C000192674

Where To Fish

2011

92nd EDITION

Edited by: Dr Colin Bradshaw

92nd Edition published 2010 by
Fish and Fly Ltd
PO Box 1079
Worth, West Sussex
RH10 4WH
England
www.fishandfly.com
info@fishandfly.com

This hardback edition
© 2010 Fish and Fly Ltd
ISBN 978-0-9566562-0-9
ISSN 1362-3842

Advertisements in this book have been inserted in the form in which they have been received from the advertisers. Care has been exercised in the acceptance of them, but the publisher accepts no responsibility for any loss through advertisers' malpractice. Advertisements have been accepted on the understanding that they do not contravene the Trades Descriptions Act 1968, the Sex Discrimination Act 1975, the Disability Discrimination Act 1995, the Wildfowl and Countryside Act 1981 or any other Act of Parliament.

The publishers regret that they can accept no responsibility for any errors or omissions within this publication, or for any expenses or loss thereby caused.

A few words included in this directory may be asserted to be proprietary names. The presence or absence of such names should not be considered to affect the legal status of any such names or trademarks.

British Library Cataloguing-in-Publication Data
A catalogue record of this book is available from the British Library

Cover Photo: Lake of Menteith by Colin Riach

Typesetting by Rowan Studios
Printed in Great Britain by CPI Antony Rowe

ABOUT WHERE TO FISH

Where to Fish is a book with a long history — first published as *The Angler's Register* in 1858 by *The Field* — and now in its 92nd Edition. It has survived as a fishing directory whilst others have come and gone. It saw out the dot com boom and has jumped through the Google hoops, yet throughout, it has retained its traditional solidity and charm. Nevertheless, changes are afoot with ebooks, websites, mobile applications and a booking service all soon to follow. Even now, URLs and email addresses are overtaking telephone numbers on its pages. Nevertheless, with many fishing organisations still without websites — *Where to Fish* continues to have a role, and deserves to be on the shelf of any keen angler.

Acknowledgements

This directory has been compiled and checked by an excellent team and many thanks go to all: Thomas Harmsworth Publishing Company, Jon Cleminson, Mark Patterson, Stan Headley, Paul King, Gillie Cawthorne and Sofi Wolstenholme.

Warning and Disclaimer

The details listed within *Where to Fish* are compiled with reasonable care, but because it has taken many months, some details may have changed even before it went to press. Because all details are subject to change, please use the information given as a guide only and use only if you accept that Fish&Fly Ltd cannot be held responsible for its accuracy or fitness for any particular purpose. In particular, always check with a fishery before you make any travel arrangements or bookings.

Please do let us know of any errors or omissions via editor@wheretofish.co.uk

About the Publisher

At Fish and Fly Ltd our mission is to develop the memberships of Fish&Fly and FishingMagic into the largest and most active fishing communities in the world. We plan to grow and nurture these communities for the benefit of members, business partners, and all like-minded people willing to share the passion, the experience, the excitement, the journey and the reward.

Fish and Fly Ltd is fast becoming one of the leading web publishers of angling titles with a portfolio that already includes some of the busiest fishing websites in the world.

www.fishandfly.com
www.flyforums.co.uk
www.flyforums.com
www.fishingmagic.com
www.speycast.com

www.wheretofish.co.uk
www.salmonatlas.com
www.troutatlas.com
www.carpatlas.com
www.watercams.co.uk

Fish&Fly Ltd. PO Box 1079, Worth, West Sussex. England. RH10 4WH.
E-mail: info@fishandfly.com

CONTENTS

Abbreviations: The following abbreviations are used throughout the book: S, salmon; T, trout; MT, migratory trout, NT, non-migratory trout; C, char; FF or FW, freshwater (ie coarse fish); RD, River Division (or its equivalent); s, season; f, fortnight; w, week; d, day; t, ticket; ns, nearest railway station; m means mile or miles, except when it is used in conjunction with t, ie, mt, when it means monthly ticket. Likewise, st means season ticket, wt weekly ticket, dt daily ticket, and so on.

Children fish for free!

Brothers Oscar and Daniel (pictured) with two fine Grassholme rainbows caught when fishing for free on their dad's day-ticket.

In the last few years over 16,000 youngsters have taken advantage of the family-friendly day tickets available from Northumbrian Water fisheries. With regular "try-it" days arranged and both bait and fly fishing encouraged, Northumbrian Water is committed to introducing more and more people to the wonderful sport of fishing. For more information and to download their fishing guide visit:

www.nwl.co.uk/Gofishing.aspx

FISHERY AGENTS

FISHING SALES - ENGLAND

Savills, Lansdowne House, 57 Berkeley Square Square, London, W1J 6ER (tel: +44 (0)20 3107 1040; web: www.savills.com).

Knight Frank LLP, 55 Baker Street, London W1U 8AN (tel: +44 (0)20 7629 8171; fax: +44 (0)20 7861 5266; email: farms.estates@knightfrank.com; web: www.knightfrank.com).

Sale & Partners, 18-20 Glendale Road, Wooler, Northumberland NE71 6DW (tel: +44 (0)1668 281611; fax: +44 (0)1668 281113; web: www.saleandpartners.co.uk; email: enquiries@saleandpartners.co.uk).

Strutt and Parker, 55 Northbrook Street, Newbury RG14 1AN (tel: +44 (0)1635 576905; fax: +44 (0)1635 581976; web: www.fishshootstalk.com; www.struttandparker.com). Fishing Agency: contact Mark Merison (email: mark.merison@struttandparker.com).

WALES

Knight Frank LLP, 22 Broad Street, Hereford HR4 9AP (tel: +44 (0)1432 273087; fax: +44 (0)1432 275935; web: www.knightfrank.com; email: hereford@knightfrank.com).

Chester-Master Ltd, Dolgarreg, North Road, Builth Wells, Powys LD2 3DD. Salmon fishing on Wye, Usk and tributaries. By the day or week (tel: +44 (0)1982-553248; fax: +44 (0)1982 553154; email: builth.wells@chester-master.co.uk; web: www.chestermaster.co.uk).

SCOTLAND

Bell-Ingram, Durn, Isla Rd, Perth PH2 7HF (tel: +44 (0)1738-621121; fax: +44 (0)1738 630904; web: www.bellingram.co.uk). Deveron, Cassley, Dee, etc.

CKD Galbraith, Lynedoch House, Barossa Place, Perth PH1 5EP (tel: +44 (0)1738 451600; fax: +44 (0)1738 451900; web: www.sportinglets.co.uk). Agents for fishing on a wide range of estates throughout Scotland.

Knight Frank LLP, 1 Edinburgh Quay, 133 Fountainbridge, Edinburgh EH3 9QG (tel: +44 (0)131 222 9600; fax: +44 (0)131 222 9639; web: www.knightfrank.com; email: edres@knightfrank.com).

FishPal, Stichill House, Kelso, Roxburghshire TD5 7TB (tel: +44 (0)1573 470612; fax: +44 (0)1573 470259; web: www.fishpal.com; email: info@fishpal.com).

Strutt and Parker, 55 Northbrook Street, Newbury RG14 1AN (tel: +44 (0)1635 576905; fax: +44 (0)1635 581976; web: www.fishshootstalk.com; www.struttandparker.com). Fishing Agency: contact Mark Merison (email: mark.merison@struttandparker.com).

FISHING HOLIDAY AGENTS

Frontiers, Kennet Cottage , Kempsford, Gloucestershire GL7 4EQ (tel: +44 (0)845 299 6212; email: info@frontierstrvl.co.uk; web: www.frontierstrvl.co.uk). Frontiers' founding principle remains their guiding light today. Strive to ensure that the experience of every trip meets and exceeds their client's.

Aardvark McLeod, RBL House, Ordnance Road, Tidworth, Hampshire SP9 7QD (tel: +44 (0)1980 847389; fax: +44 (0)1980 849161; email: mail@aardvarkmcleod.com; web: www.aardvarkmcleod.com). Arrange international fly fishing holidays worldwide, providing an exceptional level of service to the discerning fisherman.

WhereWiseMenFish, 7 Hollywood Mews, London SW10 9HU (tel: 0845 603 1552; email: info@wherewisemenfish.com; web: www.wherewisemenfish.com). Destinations & Holidays are designed to meet all expectations and skills and to appeal equally to dedicated fishing fanatics and to those in search of a relaxing 'fishing' orientated break with family or accompanying non-fishers.

Fly Odyssey, Althorne Hall Farm, Fambridge Road, Althorne, Essex CM3 6BZ (tel: +44 (0)1621 743711; email: m.mchugh@flyodyssey.co.uk; web: www.flyodyssey.co.uk). Worldwide fly fishing holidays, specialising in Australia, New Zealand and the South Pacific: we provide a comprehensive range of fly fishing packages to suit all budgets. Please contact us to discuss your next fly fishing adventures.

Go Fishing Worldwide, 2 Oxford House, 24 Oxford Road North, London W4 4DH (tel: +44 (0)20 8 742 1556; fax: +44 (0)20 8 747 4331; email: info@gofishingworldwide.co.uk; web: www.gofishingworldwide.co.uk). Offer freshwater and saltwater fishing around the world. Programme now offers an even greater variety of experiences for angling enthusiasts as well as catering for non-fishing companions with a wider range of other exciting activities.

Angling Direct Holidays, 277 Aylsham Road, Norwich, Norfolk NR3 2RE (tel: +44 (0) 1603 407596; email: info@anglingdirectholidays.com; web: www.anglingdirectholidays.com). Specialise in a vast range of destinations that can all be tailored to suit your own personal requirements, with destinations rich in culture, history, natural beauty and of course unbelievable fishing. Also specialise in accommodating non angling partners.

World Sport Fishing (tel: +44 (0)1480 403293; web: www.worldsportfishing.com). Aim to make Fishing Holiday or Shooting Holiday experience as fantastic as it should be. All destinations are hand selected and tested.

Club Fish World (web: www.clubfishworld.com). Provides fly fishing holidays to the world's finest brown trout, grayling, rainbow, sea trout and salmon rivers in the UK, Europe and North and South America.

Fly Fisher Group, Fly Fisher Travel Ltd, Manor Barns, Southrop, Lechlade, Gloucestershire GL7 3NX (tel: +44 (0) 20 3301 3300; fax: +44 (0) 870 922 3653; email: enquiries@flyfisher-travel.com; www.flyfishergroup.com). Mission is to provide an exceptional fly fishing holiday. Specialise in Iceland, Russia, Seychelles and bespoke travel.

Sportfish, Winforton, Hereford, Herefordshire HR3 6SP (tel: +44 (0) 1544 327 111; email: tuition@sportfish.co.uk; web: www.sportfish.co.uk). Trips have been designed specifically for first-time or novice anglers who want to get the most out of their week away. Not only will this be the opportunity to fish some of the best flats fishing in the world for 'Grand slam' species but it will also be a tuition based learning experience.

Farlows, 9 Pall Mall, London SW1Y 5NP (tel: +44 (0) 207 484 1000; email: info@farlows.co.uk; web: www.farlows.co.uk). A Mecca for fly fishing enthusiasts for more than a century, Farlows royal warrant is testament to a reputation of distinction. But it's not just a fishing heritage that keeps customers returning.

Roxtons Worldwide, 25 High Street, Hungerford, Berkshire RG17 0NF (tel: +44 (0)1488 689 701; fax: +44 (0)1488 689730; web: www.roxtons.com; email: fishing@roxtons.com). Salmon fishing in Russia, Norway, Iceland, Alaska, Scotland and Ireland. Trout fishing in UK, USA, Argentina, Chile, New Zealand and elsewhere. Freshwater fishing in Africa, Alaska, American West, Argentina, Brazil, Canada, England, Ireland, Iceland, New Zealand, Russia and Scotland. Saltwater and deep sea fishing in Africa, Australia, Bahamas, Cuba, Mexico, Seychelles, Belize, Venezuela, Guatemala and Dubai.

Yellow Dog, 213 South Willson Avenue, Bozeman, Montana 59715, USA (tel: +1 888 777 5060; email: info@yellowdogflyfishing.com; web: www.yellowdogflyfishing.com). Focused, full-scale destination-angling company dedicated to arranging and providing the best possible flyfishing and travel experiences in the world.

Pesca Maya, Calle Urano No. 101-A Sm. 38, Mz.19 Lote 67 C.P. 77500, Benito Juarez, Cancun, Quintana Roo, Mexico (tel: + 808 234 2104; web: www.pescamaya.com). Offers services for fishing and lodging all over the Yucatan peninsula. They take you where the action is: wether you want to catch giant tarpon, sailfish, blue or white marlin or dorado / mahi-mahi.

Steppingstones, Monkey River, Placencia, Belize (email: steppingstones.sue@gmail.com; web: www.steppingstonesbelize.com). Dedicated to two things - relaxation and fishing. If you are after top class fishing, you'll find that both Chris and Sue are keen and knowledgeable anglers who can supply the best guides and invaluable fishing tips. Steppingstones offers a unique range of fresh and saltwater fishing, and as a result, unusually in the Caribbean, they can offer really excellent fishing even when it's windy.

Avalon Cuban Fishing Centers, (web: www.cubanfishingcenters.com). Fly fishing in Cuba is far different from other destinations in the Caribbean. Only in recent years has this flats fishery been developed, and you are fishing waters that have not seen sport fishing for nearly fifty years. Cuba has given these pristine areas protection as Cuban National Marine Parks, where no commercial fishing is allowed other than for lobster. Flats fish like Tarpon, Permit, Bonefish, Snook, Mutton Snapper, Barracuda, and a variety of Jacks are found in incredible numbers and since the fishing pressure is so light in these areas the fish rarely encounter sport fishermen and are unusually easy to catch.

Country Haven, 601 Route #118, Gray Rapids, New Brunswick E9B 1G9. Canada (tel: +1 877 359-4665; email: flyhook@nbnet.nb.ca; for more details see website: www.miramichifish.com). One Stop Destination for Outdoor Vacation while visiting Eastern Canada. Located on the river banks of the Miramichi River, one of the most famous salmon rivers in the world.

Deneki Outdoors, 200 W 34th Ave PMB 1170, Anchorage, AK 99503, USA (tel: +1 907-563-9788, email: info@deneki.com; web: www.deneki.com). Own and operate fly fishing lodges in Alaska, British Columbia, the Bahamas and Southern Chile. Lodges are located in the finest unexploited fisheries, ensuring truly world-class fishing.

Loop Adventures, Box 195, S-184 22 Åkersberga, Sweden (tel: +46 8 544 101 90; fax: +46 8 544 101 99; email: travel@looptackle.se; www.loopadventures.com). Argentina, Cuba, Russia with free Loop Tackle to borrow while you are there!

Mavungana, P.O.Box 63, Dullstroom, 1110, South Africa (tel: +27 1325 40270; fax: +27 1325 40757; email: info@flyfishing.co.za; web: www.flyfishing.co.za). Hosted international fishing with Jonathan Boulton. Argentina, Mongolia, Egypt, Alaska, The Amazon and more.

Fishing Adventures Thailand, 34/13-14 City Studio, 8/21 Sukhumvit Road, Soi 13, Bangkok 10110, Thailand (tel: +668 1 846 98 94, email: info@anglingthailand.com; web: www.anglingthailand.com). The only guided fishing trip agency offering a menu of program options to meet the desires of the individual angler. Ultimate goal is to help enthusiasts discover the rich diversity of South East Asian fish species - and to catch as many as possible - while having some truly unforgettable adventures along the way.

Lax-Á Angling Club, Akurhvarf 16, 203 Kópavogur, Iceland (tel: +352 (0)557 6100; +354 531 6100; fax: +354 557 6108; web: www.lax-a.is; email: lax-a@lax-a.is). Plan and sell tours on 40 first-class salmon and trout rivers in Iceland, Argentina, Greenland, Africa, Russia, Canada, Norway, Steelhead, Scotland and Ireland; fishing on the top salmon, trout and char rivers in Iceland. Each client has a tailor-made tour, including licences, full board and lodging, guide and transfers; guesthouses, hotel and car rental also available.

Chris Hill, Dragon Trout Adventures, 8 Augusta Road, New Town, Hobart, Tasmania 7008, Australia (tel: +61 (0)3 62 282264; fax: +61 (0)3 62 284441; email: Chris@fishingtasmania.com; web: www.fishingtasmania.com). Tuition for 1-5 days, tours one or more days, trout fly fishing in Western Lakes and Central Highland lakes.

FishQuest! Global Angling Adventures, 152 N Main Street, Hiawassee, Georgia 30546, USA (tel: +1 706 896 1403; Toll Free: +1 888 891 3474; fax: +1 706 896 1467; web: www. fishquest.com; email: questhook@aol.com). Freshwater and saltwater fishing expeditions throughout Alaska, Canada, USA, Mexico, Central America, Peru, Amazon, Caribbean, Venezuela, Argentina & Chile, Australia & New Zealand and Africa to the client's specificaation. Other web sites: www.peacock-bass.com, questackle.com and payara-fishing.com).

Mike Hopley, P.O. Box 4273, Soldotna, AK 99669, USA (tel: +1 907 262 7773 (Summer); +1 360 371 8973 (Winter); fax: +1 866-672-8013; web:

www.alaskancharters.com; email: rufishn@alaska.net). Personalised guided Alaskan fishing, with accommodation, featuring Kenai River salmon, and saltwater halibut.

Marlin Lodge, Benguerua Island, Bazaruto Archipelago, Mozambique (web: www.marlinlodge.co.za). Big game fishing for sailfish and marlin, wahoo, barracuda, yellow fin, skipjack and other species; excellent accommodation available, located along beach of Flamingo Bay. Bookings can be made through **Mozambique Tourism, P O Box 2042, Rivonia, Gauteng 2128, South Africa** (tel: +27 11 803 9296/+27 11 234 0599; fax: +27 11 803 9299; web: www.mozambiquetourism.co.za; email: travel@mozambiquetourism. co.za).

Viv's Barra Sport Fishing Charters, P O Box 38220, Winnellie, NT 0821, Australia (tel: +428 877 607; fax: +889 456 374; web: www.vivsbarra.com.au; email: vbss@vivsbarra.com.au). Northern Territory Mothership (TSMY 'Swordfish') and Inland Fishing Tour specialists.

A magnificent Atlantic salmon of 54lbs for Mollie Fitzgerald of Frontiers International. Caught on fly and safely released into the River Alta, Norway.

Photo: Frontiers International Ltd

BRITISH FISH FARMS

Berkshire Trout Farm, Hungerford, Berkshire, RG17 0UN (tel: +44
(0)1488-682520; mob: +44 (0)7795 680661; fax: +44 (0)1488 685002; email:
berkshiretrout@btconnect.com; web: www.berkshiretroutfarm.com). Brown and
rainbow trout.

Bibury Trout Farm, Bibury, near Cirencester, Gloucestershire GL7 5NL. Rainbow
and brown trout bred on Coln (tel: +44 (0)1285 740212/740215; fax: +44 (0)1285
740392; web: www.biburytroutfarm.co.uk). Catch Your Own fishery on R Coln.

Brookleas Fish Farm (T. Lobb) Ludbridge Mill, East Hendred, Wantage, Oxon
OX12 8LN (tel/fax: +44 (0)1235 820 500; web: www.brookleas.co.uk; email:
brookleas@hotmail.com)

Corgary Trout Farm (H J Johnston) Castlederg, Co Tyrone BT81 7YF (tel: +44
(0)28816 71209; email brianhj@btinternet.com).

Danebridge Fisheries Ltd (L Chadwick) Danebridge, Wincle, nr Macclesfield,
Cheshire SK11 0QE (tel: +44 (0)1260 227293; www.danebridgefisheries.com;
lorne@danebridgefisheries.com); blue, golden, rainbow and brown trout.

Exe Valley Fishery Ltd, Exbridge, Dulverton, Somerset TA22 9AY (tel: +44
(0)1398 323 008; web: www.exevalleyfishery.co.uk; email: enquiries@
exevalleyfishery.co.uk). Rainbow trout available.

Hooke Springs Trout Farm (Mr & Mrs Mark Firth) Hooke, Beaminster, Dorset
DT8 3NZ (tel: +44 (0)1308 862553; web: www.hookespringstrout.co.uk).
Specialist in brown & rainbow trout.

Holbury Lakes Trout Fishery, The Fishery Manager, Holbury Lane, Lockerley,
Romsey, Hants SO51 0JR (tel: (day) 01794 341619; email:
enquiries@holburylakes.co.uk; web: www.holburylakes.co.uk).

Kilnsey Park Trout Farm (Anthony & Vanessa Roberts) Kilnsey, Skipton, North
Yorkshire BD23 5PS (tel: +44 (0)1756 752150; fax: +44 (0)1756 752224; web:
www.kilnseypark.co.uk; email: info@kilnseypark.co.uk); rainbows and brown
trout.

Lechlade Trout Fisheries (T Small) Burford Road, Lechlade, Glos. GL7 3QQ (tel:
+44 (0)1367 253266; web: www.lechladetrout.co.uk; email:
nicci@lechladetrout.co.uk). Rainbows & brown trout.

Upper Mills Trout Farm, Glyn Ceiriog, nr Llangollen LL20 7HB (tel: +44 (0)1691
718225; fax: +44 (0)1691 718188); rainbows and brown trout.

West Acre Trout Farm, Car House, West Acre, King's Lynn, Norfolk PE32 1UL
(tel: +44 (0)1760 755240; fax: +44 (0)1760 755466). Brown and rainbow trout for
immediate delivery.

See also: **British Trout Association**, The Rural Centre, West Mains, Ingliston EH28
8NZ (tel: +44 (0)0131 472 4080; fax: +44 (0)0131 472 4083; web:
www.britishtrout.co.uk; email: mail@britishtrout.co.uk).

FISHING SCHOOLS AND COURSES

The Arundell Arms Fly Fishing School, Lifton, Devon PL16 0AA (tel: +44 (0)1566 784666; fax: +44 (0)1566 784494; email: reservations@arundellarms.com; web: www.arundellarms.com). A full range of residential courses from beginners' to advanced. Private tuition also offered.

Game Angling Instructors Association, Hon Sec: Jim Gill, 3 Church Cottages, Nursery Lane, North Wootton, King's Lynn, Norfolk PE30 3QA (tel: 01553 671178; email: flystitch5@btinternet.com; www.gameanglinginstructors.co.uk). The Association has approximately 350 members both in the UK and abroad (which includes STANIC, SGAIC and APGAI qualified instructors) skilled to give a range of tuition from simple casting lessons to full residential courses. The web-site gives a full list of members, or they can be contacted through the Administrator.

Register of Experienced Fly Fishing Instructors and Schools (REFFIS). Most members of REFFIS offer fishing, as well as instruction. For full list of members, contact REFFIS via Ian Hockley of West Lake Fly Fishing, 78 Grove Street, Wantage OX12 7BG (tel: +44 (0)1235 227228; email: ian@westlakeflyfishing.co.uk; web: www.reffis.co.uk) (see below).

Blackwater Fly Fishing Instruction & Guide Service (Doug Lock) Ghillie Cottage, Kilbarry Stud, Fermoy, Co Cork, Ireland (tel: +353 2 532720; web: www.speycast-ireland.com; email: flyfish@eircom.net). Spey casting tuition and salmon fly fishing instruction on Blackwater River; REFFIS and Orvis approved.

Caithness & Sutherland Angling Services, Lesley Crawford, Askival, Reay, Caithness KW14 7RE (tel/fax: +44 (0)1847 811470; web: www.wildtroutfisher.co.uk; email: lesley@wildtroutfisher.co.uk). Tuition and guiding on many Caithness and Sutherland wild brown trout lochs, plus various renowned salmon and sea trout rivers'.

Clonanav Fly Fishing Centre, Nire Valley, Ballymacarbry, Clonmel, Co Waterford, Eire. Contact: Andrew Ryan (tel: +353 52 61 36765; fax: +353 52 61 36294; email: andrew@flyfishingireland.com; web: www.flyfishingireland.com).

Devon Fly Fishing School, The, Fox and Hounds Country Hotel, Eggesford, Chulmeigh, Devon EX18 7JZ (tel: +44 (0) 1363 82786; email: team@dsoff.com; web: www.devonschoolofflyfishing.com). Brown trout, sea trout and salmon fishing, let by day, week, or season. Private beats on Taw, and Mole.

First Nature (Pat O'Reilly APGAI & Sue Parker, STANIC) Bwlchgwyn, Rhydlewis, Llandysul SA44 5RE (tel/fax: +44 (0)1239 851952; web: www.first-nature.com; email: dreamstreams@first-nature.com). Flyfishing courses and casting instruction in the Teifi Valley, West Wales. Also free fishing and conservation lessons for young people during the school summer holidays, in conjunction with Llandysul Angling Association.

Fishhunt, Touraneena, Ballinamult, Clonmel, Co.Tipperary, Ireland (Tel: 00 353 58 47524; Mob: 00 353 87 8399345; email: philip@fishhunt.ie; web: www.fishhunt.ie). Beats on the river Blackwater (22 in total) from source to sea and prime private beats on the River Suir.

Fishing Breaks Ltd, Simon Cooper, The Mill, Heathman Street, Nether Wallop, Stockbridge, Hants SO20 8EW; (tel: 01264 781988; www.fishingbreaks.com; email: info@fishingbreaks.co.uk). Leading chalkstream fishing agents in S England (R Test, Itchen, Dever, Wallop Brook, Nadder, Kennet); fly-fishing school at Nether Wallop Mill, Stockbridge, Hants.

John Pennington, 24 Upper Burnside Drive, Thurso, Caithness, KW14 7XB, (tel: +44 (0)1847 894641; web: www.btinternet.com/~john_pennington; email: johndickpennington@tiscali.co.uk). Instruction on Halladale and Thurso River.

Test Valley School of Fly Fishing, Jerry Wakeford, 44 Butler's Close, Lockerley, Romsey, Hants SO51 0LY (tel: +44 (0)1794 341990 or +44 (0)1794 884127; web: www.learnflyfishing.co.uk; email: mail@learnflyfishing.co.uk).

Wessex Fly Fishing School, Lawrence's Farm, Southover, Tolpuddle, Dorchester, Dorset DT2 7HF (tel: 01305 789560; mob: +44 (0)7855 196332; web: www.goflyfishing.co.uk; (for instruction: www.tkfishing.com); email: sally.slocock@virgin.net). Lakes, pools, chalk-stream fishing for trout on Rivers Piddle, Bride, Hooke and Frome; catch and release river fishing for wild brown trout a particular feature; lake and river tuition from highly experienced instructors. B&B and self-catering accommodation available.

Westlake Fly Fishing, Ian Hockley, 78 Grove Street, Wantage, Oxon OX12 7BG, (tel: +44 (0)1235 227228; fax: +44 (0)1235 227227: email: ian@westlakeflyfishing.co.uk; web: www.reffis.co.uk).

A Spey casting demonstration from master spey caster, Peter S. Anderson
Photo: Colin Bradshaw

PROFESSIONAL ANGLING INSTRUCTORS

The Game Angling Instructors' Association
www.gameanglinginstructors.co.uk

ENGLAND

**Game Angling Instructors
Association**, Hon secretary:
Jim Gill, 3 Church Cottages, Nursery
Lane, North Wootton, King's Lynn,
Norfolk PE30 3QA
Tel: 01553 671178
flystitch5@btinternet.com
www.gameanglinginstructors.co.uk

**Malcolm March of Rutland
Fly Fishing**
APGAI Trout, GAIC Trout
www.rutlandflyfishing.com
Email: malcolm@mmarch.co.uk
Tel: 01780 722466

**Bob Carlson of Bob & Vera
Carlson Fly Fishing Tuition**
GAIC Trout
www.flyfishingtuition.co.uk
b9vee@lycos.com
Tel: 01539 733297 or 07502 420267
Mob: 07886 817770

**Mike Roden of Lancashire
Fly Fishing**
APGAI Trout, GAIC Trout,
GAIC Salmon
www.lancashireflyfishing.co.uk
mike@lancashireflyfishing.co.uk
Tel: 07786 682272

Bryan Martin of Devon Fly Fishing
APGAI Trout, APGAI Salmon,
GAIC Fly Dressing
www.devonflyfishing.co.uk
bryan@devonflyfishing.co.uk
Tel: 01769 550840
Mob: 07759 352194

Chris Aldred
GAIC Trout, GAIC Fly Dressing
chris@gamefishinginstruction.co.uk
Mob: 07779 725298

Alan Middleton
APGAI Trout, APGAI Fly Dressing
Email: woryem@globalnet.co.uk
Mob: 0779 0251693

John Reynolds
APGAI Trout, GAIC Trout
www.castwellflyfishing.co.uk
Tel: 07702 848417
Email: jwreynolds@onetel.com

Alan Purnell
GAIC Trout
Email: alan@flyfishing4you.co.uk
Tel: 01342 715039
Mob: 07768 032334
www.flyfishing4you.co.uk

IRELAND

Philip Maher Fishhunt Angling
APGAI Trout, APGAI Salmon,
APGAI Fly Dressing
Co Tipperary

Tel: 00353 58 47524
Mob: 00353 87 8399345
philip@fishhunt.ie
www.fishhunt.ie

NORTHERN IRELAND

Mark Patterson
APGAI Trout
County Down
Mob: 07771 892506
mark@wherewisemenfish.com

Gary Smith
GAIC Trout
County Down
Tel: 07545 197996
garysmithflyfish@gmail.com
www.fodfieldsports.com

SCOTLAND

Alberto Laidlaw
APGAI Trout, APGAI Fly Dressing,
GAIC Salmon.

Tel: 07778 526859
www.gameanglingscotland.co.uk

WALES

Gwilym Hughes, G.H.Sporting
APGAI Trout, APGAI Salmon,
APGAI Fly Dressing
Tel: 01490 412731
Mob: 07889 423986
ghughes2@btinternet.com
www.gwilymhughes.com

Mark Roberts Fly Fishing
APGAI Trout, APGAI Salmon,
APGAI Fly Dressing
Tel: 01495 312508
Mob: 07712 578764
markwgroberts@googlemail.com
www.gwentanglingsociety.co.uk

Frank Williams Fly Fishing
APGAI Trout
Tel: 01594 541229
Mob: 07824 363376
frank@frankwilliamsflyfishing.co.uk
www.frankwilliamsflyfishing.co.uk

Andrew Cartwright Game Angling
GAIC Trout
Tel: 01686 688196
Mob: 07929 469160
www.acgameangling.com
acgameangling@btinternet.com

GAIA Members gather to discuss the latest in Spey casting techniques
Photo: Colin Bradshaw

FISHING FACILITIES FOR THE DISABLED

The **Wheelyboat Trust** is a small national charity dedicated to providing disabled people with hassle-free access to waterborne activities such as angling, pleasure boating and nature watching. Formed in 1985 as *The Handicapped Anglers Trust*, it has so far supplied 144 specially designed wheelchair accessible Wheelyboats to fisheries, water parks and other venues open to the public all over the UK.

The Trust's principal role is to promote and provide Wheelyboats to fisheries and other venues enabling them to accommodate the needs of their disabled visitors. It can help these venues acquire their own Wheelyboat by fundraising to help with costs.

The features that make Wheelyboats ideal for angling also make them ideal for pleasure boating and nature watching and, consequently, the Trust is keen to meet the demand for Wheelyboats wherever it exists. Nowadays, 50% of the Wheelyboats supplied are used for activities other than fishing and, as a result, the Trust is making a bigger impact and benefiting larger numbers of disabled people.

The Trust supplies four models of Wheelyboat (as well as refurbished Mk I and Mk II models), each designed for different needs and activities. Two are multipurpose craft accommodating up to twelve people and two are purpose-built fishing boats. Designed in conjunction with JM Coulam Boatbuilders, the Coulam 15 and Coulam 16 Wheelyboats are GRP fishing boats ingeniously modified for roll-on, roll-off wheelchair access. The Coulam 15 Wheelyboat is used on large game rivers like Tweed where the disabled angler is accompanied by a boatman at the oars. The Coulam 16 Wheelyboat has been designed primarily for large stillwaters where disabled anglers want to use a boat with the performance and looks of a standard fishing boat. The Coulam 16 Wheelyboat can be used independently by disabled anglers as the deck is accessible throughout.

New Wheelyboats are being launched all the time. For more information on the work of the Trust, including the latest list of Wheelyboat venues, visit the website or contact the Director. The Wheelyboat Trust is a registered charity and relies upon the generosity of charitable organisations, companies and individuals to enable it to continue providing this important service on behalf of disabled people. Donations can be made via the Trust's website; www.wheelyboats.org.

Wheelyboats are hired like any other angling boat except that venues tend to prefer at least 24 hours notice for a booking.

THE WHEELYBOAT TRUST

Reg charity 292216

Andy Beadsley, Director.
North Lodge, Burton Park, Petworth,
West Sussex GU28 0JT.
Tel/fax: 01798 342222

Info@wheelyboats.org; www.wheelyboats.org

LIST OF WHEELYBOAT LOCATIONS

Key of Activities

Activities: T (trout), S (salmon), St (sea-trout), C (coarse), P (pleasure boating), N (bird/nature watching).

Wheelyboat Type: Mk I, Mk II, Mk III, C16Wbt, C15Wbt (Coulam 15 & 16 Wheelys).

SOUTH EAST

Arlington Reservoir
Eastbourne, East Sussex
Tel: 01323 870810
www.southeastwater.co.uk
Activity: T
Boat: Mk II

Chigboro Fisheries
Maldon, Essex
Tel: 01621 857368
www.chigboro-fisheries.co.uk
Activity: T
Boat: Mk I

Powdermill Reservoir
Sedlescombe, East Sussex
Tel: 01424 870498
www.hastingsflyfishers.co.uk
Activity: T
Boat: Mk I

Bewl Water
Lamberhurst, Kent
Tel: 01892 890352
www.bewl.co.uk
Activity: T
Boat: C16Wbt

Weir Wood Reservoir
East Grinstead, East Sussex
Tel: 01342 820650
www.weirwoodangling.co.uk
Activity: T, C
Boat: Mk II

Bough Beech Reservoir
Sevenoaks, Kent
Tel: 01732 851544
www.boughbeechfishing.com
Activity: C
Boat: Mk I

Hanningfield Reservoir
South Hanningfield, Essex
Tel: 01268 712815
www.eswater.co.uk
Activity: T
Boat: C16Wbt

Rib Valley Lake
Ware, Hertfordshire
Tel: 01920 484913
www.ribvalleyfishinglakes.com
Activity: T
Boat: Mk I

SOUTH WEST

Wimbleball Lake
Brompton Regis, Somerset
Tel: 01398 371372
www.swlakestrust.org.uk
Activity: T, P, N
Boat: Mk II

Sutton Bingham Reservoir
Yeovil, Somerset
Tel:01935 872389
www.wessexwater.co.uk
Activity: T, P, N
Boat: Mk III

Clatworthy Reservoir
Taunton, Somerset
Tel: 01984 624658
www.wessexwater.co.uk
Activity: T
Boat: Mk III

Bushyleaze Trout Fishery
Lechlade, Gloucestershire
Tel: 01367 253266
www.lechladetrout.co.uk
Activity: T
Boat: Mk II

Kennick Reservoir
Bovey Tracey, Devon
Tel: 01647 277587
www.swlakestrust.org.uk
Activity: T
Boat: Mk I

Wistlandpound Reservoir
Kentisbury, Devon
Tel: 01598 763221
www.calvert-trust.org.uk
Activity: T, P, N
Boat: Mk II

Roadford Lake
Okehampton, Devon
Tel:01409 211507
www.swlakestrust.org.uk
Activity: T, P, N
Boat: Mk II

Tamar Lakes
Bude, Devon
Tel: 01288 321712
www.swlakestrust.org.uk
Activity: C, P, N
Boat: Mk III

Stithians Reservoir
Redruth, Cornwall
Tel: 01209 860301
www.swlakestrust.org.uk
Activity: T, P, N
Boat: Mk III

River Fowey
Golant, Cornwall
Tel: 0845 5195261
Activity: P, N, Seafishing
Boat: Mk III

Siblyback Lake
Liskeard, Cornwall
Tel: 01579 346522
www.swlakestrust.org.uk
Activity: T, P, N
Boat: Mk III

Chew Valley Lake
Chew Stoke, Avon
Tel: 01275 332339
www.bristolwater.co.uk
Activity: T
Boat: Mk III

EAST ANGLIA

Blackdyke Trout Fly Fishery
Lakenheath, Norfolk
Tel: 07525 730447
www.blackdykefishing.co.uk
Activity: T, Boat: Mk I

Fritton Lake & Country Park
Great Yarmouth, Norfolk
Tel: 01493 488288
www.somerleyton.co.uk

Activity: C, P, N
Boat: Mk I

Eels Foot Inn
Ormesby Little Broad, Norfolk
Tel: 01493 730342, 740539
www.broads-authority.gov.uk
Activity: C, P, N
Boat: Mk I

The Waterside
Rollesby Broad
Norfolk
Tel: 01493 740531

www.thewatersiderollesby.co.uk
Activity: C, P N
Boat Mk III

The first Coulam 16 Wheelyboat is launched at Rutland Water.
Photo: The Wheelyboat Trust

MIDLANDS

Grafham Water
Perry, Cambridgeshire
Tel: 01480 810531
www.anglianwaterleisure.co.uk
Activity: T
Boat: C16Wbt

Westlow Mere
Congleton, Cheshire
Tel: 01260 270012
www.westlowmere.co.uk
Activity: T
Boat: Mk I

Carsington Water
Ashbourne, Derbyshire
Tel: 01629 540769, 540478
www.stwater.co.uk
Activity: T
Boat: Mk II

Press Manor Fishery
Chesterfield, Derbyshire
Tel: 01629 760996
www.pressmanorfishery.com
Activity: T
Boat: Mk I

Eyebrook Reservoir
Caldecott, Leicestershire
Tel: 01536 770264
www.eyebrook.com
Activity: T
Boat: C16Wbt, Mk II

Thornton Reservoir
Leicester, Leicestershire
Tel: 01530 230807
www.flyfishthornton.co.uk
Activity: T
Boat: Mk II

Toft Newton Reservoir
Lincoln, Lincolnshire
Tel: 01673 878453
www.toftnewton.com
Activity: T
Boat: Mk I

Elinor Trout Fishery
Kettering, Northants
Tel: 01832 720786
www.elinortf.co.uk
Activity: T
Boat: Mk I

Pitsford Water
Northants
Tel: 01604 781350
www.anglianwaterleisure.co.uk
Activity: T, Boat: Mk II

Ravensthorpe Reservoir
Ravensthorpe, Northants
Tel: 01604 770875
www.anglianwaterleisure.co.uk
Activity: T, Boat: Mk II

Blenheim Estate
Woodstock, Oxfordshire
Tel: 01993 810520
www.blenheimpalace.com
Activity: T, Boat: Mk I

Rutland Water
Oakham, Rutland
Tel: 01780 686441
www.anglianwaterleisure.co.uk
Activity: T, Boat: C16Wbt

Dearnford Lake
Whitchurch, Shropshire
Tel: 01948 665914
www.dearnford.com/dl_disabled.html
Activity: T, N, Boat: Mk II

Patshull Park
Pattingham, Shropshire
Tel: 01902 700774
www.patshull-park.co.uk
Activity: T, C
Boat: Mk III

The Mere
Ellesmere, Shropshire
Tel: 01691 622981
www.shropshire.gov.uk
Activity: C, P, N, Boat: Mk I

Blithfield Reservoir
Rugeley, Staffordshire
Tel: 01283 840284
www.blithfield.com/anglers

Activity: T
Boat: C16Wbt

Rudyard Lake
Leek, Staffordshire
Tel: 01538 306280
www.rudyardlake.com
Activity: C, P, N
Boat: Mk III

Packington Trout Fisheries
Meriden, Warwickshire
Tel: 01676 522754
www.packingtonestate.net
Activity: T
Boat: Mk I

NORTH EAST

Lockwood Beck Trout Fishery
Guisborough, Cleveland
Tel: 01287 660501, 07973 779527
www.lockwoodfishery.co.uk
Activity: T
Boat: Mk II

Hallington Reservoirs
Colwell, Northumberland
Tel: 01434 681405
www.westwaterangling.co.uk
Activity: T
Boat: Mk I

Leaplish Waterside Park
Kielder Water
Northumberland
Tel: 01434 240365
Activity: T
Boat: Mk I

Elsham Hall Country Park
Brigg, South Humberside
Tel: 01652 688698
Activity: T, Boat: Mk I

Farmire Fishery
Knaresborough, Yorkshire
Tel: 01423 866417
Activity: T
Boat: Mk I

Walton Hall Trout Fishery
Walton, Yorkshire
Tel: 01924 242990
Activity: T
Boat: Mk I

Bellflask Fishery
Ripon
Tel: 01677 470716
Activity: T
Boat: Mk I

NORTH WEST

Lake Windermere
Fell Foot Country Park
Cumbria
Tel: 015395 31273
www.nationaltrust.org.uk
Activity: T
Boat: C16Wbt

The Tranquil Otter
Carlisle
Cumbria
Tel: 01228 576661
www.thetranquilotter.co.uk
Activity: T, N
Boat: Mk I

Hawkshead Trout Fishery
Ambleside
Cumbria
Tel: 01539 436541
www.hawksheadtrout.com
Activity: T
Boat: Mk I

Stocks Reservoir
Slaidburn, Lancashire
Tel: 01200 446602
Activity: T
Boat: Mk I

SCOTLAND

Lochgilphead & District A.A
Argyll
Tel: 01546 606878
Web: www.fynetackle.com
Activity: T, Boat: Mk I

Newmill Trout Fisheries
Cleghorn, Lanarkshire
Tel: 01555 870730
Activity: T,
Boat: Mk I

River Tweed
Borders
Tel: 01896 848271, 07774 861474
www.fishtweed.co.uk
Activity: S, St, T
Boat: C15Wbt

Hillend Reservoir
Caldercruix, North Lanarkshire
Tel: 01236 843611
Activity: T,
Boat: Mk II

Castle Loch Fishery
Lochmaben, Dumfriesshire.
Tel: 07773 658136, 07952 545883
www.castlelochfisheries.co.uk
Activity: C, N
Boat: Mk III

Butterstone Loch
Dunkeld, Perthshire
Tel: 01350 724238
www.butterstonelochfishings.co.uk
Activity: T,
Boat: Mk I

Loch Achonachie
Dingwall, Highlands
Tel: 01381 620674
Activity: T,
Boat: Mk I

Fingask Loch
Blairgowrie, Perthshire
Tel: 01250 876344. 07949 540821
Activity: T,
Boat: Mk I

Storr Lochs
Portree, Skye
Tel: 01478 612612, 612482
www.portreeanglingassociation.co.uk
Activity: T,
Boat: Mk I

Lake of Menteith
Port of Menteith, Stirling
Tel: 01877 385648, 385664
www.menteith-fisheries.co.uk
Activity: T, Boat: Mk II

Invertrossachs Estate
Stirling
Tel: 01786 832212, 07788 721457
Activity: T
Boat: Mk I

Kyle of Sutherland
Lochs Migdale & Shin
Sutherland
Tel: 01863 766655
www.ksft.org
Activity: S, St, T, N, P
Boat: Mk III

Carman Trout Fishery
Alexandria, West Dunbartonshire
Tel: 07801 684578
http://sites.google.com/site/carman
troutfishery/
Activity: T
Boat: Mk I

Cobbinshaw Loch
West Calder, West Lothian
Tel: 01501 785208, 07880 601935
Activity: T
Boat: Mk II

Linlithgow Loch
Linlithgow, West Lothian
Tel: 07831 288921
Activity: T
Boat: Mk I

Raith Lake
Kirkcaldy
Tel: 01592 646466
www.raithlake.com
Activity: T
Boat: Mk I

Fly fishing for salmon on the famous Tweed from a Coulam 15 Wheelyboat.
Photo: The Wheelyboat Trust

WALES

Llyn Alaw
Holyhead, Anglesey
Tel: 01407 730762
www.dwrcymru.com
Activity: T
Boat: Mk I

Llyn Cefni
Llangefni, Anglesey
Tel: 01248 421238
www.llyncefni.co.uk
Activity: T
Boat: Mk II

Celtic Lakes Resort
Lampeter, Ceredigion
Tel: 01570 471010, 07779 990925
www.celticlakesresort.com
Activity: C
Boat: Mk III

Teglan Fishery
Lampeter, Ceredigion
Tel: 01570 471115
Activity: C
Boat: Mk I

Llyn Brenig
Cerrigydrudion, Conwy
Tel: 01490 420463
www.dwrcymru.com
Activity: T
Boat: Mk II

Llyn Trawsfynydd
Trawsfynydd, Gwynedd
Tel: 01766 540400
www.trawslake.com
Activity: T
Boat: Mk II

Llyn Nantlle
Penygroes, Gwynedd
Tel: 01248 670666
Activity: T, St
Boat: Mk II

Maes y Clawdd
Bala, Gwynedd
Tel: 01678 530239
Activity: T, N
Boat: Mk I

Tal-y-llyn
Tywyn, Gwynedd
Tel: 01654 782282
www.tynycornel.co.uk
Activity: T, P, N, S, St
Boat: Mk I I

Llandegfedd Reservoir
Pontypool, Monmouthshire
Tel: 01291 673722
www.dwrcymru.com
Activity: T
Boat: Mk III

Llys-y-Fran Reservoir
Haverfordwest, Pembrokeshire
Tel: 01437 532732, 532694
Activity: T
Boat: Mk I

Llyn Clywedog
Llanidloes, Powys
Tel: 01686 412644
www.llanidloes.com/angling_club
Activity: T
Boat: C16Wbt

NORTHERN IRELAND

Tildarg Fishery
Ballyclare, Co Antrim
028 9334 0604
Activity: T
Boat: Mk I

Corbet Lough
Banbridge, Co Down
028 4062 5039
www.banbridge.gov.uk
Activity: T
Boat: Mk II

Families at the Waterworks
Belfast
Tel 07791 910848
www.familiesatthewaterworks.piczo.
com

Activity: T
Boat: Mk I

Belleisle Estates
Lisbellaw, Co Fermanagh
028 6638 7231
www.belleisle-estate.com
Activity: T
Boat: Mk I

Parklake Fishery
Dungannon
Co Tyrone
028 8772 7327
Activity: T
Boat: Mk I

REPUBLIC OF IRELAND

Belturbet Angling Assoc
Belturbet, Co Cavan
Tel: 00 353 4995 22359, 22657
Activity: T
Boat: Mk I

Cappoquin Salmon & Trout
Anglers' Association
Co Waterford
Tel: 00 353 58 54329
www.fishcappoquin.com
Activity: S, St, C
Boat: Mk II

Lough Owel
Mullingar, Co Westmeath
Tel: 00 353 4493 48769
Activity: T
Boat: Mk III

Fermoy Town & District AC
R Blackwater, Co Cork
Tel: 00 353 89 4135120
Activity: S, P, N
Boat: Mk III

Waterford City Anglers
Lough Carrigavantra
Co Waterford
Tel: 00 353 86 399 5552
Activity: T
Boat: C16Wbt

Rinn-Shannon & District AC
Mohill
Co Leitrim
Tel: 00 353 719 651000
www.rinnshannon.com
Activity: C, T, P, N
Boat Mk III

FISHING IN ENGLAND AND WALES

THE ENVIRONMENT AGENCY

The Environment Agency is the leading public body for protecting and enhancing the environment in England and Wales. It is their role job to look after the environment and make it a better place for all, and for future generations. Your environment is the air you breathe, the water you drink and the ground you walk on. Working with business, Government and society as a whole, the EA are making your environment cleaner and healthier. For more information on the Environment Agency, please visit their website at: www.environment-agency.gov.uk.

As part of our work, we protect and improve inland fisheries. We monitor the health of fish stocks; we respond to pollution incidents and rescue fish in distress; we work with angling clubs and fishery owners to protect, improve and create new fish habitats and fishing opportunities; and we enforce fisheries laws. We also work with others to promote angling, as a widely available and healthy pastime.

Fishing licences

Any angler aged 12 or over, fishing for salmon, trout, freshwater fish, smelt or eels in England (except the River Tweed), Wales, or the Border Esk and its tributaries in Scotland, MUST have a valid rod licence.

The income raised from licence sales is only used to fund EA fisheries work.

Rod licences are available from any Post Office in England and Wales; on-line from www.environment-agency.gov.uk/rodlicence; by telephone (0844 800 5386); or from selected fisheries. You can also pay for your licence by Direct Debit. Further details about buying a rod licence, including the current prices and concessions, are available from our website – www.environment-agency.gov.uk/rodlicence.

Fishing Licence Prices (no increase is proposed for 2011)

	Non-migratory trout, char, coarse fish and eels	Salmon and migratory (sea) trout AND trout, char, coarse fish and eels
Full season (1 April to 31 March)	£27	£72
Concession (aged 65 or over)	£18	£48
Junior Concession (aged 16 or under)	£5	£5
8 day	£10	£23
1 day	£3.75	£8

- One day rod licences are valid for 24 consecutive hours.
- Eight day rod licences are valid for 192 consecutive hours from the start time and date.

Byelaws

Byelaws protect fish stocks and fisheries. They apply to all waters, whether they are owned by angling clubs, local authorities or private individuals. Owners may impose additional rules, but they cannot override byelaws that apply to their water.

Byelaws set out when you may fish for different species (open and close seasons); how you may fish (tackle, method and bait restrictions); and how many fish you may take and at what times (bag limits).

National byelaws cover the whole of England and Wales. Regional byelaws only apply locally. Please familiarise yourself with the national byelaws, as well as those that apply where you fish.

Full details of both **National and Regional** byelaws can be found on our website at: www.environment-agency.gov.uk/homeandleisure/recreation/fishing/ or, please call 08708 506 506.

Where to fish

Once you have bought your rod licence, you'll be keen to go fishing. If you can't find a suitable venue in this directory, try looking in our local fishing guides. You can download a copy from www.environment-agency.gov.uk/wheretofish or phone 08708 506 506 and we'll send you one.

River levels

Few things can be more frustrating than arriving at your favourite river only to find a raging torrent or just a trickle. Before you go fishing, check whether river levels are suitable. You can do this either on-line at www.environment-agency.gov.uk/riverlevels or, for selected rivers, by phoning our RiverCall service. Details of RiverCall are available from www.environment-agency.gov.uk/fish. Don't waste a journey – check before you travel.

Report an incident

Fish are vulnerable to many threats – from pollution and fish disease to low river levels and poaching. If you see anything you think looks wrong or suspicious, don't ignore it, report it. Please do not hesitate to report dead fish, fish in distress, illegal fishing or other environmental incidents to us on our incident hotline on 0800 80 70 60. (Freephone, 24 hour service).

Golden rules

Angling benefits our environment in many ways. If you spend hours by the water, you learn to appreciate the natural world. This often leads to an interest in protecting it. But the places you fish are important for wildlife too. Inexperience or a little carelessness with your gear can easily harm wildlife – and the good image of angling.

Anglers can follow a few "golden rules" to avoid putting wildlife at risk. You can obtain a copy from www.environment-agency.gov.uk/fish or phone 08708 506 506.

Angling events

The EA work with other angling organisations to promote angling by encouraging people to have a go at free taster and tuition events. Many of these are listed on their website (www.environment-agency.gov.uk/fish), including the National Fishing Month (www.nationalfishingmonth.co.uk), a month long program of fishing events.

Contact the Environment Agency

If you want to contact the EA either call 08708 506 506* (Mon-Fri, 8am - 6pm); email: enquiries@environment-agency.gov.uk; or by writing to Environment Agency, National Customer Contact Centre, PO Box 544, Rotherham, S60 1BY. If you need to report an incident, please call 0800 80 70 60.

Notes:

- Calls may be recorded and monitored for training and compliance purposes
- Calls from mobile phones are not free and will be charged at normal network operator's call rates.
- * Weekday Daytime calls to 0870 numbers cost 8p, plus up to 6p per minute from BT Weekend Unlimited. Mobile and other providers' charges may vary.

A lovely carp for a happy youngster.   *Photo: Ian Gemson*

FISHING LOCATIONS IN ENGLAND

Main catchments are given in alphabetical order, fishing stations listed in mouth to source order, first main river, then tributaries. Where national borders are crossed - e.g. Wye and Border Esk - allocation has been arbitrary. Some small streams have been grouped in counties rather than catchments.

Environment Agency rod licences are now required almost everywhere in England and Wales for all freshwater fishing. National and Regional Environment Agency fishing byelaws are enforce on all inland waters and are subject to change (see Chapter *Fishing in England and Wales* for contact details).

A list of fishing clubs appears at the end of each national section. 'Free fishing' means only that a riparian owner is reputed to allow fishing without making a charge. It does not imply a right and such information should be checked locally before an attempt to fish is made. All charges shown are of course subject to change. Reduced charges to juniors, the disabled, pensioners, and in some instances to ladies, are now quite commonplace. In many instances, they are specified but where they are not, they may nevertheless be in force. If in doubt, ask when booking.

ADUR

Rises SW of Horsham and flows into the English Channel at Shoreham. Sea trout, trout, and very good coarse fishing, with match weights in excess of 100lb.

Shoreham (W Sussex). Bass, codling, flats, eels, mullet from harbour and shore. Passies Perfect Tackle,

Passies Ponds, Church Farm, Coombes, Lancing BN15 0RS (tel: 01273 465257; mob: 07710 756257; www.coombes.co.uk), has 2 coarse lakes, with carp, chub, roach, etc; dt £9, conc.

Upper Beeding (W Sussex). Chub, bream, perch, rudd, roach, dace, eels and pike.

Bramber and **Steyning** (W Sussex). Bream, roach, chub, dace, pike and carp. Pulborough AS has 3m from Bramber Bridge upstream to Streatham Old Railway Bridge; on tidal water, low water best; dt £5, conc, from Bramber Newsagency; River also has run of sea trout.

Henfield (W Sussex). Henfield & Dist AS has fishing rights on 12m of Mid and Upper Adur, from Streatham Bridge to Wineham, also west arm from Locks Estate to Partridge Green, with sea trout, brown trout, very large pike, carp, perch, large shoals of bream, eels, and other coarse species, and coarse fishing in lakes and ponds, with large carp; no dt, membership: apply to Hon Sec or Prime Angling. Worthing & Dist PS has Laybrook Fishery, 3 lakes, Byron, Milton & Shelley, 2m from Ashington, (web: www.wdps.org.uk). Tackle shop: Prime Angling, 74 Brighton Rd, Worthing BN11 2EW (tel: 01903 821594) (tickets for Hassocks AS, Henfield & DAS, Pulborough AS, and Worthing & DPS); Squires Tackle, 25 Southwick Square, Brighton BN4 4FP (tel: 01273 592903).

ALDE

A small Suffolk stream, rising near Saxmundham and flowing into the North Sea at Orford Haven, 6½m NE of Felixstowe. Sea fish.

Aldeburgh (Suffolk). Bass, codling, flat-fish, etc, can be taken in estuary from jetty and boat; cod and whiting from beach; October and November best months. Coarse fishing at Chapel Barn Farm, dt £5 on site, conc; tickets Saxmundham Angling Centre, Bakery Yard, rear of Market Place, Saxmundham IP17 1AH (tel: 01728 603443). Hotels: Brudenell, White Lion, Wentworth (see also Suffolk, Sea Fishing Stations).

Snape (Suffolk). River tidal. Mullet, bass, eels below sluice. Fishing free. Other free fishing can be enjoyed at Thorpness Mere, nr Leiston. Tackle shop: Saxmundham Angling Centre, Bakery Yard, rear of Market Place, Saxmundham IP17 1AH (tel: 01728 603443): day tickets, details of local lake fishing for carp, tench, perch, bream, rudd and pike, and details of local fishing clubs. Hotel: Bell, Saxmundham.

ALN

Short Northumberland river, flowing into North Sea at Alnmouth. Trout and sea trout, occasional salmon; usually a late run river.

Alnwick (Northumberland). Aln AA water (owned by the Duke of Northumberland), 5 to 7 miles of trout, sea trout and occasional salmon; stocked yearly with brown trout, av 1 ¼lb; no fishing between old road bridge and foot bridge at Lesbury; salmon: st £70, trout £50; wt £40, dt £20, conc, from Hardy & Greys, Willowburn Trading Estate NE66 2PF (tel: 01665 602771). Tackle shop: Jobsons of Alnwick, Tower Showrooms NE66 1SX

(tel: 01665 602135; web: www.jobsonsofalnwick.co.uk) during business hours. Coquet and Till within easy reach. Hotels: White Swan, Bondgate Within; Plough, Bondgate Without; and Schooner, Alnmouth.

Chatton Northumberland). **Chatton Trout Fishery**, 2 lakes, dt on site various prices, c&r, conc, (tel: 01668 215226, see website for more info: www.chattontroutfishery.com).

ANCHOLME

This river, in South Humberside and Lincolnshire, with its tributaries drains about 240 square miles of country. Falls into the Humber at **South Ferriby**, where there is a sluice and tidal lock. The lower part is embanked for about 19 miles. The fishing rights are leased to Scunthorpe & District Angling Association; temporary membership day permits are obtainable from their bailiffs on the bankside, or from Chapmans (below). The river is abundantly stocked with coarse fish, especially roach and bream, and recently perch and tench. Winter shoals found mainly at **Brigg**. Other choice sections at **Broughton, Snitterby, Horkstow** areas. Fishing accesses: South Ferriby Sluice, 4m from Barton upon Humber: **Saxby Bridge**, 6m from Barton upon Humber: Broughton, Castlethorpe, Cadney and **Hibaldstow Bridges** near Brigg through which town river passes; **Brandy Wharf, Snitterby, Bishop Bridge**, 6m from **Market Rasen**. Improvement work completed at Scabcroft, Broughton and Brigg. Disabled fishing stands at Brigg and at Hibaldstow Bridge. The Assn also has both banks of River Rase from Harlem Lock to Carr Lane where it runs into Ancholme at Bishop

Bridge. Hull & DAA has small mixed fishery at New Holland, Windmill Lake; members only. At Barton upon Humber are **Barton Broads** mixed coarse fishery, 6½ acres, Malt Kiln Lane. For tickets, see Goole; **Pasture House Fisheries**, Barton upon Humber DN18 5RB (tel: 01652 636369) (web: www.pasturehouse.co.uk); two separate lakes covering 8.4 acres; mixed coarse fishery on banks of Humber, 97 pegs; dt £5 from Mr & Mrs Smith; also self catering holiday timber cabins to rent, new 60 seater cafe with toilets and disabled facilities; tackle shop on site. Tackle Shop: Chapmans Angling, 21-27 Beechway, Scunthorpe DN16 2HF (tel: 01724 862585; web: www.chapmansangling.co.uk); Guns & Tackle, 251 Ashby High Str, Scunthorpe DN16 2SQ (tel: 01724 865445).

ARUN

Rises on NW border of Sussex, flows past Horsham and enters English Channel at Littlehampton. Noted coarse-fish river, largely controlled by clubs. Some sea trout; May to October.

Littlehampton (Sussex). See under Sea Fishing Stations. HQ of Littlehampton & Dist AC, Fisherman's Quay, Littlehampton BN17 5BL (tel: 01903 722769; web: www.ldac.co.uk). Billingshurst AS has R Arun 7m fishing at Pallingham right up to Okehurst, and four lakes; members only; £80, conc; contact Hon Sec. Arun Angling Centre, Water Lane, Littlehampton BN16 4EP (tel: 01903 770099; see website for more info: www.arunangling.co.uk); and other Littlehampton and Worthing tackle shops.

Arundel (W Sussex). River tidal and mainly mud-bottomed. Roach and dace run large; bream, perch, pike, chub and occasional sea trout. Bass and mullet taken in fair numbers June, July, August between Ford railway bridge and Arundel, where fishing is free. Leger best method when tide running; trotting down successful in slack water. Petworth & Bognor AC has coarse fishing on 2 lakes near Fontwell Racecourse; members only; **Stemps Pond**, stocked rudd, tench, crucians, common carp and bream; members only; in **Cart Lake**, carp, roach, chub, skimmer bream. **Back Arun Fishery,** Station Approach (tel: 01903 715712); 10 acres mixed fishery; open match every Sunday; disabled access; dt £8 on site. Billingshurst AS have 7m non-tidal

river from **Pallingham** to **Bignor**; mixed coarse; members only; contact membership sec; also 1m **Wey and Arun Canal** from Newbridge to Rowner; mixed coarse; members only. Tackle shop: Tropicana, 5 & 6 Pier Rd, Littlehampton BN17 5BA (tel: 01903 715190 or 0800 0324460; web: www.thetackleshop.co.uk). **Chalk Springs Fishery**, Park Bottom, Arundel, West Sussex, BN18 0AA (tel: 01903 883742; see website for more info:: www.chalksprings.com); four lakes, clear water, stocked with brown, rainbow, and blue rainbow trout of 2-20lb; dt £45 (5 fish), £39 (4 fish); part-day £34, £26; lodge on lakes, tuition, tackle.

Amberley (W Sussex). Chub, bream, roach, dace, rudd, eel, perch, pike. Worthing & Dist PS control stretch in the area of Houghton Bridge to Bury; dt are available from local tackle shops and the tea rooms at Houghton Bridge at £10 per day (Dawn til dusk). Rother AC has two stretches on the Arun: ½m from **Greatham** north, on west bank, and 1½m from Stopham Bridge north, on west bank. The Central Association of London & Provincial Angling Clubs hold both banks downstream of Houghton Bridge to South Stoke, tidal water; Railway station 2 mins walk from fishery; dt £5 from bailiff on bank, £4 conc in advance; no night fishing on most CALPAC water. This area to Stopham involved in Sussex RD improvement scheme.

Pulborough (W Sussex). Pike, bream to 7lbs, roach to 2½lbs, chub, dace, perch, rudd, large carp. Central Association of London & Provincial ACs leases tidal stretch at Swan Meadow; station is 7 mins walk from fishery; dt £5, conc, from bailiffs; no night fishing on most CALPAC water. Petworth & Bognor AC has 1m River Arun at Hardham; members only + guests; membership £80, conc; also 1m stretch of tidal fishing; also 3 lakes in Storrington; one tench & crucians; a carp pond (fish to double figures); match lake, mixed coarse; members only. Pulborough AS has fishing on the tidal Arun from Pulborough to Greatham Bridge, approx 3m, 1m on **Rother**, 3m on **Adur**; also eleven lakes, incl **Duncans Lake**, Pulborough (good for young anglers) and **Goose Green** (6 small lakes) near **Ashington**; coarse fish; members only: st £70, conc, from Hon Sec or Tidal Angling, Lower Street, Pulborough. Cemex (formerly RMC) Angling has 1½m stretch; st (2 rods) £30, conc £22.50. (For Cemex (formerly RMC) Angling see Chertsey). At **Wisborough Green** Crawley AS has water; dt. At **Horsham** is Newells Pond Carp Fishery, one lake of 4.5 acres; st only, from Tim Cotton, Newells Pond House, Newells Lane, Lower Beeding RH13 6LN (tel: 01403 891424). Horsham & DAA has **R Arun** around Horsham and near Pulborough (both closed during the traditional close season); no dt, members only; the assn also has Roosthole, Birchenbridge (disabled swim), Island, Kerves Lane River, Sun Oak Ponds, and Foxhole, most open all year: apply Hon Sec. Worthing & Dist PS has **Laybrook Lakes** (3 lakes; mixed coarse), 2010 – 2011 membership at time of printing is full.

Rudgwick (W Sussex). Roach, bream, chub, perch, pike, carp, eels. Rudgwick AS fishes from Slinfold to Gibbons Mill; members only; st £30, conc; society also fishes 3 lakes in Cranleigh: mixed coarse. **Hazelcopse**, Baynards, nr Rudgwick RH12 3AF (tel: 01403 822878): 2 lakes of 3½ acres, with rainbows and browns; dt £30 4 fish, £25 3 fish, £20 2 fish, £15 1 fish, then c&r. **Whitevane Carp Fishery**, Mr Adam Gramston, Forest Grange, Off Forest/Pease Pottage Rd, Horsham RH13 6HX (tel: 01293 852684): 10 acre lake with large carp and mixed coarse. **Furnace Lakes**, Slinfold RH13 0QZ (tel: 01403 791163), 4m from Horsham, 6 lakes: 6 acre lake with carp to 38lbs, large rudd, bream, etc, and 2½ acre lake, mirror and common carp, roach, skimmer bream, etc; quad bike service; dt £10 2 rods, £15 3 rods, 24 hr £25 (up to 3 rods); also Specimen Lake; carp to 47lb; and Roman Lake; catfish to 91lb, carp to 47lb; dt £15 2 rods, £30 24-hour, no conc, no under 16's. Tackle shops: Tropicana, 5 & 6 Pier Rd, Littlehampton BN17 5BA (tel: 01903 715190, customer services: 0800 0324460); Prime Angling, 74 Brighton Rd, Worthing BN11 2EW (tel: 01903 821594).

Tributaries of the Arun.

WESTERN ROTHER:

Petworth (W Sussex). Pike, perch, roach, dace, chub, few trout and sea trout. Leconfield Estate operate a commercial fishery, and let trout rods on their section of the Rother; also fishing on 9 lakes, fly; contact Smiths Gore, Estate Office, Petworth GU28 0DU (tel: 01798 342502). Petworth & Bognor AC has 5½m in all, members only from Hon Sec; also stretch downstream from Coultershaw Mill to Shopham Bridge, and 1m (N bank only) from Shopham Bridge; then both banks for 1m from Fittleworth Bridge; also Coats Castle stretch; st £80 from Hon Sec; Club also has Petworth House Lower Pond; coarse; and **Bethwins Farm Ponds, Chiddingfold**; 2 ponds; mixed coarse. Contact John Hancock, Hurlands Farm, Selham, Petworth GU28 0PN (tel: 01798 861209), for 1½m stocked fly fishing on Rother for browns, 3 miles from Petworth. **Burton Mill Pond** holds good pike, perch, roach, rudd, carp, tench. **Duncton Mill**, Dye House, Dye House Lane, Duncton GU28 0LF (tel: 01798 342048; web: www.dunctonmillfishery.co.uk); members only; dt mid-Oct to mid-Mar; 11 acre Trout farm and fishery, on chalk spring fed lakes; brown, tiger and rainbow trout; fish size 2lb to 20lb, dt £30 (4 fish), £20 (2 fish); all facilities, incl club-room, tuition and rod hire; on site shop.

Selham (W Sussex). Pitshill Fly Fishing Waters: 1½m single bank downstream from Lods Bridge, contact John Hancock for st £300 (tel: 01798 861209).

Midhurst (W Sussex). Rother AC has six stretches of river and four lakes, including **Cooks Pond** at Milland, and **Minsted Pit**; coarse fish incl dace, roach, rudd, bream, tench, perch, carp, pike, eels; tickets for Rother, Rotherfield Pond, from Backshall's Garage, Dodsley Lane, Easebourne, Midhurst GU29 9BB; membership via Hon Sec.

Chithurst (W Sussex). Petersfield & Dist AC has fishing on the Arun, **Rother**, and misc stillwaters. Fishing is predominately coarse with most species, (web: www.thepdac.com). Tackle shop: Rods 'N' Reels of Farlington, 418 Havant Rd, Farlington PO6 1NF (tel: 02392 789090).

AVON (Bristol)

Coarse fishing now excellent in places. Large chub, barbel, pike, bream, roach. Trout in weir pools, including exceptional specimens occasionally, and in some tributaries. Much of Avon controlled by Amalgamated Fisheries Ltd (formerly BB&WAA), a merger of eleven clubs known as "the Amalgamation". Fishing includes many stretches of Bristol Avon, Somerset Frome, Bristol Frome, stretches on Brue, and coarse lakes. To become a permit-holder costs £45 (concessions for juniors, disabled and pensioners), obtainable from tackle shops in the main Avon centres or Hon Sec; Hon Sec also supplies for an extra £50 season night permit; dt (£6, £3 conc) waters.

Bristol. On Avon and Frome and in Somerset. Some free fishing on Environment Agency licence from Netham Weir u/s to Hanham, towpath only. Good mixed coarse for roach, bream, perch, chub and large carp to be had in and around the **Bristol Docks** system, free with EA licence. Contact Veals Fishing Tackle, Brunel Rooms, Straight St, Bristol BS2 0EJ (tel: 0117 9260790; see website for more info: www.veals4carp.com). Good sport with trout on **Blagdon Lake**, **Chew Valley** and **Barrow Reservoirs** (see Somerset streams, lakes and reservoirs). Among coarse

fishing lakes in area are **Bowood** (2m W of Calne, dt at waterside); **Longleat** (see Warminster); **Bitterwell Lake** (N of Bristol) excellent bream, roach, rudd, common, mirror and crucian carp, perch; tuck shop; tackle sold; dt on bank, £6 per rod (£3 second rod), £3 conc and after 4pm, from Mr C W Reid, The Chalet, Bitterwell Lake, Ram Hill, Coalpit Heath, Bristol BS36 2UF (tel: 01454 778960); bank fishing only. **Henleaze Lake** (north of Bristol, no dt; information on membership, send stamped self addressed envelope to: Angling Membership, Henleaze Swimming Club, PO Box 140,

Westbury-on-Trym, Bristol BS10 6YD; membership is full for 2009.

Abbots Pool, Abbots Leigh, free fishing; run by North Somerset Council, PO Box 146, Town Hall, Weston-super-Mare, BS23 1LH (tel: 01934 01934 427346). Tackle shops: Veals Fishing Tackle, Brunel Rooms, Straight St, Bristol. BS2 0EJ. (tel: 0117 9260790; see website for more info: www.veals4carp.com); Fish & Field, 60 Broad St, Chipping Sodbury BS37 6AG (tel: 01454 314034); Scott Tackle, 42 Soundwell Road, Bristol, BS16 4QP (tel: 0117 956 7371; web: www.scotttackle.co.uk); Avon Angling Centre, 348 Whitehall Road, Bristol BS5 7BW (tel: 0117 951 7250/7526); Bristol Angling Centre, 12-14 Doncaster Road, Southmead, Bristol BS10 5PL (tel: 0117 950 8723; web: www.bristolangling.com).

Keynsham (Avon). Chub, perch, eels, roach and dace. Free fishing on Environment Agency licence at R **Chew** confluence; also R Chew in Keynsham Park. Bathampton AA has one mile of single bank on R Chew at Compton Dando, nr Keynsham; trout, coarse fish; members only; from Keynsham Angling Centre, 3 Station Rd, Keynsham BS31 2BH. (tel: 0117 986 7507; see website for more info: www.keynsham-angling.co.uk); or Veals Fishing Tackle, Brunel Rooms, Straight St, Bristol BS2 0EJ (tel: 0117 9260790; see website for more info: www.veals4carp.com). Bristol & West Federation has fishing here (**The Crane**); the waters start at the junction of the lock canal behind the Marina and stretch continuously u/s to the **Pittly Brook**, opposite the Swan Inn, about 3½m, the water being divided into 4 match sections; also **Jack Whites**. All these waters are fished by arrangement with the Bristol & Bath Federation of Anglers. Tackle shop: Keynsham Garden Centre (above); Avon Angling Centre, 348 Whitehall Road, Bristol BS5 7BW

(tel: 0117 951 7250/7526). Hotels: The Grange Hotel; Manor Lodge.

Saltford (Avon). Bathampton AA has 2 ½m on Avon; Newbridge (famous for big bream bags, fish to 9lb) to Kelston (nr Bath), including Newton St Loe and Saltford; most coarse fish, including carp and tench, few large trout; st £28, conc, from local tackle shops and Hon Sec. Amalgamated Fisheries Ltd (formerly BB&WAA) has stretch at Swineford.

Bath (Avon). Coarse fish; barbel present from here to Limpley Stoke; few large trout. Also good base for Rivers Chew and Frome, with reasonable trout fishing. Some free Avon fishing at Pulteney Weir d/s to Newbridge, along towpath; Bathampton Weir u/s to car park, most of footpath. Amalgamated Fisheries Ltd (formerly BB&WAA), has water at **Kensington Meadows**; **Windsor Bridge** (a short section of left bank d/s of bridge); **Lambridge** (300 metres from the d/s end of the rugby ground to the old tip field; **Grosvenor** (from the Grosvenor footbridge d/s on the right bank for ¾m to just behind the Morrisons supermarket, plus 1 field d/s on left bank from the bridge, approx E1/4m; also **Shackells Lake**, Lower Hamswell; mixed coarse; dt £6. Good trout fishing in tributary streams, all preserved. **Kennet and Avon Canal** to Winsley Hill preserved by Bathampton AA; assn also fishes on Newton Park (mainly carp), Hunstrete (3 lakes totalling 10 acres); dt; and Lydes Farm (now re-opened), also Box Brook nr Bathford on A4 (fly only for brown trout on st only); and River Chew at Compton Dando; fly only Mar15 to Jun 15, then coarse; contact Hon Sec. National Trust has coarse (carp, chub, perch, roach) Bath Lakes (the lower of the 3 lakes at Prior Park Landscape Garden; enquire Avon & Tributaries AA; members only. Tackle shop: Bacon's Tackle, 83 Lower Bristol Rd BA2 3BQ (tel:

01225 448850) for Bathampton AA waters. Hotels: Bailbrook Lodge; Eagle House.

Bathampton (Avon). All-round fishing (barbel, roach, chub, pike, bream). Amalgamated Fisheries Ltd (formerly BB&WAA) has water at **Bathmpton Weir Pool**; the rights extend from the weir d/s a short distance; also the Amalg's **Bathford Candy's** waters extend 2 fields u/s from the tollbridge for approx 1½m; permits £45, conc £25, dt £6. Bathampton AA has water here, and at **Kelston, Newton St Loe, Newbridge, Saltford**, and on **Kennet and Avon Canal, Hunstrete, Newton Park** (possibly the most prolific carp fishery in the area) and Lydes Farm, and **Box Brook**; members only; st £28, conc, from Hon Sec and tackle shops in Bristol, Bath, Keynsham, and Chippenham. Hotels: Cranleigh; Eagle House.

Claverton (Avon). Bathampton AA has 2m; very good chub, and barbel; other coarse fish; st £28, conc, contact Hon Sec; local tackle shops. Amalgamated Fisheries Ltd (formerly BB&WAA) has 2m stretch from Midford Brook, d/s to the railway embankment, passing under Dundas Aqueduct, including Midford Brook from the B3108 road bridge to the main river; membership £45, conc £25, dt £6. Hotel: Limpley Stoke Hotel.

Warleigh (Avon). Amalgamated Fisheries Ltd (formerly BB&WAA) has fishing u/s and d/s of the Dundas Aqueduct.

Limpley Stoke (Wilts). Good all-round fishing; large carp, with tench, chub, roach bream and trout; fly-fishing on **River Frome** at Freshford and **Cam Brook** at Midford; preserved by Avon & Tributaries AA. Amalgamated Fisheries Ltd (formerly BB&WAA) has fishing at **Haydens Field** and the **Cabbage Patch**; from the mouth of Midford Brook, u/s for approx ½m; and Midford Brook itself, u/s to the B3108 road bridge. Amalg also has

Avoncliffe to Limpley Stoke, divided into 3 match zones. Bathampton AA holds **Kennet and Avon Canal** from Limpley Stoke to confluence with Avon at Bath (5½m): dt from Hon Sec, tackle shops. Hotel: Limpley Stoke Hotel.

Midford (Avon). **Midford Brook**; trout only; preserved and stocked by the Avon & Tributaries AA.

Freshford (Avon). Amalgamated Fisheries Ltd (formerly BB&WAA) has water on Avon; from behind the sewerage works, nr Freshford railway station for 1¼m d/s to the bungalows at Limpley Stoke; dt £6. **Frome**: trout, coarse fish, stocked and preserved by Avon & Tributaries AA; from Avon up to Farleigh Hungerford; limited dt for members' guests; assn also has part of Avon (coarse), Freshford to Avoncliffe; fly only water on **Midford, Wellow** and **Cam Brooks**. Amalgamated Fisheries Ltd also has water on **Cam Brook** (Dunkerton); trout and coarse; dt £6.

Bradford-on-Avon (Wilts). Coarse fish, including pike, few trout. **Kennet and Avon Canal**; coarse fish.

Melksham (Wilts). Coarse fish, few trout. Avon AC has 5m of river and 4m of canal; dt £3 from tackle shops or Hon Sec. Amalgamated Fisheries Ltd (formerly BB&WAA) has **Lacock** (National Trust) stretch, 1½m u/s from bridge; excellent barbel; permits £45 pa, conc £25; dt £6; steep banks; Amal also has 2m at **Queenfield Farm**; 3 fields left and d/s; 2 fields right and u/s to Mead Farm waters; tickets from Lacock sub-PO shop, 12 High Str, SN15 2LQ (tel: 01249 730305). Leech Pool Farm has coarse fishing at **Broughton Gifford**. Tackle shop: Avon Angling & Sports, 13 Bath Road, Melksham SN12 6LL (tel: 01225 702219).

Chippenham (Wilts). Chub, barbel, bream, perch, roach, carp, pike. Chippenham AA. see website (web: www.chippenhamac.org.uk) has water (river and lake), details from Hon Sec; st £30, dt (part river only) from Premier Angling; who also have dt for **Sabre Lake**, coarse with carp; this lake is owned by Amalgamated Fisheries Ltd (formerly BB&WAA); night annual permits on this lake £50. Amalgamated Fisheries Ltd also have Tockenham Reservoir at Lyneham; 12 acres, 94 swims; carp to 30lb, bream to 15lb, tench to 7lb, large catches of roach and crucians; full permit-holders only, £45; night fishing £50; the Amalgamation also has about 1½m of river between here and **Lacock**. Calne AA has **River Marden**, st £22, dt £3.50, from Premier Angling (below). Devizes AA waters: 15m of **Kennet** and **Avon Canal**, 1m of Avon at Beanacre, Melksham, various coarse, dt £3.50, conc. Avon AC has Avon from Beanacre to Whaddon; also Kennet and Avon Canal from Semmington Road Bridge to Kings Arms at Hilperton, st £15, dt £3, con; tickets from Premier Angling or Hon Sec. These and others from Premier Angling, 19 New Road, Chippenham SN15 1HJ (tel: 01249 659210; web: www.premierangling.com); other tackle shops: T K Fishing Tackle, 123a London Rd, Calne SN11 0AQ (tel: 01249 812003); The House of Angling, 60 Commercial Road, Swindon SN1 5NX (tel: 01793 693460/431026. Mill Farm Trout Lakes, Southcross Lane, Worton, nr Devizes SN10 5UW (tel: 01380 813138), 2 dt lakes, 3½ acres each;

£15 2 fish, £21 3 fish, £27 4 fish, £32 5 fish; Bill Coleman. Ivy House Lakes, nr Swindon SN15 4JU, all species, carp to 20lbs; dt £7 1 rod, £8 2 rods, conc; P and J Warner (tel: 01666 510368).

Christian Malford (Wilts). Several fields controlled by Amalgamated Fisheries Ltd (formerly BB&WAA) here; at Upper Christian Malford, the fishing extends for approx 2m u/s under M4 bridge to just below weir; at Lower Christian Malford, Amalg has 1½m from car park d/s; Amalgamated Fisheries Ltd also has fishing at **Hungerdown Meadow, Sutton Benger**; waters extend for one field above M4 bridge and 2 fields below, to just above Weir, approx ¾m total. Calne AA has two meadows on church side; tickets from T K Fishing Tackle, 123a London Rd, Calne SN11 0AQ (tel: 01249 812003). Somerfords FA has water upstream from Seagry to Kingsmead Mill (part of it, from Dauntsey road bridge, (is trout water) and 2m above Kingsmead Mill on left bank and 1m on right bank; good chub and perch; assn also has water on **Frome**; dt for trout and coarse fishing issued. Golden Valley FC has water at Seagry.

Malmesbury (Wilts). Amalgamated Fisheries Ltd formerly BB&WAA) has approx 1½m d/s from bridge (**Daniel Well**); permits £45 pa, conc £25, dt £6; Amalgamation also has fishing on **Burton Hill Lake**; dt £6 (available from Malmesbury main PO.

Tributaries of the Avon (Bristol)

FROME (Bristol). Rises near Chipping Sodbury and joins Avon estuary near Bristol. Small tributaries upstream provide ideal conditions for trout. Fishing on **Mells River**, **Whatley** and **Nunney Brooks**. Coarse species are barbel, bream, carp, eel, perch, roach, tench, chub and grayling. At

Stapleton, Amalgamated Fisheries Ltd (formerly BB&WAA) has water from bridge d/s on left bank to Wickham Hill Bridge, and then on both banks down to the weir; dt £6 from tackle shops.

CHEW: From confluence to Compton Dando, coarse fish; thereafter, trout.

Keynsham (Avon). Keynsham AA has fishing (see Avon).

Malmesbury (Wilts). Free fishing on Environment Agency licence at Sherston Avon u/s of Cascade at Silk Mills; Tetbury Avon u/s Station Yard Weir, Fire Station, left bank. Club also has long stretch of **Woodbridge Brook**.

Chewton Keynsham (Avon). Approx 1m of water, d/s to Rock Mill Cottages held by Amalgamated Fisheries Ltd (formerly BB&WAA); dt £6. Stretch in Keynsham Park free to licence holders.

Compton Dando (Avon). Mainly trout, grayling and dace. Keynsham AA also has water from Keynsham Mill to Compton Dando; all coarse fishing; apply Keynsham Angling Centre, 3 Station Rd, Keynsham BS31 2BH (tel: 0117 986 7507; see website for more info: www.keynsham-angling.co.uk).

Pensford (Avon). Trout and coarse fish. Lakes: **Hunstrete Complex Lakes**, nr Keynsham; three lakes with carp, tench, bream, roach, perch; Bathampton AA; members only; additional special dt must be obtained before fishing from local tackle shops; st £28, conc from Hon Sec and tackle shops; disabled platforms. Hotel: The Grange Hotel.

Stanton Drew, **Chew Magna**, **Chew Stoke** (Avon). Trout dominant; some roach and dace; no spinning; dt from local inns and Bristol tackle shops from June 15 to Sept 30 (Mon-Fri only). Amalgamated Fisheries Ltd (formerly BB&WAA) has ¾m right bank u/s from Bonds Bridge to the brook at the top of the upper meadow; dt £6. (For Chew Reservoirs, see Somerset (lakes and streams).

BOYD BROOK: Trout in upper reaches, coarse fish; Golden Valley FC has stretch above and below Bitton.

CAM BROOK: Trout. Avon & Tributaries AA has water (members

only). Cameley Trout Lakes are at Temple Cloud; st and dt, apply to J Harris, Hillcrest Farm, Cameley, Temple Cloud, Bristol BS39 5AQ (tel: 01761 452423); tickets available in car park.

BYE (BOX) BROOK: Wild brown trout, grayling. Bathampton AA has water from Shockerwick to **Box**, 2m; fly only; members only from Bath or Bristol tackle shops; st £35 and specialist information only from: A Wallace, 53 Edgeworth Rd, Kingsway, Bath BA2 2LT (tel: 01225 422491). By Brook Fly FC and Two Mills Flyfishers has water for members. Manor House Hotel, Castle Combe, Nr Bath SN14 7HR (tel: 01249 782206; see website for more info: www.manorhouse.co.uk), has ½m of good trout fishing in grounds; dt available. Tackle shop: Premier Angling, 19 New Road, Chippenham SN15 1HJ (tel: 01249 659210; web: www.premierangling.com); Steves Tackle, 35 George Street, Warminster BA12 8QB (tel: 01985 847634/847652).

FROME: Coarse fish, trout.

Frome (Som). Frome & Dist AA has twelve miles above and below town, and coarse fishing lake at Marston, 3m from Frome; regular matches.

Witham Friary Lake, coarse fishing open all year, Witham Hall Farm, Witham Friary, nr Frome (tel: 01373 836239); dt water; mixed coarse. Tackle shops: Tight Lines Angling, 20 Christchurch Street West, Frome BA11 1EG (tel: 01373 455001). Hotel: George, Market Place.

Woolverton (Avon). Trout, coarse fish.

MARDEN: Coarse fish, trout.

Calne (Wilts). Trout, barbel, chub, rudd, carp, golden orfe, tench, pike, perch, roach, dace, bream; fly fishing 1 Apr-15 Jun; 6m held by Calne AA: st & dt from T K Tackle; assn also fish section of R Avon at Christian Malford, and Spye Park Lake.

Disabled stages available, jun coaching and matches. **Bowood Lake**, large pike (to 33lb), perch, carp, tench, roach; details from Bowood Estate, Calne, Wilts SN11 0LZ (tel: 01249 812102), who issue st £195.50; North end of lake private;

note: access to lake only at Pillars Lodge entrance on Calne - Melksham road. Tickets for Sabre Lake, nr Calne, and other local waters, from T K Tackle, 123a London Rd, Calne SN11 0AQ (tel: 01249 812003).

AVON (Hampshire)

In years gone by the most famous mixed fishery in England. In its upper reaches, the Avon is a typical chalk stream, populated by free-rising trout and grayling.

Christchurch (Dorset). Avon and Stour. Excellent sea and coarse fishing in Christchurch Harbour; bass, mullet, flounders and (higher up) dace, roach, bream, carp and eels. Christchurch AC waters include several stretches of Dorset Stour lakes and gravel pits with large carp and pike; membership £140 per annum (plus joining £20); dt for these waters can be obtained from tackle shops; season June 16 to Mar 14 inclusive; stillwaters all year (members only); coarse fishing dt £11 for up to 2 rods; £6 for concessions; tackle shops will supply brochure on request and sae; permits for fishings on the Stour available locally (see also Stour, Dorset); for other salmon and sea trout fishing apply early to Hon Sec. Small coarse fisheries in vicinity: Gold Oak Farm, Hare Lane, nr Cranborne BH21 5QT (tel: 01725 517275): seven lakes with carp and tench, dt £7, £5 half day, evng £3, conc; Turf Croft Farm Fishery, Forest Rd, Burley, nr Ringwood BH24 4DF (tel: 01425 403743), dt £10; telephone for reservation; **Hordle Lakes**, Golden Hill, Ashley Lane, **New Milton** SO41 0GD (tel: 01590 672300; web: www.hordlelakes.co.uk): coarse fishery on seven lakes; dt on site. Good sea fishing at Mudeford; boats. Tackle shops: Davis Fishing Tackle Shop, 71-75 Bargates, Christchurch BH23 1QE (tel: 01202 485169; www.davistackle.co.uk). Hotel: Belvedere Guest House, 3 Twynham

Avenue BH23 1QU (tel: 01202 485 978).

Winkton (Dorset). Winkton Fishery; season is June 16 to Mar 14; large chub and barbel, pike; also dace, roach, perch; dt £11, junior & conc £6 through Christchurch Angling Centre (tel: 01202 480009)

Ringwood (Hants). Ringwood & DAC has fishing on rivers as follows: **Avon**; Breamore, 1½m (barbel, chub), Fordingbridge (trout), Ibsley, 2m (S and specimen coarse fish), side streams at Ibsley, Ringwood, 2m (coarse fish), Fordingbridge Park, ¼m (coarse fish); **Stour**; fourteen stretches totalling more than 12m (coarse fish); also seventeen still waters totalling over 200 acres; dt for some of the waters from tackle shops. Dt £11 from local tackle shops for ¾m both banks above Ringwood, Lifelands Fishery, Christchurch AC water; 1¼m E; bank below and several coarse fishing lakes, dt £11. **High Town**, Ringwood: 23 acre pit containing most coarse species; no dt; Ringwood & DAC; and several other waters in area. Tackle shops: Ringwood Tackle, 5 The Bridges, West Str, Ringwood. BH24 1EA (tel: 01425 475155; see website for more info: www.ringwood-tackle.co.uk); Hotels: Star Inn, Lamb Inn, White Hart.

Fordingbridge (Hants). Trout, grayling, perch, pike and roach. Park Recreation Ground has fishing, dt from garage next to park; Council grounds staff; Sept to Mar. Burgate Manor Farm Fishery let to Wimborne AC, see website for more info: www.wimborneanglingclub.co.uk), who also have 1m of Avon, and 11 coarse lakes; mostly members only with guests; st £102 + £10 joining fee, conc, from Wessex Angling Centre, 321 Wimborne Rd, Poole BH15 3DH (tel: 01202 668244; see web for more info: www.wessexangling.co.uk); Bournemouth Fishing Lodge, 904 Wimborne Road, Bournemouth BH9 2DW (tel: 01202 514345; web: www.bournemouthfishinglodge.co.uk). Two excellent stillwater fisheries in the vicinity: **Damerham** and **Lapsley's Fishery** (ex Allens Farm). Hotel: Ashburn.

Breamore (Hants). Bat and Ball Hotel (tel: 01725 512252) has 1½m of salmon, trout and coarse fish on dt basis.

Salisbury (Wilts). Avon, Bourne, Ebble, Nadder and Wylye; trout, grayling, coarse fish; preserved. Salisbury & Dist AC has water on Avon at the following locations: **Charford** (1m located 7m S of city); 3m of water within city limits (although in the countryside); **Durnford** (3m of chalk stream; 20 beats); **West Amesbury** (2m of double/single bank; stocked brown trout; late grayling); Ratfyn Farm and Countess Water (1m of double bank and ¾m single bank); at **Fordingbridge** there is club water (Burgate) behind the Game Conservancy; coarse fish, occasional salmon; at **Durrington** there is a joint venture between the Club and Parish Council, offering a chance to cast a fly at a trout before fishing on the Club's premium waters; the club also has coarse fishing on **Petersfinger Lakes**, 2m E of City; **Steeple Langford Lakes** (two), 10m W; **Wellow Lakes** (two), 12m E, towards Southampton; membership circa £170 (game), conc; coarse £78 + joining fee £20; limited dt for waters within city boundary from Reids Tackle or John Eadie (both

below); club also issues permits for Charlton fishing, from Post Office, Downton Cross Roads; all details from Secretary. The Piscatorial Society has Avon fishing nr **Amesbury**, members only. Other local clubs: Tisbury AC has **Wardour Castle Lake** and **Dinton Lake** with bream, carp, roach, tench, perch; and 3m of R Nadder, with brown trout, dace, roach, chub, perch etc; membership £30, conc, guest dt £5 from Hon Treasurer. Downton AA has 2½m of Avon with specimen chub, roach, barbel, etc. Membership for both these at Reids Tackle (below). London AA has **Britford Fishery**; 5m of Avon, Old River and Navigation; excellent coarse fishing, good sport with trout, some salmon; members only: st £43, conc, dt £10, conc £5, dt on bank. **Avon Springs Fisheries**, Recreation Rd, Durrington SP4 8HH (tel: 01980 653557; web: www.fishingfly.co.uk): two spring fed lakes beside R Avon, of three and five acres, stocked with rainbow trout from 2lbs to double figures; best rainbow, 17lbs 4oz; best brown, 17lbs, 9oz; prices are as follows; lakes: £404 for 10 tickets; full dt £45, 4 fish limit; half-day £35, 3 fish; evening £25, 2 fish; juv £28; river: dt £55, 2 fish limit; accom, nr fishery: Parkhouse Motel. Waldens Farm Fishery, Waldens Estate, **West Grimstead** SP5 3RJ (tel: 01722 710480), has coarse fishing on 5 lakes, total 7.5 acres; dt £7 (payable on bank), conc; has match lake with 27 pegs for hire to clubs. Tackle shops: John Eadie, 20 Catherine Str, SP1 2DA (tel: 01722 328535); Reids Tackle, Witherington Farm Fisheries, Downton, Salisbury SP5 3QT (tel: 01722 711616; see website for more info: www.reidstackle.co.uk). Hotel: Old Mill House, Warminster Rd, South Newton SP2 0QD (tel: 01722 742458; see website for more info: www.salisburymill.co.uk). (special terms for Salisbury & Dist AC members; guest house can arrange fishing); White Hart; Red Lion; Grasmere, Harnham; The Lamb on the Strand, Hinton; Bell, South Newton.

Netheravon (Wilts). Trout, grayling; preserved. The 6m from **Enford** to **Bulford** is The Services Dry Fly FA (Salisbury Plain) water; strictly members only (restricted to serving or retired service personnel and MOD employees), dt from Hon secretary.

AVON (Hampshire) tributaries

BOURNE: Enters near Salisbury. Trout, grayling, coarse fish. Fishing stations: **Porton** and **Salisbury** (Wilts). Salisbury & DAC has premium water at **Hurdcott**; ¼m of clear brook style fishing: fine trout and grayling; apply Hon Sec; waiting list for premium fisheries; club also has ¾m u/s (Upper Bourne near Gomeldon); also just above Salisbury: 1½m at Laverstock.

EBBLE: Joins Avon below Salisbury; good trout fishing, but mostly private. Salisbury & DAC has about ½m.

WYLYE: Trout, grayling.

Wilton (Wilts). 6 miles preserved by Wilton Fly Fishing Club, full-time keeper, club room, wild brown trout (stocked with fry), grayling; closed membership; no dt. Wylye Fly FC has stretches at **Steeple Langford**, **Quidhampton**, and **Barford St Martin**; members and their guests only.

Stapleford (Wilts). Salisbury & Dist AC has fishing here (3m W of Salisbury); ¾m fine dry fly; excellent autumn and winter grayling; members only; club also has fishing 12m west of Salisbury near Wylye Village; ½m single bank; also at Deverill.

Warminster (Wilts). **Longleat** Estate: excellent coarse fishing in three lakes in Longleat Park; Bottom and Middle, mixed fishing, Top Lake, specimen carp; tickets are issued by Bailiff, Nick Robbins Longleat Estate, Warminster BA12 7NW (tel: 01985 844496; mobile: 078896 25999); dt £8 (Bottom and Middle, £10 Top Lake, 7am to 7pm; 24 hr £20 3 rods (all lakes); the Estate also has

Shearwater Lake, mixed coarse, 37 acres, off A350 at Crockerton (dt £8, £15 24-hour). The Sutton Veny Estate, Eastleigh Farm, Bishopstrow, Warminster BA12 7BE (tel: 01985 212325), lets rods on 4m of Wylye, chalk stream dry fly and upstream nymph only, brown trout Autumn nymph fishing for grayling; upper beats are for wild fish; all c&r only.

NADDER: Tributary of Wylye. Trout, grayling, roach, dace, chub. Mostly preserved (landowners). Fishing stations: **Wilton**, **Tisbury**. Tisbury AC has 3m, guest tickets from Hon Treasurer (see clubs). Salisbury & DAC has a short stretch at Barford St Martin; also at Bulbridge, on the Earl of Pembroke's estate; also Nadder Meadows, a newly acquired stretch on a 3-year lease: dry fly or nymph for trout and grayling; the Club also has 2m of coarse fishing 10 mins from Salisbury, with views of Cathedral and water meadows; membership circa £170 + joining fee, conc (coarse £80 + joining); limited dt from Reids Tackle or John Eadie (below). Tisbury AC also has Old Wardour and Dinton Lakes; carp, roach, pike, tench; st £30, conc. Fishing Breaks Ltd, The Mill, Heathman Street, Netherwallop, Stockbridge, Hants. SO20 8EW (tel: 01264 781988; web: www.fishingbreaks.com) has day rods. Tackle shop: Reids Tackle, Witherington Farm Fisheries, Downton, Salisbury. SP5 3QT (tel: 01722 711616;see website for more info: www.reidstackle.co.uk); John Eadie Ltd, 5B Union Str, Andover SP10 1PA (tel: 01264 351469). Hotel: South Western; Tisbury AC HQ.

AXE

Rises in Dorset and flows south to the English Channel at Axemouth. Trout, sea trout and salmon. Fishing difficult to come by, but one or two hotels can provide facilities, and two major clubs.

Seaton (Devon). Trout, salmon, some sea trout. Axe estuary fishable (for bass, mullet, flounders, etc). Salmon, sea trout, rainbow and wild brown trout fishing on 1m at **Colyton**: dt from Mr Graham Pady, Higher Cownhayne Farm (Teasel Cottage), Colyton, EX24 6HD (tel: 01297 553040).

Axminster (Devon). Axe, Yarty; trout and salmon. Trouting good especially in April and May. At **Uplyme**, Amherst Lodge, Dorset DT7 3XH (tel: 01297 442 773): day ticket fishery with six fly fishing lakes; brown and rainbow; dt £15 c&r, 2 fish £15 to 6 fish £35; tuition by arrangement. Taunton FFC has six stretches from Forde Abbey to just s of Axminster; members only, ,apply Hon Sec; club also has one stretch of Yarty near Membury. Hotel: Bear Inn, Colyton.

Crewkerne (Som). Stoke-sub-Hamdon AA has trout fishing from Bow Mills to Creedy Bridge on **Parrett**; members only; also have **Bearley Lake**. Yeovil AA has trout and coarse fishing on **Yeo** and tributaries. Trout fishing in **Sutton Bingham Reservoir**, near Yeovil; enquiries to Fishing Lodge BA22 9QH (tel: 01935 872389). Tackle shops: Yeovil & Dist Angling Centre, 27/29 Forest Hill, Yeovil BA20 2PH (tel: 01935 476777).

BLACKWATER

Rises in NW of county, flows by Braintree to Maldon and empties into North Sea through large estuary. Coarse fish include pike, chub, rudd and some carp.

Maldon (Essex). Maldon AS has river and pond fishing in Maldon area; three stretches totalling 1½m of **R Blackwater**; all coarse; carp over 30lb, tench, roach, rudd, bream, dace, gudgeon, perch, pike; membership £70, conc; dt £5 (canal only) (night st £55) for Chelmer from bailiff on bank or tackle shop. Cemex Angling **Chigborough** gravel pits of 8½ acres; coarse fish: tench, bream, crucian, etc; st (2 rods) £70, conc £42 (for RMC Angling see Chertsey). Tackle shop: East Essex Angling Centre, 48 The Street, Heybridge, Maldon CM9 4NB (tel: 01621 840414). Hotels: Swan, White Hart, King's Head.

Chigboro Fisheries, Heybridge, Maldon, Essex CM9 4RE (tel: 01621 857368 or 852113; more on web: www.chigboro-fisheries.co.uk); 4 lakes: Home Water 16 acre lake with brown and rainbow trout of average weight 2lb 12oz, fly only; lake record, 19¼lb: 4 boats and wheelyboat; Rook Hall, 6 acres; Priory Pool, 1 acre; plus big trout water; dt £20 (1 fish + c&r, or 2 fish) all extra fish @ £6 per fish; Beanmere: £35 2 fish, av 6-7lb, min 3lb 8oz; tuition available; coarse fishing: four lakes, 20 acres total, large carp to 37lb and other species, incl catfish to 64lb; st tickets £100 for 10 visits (24 hours); dt £8; £15 24 hrs; corporate days welcome; match lakes £10/day, min 4 people.

Witham (Essex). Blackwater and **Brain**. Coarse fish. Kelvedon & DAA has 7½m from here to **Braintree**, and also below Witham towards Maldon; members only; sub £65, conc, from tackle shops, including Angling Essentials, 14 Church St, Witham CM8 2JL (tel: 01376 512255; web: www.anglingessentials.com). **Olivers Lake**, 3 acres; **Bovingdon Mere**,

Hatfield Peverel; 4 acre lake coarse fishery: Colchester APS waters.

Kelvedon (Essex). Kelvedon & DAA has numerous stretches as well as water on Suffolk **Stour**; Essex **Colne**; still waters; **Tiptree Reservoir**; three 2-acre pits at **Layer Marney** near Tiptree, Colchester; **Hunts Farm Reservoir**, near Maldon; **Shemming's Pond** near Kelvedon: all good mixed fisheries; two 6-acre **Silver End Pits** near Witham; **Seabrook's Reservoir**, at Little Leighs nr **Chelmsford**, (**Martin's Pits** (one small pit only) in Tiptree is now Colchester APS water) (all good carp waters); all members only; sub £65 (conc) from tackle shops in Chelmsford, Witham, Tiptree and Colchester. Tackle shop: Angling Essentials, 14 Church St, Witham CM8 2JL (tel: 01376 512255; web: www.anglingessentials.com).

Coggeshall (Essex). Coarse fish. Colchester APS fish Houchins Reservoirs, (see Colchester).

CHELMER and CAN: Coarse fish:

Chelmsford (Essex). River stocked: roach, dace, bream, tench, carp, pike, perch, chub. Public fishing in town parks. Chelmsford AA has fishing as follows: Boreham Mere, Blunts Mere, Cants Mere, Braxted lakes, Willows, Broads Green, danbury trout lake, and Wick Mere, **Ulting**; Broads Mere and Tuftnell Mere, **Great Waltham**; all mixed fisheries, with carp, bream, tench, rudd, roach, barbel, chub; all members only; st £64 + £6 entry, conc, plus other prices; instruction is offered, and matches are organised; contact Hon Sec; assn also has river from Chelmsford to confluence with Blackwater. Water also fished by Kelvedon & DAA. Newland Hall Fisheries, **Roxwell**, Chelmsford CM1 4LH (tel: 01245 231463), have Brook, Moat, Park and Osiers Lakes, total of approx 10 acres; the fishing is for carp, roach, tench, etc, with high match weights; platforms for disabled; dt available. Blasford Hill Fisheries, Little Waltham, nr Chelmsford CM3 3PL (tel: 01245 362772): lakes stocked with carp, tench, roach, and other species; dt £10 2 rods, conc, on bank. Tackle shops: Ronnie Crowe Ltd, 63 Maldon Rd, Gt Baddow, Chelmsford CM2 7DN (tel: 01245 471246), who has permits for local clubs. Hotels: County; White Hart, Witham.

BLYTH (Northumberland)

Rises near Throckington and flows 20m to North Sea at Blyth. Trout and grayling with coarse fish (especially roach) in lower reaches. Stretches from Stannington A1 Bridge to Bedlington controlled by Bedlington & Blagdon AA, members only, no tickets.

BRUE

Rises in Mendips and flows to Bristol Channel at Burnham. Coarse fish throughout. From West Lydford to Glastonbury, a number of weirs provide deep water in which coarse fish predominate. A good late season river, contains numbers of most coarse species.

Highbridge (Som). Roach, bream, etc. North Somerset AA fishes Brue and rivers **Kenn**, **Apex Lake**, between Highbridge and Burnham, (match record 85lb), Newtown Lake, Highbridge (carp to 20lb), Walrow Ponds, North Drain; st £25; wt £13; dt £4.50, conc (all assn waters); from local tackle shops. Weston-super-Mare AA has **River Axe** fishing, Old R Axe, South Drain. Bridgwater AA has **Huntspill River**, **Kings**

Sedgemoor Drain, North and South Drains; dt £7 from Somerset Angling (below). **Emerald Pool Fishery**, Puriton Rd, Highbridge TA9 3NL (tel: 01278 794707), purpose-made lake stocked with large carp, tench, perch, bream, etc; dt and refreshments on site. **Lands End Fisheries**, Heath House, Wedmore BS28 4UQ (tel: 07977 545882), four lakes with various carp species and 15 others; dt £6, conc. Permits for these and local fishings, and club information from tackle shops. Highbridge AA is part of N. Somerset AA. Further information from Hon Sec. BB&WAA has 3 fields u/s of Black Bull Bridge on R Brue (right bank), plus 2 fields u/s on left bank, and 2 fields d/s on right bank; as well as Pawlett Ponds and other lakes; st £45, conc £15, dt £6. Tackle shop: Veals Fishing Tackle, 1A Church Str, Highbridge TA9 3AE (tel: 01278 786934; see website for more info: www.veals4carp.com). Hotel: The George (clubs accommodated) is recommended locally, for visiting anglers.

Bason Bridge (Som). Area around milk factory noted for carp; fish run up to 35lb or so. Also roach, chub, tench, perch and pike. BB&WAA has 150 metres on right bank d/s from bridge to old station house: dt £6. Contact Veals Fishing Tackle, 1A Church Str, Highbridge TA9 3AE (tel: 01278 786934; web: www.veals4carp.com).

Mark (Som). Carp, pike, perch, roach, chub, tench. North Somerset AA has 3 to 4m on North Drain; dt and wt from Hon Sec (see Highbridge). Inn: Pack Horse.

Glastonbury (Som). Roach, bream, chub, etc, throughout the River Brue. Glaston Manor AA has approx 12m of water from Lydford to **Westhay**; membership and st from tackle shops. At **Tealham Moor**, BB&WAA has 2m from North Drain Pumping Station u/s; dt £6 from tackle shops. Tackle shops: Street Angling Centre, 144 High Str, Street. BA16 0NH (tel: 01458 447830; Thatchers Pet & Tackle, 18 Queen St, Wells BA5 2DP (tel: 01749 673513).

BUDE RIVER AND CANAL

Bude Canal AA has 1¼ miles of wider than average canal with good banks and full variety of coarse fish; dt on bank.

Bude (Cornwall). Bass from beaches, breakwater and rocks; bass and mullet in estuary of Bude River; details from Hon Sec Bude & Dist SAA. Bude AA has fishing on a total of 6½m of banks of **Tamar** and **Claw** from near Bude to half way to Launceston; wild brown trout and some dace in downstream beats; dt water; membership enquiries to Hon Sec, Bude AA. **Tamar Lake** and **Crowdy** (trout reservoir) controlled by South West Lakes Trust (see Cornwall lakes, etc). **Bude Canal** (roach, bream, eels, dace, perch, carp to 25lb and tench) 1m from town centre towards Marhamchurch leased by Bude Canal AA; dt, conc; on bank; close season April and May. Tackle shop: Waterfront Fishing & Shooting, Lower Wharf Centre, The Wharf, Bude EX23 8LG (tel: 01288 359606).

BURE

(see Norfolk and Suffolk Broads)

CAMEL

A spate river, rising on Bodmin Moor near Davidstow, flowing about 30m to enter the Atlantic between Pentire and Stepper Points. Salmon, sea trout and small brown trout. Grilse from June, with the main runs in October, November and December. Sea trout from June to Aug. Best brown trout fishing in tributary **De Lank**. Salmon fishing in upper reaches dependent on heavy rainfall. There is a voluntary restriction in operation covering the whole river. No fishing in April; in Sept all sea trout to be returned, and a limit of 2 salmon per day and 4 per week (10 per season), and 4 sea trout per day; also no selling of fish and no maggots. A salmon broodstock scheme operates Nov/Dec when rod-caught salmon can be donated to a designated hatchery (contact Jon Evans, tel: 01208 812447; web: www.rivercamel.org, for River Camel information, and the webcam for river levels). Salmon season ends 15 Dec; anglers requested to contact respective club secretaries wishing to partake in the scheme.

Wadebridge (Cornwall). Trout, sea trout, salmon; good mullet, bass and flounder fishing in tidal reaches; estuary is now a bass nursery area, restrictions apply; shore fishing allowed. Approx 6m held by Wadebridge & Dist AA at Pencarrow, Grogley, Wenford, and **River Allen** above Sladesbridge, 5½m; membership of Wadebridge & Dist, via long waiting list; dt on all waters except Grogley, salmon up to £25 (depending on season), wt £60 up to 30 Sept only; thereafter, 1 Oct to 30 Nov £100; daily limit of 4 sea trout (2 salmon) dt at £25 Oct/Nov, £15 May to Sept, conc; contact Jon Evans, Hon Sec of River Camel Fishery Assn and Fowey River Assn (tel: 01208 812447; email: jonrevans@aol.com). Accom plentiful. (For sea fishing see Padstow.)

Bodmin (Cornwall); between Camel and Fowey; Bodmin AA issues visitor permits (ten per day) on some 12 miles of the best water; details from Hon Sec; wt £45, dt £15 from May 1-Nov 30; no permits in Dec; st (long waiting list) from Hon Sec; concessions for jun for dt, and OAP on membership; free maps from Hon Sec, on receipt of email address. Liskeard & DAC has stretch of Camel; apply to local tackle shops (see Liskeard). Mr T Jackson, Butterwell, Nanstallon, Bodmin, PL30 5LQ (tel: 01208 831515; web: www.butterwellfishery.co.uk) has 1½m salmon and sea trout fishing, occasional day permits with preference given to residents, fly only, June-Aug; any method for salmon 1 Sept to 15 Dec; self-catering cottage and limited B&B. **Fenwick Trout Fishery**, Old Coach Rd, Dunmere, Bodmin PL31 2RD (tel: 01208 78296) features two acre lake stocked with rainbow trout, record 13lbs 3oz, and 570 yards of salmon fishing on R Camel; waters closed for time being owing to weed problem. Lakeview Country Club, **Lanivet** PL30 5JJ (tel: 01208 831808) has 3 coarse fishing lakes, 6 acres, stocked; specimen carp, bream, tench; dt £10. **Innis Moore Trout Fishery**, 7 acres. Contact tackle shop: Roger's Tackle Shop, Stan Mays Store, Higher Bore St, Bodmin PL31 1JW (tel: 01208 78006) (closed Wednesday), who also issue tickets for Fowey (Lostwithiel AA and Liskeard AA waters), Camel (Bodmin AA waters), Wadebridge AA on Camel. Also prime private beat on Camel: contact Bill Pope, 3 Tresarrett Manor Farm, Blisland PL30 4QQ (tel: 01208 850338).

CHESHIRE (Lakes/Reservoirs)

APPLETON RESERVOIR, nr **Warrington**. Mixed fishery and a few trout controlled by Warrington AA; members only; no dt. This is one of the larger fishing clubs of Great Britain, controlling approximately fourty plus fisheries on rivers, lakes, reservoirs, canals and pools; contact Hon Sec. Tackle shop: Baileys Bait and Tackle, 20 Parksway, Woolston, Warrington WA1 4BP (tel: 01925 823441; web: www.baileystackle.com).

ASTBURY MERE, great carp water, owned & run by Stoke-on-Trent Angling Society, membership only via website, (se website for more info: www.sotangling.co.uk), also **Bolesworth Castle**.

ARNFIELD RESERVOIR, Tintwistle, nr Manchester. Trout fishery various tariffs, (see website for more info: www.arnfield-fly-fishery.com)

BLACKSHAW MOOR LAKES, Leek. 4 acre coarse fishery; carp, tench, bream, roach. Prince Albert AS water, members only.

BOOTHS MERE run by Altrincham and District Angling club, contains bream, tench, roach, perch, pike & carp, membership and more info on website: (web: www.bagup.org.uk).

BOSLEY RESERVOIR. Fishing station: **Bosley**. Roach (good), bream, pike, perch, carp. Prince Albert AS water, members only.

BOTTOMS RESERVOIR. Macclesfield, Cheshire. Prince Albert AS; dt, conc , issued from Barlows of Bond Street, 47 Bond St, Macclesfield SK11 6QS (tel: 01625 619935); United Utilities (tel: 01457 851087).

BROOKSIDE CARP FISHERY, Church Lane, Betley, Crewe, CW3 9AY, 2 coarse lakes, (tel: 01270 820528/820271)

CAPESTHORNE POOLS, **Siddington**, including **Redesmere**. Large carp, tench, bream, roach, rudd and pike. Prince Albert AS waters, members only.

DOVE MERE, SAND MERE, Allostock, Knutsford. Prince Albert AS waters, members only; heavily stocked, including large carp.

CHESHIRE FISHING FISHERY, Tattenhall, Nr Chester, CH3 9NT, 10 lakes mixed fishery, 5 trout lakes for rainbows & 5 coarse lakes good variety of fish, many different dt prices available, tackle hire, (tel: 01829 770041; see website for more info: www.cheshirefishing.co.uk).

CLAY LANE TROUT FISHERY, Clay Lane, Mobberley, Cheshire, WA16 7BH, 2 acre lake for brown, rainbow, golden, blue, brook & tiger trout, various dt available, (tel: 01565 873337; see website for more info: www.claylanetroutfishery.co.uk).

DANEBRIDGE FISHERIES, Danebridge, Wincle, Macclesfield, SK11 0QE, trout fishing on 1 lake, dt available, also c&r tkt, (tel: 01260 227293; see website for more info: www.danebridgefisheries.com).

FIELDS FARM FISHERY, Fields Farm, Congleton Road, Sandbach, CW11 4TE, 5 pools, dt £6, conc £4, evening tkt £3, (tel: 01270 753074; web: www.fieldsfarmfisheries.co.uk).

GAWSWORTH FISHERY, Wall Pool Lodge, Church Lane, Gawsworth, Macclesfield, SK11 9RQ, 5 coarse fishing lakes & canal, most species of fish, dt £6 1 rod, £8 2 rods, (tel: 01260 223442; see website for more info: www.gawsworthfisheries.com)

GREAT BUDWORTH MERE (or **MARBURY MERE**). Nr. **Northwich**, 50-acre lake holding good bream, carp, pike, etc; Northwich AA; apply to Hon Sec; members only; holiday permit £14 for 7 days; £28 for 2 weeks; applicants must live more than 50m away; apply by post. **Pickmere** and **Petty Pool** are assn waters nearby; carp to 40lb plus.

HAMPTON SPRINGS FISHERY, Shay Lane Hampton Malpas, SY14 8AD, 8 spring fed coarse fishing lakes, match & pleasure waters and a specimen carp lake, dt £7, junr £4, £2 for extra rod, eve tkt £4 for all, (tel: 01948 820789; see website for more info: www.hamptonsprings.co.uk)

HORSECOPPICE RESERVOIR, Macclesfield. Trout fishing leased to Dystelegh Fly FC; members only.

LANGLEY BOTTOMS and **Lamaload Reservoirs**. Nr **Macclesfield**. Langley Bottoms (dt £5 from Barlows) now coarse fishing, Prince Albert AS. Lamaload, Good fly fishing for trout. Prince Albert AS. Limited dt £12, non members require key for £3, from Barlows of Bond Street, 47 Bond St, Macclesfield SK11 6QS (tel: 01625 619935); United Utilities water (tel: 01457 851087).

LEADBEATERS RESERVOIR. Controlled by Prince Albert AS, members only; United Utilities water (tel: 01457 851087). Tackle shop: Barlows of Bond Street, 47 Bond St, Macclesfield SK11 6QS (tel: 01625 619935).

LYMM DAM, Lymm, beside A56. 15 acre lake, good all year round fishing with big carp (a lot in excess of 20lb) and pike, bream (to 10lb 3oz); Bay Malton AC water, many pegs, bookable for matches to a maximum of 30 pegs; contact Hon Sec for this and seven other dt waters or ranger (tel: 01925 758195).

MARTON HEATH TROUT POOLS, Pikelow Farm, School Lane, Marton, SK11 9HD, 3 lakes for brown & rainbows, tuition, refreshments, flies, toilets and tackle are all available and the lakes are suitable for disabled anglers, (tel: 01260 224231)

MEADOW FISHERY, Mickle Trafford, Warrington Road, Chester, CH2 4EB, 3 lakes for trout fishing, (tel: 01244 300236, for more info: web: www.meadowfishery.com)

MILTON GREEN FISHERY, Tattenhall, CH3 9EE, 4 lakes for coarse fishing, for more info (tel: 01829 771 102)

OULTON MILL POOL. Fishing station: Tarporley. Well stocked with good carp, bream, tench and pike. Dt from Mill Office.

RIDGEGATE RESERVOIR, Macclesfield, brown and rainbow. Macclesfield FC, dt from Hon Sec; some river and stream fishing for members only; United Utilities water (tel: 01457 851087).

ROMAN LAKES LEISURE PARK, Marple, nr Stockport SK6 7HB (tel: 0161 4272039; see website: www.romanlakes.co.uk). Roach, perch, tench, bream to 8lb, carp to 30lbs, pike to 20lbs. Dt £5 per rod, £4 juniors under 16, at site (day permits).

ROSSMERE LAKE. 6 acres. Fishing station: **Wilmslow**. Heavily stocked; coarse. 80 match pegs. Prince Albert AS, members only.

TATTON MERE, Knutsford, WA16 6QN, species include carp, roach, bream, tench, perch and pike, dt £6, child £3, (tel: 01625 374400, for more info: web: www.tattonpark.org.uk)

TEGGSNOSE RESERVOIR, Macclesfield. Now coarse, with carp to 20lb, bream 5lb plus, tench, roach, perch; Macclesfield Waltonian AC; dt £6, only from Barlows of Bond Street, 47 Bond St, Macclesfield SK11 6QS (tel: 01625 619935); United Utilities water (tel: 01457 851087).

THORNEYCROFT HALL LAKES, Gawsworth. Prince Albert AS water, members only; carp, tench, roach, pike.

WESTLOW MERE FISHERY, Nr Congleton, 18 acres trout water, dt available, (tel: 01260 270012, and for more info: www.westlowmere.co.uk)

WINTERLEY POOL, Winterley, Crewe, CW1 5TR, coarse fishing on 2 pools, carp, tench, roach & pike, (tel: 01270 254221)

COLNE (Essex)

Rises in north of county and flows to North Sea via Colchester. Improving as coarse fishery.

Colchester (Essex). Colchester APS, (web: www.caps.org.uk) controls one short stretch, with roach, chub, perch, pike, bream, dace; no tickets; the society's other waters, with excellent catfish, carp and pike fishing, include **Layer Pit**; pike, perch, bream, roach, rudd, tench, carp; **Houchins Reservoirs**, Coggeshall, coarse, large catfish; **Snake Pit**, large carp and catfist, pike, tench; **Inworth Grange**, Tiptree (mainly carp); several stretches on Suffolk **Stour**; **Hatfield Peverell Lakes**; **Olivers Lake** at Witham; **Prestons Lake**, 20 acre mixed coarse fishery, and Bovingdon Lakes, good carp; members only on all waters, membership from Angling Essentials (below): st, conc to jun, OAP, disabled; the Society also has Joyces Chase at Goldhanger, nr Maldon; largely carp; Rockingham Farm, Layer Marney; Colne at Fordham. Colchester Piscatorial Society has water on **Langham Ponds**, 5m of **Stour** and 1m of **Colne**; st , members only; also lakes at **Ardleigh** and **Boxted**. ½m of Colne fished by Kelvedon & DAA; no dt; members' guests only; also 2 meadows of River Stour at Dedham; and stretches of Blackwater from Stisted to Kelvedon; also 6 stillwaters near Kelvedon, Braintree and Witham; membership £65, conc; apply Hon Sec. Colchester tackle shops: K D Radcliffe Ltd, 150 High Str, CO1 1PG (tel: 01206 572758); Wass's Fishing Tackle, 73a London Road, Copford, Colchester CO6 1LG (tel: 01206 212478/212492). Witham tackle shop: Angling Essentials, 14 Church St, Witham CM8 2JL (tel: 01376 512255; for more info. web: www.anglingessentials.com). Hotels: George, Red Lion.

Aldham (Essex). Colnes AS has water at Fordham and Aldham, six stretches of Stour near Bures, three reservoirs; most species; improved access for disabled; members only; contact Hon Sec or Sudbury tackle shops.

Halstead (Essex). Halstead and Hedingham AC waters are: stretch of R Colne; several miles of **R Pant**; **Halstead Reservoir**, with carp, tench, rudd; **Stebbing Reservoir**, with carp, bream, perch; Gosfield Sandpits, with tench, bream, perch, etc; membership £25, conc, from Bill's Tackle, 95-97 High St, Braintree CM7 1JS (tel: 01376 552767); no dt. For **Rayne Lodge Fishery**, Rayne Rd, Braintree CM7 2QT (tel: 01376 345719), brick-built toilets in top car park, carp, roach, rudd, bream, koi, crucian carp, tench: dt at the lakes, £8 for 1 rod, £11 for 2 rods, conc £5.

COQUET

Rises in Cheviots and enters North Sea near Warkworth. Salmon, sea trout and trout. Sport still very good. Facilities for visitors. Good run of spring salmon.

Warkworth (Northumberland). Trout, sea trout; salmon from Feb onwards to late summer and autumn. Duke of Northumberland leases large part of his water to Northumbrian Anglers Federation; st £95 salmon, £65 trout; conc for OAP; visitor all-fish all-waters (excl tidal) wt £75; dt £30; applications to Head Bailiff, 15 Woodlands, Rothbury, Morpeth, Northumberland, NE65 7XZ (tel: 01669 620984; for more info. web: www.northumbriananglersfed.co.uk), or tackle dealers for trout permits only; additional permit for tidal section £70 (additional to other permits). Permits for 2m beat, situated 1m d/s from Weldon Bridge, Longframlington,

Feb-Aug £20 or Sept-Oct £25 (salmon, brown, sea trout), from The Weldon Gun Room, Weldon Bridge, Longframlington, NE65 8AY (tel: 01665 570011; for more info. web: www.weldongunroom.co.uk).

Acklington (Northumberland). Trout, sea trout and salmon. Northumbrian AF water on Coquet and tributary, Thirston Burn.

Felton (Northumberland). Salmon, sea trout (spring and autumn), trout; river permit from water bailiff, Head Bailiff, 15 Woodlands, Rothbury, Morpeth, Northumberland, NE65 7XZ (tel: 01669 620984; www.northumbriananglersfed.co.uk).

Weldon Bridge (Northumberland). Nearest station: Morpeth, 9½m. Trout (sea trout and salmon, late summer and autumn). Anglers Arms Hotel, Weldon Bridge, Long Framlington NE65 8AX, has fishing, maximum 3 rods, on 1m north bank; free for residents, otherwise £10 dt (tel: 01665 570655).

Rothbury (Northumberland). A late salmon run and excellent sea trout fishing in June and Oct; brown trout, including fish to 3lb; Northumbrian AF has 14m of Coquet (see Warkworth). **Caistron Trout Fishery** approx 5M west of Rothbury, dt on site various pricing, boat available, (tel: 07944 178 045; web: www.caistrontroutfishery.co.uk).

Fontburn Reservoir, Ewesley, nr Rothbury, trout fishery of 87 acres with wild browns, and stocked browns, blues and rainbows; record rainbow, 26lb 8oz; brown 9lb 4oz; dt water (tel: 01669 621368); apply shop. Hotels: Queens Head, Rothbury; Newcastle House, Rothbury; Three Wheat Heads, Whitton Farm House, Thropton.

Holystone (Northumberland). Salmon (late), trout; mostly private.

Harbottle (Northumberland). Good trout and some late salmon fishing on Coquet and Alwin. Upper Coquetdale AC has extensive parts of upper river; members only.

CORNWALL (streams, lakes, etc)

ARGAL RESERVOIR, nr **Penryn**. South West Lakes Trust coarse fishery of 65 acres, with carp to 35lbs, large perch, pike to 35lb, bream, tench, eels. St £140 (day and night), £100 st (day), 24-hour £10, dt £5.50, conc £4.50; open all year, 24 hr day. Permit from self-service kiosk.

BAKE FISHING LAKES, Trerulefoot, Saltash, PL12 5BW, 4 lakes for coarse fishing, one for specimen carp, 3 lakes for rainbow & brown trout fishing, wide range of dt available, (tel: 01752 849027; web: www.bakelakes.co.uk)

BOSCATHNOE RESERVOIR, Penzance; 4 acre, stocked South West Lakes Trust coarse fishery, with bream, roach, tench, crucian carp, gudgeon, eels; st £140 (day and night), £100 st (day), 24-hour £10, dt £5.50, conc £4.50, from Newtown

Angling Centre, Newtown, Germoe, Penzance TR20 9AE (tel: 01736 763721; see website for more info: www.newtownangling.com).

BUSSOW RESERVOIR St Ives. South West Lakes Trust coarse fishery, with bream, roach, tench, carp, eels, rudd, perch, etc. Open all year, 24 hour day; St £140 (day and night), £100 st (day), 24-hour £10, dt £5.50, conc £4.50 from Newtown Angling Centre, Newtown, Germoe, Penzance TR20 9AE (tel: 01736 763721; see website for more info: www.newtownangling.com). Other coarse fisheries near St Ives: **Nance Lakes**, with carp, roach, rudd, bream; tickets from Trevarrack, Lelant, St Ives TR26 3EZ (tel: 01736 740348) or on-site; **Sharkeys Pit, Hayle**: carp, roach, rudd, gudgeon, eels (currently closed); tickets for both lakes from

Newtown Angling Centre, Newtown, Germoe, Penzance TR20 9AE (tel: 01736 763721; see website for more info: www.newtownangling.com).

CAMEL, Rises near Davidstow, Cornwall, then flows south and then north-west via Wadebridge and Padstow into the sea at Padstow Bay; salmon, sea trout.

Bodmin. Bodmin AA have day-ticket water (£15), 1 May to 31 November; apply Hon Sec or R Lashbrook, Roger's Tackle Shop, Stan May's Store, Higher Bore Str, Bodmin PL31 1DZ, (tel: 01208 78006). Liskeard & DAC share a beat with Wadebridge & DAA at Poleys Bridge. Wadebridge & DAA have 10 miles of Camel at Bodmin, Wadebridge and Wenford; dt £15 until end Sept, Oct/Nov £25 from Ego Menswear, Orchard Walk, Eddistone Road, Wadebridge (tel: 01208 813666); Roger's Tackle Shop, Stan May Stores , Higher Bore Street, Bodmin (tel: 01208 78006); also 1m River Allen at Wadebridge.

COLLIFORD LAKE, Liskeard. 900 acres. South West Lakes Trust fly fishery, with natural and stocked brown trout only. Full st £140, dt £12, conc £10; no boats; open 15 Mar-12 Oct; permits from Jamaica Inn, Bolventor (tel: 01566 86250). Just off the A30 west of Colliford Lake is **Temple Trout Fishery**, Temple Rd, Temple PL30 4HW, various dt on site, rainbow, brown, blue & golden trout, (tel: 01208 821730)

CONSTANTINE BROOK. Fishing station; **Constantine**, ns Penryn WR, 6m. Trout. Constantine joins estuary of **Helford River**. Sea fishing off Helford Mouth (see Falmouth). Ashton, near **Helston**, **Wheal Grey Pool**; stocked coarse fishery with large carp.

CROWDY RESERVOIR, Camelford. 115 acre South West Lakes Trust wild trout fishery; fly, spinning and bait fishing zoned; season Mar 15-Oct 12; free to valid EA licence holders.

Approx 8 wiles east is **Rosepark Trout Fishery**, Tresibbett, Altarnun, Bodmin Moor, PL15 7RF, 2 lakes, approx 2.5 acres of water, rainbow & brown trout, dt on site, (tel: 01566 86278.)

DRIFT RESERVOIR. Near **Penzance** (3m); sixty-five acres in quiet valley; wild brown and stocked rainbow trout (fly only); float tubing available; limit, 3 rainbows/day (max 9 per week), 3 wild browns; st, dt, eveng tickets available, from West Cornwall Angling, 1 Alexandra Road, Penzance TR18 4LY (tel: 01736 362363), Newtown Angling Centre, Newtown, Germoe, Penzance TR20 9AE (tel: 01736 763721; see website for more info: www.newtownangling.com); honesty box in boathouse. 6m from Penzance, **Tin Dene Fishery**: 2 pools with carp to 29lbs, roach, rudd, etc; dt £4, £2.50 jun: Mr John Laity, Bostrase, Millpool, Goldsithney TR20 9JG (tel: 01736 763486); wheelchair access.

HAYLE. Trout and sea trout; Estuary now a prime spot for gilthead bream, bass and mullet fishing from the Estuary; some bass on Gwithian Rocks. South West Lakes Trust has mainly coarse and fly fishing in the area. Marazion AC has coarse fishing in St Erth, nr Hayle and Whealgrey at Ashton; tickets, dt £5 (conc) from Newtown Angling Centre, Newtown, Germoe, Penzance TR20 9AE (tel: 01736 763721; see website for more info: www.newtownangling.com). Tackle shops: Angove Sports, 40 Fore St, Copperhouse, Hayle TR27 4DY (tel: 01736 752238); The County Angler, 39 Cross St, Camborne TR14 8ES (tel: 01209 718490.

TREE MEADOW TROUT FISHERY, Deveral Road, Fraddam, Nr Hayle, TR27 5EP, various dt on site & tackle shop, (tel: 01736 850899)

INNIS FLY FISHERY, Innis Moor, Penwithick, St Austell, PL26 8YH, 3 lakes for rainbow trout, 5 Fish £25, 3 fish £19, 2 fish half day £13, (tel: 01726 851162; see website for more info: www.innis-fly-fishery.co.uk).

LUXULYAN RIVER. Fishing station: **Par**. Polluted, but tributary **Redmoor River** has good head of trout. Sand-eels at Par Sands, mackerel from the bay, pollack by Gribben Head and near harbour, and bass between harbour and Shorthorne Beach. Boats for hire at Par and Polkerris. Hotels: Royal, Par; Carlyon Bay, St Austell.

LYNHER. A noted salmon and sea trout river with a reputation for early fish. Rises on Bodmin Moor, as do Fowey and Camel, and runs to Tamar estuary via Saint Germans. Smaller than Fowey but more natural, there being no big reservoirs in catchment to modify spates. Good runs of sea trout (end Mar to end May), smaller sea trout and grilse from June, and good summer night fishing for sea trout. Season ends 14 Oct, end of season has salmon fishing, given some rain.

Callington (Cornwall). Liskeard & DAC has several good beats on **Lynher**, also on **Fowey** and **Inny River** (tributary of Tamar), all providing salmon and sea trout; for sea trout only, club has beats on **Seaton** and **West Looe Rivers**. Visitor tickets from Tremar Tropicals, 11 Market St, Liskeard PL14 3JH (tel: 01579 343177; see website for more: www.tremartropicals.fsnet.co.uk); East Looe Chandlers on the quay in E Looe; or Roger's Tackle Shop, Stan Mays Store, Higher Bore St, Bodmin PL31 1JW (tel: 01208 78006) (closed Wednesday); membership applications from Trevor Sobey, Trevartha Farm, Pengover, nr Liskeard PL14 3NJ (tel: 01579 343382). **Siblyback** and **Colliford** lakes are near. Tickets from Summerlands Tackle, 16-20 Nelson Rd, Westward Ho! EX39 1LF (tel: 01237 471291; see website for more info: www.summerlands.co.uk).

MAWGAN PORTH POOLS, Retorrick Mill, Mawgan Porth, Newquay, TR8 4BH, 2 lakes 47 peg lake, plus specimen pool with 11 pegs, carp, tench, bream, gold & blue orfe, (tel: 01637 860770)

MELANHYL. Newquay. Brown trout and occasional sea trout. Contact. Sec, St Mawgan AC or The Merrymoor Inn, Mawgan Porth (tel: 01637 860258) for tickets.

OLD MILL RESERVOIR, Dartmouth. 4 acre South West Lakes Trust coarse fishery with carp, roach, rudd, bream, tench, eels; open all year, 24 hour day; season ticket syndicate only, limited availability, on application to South West Lakes Angling Assn, Lidn Park, Quarry Crescent, Pennygillam Industrial Estate, Launceston, Cornwall PL15 7PF.

PETHERICK WATER. Fishing station: **Padstow**. Small trout. Estuary now a bass nursery area, prohibiting fishing for bass. Other species scarce.

PORTH RESERVOIR, Newquay. 40 acres, South West Lakes Trust fishery, bream, rudd, tench, roach, perch, eels, and carp; open all year, 24 hour day; St £140 (day and night), £100 st (day); 24-hour £10, dt £5.50, conc £4.50 from self-service unit at car park.

RETALLACK WATERS, St Columb, TR9 6DE (tel: 01637 881160): 20 acres of water, with separate coarse and specimen lakes; carp and pike to 25lb, roach, rudd, tench, eels; dt water, tackle and bait from 'The Tackle Cabin' on site; open seven days a week. **Meadowside Fisheries**, Winnards Perch, St Columb Major TR9 6DH (tel: 01637 880544; two lakes with carp and mixed coarse fish; fishery is incorporated within the Cornish Birds of Prey Centre; members only; £80 2 rods, £100 3 rods; one-off payment £20 for net and mat which stays on site.

SEATON RIVER. Rises near Liskeard, runs through Hessenford to the sea across the beach at Seaton. It fishes well for sea trout from May onwards. Liskeard & DAC has lower stretch, which is the only fishable part of river. Tickets from Tremar Tropicals, 11 Market St, Liskeard PL14 3JH (tel: 01579 343177; see website for more: www.tremartropicals.fsnet.co.uk); East Looe Chandlers on the quay in E Looe; or Roger's Tackle Shop, Stan Mays Store, Higher Bore St, Bodmin PL31 1JW (tel: 01208 78006) (closed Wednesday).

SIBLYBACK LAKE, Liskeard. 140 acres. Fly only, premier South West Lakes Trust fishery, with stocked rainbow trout; season Mar 25-Oct 31; dt £20 from self-service kiosk; st £435, conc; Watersports Centre, Siblyback, Common Moor, Liskeard; info: (tel: 01579 346522); boats (bookable in advance) and bank fishing.

ST ALLEN RIVER, Truro. St Allen and **Kenwyn** Rivers at Truro; **Tresillian** River (3m from Truro on St Austell road); **Kennel** or **Perranarworthal** River (5m from Truro); a few sea trout run into **Lower Tresillian** River. Truro tackle shops: City Angling Centre, Palace Yard, Pydar Str, TR1 2AZ (tel: 01872 275340); WSB Tackle Ltd, Unit 3a Goonhavern Ind Est, TR4 9QL (tel: 01872 571752, 0870 7490281; web: www.wsbtackle.com).

ST TINNEY FARM, Otterham, PL32 9TA, 5 coarse lakes, dt on site, small tackle shop also on site, (tel: 01840 261274; web: www.st-tinney.co.uk)

STITHIANS RESERVOIR, Redruth. 247 acres. South West Lakes Trust brown and rainbow trout fishery; fly only; season Mar 15-Oct 31; full st £230, dt £14.50, conc £13; limited boats, bookable 24 hrs in advance; permits from Watersports Centre, Stithians (tel: 01209 860301).

TAMAR LAKE (UPPER), Bude. 81 acres, South West Lakes Trust coarse fishery with carp, bream, tench, roach, rudd, eels; st £140 (day and night), £100 st (day) from SWLT; 24-hour £10, dt £5.50, conc £4.50, from self-service kiosk on site. Tamar Lake (Lower) now closed, other than to very limited season permit holders only; apply to Trust office.

TIDDY. Fishing station: **St Germans**. Sea trout to Tideford, trout elsewhere.

VALENCY. Fishing station: **Boscastle**. Valency is 4m long; holds small trout and few sea trout. Sea fishing good for bass, mackerel, pollack, etc.

WEST LOOE RIVER. A small spate river running through Herodsfoot to the Looe estuary. Good runs of sea trout, which fish well in summer, and a small run of salmon. Liskeard & DAC has water. Information and tickets from Tremar Tropicals, 11 Market St, Liskeard PL14 3JH (tel: 01579 343177; see website for more info: www.tremartropicals.fsnet.co.uk); chandlers at The Quay, East Looe; Fishing Mayhem, 2 Higher Lux Street, Liskeard PL14 3JU (tel: 01579 340447); or Roger's Tackle Shop, Stan Mays Store, Higher Bore St, Bodmin PL31 1JW (tel: 01208 78006) (closed Wednesday). **East Looe River** also fishes well for sea trout, but local knowledge is required. Hotels: Punch Bowl, Lanreath. Looe: good sea fishing. Boats available, tackle and tickets from East Looe Chandlers on the quay in E Looe.

WHITEACRES COUNTRY PARK, White Cross, **Newquay**, TR8 4LW (tel: 01726 862519); eleven stocked coarse fishing lakes and 2 specimen lakes in 100 acres; carp to 28lb, tench 7lb, catfish to 68lb, large bream and roach; night fishing on specimen lakes, matches and competitions.

CUCKMERE

Formed by two tributaries, which join at Hellingly, and enters sea at Cuckmere Haven, west of Beachy Head. Mainly coarse fish, roach, bream, chub, carp, perch, dace and pike.

Alfriston (E Sussex). Fishing controlled by the Southdown AA (web: www.southdown-angling.org), membership from The Polegate Angling Centre or any Eastbourne tackle shop; membership £65 + £10 joining fee; conc; dt for guests only, £5, for several club fisheries. Below Alfriston Lock the river is salt and tidal, being open to mouth at Cuckmere Haven. In summer grey mullet are plentiful near Exceat Bridge (Eastbourne-Seaford road); also bass and occasionally sea trout. Cuckmere, tidal to $\frac{1}{2}$m upstream from Alfriston. At **Berwick**, Southdown AA has coarse fishing on Batbrooks Pond; club also fishes **Langney Haven**, **Hurst Haven**, **Kentland Fleet**. Tickets from Tony's Tackle, 211 Seaside, Eastbourne BN22 7NP (tel: 01323 731388; see website for more info: www.tonystackle.co.uk); Polegate Angling Centre, 101 Station Road, Polegate BN26 6EB (tel: 01323 486379).

Hailsham (E Sussex). Cuckmere 2m. Southdown AA (formed 1997 from merger of Hailsham AA and Compleat Anglers FC) has extensive fishing on Cuckmere between Alfreston and Horsebridge (Hailsham); **Wallers Haven** (3m shared with Hastings, Bexhill & Dist FAA (members only), good carp, tench and pike); **Pevensey Haven**. Polegate Angling Centre, 101 Station Road, Polegate BN26 6EB (tel: 01323 486379); Tony's Tackle, 211 Seaside, Eastbourne BN22 7NP (tel: 01323 731388; see website for more info: www.tonystackle.co.uk).

CUMBRIA (lakes)

(See English Lake District)

CUMBRIA (streams)

ANNAS. Fishing station: **Bootle**. Small trout; good sea trout and salmon; late. Millom & DAA has fishing, also water on **Esk**, **Lickle**, **Irt**, **Duddon**, **Devoke Water**, **Black Beck** and **Lazy**; st £110 + £20 entrance from Hon Sec; wt £75; dt £15 from Millom TI; Broughton TI; Haverigg PO; Waberthwaite PO; Bridge Garage, Holmrook. Environment Agency licences from Waberthwaithe P O, Haverigg PO, Millom PO.

BLACK BECK. Fishing station: **Green Road**. This stream rises on Thwaites Fell, and in $7\frac{1}{2}$m reaches Duddon Estuary. Millom & DAA has water, entrance: Race Grove, The Green, nr Millom; tickets from secretary.

CALDER. Empties into Irish Sea some 150 yards from mouth of Ehen. Salmon, sea trout, a few brown trout. Sea trout run large; 10lb and more. Best June onwards: good salmon fishing, July-Oct.

CRUMMOCK BECK (tributary of Waver). Flows into Holm Dub, tributary of Waver. Free, but difficult to fish.

Leegate (Cumbria). Waver, 1m E.

EHEN. Outflow of Ennerdale Water. Flows into Irish Sea on west coast of Cumberland. Salmon, sea trout (June to Oct) and brown trout. Egremont & Dist AA has good salmon, sea trout and brown trout fishing for 7m both banks, from **Egremont** to Sellafield;

st £40, wt £30 (visitors), no dt, conc; browns and sea trout 15 Mar-30 Sept; salmon to Oct 31 apply Hon Sec. Good fishing in upper reaches held by Wath Brow & Ennerdale AA; st and wt: from Cleator Stores, 50 Main Str, Cleator CA23 3BX (tel: 01946 810038); Wath Brow PO. Hotels: Royal Oak, Beckermet.

ELLEN. Rises on Great Lingy Hill and flows into the Solway Firth at Maryport. Salmon and sea trout runs increasing; best late July onwards. Good brown trout fishing (Mar-June best).

Aspatria (Cumbria). Trout; sea trout, and salmon from July. Hotels: Grapes, Sun.

ESK. Rises near Scawfell and flows into Irish Sea near Ravenglass. Good runs of salmon, sea trout, July onwards.

Ravenglass (Cumbria). Salmon, sea trout. Rivers Mite and Irt here join Esk estuary (see also Irt). Prince Albert AS has south bank on Esk at Ravenglass, in three stretches. Membership, wt and dt from Sec. May and June are best for trout; Sept, Oct for salmon.

Eskdale (Cumbria). Trout, sea trout, salmon; various private owners. Millom & DAA fishes Dalegarth Estate water, two beats at Gill Force and Beckfoot; good fly fishing, and worming; also stretch at Brantrake, with sea trout from June, salmon from July, Sept-Oct best months; contact Hon Sec. Inexpensive fishing on **Wastwater** and **Burnmoor Tarn**. Good sea fishing for bass within five miles.

IRT. Outflow of Wastwater, joining Esk in tidal water. **Bleng** is main tributary.

Runs of salmon, brown and sea trout July onwards, some heavy fish taken, especially sea trout; Gosforth Angler's Club has National Trust stretch; no boats, weekly permits obtainable: apply Hon Sec.

Holmrook (Cumbria). Salmon, sea trout, brown trout. Short free stretch in village. Millom & DAA holds two stretches, approx 1,200 yds, Drigg Holme Bridge and Carlton; tickets from Holmrook Garage; Waberthwaithe and Haverigg POs.

Netherwastdale (Cumbria). On **Wastwater Lake**; trout, permits (see English Lake District). Greendale Tarn and Low Tarn feed Wastwater. Sport is good in May and June.

MITE. Flows south for short course from slopes near Eskdale to join estuary of Irt and Esk at **Ravenglass**. A late river. Sea trout, good brown trout, occasional small salmon later on, but few opportunities for visitors.

POAKA BECK. Barrow AA water; no dt with membership by member sponsorship; guest tickets.

WAMPOOL. Fishing stations: **Wigton** and **Curthwaite**. Wampool, under the name of Chalk Beck, rises on Broad Moor. Sea trout in lower reaches mostly free.

WAVER. Trout stream, flowing into the Solway Firth. Some water free, but most subject to agreement by farmers and landowners. Waver has run of sea trout and herling, particularly in its lower reaches.

WHICHAM BECK. Fishing Station: **Sile Croft**. After a course of 6m runs into Haverigg Pool, which joins Duddon estuary at Haverigg.

DARENT

Rises by Westerham and enters Thames estuary at Dartford. Water retention has been improved by weirs. Modest trout fishing in upper reaches, coarse fishing downstream, roach, dace, chub.

Dartford (Kent). Dartford & DDAPS has lakes along river valley which hold coarse fish, (Brooklands, see Kent) plus stretches of **Medway**, **Beult** and **Lesser Tiese**, members only, waiting list; the Society also has **Sutton at**

Hone Lakes: carp, tench, roach, bream, rudd, pike, perch; also **Horton Kirby Lakes:** carp, tench, roach, bream, rudd, crucian carp, pike, perch; st, conc. Cemex (formerly RMC) Angling has three lakes at Sutton at Hone; 1 small lakes (No 1) is Silver permit lake with carp, tench and other species; st £38, conc £23 (2 rods); Lake 2 (4 acres) is a Gold Venue with a large head of 30lb mirror, and common carp to 45lb; ticket £350 (3 rods); waiting list; Lake 3 is Gold water; carp to 38lb, tench, bream, pike; £175 (3 rods), no conc. (For Cemex (formerly RMC) see Chertsey). **Darenth Fishing Complex** (tel: 01322 290150): two syndicate lakes, Tiplake, and Big Lake, which contain carp over 57lbs; and six day (of which 3 are night) ticket lakes, including **Long Lake**, with good head of small carp, and other coarse fish, incl occasional catfish to 65lbs; also 3 stocked beginners' ponds fish 1lb-4lb; also 36 peg match lake & specemin carp lake, fish to 30lb. Lamorbey AS fishes 3 acre lake at Lamorbey Park, **Sidcup**; 28 swims, tench, rudd, crucian carp; dt on part of water; access for disabled. Tackle shop: Mark II Angling, 24-26 High Street, Crayford DA1 4HG (tel: 01322 554545; web: www.mark2angling.co.uk); Tackle Box, 251 Watling St, Dartford DA2 6EG (tel: 01322 292400; web: www.tacklebox.co.uk); Danson Angling, 159 Blendon Road, Bexley DA5 1BT (tel: 020 8298 9090; web: www.dansononline.co.uk).

Shoreham (Kent). Trout, chub, roach, dace. Darent Valley Trout Fishers have good 2½m stretch of water between Shoreham and Eynsford; strictly members only (waiting list).

Sevenoaks (Kent). River preserved. Holmesdale A&CS has the following waters, for members and guests only: **Chipstead Lakes**, with bream, roach, perch, rudd, carp, pike; **Longford Lake**; similar variety of coarse species; carp to 30lb plus; **Montreal Park Lake** nr **Riverhead**, Sevenoaks; mainly junior water, but will become match lake in 2010; joining fee £20, annual subscription £60, conc; guests with member £6, conc, from tackle shops: Biggin Hill Angling Centre, 216-218 Main Road, Biggin Hill, Westerham TN16 3BD (tel: 01959 570265; web: www.bhac.co.uk); A & I Fishing Tackle, 33-35 High St, Green Street Green, Orpington BR6 6BG (tel: 01689 862302); Manklows Kit & Tackle, 44 Seal Road, Sevenoaks TN14 5AR (tel: 01732 454952). Manklows will supply useful general information about local fishing.

Tributary of the Darent

CRAY: Coarse fish.

Crayford (Kent). **Ruxley Pits, Orpington**, coarse fish; Orpington & Dist AA has five lakes, 40 acres in a Nature Reserve, all coarse fish, pike to 28lbs, large tench; members and guests only; no dt. Tackle shop: A & I Tackle, 33-35 High St, Green Street Green, Orpington BR6 6BG (tel: 01689 862302). Other Assn waters: R Medway and Eden nr Tonbridge; R Teise at Yalding.

DART

The East and the West Dart rise two miles apart on Dartmoor. East Dart runs to Postbridge and thence to Dartmeet, where it unites with West Dart which flows through Two Bridges. The West Dart above Dartmeet (with the exception of the right bank from Huccaby Bridge to Dartmeet), and the East Dart above Dartmeet (with the exception of the left bank from Wallabrook Junction to Dartmeet), belong to Duchy of Cornwall. The river has runs of salmon and peal (sea trout). Best months for salmon are May to Sept in the lower reaches and also higher up, depending on water. For peal May to Sept are favoured in the main river, and tidal water of Totnes Weir Pool in May and June. Wild brown trout are mainly small.

Dartmouth (Devon). In river, fishing for ray, bass (shore only), whiting, mackerel, garfish, mullet, and pouting. Coastline for dogfish, bull huss, bass, wrasse, whiting, dab, plaice, turbot, brill and conger. Boats effective in river and sea. Skerries Bank, inshore and offshore wrecks popular venues. Flatfish most prolific off Skerries Bank. Dartmouth Angling & Boating A, clubhouse open every Mon, Wed, Fri and Sat (7pm-11pm). Salmon, peal and trout fishing in Dart on Dart AA water (see Totnes, Buckfastleigh); dt £25 salmon or sea trout at Totnes Weir Pool; u/s salmon dt £20; browns £15. Lake fishing on **Old Mill Reservoir**; pike, rudd, etc (see Devonshire, small streams and lakes). Tackle shops: Brixham Bait & Tackle, 10 The Quay, Brixham TQ5 8AW (tel: 01803 853390; see website for more info: www.brixhambaitandtackle.co.uk); Devon Angling Centre, Unit 4/5 Orchard Meadow, Orchard Way, Chillington, Kingsbridge TQ7 2LB (tel: 01548 580888; web: www.anglingcentre.net). Hotels: contact Tourist Information Centre, The Engine House, Mayors Ave, Dartmouth DQ6 9YY (tel: 01803 834224).

Totnes (Devon). Salmon, peal, trout. Dart AA controls 12m Dart from Holne to Totnes; Totnes Weir salmon av 10lb; peal 3lb in April-June and about 1lb thereafter; 4lb and 5lb peal not rare; school peal run from late July to mid-Aug; nearly all peal caught after dark in normal conditions; Aug usually best; fly only for peal and trout; dt £25 salmon or sea trout at Totnes Weir Pool; u/s salmon dt £20; browns £15. Newhouse Fishery, Moreleigh, Totnes TQ9 7JS (tel: 01548 821426), has 3 lakes totalling 4 acres, trout, open all year; also 4 pools on R Avon; prices on request (no EA licence required for lakes as covered by a general licence). New Barn Angling Centre, Totnes Rd, Paignton TQ4 7PT, has 6 coarse lakes (tel: 01803 553602; see website for more info: www.newbarnfarm.com); dt £7 for 2 rods. Hotels: Seymour, Royal Seven Stars. Sea Trout Inn, TQ9 6PA (tel: 01803 762274), is close to the river at Staverton, and exclusively sells tickets on behalf of Dart AA; dt £15 brown trout, £20 sea trout (2 fish limit), £20 salmon; £25 for Totnes Weirpool salmon and seatrout.

Buckfastleigh (Devon). Salmon, peal, trout. SWW Plc has fishery, ¼m Dart, Austins Bridge to Nursery Pool; salmon, sea trout; st, 16 rods. Holne Chase Self Catering Cottages, Poundsgate, near Ashburton, TQ13 7NS (tel: 01747 828170; web: www.holne-chase.co.uk), has about 1m right bank upstream from bridge, with seven pools; fishing for holiday cottage guests only, £25 per rod day; ghillies and tuition if required; can arrange fishing on the Moor with Duchy permit, and a further 9m through the Dart between Holne and Totnes. Tickets from Sea Trout Inn, Staverton TQ9 6PA (tel: 01803 762274), dt £20 salmon, £20 sea trout (2 fish limit), £15 brown trout; fly only; salmon season 1 Feb to 30 Sept;

sea and brown trout 15 Mar to 30 Sept; no treble hook larger that No3; conc.

Princetown (Devon). Permits for salmon and trout fishing on main river, **East** and **West Dart**, **Wallabrook**, **Swincombe** and **Cherrybrook** from most tackle shops in S Devon; also the Prince Hall Hotel, Two Bridges Hotel, both Princetown; Huccabys News, 46 Fore St, Buckfastleigh TQ11 0AA (tel: 01364 643206); and Princetown Post Office (tel: 01822 890212); salmon best May-Sept; charges: S and MT, st

£150, wt £85, dt £30; T, st £70, wt £25, dt £8. Prince Hall Hotel, nr Two Bridges, Dartmoor PL20 6SA (tel: 01822 890403), has fine riverside location; hotel stocks flies and Duchy licences, and will advise on local fishing, tuition, ghillie service, etc.

Hexworthy (Devon); Salmon, sea trout (peal), brown trout. Forest Inn Hotel, Hexworthy PL20 6SD (tel: 01364 631211); dt, wt or st, at hotel, for Duchy of Cornwall water on presentation of EA licence; ghillie, instruction offered; good centre for E and W Dart and Cherrybrook.

DEBEN

Short Suffolk river (about 30 miles long) rising near Debenham and flowing to North Sea near Felixstowe. Coarse fishing.

Woodbridge (Suffolk). Tidal. Roach, pike, tench, perch above town. Club: Woodbridge & Dist AC, who also has Holton Pit and Braxhall Decoy; st £35, dt £6, conc, from Saxmundham Angling Centre; Anglia Photographics & Sport (below). Framlingham & Dist AC (tel: 01473 623228) has half mile one bank River Deben at Wickham Market; also **Hayward's Reservoirs** at **Wickham Market**, **Youngman's Reservoirs** at Charsfield, and one other still water fishery, at **Parham** near **Framlingham**; coarse fishing,

members only, st £35 from Hon Sec, conc; renewal of subscription apply Stuart Clay Traps, Melton IP12 1DG (tel: 01394 385567). Tackle Shop: Saxmundham Angling Centre, Bakery Yard, rear of Market Place, Saxmundham IP17 1AH (tel: 01728 603443); Anglia Photographics & Sports, 63 The Thoroughfare, Halesworth IP19 8AR (tel: 01986 873333). Hotels: Bull, Crown.

Wickham Market (Suffolk). Roach, perch, pike. Woodbridge AC has river and Wickham Market Reservoir.

DERWENT (Cumbria)

Rises on north side of Scafell and flows through Borrowdale, Derwentwater and Bassenthwaite Lakes to the Solway Firth at Workington. Salmon and trout practically throughout length. A late river. Best months for salmon, July to October. Trout fishing on some stretches excellent. River also holds occasional pike and perch.

Cockermouth to **Workington** (Cumbria). Salmon, sea trout, brown trout. Trout and salmon fishing may occasionally be permitted on dt; enquiries to Fishery Manager, Cockermouth Castle (tel: 01900 826320); prices on application. Permits for **Cocker** and **Derwent** also (limited); waters through town can be

fished on permit from Tourist Information Office, Town Hall, Market Place, CA13 9NP (tel: 01900 822634), by residents and visitors in town on weekly basis. Cockermouth AA has water on Cocker (members only) and also on Derwent; apply Hon Sec; and issues dt (enquire first) for **Cogra Moss**. Bowland Game FA has

$2\frac{1}{2}$ miles right bank Derwent above town, the Isel Fishings, resident bailiff; no dt, long waiting list. **Mockerkin Tarn**, stocked with carp. Fishing within reach on Bassenthwaite (LDNPA ticket), Loweswater, Crummock and Buttermere; on National Trust ticket. Nr Cockermouth are Gilcrux Springs Trout Farm, Gilcrux, Wigton, CA7 2QD (tel: 01697 322488), with brown, rainbow, and tiger trout; for evenings, book in advance. Also Ellerbeck Farm and Fishery, Brigham CA13 0SY (tel: 01900 825268), coarse fishing on day permit £5; ticket on bank; touring Caravan Club site. Tackle shops: Graham's Gun and Tackle, 9-15 South William St, Workington CA14 2ED (tel: 01900 605093). Hotels: Trout, Globe; Cockermouth, Pheasant, Bassenthwaite Lake.

Bassenthwaite (Cumbria). Derwent, 1m N; trout, salmon. Lakes: Bassenthwaite; pike, perch, trout, occasional salmon, trout (see English Lake District - Bassenthwaite). Hotels: Pheasant; Armathwaite Hall,

Keswick CA12 4RE (tel: 01768 776551).

Keswick (Cumbria). For rivers Derwent and Greta. Salmon, trout (average $\frac{1}{2}$lb), pike, perch, eels; mid August onwards for salmon. Portinscale to $\frac{1}{2}$m above Bassenthwaite Lake, Keswick AA water, see website for more info: www.keswickanglers.co.uk; assn stocks Rivers Derwent and Greta with 500 12" browns each year; fly only for trout; visitors tickets available; from Keswick PO, CA12 5JJ (tel: 017687 72269) and Youdale's Newsagents, Main Street (tel: 01768 772259); visitors st by application to Sec; tickets issued for Derwent cover Greta also; for full details of water controlled by Keswick AA, write to secretary, enclosing sae, or contact main post office.

Borrowdale (Cumbria). Trout, salmon; gin-clear as a rule and best fished after dark. Lakes: Derwent Water; trout, perch, pike; small charge for fishing. Watendlath Tarn 2m S; Blea Tarn, 4m S; trout. Hotels: Scafell; Borrowdale; Lodore Falls, Lodore, CA12 5UX (tel: 017687 77285).

Tributaries of the Derwent (Cumbria)

COCKER: Salmon, sea trout, trout. July to October best for migratory fish. Mostly private.

Scalehill (Cumbria). Cockermouth. 7m Cocker: Salmon, sea trout, trout. Privately let by National Trust lakes. Hotel: Scale Hill.

Cogra Moss. 40 acre trout reservoir 8m S of Cockermouth. Browns and rainbows. Contact Cockermouth AA; dt available; enquire Hon Sec.

NEWLANDS BECK: not worth fishing.

GRETA: Trout (av $\frac{1}{4}$lb); salmon.

Threlkeld (Cumbria). Keswick AA has fishing here (tickets see Keswick). Best months for salmon Sept and Oct; mostly spinning and worm fishing; fly only for brown trout; apply Hon Sec; st see Derwent. Glenderamackin Beck; trout; fishable throughout length, but very narrow and fish few and far between.

DEVONSHIRE (streams and lakes)

AVON. Rises on Dartmoor and flows 22m SE, entering English Channel near Thurlestone via long, twisting estuary. Tide flows to Aveton Gifford. Trout (3 or 4lb), sea trout, salmon.

Thurlestone (Devon). Near mouth of Avon estuary. Capital bass fishing off Bantham Sands at mouth.

Aveton Gifford (Devon). Sea trout (end of May onwards), some salmon; good dry-fly trout water (3 to the lb). Banks heavily wooded; good wading. Mt, ft, wt, from post office at Loddiswell.

Loddiswell. Brown trout, salmon, sea trout; Avon FA has a total of 14½m; no day tickets; tickets Loddiswell PO TQ7 4QH (tel: 01548 550329), Avonwick PO. Capital bass and pollack in Kingsbridge estuary. Hotels: King's Arms; Buttville; Torcross (for Slapton Ley).

Brent (Devon). Salmon, trout, sea trout. Red Brook, 2m N; trout. Black Brook, 2m S; trout. Hotel: Anchor Inn.

Amherst Fly Fishery, near Lyme Regis, on the Devon/Dorset border; (web: www.amherstlodge.com).

Avon Dam (8m NE of Totnes). South West Lakes Trust, brown trout fishery, zoned worm, spinning and fly fishing free to Environment Agency licence holders; no boats; season March 15-Oct 12; reservoir is about 1 ½m beyond **Shipley Bridge**, car parking on site. **Drakeland Fishery, Hemerdon,** 2 lakes, rainbow & brown trout, dt on site, (tel: 01752 344691)

BELLBROOK VALLEY TROUT FISHERY, Oakford, Tiverton EX16 9EX (tel: 01398 351292); set in picturesque Devon valley; three specimen lakes, min stock 3lb, three normal fishing lakes; specimen fishing, dt £42 4 fish, £35 3 fish, £24 2 fish; various other permits obtainable; record rainbow 2000, 25lb 12oz; tuition by arrangement; corporate party days; accommodation at fishery farmhouse; also self-catering.

BLAKEWELL FISHERY, Muddiford, Blakewell Lane, nr Barnstaple EX31 4ET; brown and rb. trout av. 3lb; various day permits from £30, 6 fish, to £23, 2 fish, from fishery; tackle hire and tuition on site (must be booked); this establishment also runs a commercial fish farm; Richard or John Nickell (tel: 01271 344533).

BURRATOR RESERVOIR, Yelverton. 150 acres, South West Lakes Trust; zoned fly fishing for brown and rainbow trout; open Mar 15-Oct 31; dt £12, st £140 (conc), from Yelverton Garage, 1 Moorland Villas, Tavistock PL20 6DT (tel: 01822 853339).

CRAFTHOLE, nr **Torpoint**. A popular little South West Lakes Trust fishery of 2 acres, dammed, stocked with carp and tench; season permit (limited), syndicate only, no dt; for st contact South West Lakes Angling Assn, Lidn Park, Quarry Crescent, Pennygillam Industrial Estate, Launceston, Cornwall, PL15 7PF.

DARRACOTT, Torrington. 3 acre coarse fishery run by South West Lakes Trust, with carp, tench, bream, roach, rudd, perch, eel; open all year, 24 hour day; st £140 (day and night), £100 st (day), 24-hour £10, dt £5.50, conc £4.50 from N Laws, Summerlands Tackle, 16-20 Nelson Road, Westward Ho! EX39 1LF (tel: 01237 471291)Summerlands Tackle, 16-20 Nelson Rd, Westward Ho! EX39 1LF (tel: 01237 471291; web: www.summerlands.co.uk); or Whiskers Pet Centre, 20 South St, Torrington EX38 8AA (tel: 01805 622859).

ERME. Rises on Dartmoor and flows 14m S to Bigbury Bay. Trout.

FERNWORTHY RESERVOIR, near **Chagford**, on Dartmoor. South West

Lakes Trust; 76 acres, natural and stocked brown trout fishing, largest 4lb 2oz; open April 1-Oct 12; dt £12, conc £10; self-service unit by Boathouse. Contact Ranger on (tel: 01647 277587 or 01647 231403).

FURZEBRAY CARP LAKES, Georgenympton Rd, South Molton, EX36 4ER, 2 lakes, Pads Pool & Specimen lake, dt £10, conc £8 also other prices available, (tel: 01769 572653; see website for more info: www.furzebraylakes.co.uk)

GOODIFORD MILL FISHERY, Kentisbeare, Cullompton, EX15 2AS. 2 coarse lakes with Roach, Rudd, Tench, Perch, Crusians, Bream along with specimen Carp to 34lb, dt £7, conc £5, £2 extra rod. Trout £16.50 (2 fish) upto £30 (5 fish), brown, rainbows & tigers stocked, (tel: 01884 266233; see website for more info: www.goodifordmillleisure.co.uk)

JENNETS RESERVOIR, Bideford. 8 acres, South West Lakes Trust coarse fishery, with carp principally, to 30lb, as well as tench, bream, roach, perch, eels; open all year, 6.30am to 10.00pm; dt £5.50, conc £4.50 from N Laws, Summerlands Tackle, 16-20 Nelson Rd, Westward Ho! EX39 1LF (tel: 01237 471291; see website for more info: www.summerlands.co.uk); also from Bideford TIC, Victoria Park, The Quay, Bideford EX39 2QQ (tel: 01237 477676).

KENNICK RESERVOIR, Christow. A South West Lakes Trust Dartmoor fishery, with stocked rainbow trout; boats bookable in advance (tel: 01647 277587); Allenard Wheelyboat for disabled; permits from self-service kiosk, £20 per day, full season £410, conc; open 25 Mar-31 Oct.

LYN, near **Lynmouth** (Devon). This beautiful river has good run of salmon, July onwards. Also sea trout and brown trout; latter small. Environment Agency (tel: 01392 316135; mob: 07768 278561) Watersmeet and Glenthorne fisheries: limits, daily limit 2 salmon, 4 sea trout and 8 brown trout subject to 6 salmon per season limit; c&r salmon until 16 June; spin all season; worm & maggot from 15 June: tickets from Tourist Information Centre, Town Hall, Lynton EX35 6BT (tel: 01598 752225); salmon season March 1-Sept 30; trout 15 Mar to 30 Sept. (See also Sea Fishing Stations).

MEAVY. Tributary of the Plym, on which Burrator Reservoir blocks salmon migration. Joins main river at Shaugh Bridge. Fishing governed by overspill when Burrator is full. Fishing stations: **Shaugh** and Clearbrook. National Trust water fished by Plymouth & Dist FAA; members only (conservation area).

MELBURY RESERVOIR, Bideford. 12 acre South West Lakes Trust reservoir, open all year, 6.30am to 10.00pm; carp, bream, roach, perch, eels; st £140 (day and night), £100 st (day), dt £5.50, conc £4.50 from N Laws, Summerlands Tackle, 16-20 Nelson Rd, Westward Ho! EX39 1LF (tel: 01237 471291; see website for more info: www.summerlands.co.uk).

MELDON RESERVOIR (3m SE of Okehampton). 57 acres, natural brown. Spinning, bait and fly fishing, South West Lakes Trust fishery, free to Environment Agency licence holders. Season Mar 15-Oct 12; contact (tel: 01409 211507).

PLYM. Devon salmon and sea trout river which rises above Lee Moor and flows south-west to Plymouth, skirts the east of the town to enter the Sound on the south side. Salmon, sea trout and brown trout; best salmon in Meavy tributary up to Burrator Reservoir.

Plymouth (Devon). Good runs of sea trout on Plym and Tavy. Salmon run late on Plym, Oct to 15 Dec. Plymouth & Dist Freshwater AA has R Plym from Plymbridge upstream for about 3m, and Tavy, north of Tavistock; annual subscription available from Hon Sec, dt (Mon-Fri only). Length above Bickleigh Bridge, controlled by Tavy, Walkham & Plym FC; club issues tickets (salmon, sea trout, brown trout) for its water, here and on Tavy, Meavy and Walkham; salmon and sea trout st £140, wt £55, dt £20, brown trout st £60, mt £25, wt £15, conc, no dt, from Osborne & Cragg (below). Tavistock Trout Fishery, Parkwood Road, Tavistock PL19 9JW (tel: 01822 615441; mob: 0797 060 8890; see website for more info: www.abigail@tavistocktroutfishery.co.uk); 5 trout fly lakes, 1 junior lake; dt £15.50 to £40 (depending on hours and number of fish), extra fish £8.50, rod hire and tuition available; Yelverton Garage, 1 Moorland Villas, Tavistock PL20 6DT (tel: 01822 853339), tickets for Burrator Reservoir and Plym, Tavy and Meavy. (see Tamar - Tavy). Sea fishing excellent. Tackle shops: Snowbee (UK) Ltd, Drakes Court, Langage Business Park, Plymouth PL7 5JY (tel: 01752 334930; web: www.snowbee.co.uk); Osborne & Cragg (DK Sports), 37 Breton Side, Plymouth PL4 0BB (tel: 01752 223141); Tackle & Bait Shop, 93 Victoria Rd, St Budeaux, Plymouth PL5 1RX (tel: 01752 361294; web: www.thetackleandbaitshop.co.uk).

OAREWATER, Brendon. Trout.

ROADFORD FISHERY, nr Okehampton. South West Lakes Trust fishery (Roadford), with wild and stocked brown trout; record 8lb 4oz; there is a campsite at lake; more than 700 acres, c&r policy, barbless hooks; open March 25 to 12 Oct; dt £12, conc, from Angling and Watersports Centre, Lower Goodacre, Broadwoodwidger, PL16 0JL; boats available; £12; wheelyboat bookable in advance; open 23 Mar-12 Oct; enquiries, (tel: 01409 211507).

SID, Sidmouth. Trout.

SLADE RESERVOIRS, Ilfracombe. South West Lakes Trust fisheries. **Lower Slade,** 6 acre coarse fishing

for pike, carp, tench, bream, roach, rudd, gudgeon and perch; st £140 (day and night), £100 st (day), 24-hour £10, dt £5.50, conc £4.50 from Variety Sports, 23 Broad St, Ilfracombe EX34 9EE (tel: 01271 862039); Summerlands Tackle, 16-20 Nelson Rd, Westward Ho! EX39 1LF (tel: 01237 471291; see website for more: www.summerlands.co.uk).

SLAPTON LEY, Dartmouth 7m. Pike, rudd, roach, eel and perch. Part of National Nature Reserve. All fishing currently suspended, moritorium in place, all enquiries to Field Centre, Slapton, Kingsbridge, TQ7 2QP (tel: 01548 580685). Tackle shops: Anchor Sports, Unit 7, Anchor Centre, Bridge St, Kingsbridge TQ7 1SB (tel: 01548 856891; web: www.anchorsportsshop.co.uk); Devon Angling Centre, Unit 4/5 Orchard Meadow, Orchard Way, Chillington, Kingsbridge TQ7 2LB (tel: 01548 580888; web: www.anglingcentre.net). Hotels: The Torcross and (in Slapton) the Tower Inn. Many guest houses.

SQUABMOOR RESERVOIR. E Budleigh. South West Lakes Trust has 4 acre water; bait fishing for coarse fish, with carp to 25lbs, tench, bream, roach, rudd, eels; st £140 (day and night), £100 st (day), 24-hour £10, dt £5.50, conc £4.50 from Exmouth Tackle and Sports, 20 The Strand, Exmouth EX8 1AF (tel: 01395 274918); Exeter Angling Centre, Smythen Street, EX1 1BN (tel: 01392 435591)Exeter Angling Centre, Smythen Street, EX1 1BN (tel: 01392 435591; see website for more info: www.exeterangling.co.uk).
Hogsbrook Lakes, 2½ acres, at Woodbury Salterton private fishery; 2 lakes; carp, tench, bream, roach and rudd; membership £275 pa; night fishing by appointment only; alcohol ban: contact bailiff, Russett Cottage, Woodbury Salterton, Exeter EX5 1EW (tel: 01395 233340).

STAFFORD MOOR FISHERY, **Winkleigh** EX19 8PP (tel: 01805 804360; see website for more info: www.staffordmoor.co.uk); five lakes of thirty acres total; all coarse; pleasure, match and specimen; tackle and bait available; rod hire; single permit £8, conc; on-site accom. Tackle shop: Veals Fishing Tackle, Brunel Rooms, Straight St, Bristol BS2 0EJ (tel: 0117 9260790; see website for more info: www.veals4carp.com).

TRENCHFORD RESERVOIR (8m NE of **Newton Abbot**). South West Lakes Trust pike fishery of 45 acres, pike to 30lb; open all year; st £140 (24-hrs), £100 st (day) from SWLT; 24-hour £10, dt £5.50, conc £4.50 from self service kiosk at Kennick; Kennick ranger (tel: 01647 277587).

VENFORD RESERVOIR, **Ashburton**. Wild brown trout; spinning and bubble-float fishing, free to licence-holders; season: March 15-Oct 12; contact South West Lakes Trust, for more details.

WISTLANDPOUND RESERVOIR, **South Molton**. South West Lakes Trust natural brown trout and stocked rainbow 41 acre fishery; fly only, open Mar 15-Oct 31; dt £14.50, conc £13, from Post Office, Challacombe EX31 4TT (tel: 01598 763229); Variety Sports, 23 Broad St, Ilfracombe EX34 9EE (tel: 01271 862039); The Calvert Trust (adjoining the water) (tel: 01598 763221).

YEALM. Rises on southern heights of Dartmoor and flows 12m south and west to English Channel, which it enters by a long estuary. Trout, sea trout, occasional late salmon. Fishing private. Estuary is now a bass nursery, bass fishing prohibited from boat.

Newton Ferrers (Devon). On estuary. One of finest deep-sea fishing stations in south-west. For Upper Yealm fishing contact for st £125 per rod, available only direct from Snowbee (UK) Ltd, Drakes Court, Langage Business Park, Plymouth PL7 5JY (tel: 01752 334930; see website for more info: www.snowbee.co.uk). Day tickets are available through the Westcountry Rivers Trust, Angling Passport scheme (tel: 01579 372140; www.angling2000.org.uk/booking_of fice.html) at £12.50 per day.

DORSET (lakes and streams)

BRIT and **ASKER**. Fishing station: **Bridport**. Trout and a few sea trout and salmon. Rivers mostly private or over-grown. Also **Radipole Lakes**; dt for latter: coarse fish; tickets from Weymouth Angling Centre or Reels and Deels. Dt £6 for **Osmington Mills Lake** (carp, roach, bream and tench) on site only (tel: 01305 832311). Trout fishing at **Watermill Lake**, well stocked with rainbows; Mangerton Mill, Bridport, DT6 3SG (tel: 01308 485224); fly only; dt £9 to £18.

CHAR. Fishing station: **Charmouth**. Char is some 7m long; trout, private. General sea fishing. Hotels: Queen's Arms.

CORFE. Rises 1m W of Corfe Castle and runs into Poole Harbour 5m down.

Coarse fishing sometimes permitted by landowners. Dt can be obtained for Arfleet Lake at Corfe Castle.

Coking Farm Fishery, West Stour, Gillingham, SP8 5SF, 5 coarse fishing lakes, carp upto 30lb, various dt prices for different lakes, for more info, (tel: 01747 839879; see website for more info: www.cokingfarmfishery.co.uk)

Eastmoors Coarse Fishing Lake, Eastmoors Lane, St Leonards, BH24 2SB, carp including common, mirror, leather & ghost, many over 20lbs, tench, some as heavy as 7lb, also golden tench, roach, perch & chub, (tel: 01202 872302; see website for more info: www.fishinglake.co.uk).

Mangerton Valley Lake, Mangerton Labe, Bradpole, DT6 3SF, 1 with carp to 28lb, also tench & roach, dt available on site, (tel: 01308 422884; web: www.mangertonlake.co.uk).

Pallington Lakes Fishery, nr Pallington Heath, 3 lakes, commons in excess of 42lbs & mirrors to over 30lbs, also tench, bream, roach, rudd, perch & eels, no dt available but open to membership, for more info, (tel: 05601 530112; see website for more info: www.pallingtonlakes.com).

Revels Fishery, Cosmore, Dorchester, DT2 7TW, 7 dt lakes, including 2 trout lakes, various prices for more info, (tel: 01300 345301; web: www.revelsfishery.fsbusiness.co.uk)

Todber Manor Fishery, Todber, Sturminster Newton, DT10 1JB, 7 coarse fishing lakes, 3 are specimen lakes, various dt prices for different lakes, 24hr tkts & wt available, (tel: 01258 820384; see website for more info: www.todbermanor.co.uk).

Whirlwind Lake, Whirlwind Rise, Dudmoor lane, Christchurch, BH23 6BQ, book by phone 01202 475255 (limited to max of 8 fishermen - no set pegs.

Wood Farm, Charmouth, DT6 6BT, membership for the fishing season April 2010 - March 2011 is £60, dt £5, wt £20, stocked with carp, rudd, roach & tench.

DURHAM (reservoirs)

DERWENT. Edmundbyers. 1,000 acre Northumbria Water trout water. Hotel: Lord Crewe Arms. Reservoir also partly in Northumberland.

SMIDDY SHAW, and **WASKERLEY**. Good trouting on this upland setting, preserved by North-West Durham AA; limited dt £10, 2 fish, Waskerley only; tickets from fishing lodge near dam wall; wild and stocked browns; Smiddy Shaw, members only; season March 22-Oct 31; for membership contact Hon Sec. Nearest towns: **Wolsingham**, **Consett** and **Stanhope**. Hotel: Royal Derwent at Allensford.

EDEN

Rises south of Kirkby Stephen and empties into Solway Firth 5m NW of Carlisle. Brown trout and grayling; few salmon. Still some spring fish, but now more a back-end river. Sea trout in lower and middle reaches and tributaries from June onwards. Trouting best in middle and upper reaches, fish run to good average size for north.

Carlisle (Cumbria). Salmon in spring and autumn, sea trout and herling in May to July, brown trout fair, good grayling. Carlisle AA has 7m on Eden, permits from tackle shops; visitors, salmon st £200, wt £125, dt £25; trout st £20, wt £10, dt £5 web: www.carlisleanglingassociation.org. Tackle shops: McHardy's Fishing Tackle, South Henry Str, Botchergate, CA1 1SF (tel: 01228 523988; web: www.mchardys.co.uk); Eddie's Fishing Tackle, 70 Shaddongate, CA2 5UG (tel: 01228 810744). Hotels: Crown and Mitre; Central; Hilltop; many guesthouses.

Wetheral (Cumbria). Salmon and sea trout preserved for 3m, both banks from Warwick Bridge upstream, by the Yorkshire Fly-fishers' Club here, no dt, and at Great Corby; Cairn Beck, 2m, Irthing, 3m N. Scotby Beck, 2m W at Scotby. Hotel: Crown.

Lazonby (Cumbria). Salmon, trout and grayling. 6thm of west bank Lazonby Parish Council fishing; dt £12 game, wt £36; dt £12, wt £40 coarse; salmon dt £15, wt £50, 6.30-10pm £7, coarse

£7, permits from Midland Hotel CA10 1BG (tel: 01768 898901) or Joiners Arms CA10 1BL (tel: 01768 898728). Tackle shop: Charles R Sykes, 4 Great Dockray, Penrith CA11 7BL (tel: 01768 862418; see website for more info: www.charlesrsykes.co.uk); John Norris, 21/22 Victoria Road, Penrith CA11 8HP (tel: 01768 864211; web: www.johnnorris.co.uk).

Langwathby (Cumbria). Salmon, trout; preserved by Yorkshire FFC.

Culgaith (Cumbria). Trout; preserved by Yorkshire FFC from Culgaith to below Langwathby apart from vicinity of Watersmeet. Winderwath, left bank is Penrith AA water, members only; (web: www.penrithanglers.co.uk). **Temple Sowerby** (Cumbria). Salmon, trout, grayling; preserved (with some miles of Eamont) by Yorkshire FFC; members only. Penrith AA (with 43m of fishing in all) has Powis House Water above Bolton Village; water upstream of Oustenstand Island; also water on River Leith; members only; The Punch Bowl Hotel, Askham, Penrith CA10 2PF (tel: 01931 712443); Langwathby PO & Stores, Langwathby, Penrith CA10 1LW (tel: 01768 881342); Pooley Bridge PO, Pooley Bridge, Penrith CA10 2NP (tel: 017684 86266). (See Penrith.) King's Arms Hotel CA10 1SB (tel: 01768 361211) has trout fishing for guests on 1½m of Eden; licences and tickets at hotel; trout average 1lb.

Kirkby Thore (Cumbria). Salmon, trout and grayling. Penrith AA preserves 2m brown trout fishing on main river and Kirkby Thore Beck near Long Marton; The Punch Bowl Hotel, Askham, Penrith CA10 2PF (tel: 01931 712443); Langwathby PO & Stores, Langwathby, Penrith CA10 2NP (tel: 01768 881342); Pooley Bridge PO, Pooley Bridge, Penrith CA10 2NP (tel: 017684 86266).

Appleby (Cumbria). Eden trout are very free risers, averaging about ¾lb with better fish to 3 and even 4lb. Appleby AA has 14m of R Eden, excellent fly fishing water, and offers dt for stretch ¾m above Jubilee Bridge (fly section and bait section), or £15 for stretch between Bolton Bridge and Ouenstands Bridge (all fly fishing); membership + entry non-resident, conc, from H Pigney and Son (below). Tufton Arms Hotel, Market Square CA16 6XA (tel: 017683 51593; web: www.tuftonarmshotel.co.uk) has tickets for guests on Appleby AA water; Tufton Arms has salmon and trout flies; good quality rods for sale; tuition and courses from John Pape; also late availability sporting agency. Tackle and permits from H Pigney & Son, Chapel St, Appleby CA16 6QR (tel: 017683 51240).

Kirkby Stephen (Cumbria). Kirkby Stephen & Dist AA has about 15m on main river and becks, fly only; (see Belah and Scandal Tributaries); visitor st £95, conc, free fishing for juniors on application, from Hon Sec; also for wt £40, dt £15. Fly fishing on 2 lakes, bait on one, at Bessy Beck Trout Fishery, Newbiggin-on-Lune CA17 4LY (tel: 015396 23303), booking advisable; 8am to dusk all year; dt from £15 (8 hours c&r) (other rates apply), tackle shop in site. Hotels: Kings Arms; Black Bull, White Lion, Croglin Castle.

Tributaries of the Eden

PETTERIL joins Eden at Carlisle. Good trout fishing. Penrith AA has 4m middle to upper reaches; members only. Lower half mostly private.

Plumpton (Cumbria). Trout.

IRTHING. Rises on Grey Fell Common and joins Eden east of Carlisle. Trout, grayling; and salmon and few sea trout, but out of season.

Brampton (Cumbria). Irthing; 1m N; Gelt, 1m S; trout, grayling (recently more prolific), chub. Brampton AS preserves 8-10m; st £29, wt £15, dt £7.50; (also grayling fly-only permit from end Sept to beginning of March £7.50 (the st covers this)) and Environment Agency licence from Brampton Post Office, Front Str, CA8 1NN (tel: 016977 2301) or licencing officer (tel: 016977 2359); trout average ½ to ¾lb, best after April; also most of River Gelt. Hotels: White Lion; Scotch Arms; Howard Arms.

EAMONT flows from Ullswater Lake. Penrith AA has approx 6m of this water; membership £140, conc half price, juv £5; dt £15 from Charles R Sykes, 4 Great Dockray, Penrith CA11 7BL (tel: 01768 862418; web: www.charlesrsykes.co.uk); The Punch Bowl Hotel, Askham, Penrith (tel: 01931 712443); Pooley Bridge PO, Pooley Bridge, Penrith CA10 2NP (tel: 017684 86266). Lake Ullswater good trout fishing; free, but Environment Agency licence required.

Penrith (Cumbria). Eamont, 1m S; trout. Upper portion (trout and salmon) preserved by Penrith AA (fly fishing only for visitors) from Pooley Bridge on both banks to below Stainton; also on **Eden**, **Lowther** and on becks. Visitors weekly ticket covering a variety of fishings, £40, dt £15, from Sykes (see below); the Punchbowl Hotel, Askham, Penrith. Trout fishing at **Blencarn Lake**, 15 acres, from Mr and Mrs J K Stamper, Blencarn Hall CA10 1TX (tel: 01768 88284); dt £22 4 fish; 5-hours 2 fish £14; fly only; facilities incl lodge with WC, piers for disabled. Yorkshire Flyfishers preserve left bank of Eamont from Brougham Castle down to Barrack Bank and then on left bank only to below Udford; members only. Other water on Eamont private. Tackle shops: Charles R Sykes, 4 Great Dockray, Penrith CA11 7BL (tel: 01768 862418; web: www.charlesrsykes.co.uk); John Norris, 21/22 Victoria Road, Penrith

CA11 8HP (tel: 01768 864211; web: www.johnnorris.co.uk).

Haweswater, 10m SE; currently, rod licence required (see Westmorland lakes). Hotels: Crown and Mitre, brampton Grange; George; Edenhall, near Langwathby. Tackle shop: Charles R Sykes, 4 Great Dockray, Penrith CA11 7BL (tel: 01768 862418; see website for more info: www.charlesrsykes.co.uk).

Pooley Bridge (Cumbria). Eamont; trout. Penrith AA water. Membership £140, conc half price, juv £5; dt £15 from Charles R Sykes, 4 Great Dockray, Penrith CA11 7BL (tel: 01768 862418; see website for more info: www.charlesrsykes.co.uk); The Punch Bowl Hotel, Askham, Penrith CA10 2PF (tel: 01931 712443); Langwathby PO & Stores, Langwathby, Penrith CA10 1LW (tel: 01768 881342); Pooley Bridge PO, Pooley Bridge, Penrith CA10 2NP (tel: 017684 86266).

Patterdale (Cumbria). The becks Goldrill, Grizedale, Deepdale and Hartsop; free. Aira Force below NT property (3m) free. N Hawes and Riggindale Becks, permits N West Water. Blea Tarn and Smallwater, N West Water. **Ullswater**. Brown trout and perch. Trout numerous, average three to pound. Evening rise during May and June yields heavy baskets; six brace of trout in evening quite common; day fishing also good; and heavier fish begin to move about middle of May; free; numerous boats but no power boats. Angle Tarn, permits. Greenside Reservoir, Red Tarn, Grizedale Tarn, free. Hotels: Ullswater, Patterdale; White Lion, Brotherswater; Glenridding Hotel (boats).

LOWTHER (tributary of Eamont). No fishing for salmon, spawning river only. Sport with trout remains good (av ¾lb). Penrith AA holds substantial stretches of good fly water on river; other assn water on Eden and Eamont;

membership £140, conc half price, juv £5; dt £15 from Charles R Sykes, 4 Great Dockray, Penrith CA11 7BL (tel: 01768 862418; see website for more info: www.charlesrsykes.co.uk); The Punch Bowl Inn, Askham, Penrith (tel: 01931 712443); Langwathby PO & Stores, Langwathby, Penrith (tel: 01768 881342); Pooley Bridge PO, Pooley Bridge, Penrith CA10 2NP (tel: 017684 86266).

LYVENNET. Good trout stream; runs in a few miles below Temple Sowerby. Leave from farmers in some parts. 1m preserved for Yorkshire Flyfishers' Club. Penrith AA has water; members only.

BELAH. Flows from Pennine fells to join Eden 2m below Kirkby Stephen. Above and below Bellah Bridge, Kirkby Stephen & Dist AA; members only.

SCANDAL BECK, Smardale (Cumbria) and **Crosby Garrett** (Cumbria). Kirkby Stephen & Dist AA has water from Soulby d/s to confluence with River Eden. (See Kirkby Stephen under Eden.)

ENGLISH LAKE DISTRICT

ATKINSON'S TARN Crook, between Bowness and Kendal. WADAA water, open all year round. 3 acre tarn; carp (to 16lb), roach, bream (to 6lb), rudd, eels; members only; apply Hon Sec.

BASSENTHWAITE, 5m Cockermouth; 8m Keswick. Long famous for its pike, roach, also perch and some salmon and brown trout; LDNPA permit required from Keswick TIC (tel: 017687 72645); st £52.50, wt £15.50, dt £4.50 (shore fishing), conc; own boat/day £6.50, £68.50/season (st holders exclusively may use electric outboard motors); salmon: dt £6.50 (1 Sepy to 31 Oct); night fishing for st holders only. Hotels: Pheasant Inn; Armathwaite Hall, Keswick CA12 4RE can arrange ghillie (tel: 01768 776551).

BIGLAND WATERS, 16 acre fly only trout lake, Bigland Trout Fishery, Mungeon Farm, Backbarrow, nr Ulverston LA12 8PB, (tel: 015395 31566 or 01229 861065; mob: 07789 502278); trout dt £24 4 fish £20 3 fish (8 hours), £16 for 6 hours 2 fish; £12 all-day sport; evng sport £8 (barbless hooks only).

BLEA TARN. About 2m above Watendlath Tarn; perch; trout. National Trust trout only; fly only, fly on bubble float only; no boats; free to EA licence holders; contact Jim Loxham or wardens at Boon Crag (tel: 015394 41197).

BLELHAM TARN. Ns **Windermere**. Pike, perch, roach and eels; National Trust water now controlled by WADAA, members only, open all year (contact Neil Birkinshaw tel: 01539 535630); assn controls fishing bank nr boathouse and rocks at northern end of tarn; livebaiting prohibited; boats not allowed; limited access.

BORRANS RESERVOIR South Lakeland. Managed by North Tyneside MBC, Educational Dept, High Borrans, Outdoor Pursuit Centre, Windermere.

BROTHERS WATER. Trout and pike, perch and eels present. National Trust, fishing free; west shore only; trout only; close season 30 Sept to 15 March; no boats (tel: 01768 482467).

BUTTERMERE. National Trust lake. Trout, char, pike, perch; no fishing from Oct 31-Mar 15; for dt £8, wt £30, st £60, conc, apply to Mr and Mrs Leck, Water End Farm, Loweswater CA13 0SU (tel: 01946 861465); which tickets also cover Crummock and Loweswater; or from Mr McKenzie, Woodhouse, Buttermere, Cockermouth CA13 9XA; rowing boats for hire; no power-craft.

CLEABARROW TARN,
Windermere. WADAA fishery, 2
acres, 20 pegs. No close season. Well
stocked, carp (20lb), tench (5lb),
bream (7lb), roach, rudd, golden rudd,
gudgeon. Fishery is weedy, strong
tackle recommended; members only;
apply Hon Sec.

CODALE TARN, 4m from **Grasmere.**
Perch, some trout; free. Hotels: (see
Grasmere).

CONISTON. Brown trout, char, eels,
perch, pike. Free, licence needed;
access on east and west banks (for
which you may have to pay); boats
from Coniston Boating Centre, Lake
Rd, Coniston LA21 8EW (tel: 015394
41366). Licences from TIC for local
club or Hon Sec, Coniston & Torver
DAA, which has fishing on Yew Tree
Tarn; fly only, dt , juv £5, conc; from
TIC, Coniston (tel: 015394 41533).
Hotels: Sun, Black Bull, Crown Inn,
Ship Inn.

CRUMMOCK WATER. National
Trust lake. Pike, trout, char, perch;
salmon and sea trout from Cocker
sometimes caught by trolling (from
July onwards); fishes best June and
July; no night fishing; st £60, wt £30,
dt £8, covering also Buttermere and
Loweswater from Mrs McKenzie,
Woodhouse, Buttermere,
Cockermouth CA13 9XA; rowing
boats for hire, £8 an hour, £20 per day,
£15 afternoon: apply to Mr and Mrs
Leck, Water End Farm, Loweswater
CA13 0SU (tel: 01946 861465); best
periods for Crummock, Buttermere
and Loweswater are: trout, late May
and early June (good mayfly hatch);
char, July and August (special
technique required: trolling 60 to 90
feet down); accom at Woodhouse,
also self-catering.

DERWENTWATER. Keswick. Trout
very good size, are best fished from a
boat in mayfly season. National Trust
and Keswick AA water.
Derwentwater is controlled by
Keswick AA and further information

can be obtained from Mike Tinnion,
tel. no. 01768 772127. Permits
available from: Rob Youdale at
Youdale's Newsagents, 83 Main
Street, Keswick, Cumbria CA12 5DT,
(tel: 01768 772259; Keswick Tourist
information, tel: 01768 772645); and
from High Hill Garage, Keswick.
Boats available from: Keswick
Launch Company, Lakeside,
Keswick, (tel: 01768 772263). Boats
for hire. No power craft. No launching
facilities. Use of live or dead
freshwater fish at any time and
maggots between 15 March and 15
June as bait is prohibited. Boats may
be hired from Nichol End Marine, and
Keswick Launch Co. Many hotels and
guest houses.

DEVOKE WATER near **Ravenglass**
(5m E). Moorland tarn offering sport
with fair sized trout. Millom & DAA
holds rights; membership and dt
obtainable from Hon Sec; Haverigg
PO; Bridge Garage, Holmrook; TI
Millom and also Waberthwaite PO.

DRUNKEN DUCK TARNS,
Ambleside. Brown trout to 4½lb,
rainbow to 6lb; dt £18 (£12 for ½ day
and £9 for sports ticket (c&r)), from
Drunken Duck Inn, Barngates LA22
0NG (tel: 015394 36347).

DUBBS TROUT FISHERY,
Windermere. A quiet upland
reservoir, controlled by WADAA,
open 15th March to 31st Dec inclusive
(although closed for dam repairs
2008/9); contact Neil Birkinshaw (tel:
015395 35630); stocked rainbow
trout, all browns to be returned; fly
only, 2 fish limit; apply from Ings
Filling Station (A591); Tourist
Information Centres; local fishing
tackle shops.

EASEDALE TARN, 3m from
Grasmere. Coarse only; free fishing;
no boats; managed by National Trust,
The Hollens, Grasmere, Cumbria
LA22 9QZ (tel: 015394 35599).

ENNERDALE, ns **Whitehaven.** Trout;
controlled by Ennerdale Lake

Fisheries formed by Wath Brow & Ennerdale Anglers and Egremont Anglers, Wath Brow; st £35 (members) and visitor wt £25 (dt £8) from Cleator Stores, 50 Main Str, Cleator CA23 3BX (tel: 01946 810038); enquiries to permit secretary (see clubs list); assn also has rainbow trout fishery, Longlands, at Cleator; st £150 (80 fish limit), dt £12 3 fish limit.

ESTHWAITE WATER (near **Hawkshead**, Cumbria). 280 acres stocked trout fishing. Rainbows to 16lb 3oz, browns to 10lb 12oz; spinning, worming or fly; also specimen pike; boats with electric o/b, also boat for disabled; dt from Esthwaite Water Trout Fishery, The Boathouse, Ridding Wood, Hawkshead LA22 0QF (tel: 015394 36541); accommodation plentiful; for Esthwaite Fly Fishers st £260 to £500 apply above; Hawkshead Anglers local membership only; pike season 1 Oct to 31 March.

FISHER TARN, ns **Kendal**, 3m. Kendal's water supply. Trout. Fisher Tarn Anglers: Hon Sec, Mr Colin Stamper, 58 Valley Drive LA9 7AG (tel: 01539 727813); dt £12 from tackle shop: Kendal Sports Shop, 30 Stramongate, Kendal LA9 4BN (tel: 01539 721554).

GHYLL HEAD TROUT FISHERY, Windermere. 11 acre WADAA stocked fishery, fly only. Open 15th March - 31st Dec. Rainbow and brown trout, 2 fish limit; all tagged fish and brown trout must be returned to the water. Dt £12 from Newby Bridge Motors on A590; Tourist Information Centre at Bowness, local tackle shops, including Carlson Tackle Shop, 64/66 Kirkland, Kendal LA9 5AP (tel/fax: 01539 724867; see website for more info: www.carlsons.co.uk); e-permits available on line.

GRASMERE, ns **Windermere**. Summer fishing, pike over 20lb regularly caught, perch, eels, roach, trout; National Trust WADAA water, open all year; live-baiting with fish is strictly prohibited, dead baiting and lure fishing are the most productive methods; find underwater drop-offs for the best sport; boat fishing can be good, boats from boathouse at northern end of lake; dt £6 (Juv/OAP £3); st £45.00 (Juv/OAP £15.00); web: www.lakedistrictfishing.net); permit also allows fishing on Rydal Water; coarse anglers should join the assn as coarse members £45; boat on Grasmere; check bait restrictions (15 Mar to 15 June incl only saltwater deadbaits allowed). Permits from: Tourist Information Centre, Grasmere (tel: 015394 35245), local fishing tackle shops, Barneys News Box, Broadgate, Grasmere, Ambleside LA22 9TA (tel: 01539 435627) (7.00am - 5.30pm); Carlson Tackle Shop, 64/66 Kirkland, Kendal LA9 5AP (tel/fax: 01539 724867; web: www.carlsons.co.uk).

GREAT RUNDALE TARN, ns **Long Marton**, 5m. Seamore Tarn and Little Rundale Tarn are in the vicinity. Small trout.

HARLOCK RESERVOIR, South Lakeland. Trout water managed by Barrow AA; brown trout; guest ticket with member from Hon Sec.

HAWESWATER, ns **Penrith** or **Shap**. A good head of wild brown trout, gwyniad and perch. Bank fishing, fly only, free to all holders of Environment Agency licence. No maggot or loose feeding; for further information contact Edward Holt, Land Agent, Northern Estates Office, The Old Sawmill, Thirlmere, Keswick CA12 4TQ (tel: 017687 72334).

HAYESWATER RESERVOIR, Patterdale. WADAA water, 34 acres, 9m north of Ambleside, open 15th March - 30th Sept; access requires a climb of 1000ft, magnificent scenery. Wild brown trout, fly only; may be taken; dt £8. Permits from: Tourist Information Centres (nearest at Glenridding (tel: 017684 82414)) or contact Neil Birkinshaw (tel: 015395 35630), local fishing tackle shops.

MOSS ECCLES TARN,
Hawkeshead. National Trust fly fishery stocked by WADAA, open 15 March-30 Sept; brown trout, fly only, c&r, no boats; dt £8 from Tourist Information, local tackle shops; Tower Bank Arms, Sawrey, Ambleside LA 22OLF (tel: 015394 36334); also Neil Birkinshaw (tel: 015395 35630).

HIGH NEWTON TROUT FISHERY, High Newton. WADAA trout fishery, 10.8 acres, open 15th March - 31st Dec, rainbow and brown trout dt £12.00. The reservoir is very well stocked throughout the year with rainbow trout. A large number of specimen tagged rainbows are introduced at the start of each season. These are sport fish and must be returned if captured, as must brown trout. The tagged fish are in addition to normal stockings which will continue as usual. All anglers must use barbless hooks (squashed barbs) and the use of buoyant lures or boobys on sunken lines is prohibited; wheelchair-accessible platform. Permits from Newby Bridge service station; tackle shops or TICs.

HOLEHIRD TARN, Windermere, 3 acre WADAA water, mo longer open to fishing.

KENTMERE FISHERY, near Windermere. WADDA water. Members only. Two lakes, of 20 and 4 acres with brown and rainbow trout; contact Neil Birkenshaw (tel: 015395 35630).

KILLINGTON RESERVOIR, near **Oxenholme**, 3m. Trout, pike, perch. Leased to Kent (Westmorland) AA; regularly stocked Mar to Oct with rainbows of over 1lb, some up to 4lb;; 2 fish limit; st £70, dt £10, Juv dt £4 from Kendal tackle shops, including Carlson Tackle Shop, 64/66 Kirkland, Kendal LA9 5AP (tel/fax: 01539 724867; web: www.carlsons.co.uk) or

Keeper, Water Keeper's Lodge at reservoir; conc st to jun.

LONGLANDS LAKE. Cleator, West Cumbria. Wath Brow & Ennerdale Anglers, stocked monthly; dt from Cleator Stores, 50 Main Str, Cleator CA23 3BX (tel: 01946 810038). Tackle shop: Wath Angling Centre, 121/2 Ennerdale Road, Wath Brow, Cleator Moor, Cumbria CA25 5LP (tel: 01946 810377).

LOUGHRIGG TARN, nr Ambleside. Pike and perch mostly, roach, rudd, dace, tench, eels, and brown trout; no boats allowed; dt £3: apply to M A Murphy, Tarn Foot Farm, Skelwith Bridge, Loughrigg, nr Ambleside LA22 9HF (tel: 015394 32596).

LOWESWATER. National Trust lake. Pike, perch, trout (av $1\frac{1}{2}$-2lb but hard to catch; fly only up to June 16); no fishing from Oct 31-Mar 15; for dt £8, wt £30, st £60; boats £8 per hour, £20 per day, £15 afternoon; apply to Mr and Mrs Leck, Water End Farm, Loweswater CA13 0SU (tel: 01946 861465); permits also cover Crummock and Buttermere.

MEADLEY RESERVOIR. Cleator Moor, West Cumbria. Brown trout and rainbow. Permits from Wath Angling Centre, 121/2 Ennerdale Road, Wath Brow, Cleator Moor, Cumbria CA25 5LP (tel: 01946 810377).

MOCKERKIN, near Loweswater. Tarn stocked with carp by Haigh AA, Whitehaven.

PENNINGTON RESERVOIR, South Lakeland. Brown and rainbow trout fishing, Barrow AA; guest ticket with member from Hon Sec.

RATHERHEATH TARN, Kendal. 5 acre WADAA coarse fishery, open all year. Carp (20lb), tench (5lb), roach (2lb), bream (7lb), rudd, crucian carp, perch, gudgeon; dt £6 (Juv £3) from: Plantation Bridge Filling Station, A591 (Open 7.00am to 9.00pm), Tourist Information Centres, local tackle shops, including Carlson Tackle Shop, 64/66 Kirkland, Kendal LA9 5AP (tel/fax: 01539 724867; web: www.carlsons.co.uk). A special platform for disabled anglers stands just inside the entrance gate ten metres from the car park; fishing is permitted from one hour before sunrise to one hour after sunset; overnight parking or night fishing is strictly prohibited.

RYDAL WATER, Ambleside. WADAA water, open all year. Pike, perch, eels, roach, trout. Rydal Water offers similar fishing to Grasmere and is a popular pike fishery producing fish to the mid-twenty pound mark. Parking is at White Moss Common or Rydal Village. Most pike are caught near underwater features around the islands and off the various points. Boat fishing is not permitted. The Association wants to conserve pike stocks in all fisheries so please use adequate tackle and have unhooking gear at hand; dt £6, under 16s free with adult. Permits (see see website for more: www.lakedistrictfishing.net) from: Tourist Information Centres, local tackle shops, Barneys News Box, Broadgate, Grasmere, Ambleside LA22 9TA (tel: 01539 435627) (7.00am - 5.30pm).

SKELSMERGH, ns Kendal, 3m. Now let to Kendal Angling; members free; with large tench, rudd and perch regularly caught; dt £5 on bank or phone D C Taylor, 2 Garnett Folds, LA8 9AS (tel: 01539 823284); or Carlsons Fishing Tackle in Kendal.

SPRINKLING TARN. Right up Stye Head Pass. Trout. Good on a favourable day until July.

STYE HEAD TARN. Same information as Sprinkling Tarn.

THIRLMERE. Perch, pike, char, trout. Wild fly fishery; leased to Windermere, Ambleside & DAA; dt, enquire Neil Birkinshaw (tel: 015395 35630); no maggots, live baits or loosefeeding; no fishing SW corner.

ULLSWATER, ns Penrith. Covers 2,200 acres; National Trust free fishing water; pike, perch, brown trout; rowing boats on water. Hotel: Inn on the Lake, Lake Ullswater, Glenridding, Penrith CA11 0PE (tel: 017684 82444).

WATENDLATH TARN. Keswick 3m. Brown, blue and rainbow trout fishery, fly only, stocked weekly; boats; open 1 March to 31 October, dt, half-day, evenings; for this National Trust trout fishery apply for tickets to Peter Tyson from the Caffel House Tea Rooms, Watendlath. Apply to Stan Edmondson for Watendlath Trout Fishery, Watendlath, Keswick CA12 5UY (tel: 017687 77293); Mr Edmondson also has day tickets for 1m fishing on **River Cocker**; also Mrs Richardson, Fold Head Farm, Watendlath.

WINDERMERE, nr Windermere. Largest English lake, 10½m long and nearly 1m wide. Good pike and perch, also eels, char and trout (trout best March-June), and roach (pike: only permitted baits are lures, spinners, flies and saltwater deadbaits). Fishing free, apart from Environment Agency licence. EA will prosecute anglers using live baits or freshwater deadbaits; this applies to several named lakes in the area (check first). National Trust access is from Fell Foot car park (free fishing) and from Harrowslack (on the nw shore), (tel: 015394 47997). Big fish taken by trolling. Boats from Bowness Bay, Waterhead Bay and Fell Foot National Trust Park. Local association, Windermere, Ambleside & Dist AA; Assn waters include 4m of Windermere Lake shore at Graythwaite Estates, near south-west end of lake; also **Grasmere, Rydal Water**, Rivers **Rothay, Brathay**, six tarns, Ghyll Head, Dubbs Reservoir, High Newton Reservoir, Kentmere Fishery; details are elsewhere in text; **Ratherheath** and **Cleabarrow** Tarns are now coarse fisheries; members only; Local tackle shops: Carlson Tackle Shop, 64/66 Kirkland, Kendal LA9 5AP (tel/fax: 01539 724867; web: www.carlsons.co.uk); and Tourist Information Centres. Hotels: Lonsdale, Lake Rd; Cragwood Country House; Applegarth; Oakthorpe. Ambleside: Skelwith Bridge; Langdale Chase; Fisherbeck.

Cragwood offers free fishing on WADAA waters.

YEW TREE TARN, near **Coniston**. Rainbow and brown trout, fly only, no boats; Coniston & Torver Angling Association water; apply Coniston Community Tourist Information Centre, Ruskin Avenue, Coniston LA21 8EH (tel: 015394 41533).

Jeremy Lucas, concentrating on the Eamont, Cumbria
Photo: Paul Sharman

ESK (Border)

Rises in Dumfriesshire and flows into the Solway Firth but is classed as an English river. The Border Esk and main tributary, Liddle Water, are primarily sea trout and salmon waters from above Langholm and from Newcastleton to the mouth. Heavy runs of sea trout and herling from June to September. Salmon run from July onwards but September and October are the best months. Chub and dace in lower reaches provide some winter fishing.

Canonbie (Dumfriesshire). Salmon, sea trout; Buccleuch Sporting Ltd, Esk & Liddle Fishery Office, Ewesbank, Langholm DG13 0ND (tel: 01387 380202) issue permits by appointment or post. Fly fishing: spinning and worming allowed only when river level exceeds markers provided; no Sunday fishing; st £51 to £272, wt £15 to £126, dt £10 to £47; children ½ price: Canonbie and Lower Liddle wt and dt from Cross Keys Hotel (below); Head Bailiff, Iain Bell at Estate Office (tel: 013873 71416) for st and information; six private beats are let on weekly basis to parties of three rods, directly by Buccleuch Sporting Ltd. Liddle tickets from Holm Hardware, Douglas Square, Newcastleton (tel: 013873 75257); also contact Stevenson and Johnstone, Bank of Scotland Buildings, Langholm, Dumfriesshire DG13 0AD (tel: 01387 380428) for all tickets. Hotels: Cross Keys in Canonbie (tel: 013873 71205) who supply wt and dt; Eskdale Hotel at Langholm supply Langholm wt and dt.

Langholm (Dumfriesshire). Salmon, sea trout. Certain stretches of Esk and its tributary the Liddle, are under the control of Buccleuch Sporting Ltd (see above). **Black Esk Reservoir**: bank fishing; fly and spinner only. Salmon and sea trout fishing on **River White Esk**, 6m, both banks, with a number of named pools, 12m from Langholm; salmon and sea trout run from late July. Hotels: Eskdale, Douglas or Cross Keys (Canonbie).

Westerkirk (Dumfries and Galloway). Salmon, sea trout, herling, trout.

Tributaries of the Border Esk

LIDDLE: Salmon, sea trout, herling, brown trout.

Newcastleton (Roxburgh). Salmon, sea trout, herling, brown trout. Buccleuch Sporting Ltd have much water. Tickets for 5m stretch. (See Canonbie). Bowland Game FA has 1½ miles, salmon, sea trout and trout fishing, left bank only, ns Longtown; members only, waiting list. Bailey Mill Farm Holidays and Trekking Centre, Bailey, Newcastleton TD9 0TR (tel: 016977 48617; web: www.baileycottages-riding-racing.com), offer fishing holidays on 7m of Liddle, with accommodation, also 12m of Esk nr **Longtown**. Oak Bank Fisheries, Longtown, have trout and carp fishing. Tickets from local tackle shops.

LYNE: Lyne rises on Bewcastle Fells and joins Esk ½m above Metal Bridge. Salmon, sea trout, herling, trout.

SARK: Trout stream about 10m long, forming for a short distance boundary between England and Scotland, and emptying into Solway at **Gretna**.

KIRTLE WATER: Stream which empties into the Solway at Kirtlefoot. Sea trout, herling, trout. Rigg and Kirtleside farm, Rigg.

Kirtlebridge (Dumfries and Galloway). Sea trout and trout; short free length. Winterhope Burn. Penoben Burn. Annan, 3m SW. Well-stocked reservoir 3m off, **Middlebie Dam**, fishable by permit; trouting very good.

Kirkpatrick (Dumfries and Galloway). Trout.

ESK (Yorkshire)

Rises on Westerdale Moor and runs into sea at Whitby. Salmon, sea trout, trout and grayling. Good runs of sea trout, river has twice held British record, 1994 was highest ever total. The River Esk Action Committee, representing riparian owners and anglers, is dedicated to the furtherance and improvement of this once great salmon river. In partnership with the National Park and Environment Agency, it is carrying out an annual programme of habitat improvement and restocking, using own hatchery; for further information, please contact Egton Estate Office (tel: 01947 895466/7).

Whitby (Yorks). Salmon, sea trout, trout, grayling, eels; largely preserved by the Esk FA from Ruswarp to Sleights. Visitors' tickets from Mr Sims, Millbeck, The Carrs, Ruswarp, Whitby YO21 1RL (tel 01947 604658 or 601610); no maggot fishing is allowed; fishing from Iburndale Beck down to Ruswarp Dam; between dam and road bridge no fishing; beyond road bridge, sea fish only; st, dt. Tackle shop: Whitby Angling Supplies, 65/67 Haggersgate, Whitby YO21 3PP (tel: 01947 603855; web: www.whitbyangling supplies.com). Hotels: Wheatsheaf; Ye Horseshoe Inn.

RUSWARP (Yorks). Salmon, sea trout, trout, grayling, eels; preserved for 2m by Esk FA. Tickets from Mr Sims, Millbeck, The Carrs, Ruswarp, Whitby YO21 1RL (tel 01947 604658 or 601610).

Sleights (Yorks). Salmon, sea trout, trout, grayling, eels; preserved by Esk Fishery Association. Tickets for water up to Sleights from Mr Sims, Millbeck, The Carrs, Ruswarp, Whitby YO21 1RL (tel 01947 604658 or 601610).

Goathland (Yorks). Murk Esk; salmon, sea trout, trout. Goathland FC water.

Grosmont (Yorks). Trout, salmon; preserved by the Esk FA above to Glaisdale, and below to Whitby.

Egton Bridge (N Yorks). Salmon, sea trout; some water preserved by the Esk FA. Other water (1¼m both banks) owned by Egton Estate, Estate Office, Egton Bridge, nr Whitby YO21 1UY (tel: 01947 895466); tickets issued throughout season (6 Apr to 31 Oct), 3 rods per day. Trout fishing in **Scaling Dam** (worm and fly). Hotels: Ye Horseshoe Inn; Wheatsheaf Inn; Postgate Inn.

Glaisdale (N Yorks). Salmon, sea trout, trout; preserved below by the Esk FA (see Whitby). Esk FA bailiff, Mark Tindall, Lease Rigg Farm, Grosmont, Whitby (tel: 01947 895352); members only; waiting list. Hotels: Wheatsheaf, Egton; Ye Horseshoe Inn, Egton Bridge.

Danby (N Yorks). Salmon, sea trout, brown trout, grayling, preserved by landowners & Danby AC. Danby AC has about 8m of water stocked each year with approx 800 11" brown trout; also water between Castleton and Lealholm; st (limited) £15, dt £4, (£6 Oct), conc, from Duke of Wellington (Danby); Post Offices, Castleton and Danby; restrictions on method according to date. Accommodation, licences, tickets, at Duke of Wellington. Tackle shops: Whitby Angling, 65 Haggersgate, Whitby YO21 3PP (tel: 01947 603855; web: www.whitbyanglingsupplies.com); Keith's Sports, 31 Milton St, Saltburn-by-Sea TS12 1DN (tel: 01287 624296; see website for more info: www.keithssports.co.uk).

Tributaries of the Esk (Yorkshire)

MURK ESK: Salmon and trout. Tributaries are: Little Beck, Brocka Beck, Eller Beck, Little Eller Beck. Fishing station: **Grosmont**.

ESSEX (streams, lakes and reservoirs)

ARDLEIGH RESERVOIR, nr **Colchester**. Off the A 137. Anglian Water joint managed; coarse fishing only, all year, excellent bream and pike; rowing boats; electrical outboards only; st £190 (incl £25 joining fee and allows night fishing), dt £7, Juv £3.50, on site; boats (must be booked in advance), min 2 persons, £25; facilities at lodge; enq to Fishery Manager, Ardleigh Reservoir, nr Colchester, Essex CO7 7PT (tel: 01206 230642; mob: 07872 679037).

CONNAUGHT WATERS, **Chingford**. Roach, bream, carp; free.

EPPING FOREST PONDS. Fishing permitted in most ponds except where prohibited by notices, namely Alexandra Lake, Eagle Pond, Shoulder of Mutton Pond; no boats; no night fishing; charges apply to the following: Ornamental Water, Perch Pond, Hollow Pond, Connaught Water (best access for disabled), Highams Park Lake, Wake Valley Pond, fishing now free in Epping Forest; further information from Forest Information Centre (tel: 020 8508 0028) or Superintendent of Epping Forest, The Warren, Loughton, Essex IG10 4RW (tel: 020 8532 1010). Tackle shop: Keswall Woodford Ltd, 618 Chigwell Road, Woodford Green IG8 8AA (tel: 020 8504 1929; see website for more info: www.keswalls.co.uk).

FISHERS GREEN, **Waltham Abbey**. Pike, carp to over 40lb, tench, bream, roach, barbel to 14lb 12oz, chub to over 7lb, perch, eels; a Cemex (formerly RMC) day and night Silver Venue fishery of 68 and 65 acre gravel pits, 3,900m of R Lea, 3,160 of **Lea Relief Channel**; st 2-rods £90 (day and night) (£65 day); conc £81 (day and night) (£58 day) (rod limit 3 (Channel and lakes); 2 for river). (For Cemex (formerly RMC) Angling, see Chertsey.)

GOSFIELD LAKE, **Halstead** (Essex). 45 acres; well-stocked with carp, perch, roach, tench, bream, pike; enquire Linda Turp, Gosfield Lake, Church Road, Gosfield CO9 1UD (tel: 01787 475043); dt (7.30 am - 7.30 pm; if arriving before 9.30am phone first) £7, conc to jun; night £13: obtainable from reception.

HANNINGFIELD RESERVOIR. Near **Chelmsford**. Excellent brown and rainbow trout fishery, average weight 2lb, good numbers of fish to 24lb 10oz; weekly stocking; bank and boat fishing, incl wheelyboats for disabled; enquiries to Fisheries Manager, Fishing Lodge, Giffords Lane, South Hanningford CM3 8HX (tel: 01245 212034) shop; (tel: 01245 212031) office; see website for more info: www.eswater.co.uk).

HATFIELD FOREST LAKE. Near Hatfield Broad Oak and Bishop's Stortford: National Trust property, 10 acre coarse lake set in ancient woodland; st, dt (tel: 01279 870678).

HOOKS MARSH; 40 acre Cemex (formerly RMC) Angling Silver Water gravel pit nr **Waltham Abbey**; bream, tench, roach, perch and pike; st (3 rods) £60, £45 (2 rods), conc £40.50. (For Cemex (formerly RMC) Angling, see Chertsey).

LAYER PITS. 6m S of **Colchester**; controlled by Colchester APS; coarse fish, large head of carp; members only.

MARDYKE: Fishing stations: **Purfleet** and **Ockendon**. Rises by East Horndon and flows 12m to Thames at Purfleet. There are some club lengths. Moor Hall & Belhus AS has two members-only coarse fisheries at South Ockendon, st on application to Sec for over 16's only.

NAZEING MEADS, Meadgate Road, Nazeing, Essex. Four gravel pits totalling 125 acres. Carp are main species (up to 45lb), with large bream (18lb), roach, tench, eels and pike (to

30lb); st (day only) £65.50, st (day & night) £111.60, conc; postal applications only to Fisheries, Holyfieldhall Farm, Stubbins Hall Lane, Waltham Abbey EN9 2EG (tel: 01992 892291).

NORTON FISHERY, Epping Lane, Stapleford Tawney, RM4 1ST, 5 acre lake, dt full day £30 (4 fish) + other ticket prices, (tel: 01708 688525; web: www.nortonfishery.com).

ONGAR. Coarse fish; good chub, roach, dace and perch.

PANT. Bocking. Upper part of R Blackwater (see Blackwater in main list).

PASSINGFORD BRIDGE. Roach, chub, pike; bream, carp, tench. Barkingside & Dist AS has 1½m downstream; bailiff on water; dt from bailiffs on bank for ¾m u/s of bridge. Woodford AS has 1½m north of bridge; Elm Park AS has water; dt from bailiff. **Romford**.

SOUTH WEALD LAKES. Thorndon is a fishing run by Essex County Council; usual freshwater fish, esp. carp; dt on bank: Weald Office, Weald Country Park, South Weald, Brentwood, Essex CM14 5QS.

STAMBRIDGE FISHERIES, Stambridge Road, **Rochford**, Essex SS4 2AR (tel: 01702 258274): two lakes, of thirty swims each, and carp to 25½lbs; mirror, common, leather and wild, also crucian carp; roach, rudd, golden rudd, bronze and silver bream, tench & sturgeon; no pike or zander; dt from £5 per rod on bank or from barn; night fishing by pre-booking; bait and tackle on site; all facilities.

STANFORD-LE-HOPE. Cemex (formerly RMC) Angling gravel pits, 13 acres, one Gold Venue, Wharf Pool (Lake 1; st 2-rods £175; 3-rod limit)

and the other dt water (Lake 2; dt £10 per 2 rods for day; £20 for 24-hours); large carp to 20lb, bream, perch, tench (For Cemex (formerly RMC) Angling, see Chertsey). Tackle shop: Stanford Tackle, 12 Wharf Road, SS17 0DH (tel: 01375 676739).

Thornwood Trout Lake, located at the very end of Carpenters Arms Lane, Thornwood, Epping, CM16 6LR, rainbow & brown trout, (tel: 07588 669255; see website for more info: www.thornwoodtroutfishery.com).

WANSTEAD & WOODFORD LAKES AND PONDS. Eagle Pond, Snaresbrook

(roach, perch, carp); **Knighton Wood Pond, Woodford**; **Hollow Pond, Whipps Cross**; all free.

OTHER TICKET WATERS. Priory Lakes, Priory Park, **Southend**; Eastwood Pit, **Rayleigh**; Essex Carp Fishery (crucian carp, bream) at Mollands Lane, **South Ockendon**; Old Hall Lake, **Herongate**; Moor Hall Farm Fishery, **Aveley**; Raphael Park Lake, **Romford**; Danbury Park Lakes, near **Chelmsford**; Harwood Hall at Corbets Tey, and Parklands Lake, both near **Upminster**; Warren Pond, **Chingford**; carp, bream. Tickets mostly from bailiffs on site. Three Lakes Angling has three mixed coarse lakes at **Boreham**, near Chelmsford; contact Hon Sec for dt. Essex tackle shops: Pro-Master Angling Centre, Fullwell Parade, Fullwell Ave, Ilford IG5 0RF (tel: 020 8551 4033; see website for more info: www.promasterangling.co.uk); Hornchurch Angling Centre, 226 Hornchurch Rd, Havering, Hornchurch RM11 1QJ (tel: 01708 620608); County Angling, 19 Suttons Lane, Hornchurch RM12 6RD (tel: 01708 477834/440016).

For Walthamstow reservoirs, see under London.

EXE

Rises in Somerset on Exmoor and runs south through Devon to Exmouth. Salmon and trout, with grayling and coarse fish in lower reaches. At several points on upper reaches trout fishing (moorland) and salmon fishing may be had by hotel guests.

Exeter (Devon). Bream, carp, dace, gudgeon, pike, perch, roach, rudd, barbel, tench and eels. **Exeter Ship** and **Tiverton Grand Western** Canals contain bream, carp, pike, perch, rudd, roach, tench, eels and dace. Hotels on canal banks: Double Locks, Turf. Exeter & DAA (amalgamation of local clubs) has coarse fishing rights on R Exe, on **Culm** and **Creedy**, from City Basin to Turf Basin on Exeter Ship Canal, and on ponds at Kingsteignton, Sampford Peveril, Feneck; also at Kia Ora pond; st £34, dt £5, conc; also salmon, trout (enquire Hon Sec). For fishing on Tiverton Canal contact Tiverton & DAC (tel: 01884 242275, Exe Valley Angling) or tackle shops. At Exwick right bank visitors may fish for ½m, and from Exwick Mills d/s 400 yds below Exwick Rd Bridge; Exeter & DAA water. South View Farm Fishery, Shillingford St George, Exeter EX2 9UP (tel: 01392 832278; web: www.southviewfishery.co.uk): 6 acres of coarse fishing on three lakes, with various species of carp to 29lb, tench, rudd and other coarse; dt on bank, facilities on site. One permit a day for salmon fishing (weekdays only) from Exeter Angling Centre, Smythen Street, EX1 1BN (tel: 01392 435591; see website for more info: www.exeterangling.co.uk).

Brampford Speke (Devon). Salmon, trout, dace, roach, chub; preserved. Pynes Water, from here down to Cowley Weir (2½m) fished by local syndicate. Exeter & Dist AA water towards Stoke Canon (see Culm).

Silverton (Devon). Trout, chub, roach, dace, pike, perch; preserved. Exeter & Dist AA has coarse fishing on Culm here (see Exeter and Culm).

Tiverton (Devon). Exe, Lowman and Little Dart; trout, salmon. **Grand Western Canal**; bream, pike, perch, roach, tench. Tiverton & DAC has river, canal and lake fishing in vicinity; canal dt from tackle shops, other waters, members only. Exe preserved for 2m both above and below town (trout and grayling) by Tiverton FFC, fly only; residential qualification, but guest tickets; st for residents only. River walk in Tiverton, ½m, free trout fishing to juv. Tackle shop: Exe Valley Angling, 19 Westexe South, Tiverton EX16 5DQ (tel: 01884 242275). Hotels: Bark House at Oakfordbridge; Fisherman's Cot, Bickleigh (beat on Exe).

Dulverton (Som). Salmon, trout, grayling. Usually good run of salmon (May onwards and autumn) to Dulverton and beyond, depending on water conditions. Trout fishing good on Exe and **Barle** (four to lb). **Exe Valley Fishery**, Exebridge, Dulverton TA22 9AY (tel: 01398 323008); one large and two small lakes stocked with rainbows averaging 2lb+, dt £6 (plus £3.50 per kilo caught) on site throughout year, 5 fish limit; also flat rate permits: £25, 5 fish; £14, 2 fish. Dulverton Angling Association has 6m of Exe and River **Haddeo**; membership £25; no dt; apply Lance Nicholson (below); also for Beasley, R Barle, 1m double bank; wild browns, occasional salmon; dt £12; at **Broford**, 5m double bank of Little Exe, with wild brown trout, fly only; dt £12, from tackle shop: Lance Nicholson, 9 & 11 High St, Dulverton TA22 9HB (tel: 01398 323409; web: www.lancenich.f9.co.uk). Hotels: Lion Hotel; The Anchor Inn, Exebridge, Dulverton, TA22 9AZ (tel: 01398 3234) with fishing rights.

Tributaries of the Exe

CREEDY: Trout, coarse fish.

Cowley Bridge (Exeter). Coarse fish. Exeter & Dist AA has rights, left bank only (see Exeter).

Crediton (Devon). Trout. Yeo 3m; trout. Crediton FFC has over 5m, mainly double bank, on Rivers **Creedy**, **Culvery** and **Yeo**, also 1½m on R Taw and 3m on River Culm; five day visitor tickets £30, a few dt at £15; contact Hon Sec; (web: www.fly-fishing-club.co.uk).

CULM: Trout, coarse fish.

Stoke Canon, **Rewe** and **Silverton** (Devon). Dace, chub, roach, perch and occasional grayling. Exeter & Dist AA has water. Crediton FFC has 3 miles of Culm near Willand; members only; £88 + £25 joining, conc; apply Hon Sec. Taunton FFC has a stretch near Culmstock; members only; apply Hon Sec.

Hemyock (Devon). Trout, small and few. Lower water preserved and stocked by Hemyock-Culmstock syndicate.

Clayhidon (Devon). Upper Culm FA preserves about 4m in this district (see Hemyock). No Sunday fishing. Inn: Half Moon.

Killerton (Devon). National Trust controls coarse fishing on Killerton Estate; tickets from tackle shops for Exeter AA water.

HADDEO. Flows into Exe 2m north of Exebridge; outflow of Wimbleball Reservoir; good stock of wild brown trout and a few grayling. Dulverton AA has 1m; membership £25; no dt; apply Lance Nicholson (see Dulverton)

BARLE. Runs through beautifully wooded valley and holds salmon (av 7-10lb) and trout (av 8-10 in).

FAL

Rises near Roche and flows about 23 miles, due south, past Grampound and Tregony to the English Channel at Falmouth. A few salmon and sea trout returning.

Falmouth (Cornwall). Trout fishing in **Argal Reservoir**, coarse fishing in **College Reservoir**: large pike and carp. Trout in some of the small streams flowing into creeks around Falmouth.

Tregony (Cornwall). Trout, 2m off runs Polglaze Brook, 4m long; trout.

FOWEY

Rises on Bodmin Moor, runs down a steep valley at Golitha and enters sea by a long estuary at Fowey. One of Cornwall's and Britain's foremost sea trout rivers, with good salmon fishing also. Run of big sea trout and some salmon in April and May and runs continue throughout the year. Peal (small sea trout) come in numbers in June and July; there is a run of grilse in September. Salmon fishing continues to mid-December, and a run of big winter fish (up to 20lb) can be expected late in the season. Circle hooks if fishing with worm 30 Sept to season end.

Fowey (Cornwall). Capital sea fishing (see Sea Fishing section).

Lostwithiel (Cornwall). Sea trout, salmon, brown trout. Lostwithiel FC has approx 4m double bank fishing; syndicate fishing; guests of members only; contact R Lashbrook, Roger's Tackle Shop, Stan Mays Store, Higher Bore St, Bodmin PL31 1DZ (tel: 01208 78006) (closed Wednesday).

Respryn Bridge (Cornwall). Most of 1m of water above and below the bridge is in the hands of Lanhydrock AA, NT Cornwall Regional Office,

Lanhydrock Park, PL30 4DE; st £60 (waiting list), wt £30, dt £15, conc; artificial bait only; voluntary catch limits; free fishing on section between Respryn Bridge and footbridge. Hotels: Royal Talbot, King's Arms, Earl of Chatham, Royal Oak, Globe, Trevone Guest House and Restormel Lodge.

Liskeard (Cornwall). Liskeard & DAC has several beats on Fowey, also **Lynher**, and on minor rivers, West Looe, Seaton, Inny & Camel; visitor tickets: st £77 + £15 joining fee, wt £55, dt £20 from Tremar Tropicals, 11 Market St, Liskeard PL14 3JH (tel: 01579 343177; see website for more: www.tremartropicals.fsnet.co.uk); East Looe Chandlers on the quay in E Looe; or Roger's Tackle Shop, Stan Mays Store, Higher Bore St, Bodmin PL31 1JW (tel: 01208 78006) (closed Wednesday). Membership (limited to 250): apply Trevor Sobey, Trevartha Farm, Pengover, nr Liskeard PL14 3NJ for membership.

FROME AND PIDDLE (Dorset)

Frome rises above Hooke in West Dorset and flows into the English Channel at Poole Harbour near Wareham. Piddle rises in a mill pond 1 mile north of Piddletrenthide and enters Poole Harbour near mouth of Frome near Wareham. Both are chalk streams and closely preserved but sport may sometimes be had. Some very good sea trout have been caught in the Frome, which also receives a run of salmon, which riparian owners are making every effort to enhance. Trout in both rivers plentiful and good. Bass run up to where the river enters Poole Harbour. Piddle carries very small stock of salmon. River is in fine condition due to successful efforts of the Frome, Piddle and West Dorset Fisheries Association.

Wareham (Dorset). On Frome and Piddle; salmon, sea trout, trout, grayling, pike, roach and dace. Free coarse fishing on towpath side of R Frome, from Wareham South Bridge downstream. EA licence required. Salmon and trout preserved. Mr Bowerman, Morden Estate Office, Charborough Park, Wareham BH20 7EN (tel: 01258 857204), sometimes has season and other rods available as follows: salmon, Frome and Piddle; trout, Piddle and Bere Stream, and River Stour, coarse fishing. Environment Agency lets 14 rods for the season (on the basis of two per day) for fishery on Piddle; salmon, sea trout; details from Area Conservation Officer (tel: 08708 506506). South Drain nr Poole Harbour is Wareham & Dist AS water; club has local waters, including two lakes (one of 10 acres), membership £45, £10 jun. Tackle shop and bait: Purbeck Angling, 28 South Str, BH20 4LU (tel: 01929 550770). Hotels: Red Lion and Black Bear.

Wool (Dorset). Frome: Salmon, sea trout. Spring salmon scarce, summer and autumn fish more plentiful. Season and other rods on 1¼m Woolbridge beat sometimes available from Mr Bowerman, Morden Estate Office, Charborough Park, Wareham BH20 7EN (tel: 01258 857204). Harry Warr, East Burton Estate, Cliff Cottage, Moreton DT2 8RL (01929 462270) has 2 stocked brown trout Frome carriers; limited salmon and sea trout; grayling and pike available; dt priced according to season and species. Dorchester & Dist AS uses the Woolbridge beat for coarse fishing only from 1 November to 28 February; contact Hon Sec. At Tolpuddle, and 7m from Dorchester, **Wessex Fly Fishing** and **Wessex Chalk Streams** Lawrences Farm, DT2 7HF (tel: 01305 848460; see website for more info: goflyfishing.co.uk): 17 chalk stream beats on Rivers Frome and Piddle, lakes and pools; tuition (REFFIS member); c&r on rivers, 10 fish limit, barbless hooks; lake dt £25

4 fish, 3 fish £21, 2 fish £16, conc, for 55yrs and over £13 2 fish, no time limits; rivers, from £40 to £80, depending on season and beat; B&B.

Dorchester (Dorset). Frome: brown trout and grayling; Dorchester FC has 6½m water in vicinity of Dorchester; u/s dry fly or nymph fishing; limited dt £35, from J Aplin (see below). Rest of river preserved by landowners; or tickets through Wessex Chalk Streams (see under Tolpuddle). Dt and licences from tackle shop. Dorchester & Dist AS has coarse fishing for 5m stretch of **Stour** near Blandford St Mary; contact Hon Sec; one dt stretch, conc from Dorchester or Weymouth tackle shops; the society also has concessions on commercial fisheries in area. For Wrackleford Estate Fishery contact Oliver Pope, Wrackleford House, Dorchester DT2 9SN (tel: 01305 267643; see website for more info: www.wrackleford.co.uk/fishing); 6 miles both banks of Frome, 8 beats; stocked brown trout; st and dt available; and wild browns on Sydling Brook; also Langford Lake, stocked with trout; dt available for up to 4 rods; has fishing lodge. Revels Coarse Fishery at Cosmore, DT2 7TW

(tel: 01300 345301); dt available £5; 24 hours £9.75; party and match bookings welcome; separate specimen lake; tackle on site. At **Kingcombe**, Higher Kingcombe Farm DT2 0EH; 7 ponds - coarse fishing; Paul Crocker (tel: 01300 320537); £5 full day, £3 evenings, £5 night. Dorchester & Dist AS has exclusive use of No 6 Lake; apply Hon Sec; no dt, st £50; the Society also has Heath Lake, Warmwell; mixed coarse, 4 acres; carp to 28lb; members only. **Rawlsbury Complex**, 4 small trout lakes let to Wimborne & DAC. **Flowers Farm Lakes**, Hilfield, Dorchester, Dorset DT2 7BA (tel/fax: 01300 341351; see website for more info: www.flowersfarmlakes.co.uk); trout fishery of 5 lakes, brown and rainbow; dt £29, half-day £23, evng £17; full day limit 4 fish; half day 3 fish; evng 2 fish; open all year. Luckfield Lake Fishery, 1½ acres, Broadmayne; strictly members of Dorchester District Angling Society only; and for R Frome fly fishing, from John Aplin, Specialist Angling Supplies, 1 Athelstan Road, Dorchester DT1 1NR (tel: 01305 266500). Hotel: King's Arms.

GIPPING (Orwell)

Rises between Stowmarket and Bury St Edmunds, and flows into the North Sea by an estuary near Ipswich. Coarse fish.

Ipswich (Suffolk). Most coarse fish. From Yarmouth Rd Bridge to Norwich Railway Bridge, 1m, dt on bank; 2m stretch from Railway Bridge to Sproughton Bridge; Gipping APS water; members only; Town section, st or dt on bank; Gipping APS controls 6m between Needham Market and Ipswich; members only; and has section of river from Bramford to Ipswich; members only; also other fishings, which include several coarse lakes in vicinity. **Alton Water**, 350 acre coarse fish reservoir at Anglian Water Services Ltd, Holbrook Rd,

Stutton, Ipswich, IP9 2RY (tel: 01473 589105), under control of AW, with bream to 9lb 2oz and pike to 27lb, plus roach and perch; st £36, dt £6 (bank), in advance £4 per rod, conc, on site or from local tackle shops. Tackle shops: Viscount Fishing Tackle, 207 Clapgate Lane, Ipswich IP3 0RF (tel: 01473 728179; see website for more info: www.viscount-tackle.co.uk); Birds Tackle, Coal Yard, Gipping Road, Great Blakenham IP6 0JB (tel: 01473 830683/834042; see website for more info: www.birdstackle.com) (agents for Colchester APS);

Markhams Tackle, 717-719 Woodbridge Rd, Ipswich IP4 4NB (tel: 01473 727841; see web for more: www.markhamsfishingtackle.co.uk); Bosmere Tackle, 57 High Str, Needham Market, Ipswich IP6 8AL (tel: 01449 721808).

Stowmarket (Suffolk). Permits to fish Green Meadow stretch from Bosmere Tackle, see below. Gipping Valley AC fishes river here, and at **Needham Market** and **Claydon**; also **Needham Lake**, 5 acres, dt £4.50 from Bosmere

Tackle: most coarse fish stocked; also Maypole Farm Lake at Buxhall, mixed coarse, members only; Manor Farm Lakes at Battisford, mixed coarse, disabled platforms; Middle Farm Lakes at Barking Tye, all platforms here have access for disabled; Gipping APS has Alderson Lake at Needham Market; and Causeway Lake at Baylham; Barham Pit (B Pit); members only. Membership from Bosmere Tackle, 57 High Str, Needham Market, Ipswich IP6 8AL (tel: 01449 721808).

GLOUCESTERSHIRE (streams & lakes)

BIDEFORD BROOK. Fishing station: **Awre**. Rises in Abbot's Wood and flows 7m to Severn estuary; coarse fish; preserved. **Blackpool Brook** enters at Awre; Forest of Dean AC; members only.

BURLEY FIELDS LAKE, Crippetts Lane, Leckhampton, GL51 4XT, carp & coarse fishery, dt on site, night fishing allowed, (tel: 01242 862905)

CONE. fishing station: **Woolaston**. Cone rises by Hewelsfield, and is 5m long. Eels and flounders.

CHAD LAKES, Stow Rd, Bledington, Nr Chipping Norton OX7 6XL, carp fishing day tickets, open all year, tackle shop on site, toilet facilities, (tel: 01451 831 470)

FROME. Rises near Cheltenham and flows into Severn estuary. Coarse fish; a few trout higher up. Fishing stations: **Stonehouse** (Glos), coarse fish, and **Stroud** (Glos), a few trout and coarse fish. Several brooks in vicinity. Pike and coarse fishing in Stroudwater Canal.

NAILSWORTH BROOK (tributary of Frome). Fishing stations: **Nailsworth** (Glos) and **Woodchester** (Glos). Brook of poor quality in parts. Lakes: Longfords Lake, pike, carp. Woodchester Park lakes: carp, pike, perch, roach, tench; no dt; NT water now preserved by Priory Angling Club.

Hillview Fisheries, Cherry Orchard Lane, Twyning, Tewkesbury, GL20 6JH, 2 lakes, Moorhen Lake, Heron Lake and The Four Canals, large range of coarse fish, dt on site £7 (1 rod), £8 (2 rods), (tel: 01684 296719; web: www.hillviewlakes.biz)

HOPE BROOK. Fishing station: **Westbury-on-Severn**, ns Grange Court, 1½m. Hope Brook rises 2m above Longhope, runs 5m to Westbury and Severn estuary (1m). Coarse fish, mostly preserved. Inn: Red Lion.

Lemington Lakes, Todenham Road, Moreton-in-Marsh, GL56 9NP, 5 coarse fishing lakes, Sunset, Priory & Abbey, dt £8, jnr £6, Westminster dt £10, £20 night (must be booked), Bishops Lake is syndicate only, (tel: 01608 650 872; see website for more info: www.lemingtonlakes.co.uk)

LITTLE AVON: Small Gloucestershire stream flowing into Severn estuary.

Berkeley (Glos). Coarse fish, trout, Waterley Brook. Fishing below Charfield preserved. Close by station rises Billow Brook, which runs thence 3m to estuary. Clubs have water on **Gloucester and Berkeley Canal**; 16m Sharpness to Gloucester.

LYD. Chub, roach, perch. Fishing station: **Lydney**. Lydney AA holds stretch on canal and Lydney Lake; dt on bank or tackle shop below; club also has **Lydney Lake** (carp to 38lb, bream to over 6lb, roach and perch), **Lydney Canal**. Tackle Shop: Forest Tackle, 15b High Street, Lydney GL15 5DP (tel: 01594 844193/844729).

Stone End Farm Fishery, Church Lane, Corse, GL19 3BX, 2 coarse fishing lakes, Front Lake & House Pond, dt £6, conc £4, eve tkt all £4, (tel: 01452 700254).

Watermark Fisheries, Wildmoorway Lane, South Cerney, GL7 5UZ, 1 trout lake for rainbows & browns, boat hire available, also trout fishing on the **River Churn**, various dt prices, no c&r tkt. Five coarse fishing lakes, Little Horseshoe, Bradleys, Hills Lake, Pike lake & Wood Pool, day & night tkts available, various prices, (tel: 01285 862680; web: www.watermarkfisheries.com).

Watersmeet Fishery, Country Inn & Hotel, can be found on the main A417 Gloucester to Ledbury road at Hartpury, 3 coarse fishing lakes for residents only, (tel: 01452 700358; www.watersmeet-hotel-angling.co.uk).

Whelford Pools, Whelford Road, Fairford, GL7 4DT, 1 dt lake & syndicate lake (no dt), large Carp, also tench, roach, perch, pike and bream, dt adults 12 years and over £9, 24hr tkt £20, conc available, (tel: 01285 713649; www.whelfordpools.co.uk).

Wildmoor Waters, The Willows, Wildmoorway Lane, South Cerney, GL7 5UZ, 2 lakes, contains numerous known fish to over 30lb, for more info, (tel: 07711 826 459; web: www.wildmoorwaters.co.uk).

The wait begins!
Photo: Ian Gemson. www.smartcarping.com

GREATER MANCHESTER RESERVOIRS

These are trout fisheries, unless otherwise stated.

ARNFIELD RESERVOIR, Glossop. Game fishing; United Utilities water (tel: 01457 851087).

BOTTOMS RESERVOIR, Glossop. United Utilities water (tel: 01457 851087); coarse (roach and chub) and brown trout fishing; Medlock Bridge AC water; club also fishes Lower Strinesdale Reservoir; and Alexandra Park, Oldham; contact Chairman (see clubs list).

BUCKLEY WOOD RESERVOIR, Rochdale. United Utilities water (tel: 01457 851087); Whitworth Anglers; members only.

CASTLESHAW (LOWER) RESERVOIR, Oldham. Trout; controlled by Oldham United Anglers; for dt contact Hon Sec; traditional fly fishing for brown and rainbow trout; no lures; United Utilities water (tel: 01457 851087).

DOVESTONE RESERVOIR, Rochdale. United Utilities water (tel: 01457 851087).

DOWRY RESERVOIR, Rochdale. Contact Nigel Bunn (tel: 0161 626 9183); United Utilities water (tel: 01457 851087).

FOUL WATER LODGE, Rochdale. United Utilities water (tel: 01457 851087); coarse fishing; members only; Medlock Bridge AC water; club also fishes Lower Strinesdale Reservoir; and Alexandra Park, Oldham; and 4m away, a pond, Cargate Pool, mixed coarse, members only; 16 pegs; contact Chairman (see clubs list).

GORTON (LOWER) RESERVOIR. Coarse permits on bank, suitable for disabled anglers. Contact Manchester City Council (below); free fishing.

GORTON (UPPER) RESERVOIR, 'Lawrence Scott Arm'; coarse; free fishing; further details from Manchester City Council, Leisure Dept, Debdale Centre, Debdale Park, 1073 Hyde Road, Gorton, Manchester M18 7LJ (tel: 0161 223 5182).

HOLLINGWORTH LAKE, **Littleborough**. Fishing for roach, perch, pike, tench, carp, bream. Contact Chief Warden, Visitors' Centre, Hollingworth Lake Country Park, Rakewood Rd, Littleborough, Lancs OL15 0AQ (tel: 01706 373421); tickets from Visitors' Centre, or from ranger on bank.

KITCLIFFE RESERVOIR, Rochdale. Trout. Controlled by Oldham FFC; for dt as guests contact Hon Sec; United Utilities water.

LITTLE SEA RESERVOIR, Oldham. Medlock Bridge AC water; club also fishes Lower Strinesdale Reservoir, United Utilities water; and Alexandra Park, Oldham; dt £4, conc, on bank; contact Chairman (see clubs list).

LUDWORTH RESERVOIR, **Stockport**. Crossland's AC. Dt for members guests only.

NEW YEARS BRIDGE RESERVOIR, Rochdale. Contact Nigel Bunn (tel: 0161 626 9183); United Utilities water (tel: 01457 851087).

OGDEN RESERVOIR, Rochdale. Rainbows with head of browns; for information contact Hon Sec; United Utilities water (tel: 01457 851087).

PIETHORNE RESERVOIR, **Rochdale**. Trout. Controlled by Oldham FFC; game fishing; for dt as guests contact Hon Sec; United Utilities water.

RUMWORTH LODGE, Bolton. Royal Ashton AC; dt water.

WALKERWOOD TROUT FISHERY, Brushes Road, **Stalybridge**, SK15 3QP (tel: 07721 619399; see website for more info: www.walkerwood.free-online.co.uk); fly only, all browns to be returned;

best brown 11lb, best rainbow 19lb; dt £20 4 fish, half day 5-hours £15 2 fish; sporting tickets all day £15, 5-hours £10, at Car Park; a range of season tickets on offer; United Utilities water (tel: 01457 851087).

WATERGROVE RESERVOIR,
Rochdale. Coarse; dt from Ernie Shufflebottom at Bay Malton AC (mob: 07762 041237); United Utilities water (tel: 01457 851087).

HAMPSHIRE (Streams, lakes and canal)

BASINGSTOKE CANAL. Fishing stations: **Greywell, North Warnborough, Odiham, Winchfield, Crookham, Fleet, Farnborough, Aldershot, Ash Vale, Woking, West Byfleet**, where canal joins R Wey. Pike, carp, roach, good tench, perch, bream (to 8lb); fishing from towpath only; dt for 32m of the canal from Greywell Tunnel to R Wey from bailiffs on bank (head bailiff Jeff Bunch (tel: 01252 326421)); The Basingstoke Canal Centre, Mytchett Place Rd, Mytchett, Surrey GU16 6DD (tel: 01252 370073); and tackle shops. Raison Brothers, 2 Park Road, Farnborough GU14 6JG (tel: 01252 543470); Goldsworth Angling Centre, 73-75 Goldsworth Rd, Woking GU21 1LJ (tel: 01483 776667; see website: www.goldsworthangling.co.uk).
Further enquiries about Basingstoke Canal to BCAA; also contact The Creel (below); dt £3 from shops (£4 on bank), juv £2, OAP/disabled £2. Farnborough & DAS also has rights on **Whitewater** at **Heckfield, Loddon** at **Winnersh, Shawfields Lake**, 3 acres, mixed, Hollybush Lakes at **Farnborough**: 3 gravel pits. At Winchfield, Farnham AS has Winchfield Pond, mainly ghost and mirror carp, and other coarse fish; apply Hon Sec; the society also has 2 Stillwater Front Lakes at Ash Vale; and Wyke Farm Pond at Ash Green; also at Baghshot Lea 3 lakes total 21 acres; mixed coarse plus catfish; at Alice Holt mixed coarse, 3 acres; members only; st £93, conc; from M J Borra (below). **Willow Park Fisheries**, Youngs Drive, Ash, nr Aldershot GU12 6RE (tel: 01252

325867; see website for more info: www.willowparkfishery.co.uk) three lakes totalling over 13 acres stocked with carp (to 33lb), tench and other coarse fish; 120 pegs; bait and refreshments on site; dt on site £10 1 rod, £15 2 rods, and £24 for 24-hours, conc; disabled facilities. Four Cemex (formerly RMC) Angling lakes at **Frimley** (Silver Water Lakes 1 & 2; £60 (2 rods) daylight hours); carp, crucian carp, bream, perch, tench, rudd, eel and pike; large specimens recorded; Lakes 3 & 4 Gold ticket waters; common carp 40lb plus; st £475, no conc, two rods (limit 3 rods). (For Cemex (formerly RMC) Angling, see Chertsey.) Tackle shops: Tackle Up, 151 Fleet Road, Fleet GU51 3PD (01252 614066; web: www.tackleupfleet.com); M J Borra, The Creel, 36 Station Road, Aldershot, Hants GU11 1HT (tel: 01252 320871; Raison Brothers, 2 Park Road, Farnborough GU14 6JG (tel: 01252 543470); Goldsworth Angling Centre, 73-75 Goldsworth Rd, Woking GU21 1LJ (tel: 01483 776667; see website for more info: www.goldsworthangling.co.uk).

BEAULIEU. The Beaulieu River is approx 7 miles long. Tickets for tidal stretch, Bailey's Hard to Needs Ore (bass, mullet), st £30, dt £5, from Harbour Master, Buckler's Hard SO42 7XB (tel: 01590 616200) or Resident Land Agent, John Montagu Building, Beaulieu (tel: 01590 614621); access from Buckler's Hard. Coarse fishing on **Hatchet Pond** (Forestry Commission); bream, carp, tench and pike; tickets from Forestry Commission, The Queen's House,

Lyndhurst SO43 7NH (tel: 02380 283141), campsite offices during camping season and local tackle shops (st £80 2 rods (£125 3 rod), wt £20, dt £6.50, VAT incl, jun conc, barbless hooks only); close season 14 Mar to 16 June. Hotel: Montagu Arms.

CHIPHALL LAKE, North Field Farm, Droxford Road, Wickham, PO17 5NZ. 1 lake for rainbow & brown trout, various dt available, (tel: 01329 833295; see website for more info: www.chiphalllake.co.uk).

DAMERHAM TROUT LAKES, The Lake House, Damerham Fisheries, **Fordingbridge**, SP6 3HW (tel: 01725 518446); six lakes, and river for st holders; r and b trout; open March to October season rods, full, half, quarter, guest, prices on application; and October to December for dt.

FLEET POND. Fishing station: **Fleet**. largest natural stillwater in SE England; heavily silted but a few swims; mixed coarse; dt from Tackle Up £3. Tackle shop: Tackle Up, 151 Fleet Road, Fleet GU51 3PD (01252 614066; see website for more info: www.tackleupfleet.com).

HAMBLE. Sea trout and trout. **Bishop's Waltham**. Fishing mostly private.

HOLBURY TROUT LAKES, Lockerley, Near **Romsey**, Hants SO51 0JR (tel: 01794 341619): fishery of four lakes, stocked with rainbow and blue trout, and ⅔m of River Dun, both banks, stocked brown trout; dry fly and nymph only on river and lakes; no c&r; various tickets, incl full dt for lakes and river; 2 or 4 fish tickets; lakes only dt £42 limit 4 fish; half day £28; full facilities on site, and tuition if required.

LYMINGTON RIVER. Fishing station: Lymington. Sea trout (2-11lb), brown trout (¾ to 1lb). Sea trout best June to Sept. Fishing improved by Brockenhurst Manor FFC; private. Mixed fishery at **Sway Lakes**, Barrows Lane, Sway, Lymington SO41 6DD (tel: 01590 682010); carp

to over 37lbs; now syndicate water; long waiting list.

MEON. Trout; sea trout in lower reaches. Fishing station: **East Meon**. Portsmouth & Dist AS holds some thirteen waters around **Portsmouth** and across Hampshire, which include coarse fishing on Hamble and Wallington; dt up to £8 on waters; club also has Lakeside at Cosham, mixed coarse; members only; also Carron Row Farm, near Titchfield Abbey, dt £8 from tackle shops; mixed coarse; also Funtley Pond, 3m W of Fareham; membership £75 per annum, conc: enquiries to Hon Sec, or local tackle shops. Other fisheries in vicinity: at Staunton Country Park, Havant PO9 5HB (tel: 023 9245 3405): a 3 acre lake with carp, bream roach, dt from Park Office (10am-5pm (4pm winter)). **Meon Springs Fly Fishery**, Whitewool Farm, East Meon, Petersfield GU32 1HW (tel: 01730 823134; see website for more info: www.meonsprings.com): 3 acres of lakes; rainbows; between East and West Meon; tickets from bailiff (mob: 07766 525840; see website for more info: www.meonsprings.com): dt £40 4 fish, £35 3 fish, £28 2 fish, £20 c&r. Tackle shops: Rovers Tackle Shop, 176-178A West St, Fareham PO16 0EQ (tel: 01329 220354); Allan's Marine, 143 Twyford Ave, Stamshaw, Portsmouth PO2 8HU (tel: 02392 671833/610777; see website for more info: www.allansmarine.co.uk). **Moorhen Trout Fishery**, Warnford, Hampshire, SO32 3LB, dt on site, £40 (4 Fish), £37 (3 Fish), £27 (2 Fish), £17 (1 Fish), rainbow trout - 2lbs into double figures, (tel: 01730 829460; www.moorhentroutfishery.co.uk).

SANDLEHEATH. Six lakes and three chalk stream beats **Rockbourne Trout Fishery**, Sandleheath, Fordingbridge, Hampshire SP6 1QG; excellent fishing for rainbow trout in lakes and brown trout, fly only, various period terms from dt £55 (5 fish), £48 (4 fish), £40 (3 fish), £30 (2 fish from 2pm); no night fishing; also fish tickets 25 fish at £275; tuition, tackle hire (tel: 01725 518603; web: www.rockbournetroutfishery.co.uk).

WAGGONERS' WELLS, near **Haslemere**. Two lakes; National Trust waters, now managed by Greyshott AC; coarse fishing; carp, roach, tench, gudgeon, a few trout; dt from Grayshott Tackle, 1 Crossways Road, Greyshott, Hindhead GU26 6HJ (tel: 01428 606122), or bailiff on bank. Hotel: Devils Punchbowl Hotel, Hindhead.

WARBURN. Dace, trout, salmon; preserved; leave sometimes from landowners; joins sea at **Key Haven**.

HERTS AND GREATER LONDON (reservoirs and lakes)

(see also London Reservoirs)

ALDENHAM (Herts). **Aldenham Country Park Reservoir**; managed by Herts CC. Coarse fishing, incl. tench, pike to 37lb, carp, plus very good roach and bream; no night fishing; dt £6 (jun, OAP £3.00); disabled free; no keepnets, barbless hooks only, no lure fishing, no night fishing; fishing punds; tickets from bailiff on site or phone Eric on 07974 272750.

Shepperton (Middx); **Ashmere Fisheries**, Felix Lane, Shepperton TW17 8NN: four lakes, total 20 acres, stocked with rainbow trout; boats; annual membership only, no dt; parking; disabled access; toilets; tuition; boat hire and tackle for sale; owner is registered coach; apply Mrs Jean Howman (tel: 01932 225445). For carp to 35lb, large head of pike (British record tench here) for **Sheepwalk Lakes** apply for associate membership tickets £50 pa to Feltham Piscatorials. For **Shepperton Marina Lake**; mixed coarse; dt available; no bait restrictions; keepnets allowed. Tackle shop: Tackle Tarts Angling, 357 Staines Rd West, Ashford, Middlesex TW15 1RP (tel: 01784 240013; see website for more info: www.tackletartsangling.com).

STANSTEAD ABBOTS. Cemex (formerly RMC) Angling coarse fishing water; the 30-acre Abbotts Lake, is noted for carp to 41lb 15oz with good bream and tench; Gold ticket water £260 st (rod limit 3); Cemex also has 2 Gold venue lakes at Amwell heavily stocked with carp; st £240 (rod limit summer/autumn 2 rods, winter 3; waiting list). (For Cemex (formerly RMC) Angling, see Chertsey.)

TRING (Herts). Large reservoirs: **Marsworth**, **Startops End** and **Wilstone** (2m from Tring) main feeders for Grand Union Canal. Good fishing for specimen hunters; bream over 16lb, former British record tench 12½lb, pike to 30lb, many large roach, specimen catfish; Sunday fishing now permitted; contact Dick Pilkington (tel: 01582 841985) for st details; dt £6 1 rod, £4 for 2nd rod, conc £4, evening £4; tickets obtainable on bank. The fourth reservoir, **Tringford Reservoir**, is a private trout fishery; ring Craig Kempster (mob: 07748 770 548); stocked rainbow trout; mostly boat fishing; fly only; st, dt by appointment only. The Tring Anglers have exclusive fishing rights on the Grand Union Canal from Tring station to Cooks Wharf (the latter venue being members only) along with the Wendover Arms and several miles of the Aylesbury Arms of the canal; also the **R Thames** at Sonning, **R Thame** at Shabbington Island and Ickford; **R Ivel** at Blunham, plus an excellent members only bream and tench lake fishery near Soulbury; also pond near Ivinghoe; mixed coarse; the Club has a comprehensive water-sharing scheme with Barnet & Dist AC; Tring

Anglers st £48, dt £5 where applicable, conc half price. Tackle shop: Chiltern Tackle, 33 Western Rd, Tring HP23 4BQ (tel: 01442 825257).

HULL

Tidal river between Hempholme and Hull is free of any permit charge and is popularly fished by an increasing number of coarse anglers. Upstream of Beverley first-class sport may be had with roach, dace, pike, chub, bream, etc. West Beck is an excellent but preserved trout fishery of chalk-stream character.

Hull (North Humberside). Drains giving good coarse fishing. Free fishing on EA licence from North Frodingham to Hull. Hull & Dist AA has water on **Derwent** at **Breighton**, **Sutton**, **Wressle**; on the **Rye** at **Butterwick**; and on the **Trent** at **Carlton**; also the **Brandsburton Ponds** (open all the year), Tilery Lake, the Broomfleet, Motorway, and other ponds, 3m of **Market Weighton Canal** (enquire first), 17m from Hull, mixed coarse fishery, 1m of **R Foulness**, north bank; membership is unrestricted. Stone Creek and Patrington Haven hold flounders; good sea fishing. **Rush Lyvars Lake**, Preston Road, Hedon HU12 8JU; coarse fishery at **Hedon**, dt water (tel: 01482 898970). **Pickering Park Lake** owned by City Council, fine pike; coarse dt around £3 from ranger on bank (tel: 01482 614966). At Aldbrough on Sea, Lambwath Lakes, 5 pond complex of 120 pegs, good match fishing for carp, tench, orfe and bream; contact 01482 796627. Tackle shops: Fishing Basket, 500 Beverley Rd, Hull HU5 1NA (tel: 01482 445284); G W Hutchinson & Co, 31 Anlaby Rd, Hull HU1 2PG (tel: 01482 223869).

Beverley (East Yorkshire). Tidal River Hull and drains give good coarse fishing; from Hull Bridge upstream through **Arram**, **Aike Wilfholme**,

Baswicke and **Hempholme** to Frodingham Beck: North East Region Environment Agency, for enquiries; weedy, June to Nov; some of best winter fishing from The Ship Yard to Weel. **Beverley Beck**, canalised stream, 1m long, 60 pegs, good access for disabled; stocked with most coarse species, but mainly roach to 2lb, bream 7lb, tench and chub, perch, pike to 30lb; dt on bank; further information: (tel: 01482 395132). **Leven Canal** (6m): coarse fish; fine tench. Tackle shop: Beverley Angling Centre, 8 Maple Drive HU17 9QJ (tel: 01482 869948). Hotel: Beverley Arms.

Brandesburton (East Yorkshire). River Hull 3m W, excellent coarse fishing in gravel pits (see Hull); at **Leven Park Lake**, 6m N of Beverley coarse lake; mixed coarse with 3 log cabins for weekly hire with own pegs; fishing included (tel: 019645 44510; web: www.levenparklake.co.uk).

Wansford (East Yorkshire). Free left bank below Lock Dow to Brigham. **Driffield Canal Fishery**, from Town Lock, Driffield along B1249 to Snake Holme Lock, $\frac{1}{2}$m west of Wansford; coarse. **West Beck** preserved by Golden Hill AS and West Beck PS; members only; dt only at Mulberry Whyen; apply at farm.

Tributaries of the Hull

FOSTON BECK (or **KELK** or **FRODINGHAM BECK**):

North Frodingham, Foston -on- the-Wolds and **Lowthorpe** (East Yorkshire). Rises in Yorkshire wolds; true chalk stream containing brown trout averaging well over the pound.

Preserved; apply at farm for Frodingham Beck dt.

DRIFFIELD BECK:

Driffield (East Yorkshire). Provides chalk stream fishing for trout and grayling of high order. Driffield AA. Kellythorpe Trout Lake now in private hands. For **Pickering Trout Lake**, Newbridge Rd, Pickering, N Yorks YO18 8JJ (tel: 01751 474219; web: www.pickeringtroutlake.co.uk); 1 acre; rainbows; £20 all day c&r; barbless hooks only; bait fishing £6 per rod; £5.35 per kg for all fish caught on that ticket.

Malham Tarn, North Yorkshire. *Photo: Rob Denson*

A fine wild brown trout from Malham Tarn. *Photo: Rob Denson*

ISLE OF MAN

The geographical nature of the Isle of Man tends to dictate the type of river, fish and hence fishing one may encounter when angling in the Island. Being a relatively mountainous place, rivers and streams are small, fast flowing and very clear. Excellent sport can be had in the numerous small trout streams, which hold fine stocks of native brown trout.

There are very few preserved stretches of river in the Island and a well chosen word with the land owner is often all that is required to enable an angler to fish in peace. Approx one half mile of the River Douglas through the Nunnery Estate is exclusively reserved for the Manx Game FC and small sections of the Rivers Dhoo and Glass can only be fished under permit from the Douglas & District Angling Club.

Natural and artificial baits are allowed on the Island's rivers, ponds and streams; however, other than in Eairy Dam, live bait, ground bait or organic matter must not be used in any reservoir. In addition, rubber worms or similar artificial bait are not allowed, including any substance with which artificial bait may be impregnated to attract fish by sense of smell. Further details of all freshwater angling can be obtained from the Freshwater Fisheries Officer, Cornaa, Maughold (tel: 01624 812224).

Anglers must abide by the regulations wherever they fish. These include: (1) Not to use or carry a gaff or tailer. (2) Not to use a line that exceeds 10lb breaking strain. (3) Not use more than one hook on a line unless (a) Pennel or Stewart tackles are being used for bait fishing; (b) a 'point with two droppers' is being used for fly fishing only; (c) a spinner is being used for spinning only. (4) Not use a spinner except (a) in a reservoir where the spinner does not exceed 10gms in weight and does not exceed 65mm in length, inclusive of hook and dressing or (b) in a river where the spinner does not exceed 15gms in weight and does not exceed 100mms in length, inclusive of hook and dressing. (5) Not to use a hook larger than No 6 Redditch scale, unless the hook is comprised in an artificial fly. (6) Return all foul hooked fish to the water. (7) Return to the water unharmed any freshwater fish hooked which is less than 18 cm in length overall. (8) Wading in the reservoirs is prohibited. (9) A landing net must be used when fishing at a reservoir at all times, and when fishing for migratory fish in rivers. (10) Fishing for salmon or sea trout from the foreshore, in any estuary or at sea is not permitted.

The river fishing season commences on 1 Apr, and finishes on the 30 Sept for trout, with an extension to the end of Oct in respect of angling for salmon and sea trout only. The reservoir season begins on 10 Mar and continues until 31 Oct.

An **'Other Waters'** fishing licence is required to fish any river or pond, and a separate licence is required should you wish to fish the reservoirs. Anglers fishing the rivers during the month of October must hold an **'Other Waters'** season licence.

There is a daily bag limit for the rivers of 6 fish, of which no more than 2 may be salmon or sea trout, and catch and release must not be continued after the 6th (final) fish is caught and killed. There is also a bag limit for the reservoirs of 4 trout per day and anglers must not continue to fish after catching and killing the maximum number of fish. Full details of all the Regulations can be obtained from the Department of Agriculture, Fisheries and Forestry; web: www.gov.im/daff/fish/inland.

Fishing Licences

Fishing licences are obligatory by law and 2009 costs are as follows; **Reservoirs:** st £137 (students £53), wt £48 (students (14-18yrs) £21), dt £15 (students £8.50), conc 2-fish bag limit £95; season 10 March to 31 Oct. **Other Waters:** st £53 (stu £21), wt £21 (stu n/a), dt £8.50 (stu £5.25); under 12s free; season trout 1 Apr to 30 Sept.

Whilst these prices are very reasonable, they are not to be ignored. It is an offence not to be in possession of a valid fishing licence whilst fishing. Failure to produce a valid licence on demand to an authorised officer could result in prosecution and confiscation of fishing tackle. Warranted Fisheries Officers and River Watchers patrol all the fisheries on a regular basis.

Licences are obtainable from: Department of Agriculture Fisheries and Forestry, Rose House, 51-59 Circular Road, Douglas (tel: 01624 685835; web: www.gov.im/tourism); from Department of Tourism and Leisure, Information Bureau, Sea Terminal, Douglas IM1 2RG (tel: 01624 686766); from Onchan Commissioners, several tackle shops, Post Offices and on-line.

No licence is required for sea fishing, which from pier, rocks or boat is excellent, especially for Pollack (locally called callig), mackerel, cod and codling, whiting and plaice. Chief bait for ground fish is mackerel, but lugworm, sand eels and shellfish are also used. Jigging with white and coloured feathers and artificial sand eel for Pollack, mackerel and cod is successful. Good centres for most species are Peel, Port Erin, Port St Mary and Ramsey.

The Department of Tourism & Leisure in Douglas issues useful booklets on sea and river fishing (tel: 01624 686766); additional information can also be obtained from their web-site: www.gov.im/tourism.

At this time there are eight reservoirs open for trout fishing **West Baldwin** lies near the centre of the Island, a large water, about a mile long and 500ft above sea level. Good access as road runs along the western side, where shallower water is to be found; fly fish or spin. The **Clypse** and **Kerrowdhoo** lie one beyond the other, about 1½ miles north of Onchan - both are fly fishing only. **Ballure** is a small reservoir nestling about 300ft in the hills, just south of Ramsey where anglers may fly fish or spin. **Cringle** reservoir is in the south of the Island; at approx 750ft it can be breezy but the mangificent views down to Langness Lighthouse make it well worth while; the western side has the deeper water but all round the underwater contours mean a variety of depths; fly fish or spin. **Sulby Reservoir** is a huge upland (c700ft) water, close to the A14 Sulby-Snaefell road; shallower water along the western edge from the car park; fly fish or spin; the dam and area to the west is well signed no fishing zone. **Block Eairy** reservoir stands at 750ft above sea level and fishing involves a steep hill walk just west of Sulby Valley; currently not fished. **Eairy Dam** is not a water supply and therefore the restrictions on the use of live organic bait do not apply; it lies to the east of the old mining village of Foxdale, about 500ft above sea level. All reservoirs hold an excellent stock of wild brown trout and have ample parking close by (apart from Block Eairy), though facilities for disabled anglers are limited.

Reservoirs are stocked on weekly basis throughout the season with Rainbow Trout reared at the Government's fish hatchery at Cornaa. All the Island's fish are raised here and visitors can visit the site to see the rearing pools and feed the fish. Opening hours are 10am - 4pm on each Wednesday during the Easter and Summer school holidays. A preliminary phone call is appreciated in the event of bad weather (tel: 01624 812224).

There is a private fishery on the island: Riverside Fishery, Patrick Road, St Johns; managed by Ken Jervis (tel: 01624 801715); limited morning tickets may be available on this 3 acre fishery; fly only and all fish are to be kept; either category of fishing licence is valid for fishing this private commercial fishery.

Salmon and sea trout are both native to the island and Manx rivers hold surprisingly good stocks of migratory fish. Given enough water, there should be sea trout in the major streams by June, with salmon arriving later in the year, usually by late September. The main streams frequented by migratory fish are the Sulby River in the northern half of the island, the Neb, which flows into the sea at Peel on the West coast and the Douglas River. Sea trout can also be found in some of the larger pools in the smaller streams. The principal rivers are as follows:

Sulby River. Starts at Sulby Reservoir and runs into the sea at Ramsey. The top section from the dam to around Sulby Bridge is a rocky, fast flowing mountain stream with alternating pools and runs. Downstream the character changes into a wider and slower running water with long deep stretches and much bankside vegetation; salmon (from Aug), sea trout.

Laxey River. 5m long; trout; rises below Snaefell and runs into the sea at Laxey. The bottom mile is difficult through the village; however, Laxey Glen is much easier; above here to Glen Roy there is 1m of very rough fishing. Fishing station: **Laxey**.

River Dhoo. Flows across the central valley to Douglas; private fishing to Braddan Bridge, above which it is slow flowing through agricultural land (somewhat polluted). **River Douglas** is formed by junction of Dhoo and Glass, half a mile above the town of **Douglas**.

River Glass. Starts at West Baldwin Reservoir and flows down to Douglas; private fishing up to the Tromode area; above here, ask permission to fish an increasingly wild stream and its little tributary, the Baldwin River. Large sections of the lower Glass are rented by Douglas & Dist AC and Manx Game FC; limited guest tickets may be available.

River Neb. Flows from the **Little London** area, through **Glen Helen**, where there are a number of deep pools to **St John's**; here **Foxdale River**, 6m long, joins on left bank; finally enters the sea at **Peel**. Trout; salmon from Sept; first class river for migratory fish.

Brown Trout Fishing: There are numerous smaller streams on the Island, many of which hold good stocks of wild brown trout. Access to the upper reaches of some of these streams may be restricted by the overgrown nature of the banks, however the lower sections are more easily reached. Many anglers chose to spin rather than fly fish due to the dense cover, however excellent results will come to the practised fly fisherman. These include:

Colby Stream: rises near Earystane Plantation and running through Colby Glen to the sea at Kentraugh; private fishing in the lower reaches.

Cornaa River: starts below North Barrule and runs through Ballaglass Glen to the sea at Port Cornaa; mainly brown trout in the pools in the Glen, although migratory fish may found in the lower sections.

Glen Maye Burn: the stream flows down through Glen Rushen and enters the sea at Glen Maye, passing through an impressive gorge; sea trout may be found in the section below the waterfall and good stocks of brown trout throughout.

Santon Burn: this stream starts in Foxdale and flows in to the sea east of Ballasalla; upper sections are narrow and overgrown, and flow through an impressive gorge with good pools in the bottom mile.

Silver Burn: starts in the St Marks area on the slopes of South Barrule and flows through open meadows to the sea at Castletown; best sport downstream for about 1 mile to Castletown.

Island Tackle Shops: Hobbytime, 12 Castle St, **Douglas** IM1 2EU (tel: 01624 625720; fax: 01624 671164); The Roland Westcott Tackle Company, 1 The Shops, Ballaquayle Rd, **Douglas** IM2 5DF (tel: 01624 629599); The Ramsey Warehouse, 37 Parliament St, **Ramsey** IM8 1AT (tel: 01624 813092); and Raymond Caley, M J Caley Post Office & Stores, Sulby Glen, nr Ramsey IM7 2HR (tel: 01624 897205).

For further information please contact: Department of Agriculture Fisheries and Forestry, Rose House, 51-59 Circular Road, Douglas, Isle of Man IM1 1AZ (tel: 01624 685835); Manx Game Fishing Club (see Clubs). (For sea fishing on the Island, see under Sea Fishing Stations.)

ISLE OF WIGHT

Freshwater fishing on the Island is better than is generally appreciated. The **Yar** from St Helens, Bembridge, to Alverstone holds fair numbers of roach, dace and rudd, with perch, carp and bream to 7lb in some stretches. Isle of Wight Freshwater AA has coarse fishing for dace, roach, carp, bream, perch, tench, pike and others at Yarbridge and Alverstone on Yar, members only;

Gunville Pond, Newport: pike to 21lb, common and mirror carp to 25lb, tench, bream, perch, roach, rudd; **Merstone Fishery**, 3 coarse lakes: carp to 30lb, bream to 14lb, perch, tench, chub, roach, rudd, **Somerton Reservoir**, Cowes: 2 acres; common and mirror carp to 20lb, roach, rudd, perch; dt from Scotties Tackle Shop (below); IWFAA membership £60 (plus £5 joining), conc; for further information, contact Hon Sec. **Hale Manor Lakes** are both 1 acre, carp and mixed coarse; one lake syndicate, one dt £6.50 (on bank); Hale Manor, Arreton PO30 3AR (tel: 01983 865204). Nettlecombe Farm, **Whitwell** PO38 2AF (tel: 01983 730783): 3 ponds of varying depth and at different levels; stocked carp, roach, tench; dt £5 per rod; ideal for children. Gillees Pond, Stag Lane, Newport: carp, rudd, roach, bream; dt from Scotties, below. Tackle shops: The Sports & Toymaster, 9 Union Str, **Ryde** PO33 2DU (tel: 01983 563836); N R Young, The Sports Shop, 70 Regent Str, **Shanklin** PO37 7AJ (tel: 01983 867947; web: www.thesportsshop.com); Scotties', 22 Fitzroy St, **Sandown** PO36 8HZ (tel: 01983 404555). Light sea fishing, for which freshwater tackle may be employed, at Whippingham (River Medina), Fishbourne (Wootton Creek) and in Bembridge Harbour; mullet, bass, flatfish, etc.

ITCHEN

Rises some miles north-west of Petersfield and flows via Winchester into Southampton Water at Southampton. Famous Hampshire chalk stream. Trout fishing excellent, but strictly preserved for most part. Some salmon and sea trout lower down, but also preserved. Principal tributaries are **Arle** and **Candover Brook**; both strictly preserved.

Southampton (Hants). Itchen and Test estuaries. Pout, whiting and eels in Southampton Water; and whiting, bass, grey mullet from the piers and quays. Free coarse fishing from public footpath between Woodmill and Mansbridge. **Lower Itchen Fishery**, Gaters Mill, Mansbridge Road, West End SO18 3HW, offers pre-booked salmon, brown trout, sea trout, grayling and night sea trout fishing on season basis, and some dt; also coarse fishing; corporate fishing days; contact Embley Ridge, Gardeners Lane, Romsey, Hants SO51 6AD (tel: 02380 814389; mob: 07885 175540; www.itchen-fishing.net). **Five Oaks Trout Lake**, Crableck Lane, Sarisbury Green, Southampton, SO31 7AL, (tel: 01489 577379). **Cadland Fishery**, c/o The Estate Office, Stanswood Farm, Stanswood Road, Fawley, Southampton SO45 1AB (tel: 023 8089 1059; mob: 07788 563007; see website for more info: www.cadlandcarpwaters.co.uk); coarse pond with specialist carp fishing, mirror, common, ghost to 26lbs plus; access for disabled; various permits, st £100 (2 lakes), conc, dt £10 (after 3.30pm £6), conc. For **Holbury Manor Pond**, with tench, carp, pike, roach, rudd contact Gang Warily Recreation and Community Centre, Newlands Rd, Fawley SO45 1GA (tel: 023 8089 3603); st £45, wt £11.35, dt £4.50, conc; **Gang Warily Pond** is for under 15's only; st £17.12, wt £4, dt £2.25. Tackle shop: Bells of Hythe, 9-10 New Rd, saltwood, Hythe, Southampton SO45 6BP (tel: 023 8084 2065; see website for more info: www.bellsofhythe.com).

Eastleigh (Hants) Trout, salmon and grayling; preserved. Eastleigh & Dist AC has various coarse and limited game fishing, incl 3 stretches of river, Upper and Lower Itchen Navigation, and 12 lakes; dt for one of these, Lakeside Park, Eastleigh, on site at cafe and from Home Stores Tackle (below). Bishopstoke FC has water, which affords excellent sport. Water holds large trout. Salmon run right up to Brambridge. Some sea trout also come up; private. Junior st from Borough Council for Bishopstoke Riverside Rd stretch. Tackle shop: Home Stores Tackle, 68 High Road, Swaythling SO16 2HZ (tel: 023 8055 1974); Eastleigh Angling Centre, 325 Market Str, SO50 5QE (tel: 023 806 53540). **Wintershill Lake**, Wintershill Estate, SO51 2AH, (tel: 02380 601421).

Bishopstoke (Hants), ns Eastleigh. Salmon, trout and grayling; preserved by Bishopstoke FC and other owners.

Winchester (Hants). Trout and grayling. Free fishing on EA licence between the city weirs, and the left bank of the **Itchen Navigation**, between Blackbridge and St Catherine's Lock. The Rod Box, King's Worthy Store, London Road, King's Worthy, Winchester S023 7QN (tel: 01962 883600; web: www.rodbox.com), offers dry fly fishing on st and dt basis and other rods on celebrated private stretches of the **Test** and on the **Itchen** and can arrange fishing on lakes; charges on request. Tackle shop: The Rod Box (above).

Itchen Abbas (Hants). Trout; preserved by riparian owners. **Avington Trout Fishery** (tel: 01962 779 312), three lakes plus stretch of R Itchen carrier, provide excellent trout fishing; browns to 22½lb. Open all year, stocked daily; dt 4 fish £69, 3 fish £57.50, 2 fish £40.25; British rainbow record broken there several times. Tackle Shop: The Rod Box, King's Worthy Store, London Road, King's Worthy, Winchester S023 7QN (tel: 01962 883600; see web for more info: www.rodbox.com). Many hotels.

Arlesford (Hants). **Candover Brook**, **Alre, Itchen**; trout; preserved by riparian owners. Grange Lakes, Alresford Pond; coarse fish; preserved.

KENT (lakes and streams)

BEWL WATER: The Fishing Lodge, **Lamberhurst**, Tunbridge Wells TN3 8JH (tel: 01892 890352); 770 acre fly-only trout fishery; st (full (7 days per week to 19 Nov 2010)) £650, 8 fish daily, extended st £775 (to 18 Feb 2011); st (weekday) £550, 8 fish daily; extended weekday st £650; evenings, £17, 4 fish (please phone if boat wanted), dt £22, 8 fish, c&r £17. Various prices for boats. Bewl Bridge Flyfishers' Club offers various advantages to members; enquiries to Treasurer (see clubs).

BROOKLANDS LAKES, Off Princes Rd, Dartford (tel: 01322 270397) 20 acres, almost in centre of Dartford. Dartford & DDAPS, variety of coarse fish, carp to 36lb, tench, bream, roach, pike to 32lb; dt £6 1 rod, £8 2 rods, £10 3 rods, conc, from bailiff on bank. Tackle shop: Mark II Angling, 24-26 High Street, Crayford DA1 4HG (tel: 01322 554545; see website for more info: www.mark2angling.co.uk).

BOUGH BEECH RESERVOIR. Near **Tonbridge**; 285 acres, st for pike, carp and coarse; apply to Mr K Crow, Honeycroft Farm, Three Elm Lane, Golden Green, Tonbridge TN11 0BS (tel: 01732 851544; see website: www.boughbeechfishing.com).

CHEQUERTREE TROUT FISHERY, Bethersden, Ashford, TN26 3JR. Coarse and trout fishing, coarse £7 1 rod, £10 2 rods; trout, dt full day £25 (4 fish), £20 (3 fish), half day £15 (2 fish). (tel: 01233 820078; web: www.chequertreefishery.co.uk).

CHIDDINGSTONE CASTLE LAKE Good coarse fishing, especially carp; no night fishing, 7-days a week June 16 to Mar 15; dt £10 from Caretaker at lakeside, no charge for juniors under 14; apply to the Administrator, Chiddingstone Castle, near **Edenbridge** TN8 7AD. (tel: 01892 870347; see website for more info: www.chiddingstonecastle.org.uk).

LONGFORD LAKE. Sevenoaks. Private water of Holmesdale A&CS, who also have junior water Montreal Park Lakes; guests with members guests only, membership from Hon Sec; from Manklows Kit & Tackle, 44 Seal Road, Sevenoaks TN14 5AR (tel: 01732 454952); A & I Fishing Tackle, 33-35 High St, Green Street Green, Orpington BR6 6BG (tel: 01689 862302).

LULLINGSTONE LAKE, near **Eynsford**. Trout. Kingfisher APS; no dt; Society also fishes stretch of River Darent at Lullingstone.

MID KENT FISHERIES, Chilham Water Mill, Ashford Rd, **Chilham** CT4 8EE (tel: 01227 730668); coarse fishing on 25 lakes, from 26 to 3 acres, well stocked with all species; catches include British record carp 67lbs 14oz, bream to 15lbs, perch, rudd, tench 13lbs, catfish 45lbs and pike to 36lbs; also available 2 rivers and 104 peg match fishing lake; membership £350 to £95; company also has **Thanington** (Milton Complex); carp, bream, tench, pike.

MOTE PARK LAKE. Maidstone (see Medway). Coarse fishery of 26 acres;

large carp, roach, tench, bream; Day tickets are available for this water, but MUST be purchased in advance. They are not available on the bank dt £5; contact Medway Victory Angling & Medway Preservation Society.

PETT POOLS. Fishing stations: **Winchelsea**, 2m; Rye, 4m. 25 acres, coarse fish; closed as we go to press for weed control; carp, rudd to 2lb, tench, bream, perch, eels and pike normally; refer to Hastings Angling Centre (below).

ROMNEY MARSH. Good fishing on marsh, especially in main drains to Rother; best in summer (large bream shoals); water on low side in winter. Clubs with water here are: Ashford & Dist APS; Cinque Ports AS; Clive Vale AC (who fish **Jury's Gap Sewer**; **Clive Vale** reservoirs (carp); Rye & Dist AS; Tenterden & Dist APS; Lydd AC; Linesmen AC (also waters on **Medway**, **Beult** and **Stour**; details: Hon Sec). Cemex (formerly RMC) has **Dungeness Long Lakes**, coastal lakes offering mixed fishing; st £40, £25 conc (2 rods only). Tackle shops; Marsh Tackle, 17 Littlestone Road, Littlestone, New Romney TN28 8LW (tel: 01797 366130); Point Tackle Shop, Allendale, Dungeness Road, Dungeness TN29 9ND (tel: 01797 320049), and Hastings tackle shops: Steve's Tackle, 38 White Rock, Hastings TN34 1JL (tel: 01424 433404; www.stevestackle.co.uk); Hastings Angling Centre, 33 The Bourne, Hastings TN34 3AY (tel: 01424 432178; see website for more info: www.hastingsangling.gbr.cc).

ROYAL MILITARY CANAL. Summer fishing only; level partially lowered in winter for drainage. Stations: **Hythe** and **Ashford**. Near Asford in the South Downs, Cemex (formerly RMC) has a 6 acre clay pit; mixed fishing; st £45 (2 rods), £28 conc; rod limit 3. Cinque Ports AS has 7m from Seabrook outfall to Giggers

Green; carp, bream, roach, rudd, tench, eels, perch, pike; most sections have dt from bailiff or tackle shops; West Hythe Ballast Pit is members and dt water. Rother FA fishes 3m from Appledore Dam to Iden Lock; dt from bailiff on bank. Sperringbrook Sewer, nr Appledore, is CALPAC water, and may be fished from Mock Hill Farm to Arrow Head Bridge; dt available from Arrowhead Cottage.

SCHOOL POOL. At Oare, $1\frac{1}{2}$m N of **Faversham**; controlled by Faversham AC; large pool containing carp (30lb plus), tench, bream, roach, rudd and pike; dt £5 1 rod, £10 2 rods, in advance only, from Mr and Mrs Kennett, 14 Millfield, Faversham ME13 8BY (tel: 01795 534516); Faversham AC also has Bysingwood Lake and Bracher Pools, Faversham, mixed fisheries;carp, tench, roach, etc; members only; also Willow Pool, near School Pool; members only; mixed coarse. **Twin Lakes**, now syndicate water, no dt. Tackle shop: Ashford Tackle, 52 St Marys Rd, Faversham ME13 8EH (tel: 01795 530160; www.ashfordtackle.co.uk), who also supply tickets for **Mansfields Lake**, Broad Oak, Canterbury; mixed coarse; dt from shop.

SPRING HILL TROUT WATERS, Albarns Farm, Pembury, TN2 4BB, 3 lakes, dt at various prices also c&r ticket, (tel: 01892 826041; web: www.springhilltroutwaters.co.uk).

STOWTING TROUT LAKE, Stowting, Ashford, 2 acre lake, dt, brown & rainbow trout, (tel: 01303 862401).

TENTERDEN TROUT WATERS, Coombe Farm, Tenterden, TN30 6XA. 3 lakes, brown & rainbow trout; dt £27 (4 fish), £17 half day (2 fish), junior £8/£13; (tel: 01580 763201; www.tenterden-trout-waters.co.uk).

WOODCHURCH TROUT FISHERY, Townland Farm, Woodchurch, TN26 3SA, dt available, (tel: 01233 860253).

LANCASHIRE AND CUMBRIA (Westmorland) streams

BELA. Cumbrian trout stream, flowing from Lily Mere to estuary of Kent at Milnthorpe. Much of its course is through low-lying country with heavy water. Size of fish better than in some northern streams; many dry-fly reaches. Salmon and sea trout below Beetham Mills private. One of the earliest of northern streams; fishing starts March 3.

Milnthorpe (Cumbria). Trout. Preserved by Milnthorpe AA and confined to members and guests; association also preserves Stainton Beck from Deepthwaite Bridge and Peasey Beck from Farleton Beck downwards and thence, from confluence of these streams, to Beetham Mills; fishing below mills private; sport very good in March, April, May and Aug; assn is considering issuing dt for waters; check with Hon Sec. Tackle from Kendal Sports, 30 Stramongate, Kendal LA9 4BN (tel: 01539 721554). Hotels at Milnthorpe: Cross Keys, Bull's Head, Coach and Horses; Wheatsheaf at Beetham.

Oxenholme (Cumbria). Bela, 2m E. Beehive Beck, 1m E. Old Hutton Beck, 3m SE. **Killington Reservoir**; large area of water, 3m E. Pike, perch and some big trout. Kent (Westmorland) AA water; regularly stocked Mar to Oct with rainbows of over 1lb, some up to 4lb; 2 fish limit; st £70, dt £10, Juv dt £4 from Kendal tackle shops, including Carlson Tackle Shop, 64/66 Kirkland, Kendal LA9 5AP (tel/fax: 01539 724867; web: www.carlsons.co.uk) or Keeper, Water Keeper's Lodge at reservoir; conc st to jun. (See Kendal).

CONDOR. Fishing station: Galgate. Brown trout and sea trout.

DUDDON. Fishing station: **Broughton-in-Furness**. Sea trout, salmon. Millom & Dist AA has rights to 366 yds of north bank from Duddon Bridge downstream, and Hall Dunnerdale stretch; assn also has water on **Esk**, **Lickle** (which joins Duddon on left bank, close to Broughton-in-Furness), **Annas**, **Irt**, **Lazy**, **Devoke Water** (salmon, sea trout, trout); **Black Beck**; also **Baystone Bank Reservoir**, Copeland, and Broughton Tower Ponds; membership; £110 + £20 entrance from Hon Sec; wt £75; dt £15 and day tickets for Assn waters from Hon Sec tel: 01229 777648; Bridge Garage, Holmrook; Waberthwaite PO; Haverigg PO, Millom TI; Broughton TI. Hon Sec supplies maps of ticket waters.

Ulpha (Cumbria). Good sea trout and salmon, few brown trout. All river below down to Ulpha Bridge private. **Devoke Water** (large trout) may also be fished from here. Millom & DAA has rights, wt and dt, limit 4 fish; applications for membership to Hon Sec. Water also held by Penny Parrock; on Duddon between the two Millom stretches. Hotel: Old King's Head.

KENT. Fast-flowing salmon, sea trout and trout stream running into Morecambe Bay. Excellent for salmon and sea trout following spates from July onwards. Good brown trout fishing all season.

Kendal (Cumbria). Salmon, sea trout, brown trout. A few spring salmon with main run and sea trout moving up about June; plentiful Aug onwards given water. South of the town to Basinghyll Bridge (mainly both banks) held by Kent (Westmorland) AA, the bottom gorge of which is fly only (National Trust - **Sizergh** Estate); also apply. Kent AC (tel: 015395 60186). **Killington Reservoir** (ns Oxenholme), is property of British Waterways; pike, perch, roach and brown and rainbow trout; fishing rights leased to Kent (Westmorland) AA, st £70, dt £10.

Tackle shops: Carlson Tackle Shop, 64/66 Kirkland, Kendal LA9 5AP (tel/fax: 01539 724867; web: www.carlsons.co.uk); permits also Ghyll Head Reservoir, High Newton Reservoir, Kentmere; Kendal Sports Shop, 30 Stramongate, Kendal LA9 4BN (tel: 01539 721554), who issue permits. Hotels: Kendal Arms; Stonecross Manor.

MINT (tributary of Kent). Best fished from Kendal. Joins Kent about 1m above town; holds good head of small trout. Kent (Westmorland) AA has lowest water (see Kendal).

SPRINT (tributary of Kent). Joins Kent at Burneside. Burneside AA (see Burneside) has about 1m of fishing from junction with Kent. Kent (Westmorland) AA has ½m (L bank only); salmon and sea trout from Aug; brown trout small; banks much wooded.

KEER. Rises 4m above Borwick, runs into Morecambe Bay 3m below **Carnforth**. Good sea trout and brown trout (no coarse fish). **Wych Elm Fly Fishery**, Milnthorpe Rd, Holme, Carnforth LA6 1PX (tel: 01524 781449): 2 acre lake with rainbow, brown, blue trout; dt £25 4 fish, £20 3 fish, £13 sport, half-dt £16 2 fish, £8 sport, evng & 3-hour £9 1 fish, £6 sport.

LEVEN: Drains Windermere, and is joined by River Crake (from Coniston Water) at Greenodd, near Ulverston, before flowing into Morecambe Bay. Salmon, sea trout, trout.

Ulverston (Cumbria). Salmon, sea trout, trout. Ulverston AA has fishing **Knottallow Tarn**, brown trout, fly only; dt from Hon Sec and Rods & Sods, The Ghyll, Ulverston; and coarse on **Ulverston Canal**, 1¼m long, specimen tench, carp, etc; restocked; dt on bank; match permits from AA Sec; assn also has Sandhall Ponds, specimen carp, members only; disabled bridge access and pegs.

Hotels: Armadale, King's, Bay Horse, Lonsdale House.

Lake Side (Cumbria). Salmon, trout, pike, perch, trout. Some free fishing; other sections of the shore private; enquire locally.

TORVER BECK (tributary of Coniston lake), Torver (Cumbria). Lakes: Coniston, 1m E; pike, perch and trout, Goat's Water, 3m NE. Beacon Tarn, 5m S. Hotel: Church House Inn.

CRAKE (tributary of Leven):

Greenodd (Cumbria). Crake; salmon, sea trout, trout. Ulverston AA offers dt on bank for **Ulverston Canal** fishing: coarse fish. **Rusland Pool River**, tributary of Leven.

Coniston (Cumbria). Yewdale Beck, Torver Beck, 2½m S. Duddon, 8m west; salmon, sea trout. Millom & DAA has water at **Duddon Bridge** and **Hall Dunnerdale**; membership and tickets, see Devoke Water. Coniston Lake: pike, perch, char, trout and eels. Char fishing very good from May to October. Lake free to holders of EA licence. For boats and tackle, see Coniston, English Lake District. River Crake flows from S end of Coniston Lake; salmon, sea trout. Esthwaite Lake, 4m east; stocked trout fishery (see Hawkshead).

RIVERS ROTHAY & BRATHAY, Ambleside. WADAA fisheries. Open, brown trout, migratory trout and salmon close seasons are as for NW Region EA fishery bye-laws. These rivers are the main feeders to Windermere and offer small river fishing for brown trout, sea-trout and the very occasional salmon. They are best fished when above normal level using worm or fly. Maggots, cheese and offal baits are prohibited. The Association does not control all the fishing on these rivers and anglers should ascertain where angling is permitted. The large pool near the head of Windermere contains pike and perch as well as trout. Autumn fishing is usually best when lake trout and sea trout take up residence in the river prior to spawning. At this time of year very large trout can be caught. Dt £8.00 (Juv/OAP £4), from Tourist Information Centre, local fishing tackle shops.

TROUTBECK (trib of L Windermere).

SCANDAL BECK, Ambleside; trout, preserved.

WINSTER. Parallel with Windermere for 6m. Joins the sea by **Grange-over-Sands**. Sea trout, brown trout, eels. Kendal & Dist AC has R Winster fishing at **Meathop**, nr Grange-over-Sands, stocked with coarse fish. Other club waters nearby

include Witherslack Hall Tarn, roach, perch, eels, pike; membership open. Wigan & Dist AA has 2m of river, trout and sea trout (no dt); 26m of Leeds and Liverpool Canal from Johnsons Lock Chorley to Saracens Head Scarisbrick; Assn also fishes fourteen stillwaters in vicinity of **Wigan**, **Chorley** and **Hindley**; and two canals, all coarse fishing with dt £2-£3, conc; also stretches of **RiversRibble** at **Elston**, **Wyre** at **St Michaels** (each of these two shared with St Helens AA) **Douglas** at **Wigan**, coarse fishing; no rivers dt, members only; st £28, juv £5, OAP £12: contact Membership secretary.

LANCASHIRE (lakes and reservoirs)

ANGLEZARKE RESERVOIR, Wigan. Coarse fishing. Southport & DAA issues dt £3 (see Upper Rivington Reservoir). Open 15 Jun to 15 Mar; no fishing both banks northern half 15 Mar to 15 June.

BANK HOUSE FLY FISHERY, Low Mill Caton, Nr Lancaster, LA2 9HX, trout fishing for brown, rainbow, tiger & blue trout, various dt prices available, also offer permit for salmon & sea trout on the **River Lune**, (tel: 01524 770412; see website for more: www.bankhouseflyfishery.co.uk).

BARNSFOLD WATERS. 7m NE of **Preston**. Two trout lakes, 22 acres, fly only; st and dt £21 to £10; boats £5 to £12: J F Casson, Barnsfold Waters Trout Fisherey, Barns Lane, Goosnargh, Preston PR3 2NJ (tel: 01995 61583).

BIRKACRE RESERVOIR, Chorley. Wigan & Dist AA water; dt £2, membership £28, juv £5, conc, from bailiff, or contact Hon Sec; no close season.

BARROW-IN-FURNESS RESERVOIRS. Barrow AA has trout fishing in five reservoirs; also Cavendish Dock for carp; st only; guest ticket with member; apply Hon

Sec; also for **Ireleth Reservoir**, **Askam in Furness**; members plus guest; rainbow trout. Furness FA (Game section) issues day tickets for stocked waters. Coarse section fishes 5 waters, 3m from Barrow-in-Furness, Ormsgill Reservoir. Angling and Hiking Centre, 275 Rawlinson Street, Barrow-in-Furness LA14 1DH (tel: 01229 829661).

BLACKMOSS RESERVOIRS, **Pendle**. Brown trout dt £12.50 for this Blackmoss FFA water from Pendle Inn, Barley (tel: 01282 614808); for further information contact Hon Sec; water consists of 2 reservoirs: Upper (browns) and Lower (browns and rainbows).

BROWNHILL RESERVOIR. Between Colne and **Foulridge**. Feeder for Leeds and Liverpool Canal. Holds brown trout; preserved by Colne AA, tickets for members' guests only.

BUCKLEY WOOD RESERVOIR, **Rochdale**. Leased by NWW to Whitworth Anglers; members only. Enquire Hon Sec (see also Mersey and Rochdale).

CANT CLOUGH RESERVOIR, Burnley. Fished by Mitre AC; dt £10 2 fish; fly only; brown trout only; season 15 Mar to 30 Sept: apply Anglers All, The Old Forge, 6 Raglan St, Colne. BB8 0ET. (tel: 01282 860515; see website for more info: www.anglers-all.co.uk).

CHURN CLOUGH RESERVOIR, Pendle. Now re-let to Colne Water AC; who also fish River Aire, limited dt from Anglers All, The Old Forge, 6 Raglan St, Colne BB8 0ET. (tel: 01282 860515; see website for more info: www.anglers-all.co.uk).

CLEVELEY MERE, Cleveley Bank Lane, Forton, Lancaster, PR3 1BY, 24 acre lake for brown & rainbow trout, 14 boats, various dt prices available, (tel: 01524 793644; see website for more info: www.cleveleymere.com).

CLOWBRIDGE RESERVOIR, Rossendale. Coarse dt on site at Rossendale Valley Sailing Club Shop; United Utilities (tel: 01204 664305) reservoir.

COWPE RESERVOIR, Cowpe Road, off A681 at Waterfoot, rainbow & brown trout fishing, dt £18 from Mace Express Newsagents, 63 Burnley Rd East, Waterfoot, tel 01706 214892, EA Rod licence required before issue.

DEAN CLOUGH RESERVOIR, Hyndburn. Brown and Rainbow trout, fly only (tel: 01706 227548). Hyndburn Angling & Darts Centre, 71 Abbey Str, Accrington BB5 1EH (tel: 01254 397612).

DILWORTH (UPPER) RESERVOIR, Ribble Valley. Trout; Ribchester & DAC has water; dt apply Hon Sec.

DINGLE RESERVOIR, Blackburn. Dingle Fly Fishing Club; enquire locally.

EARNSDALE RESERVOIR, Darwen. Brown and rainbow trout. Darwen AA has rights on reservoir; good fly water.

ENTWISTLE RESERVOIR, Blackburn. Entwistle Flyfishers; dt water.

FORREST HILLS, Hazelrigg Lane, Ellel, Lancaster, LA2 0PL, 4 acre fly fishing lake for mainly rainbow trout, occ' brown, tiger & blue trout, dt full day 4 fish £22, sporting £15, half day 2 fish £15, half day sporting £10, also offers fishing on the **River Conder**.

GRIZEDALE LEA RESERVOIR. 9m south of Lancaster. Rainbow trout, 1 Apr-30 Nov; Kirkham & Dist FFC water, fly only, limit 3 (4 later in season); membership £175 plus £175 joining fee; dt (limited), from Hon Sec, or from A F Hodgson, 5 Hillside Ave, Kirkham, Preston PR4 2YR; or G Steel, 114 Highcross Ave, Poulton-le-Fylde FY6 8XB.

HAGGS RESERVOIRS. Hynburn Road, **Accrington**. Roach, carp, chub, tench, Accrington New Anglers water; members only; water has disabled platform.

HEAPY RESERVOIRS. Chorley. Reservoirs 1,2,3 and 6: roach, carp, perch, bream, tench; Wigan & Dist AA water; no dt; st £28, juv £5, OAP £12; Map books £1.50 + sae from Membership Sec or from bailiffs.

HODDLESDEN RESERVOIR, Blackburn; mixed coarse, Darwen Loyal Anglers; dt £3 from Angler's Den, 19 Blackburn Road, Darwen BB3 1EJ (tel: 01254 706713).

HULLOWN FISHERY, Laneshawbridge, Nr Colne, fishing for rainbow & brown trout on 2 acre lake, dt available, (tel: 01282 869789).

JUMBLES RESERVOIR, Turton ; mixed coarse, Darwen Loyal Anglers; dt £3 from Angler's Den, 19 Blackburn Road, Darwen BB3 1EJ (tel: 01254 706713).

LANESHAW RESERVOIR, Pendle. Brown and rainbow trout, fly only, barbless hooks; dt £15 (2 fish), evng £10 (1 fish) from Anglers All, The Old Forge, 6 Raglan St, Colne BB8 0ET (tel: 01282 860515; web: www.anglers-all.co.uk).

MEREBECK FISHERY, Mere Lane, Mere Brow, Tarleton, PR4 6JU, 8 acre fly fishing water for rainbow, brown & blue trout, (tel: 01704 821006; web: www.merebeck.co.uk).

MITCHELS HOUSE RESERVOIRS, Higher Baxenden: wild browns, rainbows.

OGDEN RESERVOIR, Rossendale. Haslingden & Dist Fly FC; trout fishing dt £15, 3 fish limit; also has **Holden Wood Reservoir**, Grane, Haslingden (no dt, members only): contact Hon Sec.

PARSONAGE RESERVOIR, Hyndburn. Trout fishing (rainbows), Bowland Game FA (see clubs); dt £17 locally (see notice board at entrance).

PENDLE VIEW FISHERY, A59 Bypass, Barrow, Clitheroe, BB7 9DH, 3 lakes, 2 coarse & 1 trout lake, various dt prices, tel: 01254 822 208; web: www.pendleviewfishery.com

PENNINGTON FLASH, Leigh. Good coarse fishing. Pennington Flash AA (now Leigh & DAA) issues st and dt £3 on bank, conc; enquiries to Hon Sec; assoc also fish Firs Park in Leigh; mixed coarse; dt water; and Bridgwater Canal from Leigh town centre to A580 towards Manchester; dt £3; and at Bickershaw, Leigh, 2 lakes, one specimen (dt £6 one rod), and smaller lake, 34 pegs (dt £3); assn also Pennington Brook (by golf course); dt on bank.

ROUGH LEE TROUT FISHERY, Roughlee, Barrowford, BB9 6NR, 2.5 acre lake, rainbow, blue & brown trout, various dt prices available, (tel: 07835347875, see website for more: www.roughleetroutfishery.com).

STOCKS RESERVOIR. Slaidburn. 350 acre trout fishery, stocked weekly with brown, blues and rainbow trout to 22½lb, also indigenous stock of wild browns. Fly only, there is a close season. 24 boats with motors; and

bank fishing, tackle on site, Wheelyboat for disabled; st, dt and sporting tickets; 5, 3, 2 fish limit, and sporting; juv free with paying adult; tickets from Mr Ben Dobson, Stocks Fly Fishery, Catlow Rd, Slaidburn BB7 3AQ (tel: 01200 446602; web: www.stocksreservoir.com (daily reports)); telephone for boat before coming; ghillie and guiding service; tackle shop and cafe on site; tuition. Tackle shop: Anglers All, The Old Forge, 6 Raglan St, Colne BB8 0ET (tel: 01282 860515; see website for more info: www.anglers-all.co.uk).

SWINDEN RESERVOIR, Burnley, ten minutes drive from town centre. Trout fishing (blue, rainbow, brown and golden), Burnley AS; dt £15, 2 fish dawn to dusk from Roggerham Gate Inn, Todmorden Road, Briercliffe, Burnley BB10 3PQ (tel: 01282 422039) below reservoir; all browns to be returned.

UPPER RIVINGTON RESERVOIR. Closed 15 Mar to 15 Jun; Southport & DAA water; 57 acres; mixed coarse; no keep nets; no barbed hooks; no gravel bait &c; dt £3 from Crown Tackle, 4a Chorley New Road, Horwich BL6 7QH (tel: 01204 668223).

UPPER RODDLESWORTH RESERVOIR. 25 acres in West Pennine Moors, managed by Horwich & Dist FFC; stocked with rainbows to 8lbs, blue trout, and wild brown population; dt £11; from The Black Dog Inn, Belmont.

LOWER RODDLESWORTH and **RAKE BROOK RESERVOIRS**, Chorley. Coarse fisheries with pike to 30lbs, managed by Withnell AC; dt £6; from Brinscall Post Office, School Lane, Brinscall PR6 8QP (tel: 01254 830225); also for the Shale Holes, dt; for further information contact Hon Sec; (see website for more info: www.withnell-angling-club.co.uk).

WALVERDEN RESERVOIR, Pendle. Coarse fishing for perch,

tench, pike, eels, carp, roach; dt £5 on bank, st £30, conc available. (web: www.pendleburnley-districtanglingas sociation.co.uk).

WORTHINGTON RESERVOIRS. Standish, **Wigan**. 3 reservoirs of 5, 7 and 3 acres (Worthington, Arley, Adlington Reservoirs), all coarse with roach, perch, carp, bream, barbel; now Warrington AA; see website for more info: www.warrington-anglers.org.uk; open membership, dt from Georges Fishing Tackle. Tackle shops: Georges Fishing Tackle, 15 Frog Lane, Wigan WN6 7DE (tel: 01942 241932). **Orrell Water Park**, Lodge Rd, Orrell; 2 lakes; dt on bank, (tel: 01695 625338); and many others in Chorley, Westhoughton, Blackburn, Leyland, and Preston.

LEE or LEA

Walton's river; flows through Bedfordshire and Hertfordshire then along boundary between Essex and Middlesex to join Thames near Blackwall; 46m long. Urban development and canalization have largely removed its charm, but still holds good quantities of barbel, and large bream, carp, pike, chub, perch. Very little free fishing, but permits are obtainable from bailiffs on most stretches and fishing is allowed from Cheshunt to Bow throughout the 'old close season.'

Tottenham (London). **Bow** to **Ponders End** controlled by Lee Anglers' Consortium (LAC) (see clubs); st £25, dt £3, conc. Good access points are at Lea Bridge Rd, Hackney Marshes, Carpenters Rd, Dace Rd; dt from bailiffs; **Picketts Lock** and **Stonebridge Lock**, where there are permanent platforms on the Tottenham Marshes bank (currently out of order), are fisheries with roach, carp and bream; bailiff on bank for assistance, Tom Rowley (see clubs); other LAC water: at Edmonton, north of A406, there are permanent platforms on the **Lee Park Way** (opposite the tow path) where roach and bream show well from May onwards; winter hotspot is under A406 road bridge; above and below Picketts Lock for bream and roach; skimmers and good bream are caught opposite Ford factory (see local table signs). TW reservoirs close to Tottenham Hale (roach, perch, carp, bream, pike; or stocked with brown and rainbow trout) (see under London). Tackle shop: Don's of Edmonton, 239 Fore Str, Edmonton N18 2TZ (tel: 020 8807 5396); J&B's Fishing Tackle, 594 Hertford Rd, Edmonton N9 8AH (tel: 020 8805 8675/6050).

Enfield Lock (Middx). Plenty of roach, perch, bream, tench, double figure carp and pike; dt; controlled by LAC (see Tottenham) from Enfield Lock to **Ponders End**; access for Ponders End up to Enfield from Wharf Rd, Ponders End; access from South Ordnance Rd for Enfield Lock to Rammey Marsh Lock; bream, skimmers, roach and carp from near bridges, locks, opposite the Navigation Inn and new footbridge from behind 'Makros' (off Mollison Ave); the 'canopy' area up to the Turkey Brook noted for large shoals of bream, but proving hard to catch.

Waltham Abbey (Herts): **Lee Relief Channel**, now called Walton's Walk, from David Stoker Sluices to Highbridge St, Waltham Abbey: 1½m of bank, mixed coarse fishing, with chub, tench, bream, carp, pike, and occasional bags of roach. This fishery is run by Garry Smith, LVRPA Fisheries, Holyfield Hall Farm, Stubbins Hall Lane, Waltham Abbey EN9 2EG (tel: 01992 892291; web: www.leevalleypark.org.uk); apply to LVRPA. From **Waltham Cross** to **Rammey Marsh Lock**; roach, tench, carp and skimmers; controlled by LAC; car park in High Bridge Str gives access to upper section; parking at bottom of Lee Rd provides access down, under M25 to Rammey Marsh Lock; this stretch is known for its large tench, carp and winter pike. There is mixed coarse fishing on 2 4-acre lakes, **Claver Hambury Lakes**; dt; club bookings available; tickets on bank. Tackle shop: Simpsons of Turnford, 2 Nunsbury Drive, Broxbourne EN10 6AH (tel: 01992 468799.

Cheshunt (Herts). Good chub, roach, tench, bream fishing, controlled by LAC. (See Tottenham). Lee Navigation to Cheshunt: from **Aquaduct Lock** downstream, the R Lee becomes a canal; access from Hertford Rd (off A10) to Cadmore Lane and Windmill Lane for the Cheshunt to Waltham Common Lock section. Nr Aqueduct Lock Hertford AC share 4 pits, Slipe Lane Pits; coarse, members only: st available, apply Hon Sec; club also has extensive river fishing; dt on bank. Kings Arms and Cheshunt AS run Brookfield Lake, with carp, tench, bream, perch; dt £5, two rods, conc, from Simpsons below; other society waters include local rivers, lakes and gravel pits; matches, outings, newsletter organised, new members welcome. **North Met Pit**, gravel pit of 58 acres, various coarse species incl large carp (to 44lbs), pike (to 30lbs), tench (to 10lbs 2oz); LVRPA water (see Waltham Abbey). Also **Bowyers Water**, 35 acre gravel pit, with carp (to 41lbs 8oz) and pike; day & night st £156.60, conc; contact LVRPA (see Waltham Abbey) for details on current waiting list position. **Wormley** (Herts). **Slipe Lane Pits**, four gravel pits of 25 acres with large tench, bream (to 10lbs 4oz), carp (to 37lbs), pike (to 29lbs); st (day only) £38.50, conc; night fishing; £69.50 day & night, conc; run by LVRPA (see Waltham Abbey).

Broxbourne (Herts). **Carthagena Fishery**, consisting of Weir Pool, 2 lakes (one with carp to 40lbs); ¾m of Old R Lee, 1m of Lee Navigation, bream, tench, carp, chub, roach, rudd; st only for Weir Pool, river and stream, £65,winter ticket £45 starts 1 Oct; juv, OAP £45; dt for carp lake £10; Carthagena Lake, syndicate only: from Jerry Hammond, Carthagena Lock (tel: 01992 463656); towpath from Nazeing New Rd to Dobbs Weir, dt £3-£1.50, from bailiff on bank. **Old Mill and Lee Navigation Fishery**, Mill Lane, Weirpool, Lee Navigation, with roach, chub, pike, perch; dt £3.40 (1 rod), £5.60 (2 rods), conc; run by LVRPA (see Waltham Abbey); day tickets from bailiff on bank.

Hoddesdon (Herts), ns Rye House or Broxbourne. On Lee, Stort and New River Lee. **Admiral's Walk Lake**, 25 acre gravel pit at Conker lane, pike (to 29lb 8oz), tench, bream, roach, carp; st £40.10, no dt, conc; **Dobbs Weir Fishery**, coarse fish (carp to 26lbs 5oz); rainbow to 4lbs 4oz; British record chub 8lb 13oz); dt £3.40 (1 rod), £5.60 (2 rods), conc; dt on bank; night tickets £5.60 (night tickets must be booked in advance through baliff (tel: 07908 948066 from 20:00-08.00 hrs), no conc; both fisheries run by LVRPA (see Waltham Abbey).

Rye House (Herts). Roach, chub, dace, bream, pike, perch, tench. Rye House Bridge to October Hole is London AA water; additional fisheries at Wormley on canal, and Kings Weir Canal and Old River; barbel, dace, chub, roach; members only: st £43, conc, dt £4 from fishery keeper on bank. West Ham AC controls east bank and LAC, west bank, at Feildes Weir; dt from bailiff; LAC now has 8 purpose-built disabled anglers' platforms; LAC also has **Rye House** d/s of road bridge ; roach, perch; parking; dt on bank.

St Margaret's (Herts). River Lee. River fishing from towpath; LAC; roach, perch; dt on bank (see Tottenham).

Ware (Herts). River Lee Navigation, controlled by LAC; deep flowing section through Ware town, weedy in summer, with roach, perch and chub; above the lock there is fishing to Hertford; roach, perch and chub. Below the Ware town road bridge, pegs 46 to 70: roach, perch and skimmers; Hardmead Lock to Amwell Section; slow flowing with good specimen carp, bream and chub for the specialist angler; also LAC water (see Tottenham). Ware AC, members of Turnford Angling Consortium (with lakes at Wormley) have members only carp ponds; also almost 1m offside bank of Lee Navigation between Stanstead and Hardmead Locks; also Pretty Lake at Ware, mixed coarse; membership £53 (incl joining fee), conc; apply Hon Sec. Rib Valley Fishing Lake, Westmill Farm, Ware SG14 3HJ (tel: 01920 462200 (tackle shop); see website for more info: ribvalleyfishinglakes.com) 13 acres, 3 lakes, fly or coarse; rainbow trout from 2lbs; dt available, plus other ticket options; tickets available from tackle shop on site; toilet facilities; wheelyboat on trout lake.

Hertford (Herts). For **Lee, Mimram, Beane, Rib** and **New River**. Abbey Cross AS have water; members only: apply Hon Sec. Hertford town (Folly Bridge) downstream to Marina: fast, deep flowing section, with summer streamer weed. Good specimen fish area for chub, bream, carp and barbel. Downstream of Hertford Marina,

there is Dicker Mill canalised section and The Meads below Hertford Lock; good for carp, roach, perch and bream; permanent platforms: LAC water. London AA has stretch from Town Mill gate to junction with Lee Navigation (¾m): st £41, conc, dt £3.50 from LAA; also from Folly Sluices, Hertford, to confluence of River Beane. For Hertford AC contact Hon Sec. For Ware AC Hon Sec; both clubs have local fishing. Hotels: Salisbury Arms, White Hart.

Hatfield (Herts). Hatfield & Dist AS has rights on river from Mill Green to Essendon (about 2½m); including seven-acre Broadwater (large carp and bream); members only. Tackle Shop: Old Hatfield Angling Centre, 3 The Broadway AL9 5BG (tel: 01707 883131).

Luton (Beds). Tring Reservoirs; Grand Union Canal; Great Ouse. Club: Leighton Buzzard AC has Tiddenfoot Lake at Leighton Buzzard; mixed coarse; members only; Rackley Hills Lake; mixed fishery. Luton AC members have 2 one-acre lakes; mixed coarse; float only; members only; at Home Farm, Tingrith, near Toddington. Vauxhall AC has Manor Lake near Westoning in Tingrith; 3 acre carp lake; strictly members only; apply Hon Sec. Tackle shop: Tavistock Angling, 95 Tavistock St, Bedford MK40 2RR (tel: 01234 267145).

Tributaries of the Lee

STORT: Preserved from source to Bishops Stortford.

Roydon (Essex). Roach, dace, perch, pike, chub, bream, carp, rudd, gudgeon, eels, bleak, pope. Globe AS fishes Stort and backwaters here, with the species listed; members only. Ware AC has water between Hunsdon Mill Lock and Parndon Mill Lock; members only; st £53 incl joining fee; contact Hon Sec.

Harlow (Essex). Coarse fishing at Netteswell Pond, Oakwood South Pond (currently silted-up) and on south bank of Stort Navigation between Burnt Mill Lock and Harlow Lock, all managed under agreement between Harlow Council and Stort Valley AC; species are carp, roach, rudd, bream, tench, perch, pike, etc; dt £4, conc, on bank; more details from either club Secretary (tel: 01279 437888); or bailiff 01279 864874);

enquiries to Harlow District Council, Parks and Landscapes Service, Mead Park Depot, River Way, Harlow CM20 2SE (tel: 01279 446998). For stretch of Stort Navigation: Harlow DC. See Boxmoor. London AA has water at **Spellbrook** membership £43, conc; club also has water at **Pole Hole Fishery**, nr Eastwick; enquiries to office. Tackle shop: Harlow Angling Centre, 5 Long House, Bush Fair, CM18 6NR (tel: 01279 444249), who issue tickets for Cemex and Nets Well Pond.

Sawbridgeworth (Herts). Good head of all coarse fish with many large roach; fishes best April. Sawbridgeworth AS has from confluence of Little Hallingbury Brook to Harlow Mill road bridge, left hand bank; pike fishing; visiting parties welcome; apply Hon Sec for reservation; mixed lake fishery ½m from Sawbridgeworth Station, on Little Hallingbury Rd; members only, £3 per rod.

Bishop's Stortford (Herts). Navigational stretch opened by British Waterways; Bishop's Stortford & Dist AS has coarse fishing to Spellbrook Lock (tickets), a length at Harlow, Cam at Clayhithe, lakes, 10 acre gravel pit; contact Hon Sec, (web: www.bsdas.org.uk). Hotel: George.

ASH. Fishing stations: **Widford** (Herts) and **Hadham** (Essex); a few trout, pike, etc; preserved.

RIB: Trout, coarse fish. For Rib Valley Fishing Lake (see Ware).

BEANE: This once-excellent trout stream has been largely ruined by abstraction. Some stretches still hold good fish, however. No public fishing except at Hartham Common, Herts.

MIMRAM: Trout, preserved.

LINCOLNSHIRE (small streams)

GREAT EAU or **WITHERN**. Rises above Aby and flows some 12m to sea at Saltfleet; coarse fish; much free water; fishes best in autumn.

Saltfleet (Lincs), ns Saltfleet, 3m. Grayfleet, South Eau, and Mar Dyke; coarse fish; some free water. At Saltfleetby St Peters is pond on which fishing is permitted by dt, purchased from shop near pond; no Sunday fishing. Sea trout in Haven in Sept; also flounders.

Louth (Lincs). Great Eau private above bridge on main Louth-**Mablethorpe** road, including Calceby Brook, Aby and South Ormesby Park; free below to licence holders as far as Gayton lugs. Louth Crown & Woolpack AC has small coarse pond at Charles St, good tench, membership available to locals, conc. **Theddlethorpe** (apply caravan park at Saltfleet); and free below Cloves Bridge. Altogether 10m free fishing to licence holders; coarse fish, including good roach, bream, perch, pike, rainbow trout (few and mostly small) and grayling (apply local farmers). **Lud** generally free below Louth to Alvingham. Coarse fishing in ponds at **Louth**, **North** and **South Somercotes**, **Fulstow**, **Saltfleetby**, **Legbourne**, **West Ashby**, **Hogsthorpe**, **Chapel St Leonards**, **Skegness**, **Wainfleet**, **Authorpe**, **Addlethorpe**, **Alford**, **Farlesthorpe** (members only), **Spilsby**, all on dt on bank. Sutton Brick Pits, Alfred Rd, **Sutton-on-Sea**; dt at adjacent houses. Hatton Lake; dt (tel: 01673 858682). Tackle shops: Castaline, 18/20 Upgate, Louth LN11 9ET (tel: 01507 602149; web: www.castaline.co.uk); Belas Sport, 54 High Str, Mablethorpe LN12 1AD (tel: 01507 473328). Hotels: Kings Head, Lincolnshire Poacher, both Louth.

STEEPING. Rises 5m above **Spilsby** (1m off on left bank), runs thence to **Wainfleet** and joins the sea 4m below near **Skegness**; coarse fish; Wainfleet AC controls Steeping and **Wainfleet Relief Channel**; st £10, dt £2.50,

conc: Storr's Fishing Tackle, 37/38 High St, Wainfleet, Skegness PE24 4BJ (tel: 01754 880378).

LINCOLNSHIRE (small lakes and ponds)

ASHBY PARK FISHERIES, Horncastle LN9 5PP (tel: 01507 527966): 7 lakes, mixed coarse fishing with carp to 30lb, bream to 14lb, and most other species, incl eels to 5¾lb; dt £5 and bait on site.

BAINTON FISHERIES, Lolham Level Crossing, West Deeping. 7 gravel pits between Peterborough and Stamford in the Welland Valley; excellent summer tench venue, with good carp to 45lb; also rudd, bream, chub, perch, eels, pike to 32lb, catfish, crucian carp; st and syndicate members only from fisheries (see website for more info: www.predator-fishing.co.uk).

BELLEAU BRIDGE LAKE, Belleau Bridge Farm, **Alford** LN13 0BP. 6 acre coarse fishery, dt from Mr Harrop (tel: 01507 480480).

BRICKYARD FISHERY, South Rd, South Somercotes, Louth LN11 7PY (tel: 01507 358331). 4 acre coarse fishing water, dt £5 on site.

CHARLES STREET POND, Louth. 1 acre lake with crucian carp and tench; st only, from local tackle shops, open all year.

GOLTHO LAKE, Goltho, Wragby LN8 5JD; contact Mrs Rusby (tel: 01673 858671). Lincoln, 10m. 2 acre mixed coarse fishery, dt £4 on site; phone for seasonal changes.

GRANGE FARM LEISURE, Mablethorpe LN12 1NE. 4 coarse lakes, 1 trout and 1 carp lake; dt only £4.50 (coarse), evng £2.50, conc, sold on site; fly dt £18 (4 fish), c&r £10; also tackle and bait shop, and cafe (tel: 01507 472814); sells EA permits.

GRIMSTHORPE LAKE, private fishing only.

HATTON TROUT LAKE, Hatton, nr Wragby LN8 5QE (tel: 01673 858682); coarse; dt on site, £5.

HAVERHOLME PARK LAKE, nr Sleaford; contact Mr Dave Gash (tel: 01526 832125); carp average 7-8lbs, roach, bream, perch; dt £5 on bank.

HILL VIEW LAKES, Skegness Rd, Hogsthorpe, Chapel St Leonards PE24 5NR (tel: 01754 872979); four lakes, mixed coarse; dt from cafe; barbless hooks only.

HOLLANDS PARK, Wedland Lane, Thorpe St Peter PE24 4PW (tel: 01754 880218); 2 coarse, 2 carp fishing lakes, dt £3.00 on bank.

LAKE HELEN, Mill Lane, Sutterton PE20 2EN. Mixed coarse fishery of 2¾ acres; contact H Greeves; dt £5 (tel: 01205 460681).

LAKESIDE LEISURE LTD, Chapel St Leonards, PE24 5TU (tel: 01754 872631); four mixed coarse lakes, two with 10 species, the others 20 and 24 species respectively, dt on site, £5.50, £8.50 double; tackle on site.

OHAM LAKES, Alford, LN13 0JP. 3 acre coarse fishery, with tackle shop and other facilities on site; dt £5, conc; contact D Higham, Maltby le Marsh, Alford LN13 0JP (tel: 01507 450623).

ROSSWAYS WATER, 189 London Rd, Wyberton PE21 7HG (tel: 01205 361643); two lakes mixed coarse fishing, carp to 22lb, large bream and tench; dt £5 (£7 2 rods), subject to availability; barbless hooks only; cabins to let on site.

SALTFLEETBY FISHERIES. Saltfleetby Fisheries, Main Road, Saltfleetby, Louth LN11 7SS (tel: 01507 338272); 3 ponds with tench, bream, carp, chub, roach; dt £6, 2 rods £8, conc £4; new café, bait & tackle shop; no groundbait, and carp over 3lb not to be kept in nets; or contact Castaline (above).

SKEGNESS WATER LEISURE PARK, Walls Lane, Ingoldmells, Skegness PE25 1JF (tel: 01754 769019); 7 acre lake with tench, perch, bream, golden orfe, and carp; dt at lakeside.

STARMERS PIT, Tritton Rd, **Lincoln** (tel: 01522 534174) Lincoln & Dist AA water; 7 acre lake, mixed coarse fishery with large pike, eels, carp, bream and tench; dt £4, conc £3, on site; details of membership (£25), conc, from Hon Sec, also for night fishing (syndicate only); also information on **Boultham Park Lake** and Blue Lagoon, 3 acres; mixed coarse.

SYCAMORE LAKES, Skegness Rd, **Burgh-le-Marsh**, PE24 5LN (tel: 01754 811411); 6 acre mixed coarse fishery of four lakes, with carp from 2lb to 30lb, tench, rudd, roach, perch, orfe; Woodland Lake stocked with smaller fish, ideal for pole fishing; dt £6, conc, at lakeside; tackle and bait shop, lakeside cafe, accom on site; caravan park.

TATTERSHALL LAKES & COUNTRY PARK, Sleaford Rd LN4 4LR (tel: 01526 348800; web: www.tattershallpark.co.uk); 4 lakes, mixed coarse fishing, disabled access; dt on site.

THORPE LE VALE FISHERY, Ludford, Market Raisen LN8 6AR (tel: 01472 398978); 5 acre trout fishery, brown & rainbow; fly only; dt £12.50 (2 fish + c&r), £10 c&r; open all year.

TOFT NEWTON FISHERY, Toft-next-Newton, **Market Rasen** LN8 3NE (tel: 01673 878453; web: www.toftnewton.com); 40 acre reservoir, bank and boat fly only fishing, stocked weekly, rainbow and brown trout; season varies, usually 1 Feb to mid-Dec; dt £21, 6 fish, £17.50, 4 fish, £13.50, 2 fish, then c&r, c&r only £11; boat £10, £6.00 ½ day; Wheelyboat and facilities; tackle hire and tuition on site.

WILLOW LAKES, Newark Hill,Foston, nr **Grantham**, NG32 2LF; 7 lakes: 6 mixed coarse: 3 dedicated match lakes, and 3 dt lakes, dt £5, conc £4, tickets on site, also evening ticket from machine in car park; contact Mr Chilton, Willow Lodge, Newark Rd, Foston, Grantham NG32 2LF (tel: 01400 282190).

WOODLANDS FISHERIES, Ashby Rd, **Spilsby** PE23 5DW (tel: 01790 754252); five coarse lakes with mixed species, best carp 22lb, tench over 5lb, roach 2lb; dt available, conc; tackle and refreshments on site.

LONDON (Thames Water Reservoirs)

Most of the waters referred to below are in the area termed Greater London. All are easily accessible from Central London. A number are rented by angling clubs and reserved for members, but at others fishing is offered to the general public at modest charges on season or day ticket basis.

It seems appropriate to mention here two important angling bodies: first, the **London Anglers' Association**, which has water on many miles on rivers, streams and lakes (125 fisheries in all). The Association now has about 3,000 full members through 100 affiliated clubs. It has offices at Izaak Walton House, 2A Hervey Park Road, Walthamstow, London E17 6LJ (tel: 020 8520 7477). For a brochure and application form please send a stamped addressed envelope to the above address. Annual membership (associate membership) senior £41.00, partners £60.00, senior citizen permit £24, jun associate membership £23; registered disabled £24.

The Central Association of London and Provincial Angling Clubs (CALPAC) has about 120 affiliated clubs and fisheries on rivers, canals and lakes in the South of England. Membership £46 plus £16 joining fee, conc: 16-18 years, £37; under 16 years at 15 June £28; over 65s £28; regd disabled £28. Day tickets issued for many fisheries; £5; no night fishing on most CALPAC waters (but allowed on Padworth stretch of Kennet, Stew Ponds at Epsom and Manor Pond at Cobham; tickets £30). Full details from Hon Sec.

Among tackle shops in Central London are: Farlows of Pall Mall, 9 Pall Mall, SW1Y 5NP (tel: 020 7484 1000; web: www.farlows.co.uk). Tackle dealers in the suburbs are too numerous to list. Tackle shops in Metropolitan area listed under individual centres.

Thames Water Reservoirs where fishing rights are let to clubs include the following:

Cheshunt (North) to Kings Arms AC.

Reservoirs open to the public for game fishing (stocked with rainbow or brown trout).

Walthamstow Nos 4 & 5 are stocked with brown and rainbow trout. Bank fishing, fly only on both; 7 days/week from 7am (mob: 07747 641179).

East Warwick, fly only, let to Walthamstow FFC; members only; c&r; contact Steven Mills (via tel: 07957 301212; web: www.walthamstowffc.org.uk).

Farmoor 2, Cumnor Road, Farmoor, Oxon OX 2 9NS; st, dt and half day; fly only from boat or bank; fully stocked tackle shop on site.

Reservoirs open to the public for coarse fishing.

West Warwick Reservoir, **Walthamstow Nos 1, 2 & 3**, **High** and **Low Maynard**, **Coppermill Stream**. Dt on all. Best catches to date include carp 42lb, pike 32lb, bream 16lb, perch 4lb 10oz, plus large roach, barbel, chub and few dace.

LUNE

Rises on Ravenstonedale Common (Westmorland) and flows through beautiful valley into Irish Sea near Lancaster. Excellent sport with salmon, sea trout and brown. August to October best for salmon and sea trout.

Lancaster (Lancs). Salmon, sea trout, trout, coarse fish. Environment Agency has Halton and Skerton Fisheries; salmon, 16 Jun to 31 Oct; sea trout, 1 Apr to 30 Sept; brown trout 15 Mar to 30 Sept; coarse fishing 16 Jun to 14 Mar, all weekdays only; salmon, c&r only after 1 fish per year, on EA waters; evening permits for sea trout on both beats at Halton; salmon £15.00 dt or night ticket; £5 dt trout and coarse, from Bankhouse Fly Fishery, Lancaster Road, Caton LA2 9HX (tel: 01524 770412; web: www.stocksreservoir.com); who also have 2 acre Mill Pond, trout, various dt. Scarthwaite Country House Hotel, Crook O Lune LA2 9HR (tel: 01524 770267) sells permits for Lancaster & Dist AA, Caton fishing. Lansil Sports and Social Club LA1 3PE (tel: 01524 39269) has 1½m both banks just above tidal stretch, with additional coarse fishing for usual species plus specimen bream (12lb+);st £75 + £25 joining fee, other fishing (coarse & brown trout) £35 + £10 joining, conc. Littledale Fishery, nr Caton, mixed coarse; tickets from Morecambe Angling Centre, Grand gar, Thornton Rd LA4 5PB (tel: 01524 832332). Lonsdale AC fishes Upper Swantley; mixed fishery; open but restricted membership. Tackle shops: Stephen J Fawcett, Gunsmiths, Fishing Tackle & Countrywear, 7 Great John Str, Lancaster LA1 1NQ (tel: 01524 32033; see website for more info:

www.fawcettsonline.com), who supply licences and specialist information on Lune, Greta, Wyre and Wenning; Gerry's of Morecambe, 5&7 Parliament St, Morecambe LA3 1RQ (tel: 01524 422146; web: www.gerrysfishing.com); Morecambe Angling Centre (above); Carlsons Tackle Shop, 64/66 Kirkland, Kendal LA9 5AP (tel/fax: 01539 724867; see website for more info: www.carlsons.co.uk).

Caton (Lancs). Lancaster & Dist AA has fishing over 1½m both banks for which dt is available; long waiting list for membership; permits £10 to £20 depending on season, weekdays only, from Scarthwaite Country House Hotel, Crook O Lune LA2 9HR (tel: 01524 770267); no dt Saturdays and Sundays, though Sunday fishing is allowed to members; fly only when water level 1ft 6in or below; worm prohibited in October, except at water level of 3 ft; no maggot, shrimp, prawn or grub fishing; no boat fishing, no dogs. Prince Albert AS also have water, and at **Killington**, members only. Bank House Fly Fishery (Ben, David or Jan Dobson; (tel: 01524 770412; see website for more info: www.bankhouseflyfishery.co.uk), Low Mill, Caton LA2 9HX, has 2½ acres stocked brown, rainbow, tiger and blue trout fishing; dt £24.00 (10 hrs) (4 fish) and half-dt (5 hrs) £17.50 (2 fish), other tariffs available non-residential fishing lodge, with all facilities, piers for disabled.

Hornby (Lancs). Salmon, sea trout, trout. Lancaster AA has Claughton stretch (see Caton); no dt. From Wenning Foot (North) for ¾m, Southport Fly Fishers, members only.

Kirkby Lonsdale (Cumbria). Salmon, sea trout, trout. Trout and sea trout fishing is very good; average 1½lb; sea trout up to 8lb. Kirkby Lonsdale & DAA has approx 4m of water, upstream and downstream of town; members only £260 + £30 joining.

Clitheroe AA has water commencing 10yds from Stanley Bridge d/s, on left bank to water board pipe bridge; dt for members' guests only. Lancaster & Dist AA has water. Lancashire FFA has fishing here and at Tebay. Redwell Carp and Coarse Lakes: four lakes of stocked fishing, dt £7 (1 rod) £10 (2 rods), conc; contact Ken Hall, Kirkby Lonsdale Rd, Arkholme LA6 1BQ (tel: 015242 21979). Hotels: Red Dragon; King's Arms; Sun; Snooty Fox; Orange Tree. Pheasant Hotel at Casterton, 1m upstream, is convenient for assn waters. Salmon (best August, September); sea trout (June onwards), trout.

Barbon (Cumbria). Lune, 1m W Barbon Beck. Barbon is good centre for Kirkby Lonsdale & DAA water; members only. Hotel: Barbon Inn.

Sedbergh (Cumbria). Bowland Game FA has right bank of River Rawthey at its confluence with the Lune; members only; long waiting list; also left bank of Lune u/s from confluence for ¼m; assn also a further beat u/s: 1½ miles both banks at **Low Gill**. Sedbergh & DAA has approx 3m on Lune and tributaries, 16m **Rawthey**, from source to Lune, 4m **Dee** and 2m **Clough**; brown trout stocked annually; salmon and sea trout from July; visitors st £150 from Visitors Hon Sec; dt £20, wt £50 & conc, from Three Peaks Outdoors Ltd, 25 Main Str, LA10 5BN (tel: 01539 620446; web: www.3-peaks.com). Mr Metcalfe, Holme Open Farm, Sedbergh LA10 5ET (tel: 01539 620654) has stretch of R Rawthey; tickets at the farm. Hotels: The Bull, The Dalesman.

Tebay (Cumbria). Salmon and sea trout (August onwards best), trout (average 3 to lb). Tebay AA has 17m of good water; wt apply Hon Sec; limited dt from Cross Keys Inn, Tebay CA10 3UY (tel: 01539 624240); occasional season permits, from Secretary. Hotel: Cross Keys.

Tributaries of the Lune

RAWTHEY. Trout, with sea trout and occasional salmon late in season. Sedbergh & DAA has virtually whole of river from its source at Fell End down to Lune, and tributaries Dee 2m, and Clough, 1m; visitor's dt £20 available from Three Peaks Outdoors Ltd, 25 Main Str, LA10 5BN (tel: 01539 620446; see website for more info: www.3-peaks.com).

WENNING. Sea trout (good), brown trout, few salmon (late). Best latter part of season. Fishing station:

High Bentham (Yorks). Bentham AA has about 3½m of water; fast stream, good sport; visitors' tickets: st, wt, dt (jun ½) from Hon Sec (by post only c/o 1 Ashbank Villas, High Bentham, Lancaster LA2 7HX). Prince Albert AS has stretches of Wenning at Hornby Castle, Clintsfield Farm and Robert Hall Estate (game). Barnoldswick AC have two stretches of Wenning, upstream from Farrars Viaduct, downstream from Clintsfield Viaduct. Hotels: The Coach House, Black Bull Inn. Punch Bowl Hotel also has ¾m private trout and sea trout fishing and issues dt (tel: 01524 261344). Clapham accom: Flying Horseshoe Hotel; New Inn, Arbutus House.

GRETA. Trout (4 to 1b) and late run of salmon and sea trout. Nearest towns: **Ingleton** and **Burton-in-Lonsdale** (Yorks). Trout. Hotel: Punch Bowl, Burton-in-Lonsdale (licences).

MEDWAY

Kentish river joining estuary of Thames at Sheerness through estuary of its own. Coarse fish (abundant bream, record barbel, 1993) with few trout in upper reaches.

Maidstone (Kent). Free on EA licence from Maidstone to East Farleigh, North Bank, except new mooring area. Maidstone Victory Angling and Medway PS have first class fishing from Yalding down to Maidstone, **R Beult** fishing, and various stillwaters (see website), dt £5 for river in advance from tackle shops; also specialist carp lake at Larkfield, members only; membership from Hon Sec and local tackle shops. For fishing on Brookland Lake (Medway Valley Fisheries), contact James Chatten (mob: 07880 574614); membership available; also for dt water on Woodlands Lake (formerly known as Holborough Lake. Mallards Way Lake, details from Len Valley A & PS. Sittingbourne AC has 4 coarse lakes in vicinity, membership £75 + £25 joining from Hon Sec (www.sittingbourneanglingclub. co.uk). Mid Kent Fisheries water: Larkfield, nr Maidstone; Over 20 Lakes from 46 acres to 20 acres: carp, tench, bream, pike; members only: various ticket prices: contact fishery at Chilham Water Mill, Ashford Rd, Chilham CT4 8EE (tel: 01227 730668) (see Kent Lakes and Streams); Bluebell FC has 2 small ponds; good carp; apply Maidstone Angling Centre; also for dt £5, conc, for Mote Park. Tackle shops: Maidstone Angling Centre, 15 Perryfield Str, ME14 2SY (tel: 01622 200000/677326; see website for more info: www.maidstoneangling.com); Nicks Tackle Exchange, 10 Knightrider Str, ME15 6LP (tel: 01622 673899). Medway Bait and Tackle, 64B St Johns Road, Gillingham ME7 5NB (tel: 01634 856948). Inns: Medway; West Kent; Rose and Crown; Queen's Head.

East Farleigh (Kent). Free fishing as described under Maidstone; thence mostly Maidstone Victory Angling and Medway Preservation Soc water; weekday dt from Maidstone tackle shops. Inn: Victory.

Wateringbury (Kent). Large carp and tench, chub, bream, roach. Maidstone Victory Angling and Medway Pres Soc has most of towpath bank here and at **Teston**; dt. Medway Wharf Marina, Bow Bridge ME18 5ED, has fishing for boat and caravan owners using their services; dt available; (tel: 01622 813927). Barking AS has a meadow; members only but open to visiting clubs. CALPAC shares 1m of Medway here shared with the Warlingham & DAA; coarse; closed 15 Mar to 15 June incl; no keepnets, barbless hooks. Inn: King's Head.

Yalding (Kent). Chub, bream, perch, rudd, dace, roach, eels, and pike. Free fishing on EA licence u/s from Yalding Sluice 200m, south bank. Maidstone Victory Angling and Medway Preservation Soc has towpath bank downstream of Railway Inn, also Medway at **Nettlestead**, **Teston**, **Barming**, weekday tickets from tackle shops; on bank for Teston fishing. Yalding AS has water; dt (weekdays only). Orpington & Dist AA has water on **R Teise** here, members only. Central Assn of London and Prov AC has one meadow at junction of Medway and **Beult**; members only, membership open, key required; other CALPAC stretch, 1,200 yds Yalding Medway, dt £5, conc, from bailiff on bank; no night fishing on most CALPAC water; closed 15 March to 15 June incl; no keepnets; barbless hooks. Inns: Railway (tackle, but no accommodation); George; Anchor (boats).

Tonbridge (Kent). Tonbridge & Dist A & FPS has 9m of Medway, 1½m of Eden and 8 pits of 4 to 30 acres; the 2 large ones are dt water; dt £5/rod; for parts of Medway £4; contact Sec for details; vacancies for membership; £45 + £10 joining fee, concessions for OAP, ladies and juniors. Paddock Wood A&CS has water at **Gedges Lake**, coarse fishing (tel: 01892 832730); members only; disabled car park; st £45 + £30 joining, conc; club also has 4 lakes at Pettridge; members only, and stretches of Medway at East Peckham, and Teise at Laddingford; and Beult at Hunton; and Rother at Newenden. **Mousehole Lake Fishery**, 4 acre coarse fishery, on B2015 at Nettleshead Green (tel: 01622 871447); carp, perch, tench, roach, gudgeon, rudd, bream, barble; dt on site all year; booking advisable. Orpington & Dist AA fishes Medway and Eden, near Tonbridge; members only. Tackle shops: Tonbridge Rod and Line, 17a Priory Rd, TN9 2AQ (tel: 01732 352450); Medway Tackle, 103 Shipbourne Rd, TN10 3EJ (tel: 01732 360690; see website for more info: www.medwaytackle.co.uk).

Tunbridge Wells (Kent). Royal Tunbridge Wells AS has coarse fishery at **Ashurst** and **Fordcombe**, trout waters, stock in spring, on **Medway** from Hartfield to Ashurst, and coarse fishing from Hartfield to Poundsbridge (11m), also on **Teise** below Lamberhurst Village to Finchcock's Bridge, **Goudhurst**; on Medway: grayling and barbel in places; fishing on three ponds also; membership limited; annual subscription £75, joining fee £15, concessions for married couples and jun; Society also has Colebrook Park, 1m north of Tunbridge Wells; members and guests only; society also has access to Weirwood Reservoir; coarse; members only. Crowborough AA have several ponds and lakes local to **Crowborough**, with large pike, carp, tench, bream; st available, conc. Tackle shop: Friendly Fisherman, 25 Camden Rd, TN1 2PS (tel: 01892 528677 (coarse), 01892 619677 (fly); www.thefriendlyfisherman.co.uk); M A Wickham, 4 Middle Row, E Grinstead RH19 3AX (tel: 01342 315073).

Ashurst (Kent). Coarse fish, some trout, grayling, barbel to 17lb. Royal Tunbridge Wells AS has water (see above); limited tickets for members' guests only.

Fordcombe (Kent). Trout, coarse fish, barbel to 16¼lb, large carp. Royal Tunbridge Wells AS has water, limited tickets for members' guests.

Tributaries of the Medway

BEULT: Excellent coarse fishing; lower reaches noted for chub, bream and tench; trout higher. Gravesend Kingfisher A & PA (stretches at **Smarden, Hunton, Headcorn** and **Staplehurst**; members only); London AA has water at **Hunton** and **Linton**; members only; membership £41, conc. Dartford AA has fishing. CALPAC has 400 yds at Medway junction, members only.

EDEN: Coarse fish.

Penshurst (Kent). On Eden and Medway; coarse fish. Penshurst AS has rights from Ensfield Bridge to Pounds Bridge and from The Point on Medway to weir on Eden; members only; no dt.

Edenbridge (Kent). Coarse fish. 8m controlled by Edenbridge AS (members only, no dt) also a mile at Penshurst. Short stretches rented by Holland AS, also Crawley AS. Edenbridge AS also has good carp lake and a new lottery-funded mixed coarse lake; members only; and they fish the River Rother: apply Hon Sec for membership. CALPAC has half mile of river at Skeynes Farm, 2m from Edenbridge; dt on bank £5; no keep nets; barbless hooks; closed 14 Mar to 16 June incl. Tackle Shop: M A

Wickham, 4 Middle Row, E Grinstead RH19 3AX (tel: 01342 315073); Biggin Hill Angling Centre, 216-218 Main Road, Biggin Hill, Westerham TN16 3BD (tel: 01959 570265; web: www.bhac.co.uk).

TEISE: Joins Medway at Yalding. Trout, coarse fish.

Laddingford (Kent). London AA has water for members only at Mileham Farm, Hunton Bridge and Reed Court Farm; good for roach, tench and carp; plenty of pike but most are small; membership £41, conc. Paddock Wood A&FPS has water; members only.

Goudhurst (Kent). Teise Anglers' and Owners' Association holds 7m of water from above Goudhurst to below Marden; brown, natural browns and rainbow trout; mainly fly only, and winter grayling and coarse fishing; members only (fee on application); juniors welcomed; assn also has stocked farm reservoir for rainbow trout fishing at Marden; apply to Hon Sec. Season: April 3 to Oct 31; winter Nov 1 to March 14.

Lamberhurst (Kent). Royal Tunbridge Wells AS has trout and coarse fishing water d/s of the Chequers Hotel for approx 3m; members and guests only.

ANGLING TRUST

THE VOICE OF ANGLING

Join today ! www.anglingtrust.net

MERSEY

Forms Liverpool Channel and seaport. Main river, having been polluted for 100 years and of no account for fishing except in higher reaches has, thanks to Environment Agency initiatives with industry, seen salmon return to the river basin. Tributaries contain trout.

Liverpool (Merseyside). Liverpool & Dist AA has 26m stretch on **Leeds & Liverpool Canal**; st £20, conc £15, jun free (under 16); dt on bank apply or local tackle shops. Northern AA has stretches on Macclesfield Canal and **R Weaver** at **Vale Royal**; dt on rivers and canals (see British Waterways Angling Together scheme), conc. For **Shropshire Union Canal**, see English Canal Fishing. Taskers, and Johnsons, have information on all Liverpool park lakes: Sefton, Walton, Greenbank, Stanley, Calderstones and Newsham: dt waters from banks; parks lakes free. Tackle shops: Johnson's Angling Centre, 469 Rice Lane, Liverpool L9 8AP (tel: 0151 525 5574); Taskers Angling Superstore, 25-29 Utting Avenue, Liverpool L4 7UN (tel: 0151 260 6015; see website for more info: www.taskers-angling.co.uk); Hoppy's, 12 Sefton Str, Liverpool L21 7LB (tel: 0151 260 6015).

Wirral (Cheshire). Assn of Wirral Angling Clubs comprises seven clubs, and actively promotes lake and pond fishing on Wirral; club coarse fishing waters include Birkenhead Park Upper (matches Sat/Sun, otherwise open) (now re-opened) and Lower Lakes (recently restocked with 23,000 fish); Central Park Lake, Wallasey; Arrow Country Park Lake; Captain's Pit, Wallasey; and other waters; annual and monthly permits from bailiffs and tackle shops. Caldy Anglers have Caldy Ponds, Wirral, also 43m canal fishing; members only; also AWAC waters (local parks).

St Helens (Merseyside). Two NNW coarse fisheries in vicinity: **Leg O'Mutton Dam**, controlled by St Helens AA; and **Paddock Dam**, Holme Rd, Eccleston, with bream, roach, tench, perch, carp, pike; controlled by St Helens Ramblers AS; members only; st £20, conc, from tackle shops; good carp, roach, chub, tench and dace in **St Helen's Canal** (Church Street length); and Blackbrook Canal, both St Helens AA waters; club also has The Brook, the outfall of Carr Mill Dam; also Carr Mill Dam itself; club also has The Dig Pit and Taylor Park Lake (for this, apply at boathouse; free to locals). Wigan Angling Centre, 15 Orrell Rd, Orrell, Wigan WN5 8EY (tel: 01942 226427) supply licences for **Carr Mill Dam**, 10 acres; no dt; also for Island Dam; mixed coarse; st only. St Helens Tackle shop: Star Angling, 101 Duke Str, WA10 2JG (tel: 01744 738605).

Warrington (Cheshire). Warrington AA water, both banks of Mersey from Woolston to Warrington, mainly coarse, a few set trout; also a forty mile stretch of **Bridgewater Canal** as well as water on Dee, **Ribble**, **Severn** and tributaries and **Dane**, **Wye**, **Derwent** and **Dove**; reservoirs, meres, etc, including **Appleton Reservoir**, Stockton Heath (mixed coarse) and **Worthington Reservoirs**, Wigan; almost all of their waters are members only; st £36 + £34 joining; no joining fees for juniors (£14), intermediate and ladies (£21) or OAPs (£36); apply Hon Sec. Tackle shop: Baileys Tackle, 20 Parksway, Woolston, Warrington WA1 4BP (tel: 01925 823441; web: www.baileystackle.com).

Stockport (Cheshire). Stockport & Dist AF has **River Goyt**, Marple to Stockport; members only; also **Poynton Pool** on A523; also **New House Farm Pool**, Chudleigh Close,

Bramhall; **Woodbank Park Pool**, Offerton; **Compstall Reservoir** in Etherow Country Park off B6104; apply: Hazel Grove Angling Centre, 2 Fiveways Parade, Hazel Grove, Stockport SK7 6DG (tel: 01625 858643; see website for more info: www.hazelgroveangling.co.uk).

Whaley Bridge (Derbyshire). River here known as **Goyt**; no longer polluted; dt (not Sundays), for one bank only. **Cote Lodge Reservoir**, High Peak; coarse, Old Glossop AC, dt obtainable: contact Hon Sec Ron North (tel: 0161 3308872); United Utilities water (tel: 01457 851087).

Errwood Reservoir, High Peak, is the headwater of the Goyt in an area of outstanding natural beauty; 80 acres, trout water stocked monthly; Errwood FFC; dt £15 (3 fish); (season 3rd Sat in March to end Nov) from tackle shops in Whalley Bridge, Macclesfield and elsewhere, including Stockport Fly Fishing Supplies, 11 Shaw Road SK4 4AG (tel: 0161 431 7474; web: www.flyfishingsupplies.co.uk); United Utilities water (tel: 01457 851087). **Peak Forest Canal** starts here; coarse, sport patchy. Lock pools at **Marple** stocked with carp and tench. Canal to Ashton Junction being opened and dredged.

Tributaries of the Mersey

NEWTON BROOK (tributary of Sankey Brook):

BOLLIN:

Heatley (Cheshire). Occasional trout, roach, dace, pike. Lymm AC has several lengths of Bollin at Reddish and Little Heatley, near Lymm, part double bank, mostly single; club also controls a large number of fisheries on Severn, Vyrnwy, Dane and others; and many (23) lakes and ponds about the north of Cheshire with trout and coarse fishing; some of these are dt waters, membership costs £60 per annum, joining fee £60, conc, apply to N Jupp, Secretary.

Ashley (Cheshire). Bollin, 1m N; trout, roach, dace, pike; Bollin and Birkin AA; private.

BIRKIN (tributary of Bollin):

Knutsford (Cheshire). Birkin, 4m; Bollin and Birkin AA has water; private. **Tabley Mere**, 3m, is let to Lymm AC; no permits. Toft Hall Pool, 1½m S; occasional permits. **Tatton Mere**, Knutsford, coarse fishing; dt on bank. **Redesmere** and **Capesthorne Lakes** (6m S of Wilmslow on A34 road); Prince Albert AS waters, members only; also **Fanshawe Pool**; carp to 38lb, tench, rudd, also members only; Capesthorne Hall

stock pond: very good carp fishing, no dt. Tackle shop: Trev's Tackle, c/o North West Angling Centre Ltd, Chapel Str, Hindley, Wigan, WN2 3AD (tel: 01942 255993; web: www.trevstackle.com).

IRWELL:

Manchester. Some river waters have been leased to clubs. At **Poynton**, 10m out, Stockport & Dist FA has pool; st only. 18m from Manchester, at Northwich, is coarse fishing in Weaver (see Weaver). Bolton & Dist AA has **Manchester, Bolton & Bury Canal,** from Hall Lane to Blue Wall length, 6 reservoirs, and other fisheries; no day tickets, but st £22, conc, from tackle shops in district. Warrington AA has a forty mile stretch of **Bridgewater Canal** as well as water on Dee, **Ribble**, **Severn** and tributaries and **Dane**, Mersey, Wye, reservoirs, meres, etc; apply Hon Sec. Victoria AC controls **Turks Head Reservoir**, members only. Chorlton Water Park, Maitland Ave, Chorlton M21 7WH (tel: 0161 881 5639): dt £6, conc, and st £30, conc, fishing for large carp to 30lb and pike to 15lb, roach, bream, perch. Tackle shops: Swinton Angling Centre, 57 Worsley Road, Swinton, Manchester M27 5NE (tel: 0161 794 2784); Trafford

Angling Supplies, 34-36 Moss Rd, Stretford M32 0AY (tel: 0161 8641211; see website for more info: www.traffordangling.co.uk). **Bolton** tackle shop: Bolton Angling Centre, 185 St Helens Rd, Bolton BL3 3PS (tel: 01204 658989).

ROCH:

Bury (G. Manchester). Bury & Dist AS and has stretches of R Irwell, several small ponds; mostly coarse fishing; membership £30, concessions. Bury AA (connected to Elton Sailing Club) fishes **Elton** Reservoir. Trout fishing at Entwistle (Entwistle FFC) and Dingle (Dingle FFC). **Haggs Reservoir**, Hyndburn Rd, Accrington, Accrington New Anglers water; members only.

Rochdale (G. Manchester). Rochdale Walton AS; Healey Dell Lodge, dt (accompanied by member, or from Rochdale Angling (below); also Syke Reservoir. Todmorden AS has coarse fishing on **Rochdale Canal**, from Lock 37 (Summit West) to Lock 51 (Castleton, Manchester Road); st £35 + £10 entry fee only after end Jan, conc, from tackle shops. Tackle shops: Towers of Rochdale, 52 Whitworth Rd, OL12 0EZ (tel: 01706 646171; see website for more info: www.towersofrochdale.co.uk); Rochdale Angling Centre, 161 Yorkshire Str, OL12 0DR (tel: 01706 527604), who issues tickets for Todmorden AS, Newhay Anglers and Bury & Dist AS. For Rochdale Canal see also Calder (Yorks) - Hebden.

TAME:

Ashton-under-Lyne (G. Manchester). NWW reservoir **Walker Wood**, 2m NE; trout.

MIDLANDS (reservoirs and lakes)

BARKER'S LAKE, Ringstead, 25 acres stocked with carp to 25lb, bream to 6lb, tench, good pike in winter; part of Ringstead Island complex, with Brightwell's Lake, backwater and main R Nene; Wellingborough & District Nene AC water.

BLENHEIM LAKE. Woodstock, Oxon. Excellent tench, perch, roach, bream in summer; pike in winter to 40lb; boat fishing only for visitors; apply on-line only to www.blenheimpalace.com; if necessary apply The Estate Office, Blenheim Palace, Woodstock, Oxon 0X20 1PP (tel: 01993 810500). Tackle shop: Predator Angling Centre, 6 The Kidlington Centre, High Street, Kidlington OX5 2DL (tel: 01865 372066; web: www.predatoranglingcentre.com); who also sell dt £8 for Manor Lake, **Kirtlington**: tench, carp to over 20lb, roach, perch, bream; as do J & K Tackle, 62/64 Sheep St, Bicester OX26 6LG (tel: 01869 242589; web: www.jktackle.co.uk) (tickets must be pre-bought; no night fishing).

BODDINGTON RESERVOIR, Byfield (Northants). 65 acres; carp, roach, tench, perch and pike to 40lb; dt conc, no night fishing; 24 hour information line: 0113 281 6895; or contact Fisheries and Environmental Manager, British Waterways, South East Waterways, Ground Floor, Witan Gate House, 500-600 Witan Gate, Central Milton Keynes MK9 1BW (tel: 01908 302556); contact on the bank: Head Bailiff (tel: 07740 534 891); match booking welcome; record match weight at 650lbs.

CARSINGTON WATER, nr **Ashbourne**, Derbyshire. Owned by Severn Trent Water Ltd, Carsington Water, Visitor Centre, Ashbourne, Derbys DE6 1ST (tel: 01629 540769); opened as predominately a brown trout fishery in 1994 but now a mixed fishery of rainbows and browns; season 20 Mar-24 Oct 2010; fish stocked weekly; day and part-day tickets for bank and boats; dt £19 (6 fish), evng £11 (2 fish); boats (single occupancy Mon to Thur) £17 p/day, £12 half day; wheelyboat £14/day, £10 half day, £8 evening, should be pre-booked; contact Watersports Centre (tel: 01629 540478) for day-to-day bookings; facilities and catering on site; enquiries to the Fishery Office (above). **Alton Manor Farm** is just west off the B5023 Wirksworth road, 3 lakes, dt on site, no café or tackle shop.

BARLOW FISHERY, Crowhole, Barlow, Dronfield, S18 7TJ. Trout & coarse fish, trout £16 (4 fish), £14 (3 fish), £12 (2 fish), coarse £5 full day, other prices available, (tel: 0114 289 0543; web: www.barlowlakes.co.uk).

CASTLE ASHBY LAKES.
   Northampton 7m; coarse fishing in three lakes, all mixed coarse, leased to Mr M A Hewlett, Castle Ashby Fisheries, 18 Hoylake Drive, Linksview, Northampton, NN2 7NL (tel: 01604 712346; web: www.castleashbyfisheries.co.uk); dt waters, from bailiff on bank. **Menagerie Pond** (specimen carp fishery, with bream, roach); membership £175; details from Estate Office, Castle Ashby, Northampton NN7 1LJ (tel: 01604 696232, bailiff tel: 07515 850375.)

CLATTERCOTE RESERVOIR,
   Banbury (Oxon). 20 acres, principally carp to 28lb, chub, roach, perch, tench to 7lb, much bream recently, crucian carp to 3lb; dt available, night fishing for 24-hours 2 rods; contact bailiff (tel: 07740 534892); match bookings welcome: record match weight 220lb; 24 hour information line: 0113 281 6895. Tackle shop: J & K Tackle, 62/64 Sheep St, Bicester OX26 6LG (tel: 01869 242589; web: www.jktackle.co.uk).

CLAYDON LAKES. Buckingham, 6m. Upper and Middle Lakes at Middle Claydon, near Winslow, are Leighton Buzzard AC water;

Danubian catfish, pike-perch, large bream, big carp; members only.

CLUMBER PARK LAKE (83 acres). National Trust property, 4½m from **Worksop** (tel: 01909 476592); coarse fish (including pike); 16 June to 14 March, 7am to dusk; st £70 (which includes free parking), dt £5.00 (jun and dis £4.00) from bailiff on bank; or from estate office in advance.

COSGROVE LEISURE PARK
   Milton Keynes, 2m (Bucks). Coarse fishing on 10 lakes from 2 to 25 acres, and Rivers Tove and Great Ouse; 2 lakes: members and caravans only; tackle and bait shop on site, food and refreshments, camping, caravan site; contact Manager, Cosgrove Leisure Park, Main Street, Milton Keynes MK19 7JP (tel: 01908 563360). Tackle shop: Milton Keynes Angling Centre, St Giles House, Victoria Road, Bletchley, Milton Keynes MK2 2QH (tel: 01908 374400).

CRANFLEET CANAL. Roach, perch, gudgeon. Trent Lock held by Long Eaton Victoria AS, also Erewash Canal, Long Eaton Lock to Trent Lock; dt, membership £24, concessions.

DENTON RESERVOIR. Denton (Lincs). Excellent mixed coarse fishing with large carp; held by Grantham AA; enquiries to Hon Sec.

DRAYCOTE WATER FISHERIES, near **Rugby** (Warks). 600 acre reservoir owned by Severn Trent Water Ltd. Brown and rainbow trout. 50,000 rainbows stocked over the season twice-weekly over Mar-Oct; dt £21, 8 fish limit (£17 2 fish and c&r); evngs £16, 5 fish limit, also morning or afternoon tickets at same price; OAP, jun, dis, £16 (5 fish); motor boats £24, after 2pm £17 (2 people); single occupancy £13, half day £13; disabled facilities, catering and courses; optional c&r; information from Keith Causer, Fishing Lodge (tel: 01788 812018).

DRAYTON RESERVOIR, Daventry. 20 acres, principally carp to 40lbs, also roach, perch and tench, pike to 31lb; average catches, 100lb plus, with 200lb per day often recorded, match record 405lbs; dt £6 Mon-Fri (1 rod), £10 2 rods), £6 w/ends from patrolling bailiff, £4 conc; match bookings welcome, 120 pegs; night fishing, £25, first come first served, barbless hooks only, no braid, must have unhooking mats; fish & chip service to pegs (not Sunday); contact Fisheries and Environmental Manager, British Waterways, South East Waterways, Ground Floor, Witan Gate House, 500-600 Witan Gate, Central Milton Keynes MK9 1BW (tel: 01908 302556); contact on the bank: Head Bailiff, Mark (tel: 07889 532563); 24 hour BW information line (tel: 01132 816895) updated weekly.

DUKERIES LAKES, **Worksop**. Welbeck Estate fisheries controlled by Welbeck Estate Office (tel: 01909 500211); members only. Worksop & DAA, has rights on **Sandhill Lake**, (80 pegs), with bream, tench, roach, rudd, carp, perch; **Woodsetts Quarry Pond**, dt £3 on the bank, conc; night fishing, limited pegs; £7.50 per night.

EYEBROOK RESERVOIR.

Caldecott (Leicestershire), off A6003 Uppingham to Corby Rd, south of Caldecott village, follow brown TI signs; 400 acres of excellent trout fishing; well-stocked water, mostly rainbows, a few browns; fly only, good bank and boat fishing; season 25 Mar-28 Nov (bank fishing); season and day tickets obtainable from new, purpose-built fishing lodge with disabled access; all bookings and enquiries to Eyebrook Trout Fishery, The Fishing Lodge, Eyebrook Reservoir, Great Easton Road, Caldecott, Leics LE16 8RP (tel: 01536 770264; web: www.eyebrook.com); st £395, dt £18, half-day £14, 3-day £155, conc dt £14; boats £20/day motor, half-day

£14; 2 wheelyboats £12 a day. Hotels: Falcon, High Str East, Uppingham; Vaults, Uppingham, 5m N; Corby Hilton, Corby. B&B at Mrs J Wainwright, Homestead House, Ashley Rd, Medbourne, Market Harborough LE16 8DL (tel: 01858 565724; see website for more info: www.homesteadhouse.co.uk); Post Office, Great Easton LE16 8ST (Elaine Hankey) (tel: 01536 770309).

FOREMARK RESERVOIR. Nr **Repton**, Derbys DE65 6EG. 230 acres, leased by Severn Trent Water Ltd. Season 2010 6th March to 28 Nov; rainbows stocked weekly; various permits and prices; disabled facilities, catering and courses; enquiries contact the lodge (tel: 01283 703202).

GRAFHAM WATER. **St Neots** (Hunts). 3m off A1 at Buckden: 1,560-acre reservoir stocked with brown and rainbow trout; pike Oct/Nov; managed by Anglian Water Services from the lodge at Mander Car Park, West Perry PE28 0BX (tel: 01480 810531; fax: 01480 812488); records include b trout 19lb 12oz, r 13lb 3oz; st £199 (beginners), then £349 to £709 (which covers 4 main reservoirs); dt £19, 8 fish limit, conc; c&r option; beginners dt £7, 1 fish; motor boats £12 to £25; also 3-day boat package; it is advisable to book these in advance; new fishing lodge on site with tackle shop, restaurant, access for disabled; wheelyboat; group bookings.

GRIMSBURY RESERVOIR.

Banbury (Oxon). Coarse fishery leased to Banbury & DAA; dt for non members, concessions for juniors, on bank, or from local tackle shops (see Banbury).

HARLESTHORPE DAM. **Clowne**, Derbys. Coarse fish, with pike to 22lb, carp to 32lb. St £120, dt £6 (£6 w/e) (£7 w/e for 2 rods), £5 after 3 pm, on site; night fishing on island only (by appointment); enquiries to owner

Carol Sibbring (tel: 01246 810231; web:www.harlesthorpedam.co.uk).

LADYBOWER RESERVOIR,
Ashopton Rd, **Bamford**, S33 0AZ (Derbyshire); dt, st available, limited permits from warden for fly fishing on R Derwent below Ladybower Dam; also 2 reservoirs, **Derwent** and **Howden**; both bookable in advance; 2 rods per day only; all prices include VAT; enquiries to Alan Pernell, Fishery Office (tel: 01433 651254).

NANPANTAN RESERVOIR. 2m S of **Loughborough**. 5-acre coarse fishery, (tel: 0870 0627777); dt £5 from Bennett's Angling Store, 9 Market Place, Mountsorrel LE12 7BA (tel: 0116 2302818

NASEBY RESERVOIR, Northants. 85 acres. Carp to 36lb, tench to 9lb 8oz, catfish to 65lb, rudd; dt £6; night fishing (24 hrs) £20; contact bailiff, Harry Bosworth (mob: 0790 4493417).

OGSTON RESERVOIR, near **Chesterfield**, Derbyshire. 203-acre trout fly fishery owned by Severn-Trent Water Plc, and fished by Derbyshire County AC, no day tickets **PACKINGTON FISHERIES, Meriden** (Warks). Excellent trout fishing on 4 lakes ; st from £270, dt £27 - 5 fish, £19 - 2 fish, c&r only £19 other prices available; good coarse fishing on **Somers** fishery for carp, tench, roach, perch, bream and rudd; 11 lakes (wheelyboat on trout fishery, must be booked in advance) and 1m of Blythe; dt £7, conc £5; apply Packington Fisheries, Somers Lodge, Somers Lane, Meriden, nr Coventry CV7 7PL (tel: 01676 523833: coarse; trout: 01676 522754); cafe, toilets and tackle shop on site.

PITSFORD WATER, Northampton 5m. 750 acres, managed by Anglian Water Services; rainbow and brown trout, around 30,000 fish released during season; b record 14lb 3oz; r record 15lb 11oz; good fly hatches all season; st £349 to £709, conc for beginners (which covers the 4 main reservoirs), dt (8 fish/c&r) £19, conc; half day £13 (4 fish); beginners £7 (1 fish/c&r); boats £22 to £12; pike fishing from 16 June on selected dates; access for disabled; wheelyboat; permits and tackle from Pitsford Water Fishing Lodge, Brixworth Rd, Holcot NN6 9SJ (tel: 01604 781350; www.anglingwater.co.uk/leisure/).

RAVENSTHORPE RESERVOIR, Northampton 8m. 100 acres, the home of modern reservoir trout fishing, established 1891; managed by Anglian Water Services; brown and rainbow trout; record b 10lb; record r 16lb 14oz; ; st £349 to £709, conc for beginners (which covers the 4 main reservoirs), dt (8 fish/c&r) £19, conc; half day £13 (4 fish); beginners £7 (1 fish/c&r); boats £22 to £12; wheelyboat for disabled; apply to Ravensthorpe Fishing Lodge, Ravensthorpe Reservoir, Teeton Road, Raversthorpe NN6 8LA (tel: 01604 770875). Accom Poplars Hotel, Moulton.

RUTLAND WATER, Leics. **Stamford** & A1 5m, **Oakham** 3m; managed by Anglian Water Services; Normanton Fishing Lodge, Rutland Water South Shore, Edith Weston, Oakham, LE15 8HD (tel: 01780 686446); 3,100 acres, 17m of fishing bank, largest stocked trout fishery in Britain; browns to 15 lbs and rainbows to 14 lbs, 100,000 plus released per season; pike fishing in late Oct-early Nov; 65 motor boats; including single manned; competition facilities; st £349 to £709, conc for beginners (which covers the 4 main reservoirs), dt (8 fish/c&r) £19, conc; half day £13 (4 fish); beginners £7 (1 fish/c&r); boats £22 to £12; catch-and-release option (except June to Sept; ring first); disabled (wheelyboat); full restaurant facilities, access for disabled and tackle shop on site.

SHUSTOKE RESERVOIR.
Shustoke; **Coleshill** 3m. Leased to

Shustoke FF by STW; tel 01675 481733 or 01676 533091.

STAUNTON HAROLD RESERVOIR, near Melbourne, Derbys. Severn-Trent W coarse fishery, 209 acres, leased to Burton Mutual; bream, roach, pike; dt on bank. Tackle shop, Melbourne Tackle and Gun, 64 Church St, Melbourne DE73 8EJ (tel: 01332 862091; see website for more info: www.melbournegun.co.uk); issues dt £6 for 20-acre Melbourne Pool, specimen tench, bream, carp.

SULBY RESERVOIR. 1m **Welford,** 14m **Northampton**. Coarse fishing; exclusive syndicate fishery of 100 anglers, with specimen carp to around 35lb; limited st only. **SYWELL RESERVOIR. Northampton** 6m; now a County Park (Northampton County Council); tench to 13lb, pike (over 30lb), perch, roach and carp (tel: 01604 810970); st available and winter pike ticket (please ring), dt £8, night £12, conc; from box next to rangers office.

THORNTON RESERVOIR. **Cambrian Fisheries,** Fishing Lodge, Reservoir Rd, Thornton, **Leicester** LE67 1AR (tel: 01530 230807; web: www.flyfishthornton.co.uk); 70 acres; open 1 Feb; trout, annual stocking of 17,000, fly only; 2010 st range from £512 to £147; dt £20 to £11.50, according to limit, which varies from 6 fish to 1 fish + c&r; boats £20 and £4 contact lodge for boat before going; tickets on site; also tuition; tackle available.

TRIMPLEY RESERVOIR, near **Bewdley,** Worcs. Trout, fly only, from 1 March-June 30; Jul 1-Oct 15, mixed fishery; then coarse fishing until Jan 31; st 7-day £214, £146 weekday, £98 weekend; mixed £48; coarse £21; there is a £15 joining fee; dt for guests of members only; write for details to permit officer, Trimpley AA, Anthea Harvey (tel: 01299 402099). Tackle shop: Malcolm Storey Angling Centre, 129 Sutton Road, Kidderminster DY11 6QR (tel: 01562 745221).

NENE

Rises in West Northamptonshire and flows to Wash. Good, all-round coarse fishery slow-running for most part. Roach and bream predominate, the bream in particular running to a good average size; also carp, chub, perch, pike.

Wisbech (Cambs). Centre of intricate system of rivers and drains, including the Nene-Ouse Navigation Link; all waters well stocked with pike, bream, roach, perch and some good tench. Fenland Assn of Anglers is centred in Wisbech. King's Lynn AA has **Middle Level Main Drain** (12 miles of fishing); assn st £36, conc, wt £15, dt £4; **Great Ouse Relief Channel** provides 11m of fishing from Denver Sluice to King's Lynn. Tackle shops: March Angling Centre, 88A High St, March PE15 9LQ (tel: 01354 658747). Hotels: Rose and Crown, Marmion House.

Peterborough. Excellent centre for roach, bream, chub, tench, carp, rudd,

zander, eels and pike. Peterborough & DAA now controls most of the N bank of the Nene from **Wansford** to the Dog in a Doublet and some fishings on the S bank in the same area; dt **Ferry Meadows Lakes,** £4, conc, book £24, £8 seniors, £5 juniors from bailiffs or tackle shops; close season fishing will be allowed on certain areas of Ferry Meadows Lakes (notice board for which pegs). Whittlesey AA has local fishing on fenland dykes: **Bevilles Leam** from Ponders Bridge to Goosetree Corner; and **Whittlesey Dyke** from Ashline Sluice to Floods Ferry; st £14, dt £3, juv £1, from bailiff or from local tackle shops. Deeping St James AC has Nene fishing at Wansford and Stibbington;

dt £3.50 on bank. At **Wansford** A1 road bridge, Stamford Welland AAA have ½m of south bank, downstream; first-class sport in fen drains and brick pits, but many pits being filled in. Eldernell Carp Lake, Coates, Whittlesay: £5 dt on bank for carp, tench, roach, etc; barbless hooks only, no groundbait, hemp; licences, st, wt and dt from bailiffs; and local coarse fisheries **Gerards Pit** at **Maxey**, **Tallington Lakes**. Sibson Fisheries, New Lane, Stibbington, PE8 6LW, have coarse lake with large carp, tench, bream; dt £10 on bank; memb £90, conc (tel: 01780 782621). At Northey Park PE6 7YX is a mixed fishery (tel: 07889 711555). At Turves is **Kingsland Reservoir**: 2 carp lakes, one silverfish; dt £5 (tel: 01733 840312). At Eastrea are **Decoy Lakes**: mixed coarse fishery of 12 lakes, 250 pegs total; dt £6, £3 for under 18s (must be accompanied by adult); tackle shop (tel: 01733 202230). Tackle shops: Webbs Fishing Tackle, 196 Newark Ave, Peterborough PE1 4NP (tel: 01733 566466), information and permits on various local waters; Sheltons of Peterborough Ltd, 67A South Str, Stanground, Peterborough PE2 8EX (tel: 01733 565287; web: www.sheltonsfishing.co.uk), all local handbooks available; F Wade & Son, 247 High St, Old Fletton, Peterborough PE2 9EH (tel: 01733 565159); Stamford Tackle, 13a Foundry Road, Stamford, Lincs PE9 2PY (tel: 01780 754541).

Elton (Northants). Leicester & DASA has a stretch below Elton (Iron Bridge stretch, 12 pegs); members only; apply Hon Sec; st £15. Coventry & Dist AA has 70 pegs at Fotheringhay; good head of carp, tench, roach and chub; full bk £25, conc, dt on bank.

Warmington (Northants). Warmington AC has 2 to 3 miles from d/s of Fotheringhay to u/s of Elton, members only; £12 pa, no dt; water let to clubs for matches, of up to 50 pegs. Bluebell Lakes, Tansor, Oundle PE8 5HP (tel:

01832 226042): fishery consists of Kingfisher, Swan, Sandmartin, Mallard, Wood Pool and Bluebell Lakes (tel: 01832 226042: web: www.bluebell-lakes.co.uk), 1½m stretch of Nene, and Willow Creek, a backwater of 750 yds; good coarse fishing with large carp, chub, bream, tench and pike; tackle shop; membership and dt sold at reception. Deeping St James AC fishes two stretches of Nene and coarse lake at **Stibbington**; dt £3.50 on bank.

Oundle (Northants). Roach, bream, carp, tench, dace, etc. Oundle AA has water on Oundle bank; limited st £12, dt £3; conc. Wellingborough & District Nene AC has 3m at Barnwell, just upstream of Oundle and 2 acre gravel pit (tench, pike, perch and rudd); members only. **Elinor Trout Fishery**, Aldwincle, 50 acre lake stocked weekly with browns and rainbows, fly only; dt, evening, boats; enquiries to Lowick Rd, Aldwincle, Kettering NN14 3EE (tel: 01832 720786; web: www.elinortf.co.uk). Tackle shop: Alans Angling Mart, 86 Rockingham Rd, Corby, Northants NN17 1AE (tel: 01536 202900; web: www.alansanglingmart.co.uk); who have Biggin Lake on Oundle golf course; 7 acre mixed coarse; dt £5, £3 conc, st available Hotels: Talbot; Ship; Chequered Skipper, Ashton; George, Oundle for Oundle FC HQ.

Thrapston (Northants). Kettering, Thrapston & Dist AA has two coarse lakes at Thrapston; dt £3 from bailiff on banks or tackle shops, including Alans Angling Mart (above). Earls Barton AC controls ½m R Nene at Ringstead, nr Thrapston, although as we go to press the water may be discontinued; 1m at Cogenhoe; and 1½m at **Earls Barton**; also Hardwater Lake, Earls Barton; members only.

Rushden, **Higham Ferrers** and **Irchester** (Northants). Coarse fish. With new sewage works completed, fishing now showing marked improvement. Rushden & Higham

Ferrers Irchester AA have water at **Turvey** and **Sharnbrook** on Ouse: barbel, chub, bream, pike, perch; members only; st £20, £10 juv, from Turvey PO, Bedford; tackle shops. Information, tackle and Rushden club cards from Bob Webster (below). Shefford & DAA has 2 lakes, one of 56 acres; mixed coarse; members only; apply Hon Sec; also 300 metres Great Ouse on same site; members and guests; st £55, conc for all waters; also night permit (extra) for stillwaters. Excellent trout fishery at **Ringstead Grange**, Ringstead, Kettering NN14 4DT (tel: 01933 622960); 36 acres, well-stocked with large fish; record brown 10lb 6oz, record rainbow, 14lb 4oz; st £400, dt £18.50, limit 6 fish, conc £12.50; evngs £12.50, 3 fish; boat for one or two £8 extra, evening £5, from bailiff on site. Tackle shop: Bob Webster & Sons, 37 High St, Irthlingborough NN9 5TE (tel: 01933 650110); tickets for Vauxhall AC, Wellingborough & District Nene AC, Rushden & Higham Ferrers Irchester AA; Kettering, Thrapston & District AA; Andy's Angling Centre, 19 High Street, Shefford SG17 5DD (tel: 01462 850061; see website for more info: www.andysangling.co.uk).

Wellingborough (Northants). Wellingborough & District Nene AC have from one meadow above Hardwater Crossing to Ditchford Weir, plus nine other Nene stretches; other club waters: **Great Ouse** at **Harrold**, 2 stretches; **Barker's Lake**, Brightwells and 2 new lakes, pond, and backwaters at Barnwell, and Ringstead; also 2 small carp ponds at Grendon; these fisheries contain many large carp; membership £30, conc, from Hon Sec. Kettering, Thrapston & Dist AA has Nene fishing between Denford and Pilton. **Aldwinkle Pits** nr Thrapston; now syndicate water. Northampton Nene AC has Newton Blossomville, Carlton, and Turvey a prime barbel

water that is quite capable of, and quite often does produce fish to in excess of 14lbs. Earls Barton AC has The Dam; 2 acres; coarse; members only. Tackle shops: Aquaflow, 63 Park Rd NN8 4QE (tel: 01933 270463/270492).

Castle Ashby (Northants). Pike, perch, bream, tench, roach; preserved for most part. Lakes on **Castle Ashby Fishery** (1¼m S); carp, pike, bream, tench, perch, roach; dt from bailiff at waterside (mob: 07515 850375); estate office (tel: 01604 712346). Hotel: Falcon.

Billing (Northants). Pike, roach, perch, bream, tench, chub: preserved by Northampton Nene AC which issues dt for 1½m on bank of river opposite Ecton Pits. Good coarse fishing at **Billing Aquadrome** (tel: 01604 408181); nine lakes open all year (river: from June 16 to Oct 16), wt £25, dt £5; all on site. At Earls Barton, Hardwater Lake, large mixed coarse gravel pit; Earls Barton AC; members only; membership, conc; apply Hon Sec or tackle shop: M F Perkins, 3 Station Road, Earls Barton NN6 0NT (tel: 01604 810274).

Northampton (Northants). Pike, perch, bream, chub, roach, carp, etc; Northampton Nene AC controls north bank from Weston Mill to Clifford Hill Lock; also Swan Valley Lake (members only) and Shelfeys Lake (dt £4 on bank); mixed coarse. Castle AA fishing includes north bank Nene by Carlsberg Brewery, Barnes Meadow (north bank), Midsummer Meadow, Crescent Lake, Green Farm, Sixfields Reservoir and lakes at Canons Ashby dt £7, conc £4, membership £45; Northampton good centre for lake and reservoir fishing. **Heyford Fishery**, Weedon Rd, Nether Heyford, NN7 3LG (tel: 01327 340002): a purpose-built match fishery, 1,200m long, 132 pegs, with annual regular stocking of carp, roach, bream, and other coarse species; also specimen carp lake and juniors lake.

Northampton Britannia AC controls 2m local canal fishing, dt in advance; club has amalgamated with Towcester & DAC; cards from local tackle shops: Gilders, 250/2 Wellingborough Rd, NN1 4EJ (tel: 01604 636723; web: www.gilderscountrysports.co.uk); The Sportsmans Lodge, 44 Kingsthorpe Rd, Kingsthorpe Hollow NN2 6EZ (tel: 01604 713399).

Weedon (Northants). Pike, perch, bream, roach. **Grand Union Canal**. Northampton Nene AC has rights from Bridge 22 at Dogford above Weedon to Yardley Gobion (Bridge 64) (16m); also a further 5m on Northampton Arm; dt from bailiff; available for match bookings; also Blue Lagoon and Meadow Lake: dt on bank. **Hollowell Reservoir**, 140 acres Anglian Water managed, pike to 35lb, large roach and rudd; st £100, winter st £50, only available no dt; 1 Apr to 31 Mar for st; 1 Oct to 31 Mar (winter); bank only; night fishing allowed; no keepnets; st available from Pitsford Water tackle shop. The Fishery Warden, c/o Pitsford Water, Holcot, NN6 9SJ (tel: 01604 781350).

Tributaries of the Nene

OLD RIVER NENE:

March (Cambs). Pike, perch, bream, rudd, roach, tench. Fen drains. **Old River Nene** mostly free to licence-holders. **Reed Fen** (south bank) is now private fishing. **Twenty Foot** controlled by March & Dist AA (tickets on bank). **Middle Level** is King's Lynn waters; dt on bank £4. **Forty Foot** is now leased by Chatteris WMC; dt on bank. **Mortens Leam**, 5m from March, 7m of river fishing from Rings End to Whittlesey; wide variety of coarse fish; dt on bank. Cambridge FPAS has Block Fen Lakes; coarse; dt £5 on bank. Fields End Water Caravan Park & Fishery, Fields End, Benwick Road, Doddington PE15 0TY (tel 01354 740373) has coarse fishing; carp and silver fish; 2 dt (from £4.50) lakes total 5 acres; tickts from bait shop. Tackle shop: March Angling Centre, 88A High St, March PE15 9LQ (tel: 01354 658747). Hotels: Griffen; Station.

Ramsey (Hunts). Pike, perch, bream, etc. Ramsey & DAS has fishing on **Forty Foot Drain**, and **Old River Nene** at Ramsey St Mary's and Benwick: roach, bream, perch, tench, pike, carp, zander and eels; dt waters £3. Yaxley Farcet Holme & Dist AA have fishing on one bank from Horsey Toll to Ashline Sluice; also Yaxley Lode to North West Cut; also Monks Lode; also Raveley Drain; contact Hon Sec; dt waters £4 on bank. Tackle shop: F Wade & Son, 247 High St, Old Fletton, Peterborough PE2 9EH (tel: 01733 565159); H R Wade & Sons, 74/78 Great Whyte, Ramsey PE26 1HU (tel: 01487 813537; web: www.hrwade.co.uk); bait and Ramsey & DAS tickets etc.

WILLOW BROOK: Trout, coarse fish; preserved.

King's Cliffe (Northants). Willow Brook. Welland, 3m NW.

ISE:

Kettering (Northants). **Cransley Reservoir** (syndicate only); roach, perch and tench; syndicate water. For water on **Nene** at **Thrapston**, apply Kettering, Thrapston & Dist AA. Tackle and licences from Alans Angling Mart, 86 Rockingham Rd, Corby, Northants NN17 1AE (tel: 01536 202900; see website for more info: www.alansanglingmart.co.uk).

Geddington (Northants). Preserved to Warkton.

STRECK:

Crick (Northants). Streck, 2m S. Dunsland Reservoirs (pike, perch, etc) 3m SW; private.

Daventry (Northants). Long Buckby AA has 6m single bank of Grand Union Canal from southern end of Braunston Tunnel to Whilton Marina, and from A5 to south end of Crick tunnel; mixed coarse; dt £3 on bank, conc. **Daventry Reservoir**, Daventry Country Park, Northern Way, Daventry NN11 5JB (tel: 01327 877193); coarse fishery, good pike fishing in winter, bream in late summer and autumn; dt on bank. **Drayton Reservoir** (see Midlands reservoirs and lakes). Hellidon Lakes Hotel, Hellidon NN11 6GG has fishing (tel: 01327 262550).

NORFOLK AND SUFFOLK BROADS

(Rivers Bure, Waveney and Yare)

Rivers Bure, Waveney and Yare, their tributaries and Broads are among the finest coarse fisheries in England. They contain pike, perch, roach, dace and large chub. Some banks of tidal water which may be fished free. For details, contact Environment Agency Fisheries (tel: 08708 506506). Some Broads are preserved and can be fished on payment. Rivers and most Broads very busy with boating traffic in summer, so early morning and late evening fishing advised. Best sport in autumn and winter at Wroxham or in the boatyards. Boats are essential for the most part.

BURE

Strong current from Yarmouth to little above Acle; upper reaches gentle and ideal for float fishing. The river contains a good head of coarse fish. Excellent roach, bream and pike etc, at Thurne Mouth, St Benets, Horning, Wroxham. Several Broads are connected and can be fished as well as tributaries Thurne and Ant.

Stokesby (Norfolk). Bream, roach, pike, perch. Strong tides and sometimes brackish; legering best; free.

Acle (Norfolk). Bream, roach, pike, perch. Tides often strong. River traffic heavy in summer. Acle and Burgh Marshes free fishing on EA licence. Inns: East Norwich Inn; Travel Lodge, A47 By Pass, Acle.

South Walsham and **Upton**: 4¾m R bank from South Walsham Broad to Bure confluence and d/s past **Upton Dyke** is EA water free to licence-holders.

St Benets Abbey, bream and roach. North bank from Ant d/s, Norwich & DAA; dt for St Benets Abbey and Cold Harbour from A T Thrower & Son, Ludham PO NR29 5QQ; also Ludham Bridge Stores.

Horning (Norfolk); ns Wroxham, 3½m. Good coarse fishing; free to licence holders; boat almost essential; roach, rudd, bream, perch, pike, tench; river very busy in summer, hence early morning and late evening fishing gives best results. At **Woodbastwick** opposite Horning Ferry public house Environment Agency has 100m of right bank, tidal; free to licence-holders. Broads: **Ranworth** (tickets for Inner Ranworth from store on Staithe); **Decoy** (club water), **Salhouse** (dt issued); and **Wroxham**, small charge, upstream. Tackle shop: Horning Fishing Tackle and Chandlery, 106 Lower Str, NR12 8PU (tel: 01692 631401). Several boat yards. Hotels: Swan, Kepplegate.

Wroxham (Norfolk). Roach, rudd, bream, pike, perch, tench; good pike and bream in winter; boats only. Much river traffic, summer. Broads: **Wroxham Broad, Bridge Broad, Salhouse Broad**, mainly boats. Tackle shop: Wroxham Angling and Gift Centre, Station Rd, Hoveton,

NR12 8UR (tel: 01603 782453). Hotels: Broads; Hotel Wroxham.

Coltishall (Norfolk). Boats in vicinity. Hotels: King's Head; Norfolk Mead.

Buxton Lamas (Norfolk). All banks now private.

Abbots Hall (Norfolk). Ingworth. Brown trout, stocked 4 times during season. 1m both banks, dry fly, or upstream nymph only, open to Salmon & Trout Assn members only; dt £17.50 (weekdays only); applications to Vic Purdy (tel: 01263 833593). Tackle shop: Angling Direct, 279 Aylsham Road, Norwich NR3 2RE (tel: 01603 400757; see website for more info: www.anglingdirect.com).

Blickling (Norfolk). Dt for **Blickling Lake** (20 acres), from bailiff at 1 Park Gates, Blickling NR11 6NJ; £5, conc; no night fishing; tickets on bank in summer; pike season Oct 1 to Mar 14.

Tributaries of the Bure

THURNE: Slow-flowing, typical Broadland river; tidal below Potter Heigham. Coarse fish, good bream, pike and roach. Environment Agency free fishing at **Potter Heigham**, **Martham**, **Thurne Marshes**. In the spring of 2003 the Environment Agency built new stages along river (Potter Heigham) especially for disabled.

Thurne Mouth (Norfolk). Good roach, bream, rudd, perch and eels. Hedera House (tel: 01692 670242), has fishing on river for guests at self-catering chalets; contact Miss C Delf.

Potter Heigham (Norfolk). Popular centre; good roach and bream; fair-sized eels. Bure. 3m, S. Broads: **Womack**, 1½m; **Hickling Broad** and **Heigham Sound** (tench, bream, roach, perch). Approx 3½m left bank, Martham to Repps and 4½m right bank Martham to Coldharbour free to licence-holders. Access points at Ferry Rd, Martham; Potter Heigham Bridge and Repp's Staithe; best access for Hickling Broad via boatyard. Boats from Whispering Reeds Boatyard, Staithe Rd, Hickling, Norwich NR12 0YW (tel: 01692 598314; see website for more info: www.whisperingreeds.net). Tackle shop: Lathams of Potter Heigham, Bridge Rd, Potter Heigham NR29 5JE (tel: 01692 670080; web: www.lathams-fishing.co.uk). Hotels: Broads Haven.

Martham (Norfolk). Rudd, tench, bream, roach, perch, pike; fishing platforms upstream of Martham Ferry; free fishing; **Heigham Sound** 1m free on EA licence. Martham & Dist AC fishes **Martham Pits**, Staithe Rd, 3½ acres good coarse fishing, with tench to 8lbs, bream over 8lbs, carp over 22lbs, good stock of silver fish; good sized rudd, perch and crucian carp over 3lb; dt £5 from Co-op, 88 Repps Road, Martham, NR29 4QZ (tel: 01493 740190); membership £40 p/a (long waiting list), conc. Boats all the year round: Whispering Reeds Boatyard, Staithe Rd, Hickling, Norwich NR12 0YW (tel: 01692 598314; see website for more info: www.whisperingreeds.net). Tackle shop: Lathams of Potter Heigham, Bridge Rd, Potter Heigham NR29 5JE (tel: 01692 670080; web: www.lathams-fishing.co.uk).

ANT:

Ludham. Roach, bream, eels, perch, pike. 2¼m of the river, upstream and downstream of Ludham Bridge, free to licence-holders.

Irstead and **Neatishead** (Norfolk). Good bream, perch, rudd, pike; also tench and roach. Fishing free.

Stalham (Norfolk). River clear, slow-running and weedy in summer; roach, rudd, bream, perch, pike and few tench. Broads: **Barton**, 1m; bream, roach, eels, perch and big pike; rod licence needed; can only be fished from a boat. **Hickling**, 3m by road; good pike, bream, etc. Sutton Broad overgrown. Tackle shops: Broadland Angling and Pet Centre, 24-26 High Str, Stalham, Norwich NR12 9AN (tel: 01692 580959); Wroxham Angling and Gift Centre, Station Rd, Hoveton, Norwich NR12 8UR (tel: 01603 782453). Hotels: Sutton Staithe Hotel and Kingfisher.

Wayford Bridge (Norfolk). Upper Ant; head of navigation; fishing free to licence-holders; roach, rudd, perch, pike, tench, bream; boat advisable; river is narrow and fairly busy at times in summer; weedy and clear. Bait and tackle from Stalham. Good fishing also above the head of Ant Navigation in Dilham and North Walsham Canal, navigable to rowing boats as far as Honing Lock. Caravan site and food at Wood Farm Inn.

North Walsham (Norfolk). Several coarse fisheries in locality. Gimmingham Lakes, with carp to 30lbs, Roughton, with carp, tench, bream, roach, and perch; Felmington, with roach, perch, tench, carp; dt for all of these, and other local information from tackle shop: Angling Direct, 279 Aylsham Road, Norwich NR3 2RE (tel: 01603 400757; see website for more info: www.anglingdirect.com). Inns; Ockley House; Toll Barn.

SAW MILL LAKE: Fishing station: **Gunton** (Norfolk) near Cromer; 16 acre lake in Gunton Park, 3m; coarse fish; dt from machine on bank. Tackle shop: Team Sabre Tackle, 21 New St, Cromer NR27 9HP (tel: 01263 513676).

Horning (Norfolk). **Salhouse Broad**; too much traffic in summer, but good fishing in early mornings and from Oct to March. Dt issued. **Ranworth Broad** (tickets for Inner Ranworth from store on Staithe). **Malthouse Broad**; free. **Decoy Broad**; now open only to clubs. Tackle shop: Horning Fishing Tackle and Chandlery, 106 Lower Str, NR12 8PU (tel: 01692 631401). Licences from Post Office.

Ormesby, **Rollesby** and **Filby**. Fishing by boat only, from Filby and Eels Foot Inn. These Broads are connected and undisturbed by motor cruisers and yachts, but electric outboards may be used. Fishing good everywhere. Excellent pike in winter. Wt available. **Little Ormesby Broad**, free fishing by boat only.

Salhouse (Norfolk). Salhouse Broad, 1m NE; few pike in winter.

Broads connected with the Bure

Wroxham Broad, 1m N; (see Wroxham); Information and boat-hire from Wroxham Angling Centre, Station Rd NR12 8UR (tel: 01603 782453). **Decoy** or **Woodbastwick Broad**, 2m NE; fishing on payment; **Ranworth Broad**, 3m E; good for bream; these three are controlled by Norwich & DAA; no dt. **South Walsham Broad**, 5m E; public access; boat necessary; good bream and pike fishing.

Wroxham (Norfolk). **Wroxham Broad**, boat fishing, and part bank fishing by yacht club. **Salhouse Broad**, right bank, 2m SE; mainly boat fishing, but bank fishing after a long walk. Charges may be made on bank or through boat hire. Tackle shop: Wroxham Angling Centre, Station Rd NR12 8UR (tel: 01603 782453).

Broads connected with the Thurne and Ant

Potter Heigham (Norfolk). **Heigham Sounds**; fine fishing in summer; pike fishing, roach and bream in winter (free). Pike fishing on Horsey (no live-baiting). Womack Water dredged and cleared of weed, and may be fished from quay below. (For hotels, boats, etc, see entry under Thurne.)

Hickling (Norfolk). **Horsey, Barton** and **Hickling Broads**, bream, roach, pike, perch. All free except Horsey: dt from keepers. Licences from Post Office and stores; boats for hire.

Martham (Norfolk). R Thurne. Bream.

WAVENEY

Flows along Norfolk-Suffolk border. Fishing from tidal limit at Ellingham. Between Geldeston Lock and St Olaves, the tidal river gives some wonderful sport with bream in summer, winter roach and pike at Beccles Quay.

Lowestoft (Suffolk). Oulton Broad and Waveney, which connects with Broad; bream, perch, roach, pike, etc; boats at Broad. Flounders and smelts in harbour. Good sea fishing in Oct, Nov and Dec from boats and beach for whiting, cod and flatfish. Several Broads within easy reach. Much of **River Hundred** is Kessingland AC water. **Oulton Broad** (Suffolk). Broad gives good sport with eels to 5lb, bream, roach, perch, etc, but crowded with boats in summer. Bank fishing from Nicholas Everitt Park. EA 2m of free fishing at Puddingmoor Lane, **Barsham**; and 170 yds at **Worlingham**; boat fishing best on tidal river. Good perch and pike (best Oct-March); roach (good all season, best Jan, Feb, Mar); bream (moderate, best June-Nov); dace. **North Cove**; 400 yards with bream to 7lb, big pike, st from Post Office. **Oulton Dyke** (north side only); bream (excellent Aug, Sept, Oct); perch, roach, eels. Club: Oulton Broad Piscatorial Society. Tackle shops: Ted Bean, 175 London Rd North NR32 1HG (tel: 01502 565832). Hotels: Wherry; George Borrow; Broadlands.

Haddiscoe (Norfolk). **New Cut**: good coarse fishing; free. **Fritton Lake**, Countryworld, Fritton, Gt Yarmouth NR31 9HA (tel: 01493 488288): 163 acres; well known for bream in summer, and pike in winter, also perch, roach, rudd, tench, eel, carp; seasonal opening; dt, boats for hire; holiday cottages to let, with fishing included.

Worlingham (Suffolk). 170 yds of Suffolk bank free fishing via Marsh Lane.

Beccles (Suffolk). Good roach, bream, pike, etc; best early or late in summer but especially good Oct onwards, when river traffic eases off. Free fishing from Beccles Quay. 400 yds stretch at **Aldeby** is George Prior AC water. **Aldeby Pits** coarse fishery (tel: 01502 677363) is 5m from Beccles, on Waveney. Tackle shop (see below) is helpful, and issue st and dt for waters belonging to Beccles, Bungay Cherry Tree AC, and Harleston and Wortwell clubs, on river and lakes; charges range from st £26 to £50 (also depending on how many rods); dt £5, wt £10. Tackle shop: Angling (Direct) Suffolk, Site 3, Ellough Industrial Estate NR34 7TD (tel: 01502 713566). Hotels: King's Head; Waveney House; Ship House.

Geldeston (Norfolk). Good pike, roach, perch, bream, etc; free. Inns: Wherry (licences) and Geldeston Lock. Tackle shop in Beccles (3m).

Barsham (Suffolk). 2m free fishing on Suffolk bank from Puddingmoor Lane.

Bungay (Suffolk). Good roach, chub, bream, perch, pike and tench; fishes well all season. For more info on other fisheries in the Bungay area see web: www.bungay-suffolk.com/activities/ **Homersfield** (Suffolk). Pike, perch, roach (large), dace, tench. 300 yds of free fishing. Inn: Black Swan, Homersfield IP20 0ET.

Harleston (Norfolk). Waveney, 1m S; coarse fish. Harleston, Wortwell & Dist AC has fishing on Weybread Pits; disabled platforms; 6 lakes stocked with most coarse species; dt £5 1 rod, £7.50 for 2, conc, coaching for juniors, tickets from Waveney Angling and others; also 4½m of Upper Waveney centred on Shotford Bridge; members only. Weybread Fishery, Mill Lane, Weybread IP21 5TP has dt (booking only) (tel: 01379 588141) has mixed coarse fish; one lake 3 acres; carp to 28lb, large roach and perch; B&B. Waveney Valley Lakes, Wortwell IP20 0EJ (tel: 01986 788676), dt bookable in advance; caraval & lodge fishing holidays. Waveney Angling, 5 London Road, Harleston IP20 9BH (tel: 01379 854886); Angling (Direct) Suffolk, Site 3, Ellough Industrial Estate NR34 7TD (tel: 01502 713379).

Eye (Suffolk). **Dove Brook**; large dace. Fishing in Waveney at Hoxne, 3m.

Diss (Norfolk). **Waveney** and **Dove**. Diss & Dist AC has good quality stocked water on Waveney at Scole, Billingford, Hoxne, Brockdish, 6m total, best end Sept onwards; Dove at Oakley, d/s of bridge, roach, rudd, bream, pike, tench; **Diss Mere**, 5 acres, mirror carp, tench, roach and crucian carp; no dt; st £26, 2-week ticket half st price, conc £13, for all fisheries from Pegg Angling Supplies, Wills Yard, Chapel St, Diss IP22 4AP (tel: 01379 640430). Hotel: Saracens Head.

YARE

Rises few miles from East Dereham and flows through Norwich to Yarmouth. Tidal, still one of the best Broads rivers for roach and bream, the main species; specially good for roach in middle reaches, bream in lower.

Great Yarmouth (Norfolk). Broads and rivers. Rivers Yare, Bure and Waveney fall into **Breydon Water** (Bure joined in upper reaches by Thurne and Ant). In all, some 200 miles of rivers well suited to boat and bank angling are within easy reach; some Broads are landlocked, strictly reserved for angling and free from river traffic; others connected to rivers, but mostly best fished from boat. Many Broads easily accessible; also rivers **Bure**, **Thurne**, **Ant** and **Waveney**. Trout in Bure. Also good sea fishing. Tackle shops: Pownall and Son, 74 Regent Rd NR30 2AJ (tel: 01493 851120/842873; web: www.pownalls.com); Gorleston Tackle Centre, 7 & 8 Pier Walk, Gorleston-on-Sea NR31 6DA (tel: 01493 662448; see website for more info: www.gorlestontackle.co.uk); Paul Dyble, Dabs & Crabs, Hemsby Rd, Scratby, Great Yarmouth NR29 3PQ (tel: 01493 731305) for fishing boat trips.

Reedham (Norfolk). Strong tide; legering best; roach, perch, bream, eels; free at Langley on EA licence. Hotel: Ship.

Cantley (Norfolk). Roach, bream, perch; bream and perch plentiful; fishing free to licence-holders; mostly by leger. Inn: The Reedcutter.

Buckenham (Norfolk). Carp, bream, roach, perch; pike; Great Yarmouth & Norfolk CAA has fishing here and at Claxton, Rockland and Langley, 2,900 yds left bank and 5,200 right bank; mouth of Hassingham Dyke is good spot; dt £3.50 from Beauchamp Arms; lakes Strumpshaw Broad, 1m

NW; Rockland Broad, 1½m SW on other bank of river; free.

Brundall (Norfolk). Roach, bream, perch in Yare. Several reaches between Coldham Hall and Surlingham Ferry can be fished by boat. Much fishing private. Surlingham Broad; fishing only fair in summer; water shallow and weedy; pike in winter.

Norwich (Norfolk). Free fishing at Earlham Bridge to Cringleford Bridge, 2m of left bank, with dace, roach, chub, bream, pike. **Wensum** above city holds fine roach, perch, dace, chub and pike. Good roach and bream fishing at **Rockland Broad**; 7m from Norwich; but poor access to banks. 10m from Norwich, Haveringland Hall Country Park, Cawston NR10 4PN, has excellent coarse fishing lake, open all year on permit, dt £6 2-rods, conc, from manager's office (tel: 01603 87 1302) or on bank. Norwich & DAA has water on **Bure**, **Thurne**, and **Ant**, **Ranworth** **Broad** and **Woodbastwick Decoy** (fishing by boat only on last two waters); dt (Coldharbour and St Benets) from Hon Sec and tackle shops. Anglian Water coarse fishery: **Taverham Mill Lake**, Taverham, Norwich NR8 6TA (tel: 01603 861014; see website for more info: www.taverham-mill.com); lake, with carp, roach, pike, bream, etc; and stretch of R Wensum with barbel, chub, roach, dace; tackle shop, self-catering accom on site; st and dt for lake; st only on river; free to lodge residents on both. Nr **Attleborough** is Manor Lake, part of Rockland Manor, Scoulton Rd, Rocklands NR17 1UW (tel: 01953 483226); crucian, mirror, common and ghost carp (to 25lb), tench, rudd, perch; st £100, conc; apply Rockland Manor. Tackle shops: Gallyon's Country Clothing and Fishing Tackle, 7 Bedford Str, NR2 1AR (tel: 01603 622845; web: www.gallyonsclothing.co.uk). Hotel: Maids Head.

Tributaries of the Yare

CHET:

Loddon (Norfolk). Free coarse fishing in Chet at Loddon Staithe: roach, bream. This water now navigable and fishes best in autumn and winter when traffic finishes. Hotels: Swan, and Angel Inn, Loddon; Hardley Floods preserved. White Horse, Chedgrave.

WENSUM: Coarse fish (good chub and barbel).

Norwich (Norfolk). Tidal. Riverside Rd, Oak Str and Hellesdon Mill controlled by City Amenities Dept; chub, barbel &c. Free fishing at Fye Bridge Steps, Cow Tower, Bishop Bridge, Yacht Station and d/s of Foundry Bridge to apprx 100yds d/s of Carrow Bridge.

Costessey (Norfolk). Chub, roach, dace, bream and pike. Norwich & DAA have has Wensum Fisheries; 3 lakes; members only; association also has almost 1 mile of River Wensum behind the lakes; members only. **Costessey Lakes**, 3 lakes Anglian Water coarse fishery, carp to 35lb, st and dt from Taverham Mill Fishery Tackle Shop, Taverham, Norwich NR8 6TA (tel: 01603 861014; web: www.taverham-mill.com). **ShallowBrook Lakes**, Norwich Rd, New Costessey NR5 0LA: 4 lakes totalling 11 acres, coarse fish, st available, dt £6, £4 half day;(tel: 01603 747667; see website for more info: www.shallowbrook.co.uk).

Drayton (Norfolk). Free fishing at Drayton Green Lane for half mile, with roach, chub, bream, dace and pike.

Attlebridge (Norfolk). Good trout fishing here, some miles of water being preserved. Tud, 4m S; private. **Reepham Fishery**, Beck Farm, Norwich Road, Reepham NR10 4NR (tel: 01603 870829; web:

www.reephamfishery.co.uk); 3½ acre spring-fed lake, plus match lake with 20 pegs (available for booking), with carp to 28lb, tench to 4lb, roach, rudd; crucian carp to 4lb, also koi, chubb, golden orfe; dt £9, conc, from bailiff on bank; disabled swims, facilities on site; open 7am to dusk (or 7pm latest); closed on Mondays (except bank holidays). At Clay Lane, **Swannington** is Five Ways Fishing Lakes, 10m NW of Norwich (tel: 01603 260303); 30 pegs; carp, tench, bream, roach, perch, rudd; members only; enquire Five Ways Farm NR9 5NW.

Lenwade (Norfolk). Fishing in three old gravel pits set in 25 acres, administered by the trustees of two Great Witchingham charities. There is a lake with carp to 30lbs, plus mixed coarse fishing; permits from bailiff.

Swanton Morley (Norfolk). Dereham & Dist AC has water, see Lyng, below. **Swanton Morley Fishery**, bream roach, rudd, tench, perch, pike, carp; dt £5 on bank; permits and information from F W Myhill & Sons, 7 Church St, Dereham NR19 1DJ. (tel: 01362 692975; see website: www.myhillspetandgarden.co.uk). Accom with free fishing on R Wensum: J Carrick, Park Farm, Swanton Morley NR20 4JU (tel: 01362 637457). Fishing parties welcome at Wensum Valley Hotel Golf & Leisure Club, Beech Avenue, Taverham, Norwich NR8 6HP (tel: 01603 261012; see website for more: www.wensumvalleyhotel.co.uk).

Hellesdon (Norfolk). Roach, chub, dace, carp, pike. Free fishing from Mill Pool to New Mills.

Lyng (Norfolk). Fine roach, dace and some trout. Dereham & Dist AC has Wensum here, and at **Swanton Morley**, (2 stretches); chub, pike, roach, dace, etc; **Lyng Pit**; carp, tench, bream, pike, roach; five pits at Swanton Morley with pike, bream, tench, roach and carp, perch, chub;

membership £50, conc, from Myhills (below), or from Hon Sec. Near East Dereham, Salmon & Trout Assn has **Roosting Hill Fishery**, Beetley, North Elmham; two rainbow lakes (6 and 2 acres); S&TA members syndicate only; dt £15 for S&TA members; 1 May to end Nov; contact R G Bunning, Gressenhall NR20 4DT (tel: 01362 860352, or 01362 860633 evng). Mr Rogers, Lakeside Country Club, Lyng, Norwich NR9 5RS (tel: 01603 870400; see website for more: www.lakesidecountryclub.co.uk), has 35 acres of coarse fishing, the largest of 26 acres; carp, bream, pike; accom and catering on site; Kingfisher Lakes FC has 1m of Wensum and 1 lake at Lenwade Country House Hotel; free to residents or dt £5 from hotel, or apply to Mr Rogers (above). Tackle Shop: F W Myhill & Sons, 7 Church St, Dereham NR19 1DJ (tel: 01362 692975; see website for more info: www.myhillspetandgarden.co.uk). Other tackle shop: Churchills of Dereham, 26 Norwich St, Dereham NR19 1BX (tel: 01362 696926; web: www.churchillsofdereham.co.uk). Accom, Park Farm, Swanton Morley.

North Elmham (Norfolk). Fishing in Wensum for pike, roach, perch, dace and good trout. Fakenham AC has Railway Lake, 1 acre, mixed coarse; dt water; tickets from Dave's Fishing Tackle (see below).

Fakenham (Norfolk). Salmon & Trout Assn (S&TA) has Bintry Mill Trout Fishery on Wensum; browns; 2m mostly double bank; dt on two beats (lower two) £25; dry fly and nymph only; contact Terry Lawton (tel: 01603 872393). Trout, dace, roach, perch, gudgeon, eels; Fakenham AC has 2m, dt water, also **Willsmore Lake**, Hayes Lane, with carp, bream, tench, etc; 6 tickets daily on lake, Mon-Sat from Dave's Fishing Tackle, 33b Bridge Street NR21 9AG (tel: 01328 862543; see website for more info: www.davesfishingtackle.co.uk). Nr **Beeston** (8m south) is **Bridge**

Farm Fisheries, Dereham Rd, Litcham, King's Lyn PE32 2RN (tel: 01328 701699; see website for more info: www.bridgefarmfisheries.co.uk) 2 coarse lakes; 40 pegs; carp, tench, roach, rudd, golden rudd, golden orfe, koi carp; dt, conc, bed and breakfast accommodation; disabled facilities.

TASS or TAES:

Swainsthorpe (Norfolk). Yare, 3m N. **Taswood Lakes,** Mill Rd, Flordon NR15 1LX (tel: 01508 470919; web: www.taswoodlakes.co.uk); good carp and other coarse fish; dt available; night by appointment.

BASS:

Wymondham (Norfolk). Yare, 4m N at Barford and 6m N at Marlingford; roach. Club: Wymondham & DAC: st & dt. Tackle shop: F W Myhill & Son Ltd, 36 Fairland St, NR18 0AW (tel: 01953 602272; see website for more: www.myhillspetandgarden.co.uk).

BLACKWATER: Trout; preserved.

Booton (Norfolk). Booton Clay Pit, with carp to 30lb, bream to 10lb and large roach, tench, etc; stocked; 24 hour dt £15, dt £5 from bailiff on bank; for further details contact S Brownsell, 27 Holman Close, Aylsham NR11 6DD (tel: 01263 732263).

Broads connected with the Yare

Buckenham (Norfolk). **Rockland Broad,** 1½m SW; good roach fishing and pike fishing in winter; free; boat required; slipway available; also free

fishing at Rockland Staithe (winter best).

Brundall (Norfolk). Belongs to National Trust; shallow water grown up in summer, but good for pike in winter.

NORFOLK (small streams)

BABINGLEY RIVER. Fishing station: **Castle Rising**. Reduced water levels; little fishing and limited access.

GLAVEN. Rises 3m E of **Holt** and joins sea at **Cley**, 6m down. 1m at Cley. Fishing now held privately. No permits. There are several small coarse lakes in this area. **Letheringsett, Booton** at **Cawston**, **Selbrigg** at **Hemstead**; dt on bank.

NAR. Rises above **Narborough** to enter the Wash at **King's Lynn**. Chalk stream brown trout fishing; private. 2m both banks below Narborough Mill, stocked, fish 11" upwards, dry fly and upstream nymph fishing only,

reserved for Salmon & Trout Assn syndicate members; S&TA members can apply for dt £20 (3 fish); contact J Peppitt (tel: 01328 878355). At Narborough, trout (3) (various prices) and coarse lakes (1) (dt £8; £16 24 hours booking obligatory) plus trout stream; dt £8 trout on stream, plus £3.86 per kg; enq to Narborough Trout and Coarse Lakes, Main Rd, Narborough, nr King's Lynn PE32 1TE (tel: 01760 338005; web: narfish.co.uk).

TASS. Rises N of **Wacton**, 11m S of **Norwich**, to enter Yare on outskirts of city.

OTTER

Noted Devonshire trout stream flowing into English Channel immediately east of Exe. Mullet in estuary and some sea trout, with brown trout of good average size for West Country higher up, where hotels have some excellent dry-fly water.

Budleigh Salterton (Devon). Tidal. Free fishing from river mouth to Clamour Bridge (about 1½m, both banks) to visitors staying in East Budleigh or Budleigh Salterton. Sea trout, brown trout, grey mullet plentiful but difficult to catch. Fishing on both banks from Clamour Bridge to Newton Poppleford. Sea fishing; bass, flatfish, etc, from extensive beach. (see Sea Fishing Stations under Sidmouth).

Ottery St Mary (Devon). Some good trout water in vicinity.

Honiton (Devon). Deer Park Hotel, Buckerell Village EX14 3PG has 3m (both banks) of wild brown trout fishing; trout up to 2lb, average 1lb; dt £30, £15 after 5pm, from Otter Country Sports, 3 Black Lion Court, Honiton EX14 1ES (tel: 01404 41010). Otter Inn, **Warton**, has trout fishing on 100 yds of Otter. Coarse fishing on 2 lake at Lakeview Manor, Dunkeswell, EX14 4SH (tel: 01404 891358); carp, rudd, tench, and roach; no day tickets; st £160, conc, sold at hotel. Hollies Trout Farm and Fisheries, Sheldon EX14 0SQ (tel: 01404 841428), trout pond of 1½ acres, spring fed; open all year, or apply Otter Country Sports, 3 Black Lion Court, Honiton EX14 1ES (tel: 01404 41010).

OUSE (Great)

Rises in Buckinghamshire and flows north-east through Northamptonshire, Bedfordshire, Cambridgeshire, Huntingdonshire and Norfolk, entering the North Sea by The Wash. Coarse fishing throughout. Slow, winding river for most part. Roach and dace are to be found in quantity, together with barbel and bream. Between Newport Pagnell and Bedford there are large chub and barbel.

King's Lynn (Norfolk). Coarse fish of all kinds except barbel. King's Lynn AA has water on the Ouse from Modney Court to Denver Sluice east bank; Denver Sluice to Danby's Drove, west bank; on the Wissey, from Dereham Belt to R Ouse; on the **Relief Channel Drain**, King's Lynn to Denver Sluice; on the **Middle Level Drain** from St Germans to Three Holes, 8m; Ten Mile Bank, and 4 lakes (members only + £10); senior st £36, junior £6, conc £21 (conc rod licence ticket to be shown), wt £15, dt £4, from bailiffs. Gatton Waters, Hillington, nr Sandringham PE31 6BJ: coarse fishing in 8 acre lake, for visiting campers only, and caravans; contact Mr Donaldson (tel: 01485 600643). Woodlakes Holiday Park, Holme Rd, Stow Bridge, PE34 3PX (tel: 01553 810414), 8m south of King's Lynn, coarse fishing on five lakes, the largest 12 and 10 acres; carp to 37lbs, pike, roach, tench, bream, rudd, perch, etc; dt £8 mid-week, £10 w/e and bank holidays, conc for juv, OAP. Swaffham AC has Bradmoor lakes, Narborough, stocked with carp, bream, etc; st £33 (£50 night), conc, (photo required) from Kev's Tackle. Tackle shops: Anglers Corner, 22 Windsor Rd PE30 5PL (tel: 01553 775852); Tackle Box, 38 Tower St, King's Lynn PE30 1EJ (tel: 01553 761293); Kev's Tackle, 2 Mangate St, Swaffam PE37 7QN (tel: 01760 720188). Hotel: Park View.

Downham Market (Norfolk). Coarse fish, sea trout; tidal. **Cut Off Channel** is King's Lynn AA water, 12m from Wretton Fen Drove to Denver Sluice;

also Old Bedford River at Salters Lode; 3m u/s; dt £4 on bank; also 5m from town Tottenhill Lake; small carp, tench, bream members only lake. Tackle shop: Howlett Cycles and Fishing, 53 High St, PE38 9HF (tel: 01366 386067).

Hilgay (Norfolk). King's Lynn AA water on Ouse and **Wissey**; also **Cut Off Channel** (see King's Lynn). London AA has water on Ouse; dt £3.50, conc, from bailiffs.

Littleport (Cambs). Ouse and **Lark**; coarse fish, except barbel, good pike and bream, with roach, perch, zander; Littleport AC has fishing on Ouse: old Littleport A10 Bridge u/s to Sandhills Bridge, both banks, except Boat Haven on west bank; bream to 7lb, roach, rudd, perch, eels, pike, zander, carp; permits £5 from bailiff on bank; club books from tackle shop, Littleport Angling Centre; full membership £15, conc. London AA controls 14m of water from Littleport Bridge to Southery (Norfolk), both banks; dt from bailiffs; night permit available, also 24-hour ticket. D/s of Littleport King's Lynn AA has 2m of single bank on road side on Little Ouse, u/s of Iron Bridge at Little Ouse Village; dt from bailiff. Tackle shop: Littleport Angling Centre, 15 Granby Str, Littleport CB6 1NE (tel: 01353 860419); Benwick Sports, Unit 22, Northfield Road, Soham, Ely CB7 5UF (tel: 01353 721009; web: www.benwicksports.co.uk).

Ely (Cambs). Free fishing in Ely town centre. Coopers AC have ½m downstream of railway bridge; dt £4 on bank; wheelchair access; bookings from Hon Sec; Ely Beet Sports & Social Club, Lynn Rd, Ely CB6 1DD (tel: 01353 662029) has fishing on both banks of Ouse at confluence; contact Dave Newman; dt £5 on bank; also Roswell Pits, Ely, all year round; dt £5. Littleport AC have ¾m from Sandhill Bridge downstream; dt on bank: bookings from Paul Frost (tel:

01353 860353). Tackle shop: Littleport Angling Centre, 15 Granby Str, Littleport, CB6 1NE (tel: 01353 860419); Benwick Sports, Unit 22, Northfield Road, Soham, Ely CB7 5UF (tel: 01353 721009; web: www.benwicksports.co.uk).

Earith (Hunts). Histon & Dist AC has apprx 1m opposite village, members only; st; also **Old West River** Earith Bridge to Smithey Fen. At Streatham, Cambridge Albion AS; good coarse fishing; **Old Bedford River** from Earith to Welches Dam controlled by Cambridge Albion AS; members only but dt £5 on bank (£4 from Hon Sec). Ploughman's Pit (good carp, bream, pike. The Hundred Foot (Earith to Sutton Gault), rented by Cambridge FPAS, tidal; practically all coarse fish, except barbel; **Borrow Pit** nr Ely, coarse fish, dt £5 (£4 in advance), from Hon Sec or local inns for Cambridge FPAS water.

Over and **Swavesey** (Cambs). Bream, perch, chub, rudd, tench, large carp to 37lb, pike, dace and zander. Sea trout runs up to the locks; fish over 12lb taken. Occasional salmon.

Holywell Ferry (Hunts). Hotel: Ferry Boat. Pike, bream, roach, rudd, chub, etc; free; boats; good fishing, especially roach.

St Ives (Hunts). All coarse fish, bream, dace, perch, chub, gudgeon, also carp, barbel, rudd and tench; ample bank fishing, but boats for hire; St Ives & DFPAS has 3m water; st £16, dt on bank £5, conc, under 16s free. Adjoining water at Bluntisham (members only (st £41), plus lake at Hemmingford Grey, nr St Ives (dt £4, conc, to be purchased only on bank; night permits for members only), held by London AA. Tackle shop: Petzone, 3 Station Road, PE27 5BH (tel: 01480 462807). Hotels: Golden Lion, Slepe Hall.

Godmanchester (Hunts). Good bream, roach, chub and chance of carp. Godmanchester A & FPS has about

10m; tickets from Hon Sec or tackle shop; st £12, dt £3 from Stanjay Tackle, £4 on bank. London AA has Portholme Meadow, Berry Lane Meadows and 1¼m Old West River at Stretham (members only); boats from Huntingdon; no free fishing. Tackle shop: Stanjay Sports, 7 Old Court Hall, Godmanchester PE29 2HS (tel: 01480 453303; see website for more: www.stanjayfishingandtrophies.co.uk), who manage **Woolpack Fishery**, Cow Lane, 60 acres of well stocked coarse fishing; gold ticket £300 all lakes; lakes 1, 2, 3 & 8 white st £45, green ticket (24-hour) £80 2 rods, £100 3 rods, conc; dt £5 in shop only; Stanjay also has Cromwell Lake, 2½ acres, 36 match pegs (bookable) st £70, dt from shop £5 (1 rod) £7 (2 rods); large coarse fish water. Hotels: Black Bull, Exhibition, Bridge and George.

Huntingdon (Cambs). Chub, bream, roach and tench; good when boat traffic declines. Huntingdon A&FPS has water from Town Bridge to Hartford Church; platforms for disabled; permits, st £12, conc, juv st £6, no dt, from tackle shops. London AA (see Clubs) has **Portholme Meadow**, **Alconbury Brook** (Huntingdon), **West Meadow**, **Lea Brook** (Godmanchester) and **Willow Tree Island** (at Offord); **Brampton Mill Pool** and millstream, and also lake and river at **Brampton**; all members only; membership £43, conc. Brampton (Cambs) AS has one stretch of Ouse, 2 brooks and 2 lakes; mainly st (£20) but dt £4 on rivers and one lake; on bank or from Stanjay. Biggleswade, Hitchin AA has 1m at Brampton; members only. Tackle shops: Sports & Fashions, 51 High Str, Huntingdon PE29 3AQ (tel: 01480 413435/454541); Stanjay Sports, 7 Old Court Hall, Godmanchester PE29 2HS (tel: 01480 453303; see website for more: www.stanjayfishingandtrophies.co.uk); Ouse Valley Specialist Angling, 25/31 Huntingdon St, St Neots PE19

1BG (tel: 01480 386088; web: www.ousevalleyangling.co.uk).

Offord Cluny (Hunts). Stocked by Environment Agency. Chub, roach, bream, tench, carp, barbel, catfish. Offord & Buckden AS has 3m of Great Ouse between St Neots and Huntingdon, incl two weir pools; membership £15, dt £4, conc, from bank by car park; from Stanjay, Godmanchester. **St Neots** (Hunts). St Neots & Dist A&FPS has several stretches and are expanding their fishings; Wilden Reservoir (members only); good tench, chub to 7lbs, bream, roach and big carp; st, conc, from tackle shops; dt for most of R Ouse fishing (not Wray House), from bailiffs; also Hen Brook and Pocket Park, both part of Ouse; dt on bank. Shefford & DAA has 1500 metre stretch d/s of town at Little Paxton; members only; apply Hon Sec. Luton AC has 3 stretches on Great Ouse: Black Cat, Wyboston Lakes and Eaton Ford; also at Wyboston 2 coarse lakes, one dt (South Lagoon); dt £6 on bank, conc. London AA has water at **Tempsford** and **Blunham** (see Ivel). Tackle shops: Ouse Valley Specialist Angling, 25/31 Huntingdon St, St Neots PE19 1BG (tel: 01480 386088; web: www.ousevalleyangling.co.uk).

Biggleswade (Beds). Ouse, Ivel; Biggleswade, Hitchin AA, a founder member of the Ivel Protection Assn which gives members access to all IPA-controlled fishings; Assn has 7m on mid Ouse, starting at Tempsford, and 15 acre **Gingerbread Lake** at Eaton Socon with large carp, tench, rudd, bream, with access also to the river here; st £60, conc, from Memb Sec and local tackle shops; club also has **Links Pool** nearby; mixed coarse; members only; near Sandy railway station the Assn has 2 lakes, New Road Lake, specimen bream and carp, and McGregor Lake, mixed coarse, members only. Under sharing arrangements with Cemex (formerly RMC) Angling, Milton Keynes AA has access to 1m of R Ouse at **Harrold** in Beds and 1m of R Ivel near **Biggleswade**, Beds (for further information contact Cemex or Milton Keynes, chairman, Trevor Johnson (see Clubs)). Shefford & DAA has Broom Lake at Broom Village; mixed coarse; members only. Blue Lagoon and Green Lagoon, **Arlesey** (4m S); large coarse lake, Letchworth Garden City AA; dt on Green Lagoon only £7, membership £58, conc. Tackle Shop: Mainly Tackle.

Bedford (Beds). Approx 4m water in town centre and above, free to EA rod licence-holders. Council controls three lakes at Priory Country Park, dt on bank. Bedford AC has fishing and issues limited dt at £7, obtainable from Tavistock Angling, other tackleists or Hon Sec. Shefford & DAA has Willington Lake; mixed coarse (carp to 35lb); members only; assn also fishes Great Ouse here; barbel water. Vauxhall AC controls **Radwell** complex, 6m of Ouse (both banks in many places), and seven gravel pits of total 100 acres at Sharnbrook; ¾m R Ouse at **Felmersham**; club also has 600 yds at **Kempston**, and ½m at **Willington**; also 8 acre coarse lake, **Woburn Sands**; and holds stretch of **R Ivel** close to Sandy (Girtford Bridge); members only plus guests; st £37, conc; membership details from Membership Sec. Biggleswade, Hitchin AA has **Sandy Lakes Fishery**; mixed coarse; members only; apply membership secretary, Anthony Pogmore (tel: 01767 223147). Kempston AC, now amalgamated with Vauxhall AC, has 2 ½m at Kempston Mill on the Ouse; st from Tavistock Angling or Hon Sec. Luton AC has 40-peg stretch at Biddenham Baulk; members only; apply Hon Sec; club also has ¾m left bank at Lavendon Mill; members only; also 5 acre reservoir at Steppingley, near Ampthill; mixed coarse; members only. Biggleswade, Hitchin AA has river at Lavendon

from A428 at Cold Brayfield for 2 meadows towards Olney; also at Priory Farm, Harrold, 4 meadows, access via the Lavendon-Harrold B road; st £60 from membership secretary. Blunham & DAC has stretches at Gt Barford, 1,000 yds; Willington, 2,000 yds; and Oakley, 1,500 yds, good mixed coarse fishing with roach, chub, bream, barbel, etc; members only, £40, £20 conc. Ampthill AFPS fish **Ampthill Reservoir**, **Westminster Pool**, **Brogborough Lake**, and **Marston Pits**; membership £38; guest tickets (accompanied by member); also stretch of river at **Stoke Goldington**. Tackle shops: Tavistock Angling, 95 Tavistock Str, MK40 2RR (tel: 01234 267145); Sportsmans Lodge, 147 Harrowden Road, Bedford MK42 0RU (tel: 01234 269724); Bleak Hall Sports, 1 & 65 High Street, Kempston MK42 7BT (tel: 01234 852530; web: www.bleakhallsports.co.uk). Hotels: Embankment, Swan.

Felmersham (7m N of Bedford). Vauxhall AC fishes ¾m here and ¼m at **Willington**, membership £37, conc. Letchworth Garden City AA has left bank d/s of road bridge; no dt, membership £58, conc.

Sharnbrook (Beds). Vauxhall AC has water; 1500 yards on Country Park side; also **Harrold Country Park**; 2 lakes; mixed coarse; members only. Cemex (formerly RMC) Angling has (Silver Water) **Harrold Fishery** (1,500m Ouse, 1,200m Ivel at Lower Caldecott), with carp, chub, roach, dace, pike, catfish, barbel; st £30, conc £20; 2 rod limit; (For Cemex (formerly RMC) Angling see Chertsey).

Newton Blossomville (Bucks). Coarse fish (large barbel). Northampton Nene AC has water; strictly limited; members only from Hon Sec or local tackle shops; also at Turvey.

Newport Pagnell (Bucks). Good barbel, roach, bream, chub, perch. Stretch fishes well in winter. Newport Pagnell

FA leases Newport Pagnell Lakes from AW; and fishes 5m of river; members only (£33, conc) + guests £5; £7 key to car park and access to pits; contact Hon Sec. Milton Keynes AA has 6/7m of bank on R Ouzel from Bletchley, through Milton Keynes towards Newport Pagnell and 12m of tow path on Grand Union Canal in **Milton Keynes** (for further information see Hon Sec below).

Stony Stratford (Bucks). Deanshanger & The Stratfords AA has 6m of Ouse; bream, roach, perch, chub and pike, plus Grand Union Canal at **Castlethorpe**, st £15, dt £4 on bank, or from Gone Fishing, 26 Church St, Wolverton, Milton Keynes, Bucks MK12 5JN (tel: 01908 313158; web: www.gone-fishin.co.uk). Milton Keynes AA has approx 6m of bank on Great Ouse between **Stony Stratford** and **Newport Pagnell**; 1m of bank on R Tove at **Castlethorpe**; approx 16 lakes totalling 345 acres in Milton Keynes area (including Furzeton, Caldecotte, Tear Drops (3), Lodge Lake, Willen Lakes (2), Bradwell Lake, Dimmocks Pit); finally access to **Emberton Park** at **Olney** (just outside Milton Keynes): 6 lakes totalling 60 acres (incl. Heron, Glebe and Willow lakes); also ¾m of the Great Ouse; assn controls the Adams Mill barbel fishery on the Ouse; for further information contact Milton Keynes, chairman, Trevor Johnson (see Clubs).

Cosgrove Lodge lakes at Cosgrove (Northants): noted for roach, tench, bream, pike; dt on water. Hotels: Cock; Bull.

Buckingham (Bucks). Chub, roach, perch, dace, bream, pike. Buckingham & Dist AA has several miles of fishing on upper Ouse and tributary Padbury Brook, plus two stillwaters in area; good quality coarse fishing throughout, with increased water flows of winter months bringing out best in the river; assn records include carp 39lb 4oz, pike 27lb 4oz, perch 5lb 6oz, bream, chub and tench over 7lb; adult membership £39, dt £6, conc (disabled via membership sec; proof must be provided in 1st season): from Jakeman Sport, 5 Bourbon St, Aylesbury HP20 2PZ (tel: 01296 486613); J & K Tackle, 62/64 Sheep St, Bicester OX26 6LG (tel: 01869 242589; web: www.jktackle.co.uk); Tingewick P O, Main St, Twyford, Buckingham MK18 4EP (tel: 01280 848374). Mountmill Angling Syndicate has 2m between Beachampton and Deanshanger, mostly double bank, with large perch, pike, roach, dace, bream, barbel; membership limited, contact P Welling, 1 South Park Gardens, Berkhamsted, HP4 1JA (mob: 07770 632296). Leighton Buzzard AA, Claydon Lakes, 6m; no dt. At Stowe, Landscape Garden National Trust has 3 coarse lakes; carp, perch, pike, roach, rudd and tench; Stowe AC water; long waiting list; contact Seahawk Supplies, Brewery House, 4 Castle St, Buckingham MK18 1BS (tel: 01280 822872; see website for more info: www.seahawksupplies.co.uk). At **Mursley**, Church Hill Fishery, Swanbourne Rd, MK17 0JA: 3 lakes of 15 acres stocked with r and b trout; dt £35, half-day £25, 4 and 2 fish (tel: 0129672 0524). Pimlico Farm Pools, Tusmore, Bicester OX27 7SL (tel: 01869 810306; see website for more info: www.pimlicofarm.co.uk): 3 lakes with carp, perch, roach, rudd, tench; 50 pegs, open dawn till dusk; disabled anglers free fishing, matches, self-catering accom with fishing included.

Tributaries of the Ouse (Great)

WISSEY:

Hilgay (Norfolk). King's Lynn AA have 2m of both banks down to Ouse; St £36, wt £15, dt £4, conc. London AA issues dt for Five Mile House Farm; dt £3.50 on bank; also 24-hour ticket; good for zander.

LITTLE OUSE: Good bream and roach.

Brandon (Suffolk). The above species, plus dace, perch, pike (good), a few chub and zander. Brandon & Dist AC has 2 ponds and ¾m river at Recreation Park; no dt, membership £22 annually with concessions, from Recreation Centre. Hotel: The Ram.

Thetford (Norfolk). Little Ouse and Thet. Roach, rudd, tench, chub and pike; and dace to specimen size. Fishing free for 7 miles through town centre out to Santon Downham.

LARK: Trout and coarse fish.

Mildenhall (Suffolk). Brown trout, carp, rudd, roach, tench, bream, pike, dace, gudgeon, chub. Mildenhall AC has several stretches excellent coarse fishing on Lark at Mildenhall, u/s and d/s at Isleham Lock; for st contact Hon Sec. Lark APS has fly fishing for browns between Lackford and Barton Mills; coarse fishing on various stretches from Barton Mills to West Row Fen; fly only, trout; membership £125 (st only); coarse st £20, conc £10 (under 12's free) from Hon Sec; dt £4 from Barton Mills PO or £5 on bank; disabled facilities at Barton Mills (ten platforms), where there is also a lake, and Mildenhall (three platforms). Tackle shops: Tackle Up, 49a St Johns St, Bury St Edmunds IP33 1SP (tel: 01284 755022); Hooked, 88 All Saints Rd, Newmarket CB8 8HF (tel: 01638 661594); Matthews Florist & Garden Centre, 18 High St, Lakenheath, Brandon IP27 9JS (tel: 01842 860284). Hotels: White Hart, High St; Riverside, Mill St.

Bury St Edmunds (Suffolk). Coarse fish. Bury St Edmunds AA has Little Ouse (Redmere stretch), stretches on Blackbourne; and 3 lakes: at Barrow; Middle Reservoir; Water Lane Lakes: coarse; st £55, conc, dt £7.50 (no dt Sunday fishing), no conc; tickets from Tackle-Up (below). For fishing **Larkwood Trout Fishery** contact I D McGregor, Icklingham Road, West Stow, Bury St Edmunds IP28 6EZ (tel: 01284 728612; see website for more info: www.larkwoodfishery.co.uk); 2 3-acre lakes; open all year; dt water; tuition, corporate days, lodge, tackle shop. Tackle shop: Tackle Up, 49a St Johns St, Bury St Edmunds IP33 1SP (tel: 01284 755022; web: www.tackle-up.com); which has information on a variety of coarse fisheries in area, incl Weybread Fishery, with large carp, roach etc; Marsh Farm Lakes, Saxmundham; Barway Lake, nr Ely; Cross Drove Fishery, Hockwold-cum-Wilton; Swangey Lakes, Gt Ellingham.

CAM or **RHEE**: Excellent fishery, with good roach and pike. Best catches between Baitsbite Lock and Clayhithe Bridge.

Waterbeach (Cambs). Letchworth Garden City AA has 1200 yards right bank d/s of Clayhithe Bridge; dt on bank. Contact Hon Sec. Cambridge FPAS has Reach, Burwell and Wicken Lodes; dt £5 on bank (£4 in advance).

Cambridge. R Cam can fish well, with roach, chub, dace, and many other species. Fishing disallowed on college property. University Sports and Social Club controls R Cam at Cantelupe Farm; permits from club. Cam from near Pike and Eel Pub, Chesterton, d/s through Baitsbite Lock to Clayhith Bridge, Cambridge FPAS; st £25, conc, dt £4 in advance, from Hon Sec local tackle shops; also lakes; enquire Hon Sec for permits. Waterbeach AC controls Cam, Baitside Lock area, also at **Upware**; club also has rights on

Swaffham Bulbeck Lode, and Atkin and Leland Waters, Landbeach which is for members only; st £25, dt £6; club also has Magpie Lake here; mainly carp for match and dt; club also has **Wrights Reservoir** at Frolic Farm, Lode Fen; members only. Cambridge Izaak Walton Soc has ¾m at Dernford Farm, Stapleford (**Granta**); brown trout, chub, dace, perch; members only; contact Hon Sec. Cambridge Albion AS controls Cam at Wicken; Dimmocks Cote to Upware; and d/s towards Fish & Duck Pub; st £20, dt £5, on bank or from tackle shops; the Old West River at Stretton Bridge, and **Old Bedford River** from **Earith** to Welches Dam, a good pike water. Histon & Dist AS controls **Old West River** from Hermitage Lock to old pump engine, and two other stretches; should be fished early in day, owing to boat traffic; st £15, conc, dt £3 in advance; and Counterwash Drain from Earith to Manea on both banks; tench, roach, rudd, pike, etc; the society also has from Earith Bridge to Sutton Gault on Old Bedford River; members only. For **Drayton Fen**, 80 acres, with good carp, tench, pike, also Holywell and Swavesey Lakes and Gt Ouse; enquire Coopers (below). London AA has water for members only at **Swaffham Prior** and **Upware**; members only; membership £41, conc. Tackle shop: FJ & FJ Farrington, 2 Ferry Lane, Cambridge CB4 1NT (tel: 01223 461361); Cooper & Sons, 1 Carlton Terrace, Carlton Way, Cambridge CB4 2DA (tel: 01223 365987).

Barrington. Cambridge Izaak Walton Soc has ¾m here; chub, dace, pike; members only; contact Hon Sec.

OLD WEST RIVER: Good stock of coarse fish. **Milton Lake**. Large carp and other coarse fish.

IVEL: Dace, roach, barbel, bream, chub and perch.

Tempsford (Beds). Ouse and Ivel. Biggleswade, Hitchin AA has water on Ivel; members only; st £60; family £70, conc. London AA has several miles on Ouse here and at Blunham; members only; membership £41, conc.

Blunham (Beds). Ouse (1m W). Blunham & DAC controls 1,000 yds local fishing on River Ivel; also Gt Ouse at Oakley, Willington and Gt Barford; Halls Pit, nr Sandy; Barford Lake, Gt Barford; Willington Gravel Pits; members only, £40, £20 conc. Below Blunham Bridge to Ouse held by Biggleswade, Hitchin AA; club also has right bank of Ivel, stretch between Langford Mill and Broom Mill; 2 gravel pits at Sandy New Road; no dt; club also has right bank u/s of Langford Mill. Shefford & DAA has left bank, at **Shefford**; members only. Tackle shop at Shefford, Andy's Angling, 19 High Street, Shefford SG17 5DD (tel: 01462 850061).

Lower Caldecote (Beds).

Langford (Beds). Letchworth Garden City AA has fishing opposite garden centre; no dt; Assn fishes most of Ivel through its membership of the Ivel Protection Association. River also fished by Shefford & DAA here; members only.

FLIT (Ivel Navigation). Enters Ivel at Langford. Mixed fishery with roach, chub, perch, pike. Shefford & DAA has from Langford to Shefford; members only; apply Hon Sec; st £55.

Henlow (Beds). Letchworth Garden City AA fishes Poppy Hill Complex in Henlow: 5 lakes and river at Henlow Village, entry via Park Lane; no dt. Shefford & DAA fishes Airman Pit, 1m west; mixed coarse, mainly carp and catfish up to 45lb; members only; apply Hon Sec.

HIZ (tributary of Ivel). Ivel Protection Assn has a stretch.

OUZEL: Coarse fish.

Leighton Buzzard (Beds). Luton AC has 12m **Grand Union Canal** from

Pitstone, through Leighton Buzzard to Stoke Hammond; towpath; dt £5, conc, from bank; mixed coarse. Leighton Buzzard AC has 2m from Stoke Hammond to Bletchley A5; mixed coarse; st £35, apply Hon Sec or agents (see web site - clubs list). Leighton Buzzard AC also fish **Claydon Lakes**, **Tiddenfoot** (tench to double figures, catfish to 60lb) and Rackley Hills Pits and other pits; concessions to jun & OAP £12. Berkhamsted & DAS controls Bridigo Pond, Linslade, nr Leighton Buzzard; mixed carp and coarse fishery; also Steart Farm, Cublington, carp fishery, both members only; £35, £45 family, conc. Cemex (formerly RMC) Angling has 2 small lakes, including

Jones Pit, famous for catfish; stocked also with carp; Gold Water: st (2 rods) £220; 3 rod limit; waiting list; (For Cemex (formerly RMC) Angling, see Chertsey).

RELIEF CHANNEL: not strictly a tributary but included here because of its traditional status as an excellent coarse fishery in its own right, now re-established as such, after a difficult period with zander, by an intensive programme of investigation and re-stocking by AWA. Rented to Wisbech & Dist AA which issues dt.

TOVE: Coarse fish. Towcester & DAC fish 3m mostly both banks; dt in advance from tackle shops (see clubs list).

OUSE (Sussex)

Rises few miles south-east of Horsham and flows for 33 miles to enter English Channel at Newhaven. Tidal for 12 miles from mouth to point 4m upstream of Lewes. Coarse fish and trout, but notable for run of big sea trout.

Lewes and **Barcombe Mills** (E Sussex). Sea trout (good), barbel, tench, perch, bream, roach, dace, chub, rudd, carp over 30lb and pike over 30lb. Ouse APS has west bank from Hamsey to Barcombe Mills (about 4m) and certain stretches of non tidal water above the mills; sea trout from May to Oct, but June to October best, given rain; also water shared with Copthorne & DAS: west bank for 4m between Anchor Inn and Newick; permits; contact Andrew Woolley, 14 The Martlets, Mill Lane, South Chailey, BN8 4QG (tel: 01273 891312); Barcombe Mills Pool and side streams reserved for sea-trout fishing and open to permit holders at additional charge bookable in advance. Decoy Wood Fisheries, 3 Decoy Cottages, Laugthon Rd, Ringmer BN8 6DJ. tel: 01273 814344; see website for more: www.decoycottages-holidaylets.com: coarse fishing in 4 acre lake; good stock of carp, rudd, roach, tench, perch, the odd pike; book 24 hours in advance; self catering cottages, fishing included. Tackle shop: Percy's Fishing Tackle, 9 Cliffe High Street (tel: 01273 473207); Uckfield Angling Centre, 212A High St, Uckfield TN22 1RD (tel: 01825 760300; see website: www.uckfieldangling.com). Hotels: Shelleys; White Hart; Crown (all Lewes); for Barcombe Mills: Anchor Inn.

Isfield (E Sussex). Coarse fish, trout and sea trout. Isfield & Dist AC has sections of Ouse at Isfield and Barcombe Mills; also has stretches of **Uck** at **Uckfield**, and lakes around **E Grinstead**, **Uckfield**, **Horsted Keynes** and elsewhere, thirty fisheries in all; large carp, tench, bream, perch, eels and pike; st £65 plus £15 joining fee, conc, from Memb Sec (sae); no dt. Hotel: Laughing Fish, Isfield. (Tackle see Lewes).

Haywards Heath (W Sussex). Coarse fish and trout. Haywards Heath & Dist AS has 11½m mainly single bank of **Ouse** from **Linfield** down to **Newick**, and several lakes, including **Balcombe Lake**, **Slaugham Mill Pond**, **Valebridge Mill Pond**; fishing coarse mainly, trout in river, and is for members only; membership open to approved applicants, with concessions; a few river guest tickets. Tackle shops: Sporting Chance, Unit 2, 29 Boltro Rd, Haywards Heath RH16 1BP (tel: 01444 454095); Burgess Hill Angling Centre, 143 Lower Church Rd, Burgess Hill RH15 9AA (tel: 01444 232287; web: www.burgesshillanglingcentre.co.uk) for Hassocks AS and Henfield & DAS and Haywards Heath & DAS.

UCK: mainly coarse fishing below Uckfield with occasional sea trout. Joins Ouse at Isfield. Isfield & Dist AC has water at Uckfield

Isfield (E Sussex). Coarse fish and trout. Isfield & Dist AC has water from here to **Uckfield** (members only), with excellent coarse fishing and trout to 3lb.

OUSE (Yorkshire)

Forms with Trent the estuary of the Humber. Coarse fish, with some trout. Dunsforth, Beningbrough and Poppleton reaches noted for barbel and chub. Large bream present but difficult to catch. Most water held by Leeds and York clubs. Tributaries give excellent coarse fishing, and trout in upper reaches.

Goole (E Yorkshire). Don enters Ouse here. Several different clubs have amalgamated for fishing the **Aire & Calder Canal** from Goole to Crowcroft Bridge nr Pollington; information from R S Tackle and Guns; as for West Cowick Pond, and Big Hole Pond at Rawcliffe. Bradford No 1 AA has 9 miles of canal between Great Heck and Goole; members only. Selby AC offers dt £2.50 (yearbook £10) on bank at Selby Canal between Brayton and Burn Bridges, with roach, perch, pike and other species. Selby tackle shops: Selby Angling Centre, 69 Brook Str, Selby YO8 4AL (tel: 01757 703471); Field Sports, 24/26 New St, Selby, YO8 4PT (tel: 01757 709607); R S Tackle and Guns, Unit 1, Carlisle St, Goole DN14 5DS (tel: 01405 720292).

Acaster (N Yorks). Coarse fishing. Castleford Anglers fish on 150 yds below old salmon hut; dt on bank. Fish include barbel; above dam, trout and coarse fish. Hotel: Manor Country House.

Naburn (N Yorks). Below dam, right bank to old salmon hut, York Amalgamated; left bank, tickets from lock keeper, yearbook available.

York (N Yorks). Coarse fish; some free fishing on public waters. On left bank nearly all free except 8m from Rawcliffe Ings and Clifton Ings up to Aldwark. York & DAA is an amalgamation of 20 clubs, and has fishing on **Ouse**, **Derwent**, **Nidd** (at Skipbridge), **Foss**, **Rye**, and **Seven** as well as canals Pocklington, Selby and Aire and Calder; and several still waters; st £36 (plus £4 for Laybourn Lakes at Hessay), conc, dt £5 from local tackle shops for lower Nidd; ½m on Derwent, each fishery members only. Tackle shops: Anglers Corner, 41 Huby Court, Walmgate, York YO1 9UD (tel: 01904 629773).

Poppleton and **Newton** (N Yorks). Good barbel, pike, etc. York Amalgamation has extensive stretches; including National Trust water at Beningbrough Hall; coarse: barbel, bream, eel, gudgeon, roach, ruffe; dt from York tackle shops. Newton on Ouse AC also fishes this water; dt from Blacksmith's Arms, Newton on Ouse YO30 2BN (tel: 01347 848249).

Lower Dunsforth. From Lower Dunsforth to Aldwark Bridge (about 4m right bank) fishing is largely in the hands of Leeds & Dist ASA; association also has good length at **Hunterslodge** on opposite side below Aldwark bridge (left bank); and a futher length at Linton-on-Ouse adjoining bottom of Hunterslodge to canal mouth; members only.

Tributaries of the Ouse (Yorkshire)

DON. Rises on Wike Head and flows through Sheffield and Doncaster to the estuary of the Ouse; after 150 years of pollution from the Sheffield steel industry, this river is once more fishable. The Environment Agency has stocked over past twelve years, and 30lb nets of roach have been caught. Hemp and tares are best summer baits, maggots and casters in winter.

Doncaster (S Yorks). Doncaster & Dist AA has much widespread coarse fishing, including water on the canalised Don and **South Yorkshire Navigation Canal** at **Sprotborough**, 4m d/s to Doncaster Prison; 6m of the **Torne** fromEpworth road bridge to Pilfrey bridge; the 6m of **New Junction Canal** from Barnby Dun to the **Aire & Calder** junction; also BW **Southfield Reservoirs**, **Cowick**, 110 acres total, 70lb bags of roach and bream; dt £3 on banks at many of these fisheries. **Thrybergh Reservoir**, 34 acres, near **Rotherham**; Rotherham MBC trout fishery; permits on site; Rotherham MBC also has **Fitzwilliam Canal**, Rotherham 1m, dt. BW Castleford Anglers have **Woodnook Reservoir**; st from Assn HQ and tackle shops. **Hayfield Fishing Lakes**, Hayfield Lane, Auckley, DN9 3NP (tel: 01302 864555); 2 lakes with 161 pegs, mainly carp, roach, rudd, tench, gudgeon, barbel, etc; dt £5 available, conc; bait bar on site, plus refreshments. Tackle shops: Doncaster Fishing Centre, 207 Carr House Rd, Belle Vue, Doncaster DN4 5DR (tel: 01302 363629; web: www.doncasterfishingcentre.co.uk). R & R Sports, 40 High Str, Bawtry DN10 6JE (tel: 01302 711130); has dt for a variety of coarse fishings in area, incl Chesterfield Canal, R Idle.

Sheffield (S Yorks). **Damflask Coarse Fishery** (YW reservoir), 5m W; contact bailiff (mob: 07952 485798); 2-mt and dt £4.30 from machine on site, adjacent to Dam House; bream in summer and autumn, specimen pike in winter; roach perch and chub through year; numbers of specimen fish is increasing. **Underbank**, corporation reservoir, now a club water, coarse fishing; tickets on bank. Further information under 'Yorkshire Lakes'. Sheffield & Dist AA has water on Rivers **Trent**, and **Chesterfield Canal** from A631 to Trent junction; dt £3 (before fishing) issued for all waters; various outlets. **Stainforth and Keadby Canal** controlled by joint committee including Rotherham, Doncaster, and British Railways clubs; dt on bank. Sheffield & Dist AA also has 2m of Three Rivers at Keadby Pump House; mixed coarse, good roach and pike and tench; dt before fishing at Keadby PO. At **Staveley** Urban District Council have five acre lake stocked annually with coarse fish; dt and st; also **Foxtone Dam**; dt. Chapeltown & Dist AA fish **Westwood** and **Howbrook Reservoirs**, and ponds, various coarse species. Tackle shop: Kerfoots Fishing Tackle, 6 Southey Green Rd, Sheffield S5 8GW (tel: 0114 231 3265); Bennetts of Sheffield, 1-5 Stanley St, Sheffield, S3 8JP (tel: 0114 275 6756; web: www.bosfish.co.uk).

Oughtibridge (S Yorks). Sheffield 6m; free fishing, mainly roach, trout, dace, chub, barbel, with some grayling, perch. Mainly shallow, some pools and disused weirpools.

DEARNE (tributary of Don):

Barnsley (S Yorks). Dearne; Free fishing on length within Hoyle Mill Country Park. Mainly free, between here and **Darfield**, and through common near Wombwell. Stocked at **Haigh**, where Wakefield AC has water; occasional trout, and chub, perch and roach; club also has 9 lakes near **Wakefield**, fishing on R Calder; and Horbury Canal, Aire & Calder, and Walton Canal; membership from Wakefield tackle shops; no night fishing. Darfield Colliery AC has Netherwood Country Park Lake, Bradberry Balk Lane, Wombwell; dt £3 (OAP/jun conc) on bank; st/books from Hon Sec. Barnsley MBC owns **Cannon Hall Lake**, Barkhouse Lane, Cawthorne (tickets from machine); contact David Haigh (tel: 01226 790270); **Dearne Valley Park Lake (Hoyle Mill)** now Hoyle Mill AC water; contact Fred Wilson, Hon Sec (tel: 01226 213686; mob: 079773 17085) tickets on lake bank; memb £15, conc, dt £2, conc, for this club water; Barnsley MBC free fishing on selected sections of river; information from Trevor Mayne, Countryside Officer, Barnsley MBC, Parks Services, Westgate Plaza One, POBox 605, Barnsley, S70 9FF (tel: 01226 772646). Barnsley & Dist AAS fish **Brampton Canal**; dt £3, conc, (full book £25); **Worsbrough Country Park** fishing, Worsbrough Bridge; Assn also has Sally Walshes Dam, 13 acres, 6m s of town at Emsworth; dt on bank; excellent coarse carp fishery. **Barnsley Canal**, fishing on north bank only. Barnsley & Dist AAS also has **Smithies Reservoir**, Smithies Lane; dt £3 on bank or contact Hon Sec; the society also has Sally Walshes Dam; mixed coarse with specimen carp; dt £3 on bank; carp dt £7 on bank; in Barnsley the society has Tinkers Ponds; mixed coarse with specimen carp, dt £3 for both ponds. Tackle shop: Barnsley Bait Co, 85 Towngate, Mapplewell

S75 6AS (tel: 01226 210183; web: www.barnsleybaitcompany.com).

Claycross (Derby). Lakes: Williamthorpe Ponds, 2m NE. Wingerworth Hall Lakes (two), 2½m NW. Great Dam, 3½m NW.

ROTHER (tributary of Don):

Killamarsh (Derby). Short Brook. Lakes: Woodhall Moor Dams, 2m E. Barlborough Hall Lake, 3m SE. Pebley Dam, 3m SE. Harthill Reservoir, 3m E. Woodhall Pond, 3m E.

AIRE: Issues from ground at Aire Head, half a mile south of Malham village. Its upper reaches contain quality trout and grayling, which give place to coarse fish between Steeton and Keighley. Bradford No 1 AA has 600 yards left bank below the beck. Keighley AC has stretch at Marley and several more at Keighley and Skipton, with trout, chub, barbel (stocked), roach, pike, plus other fishing on ponds and 10m Leeds & Liverpool Canal from Leaches Bridge, Keighley, to Belmont Bridge, Skipton; st £26, dt £4, conc. Tackle shops in Keighley. (For Malham Tarn see Yorkshire lakes, Reservoirs, etc).

Beale (W Yorks). Bradford No 1 AA has 3m left bank above and below bridge, and a further 1½m u/s; coarse, mainly roach; members only.

Leeds (W Yorks). Contains roach, bream, chub, trout, perch. Adel Beck and Dam (private). **Roundhay Park Lakes**, 4m NE. Leeds & Dist ASA have fishing, currently free. Larger lake (Waterloo) contains trout, pike, perch, roach, tench, carp, etc; no fishing on small lake; trout under 10ins to be returned immediately; 3-fish limit; assn has extensive fishing on Ouse and tributaries, canals and lakes, dt £4 for many waters; full details from Hon Sec. Also trout at Pool and Arthington (see Ouse (Yorks) - Wharfe). Castleford & Dist SA fish Fairburn Ings and Fairburn Cut; dt on site. At **Swinsty** and

Fewston is Washburn Valley Game Fishery and Thruscross Reservoir (wild browns, c&r), 5m W of Harrogate, YWS reservoirs (see Damflask Coarse Fishery), containing rainbow trout, also wild brown; visitors' dt can be had from machine at Swinsty Moor car park; st from Fishing Warden at Reservoir Lodge, Fewston, Harrogate HG2 1SV (tel: 01943 880658 see website for more: http://recreation.yorkshirewater.com) fly only. Tackle shops: Tackle2u, 95 Kirkgate, Leeds LS2 7DJ (tel: 0113 243 4880; web: tackle2u.com); Bob's Tackle Shop, Unit 4, Ash Lane, Garforth, Leeds LS25 2HG (tel: 0113 286 7112); Eric's Angling Centre, 401 Selby Road, Leeds LS15 7AX (tel: 0113 264 6883; see website for more info: www.ericsangling.co.uk).

Bradford (W Yorks). Aire, 7m N. Stockton AL have small stretch at Middleham; members only; apply Hon Sec. Bradford City AA has extensive rights here and on water on the canals at **Apperley Bridge** and near Skipton; on **Wharfe**, **Ure** and **Swale**, reservoirs and lakes; assn fishes Saltaires length of **Leeds and Liverpool Canal**. Bradford No 1 AA, a very major club, has water on **Wharfe** at **Addingham**, Denton, **Aire** near **Skipton**; **Swale** at **Gatenby**, **Ure** at Middleham, **Nidd** at Ramsgill, Cowthorpe and Nun Monkton, **Derwent**, also **R Calder** at Elland, and reservoirs; Association also has 1000 yards of River Ouse at Nun Monkton; membership £38, entrance £20, conc. Tackle shops: Westgate Anglers, 63 Westgate BD1 2RD (tel: 01274 729570); Wibsey Angling Centre, 208 High St, Wibsey, Bradford BD6 1QP (tel: 01274 604542).

Bingley, **Saltaire** (W Yorks). Trout, coarse fish; Bingley AC has 1m through Bingley, coarse fish; restocked annually with trout; 2m of Leeds and Liverpool Canal, with large carp and others; st £28 and dt £2, from tackle shop; club has good trout fishing on **Sunnydale Reservoir**, Eastmorton; trout and coarse fish, no dt; also two dams and beck; trout waters are for members only. Bradford No 1 AA has a length, left bank, along Bingley Cricket; members only. Trout and coarse preserve in **Myrtle Park**; water restocked; dt £2, conc; dt £2 for **Leeds & Liverpool Canal**; Saltaire AA (HQ Ring of Bells, Bradford Rd, Shipley) has 4m stretch of Aire, mixed fishery, dt water, best match bag 2003, 30lbs chub; and **Tong Park Dam**, brown and rainbow trout, from Wibsey Angling Centre, 208 High St, Wibsey, Bradford BD6 1QP (tel: 01274 604542) (no tickets for Tong Park Dam; Westpark Angling, 572 Thornton Road, Bradford BD8 9NF (tel: 01274 548289). From Bankfield Hotel downstream to Baildon Bridge (both banks, except Roberts Park) is also Saltaire AA water.

Keighley (W Yorks). Trout, grayling, coarse fish, chub plentiful. Sport improved after restocking. Keighley AC has 14m; trout to 5 lbs; best May-June and Sept; club also has fishing on the **Leeds-Liverpool Canal**; and has fishing on **Whitefields Reservoir**, stocked with carp, large pike, tench, roach and perch, and, for members only, **Roberts Pond** (large tench, carp, pike, roach and chub); membership open; dt for R Aire and canal; Aire is 10 lengths from Kildwick to Stockbridge; see notice boards; good grayling, trout and coarse fish; club adding barbel. (See also Yorkshire lakes, reservoirs, etc). Tackle shops: K L Tackle, 127 North Str, BD21 3AB (tel: 01535 667574); Wet Nets, 14 Royal Arcade, Low Street BD21 3QP (tel: 01535 611579).

Cononley (W Yorks). Trout, perch, chub, roach, dace, bream, grayling; Bradford City AA water, no dt; st £30 + £15 joining, conc, from tackle shops.

Skipton (N Yorks). Trout, grayling, pike, chub, roach, perch. At Skipton, Skipton AA has three miles of fishing, mainly both banks; st £61 (entrance fee £10), conc, dt £5, from Hon Sec or tackle shops; the assn also issues a ticket for Winnygill and River Aire only, £29 (+ £10 joining), conc; association also has rights on **Embsay Reservoir** (trout) (mt £28, dt £12), **Whinnygill Reservoirs** (trout and coarse fish) dt £6; the club shares water with Bradford City AA from Carleton to Snaygill; dt £5 from outlets and Hon Sec; also from PO, Embsay. Near Skipton at **Kilnsey Park** BD23 5PS, are two trout lakes of 3 acres (tel: 01756 752150); dt £16 (2 fish), £12 c&r, juv £10. Bradford No 1 AA has **Bradley**, **Broughton** and **Sandbeds** fisheries, left bank; members only. Bowland Game FA has 2 beats on Aire; excellent brown trout fishing, one at Hanlith, the other at Airton, 3 miles of double bank; members only, waiting list; c&r only. Hotels: Highfield, Devonshire Arms Country House.

Bell Busk (N Yorks). Trout; preserved by owners. Lakes: **Conniston House**; trout. **Eshton Tarn**, 2m NE; pike. **Malham Tarn**, 8m N; trout and perch; tickets (for Malham Tarn see Yorkshire lakes, Reservoirs, etc).

CALDER (tributary of Aire): Good coarse fishing from Brighouse to Sowerby Bridge. River Calder and Calder Canal run side by side for 2½m at Wakefield Rd, Sowerby Bridge, Halifax (7 access roads and ample parking facilities) making access the same for both. Grayling to 1½lb, brown and rainbow trout in river.

Halifax (W Yorks). Calder 2m S. Clubs: Ryburn & Halifax AS (formerly Dean Clough & Ryburn AS) has 4m good coarse fishing on Calder, Sowerby Bridge to Luddenden Foot; 3m of **Calder and Hebble Navigation**; and some good brown trout and grayling fishing at Sowerby Bridge; st £20, conc, dt £5, from Jewsons (see below), and other local tackle shops. Other societies: Brighouse AA has

stretch of river from Elland Bridge d/s left bank for 40 metres; right bank d/s to end of Lowfields Ind Est; also stocked coarse fishery, Brookfoot Fisheries: lake is dt water, and Tony Riley's Pond, members only; st £25, conc; dt for canal £4 (which covers lake), conc from tackle shops below. Ripponden Flyfishers have good trout fishing in **Ryburn Reservoir**, Ripponden. Brighouse AA and Bradford No 1 AA control 14m on Calder above and below **Brighouse**; heavily restocked and now provides sport with good-quality trout to 4lb, grayling to 2lb 8oz, roach and chub; st £38 + £20 joining fee from Jewson; dt. Brighouse AA also has water on canal from Brighouse to Salter Hebble; also Brookfoot Lake; 3.5 acres mixed coarse, plus specimen carp to 20lb; dt £4, conc, from tackle shops. Hebden Bridge AC has canal fishing and brown trout fishing in area. Tackle shops: A J Jewson, 28 Horton St, Halifax HX1 1PU (tel: 01422 354146; web: www.ajjewson.co.uk); Calder Anglers Supplies, 39a Rastrick Common, Brighouse HD6 3DW (01484 711063). Hotels: Corus Imperial Crown; Black Horse Inn, Brighouse.

Hebden (W Yorks). At **Todmorden** (Yorks, postal address Lancs), Todmorden AS has mixed coarse fishing which includes the **Rochdale Canal** (Locks 13-51) within the Todmorden boundary; **New Mill Dam**; **Walsden Printing Co Lodge** (now Ramsden Wood Fishery); **R Calder**; **Portsmouth Reservoir**; Cliviger Fishponds; also (at Littleborough) **Grove Fishery**, **Croft Head** and **Lower Townhouse Fishery**, and **Whiteley Knowl Reservoir**; all members only except: Cliviger Fishponds; Grove Fishery which are dt waters (must be in advance); annual membership £35 + £10 entry only after end Jan, conc (from local tackle shops). Ryburn & Halifax AS (formerly Dean Clough &

Ryburn AS) have 4m Calder fishing from Luddeden Foot to Stainland Road, trout, grayling (on river), coarse; 3m of **Calder and Hebble Canal**, from Sowerby Bridge Marina to Salterhebble Lock (200 pegs); 2m of **River Hebden**, from Hardcastle Crags to Hebden Bridge (trout only); **Swamp Dam**, from Finkle St, Luddeden Foot; no boats on Society waters; match availability; st £20, dt £5, conc; tickets from surrounding tackle shops. **Calder and Hebble Navigation**: from Salterhebble Top Lock, through Brighouse, Lower Hopton Bridge, Thornhill, to upstream of Ganny Lock, the following clubs have water: Bradford No 1, Thornhill C & BC. Ryburn & Halifax AS has Dead Arm to Salterhebble Locks; and Watermill Travel Lodge to Salterhebble Lock, 200 meters; Brighouse AA has Calder and Hebble Canal, from Salterhebble Locks to Brighouse; Hebden Bridge AC has Rochdale Canal from end of Tods Waters to Sowerby Bridge Marina; also part of Calder. Brighouse AC has fishing on R Calder; Unity AC has Milby Cut, **Boroughbridge**; Dyehouse Dam, Oakenshaw; all waters contain coarse fish, roach, rudd, bream, tench, perch, etc, members only on most; membership £12, conc. Tackle shops: A J Jewson, 28 Horton St, Halifax HX1 1PU (tel: 01422 354146; see website for more info: www.ajjewson.co.uk); Chris Roberts Fishing Tackle, 22 Chapel Hill, Huddersfield HD1 3EB (tel: 01484 545032); Wibsey Angling Centre, 208 High St, Wibsey, Bradford BD6 1QP (tel: 01274 604542); Unity AC membership. Hotel: Queen.

COLNE (tributary of Calder):

Huddersfield (W Yorks). Holme Valley PA fishes **R Calder** from Battyeford to Mirfield, Magdale Dam and pond at Holmfirth; dt on river; and pond from tackle shops; facilities for the disabled. **Hill Top**, **Sparth**, and **Longwood Compensation Reservoirs**, **Huddersfield Narrow Canal** are dt waters; (and **Push Dam** which is members and guests only), all Slaithwaite & Dist AC waters, dt from tackle shops below. Tickets from Chris Roberts Fishing Tackle, (below); Holme Valley Sports, 76 Huddersfield Road, Holmfirth HD9 3A (tel: 01484 684128). Hotel: Huddersfield and many others.

Slaithwaite (W Yorks). Slaithwaite & Dist AC has fly only trout fishery from Marsden to Slaithwaite, no fishing in village centre, then east stretch from Linthwaithe Steps, all members only, no dt; **Narrow Canal**, Slaithwaite to Bargate and three other stretches, three reservoirs, dams and ponds; trout, coarse fish; st £28 (extra £10 for trout and grayling on river), conc, enquiries to Hon Sec; for membership contact Ray Collier (tel: 01484 656389 evngs). Tackle shop: Chris Roberts Fishing Tackle, 22 Chapel Hill, Huddersfield HD1 3EB (tel: 01484 545032).

HOLME (tributary of Colne);

Holmfirth (W Yorks). River has wild brown trout, as well as usual coarse species. Holme Valley PA has water from Holmfirth to Steps Mill, Honley, except 50 yard stretch by old Robinson Mill Dam; assn also controls stretch of R Calder; Magdale Dam, members only, and Cinderhills Pond; all waters coarse fishing, with roach, tench, perch, etc; dt on pond and on Calder, from Sec or Holmfirth Information Centre; membership £20 plus joining, conc; wheelchairs free. Slaithwaite & Dist AC fishes most of stretch from Holmebridge to Bottoms Dam, river is extremely shallow and overhung, with many small wild trout; members only. **Holmstyes Reservoir**; trout (Huddersfield 8m) preserved by Huddersfield AA; st available; waiting list; **Boshaw Reservoir** (Huddersfield 8m); preserved as above. Tackle shop: Chris Roberts Fishing Tackle, 22

Chapel Hill, Huddersfield HD1 3EB (tel: 01484 545032).

DERWENT: Rises in high moors and flows almost to coast near Scarborough where it turns south and enters estuary of Ouse. Its upper reaches, most easily reached from Scarborough, are trout and grayling waters (see Ayton). Lower down coarse fish predominate, barbel included.

Wressle (East Yorkshire). Coarse fish free, some access.

Breighton (East Yorkshire); ns Wressle 1m. Bubwith 1m. Chub, dace, pike, etc; fishing free.

Bubwith (East Yorkshire). Coarse fish; fishing free with EA licence from Bubwith bridge u/s for 4m to Ellerton Landing.

Ellerton; roach, perch, dace, bream, chub, eels and pike; flatfish lower down; fishing free with EA licence.

East Cottingwith (N Yorks); ns High Field, 4m. Coarse fish (pike and chub very good). York AA controls East Cottingwith Water (2m). Tackle shop: York Tackle Shop, 31 Yarburgh Way, York YO10 5HD (tel: 01904 411210; web: www.yorktackle.com). York & YDAA has 10m of good coarse fishing on **Pocklington Canal**; dt from local tackle shops.

Pocklington (N Yorks). **Pocklington Canal**; Well stocked with bream, roach, perch, pike, etc. York & DAA water.

Ellerton Landing (N Yorks). Hotel: White Swan, Bubwith.

Kexby (N Yorks). Pike, chub, etc. York, and Leeds Amalgamated, societies have water; members only.

Stamford Bridge (N Yorks). Excellent for roach, pike, chub, dace. York & DAA has fishing on good length; on right bank down to Kexby; on left bank 2 fields below car park; also pits; dt £5 at cafes in Stamford Bridge.

Howsham (N Yorks). Coarse fishing. York & DAA has water on Derwent and Barton Hill Beck, from Kirkham Abbey to Howsham (less 2 fields), members only; Bradford No 1 AA has left bank at Howsham Wood, large barbel to 12 lb; members only.

Kirkham Abbey (N Yorks). Coarse fish, some trout and occasional grayling. Leeds and York Amalgamations have water; members only. Malton & Norton AC has water; book £15, conc; members only.

Castle Howard (N Yorks). **Castle Howard Great Lake** contains specimen coarse fish, including pike, perch, tench, bream, roach; bank fishing only. However due to over-fishing in the North Sea, cormorants have significantly reduced lake stocks. For further details, see 'Yorkshire Lakes.'

Huttons Ambo (Yorks). Roach, pike, dace, eels, gudgeon, perch, grayling, and few trout. South bank, 1m down and 1m up, held by Malton & Norton AC, no dt, membership £15 pa. North bank held by Huttons Ambo AC for 2m down and 2m up; membership, for people resident within 10m Malton; dt from village post office (open Sundays); bream and roach heavily stocked.

Malton (Yorks). Coarse fish, mainly roach. Malton & Norton AC: waters extend to 1m below Huttons Ambo; membership discretionary, issued by Hon Sec, and C Swift (below); club has 15m of Derwent and Rye; members only; st £15, conc; also mixed coarse pond (1 acre), Howthorpe Ponds, at Terrington. Some water on Derwent (between road bridges in Malton) and Rye. Tackle shops: C Swift, 25 Castlegate, York YO17 0DP (tel: 01653 694580); tickets for Malton & Norton AC waters. Hotel: Green Man.

Yedingham (Yorks). Coarse fish. Providence Inn, Yedingham, Malton

YO17 8SL (tel: 01944 728231) has private stretch; enquire of landlord.

Ganton (Yorks). Chub, pike, dace, grayling; dt for 1m each way from Hay Bridge, from, Bogg Hall Farm YO12 4PB (tel: 01944 710391), at first house across railway crossing at Ganton; dt. Ruston Beck, 2m W. Dt waters at **Seamer** (Malton Rd), from house by stream.

Hackness (Yorks). Derwent AC, controls 10m of trout (brown and rainbow) and grayling fishing down to **East Ayton**; members only plus guests.

FOSS BECK (tributary of Derwent). Fishing station: **Fangfoss** (Yorks); fishing private.

SPITTLE BECK (tributary of Derwent).

Barton Hill (Yorks). Derwent, 2m E. Whitecarr Beck, 4m SE. Loppington Beck, 4m SE. Swallowpits Beck, 5m SE at Scrayingham. York & DAA have trout water **Barton Hill Beck**, members only.

RYE (tributary of Derwent): Trout, grayling, other coarse fish.

Ryton (Yorks).

PICKERING BECK (tributary of Rye) and **Costa Beck** (chalk stream). Trout, grayling.

Pickering (Yorks). About 1m of free fishing in town; private above, preserved below (3m) by Pickering FA; fly only; membership limited to 120. Water also on **Costa Beck** and **Oxfold Becks**, trout and grayling, and Duchy of Lancaster water, **Newbridge**; two trout lakes; dt for members' guests only. Club HQ: Bay Horse Hotel. Hazelhead Lake, Newgate Foot Farm, Saltersgate, Pickering YO18 7NR (tel: 01751 460215); one 2-acre lake is 9m from Pickering, wild and stocked brown trout fishing: open 1 Apr to 31 Oct; dt £15 (4 fish), 4hr £10 (2 fish). **Pickering Trout Lake**, Newbridge Rd, Pickering, N Yorks YO18 8JJ (tel:

01751 474219; see website for more info: www.pickeringtroutlake.co.uk); 1 acre; rainbows; £20 all day c&r; barbless hooks only; bait fishing £6 per rod; £5.35 per kg for all fish caught on that ticket. Hotels: White Swan, Black Swan, Forest and Vale.

SEVEN (tributary of Rye): Trout, grayling; some coarse fish.

Newsham Bridge (Yorks). York & DAA has water (one field) on Seven and 4½m Rye; dt available £5 from Hon Sec and tackle shops.

Marton (Yorks). Private from mill to Marton; below Marton some free water; grayling, pike, chub, dace and a few trout. Tackle shop in Malton, 12m.

Sinnington (Yorks). Seven AC has 2½m downstream from the main road; brown, rainbow trout, some grayling; members only, waiting list; fly fishing and coarse fishing (latter only after end of trout season) below large weir and bottom farm.

WATH BECK (tributary of Rye):

Slingsby (Yorks). Trout; preserved. Rye, NE.

DOVE-IN-FARNDALE (tributary of Rye):

Kirby Moorside (N Yorks). Dove-in-Farndale, 1m E; trout; private. Dt for stretches downstream of Kirby Moorside from some of the farms. Hodge Beck, in Sleightholme Dale, 1m W, trout only. Hotel: King's Head.

THORNTON BECK (tributary of Derwent):

Thornton-le-Dale (N Yorks). Trout and grayling; preserved. Pickering Beck, 3m W. Derwent, 3m S. Hotel: The Buck; Thornton-le-Dale.

WHARFE: Rises on Cam Fell and flows 60m south-east to join Ouse near Cawood. Trout in upper reaches, with coarse fish downstream.

Ryther (N Yorks); ns Ulleskelf, 3m. Castleford & Dist ASA has water;

mainly coarse fish. Hotel: Rythre Arms.

Ulleskelf (N Yorks). Coarse fish; preserved by Leeds & Dist ASA; dt from the Ulleskelf Arms, Church Fenton Lane, Tadcaster LS24 9DW (tel: 01937 832136).

Tadcaster (N Yorks). Trout, chub and dace, good head of barbel perch and bream; preserved by Tadcaster Angling and Preservation Association on both banks downstream from road bridge, ¾m east bank, and 1½m west bank Grimston Park; st £25 for locals only; dt £2.50, conc. Tickets from Hon Sec; The Bay Horse, 11 Commercial St LS24 8AB (tel: 01937 832299); The Old Chocolate Box, 28 Kirkgate, Tadcaster LS24 9AD (tel: 01937 835170).

Boston Spa (W Yorks). Trout, grayling, coarse fish (chub, barbel and pike good; bream introduced). Most rights held by Boston Spa AC; dt £3.50 from Super Shop Newsagents, High Street; also Tackle2u, Leeds; club stocks water with trout and grayling; limit two trout, or two grayling, but not more than three fish total in a day; trout/grayling 12"; May best month for trout and August and September for barbel and chub.

Wetherby (W Yorks). Wetherby & Dist AC water (stocked with trout and coarse fish) extends from Collingham Beck to Wetherby Weir, south bank (about 350 yards in Collingham Wood, south bank is private); club also has four fields between golf course and playing fields, north bank; this water is open for visitors on st (above weir), and dt; members only below and on weir, but visitors may fish if accompanied by a member; same charge as above; no legitimate bait or lure barred; trout limit 11"; dt (no tackle) from Touchwood DIY, 20 High St, Wetherby, LS22 6LT (tel: 01937 585726).

Collingham (W Yorks). Wetherby AC has water here; trout and coarse fish including barbel, grayling and good dace.

Pool (W Yorks). Grayling, trout, dace, chub; preserved by the Leeds & Dist ASA which has 5m of fishing from River **Washburn** to Castley Beck on left bank; no wading 25 March to 15 June; 3 trout/grayling limit; dt £4 from Leeds and Otley tackle shops and filling station in Pool. Members of Leeds AA, small private club, may fish Harewood Estate preserves, 3m right bank, 2m left bank.

Otley (W Yorks). Otley AC hold 2m left bank and 2½m right bank below Otley Bridge, and two lengths above the bridge; fishing for members only, no dt. Dt £4 for Leeds & Dist ASA **Knotford Lagoon**, near Otley; large carp and other coarse fish; stocked; also some rainbow trout; no wading. Bradford No 1 AA has second Knotford Lagoon; members only. At Yeadon (6m) Airboro' & Dist AA has **Yeadon Tarn**, Cemetery Rd; good catches of roach, perch, carp, bream, tench; dt £4 from newsagent in same road, and tackle shop in Otley: Angling and Country Sports, 36 Cross Green, Pool Road, Otley LS21 1HD (tel: 01943 462770; see website for more: www.otleyanglingclub.co.uk).

Burley and **Askwith** (W Yorks). Trout, grayling, chub, dace. Bradford clubs have rights for members only.

Addingham (W Yorks). Bradford No 1 AA has four lengths on left and right bank, and Steven Bank Fishery, no dt obtainable; also some left bank at Denton, members only. Addingham AA has river from High Mill caravan site to Farfield Cottages on left bank, and right bank from Stephen Bank to Kexgill Beck, with trout (stocked twice a year with browns 1¼ to 2½lbs); grayling; dt £15 from Addingham PO; membership limited to 50, hence waiting list (except for juniors); apply Hon Sec. Tackle shops at Keighley and Harrogate.

Ilkley (W Yorks). Ilkley & Dist AA have water from Old Bridge to Stepping Stones, both banks, with trout, grayling, dace, barbel and chub; dt £11 (April 15-Sept 30 inc); dt available for grayling in winter (enquire about price): from Tourist Information Centre, Station Rd, Ilkley, LS29 8HA (tel: 01943 602319); membership £72 + £50 joining, jun £25 (no joining fee), OAP £38, some vacancies; club also has two coarse ponds at **Benrhydding**; also stretch of River Wharfe at **Otley**, north bank only; and gravel pit adjacent to this stretch; contact Hon Sec. Addingham AA has river between Addingham and Bolton Abbey, brown trout and grayling only; dt £15; apply Hon Sec. Hotels: Craiglands, Cow and Calf.

Bolton Abbey (N Yorks). Trout and grayling. 5 miles stretch (both banks) on R Wharfe, fly only; bailiffed, concentrating on wild trout fishery, light stocking only; trout March 25-Sept 30; grayling only 1 Oct to 21 Dec; all grayling to be returned; st £300, wt £90, dt £30 (grayling £15 Oct-Dec); c&r; 4 fish limit (not less than 10"); fishing not recommended on Sundays and Bank holidays; contact River Keeper (tel: 07752 887556) or Estate Office, Bolton Abbey, Skipton BD23 6EX (tel: 01756 718000; see website for more info: www.boltonabbey.com). Hotels: Devonshire Arms, Bolton Abbey; Devonshire Fell, Burnsall.

Burnsall (N Yorks). Brown trout (av ½lb-1lb; many large fish), grayling; preserved by Appletreewick, Barden and Burnsall AC from Linton Stepping Stones, below Grassington, to Barden Bridge, some 7m mostly double bank fishing; joining fee £200, membership £550; dt £35 for trout, 1 June to 30 Sept (excluding June and Sept week-ends); wt £140 (includes June and Sept w/e), conc, fly only;

limit three brace (then c&r with barbless hooks); grayling (all of which must be returned) dt £15 Nov-Jan (fly only); waters re-stocked regularly with trout from ½ to 1lb and over; club also has **Lower Barden Reservoir**; no dt; tickets from Red Lion Hotel (tel: 01756 720204; see website for more info: www.redlion.co.uk); half price juvenile tickets are available for those under 18 years, and those under 15 must be accompanied by an adult.

Grassington (N Yorks). Trout (av ¾lb), grayling (av ¾lb); preserved by Linton, Threshfield and Grassington AC for 3m both banks (also in Captain Beck and Linton and Threshfield Becks until August 31); wt £60, dt £18 for fly-fishing only; waiting list for membership; no night fishing; no canoeing; trout season: March 25 to Sept 30 inclusive; grayling (few) only from Oct 1 to Feb 28; no visitor tickets presently; fly only during Oct; tickets: Black Horse Hotel, Grassington or PO. Saltaire AA also has left bank at **Linton**, no dt; fishing best in May. **Eller Beck**, **Hebden Beck**, 2m E. Lakes: **Blea Beck** dams 4m NE. Hotels: Black Horse (Saltaire AA HQ), and others.

Kilnsey (N Yorks). Brown trout. Preserved by Kilnsey AC (National Trust, Upper Wharfedale) of 65 members, from Chapel House Farm u/s to Beckamonds; artificial fly only, limit three brace over 10"; dt £35 (bought between 9am and 10am) (number limited, and none on Sundays or Bank Holidays) from Keeper, Ken Slaymaker, Tennant Arms Hotel, Kilnsey, via Skipton BD23 5PS Hotels: Tennant Arms, Falcon.

Buckden (N Yorks). Trout. Bradford City AA has 2m; no dt. Other fishing for guests at Buck Inn BD23 5JA; dt issued.

SKIRFARE (tributary of Wharfe); lower reaches well stocked with brown trout, average 1lb.

Arncliffe (N Yorks). Some Skirfare Fishing preserved by Kilnsey AC, dt water (see Kilnsey). 2½m on upper reaches of Skirfare, unstocked; open to guests at Falcon Inn, BD23 5QE (see advt); dt water, no Sunday fishing.

FOSS (tributary of Ouse): Trout.

Earswick (N Yorks). Free fishing on right bank. Owners are Joseph Rowntree Trust.

Strensall (N Yorks). Foss Navigation Cut, 1m NE. **Whitecar Beck**, 1m NE. York & DAA has coarse fishing here and at **Towthorpe**; members only.

NIDD: About 1½m from Pateley Bridge the river flows from the outlets of its Gouthwaite compensation reservoir, meandering through Nidderdale. Brown trout and grayling; with coarse fish from Birstwith downstream in increasing numbers. Nidderdale AC waters.

Nun Monkton (N Yorks). Coarse fish. Bradford No 1 AA has 1m good coarse fishing here on left bank, both banks at **Ramsgill** and left bank at **Summerbridge**, for members only; also 2½m right bank at **Cowthorpe**.

Kirk Hammerton (N Yorks). Coarse fish. Following on Harrogate AA water (see Goldsborough) almost all fishing downstream to where Nidd joins the Ouse controlled by Leeds and York Amalgamations. York & DAA holds York side of river from Skip Bridge on Boroughbridge Rd upstream for about 1m to the railway bridge and also for about 1m above Hammerton Mill dam. Tickets from York tackle shops; and Aykroyd.

Goldsborough (N Yorks). Trout, grayling and mixed coarse fishing, including pike and barbel. From Little Ribston downstream through Walshford Bridge to first meadow below Cattall Bridge belongs to Harrogate AA; association also has both banks of **Crimple Beck** from confluence with Nidd above Walshford Bridge up to Spofforth; waiting list for membership; dt issued by Hon Sec to members' guests only. York & DAA have 1m left bank; dt £6; for access see; (web: www.ydaa.org.uk). Water otherwise strictly preserved.

Knaresborough (N Yorks). Trout, grayling and coarse fish, including barbel. Practically all fishing in vicinity controlled by Knaresborough AC and Knaresborough Piscatorials; former issues st £25 and dt £5 for good stretch upstream from Little Ribston village; club also owns fly only trout lake in Knaresborough area, members only; full membership £230 plus £200 entry fee; club also fishes River Nidd between Killinghall Bridge and Hampsthwaite Bridge; fly only dt £15, anglers limit (advance book with M H & C Johnson (below); Knaresborough Piscatorials fish 8 miles of Nidd, plus various stretches of Ure and Swale, mostly in area of Knaresborough. Trout, chub, specimen barbel, roach, bream, perch, few rudd, dace, pike, may be caught in club waters; fees, £80 pa + £20 entry fee, conc. York & DAA; (web: www.ydaa.org.uk), has good stretches here; from sewage to Haughs Farm on right bank; dt £5; tickets for Knaresborough Piscatorial water from Harrogate Angling Supplies, High Street, Starbeck, Harrogate (tel: 01423 883270). Free fishing on Nidd, rt bank, 1m: downstream limit - A59 road bridge (access at side of Yorkshire Lass Pub House); upstream limit - top of 'Horseshoe' Field above private single track vehicular bridge.

Ripley, Nidd Bridge (N Yorks). Trout, grayling and coarse fish. Knaresborough AC holds left bank u/s to Hampsthwaite, fly only, members only.

Birstwith (N Yorks). Trout and grayling above Birstwith Dam upstream to upper reaches of Nidd. Below Dam there are also coarse fish.

Knaresborough AC has right and left bank downstream from Hampsthwaite Bridge; members and their guests only.

Pateley Bridge (N Yorks). Trout and grayling. From Gouthwaite, 1½m above Pateley Bridge down to below **Summer bridge**, 11m total, owned and rented by Nidderdale AC, who hold nearly all water, both banks, except short pieces here and there which are private; half is dt water; also Scar House Reservoir; permits: wt £30, dt £10; jnr wt £15, dt £5, for three lengths of river and Scar House, at Royal Oak (below); or local post offices in Lofthouse, Pateley Bridge, and Summerbridge; anglers must obtain tickets before fishing. Disabled platforms on one length of dt water. Royal Oak Hotel, Dacre Banks, Harrogate HG3 4EN (tel: 01423 780200; see website for more info: www.the-royaloak-dacre.co.uk), offers two-day fishing breaks from March to October, with en-suite B&B, packed lunches, evening meals, and trout fishing on R Nidd and Scar House Reservoir; £120 per head. Hotels: Roslyn, Pateley Bridge, and The Sportman, Wath, Pateley Bridge.

Gouthwaite (N Yorks). River enters **Gouthwaite Reservoir**, privately owned and fished; no permits. Below reservoir Nidd private on left bank downstream; other bank Nidderdale AC water.

CRIMPLE (tributary of Nidd). This river is now private fishing.

Harrogate (N Yorks). Trout and coarse fishing, within easy reach of town in Nidd, Wharfe and Ure, and stillwaters. Tickets, tuition and guiding services from Orvis Co (see below). Coarse river fishing on the R Ure at Newby Hall, **Skelton-on-Ure**; dt available from the Estate Office, Newby Hall, Skelton-on-Ure, Ripon HG4 5AE (tel: 01423 322583 (after 9am); web: www.newbyhall.com) or Water Bailiff (Bishop Monkton side only).

Tackle shops: Linsley Bros, 55 Tower Str, Harrogate HG1 1HS (tel: 01423 505677; see website for more info: www.linsleybros.co.uk); Orvis, 21-22 West Park, Harrogate HG1 1BJ (tel: 01423 561354; see website for more info: www.orvis.co.uk); Harrogate Angling Supplies, 61 High Street, HG2 7LQ (tel: 01423 883270). Hotels: Crown, Barcelo Majestic, Old Swan, St George, Cairn, Prospect.

KYLE: Coarse fish.

Tollerton (N Yorks). Coarse fishing free down to Alne. Ouse at Aldwark, 4m W, and Linton Lock, 3m S and 7m NE, at Stillington.

URE (or **YORE**): Noted for grayling, but also holds few trout. Coarse fish, barbel increasing, from Middleham downstream.

Boroughbridge (N Yorks). Fine coarse fishing (especially chub, barbel, pike and roach; bream increasing); few trout and grayling; Boroughbridge & Dist AC, issues dt £3 (weekdays only, from June 16 to end of season) sold at Ann's News, Horsefair; Fish-N-Things, 5 Horsefair YO51 9LF (tel: 01423 324776). Bradford No 1 AA has Langthorpe stretch, left bank, and Roecliffe, right bank, members only. Tackle shop: Wibsey Angling Centre, 208 High St, Wibsey, Bradford BD6 1QP (tel: 01274 604542). Hotel: Crown.

Ripon (N Yorks). Trout, dace, pike, perch, chub (nets to 100lb), bream, barbel, roach; preserved for 6m largely both banks by Ripon Piscatorial Assn; Assn also has **Ripon Canal**,(roach, bream, carp, perch); Racecourse Lake (carp to 30lb, bream, pike, roach, perch, chub); Ure Bank Pond (no dt); roach, bream, tench, carp; and under 1m on **R Laver** (brown trout, grayling; fly only; worm from 30 Sept); visitors dt £6, st £44 (from Membership Sec); dt from Bondgate PO. Ripon AC has 1½m both banks **R Skell** at Ripon and 1m on Ure, 2m u/s of Ripon; members and guests only, no dt; waiting list for membership. Lakes: Queen Mary's Ponds; coarse fish; Bradford No 1 AA; members only; permit required. Roger's Pond, coarse dt £5 from Angling Centre. **Leighton Reservoir**, Swinton Estate Office, Masham, Ripon HG4 4JH (tel: 01765 689224); 100 acre trout fishery, dt £18, evng £12, conc, from fishing hut.

Tanfield (N Yorks). Trout, grayling; preserved for about 5m, mostly both banks, by Tanfield AC; guests must be accompanied by member; full time bailiff employed. Two trout fisheries at West Tanfield: Bellflask, brown and rainbow, dt £20, 4 fish; run as fishery and nature reserve, barbless hooks; contact Brian Moreland (tel: 01677 470716). Tanfield Lodge Lake, West Tanfield, Ripon HG4 5LE (tel: 01677 470385); brown and rainbow, 11½ acres, disabled access; open 15 Mar to 5 Oct; dt £12, 4 fish, £6 evening 2 fish; juv 2 fish; no wading: tickets from hut on site; toilet facilities.

Masham (N Yorks). Trout (stocked), grayling. 6½m west bank belongs to Swinton Estate; block tickets; details from Estate Office, Swinton, Masham; well stocked 2½m stretch of Swinton water fished by Masham AC; brown trout and grayling; waiting list: st £170 + £30 joining fee; jun conc; grayling membership Oct-end Feb, £55; apply to S Goodburn, River Keeper, 2 Westholme Crescent, Masham HG4 4EY (tel: 01765 688027; mob: 0788 9012783). Yorkshire Flyfishers hold Clifton Castle water (about 2m) above Masham; no tickets; tackle, information, and large selection of flies, from A Plumpton, Hairdresser, Silver St. Hotel: King's Head. **Leighton Reservoir** near here (see Yorkshire Lakes).

Cover Bridge (N Yorks). Trout, grayling. East Witton Estate issue dt on **R Cover** from Hullo Bridge to Cover Bridge; mostly both banks, fly only; dt £6.50 from Cover Bridge Inn, East Witton, Leyburn DL8 4SQ (tel: 01969 623250), who also sell tickets for River Ure (see below).

Middleham (N Yorks). Trout, chub, grayling. Bradford No 1 AA has right bank here, left bank at **Langthorpe**, and right bank at **Roecliffe**, members only; they also have right bank at Ullshaw Bridge. Fishing may be had in Leeds & Dist ASA stretch of Ure 1 ½m downstream from Middleham Bridge, left bank; excellent barbel, chub, grayling, a few large trout, and the odd salmon; dt £4.50 from Cover Bridge Inn, East Witton, Leyburn DL8 4SQ (tel: 01969 623250).

Redmire (N Yorks). Trout, grayling; preserved. Restocked; fly only; all fishing now by st only; numbers limited; apply Estate Office, Leyburn DL8 5EW; trout best April, May and June; grayling Oct and Nov. Richmond & Dist AS has 1m stretch of River **Bain**, single (right) bank; dt from Gilsan Sports, 5 Market Place, Richmond DL10 4HU (tel: 01748 822105). Hotels: King's Arms, Redmire; White Swan, Middleham; Rose and Crown, Bainbridge; Wensleydale Heifer, West Witton.

Aysgarth (N Yorks). Trout, grayling. Bradford City AA has approx 2m from footbridge, both banks, 3¾m both banks at **Worton Bridge**. Palmer Flatt Hotel has short stretch. Wensleydale AA water extends from 2m west of Hawes to Worton Bridge, plus ¾m beyond on north bank only; st £40, wt £20, dt £10, conc; grayling only st £15, dt £5; tickets from The Rose & Crown, Bainbridge; The Crown Inn, Askrigg and The Victoria Arms, Worton. HQ: Rose & Crown Hotel, Bainbridge, Wensleydale DL8 3EE (tel: 01969 650225).

Askrigg (N Yorks). Trout, grayling; preserved by Wensleydale AA, (see above); tickets from The Rose & Crown, Bainbridge; The Crown Inn,

Askrigg and The Victoria Arms, Worton. Hotel: King's Arms.

Bainbridge (N Yorks); Wensleydale AA water includes 6m on Ure (and the feeder streams), both banks of **R Bain**, upstream from the Ure; half-way to Semer Water, and the west bank all the way; the south-east shore of the lake; for tickets, see above. Hotel: Rose & Crown Hotel (above).

Hawes (N Yorks). Brown trout, grayling; Hawes & High Abbotside AA has upper reaches of river, including tributaries; the fishing is pleasant, peaceful and not crowded; Sunday fishing, no ground bait, platforms for disabled; visitors welcome: st £60, wt £30, dt £16, conc 50%, from Hon Sec, "Three Peaks Ltd", Riverside House, Bridge End, Hawes DL8 3NH (tel: 01969 667443); The Gift Shop; or Caravan Club site, all in Hawes; below Hawes the association has several miles of excellent water; disabled anglers may fish Widdale Beck at Apperset, near Hawes. Hotel: White Hart.

SWALE: Good chub and barbel water. Trouting best in upper reaches, water improving.

Helperby (N Yorks). Coarse fish; right bank from Swing Bridge to Myton Plantation controlled by Leeds & Dist ASA; (car parking (charged) at Oak Tree pub in village); members only. Bradford No 1 AA has water above and below Thornton Bridge; members only; also Raskelf Lake, 6 acres, 45 pegs, mixed coarse, especially tench. Helperby & Brafferton AC have left bank from footbridge d/s for ¾m, also **Fawdington Fishery**, from ½m above Thornton Bridge, approx 1½m u/s to Fawdington Beck mouth; chub, barbel, dace, pike, roach, perch; dt £4, conc, for both these waters, 16 Jun-14 March, from Post Office; Oak Tree Inn, Helperby; B&B also offered at farm.

Topcliffe (N Yorks). Noted coarse fishing centre; especially good for chub and barbel. Thirsk AC has Skipton fishing, dt from Woodlands Lakes, Carlton Miniott village (tel: 01845 526110), also Northallerton Angling Centre, 4a Zetland Street, Northallerton DL6 1NA (tel: 01609 779140; see website for more info: www.parklands4u.co.uk). Also has caravan park with new facilities). Bradford No 1 AA has 900 yds at **Catton**, and further water at Topcliffe, members only. **Cod Beck**; mixed fishery; preserved by Bradford City AA; members only.

Pickhill (N Yorks). Coarse fish; trout. Bradford No 1 AA fishes 1,800 yards, right bank; members only.

Maunby (N Yorks). Bradford No 1 AA has two lengths left bank, members only.

Gatenby (N Yorks). Bradford No 1 AA has stretches of right bank here; members only.

Morton-on-Swale (N Yorks). Trout grayling, pike, chub, dace, barbel; fishing good. Northallerton AC has 2½m left bank downstream from A684 road bridge; also 1½m u/s on one bank and 1m on other; no dt u/s other than for guests of members; dt for d/s £5 from PO/shop in village.

Great Langton (N Yorks). Trout, grayling, coarse fish; Kirkby Fleetham AC has both banks for 2m downstream from Langton Bridge; fly only; no tickets; membership limited, by introduction, with preference given to local residents.

Catterick (N Yorks). Good mixed fishing; trout, grayling, dace, chub, barbel, few roach and pike. Trout from 8oz to 1lb; fast takers. Richmond & Dist AS has 14m of water on both banks, Richmond being the centre; dt from Gilsan Sports (see below). Ferryhill & DAC also has 1½m trout and coarse fishing above and below village, good barbel, chub, grayling, no dt. Inns: Farmers' Arms; Angel Inn; Hotel: Bridge House Hotel.

Richmond (N Yorks). Richmond & Dist AS preserves 10 miles above and below town centre, stocked with trout, plus most coarse species; st £30 + £5 joining, wt £16, dt £6, conc; also water at Bedale and Thorpe Perrow; from tackle shop: Gilsan Sports, 5 Market Place DH10 4HU (tel: 01748 822105).

Reeth (N Yorks). Swale; trout. Black Bull Hotel, High Row DL11 6SZ (tel: 01748 884213; see website for more info: www.theblackbullreeth.co.uk) has water for residents; dt.

Muker (N Yorks). Trout; strictly preserved. Muker Beck; trout; Thwaite Beck, 1m W; trout; free. Summer Lodge Beck, 5m E; trout; preserved.

Keld (N Yorks). Trout; plentiful but small; preserved.

GUN BECK (tributary of Swale):

Husthwaite (N Yorks). Centre for good trout fishing on **Husthwaite Beck**; dt from York tackle shops.

Coxwold (N Yorks). Hole Beck and Gun Beck preserved.

BEDALE BECK (tributary of Swale):

Leeming (N Yorks). Swale, 2m NE; preserved by Black Ox AC from A1 road to confluence with Swale, excepting only two small fields above Leeming Bridge; trout and coarse fish; st £15 from Rex Dale, Danby Wiske, Northallerton DL7 0NA (tel: 01609 771117).

COD BECK (tributary of Swale); good trout water.

Thirsk (N Yorks). Good local fishing for barbel and chub. Thirsk AC has water on Swale and Cod Beck; dt from Elliot Angling Supplies, (tel: 01845

574550). York & DAA have 5½ acre lake at **Sand Hutton**; also Park View and Claxton Ponds, 20m SE, all members only. Hotels: Royal Oak, Three Tuns, Thirsk.

Sessay (N Yorks). Cod Beck, 2m W; Thirsk AC, Swale, 2m SW; Bradford club now has fishing on P J Till's farm (The Heights). The Oaks Fishery, David, Thomas and Rachel Kay, The Oaks, Sessay, nr Thirsk YO7 3BG (tel: 01845 501321): 7 lakes with carp and other coarse species; disabled access; dt £7, conc; night fishing available (please ring); tackle and cafe. Inn: Moor & Pheasant, Dalton; Horsebreakers Arms, Sessay.

Brawith (N Yorks). Trout; preserved.

Topcliffe (N Yorks). Bradford City AA has water here, and on **Cod Beck**; members only.

WISKE (tributary of Swale).

Otterington (N Yorks). Cod Beck, 2m E. Broad Beck. Sorrow Beck, 4m E.

Northallerton (N Yorks). Dace, chub, pike; preserved: fishing good. Northallerton AC has fishing on several miles of water on the Swale at Morton Bridge; dt £5 from PO/shop in Morton-on-Swale. Richmond & Dist AS has Great Langton Quarry; mixed coarse; dt £6 from tackleist below. 1m north-west is Parklands Fishery, 3 acres, stocked with carp, tench, roach, rudd, perch, barbel &c; dt on bank £6, conc £5; tickets from tackle shop: Northallerton Angling Centre, 4a Zetland Str, DL6 1NA (tel: 01609 779140; see website for more info: www.parklands4u.co.uk). Also has caravan park with new facilities. (see also Morton-on-Swale).

PARRETT

Rises in hills on border of Somerset and Dorset, and flows into Bristol Channel near Bridgwater. Roach, bream and dace predominate. Thorney-Middle Chinnock stretch and some of tributaries hold trout. Occasional salmon and sea trout run through into Tone.

Bridgwater (Som). River tidal here. Docks now a Marina. Bridgwater AA fisheries are as follows: **King's Sedgemoor Drain** from ¾m above Greylake Bridge, where 18ft Rhyne enters Cary River to A38 Road bridge at Dunball; good roach, rudd, pike, tench, bream, carp and perch; **North Drain** (jointly held with North Somerset AA and Yeovil & Sherborne AA), **South Drain** (jointly held with Glaston Manor AA); **Huntspill River**; (**Cripps River**, from Gold Corner to R Brue may be fished free); **Bridgwater and Taunton Canal**; **Dunwear**, **Screech Owl**, and **Combwich Ponds**, (carp, bream, roach, rudd, tench, perch); also **Walrow Ponds** (with North Somerset AA) at Highdridge; mixed coarse; assn also has access to Somerset Levels Association of Clubs (SLAC) waters on Rivers **Parrett** and **Isle**; st £35, wt £27, dt £7, from tackle shops in area or Hon Sec, with concessions for jun, OAP; permits cover all waters. Pawlett Ponds, River Rd, **Pawlett**, 4 lakes, Amalgamated Fisheries Ltd (formerly BB&WAA) water, with carp, bream, tench, large roach, perch etc; dt £6 from PO and Pawlett General Stores. Tackle shop: Veals Fishing Tackle, Brunel Rooms, Straight St, Bristol BS2 0EJ (tel: 0117 9260790; see website for more info: www.veals4carp.com); Somerset Angling, 74 Bath Rd TA6 4PL (tel: 01278 431777). Accommodation: Crossways Inn, With Rd, West Huntspill, Highbridge TA9 3RA (tel: 01278 783756; see website for more info: www.crossways-inn.com).

Langport (Som). Parrett; pike to 30lbs, large perch, carp, bream, roach, hybrids, tench, chub, rudd, eels. Langport & Dist AA has rights to 6½m; Assn is member of Somerset Levels Association of Clubs (SLAC); st holders may fish SLAC waters on Parrett and Isle; Assn also owns 2¼ acre **Coombe Lake**, stocked with bream, a few carp (extremely difficult to catch) and others; st £15, wt £5 and dt £3, conc, obtainable from Fosters Newsagents, Bow St; Yeovil & Dist Angling Centre, 27/29 Forest Hill, Yeovil BA20 2PH (tel: 01935 476777). Stoke-sub-Hamdon & DAS has stretches at **West Chinnock** to **Thorney Lakes**:dt £6, conc £4. Thorney Lakes & Caravan Park, Muchelney, Langport TA10 0DW (tel: 01458 250811; web: www.thorneylakes.co.uk, has coarse fishing, with carp to 25lb, and other species; both lakes closed at night. **Viaduct Fishery**, Cary Valley, Somerton TA11 6LJ (tel: 01458 274022; see website for more info: www.viaductfishery.com); 6 coarse lakes; includes tackle shop, bait, tuition; toilet facilities; refreshments; 136 pegs; dt £7 (£9 2 rods), conc, from fishery's tackle shop. Tackle shop: Veals Fishing Tackle, Brunel Rooms, Straight St, Bristol BS2 0EJ. (tel: 0117 9260790; see website for more info: www.veals4carp.com). Hotels: Langport Arms Hotel; Dolphin Hotel, Ilchester.

Crewkerne (Som). Trout, coarse fish. Seven miles above and below Stoke-sub-Hamdon controlled by Stoke-sub-Hamdon & DAS; trout fishing (with restocking) from Bow Mills to Hurdle Pool; 1 Apr to 31 Oct (trout av ¾lb); members only; coarse fishing, 12 different species including 3 types of carp, from Hurdle Pool to Thorney Mill; tickets from local tackle shops. Tackle shop: Yeovil & Dist Angling Centre, 27/29 Forest Hill,

Yeovil BA20 2PH (tel: 01935 476777).

TONE: Trout and coarse fish above Taunton; below, most species of coarse. Summer weeds below **Taunton** have recently been cleared; provides first-class coarse fishing in winter. Fast stretch at Taunton to Bathpool, Creech, Ham, Knapp and Newbridge.

Taunton (Som). Good coarse fishing free on town stretch. Taunton FFC has several stretches from just south of Taunton to the headwaters; members only, waiting list; contact Hon Sec. Taunton AA has water on **Bridgwater Canal** at Taunton; **West Sedgemoor Drain** from Pincombe Bridge, Stathe, now de-silted; **R Tone** fast stretch at Taunton, Creech and Ham; Ponds at Walton and Wych Lodge (3 acres); assn also has Maunsel Ponds, 5m NE of Taunton; 2 ponds situated in the grounds of Maunsel House; well stocked with roach, rudd, tench, carp, perch; st £34, wt £15, dt £5, conc, from tackle shops (below). Tackle shops: Taunton Angling Centre, 63 Station Rd, Taunton TA1 1PA (tel: 01823 282518; see website for more info: www.taunton-angling.co.uk); Enterprise Angling, 42 East Reach, Taunton TA1 3ES (tel: 01823 282623). Hotels: Castle (which advises visiting anglers on local facilities).

HILLFARRANCE BROOK (a Tone tributary, from Hillfarrance to confluence with Tone). Trout, grayling. Axe contains trout and sea trout in lower stretches; no tickets.

Wellington (Som). Trout, roach, dace; trout average ½lb. Wellington AA has water from Fox Bros' works 2m up stream, and 2m below; brown trout, grayling, roach, dace; members only; apply by letter to Hon Sec. Thereafter preserved by owners. **Langford Lakes**, Langford Budville, Wellington, TA21 0RS (tel: 01823

400476; see website for more info: www.langfordlakes.co.uk): four stocked coarse fishing lakes on conifer plantation, with mixed, carp to 25lbs, tench and bream fishing; barbless hooks only; no keepnets, natural bait only; £6 2 rods, £5 1 rod; no night fishing; toilet facilities on site; holiday cabins tickets from office. Tackle shop: Wellington Country Sports, 24 High Str, Wellington TA21 8RA (tel: 01823 662120).

Wiveliscombe (Som). Tone, Milverton Brook and Norton Brook; trout; banks bushed.

NORTON BROOK (tributary of Tone):

Bishops Lydeard (Som). Trout; banks overgrown.

MILVERTON BROOK (tributary of Tone).

Milverton (Som). Trout; private; banks bushed.

YEO: Coarse fish, some trout.

Long Load (Som). Good coarse fishing on Long Load Drain; also Kingsmoor Drain, controlled by Yeovil & Sherborne AA; club also has 1m upstream, both banks; st £12 Yeovil tackle shop.

Ilchester (Som). Mainly roach, dace, good chub fishing. St and wt for 6m stretch u/s and d/s of Ilchester, plus Long Load Drain, from Yeovil & Dist Angling Centre (see Yeovil). Ilchester & Dist AA has 6m fishing above and below Ilchester on **Yeo** and **Cam**; st £12, conc. At **Martock** are **Ash Lakes**; coarse fishing on three ponds; dt on bank; contact Ash Lakes, Ash, Martock TA12 6NZ (tel: 01935 823459). Tackle shop: Yeovil & Dist Angling Centre, 27/29 Forest Hill, Yeovil BA20 2PH (tel: 01935 476777).

Yeovil (Som). Roach, dace, chub. Yeovil & Sherborne AA have water downstream of **Sherborne Lake**, **Sutton Bingham Stream** from Filter

Station to Yeovil Junction and R Wriggle from Yetminster to R Yeo, trout; Halfway House lake, mixed coarse; st £12, conc from tackleist below; assn also has Sherborne Lake, mixed coarse; members only (separate ticket required), no dt. Lyons Gate Caravan Park, Cerne Abbas, DT2 7AZ (tel: 01300 345260) has four good coarse lakes with carp to over 35lb, roach, tench, orfe, barbel, chub, bream; dt £5. At Stoford is the Old Mill Fishery, Tucking Mill Farm BA22 9TX (tel: 01935 414771); over 21 species of coarse fish in four lakes and river; dt £6, night £5 (ring first), evng £3, conc. Mudford AC has 3m of river from Mudford to Chilton Cantelo; st £12.50 from tackle shop. Tackle shop: Yeovil & Dist Angling Centre, 27/29 Forest Hill, Yeovil BA20 2PH (tel: 01935 476777). Hotels: Mermaid; Manor.

ISLE: Prolific chub water; also roach, dace, etc. First E1/2 mile from junction with Parrett held by Somerset Levels Association of Clubs (SLAC) of Anglers.

Isle Brewers (Som). Roach, chub, dace, some trout from Fivehead Rd to Hambridge; Newton Abbot FA has many coarse lakes and ponds. See Newton Abbot.

Ilminster (Som). Roach, chub, dace. Chard & DAC has 1½m of water from Horlicksbridge, Ilminster, to Winterhay; members only, st £17, conc. Ilminster AA has 5m from Ilminster to Isle Brewers; st, conc, from tackle shop: Yeovil & Dist Angling Centre, 27/29 Forest Hill, Yeovil BA20 2PH (tel: 01935 476777).

Chard (Som). Chard Reservoir; carp, bream, roach, tench, eels and perch; dt £8 on bank; Chard & DAC has Perry Street Pond; 1½ acres; mixed coarse; st £17; apply Hon Sec; club also has 9 peg water; mainly carp; Sadborrow Pond; members only.

RIBBLE

Rises in the Pennines and flows 69 miles into the Irish Sea between St Anne's and Southport. Good coarse fishing lower down, between Ribchester and Preston. Also coarse fishing in Church Deeps. Best salmon, sea trout, brown trout and grayling fishing is between Settle and Ribchester. Tributary Hodder has good salmon, sea trout, grayling and brown trout fishing throughout length but affected by water abstraction. Upper waters impounded in Stocks Reservoir. Its main tributary, the Loud, also provides good trout and sea trout fishing.

Preston (Lancs). Coarse fish, few salmon and sea trout. 2m of former Preston Federated Anglers water through town now fished free and also **Rufford Canal**. Wigan & DAA have their waters on **Ribble** and **Wyre**. Through Wigan & DAA tickets Ribble & Wyre FA is fished on a broken 3-4 miles of Wyre; members only; st £28, which entitles anglers to fish 1m of Ribble; Heapy Reservoirs at Chorley and 21m of Leeds & Liverpool Canal from Johnsons Hill Locks (Blackburn) to Red Lion Bridge at Scarisbrick (Southport); also Fan Lodge at Bickershaw (Wigan); also Morans Moat here, coarse fish, disabled pegs; and other Wigan fisheries; these fisheries can be fished by holders of Wigan & DAA permits. **Twin Lakes Trout Fishery**, Croston PR26 9AA (tel: 01772 601093): one lake 8 acres, stocked mainly fly only; rainbow, blue and brown trout, best rainbow 19lbs 6ozs; dt £25 (4 fish), ½ day £17.50 (2 fish), 3-hour £12 (1 fish); plus 6 acre mixed coarse lake; dt £6. Other local fishing: Greenhalgh Lodge Fishery, Greenhalgh Lane, nr Kirkham PR4 3HL (tel: 01253 836348; web:

www.greenhalghlodge.co.uk); 3 acre, 38 peg lake; carp; dt £7, conc £5.50; cafe on site, refreshments. Hudson's Farm, Rawcliffe Rd, St Michaels PR3 0UH (tel: 01995 679654): mixed coarse fishery of 2 ponds and 2 lakes: large carp, bream, tench; dt £6, up to 3 rods, £4 conc; tickets on bank. R **Crossens**, 1m from Southport, fished by Southport & Dist AA; dt must be bought prior to fishing from local outlets; no tickets on bank. Tackle shops: Catch 22 Fishing Tackle, Unit 17, Birkdale Trad Est, Liverpool Rd, Southport PR8 4PZ (tel: 01704 568450). Tackle shop in Preston: Carters Fishing Tackle, 85/89 Church Str, PR1 3BS (tel: 01772 253476; web: www.tedcarter.co.uk), has information on much Lancashire fishing; tickets for Wigan AA, and dt for Windermere, Ambleside & DAA; dt for Southport & DAA, st for Lakewood Reservoir.

Longridge (Lancs). Ribble, 3m SE. Hodder, 5m NE. Salmon, sea trout and trout. Loud 2m N. Most of right bank preserved by Loud & Hodder AA; visitors' tickets issued if accompanied by member. Prince Albert AS, Macclesfield, own several miles above and a little below M6 bridge. Warrington AA has 1½m stretch at **Hurst Green**; members only; coarse, sea trout, salmon.

Ribchester (Lancs). Lancashire FFA have 1m here, and water at **Gisburn** and at **Walton-le-Dale**, although much is free fishing here; also **Hodder** at **Newton** and **Chaigley**, **Lune** at Kirkby Lonsdale and Tebay; **Irt** at Santon Bridge, all with salmon, sea trout, some browns; for membership apply Hon Sec; tickets only to members' guests. Warrington AA has stretch; members only; contact Hon Sec. Other local body is Ribchester & DAC; dt £4; barbel, chub, dace, gudgeon, pike, eels and roach; tickets for Ribchester Village Front from Spar, Church Str (after 7.00am) or White Bull (during opening hrs); dt coarse only from 15 June to 15 March.

Mitton (Lancs); ns Whalley, 2m. Salmon, sea trout, trout and coarse fish. Environment Agency controls left bank d/s from Mitton Bridge; Salmon fishing open Feb 1-Oct 31; brown trout Mar 15-Sept 30; coarse, June 16-Mar 14; permits from Aspinall Arms Hotel, Mitton Rd, Mitton, Clitheroe BB7 9PQ (tel: 01254 822727). Mid-Ribble AS has over 2.6m right bank of **R Hodder** above and below Lower Hodder bridge, nr Stonyhurst, down to Hodder Foot, also right bank Ribble from Hodder Foot to Starling Brook (½m below Dinckley Bridge), and left bank of Ribble at **Long Preston**; waters stocked annually with trout, good returns for migratory fish, also coarse fishing; members only, limited guest tickets; membership limited to 60 (web: www.midribble.co.uk); details from Hon Sec.

Clitheroe (Lancs). Trout, salmon, sea trout. Clitheroe AA Ltd fishes 3m of Ribble, mostly double bank, and half mile of **Lune**, at **Kirkby Lonsdale**; members only, no dt; members guests' dt for trout and grayling only. Ribblesdale AA has 3m between W Bradford and Low Moor, mostly double bank; members only; waiting list; Assn also fishes Hodder and Calder Foot. The Inn at Whitewell, in the Forest of Bowland, offers fishing to guests at price per day depending on season; salmon best towards end of season (see Whitewell). By the A59 between Clitheroe and Accrington, Pendle View Fishery A59 By-Pass BB7 9DH, coarse and sport fishing; dt £12 3 rods, £9 2 rods, £6 1 rod on bank, conc, 24-hours £20 1-3 rods; phone (tel: 01254 822208) for details. Bowland Game FA have several miles on Ribble and other fisheries on **Lune**, **Wenning**, **Hodder** 3 beats over 3 miles, **Derwent**, **Aire** and **Parsonage Reservoir**. Ribble Valley Borough Council, issues st £40 to residents (£50 non residents), conc, for water at Brungerley and below Edisford Bridge; wt £25 for visitors, all from Visitor Information Centre, Church Walk, Clitheroe BB7 2RA (tel: 01200 425566). Two rods on Hodder 2 days a week, fly only, for residents only of Red Pump Hotel, Bashall Eaves (tel: 01254 826227). Tackle shop: Ken Varey's Outdoor World, 4 Newmarket St, Clitheroe BB7 2JW (tel: 01200 423267; see also website: www.kenvarey.co.uk). Hotels: Inn at Whitewell; Gibbon Bridge Hotel; Parkers Arms.

Sawley (N Yorks). On Ribble. Salmon, sea trout, trout and grayling. Trout and salmon fishing good. Several miles preserved by Yorkshire FFC (visitors' tickets through members only). Inn: Spread Eagle.

Gisburn (N Yorks). Trout, salmon. Lancashire FFA have water at Ribchester and Gisburn, and at Walton le Dale; fly fishing for members only. Hotel: Stirk House.

Long Preston (N Yorks). Ribble, 1m W. Trout, grayling, odd salmon, coarse fish. Left bank is preserve of Mid Ribble AS; members only + guests. Staincliffe AC also have water, members plus 5 tickets for their guests. Hotels: Boar's Head; Maypole Inn.

Settle (N Yorks). Settle AA has 7½m of good trout and grayling fishing in Ribble between Langcliffe, Settle and vicinity of Long Preston; wt £75, dt £25 from Sweet Corner, Settle; fly only; limit 1½ brace; water stocked yearly. **Malham Tarn**, National Trust water, is 6m from Settle and holds large wild trout, fly only; c&r policy; dt water (boats only) (see Yorkshire lakes, Reservoirs, etc). Further north are Manchester AA's waters. Licences from post offices. Other hotels at Settle: Falcon Manor and Golden Lion.

Horton in Ribblesdale (N Yorks). Trout; preserved from source to Helwith Bridge, including all tributaries, by Manchester AA; assn also has **Newhouses Tarn** (fly only); stocked b and r trout; no tickets.

Tributaries of the Ribble

HODDER: Good salmon and trout water.

Higher Hodder Bridge (Lancs and Yorks). Salmon, sea trout, trout, grayling and few chub.

Whalley (Lancs). Bowland Game FA has 3 beats, 4 miles in all (middle beat sells dt from Red Pump Inn at Bashall Eaves if a resident (see below)); single and double bank; otherwise members only, waiting list.

Chipping (Lancs). Hodder, 1½m E. Salmon, sea trout and grayling. Loud, 1m SE. Trout and sea trout. About ½m of Hodder below Doeford Bridge on right bank and several miles of **River Loud** are preserved by Loud & Hodder AA; tickets if accompanied by member. Hotel: Derby Arms.

Whitewell (Lancs). Salmon, sea trout, trout, grayling. The Inn at Whitewell, Forest of Bowland BB7 3AT (tel: 01200 448222; fax: 01200 448298), has four rods for residents only on 7m of Whitewell FA water (both banks); dt £15-£60 depending on season; salmon runs best towards end of season. The Red Pump Inn, Clitheroe Road, Bashall Eaves BB7 3DA (tel: 01254 826227; see website for more: www.theredpumpinn.co.uk), has 2 rods 8m further down the river for residents; pre-booking is required.

Newton (Lancs); Lancashire FFA have water downstream from Newton to Dunsop Bridge.

Slaidburn (Lancs); ns Clitheroe, 8½m. Hodder; salmon, sea trout and trout. Tickets for several miles of Hodder from Slaidburn PO.

Stocks Reservoir in vicinity: excellent trout fishery with tackle shop and 24 boats and Wheelyboat for disabled; for dt contact Stocks Fly Fishery, Stocks Reservoir, Catlow Road, Slaidburn BB7 3AQ (tel: 01200 446602; see website for more info: www.stocksreservoir.com). Hotel: Moorcock Inn.

CALDER: Coarse fishing. Some club water.

Elland (Yorks). Bradford No 1 AA fishery extends u/s of Elland Road Bridge for approx 1,800 yds; members only.

Whalley (Lancs). West Calder. Ribble, 2m W; salmon, sea trout and coarse fish. Hodder, 2m W; salmon, sea trout and trout.

Barrowford (Lancs). Pendle Water; trout. Colne Water and Pendle join near Barrowford to form Calder. **Leeds and Liverpool Canal** from Barnoldswick to East Marton (10m), and 1½m at Keighley leased to Marsden Star AS; dt £3 water; tickets from tackle shops.

Burnley (Lancs). **Hapton Lodges Reservoir** at Hapton now coarse; Blythe AC. Marsden Star AS fishes Gawthorpe Hall Pool at Padiham, members only, tench, carp, perch fishing; also Heasandford Lodge, Netherwood Road; dt £4 from nearby filling station (Eastern Avenue); mainly carp. At **Lowerhouse Lodge**; carp, bream, roach, perch, tench, pike; Pendle & Burnley & Dist AS water; st £27, dt £5 on bank, conc £3. Tackle shop: Macks Fishing Tackle, Unit 8, Dean Mill, Plumbe St, Burnley BB11 3AJ (tel: 01282 427386).

COLNE (tributary of Calder). Free now of pollution; holds some trout and coarse fish.

Colne (Lancs). Colne; trout. Water held by Colne Water AS. **Leeds and Liverpool Canal** held by Marsden Star AS (10m from Barnoldswick to Bank Newton, and 1½m Howden to Morton); pike, trout, tench, bream, roach, rudd, carp and perch; st £20 and dt for waters for both clubs. Marsden Star AS also fishes Gawthorpe Hall Pond, Padiham, members only; no dt. Barrowford AA fishes Knotts Lane Ponds at Colne; coarse fish; members only; apply Anglers All. Pendle Leisure Services, supplies tickets for **Foulridge Lower Reservoir**, roach, bream, pike, tench, carp; dt also on bank; also **Ball Grove Lake**. For more information, contact Jackson's (below). Tackle shops: Anglers All, The Old Forge, 6 Raglan St, Colne BB8 0ET (tel: 01282 860515; web: www.anglers-all.co.uk); Jackson's Fishing Tackle, 27 Albion Str, Earby, Barnoldswick BB18 6QA (tel: 01282 843333; web: www.jackfish.net); Boyces, 44 Manchester Road, Nelson BB9 7EJ (tel: 01282 614412).

Foulridge (Lancs). Four British Waterways reservoirs: **Lower Foulridge** (or **Burwains**), **Upper Foulridge**, **Slipperhill**, **White Moor**. Let to clubs: coarse fishing, dt on bank at Lower Foulridge from Pendle Leisure Services.

ROTHER

Rises near Rotherfield and reaches the sea at Rye Bay. Mostly coarse fish, with trout in upper reaches and tributaries but runs of sea trout increasing. Mullet and bass in estuary.

Rye (E Sussex). Near mouth of Rother; coarse fish. Free fishing from roadside bank between Iden and Scots Float, nr Rye. Clive Vale AC has 1m of **Tillingham River** above Rye and **Rother** at Wittersham to Iden Bridge; south bank footpath for 2 fields on **Royal Military Canal** at Winchelsea; st £40, conc from Hon Sec or local tackle shops. Romney Marsh is close by. Several clubs have water, including Rother FA which has 12m of Rother and Royal Military Canal; dt on bank £3. Clive Vale AC has **Saunders Gravel Pits**, Rye Harbour; carp to 25lb, tench, roach, rudd, eels etc. Members only, st £40, conc.

Wittersham (Kent). Roach, chub, bream, perch, pike, tench, bleak, eels, and other species. Rother FA has 7m of Rother, accessible at Robertsbridge, Salehurst, Udiam, Bodiam, Newenden, Potmans Heath and Blackwall Bridge at Wittersham, also 3m of Royal Military Canal from Iden Lock to Appledore; membership open to clubs, not individuals; mostly members only, but £3 dt on canal and Blackwall Bridge, £1.50 juv, from bailiff on bank; clubs can book matches on both: contact G Parry, Tackle & Gun Shop, Tenterden. Clive Vale AC has a good stretch d/s at Blackwall Bridge; st £40, conc, from Hon Sec or Hastings tackle shops. Hastings, Bexhill & Dist FAA has **Rother and Hexden Channel** between Rolvenden and Wittersham; st £40, with concessions.

Newenden (E Sussex). Large bream, chub and roach; Rother Fishery Assn has fishing rights, terms described under Wittersham.

Bodiam (E Sussex). Few trout (small) or sea trout in upper reaches, coarse fish. Hastings, Bexhill & Dist FAA has 500 yds fishing on south bank with prime chub and dace, membership £40, conc. Edenbridge AS has 2 sections d/s of Bodiam Castle; members only, no dt; contact Hon Sec. Hotels: Castle, Justins.

Etchingham (E Sussex). Burwash FC has National Trust and other water on **River Dudwell** (tributary of the Rother); trout; members only. Hastings, Bexhill & Dist FAA has **Wishing Tree Reservoir**, a lake, dt £7 on bank, conc; also **Bucks Hole Reservoir** in Alexander Park; prime carp water (to 34lb); dt £7 on bank; night fishing members only; also **Harmers Pond**; wheelchair access to

bank; carp to 21lb, mixed coarse; dt on bank. CALPAC control **Speringbrook Sewer**, Snargate, nr **Appledore**, fen-like fishing of about 2,000 yds, with chub, roach, bream, dace, perch, pike; dt £5 from Arrowhead Cottage; no night fishing on most CALPAC water; no keepnets; barbless hooks; open all year. At **Burwash** is **Lakedown Trout Fisheries**, 4 lakes, 26 acres total, b and r trout from $2\frac{1}{2}$lb to 16lb; for tickets contact Lakedown Trout Fisheries, Swife Lane, Broad Oak, Heathfield TN21 8UX (tel: 01435 883449; web: www.lakedowntroutfishery.co.uk).

Stonegate (E Sussex). Wadhurst AS has trout water; dt to members' guests only. Hotel: Stone Bridge.

Tenterden (Kent). Tackle & Gun has tickets for a large number of local fisheries. These include Rother FA (see Wittersham), Tenterden AC (incl various ponds, Dowels Sewer, Hexden Channel, Rother at Potmans Heath); Northiam AC (carp lakes and several miles of Rother); Rye AC (R Tillingham and R Brede, good coarse fishing); Headcorn AC (carp ponds in Biddenden area); also info on **Hawkhurst Fishery** (tel: 01580 753813), 11 lakes, with trout and coarse fishing; Tenterden Trout Waters, Combe Farm, Tenterden TN30 6XA (tel: 01580 763201): 3 lakes of 5 acres total, stocked for fly fishing; day £27, conc, and half-day permits £17 from 8.30am to dusk; basket system allows continuous fishing. Tackle shop: Tackle & Gun, 3 Eastwell Parade, High St, Tenterden TN30 6AH (tel: 01580 764851).

BREDE: Rother tributary; chub to 5lb, bream to 7lb, roach, rudd, tench, pike to 25lb and mullet in summer; also run of sea trout. Barbel introduced upstream; a few small trout in upper reaches; approx 6 miles controlled by Clive Vale AC; members only, st £40, conc, from Hon Sec or local tackle shops. Fishing locations **Rye**, **Winchelsea**.

SEVERN

Longest river in England. Rises in Wales (N Powys) and flows 180m into Bristol Channel. Fair salmon river, with commercial fisheries near mouth; spring salmon in January/April and May. Average size good. Some trout and grayling in upper reaches, but river noted chiefly for coarse fishing, especially for chub in the upper reaches and barbel in the middle river. Shad run up river in May and are taken on rod and line, principally at Tewkesbury Weir.

Sharpness (Glos). Coarse fishing in the **Gloucester and Berkeley Canal** from Severn Bridge to Hempstead Bridge, Gloucester (about 16m); bank licence from any bridge house.

Gloucester (Glos). Gloucester United AA controls several miles of Severn from Hawbridge u/s and d/s, one bank, and Stank Lane; st £11, conc, dt £4, from tackle shops; Assn also has water from **Lower Lode** to **Deerhurst**, also Rymers; on gravel pit at **Saul** (Gardners Pool); BW dt on bank or from tackle shops for **Gloucester Sharpness Canal),** stretch behind cinema and also Baxters up and down of new bridge; dt £4 from bailiffs. Red Lion Inn, Wainlode Hill, Norton GL2 9LW (tel: 01452 730251), has Severn fishing; tickets from hotel; all freshwater and some game fish; dt £5 at Inn and camp-site shop. **Witcombe Reservoirs**: three lakes of 12, 9, and 5 acres, fly only; Troutmaster water, stocked rainbow trout of 2lbs 8oz av; st £710-£300, dt £38-£15.50p, depending on limit; boats bookable in advance: Mrs M Hicks Beach, Witcombe Farm, Great Witcombe GL3 4TR (tel: 01452 863591/864413). Staunton Court, Ledbury Rd, Staunton GL19 3QS (tel: 01452 840230; see website for more: www.stauntoncourtfishing.com), has stocked coarse fishing on Match Lake, Dovecote Lake and Pleck Pool, with carp to 34lbs, roach to 2lbs, rudd, tench to 8lbs, etc; £6 dt; tackle shop on site (fresh bait and equipment). Tackle shops: Gloucester Angling Centre, 47 Bristol Road, Gloucester GL1 5SA (tel: 01452 520074); Allsports, 126/128 Eastgate Str,

Gloucester GL1 1QT (tel: 01452 522756; see website for more info: www.allsportsguns.co.uk); Tredworth Fishing Tackle, 78 High Str, Tredworth GL1 4SR (tel: 01452 539492); Cheltenham Angling Centre 442 High St, Cheltenham GL50 3JA (tel: 01242 582270). Hotels: New County, Fleece, New Inn.

Tewkesbury (Glos). Salmon, twait and coarse fish. Avon: coarse fish. Below weir shoals of big bream. Birmingham AA has 34 stretches on Severn including those at Bushley, Ripple, Ukinghall Pool, Severn Stoke, Deerhurst, Apperley (2 pools at Apperley, also). Tewkesbury Popular AA has 60 pegs on Severn from mouth of Avon to Lower Load, with bream, chub, barbel, eels, gudgeon, pike and bleak, and **Avon** from Healings Mill to Abbey Mill, Ham side; also from Abbey Mill to Severn confluence, both bans; bream, roach, chub, skimmer, bleak, gudgeon; membership £20, conc, from Robert Danter at Tewkesbury Fishing Tackle (below). Gloucester United AA have water at Drirhurst; dt from tackle shops and Hon Sec. Tackle shop: Tewkesbury Fishing Tackle Shop, 31 Barton Str, GL20 5PR (tel: 01684 293234); Cheltenham Angling Centre, 442 High St, Cheltenham GL50 3JA (tel: 01242 582270). Hotels: Abbey; many others.

Ripple (Worcs). Bream, pike, perch, chub, dace, roach. Environment Agency fishery, 1900 yds free to licence holders, is on left bank, at M50 viaduct.

Upton upon Severn (Worcs). Chub, barbel, bream, roach, dace, perch and pike. Environment Agency has 1200 yds of west bank above old railway embankment, free to licence holders, mainly bream, barbel and roach fishing. Upton upon Severn AA has 10 pegs at Hanley Rd, 42 pegs at Upper Ham. Free parking. Dt £2 from G Shinn, tackle shop, 21 Old Str, WR8 0HN (tel: 01684 592102). Birmingham AA has 4 meadows, dt £5 from tackle shops. Hotel: Star Inn.

Worcester (Worcs). Barbel, bream, chub, roach. Free fishing behind cricket ground. Worcester & Dist United AA has stretches below Worcester, 350m l bank; Pixham Ferry, 800m r bank; West Diglis, 900m r bank; East Diglis, 350m l bank; Pitchcroft, 800m l bank, and opposite Pitchcroft, Hallow Tip, mixed coarse; Bourley above Holtfleet, 1000m, 40 pegs; assn also has stretches of **Avon**, and 1,500m l bank **Teme** at Knightwick; dt, £4 through Hon Sec or through tackle shop (see below). Dt £5 Mon-Fri (Sat/Sun is syndicate fishing) on bank for 6 pegs at Bevere Lock (tel: 01905 640275). Birmingham AA has stretches at Severn Stoke, Hallow, Grimley, rights on Worcester and Birmingham Canal from King's Norton to Blackpole (near Worcester); bream, roach, perch, pike. Tackle shop: Alan's Fishing Tackle, 26-30 Malvern Road, Worcester WR2 4LG (tel: 01905 422107; website has more: www.alansfishingtackle.co.uk) has tickets for Evesbatch Fisheries, two lakes with carp and roach.

Lincombe and **Holt** (Worcs). Wharf Inn, Holt Heath, Worcester WR6 6NN (tel: 01905 620289) has section at Holt Fleet, 19 pegs with barbel and bream; disabled access, dt £4 from inn. For 2 carp pools, 6 acres; contact Jim Parker; dt £6, conc (mob: 07714 907603). Dt £5 for Lincombe Lock DY13 9PP, 180m l bank, from keeper on site (tel: 01299 822887).

Stourport-on-Severn (Worcs). At confluence of Severn and Stour:

barbel, chub and large roach; also **Staffordshire and Worcestershire Canal**: coarse fish. Lyttelton AA has 80 pegs right bank u/s of Stourport; tickets from Marks only. Birmingham AA has ½m both banks; also Ribbesford, Lickhill and Newhalls; dt £5 from tackle shops. Tackle shop: BMB Mould Tools, 81 Barracks Rd, Stourport-on-Severn DY13 9QB (tel: 01299 877784); Marks Fishing Tackle, 11 Raven Street, Stourport-on-Severn DY13 8UU (tel: 01299 871735), where Lyttelton AA tickets are sold; also Birmingham AA dt for Severn and Teme.

Bewdley (Worcs). Chub, roach, pike, perch, dace, barbel. Telford AA has 2,000m l bank from Buildwas village to Dale End Park, information from Hon Sec; dt £4, conc, on bank or tackle shop, Rod & Gun. Kidderminster & DAA has 120 pegs, 2½m water, above and below town (Bewdley); 34 pegs at **Winnalls** below Stourport; membership cards £35; wt £10; dt £5 from tackleists, also £5 on bank, conc. Birmingham AA has six stretches in vicinity, incl Lyth Farm and Ladyham; dt £5. Cards for both Assns from Stan Lewis, (see below); Stan Lewis runs riverside guest-house with B&B and clubroom, and issues tickets for 1½m Severn at Bewdley (with record roach) and certain local pools under his own supervision, with excellent roach, chub, and pike to 26lbs 8 ozs. Tackle shops; Rod & Gun, 3-5 High Str, Dawley, Telford TF4 2ET (tel: 01952 503550; Stan Lewis, 2 Severn Side South, Bewdley DY12 2DX (tel: 01299 403358); Marks Fishing Tackle, 11 Raven Str, Stourport-on-Severn DY13 8UU (tel: 01299 871735). Hotels: George; Horn & Trumpet; Stourport Manor Hotel.

Upper Arley (Worcs). Salmon, trout, grayling, chub, dace, pike, etc. Dowles Brook, 3m S. Birmingham AA has stretches at **Arley Stanley**, **Arley Kinlet**, **Arley**, **Aveley** and **Trimpley**; dt £5 from tackle shops. Hotels:

Harbour and Unicorn (last two issue dt).

Hampton Loade (Salop). Birmingham AA has extensive fishing here, on both banks, and at **Alveley**; dt £5 from tackle shops.

Bridgnorth (Salop). Barbel, roach. Ship Inn (tel: 01746 861219) has 270m west bank, dt £5 on bank. Birmingham AA has stretches at **Knowle Sands, Danery, Quatford** and **Eardington; Nordley Pools** at **Broseley** (5m); dt £5 from tackle shops. At Quatt 4m SE National Trust have Dudmaston Pools; Kniver Freeliners AC water; coarse fish; members only; also Birmingham AA's 1½m of bank running through the estate; salmon & coarse; dt £5 from tackle shops. **Boldings Pools**, Astley Abbotts, Bridgnorth WV16 4SS: twelve lakes with carp and tench and other coarse species, dt £5.50, conc; disabled access, toilets (tel: 01746 763255; see website for more info: www.boldingspools.co.uk). **Shatterford Lakes**, Bridgnorth Rd, Shatterford DY12 1TW (tel: 01299 861597): one trout lake; 2 silver fish lakes; 2 specimen lakes (catfish to over 60lb and carp to over 40lb); prices according to lake; conc; dt available; most lakes accessible to disabled; well-stocked tackle shop at fishery. Kingsnordley Fisheries, **Kingsnordley**, Bridgnorth WV15 6EU (tel: 01746 780247): 12 day-ticket pools, with bream, barbel, tench, roach, chub, and large carp; dt on bank, extra rod £1, specimen pool £7, extra rod £1.50. Astbury Falls Fish Farm WV16 6AT (tel: 01746 766797), has £15 half dt (5 hours) 2 trout; £20 full day, 3 trout. Tackle shop: Malcolm Storey Angling Centre, 129 Sutton Road, Kidderminster DY11 6QR (tel: 01562 745221). Hotels: Severn Arms; Falcon; Croft; Kings Head.

Coalport (Salop). Chub, barbel, pike, etc, fewer roach and dace than are found farther downstream. Some free

water. Rowley Regis & Dist AS has stretch on right bank; no tickets. Telford AA has Sweeneycliffe House fishery, 700m l bank; also right bank upstream to Tile Museum, about 800m; dt £4 on bank, or from Rod & Gun, 3-5 High Str, Dawley, Telford TF4 2ET (tel: 01952 503550).

Ironbridge (Salop). Barbel, chub, roach, perch, etc. Environment Agency has 600 yds of fishing on left bank free to licence-holders (tel: 08708 506506), for information. Dawley AS has right bank d/s from power station fence to Free Bridge, also pools at **Telford, Broseley** and **Dawley**; dt £4, conc, on all waters from bailiffs. Telford AA has Horsehay Pool, near Dawley; Wide Waters, Castle Pool and Dandy Pool at Little Dawley; also Middle Pool and Trench Pool; also Blue and Randlay Pools and Holmer Lake; and Priorslee Flash; coarse: roach, bream tench, crucian &c; dt £4 on bank or from Rod & Gun; assn also has left bank from bend below rowing club steps u/s to railway bridge; and from fence above private gardens to top of the island opp power station (about 1200m); also 2 meadows opp Buildwas Church (1200m); dt on bank. Tackle shops: Rod & Gun, 3-5 High Str, Dawley, Telford TF4 2ET (tel: 01952 503550; WAC Tackle, 5 Anstice Square, Madley, Telford TF7 5BD (tel: 01952 586786; see website for more info: www.wactackle.com). Hotel: Tontine.

Atcham (Salop). Barbel, chub. Environment Agency has 2,895m r bank. Macclesfield Prince Albert AS has members only fisheries here, at **Bicton, Melverley, Longnor, Royal Hill, The Isle, Welshpool, Newton**, and elsewhere, a total of twenty nine Severn beats. Also fishings on the rivers **Gam, Vyrnwy** and **Banwy**, members only.

Shrewsbury (Salop). Town waters, 1800m both banks, dt £4 from tackle shop (below), or £6 on the banks;

waters managed by Shrewsbury Angling Management Committee; good winter fishing for barbel, pike, chub, roach. The Wingfield Arms, SY4 1EB (tel: 01743 850750), 4m west of town at Montford Bridge, has 1m; barbel, eels and good pike. Old LMS AC has fine stretch at **Emstry**, with fords and runs; dt from local tackle shops. St Helens Ramblers AS have two stretches at Shrewsbury, permits only, shared with St Helens AA. Birmingham AA has stretches at **Underdale**, Shrewsbury, **Pool Quay** and **Buttington Bridge**, west of the town; dt £5 and permits from Sundorne Fishing Tackle. Warrington AA has water at Montford Bridge with large chub and barbel; members only. At Atcham National Trust has Attingham Park; part coarse only, part salmon and coarse, they issue dt; Lymm AC has water, u/s and d/s of confluence with River Tern; membership only; membership apply Hon Sec; dt available. **River Tern** also fished at Waters Upton near Hodnet by Nantwich AS; members only; mixed coarse. Wolverhampton AA has ¾m at **Montford Bridge**; dt £2.50 from bailiff on bank; assoc also has 13m of Shropshire Union Canal at Pendiford; dt on bank; also Staffs Worcester Canal at **Penkridge**, and at **Wombourn**. Tackle shops: Walkers of Shrewsbury, 88-90 Frankwell, Shrewsbury SY3 8JR (tel: 01743 361535); Montgomery Canal tickets; dt £3; Total Angling, Vanguard Trading Park, Vanguard Way, Battlefield Enterprise Park SY1 3TG (tel: 01743 462699); ask for Andy Jones re Montgomeryshire AA tickets.

Melverley (Salop). Chub, dace. Environment Agency has two meadows on left bank, about 500 yds, free to licence holders (tel: 08708 506506, for details). Chester AA has 800yds immediately d/s of Environment Agency stretch.

Llandrinio (Montgomery). Chub, dace, trout, barbel, salmon; leave from farmers. Lymm AC has water on Severn and Vyrnwy, members only. Canal; coarse fish, tickets (see Welshpool). **Maerdy Brook**, 2m SW. Arddleen Brook, excellent trout, dace and chub. Hotel: Golden Lion.

Welshpool (Powys). Salmon, trout, coarse fish (inc grayling). Trout small in streams, few but big in river. Welshpool & Dist AC (now in Montgomeryshire AA) which has 1m of coarse and game fishing in **Severn**, **Camlad**, **Vyrnwy**, **Banwy**; also 6m of **Montgomery Canal** (coarse fishing); the Welshpool river stretch is at **Lower Leighton**, 750m and 1,500m; club also has 2 pools at Groes, Garth Pools, 3m east, mixed coarse; dt from TI in Welshpool and Grants Newsagents. Nantwich AS fishes 1m mostly double bank; members only; apply Hon Sec; excellent barbel stretch. Black Pools trout fishery, fly only, is 1m from Welshpool on Llanfair Rd; put and take. Bank and (your own) boat fishing (limited dt £5; enquire first) on Marton Pool, Marton, 5m SE; good coarse fishing; apply to Site Manager, Marton Pool Caravan Park, Marton SY21 8JX (tel: 01743 891306). Warrington AA has Hope Farm stretch, Welshpool; members only. For **Glyndwr Fishery**, Dolanog, Welshpool, contact Howard Thresher (tel: 01363 777783). Tackle shop: Sport Hafren, Church Street, Welshpool (tel: 01938 552202). Hotels: Westwood Park; Bear, Newton; Black Lion, Llanfair Caereinion.

Forden (Powys). Montgomery, 3m. Trout, salmon, chub, dace, etc. Birmingham AA has 3m; dt £5 from tackle shops. Camlad; trout, grayling, chub; Montgomeryshire AA has water on river; tickets from tackle shops.

Montgomery (Powys). Severn, 2m; trout, salmon, grayling, chub, pike and perch. **Camlad**, 2m N; good trout, grayling, chub. Montgomeryshire AA has water; tickets cover all assoc waters; st £22, conc; dt £3, no conc.

Warrington AA has waters at Caerhowell Hall, **Dolwen**, **Fron** and **Llanidloes**; also **Vyrnwy**, **Dee**, canals and pools. Tackle shops in Welshpool and Newtown.

Abermule (Powys). **Severn** and **Mule**; salmon, trout, grayling, coarse fish; mostly private but dt for some lengths. Water not always fishable in summer. Montgomeryshire AA has Mule from Abermule village u/s for 4 miles both banks; dt from tackle shops; st £22, conc, wt £10, dt £3. Lymm AC has 1,000 yds, members only, trout and grayling.

Newtown (Powys). Salmon, trout, grayling, pike, chub, dace; 3m, mainly right bank, beginning at municipal car park; information from Newtown AC. Environment Agency has free fishery of 500yds north bank beside sewage farm at **Penarth**, with chub and dace (tel: 08708 506506 for details). Newtown & Dist FC control **Fachwen Pool** (now a coarse fishery with all types of fish and carp up to 30lb); dt from Newtown & Dist AC; Assn also controls the river upstream from the park for 2m, which incl **Vaynor Estate** and **Penstrowed**; st £25 and dt £6 from Newtown Angling. Severnside AC has extensive Severn fishing at Newtown, Vaynor, Dolerw Park and pools; dt from Newtown Angling; also mixed coarse fishing 3m N of Newtown: Fachwen Pool. Prince Albert AS has stretch here. Penllwyn Lodges (tel: 01686 640269; see website for more info: www.penllwynlodges.co.uk) offers self-catering log cabins with fishing in 600 yards of canal plus small lake; tench, chub, carp. Tackle shop has dt for canal at **Abermule**. Tackle shop: Newtown Angling, 3 Severnside Centre, Short Bridge Str, SY16 1AA (tel: 01686 624044). Hotels: Maesmawr Hall and others.

Caersws (Powys). Maesmawr Hall Hotel, SY17 5SF (tel: 01686 688255) sell dt. Trout, coarse fish, some salmon. Caersws AA has 7m double bank in vicinity of Caersws and Llandinam with good brown trout and grayling; fly, spinning and worm; st £80, dt £10, conc, (also covers Llandinam fishery) from Spar shop; Llandinam PO; Maesmawr Hall Hotel. For trout fishing at **Caersws** and at **Clewedog Dam**, apply to Kingfisher Angling Centre, 9 New St, Shrewsbury SY3 8JN (tel: 01743 240602) for dt and information. Hotels: Maesmawr Hall; Buck; Red Lion; Unicorn.

Llandinam (Powys). Trout and grayling fishing on both banks. Caersws AA controls Dinam Fishery, fly only, st £90, dt £12, conc; from Llandinam PO and Stores SY17 5BY (tel: 01686 688843), or see Caersws. Hotel: The Lion.

Llanidloes (Montgomery). Trout, salmon, pike, chub, dace, grayling. Llanidloes AA has about 12m fishing on upper **Severn**, **Afon Clywedog** and other tributaries; st and dt from Hon Sec. Warrington AA has Dolwen Bridge to Llanidloes; members only. Environment Agency has 805m on right bank beginning at sewage works, which is free fishing to licence holders, mostly chub, dace, with grayling (tel: 08708 506506 for details). Warrington AA, has water downstream. At **Trefeglwys** (4m N) is caravan park with fishing (trout and coarse) on **Trannon**; best months for trout April-July. **Llyn Ebyr**, 30 acre coarse lake with perch, pike; tickets £5 per rod which includes boat from E J Williams, Llyn Ebyr SY17 5PY (tel: 01686 430236). Hotels: Lloyds, Unicorn, Queen's Head, Angel, Temperance, Royal Oak, Red Lion.

Tributaries of the Severn.

LEADON: Trout, coarse fish (some barbel introduced).

Ledbury (Hereford). Ledbury AA has trout water, no dt. Castlemorton Lake; coarse fishing; free, but licence necessary. Three Counties Fisheries, Field Cottage, Ryton, Nr Dymock GL18 2DH (tel: 01531 890455; web: www.threecountiesfisheries.co.uk) have 25 peg carp pool here, with roach, tench and rudd; management also runs 2 pools at Redbank Farm; coarse: carp, roach, rudd, tench, bream; also Pixley Pool, carp only; and near Ross-on-Wye Biddlestone Pool; carp, tench and bream; dt on banks. Hotels: Royal Oak, 5 The Southend.

AVON: The principal tributary of the lower Severn. Roach, chub, dace and perch dominate higher reaches; bream, barbel and pike, the latter patchily distributed.

Tewkesbury (Glos). Confluence of Avon and Severn, connected also by 'Mill Avon'. Weirs and weir-pool fishing, including twaite shad during the spawning run. Eckington AC controls 2m of Avon at Corpus Christi by **Strensham** village; good coarse fishing, chub, roach, bream, perch, pike included; membership £12, no dt, conc, from Hon Sec, Cheltenham tackle shops or the Bell Inn, Church St, Pershore, Eckington WR10 3AN (tel: 01386 750033). Mythe Pool, Tewkesbury: 10 acre coarse lake with bream, roach; tickets from Alan's Fishing Tackle, 26 Malvern Road, Worcester WR2 4LG (tel: 01905 422107; see website for more info: www.alansfishingtackle.co.uk). Birmingham AA also has water at Birdsmeadow; dt £5 from tackle shops.

Twyning (Glos). Chub, dace, roach, pike, perch, bream. Birmingham AA has ½m stretch; dt £5 from tackle shops.

Eckington (Worcs). Most species of coarse fish, principally bream, big head of roach. Hotel: Bell Inn WR10 3AN (tel: 01386 750033), ¼m from river, is HQ of Eckington AC, which controls over 4m, 200 pegs of lower Avon, with many coarse species; permits obtainable.

Pershore (Worcs). Roach, bream. Worcester & Dist United AA has 900m at Burlington, and 1,000m at Pensham. Information from Hon Sec; dt from Alan's Fishing Tackle, 26 Malvern Road, Worcester WR2 4LG (tel: 01905 422107; web: www.alansfishingtackle.co.uk). Birmingham AA has water here, both banks and at Pensham, **Nafford**, **Eckington**, **Twyning**, and at Mythe Farm and Wood End; dt £5 from tackle shops. Some free water in recreation ground. Hotel: Angel.

Evesham (Worcs). Pike, perch, bream, roach, dace, gudgeon, chub, bleak and barbel. Evesham & DAA has 40 pegs in town, and 26 pegs behind football club, dt £2.80 from bailiff on bank; there is free fishing for jun and disabled at Workman Gardens, Waterside; dt on bank for Crown & Corp Meadows, 40 pegs. At **Hampton Ferry**: E W Huxley & Son, Hampton Ferry Fishery WR11 4BP (tel: 01386 442458), has 40 pegs; dt £4.50 (incl car park) from bailiffs or Raphael's Restaurant. Anchor Meadows Fisheries, **Harvington**: 500m right bank with barbel, large carp and chub, dt on bank, or The Bungalow, Anchor Meadows WR11 8PA (tel: 01386 48065). Birmingham AA has fisheries at Swifts, **Wood Norton**, **Chadbury**, **Charlton**, **Cropthorne**, **Fladbury**, **Lower Moor** and **Wick**; dt £5 from tackle shops. Manor Farm Leisure (caravan holidays), Anchor Lane, Harvington WR11 8PA (tel: 01386 870039), has ¾m coarse fishing on Avon. 1m north bank of Avon at **Wilmots Waters**; 30 pegs (parking behind); dt, conc, from Baitbox shop. Waterside and Workman Gardens, reserved for disabled and juv anglers. Twyford Farm, Evesham, has ½m right bank, chub, roach; tickets on bank; licences from post office. **The Lenches Lakes**, Hill Barn Orchard, Evesham Rd, Church Lench, Evesham WR11 4UB (tel: 01386 871035 see website for more info: www.lencheslakes.co.uk): stocked rainbow trout fly fishing on two lakes of 3½ acres each; fish av 2lbs-2½lbs; various priced dt available, st; tackle sold on site.

Stratford-upon-Avon (Warwick). Royal Leamington Spa AA has Lido and Recreation Ground fishing on R Avon, dt £3.50 on bank; R Avon and College Pool at Wasperton; members only; also Snitterfield Reservoir, excellent crucians and bream, members only. Local club, Stratford-upon-Avon AA has 200 pegs on R Avon at Luddington and Manor Farm, and **R Stour** at Preston-on-Stour and Wimpstone, with good variety of coarse fish in both; assn also has water between Luddington and Seven Meadows; also section of Stratford canal at Wilmcote; membership £27, dt £4 (no dt for Stour), conc, from Stuart's Angling Centre before fishing; club also has 50 pegs on Stratford Canal at Wilmcote; dt on bank; also 7 meadows on Avon at Stratford (60 pegs); and 30 pegs on Hampton Lucy Brook; dt in advance from Stuart's. Stuart's also issue tickets for ADAC water: 27 pegs Luddington Village Hall; 100 pegs South Stratford Canal; membership £24, dt £3 before fishing, conc. Lifford AC has North Stratford Canal, Lifford Lane to Brandwood Tunnel, 60 pegs. Birmingham AA has stretches at **Barton**, **Bidford**, **Marlcliff**, **Cleeve Prior** and **Salford Priors**; dt £5 from tackle shops; good chub and dace. Alveston Village Assn AC has 45 pegs on Avon at **Alveston**, with chub, bream, roach, carp, barbel,

dt £3, conc, from Hon Sec. At **Moreton in Marsh**, Lemington Lakes: five pools with carp, rudd, roach, tench, bream, dt from £8 at shop on site (tel: 01608 650872). Tackle shop: Stuart's Angling Centre, 17 Evesham Rd CV37 9AA (tel: 01789 293950). Hotels: Welcombe, Falcon and many others.

Leamington (Warwick). Bream, chub, dace, roach, pike, perch. Avon at **Wasperton** and **Stratford** Lido and Recreation Ground preserved by Royal Leamington Spa AA; Assn, also has R **Leam**, **Offchurch**; members only; R Leam Newbold Comyn to Princes Drive; dt £3 on bank, conc, for most of these; annual membership £28, conc, from Baileys. Tackle shop: Baileys Fishing Tackle, 30 Emscote Rd, Warwick CV34 4PP (tel: 01926 490636).

Rugby (Warwick). Chub, roach fishing. Environment Agency has free fishery at Avon Mill, ½m north bank beside B4112 road (for details, tel: 08708 506506). Avon Ho AC have water on Oxford Canal nr Barby; club also has 3 pools at Kings Newnham and stretch of upper Avon; membership from Banks and Burr (below). Old Kings Head AC fishes 4m of Grand Union Canal, from Crick Tunnel to **Yelvertoft**; large carp, eels, bream, and good stocks of smaller fish; st £12 (£6 after 1 Oct) from Knightley Arms, conc, or from Yelvertoft PO or Crick PO. **Foxholes Fisheries**, **Crick**, Northants NN6 7US (tel: 01788 823967; see website for more info: www.foxholesfisheries.co.uk): 4 pools fishable on season ticket; all species stocked; one lake is general, 3 carp (to 40lbs); open 1 May - 31 December; no dt: contact Roger Chaplin. **Spring Pools** are three pools close to Rugby at Newton; all species, dt on bank, or (tel: 0799 0710666). **Clifton Lakes** on A5 offer 8 pools and 1 lake plus length of R Avon; season ticket from riparian owner. **Newbold Quarry**, old established water for good tench and roach fishing; fishing is free. Draycote Water close by Dunchurch, dt from lodge on site. For st and dt for **Coombe Pool**, 85 acres nr Coventry; bream, carp, (tel: 02476 453720). Tackle shops: Banks & Burr, 25/27 Claremont Road, Rugby CV21 3NA (tel: 01788 576782; web: www.tackleup.com); Rugby Tackle Mail Order, 155A Bilton Rd, Rugby CV22 7DS (tel: 01788 570645; web: www.rugbytackle.co.uk); Old Town Tackle, 25b Clemens Street, Leamington Spa CV31 2DP (tel: 01926 421855). Hotels: Grosvenor; Three Horseshoes, both Rugby; Holiday Inn, Crick.

ARROW joined by the **Alne** at Alcester; flows into Avon at Salford Priors: Coarse fish, some trout.

Salford Priors (Worcs). Arrow and Avon; coarse fish. Birmingham AA has ¾m; dt £5 from tackle shops.

Wixford (Warwick). Pike, perch, roach, dace, chub and bream; dt for about 1m of water on Ragley Park Estate from Fish Inn, Wixford B49 6DA (tel: 01789 778593), or from bailiff on bank. Lakes: Ragley Park, 1m NW. B&B next door to inn.

Redditch (Worcs). Redditch & Dist FA are local federation, who fish **Arrow Valley Lake**, with carp to 25lb, large roach and other coarse fish; dt on site, Avon at Wick nr **Pershore** and **Birmingham - Stratford Canal**; for Arrow Valley Lake contact Countryside Centre (tel: 01527 464000); st available, dt £5.00, conc. Tackle shop: Corn Stores, 360 Evesham Rd, Crabbs Cross B97 5JB (tel: 01527 541982). Hotels: Thistle, Southcrest Manor.

Alvechurch (Worcs). Barnt Green FC has rights on **Upper and Lower Bittell Reservoirs**, **Arrow Pools** (Upper and Lower) and **Canal feeder**; **Lower Bittell** and **Mill Shrub** trout (fly only), remainder coarse fish; fishing for members and their guests.

STOUR (tributary of Avon): Coarse fish, trout, mostly preserved.

Shipston (Warwick). Shipston-on-Stour AC has water; members only; contact Hon Sec: (tel: 01608 664026**LEAM** (tributary of Avon): Coarse fish.

Eathorpe (Warwick). Warwick DC has 750m at Pump Room Gardens, Leamington Spa; dt on bank; and Leamington Mill Gardens, 350m l bank; both with roach, perch.

HAM BROOK (tributary of Leam): Coarse fish.

Fenny Compton (Warwick): Good pike, bream, tench, roach in **Oxford Canal**. **Claydon**.

SOWE (tributary of Avon): few fish.

Coventry (W Midlands). Excellent trout and coarse fishing on **Packington Estate**. **Meriden**. More than five miles of river fishing and 160 acres of lakes. Rainbow and brown trout; also coarse fishery 2m off. (For details see Midlands (reservoirs and lakes)). Coventry & Dist AA has extensive fishing on rivers and reservoirs and coarse fishing in **Ouse** at Turvey, **Nene**; day tickets for some of this fishing may be had from tackle shops in Coventry area or Hon Sec; dt from bailiffs, for Assn's **Napton Reservoirs**, Coventry AA water, dt available, good tench, carp & bream. **Hopsford Hall Fishery**, Withybrook Lane, nr Shilton CV7 9HY (tel: 01455 220375); carp to 20lb and other coarse species; good access for disabled; dt, conc, from bailiff on bank. Royal Leamington Spa AA control **Jubilee Pools**, at Ryton-on-Dunsmore; also Ryton Pools Country Park; for membership, see Leamington. **Lavender Hall Premier Coarse Fishery**, Lavender Hall Lane, Berkswell CV7 7BN (tel: 01676 530299; see website for more info: www.fisheries.co.uk/lavenderhall): five well stocked lakes with carp, tench, bream, roach, etc; dt £7.00, conc; tackle shop; cafe facilities; from lodge. **Coombe Pool**, Coombe

Country Park, Brinklow Rd, Binley CV3 2AB (tel: 02476 453720; web: www.fisheries.co.uk/coombe); 85 acres nr Coventry; bream, carp, st from centre £70 (24-hour); dt £4 1 rod, £5 specimen (3 rods) on bank. Tackle shops: Rugby Tackle Mail Order, 155A Bilton Rd, Rugby CV22 7DS (tel: 01788 570645; web: www.rugbytackle.co.uk); Lanes Fishing Tackle & Country Clothing, 31 London Road, Coventry CV1 2JP (tel: 024 7622 3316) (assn cards). Hotel: Brandon Hall Hotel, Brandon.

TEME: Trout and coarse fish, with a few salmon; grayling. Very large barbel, strong tackle recommended. Trout in upper reaches.

Worcester (Worcs). Barbel, chub. Worcester & Dist UAA has 1,200m l bank at Knightwick; also 250 pegs at the **Worcester Birmingham Canal**; Birmingham AA has water at Cotheridge, 4m west of Worcester; dt £6 from (see below Broadwas). The Talbot at Knightwick WR6 5PH (tel: 018868 21235) has fishing; dt £6. Tackle shop: Alan's Fishing Tackle, 26-28 Malvern Road, Worcester WR2 4LG (tel: 01905 422107; web: www.alansfishingtackle.co.uk).

Leigh (Worcs). Trout, chub, dace, grayling, pike, perch, salmon. Bransford AS and local clubs rent Bransford to Powick; dt from Alan's (above). Birmingham AA has water here (Leigh and Brockamin); dt £5 from tackle shops.

Broadwas (Worcs). Trout, grayling, chub, dace. Birmingham AA has stretch of left bank here and at Eardiston, 1¼m; dt £6 must be booked in advanced from (tel: 0121 454 9111; web: www.baa.uk.com).

Tenbury (Worcs). Barbel, chub. Peacock Waters (tel: 01584 881411) has 900m l bank; st. Tickets (campers only) for Little Hereford, 500m right bank d/s of bridge, A Jones, Westbrook Farm, Little Hereford, Ludlow SY8 4AU (tel: 01584

711280). Tenbury FA has approx 4m of Teme above and 1m of **Ledwyche Brook**, trout, salmon and grayling, and barbel, chub, pike etc; membership £95 (first year) then £90; £20 salmon dt, dt £15 game, £10 coarse; from Hon Sec (tel: 01584 810345/695). St Michaels Pools, New House Farm, St Michaels, Tenbury WR15 8TW (mob: 077101 52464, Mr Jones): 2 pools; dt £25, £10 c&r, conc; brown and rainbow trout, fly only. Hotels: Crow; Royal Oak; B&B at Deepcroft Farmhouse.

Ludlow (Salop). Birmingham AA has water from Eastham Bridge to Eardiston, incorporating Lindridge and Puddleford; dt £6 from Ludlow Tackle Shops or (tel: 0121 454 9111; web: www.baa.uk.com). **Delbury Hall Trout Fishery**, Diddlebury SY7 9DH (tel: 01584 841267; web: www.delbury.com); dt £25, 2 fish limit; 2 trout lakes; 5.5 acres; fly only; barbless hooks. Dt for **Hyde Pool** at Wooferton (coarse); **Lower Bromden Pools**, Wheathill (5 pools: coarse) from Ludlow Tackle. Tickets for **Little Hereford Carp Pool** from 'Haynall-Villa', Little Hereford SY8 4BG (tel: 01584 711589; web: www.haynallvilla.co.uk); 1 acre; carp; dt. Tackle shop: Ludlow Tackle, Old Service Station, Bromfield Rd SY8 1DW (tel: 01584 875886; web: www.ludlowtackle.co.uk) supplies river reports, directions and information on venues in the area. Hotels: The Feathers, Angel, Bull, Charlton Arms, and Exchange.

Knighton (Powys). Mainly trout; preserved except for 1m free to licence-holders. Hotel: Knighton Hotel.

ONNY: Good trout, chub, etc.

Plowden (Salop). Trout, chub; private water. Plowden Club has 4m trout fishing at Plowden Estate, members and guests only, no dt; occasional membership.

SALWARPE: Trout, coarse fish. Birmingham AA has 1,300 yds at **Claines**; dt £5 from tackle shops.

Droitwich (Worcs). Trout above, coarse fish below. Severn 6m W. Droitwich & District AS has water at **Holt Fleet**; noted chub waters; society also has **Heriotts Pool** (large carp); two sections of Droitwich Canal at Porters Mill: 36 pegs, stocked with carp, chub, bream, roach and rudd: dt on bank. **Astwood Fishery**, Stoke Prior, Bromsgrove B60 4BB (tel: 01905 770092; see website for more info: www.fisheries.co.uk/astwood) 2 acre pool and 2 1-acre pools with carp to 30lb and bream to 8lb, tench; dt on bank. Tackle shop: Droitwich Angling Centre, 18 & 19 North Street Ind. Est., Droitwich WR9 8JB (tel: 01905 779300; see website for more info: www.droitwichangling.co.uk); BAA, Worcester AS tickets.

Bromsgrove (Worcs). Tardebigge Reservoir now syndicate water 2010 membership full. Upper and Lower Bittel Reservoirs owned by Barnt Green FC; members only (see also Arrow-Alvechurch). Hewell Grange Lake; st only via Colin Pace, Hewell Grange Prison. (See also Worcester and Birmingham Canal). Upton Warren Lake, 18 acres with carp, bream, roach etc; dt on bank for 12 pegs (majority for members only; boat and several pegs for disabled. Tackle shops; Ensign Fishing Tackle, 3 Stoke Rd, B60 3EQ (tel: 01527 833322; www.ensign-fishingtackle.co.uk).

STOUR: Once heavily polluted, but fish now returning in some areas, principally lower river.

Stourbridge (Worcs). **Staffordshire and Worcestershire Canal**; coarse fish. Tackle shop: Club 2000 Fishing Tackle, First Floor, 76-78 Wynall Lane, Wollescote, DY9 9AQ (tel: 01384 892892; see website for more info: www.C2kft.co.uk).

Dudley (W Midlands). Lakes: Pensnett Grove Pool, Middle Pool, Fenns Pool,

3m SW (see Brierley Hill). Himley Park Lakes (Dudley Corporation); 16 acres good coarse fishing with carp and tench, dt on bank; swims accessible to disabled. Plenty of fishing in canals within 6m radius. Lodge Farm Reservoir; Dudley Corporation. At Parkes Hall, **Coseley**, 2½m away, is good pool for which dt can be had; coarse fish (Dudley Corporation). Tackle from Hingley All Sports & Hobbies, 164 Lower High St, Stourbridge DY8 1TT (tel: 01384 395438).

SMESTOW (tributary of Stour): Polluted.

Wolverhampton (W Midlands). Smestow, 2m W; polluted. Some fishing in **Penk** at Penkridge. Most local water on Severn held by Birmingham AA; dt £5 from tackle shops. Patshull Park Fishery, nr Pattingham WV6 7HR (tel: 01902 700774; see website for more info: www.patshullpark.co.uk) trout & coarse, various dt prices, boats available. Pool Hall Fisheries, Trescott WV4 4XN (tel: 01902 763031; see website for more info: www.poolhallfisheries.co.uk), carp and other coarse, dt from car park shop. Lakes at Himley Park have dt (on bank). Swan Pool, Sandwell Park Farm, **West Bromwich** B71 3SZ (tel: 0121 553 0220; see web: www.sandwell.gov.uk for other pools also), 202 acres with carp and pike, dt on bank; st available from Sandwell Park farm. **Staffordshire Worcester Canal** is Wolverhampton AA water; contact 01902 457906. Tickets from local tackle shops. Tackle shops: Britton's of Wednesfield, 85 Lichfield Road WV11 3HP (tel: 01902 722231; www.brittonsofwednesfield.pwp.blue yonder.co.uk); who sell Wolverhampton AA; British Waterways for Essington and Worley Canal; Blachfords Progressive AC (4 waters incl Calf Heath, Kingswood Lake, and Leacroft and Turf Pool;

mixed coarse st £20); **TERN**: Coarse fish, some trout.

Telford (Salop). Tickets from tackleist WAC Tackle, Madeley (tel: 01952 610497; web: www.wactackle.com), for Telford AA and other local clubs, including a good stretch at Ironbridge for barbel; also pools, flashes and lakes, including **Holmer Lake**, noted for roach (to 3lb) and bream (to 10lb); assn also has Apley Pool, Wellington, good quantities of carp; Little Apley Pool opp Blessed Robert Johnson School, Wellington, very suitable for disabled; also Middle Pool, Oakengates; carp, bream, tench, roach, pike; and Trench Pool nearby, dt £4; also Priorslee Flash at St George's; Randlay Pool and Blue Pool, Telford Town Park: dt for each on bank; assn also has Madebrook Pools, created for the disabled, adjacent to Stirchley Leisure Centre; 15 anglers; for all Assn contest bookings: contact Mrs Ellen Rogers (tel: 01952 410789). Uppington Estate Waters: tickets for stretch in Wroxeter; from Estate Office, Uppington Estate, Uppington TF6 5HN (tel: 01952 740223); Uppington Estate fishing between Cressage Bridge and the Rocks at Eyton on Severn has been let to Prince Albert AS. 10 minutes from Junction 6 of M54 are **Swann Pool** (25 pegs, dt) and **Malthouse Pool** (40 pegs, dt); apply in advance to Rod & Gun, 3-5 High Str, Dawley, Telford TF4 2ET (tel: 01952 503550).

Crudgington (Salop). A few trout and coarse fish.

Hodnet (Salop). Tern. 1m E; a few trout and coarse fish. Strine Brook, 2m E. Lakes: Rose Hill Ponds, 4m NE. **Hawkstone Park Lake**, 3½m; excellent tench and carp water (40lb bags not uncommon) and large roach, rudd, pike and eels; private preserve of Wem AC, membership closed.

Market Drayton (Shrops/Staffs). Trout and coarse fish. Environment Agency has free fishery of 1,200 yds on right bank, mainly d/s of Walkmill Bridge, around sewage works; details from EA. At **Great Sowdley**, 7m SE, are canal reservoirs; perch, pike, roach, tench, carp. Market Drayton AC fishes Shropshire Union Canal at Knighton, Bridges 45-47, dt on bank. Fenton & Dist AS has **White Farm Pools** at **Ashley**, and **Peaks Pool** at **Eccleshall**; members only.

MEESE (tributary of Tern); Trout, coarse fish.

Newport (Salop). Meese, 1m N; trout; private. Lakes: Chetwynd Park Pond, 1m N. Minton's, Limekiln and Wildmoor Pools, 3m S. Moss Pool, 1½m NE. Telford AA, Honeysuckle AC, Lilleshaw AS and Audco AC have 1m of disused Newport & Shrewsbury Canal (SSSI) in town centre; dt £4 on bank or Newport Tackle. Tackle shop: Newport Tackle, 74 High St, TF10 7AY (tel: 01952 820334).

REA: Trout, grayling; preserved.

Minsterley (Salop). Trout, grayling, Minsterley Brook. Habberley Brook, 3m SE. Lake: Marton Pool, 7m SW.

SHELL BROOK (tributary of Roden):

Ellesmere (Salop). Shell Brook, 2m NW; preserved. Halghton Brook, 4m N. Roden, 6m SE. Lakes: **Ellesmere Meres**, noted for bream (12lb plus). Ellesmere AC (most waters are st for locals and outside members; contact Hon Sec) has **Whitemere** and **Blakemere**; Sunday fishing is allowed; boats on most assn waters for members only; club members may fish 4m stretch of **Shropshire Union Canal**; coarse fish. Hotels: Black Lion, Ellesmere Hotel, Red Lion; tickets (see also Shropshire lakes).

PERRY: Trout, preserved.

Ruyton-Eleven-Towns (Salop). 300m stretch on 1 bank with chub and pike; dt from Bridge Inn.

VYRNWY; Provides sport with trout, grayling, coarse fish and salmon.

Llanymynech (Salop). Trout, salmon, grayling, roach, perch, pike, eels, chub, barbel, etc. Oswestry AC has water here, members only, st, conc. For Lord Bradford's water at Lower House Farm, enquire of agent, Llanymynech. Hotels: Bradford Arms, Cross Keys, Dolphin. Good trout fishing at **Lake Vrynwy** (see lakes in Welsh section).

Llansantffraid (Powys). Warrington AA has water here on Vyrnwy and **R Cain**, on Vrynwy at **Four Crosses**, and **Cross Keys**; members only.

Meiford (Powys). Montgomeryshire AA has 750m l bank at Great Dufford Farm, 12 miles away, with barbel and chub and good grayling; st £22; dt £3 from TI.

MORDA (tributary of Vyrnwy): mostly trout, but some coarse fish in lower reaches.

Oswestry (Salop). Most river fishing preserved. The Moat, Deythaur, Llansantffraid (tel: 01691 828147), mixed coarse; Farm Pool (fly only) trout fishing; Prince Albert AC water; members only; club also has 4m of River Vyrnwy. Tickets from Shropshire County Council; West Lake Fishery, 2½ acres. Trench Farm, Redhall Lane, Penley LL13 0NA (tel: 01978 710098); carp fishing on three pools, dt £6, conc; coarse, carp to 38lb. Five coarse fishing ponds: Middle Sontley Farm, Wrexham LL13 0YP (tel: 07710 932094); dt £3 on bank;

mirror carp to 29lb, common carp to 26lb, tench and bream to 8lb; night fishing £6, phone first. Tackle shops: Morgans Angling Centre, 100 Castle Street SY11 1AZ (tel: 01691 657717).

TANAT (tributary of Vyrnwy): Trout (good average size), chub and grayling.

Llan-y-Blodwel (Salop). Horseshoe Inn (tel: 01691 828969) has 1½m (dt), 3 rods per day, fly only; and Green Inn, Llangedwyn, has short stretch; dt issued (3 rods only); fly only (tel: 01691 828234).

Llanrhaiadr-y-Mochnant (Powys); trout; free. Tanat, 1m; trout, grayling, chub, etc; 6m from Llangedwyn to Llangynog strictly preserved; no dt.

CAIN (tributary of Vyrnwy): Trout, coarse fish.

Llansantffraid (Powys). Trout. Warrington AA has two stretches; members only.

BANWY (tributary of Vyrnwy): Trout, grayling, chub, dace and chance of salmon here and there.

Llanfair-Caereinion (Powys). Montgomeryshire AA has right bank downstream from town bridge to boundary fence; mainly trout, some chub and dace; dt £3 from tackle shops. At **Cyffronydd** Warrington AA has 610 yds; 700 yds right bank at **Neuadd Bridge**; members only. Hotels: Caereinion Hotel; Wynnstay Arms.

SHROPSHIRE LAKES

ELLESMERE LAKES. Fishing station: **Ellesmere**; dt for this Mere from warden at local Council wildlife station on Mere frontage; excellent coarse fishing (noted for bream), punts for hire. **Crosemere, Newton Mere, Blakemere, Whitemere** also

controlled by Ellesmere AC, members only, contact Hon Sec.

WALCOT LAKES. Lydbury North, 3m NE of Clun. Two extensive lakes, Walcot East controlled by Birmingham AA; tench, pike and other coarse fish; dt £6 in advance only from tackle shops; (web: www.baa.uk.com).

SOMERSET (streams, lakes and reservoirs)

AXE. Rises on Mendips and flows 25m NW to Bristol Channel near Weston-super-Mare. A few trout in upper reaches and tributaries, but essentially a coarse fish river, containing a mixture of the usual species, with roach now predominating.

Weston-super-Mare and **Bleadon** (Som). Weston-super-Mare & Dist AA fishes Old R Axe, Hobbs Boat to Cowbridge NB, and Lympsham to Crab Hole; South Drain, Gold Corner to Edington Junction; North Drain, Pumping Station to Blakeway Bridge; R Brue, at Manor of Mark; also Summer Lane Pond(mainly carp) and Locking Pits, 2 small coarse fisheries; assn waters contain roach, bream, carp, perch, rudd, pike, eels; no night fishing; active junior section; st £30, conc, wt £15 and dt £5 from Hon Sec not sold on bank (web: www.wsmaa.co.uk). North Somerset AA has water on **Brue** near **Highbridge**, **Old River Kenn (Blind Yeo)**, **Congresbury Yeo**, and **North Drain**, Newtown and Apex Lakes, and Walrow Pond (jointly with Bridgwater AA), together with some smaller rivers. Clevedon & Dist Freshwater AC fish Old River Kenn and R Kenn (Blind Yeo) at **Clevedon**; mainly bream, roach, tench, pike, a few trout; contact tackle shops. Somerset Levels Association of Clubs (SLAC) have **Parrett** from Thorney to Yeo, and below Langport. Two coarse fisheries near Clevedon: Plantations Lakes, Middle Lane, Kingston Seymour BS21 6XW (tel: 01934 832325; see website for more info: www.plantationlakes.co.uk), 3 lakes, stocked with 12 species, carp to 22lbs, restaurant on site; dt. Bullock Farm Fishing Lakes, Kingston Seymour BS21 6XA (tel: 01934 835020; see website for more info: www.bullockfarm.co.uk), five lakes with 143 swims, stocked with large variety of species; dt £6, conc, at lakeside; refreshments; self-catering cottages with free fishing for residents; 2.5 acre campsite. Tackle shops: Veals Fishing Tackle, 1A Church Str, Highbridge, Somerset TA9 3AE (tel: 01278 786934; web: www.veals4carp.com); Weston Angling Centre, 25a Locking Road, Weston Super Mare BS23 3BY (tel: 01934 631140); Chris's Angling Centre, 12 Regent St, Burnham-on-Sea TA8 1AX (tel: 01278 794442).

BRISTOL RESERVOIRS:

Chew Valley, **Blagdon** and **Barrow** reservoirs provide some of the best lake trout fishing in Europe, with a total annual catch of over 50,000 fish of high average size. Season and day tickets obtainable. All fishing is fly only. For all waters, st, dt various prices, boats available,(tel: 01275 332339; see website for more info: www.blagdon-lake.net); details as follows: **Barrow Reservoirs** - **Barrow Gurney**; 3 lakes, open March to November; brown and rainbow trout; bank fishing only; dt £13.50 and evng £12 from self-service kiosk; st also available, conc for juniors, OAPs and registered disabled; tackle hire & tuition can be arranged. Contact Woodford Lodge, Stoke Hill, Chew Stoke, Bristol BS40 8XH (tel: 01275 331365).

Blagdon Lake - **Blagdon**; Open March to November; noted brown and rainbow trout water. Bank dt and part dt from self-service kiosk, st available. Rowing boats from Blagdon Lodge office (advance booking recommended); dt £18 obtainable on all waters; disabled boat anglers catered for (wheelyboat must be advance-booked); concessions for jun (under 18), OAP and registered disabled; tackle shop, tackle hire and tuition arranged; contact Woodford Lodge, Stoke Hill, Chew Stoke,

Bristol BS40 8XH (tel: 01275 332339).

Chew Valley Lake - Chew Stoke. Open March to November; noted brown and rainbow trout water where fish run large. Bank dt and evng from self-service kiosk. Motor boats from Woodford Lodge office (advance booking recommended). St available, dt £15.50 tickets are obtainable on all waters; disabled boat anglers catered for (wheelyboat). Concessions for jun (under 18), OAP and registered disabled; tackle shop and restaurant at Woodford Lodge; tackle hire and tuition arranged. Pike fishing; Oct and Nov, advance booking essential, from Woodford Lodge, Stoke Hill, Chew Stoke, Bristol BS40 8XH (tel: 01275 332339).

Cheddar Reservoir, Cheddar. Coarse fishery managed by Cheddar AC; st £45, dt £6, conc; permits and tickets from Broadway House Caravan Park, Axbridge Rd BS27 3DB (tel: 01934 742610; see website for more info: www.broadwayhousepark.co.uk), on main Cheddar to Axbridge road, opposite reservoir; no tickets available at the water: Bristol Angling Centre, 12 Doncaster Rd, Southmead, Bristol BS10 5PL (tel: 0117 950 8723; more on web: www.bristolangling.com); Veals Fishing Tackle, 1A Church Str, Highbridge, Somerset TA9 3AE (tel: 01278 786934; see website for more information: www.veals4carp.com); Thatcher's Pet & Tackle, 18 Queen St, Wells BA5 2DP (tel: 01749 673513).

WESSEX WATER RESERVOIRS: Wessex Water, Claverton Down Road, Claverton Down, Bath BA2 7WW; brochure enquiries (tel: 0845 6004600); st from above address; dt from dispensing units at reservoirs; season ticket covering a specific reservoir: £400 (4 days/week); dt £18, conc £15, evng £10, tkt book ticket £90 conc £78; boat £15 (2 anglers max). limits: 4 fish on st, 5 fish on dt, 2 fish on evening ticket. **Clatworthy Reservoir**. 12m from **Taunton** in Brendon Hills; 130 acres brown and rainbow trout; fly only; $2\frac{1}{4}$m bank fishing; season: mid-Mar to beginning of Oct; permits from Fishing Lodge; wheelyboat for disabled; st, dt, tkt book available, conc; for further info, contact ranger (tel: 01984 624658).

Durleigh Reservoir. 2m W of **Bridgwater**. 80 acres; coarse fishing, carp, roach, bream, pike. Biggest recently, pike 27lb, carp 24lb, bream 7lb. Dt £6.50, evngs £4.50, conc £4.50, book of 10 tkts £50, (for more information, (tel: 01278 424786, Wessex Water).

Hawkridge Reservoir. 7m W of Bridgwater. 32 acres. Brown and rainbow trout; fly only. Season mid-Mar beginning Oct; st, dt, block available, conc, strictly no dogs, Boat or bank (tel: 01278 671840; Wessex Water).

Otterhead Lakes. About 1m from **Churchingford** nr Taunton. Two lakes of $2\frac{3}{4}$ and 2 acres; wild brown trout; fly only; no boats; season 15 March-30 Sept; members only, no dt; controlled by Wessex Water; very overgrown; leased to local club, Taunton FFC.

Sutton Bingham Reservoir. 4m S of **Yeovil**. 142 acres. Brown and rainbow trout; average rod 2lb; fly only, bank or boat; Wheelyboat available for disabled. Season 18 March-11 October; dt £16 from Ivan Tinsley,the ranger. Sutton Bingham Fishing Lodge, 1 Abbotts Mill BA22 2QL (tel: 01935 872389), conc; st available.

AVALON FISHERIES, Nr Westhay, BA6 9TT, coarse fishing on 2 lakes, pleasure lake, dt on site £7 (1 rod), £9 (2rods), conc available, holds carp from 2lbs - 15lbs plus good stock of skimmers, bream, tench, roach, rudd, perch and crucians plus pike into double figures & specimen carp lake, dt on site £10 max 2 rods, 24hr tkt available, must be booked in advance, (tel: 07855 825059; see website for more: www.avalonfisheries.co.uk).

BULLOCK FARM FISHING LAKES, coarse fishing lake complex (five lakes including specimen carp lake) just 4.5 miles from J20 off the M5 and 15 miles south of the city of Bristol, dt £7 adults, £5 junior/OAP/disabled (no charge for extra rods), (tel: 01934 835020; web: www.bullockfarm.co.uk).

BURTON SPRINGS FISHERY, Lawson Farm, Burton, Nr Bridgwater, TA5 1QB. Mixed coarse & trout fishing on 2 lakes, coarse many double figure carp up to 30 lbs, perch to 4lbs and tench up to 7lbs, few bream present, dt £8 (2 rods), 24 tkt £15, available via appointment only. Trout lake for rainbows, browns & blues & occas' tiger, dt on site £26 (4fish) half day £20 (2 fish), c&r (6 fish) £15, (tel: 01278 732135; see website for more information: www.burtonspringsfishery.com).

CHARGOT WATER, Luxborough. 3 ponds. Trout; fly only.

CIDER FARM LAKES, Dobunni Farm, Wick Road, Lympsham, BS24 0HA, 3 pleasure lakes and 2 dedicated match lakes, on site bait shop & drinks & hot food are available all day from the farm shop, dt on site £7 (1 rod), £9 (2 rods), conc available, (tel: 01278 751401; see website for more info: www.ciderfarmlakes.co.uk).

DONIFORD STREAM (Swill River at Doniford) and **WASHFORD RIVER, Taunton**. Trout; preserved.

EDNEYS FISHERIES, Mells, Frome, BA11 3RF, 3 mixed coarse lakes with carp up to 30lb, most swims are disabled friendly, dt £6, juv £4, night tkts £6, st £85, (tel: 01373 812294; web: www.edneysfisheries.co.uk).

EXE VALLEY FISHERY, Exebridge, rainbow trout fishing on 1 lake, dt are Option 1: £6 to fish with a per kilo charge of £3.50 (available until 4.30pm each day), Option 2: Flat rate charges (available 8.00am until sunset each day) 2 Fish - £14, 3 Fish - £18, 4 Fish - £22, 5 Fish - £25, (tel: 01398 323008; see website for more info: www.exevalleyfishery.co.uk).

FOLLY FOOT FISHERY, Taunton Road, North Petherton, TA6 6NW, 1 lake (3 acres) and is well stocked with a variety of koi, mirror, common and ghost carp, dt £8 (7:30am till dusk), night/24 hours £15, eve tkt (summer only) £5, (tel: 01278 662 979; web: www.follyfootfishery.co.uk).

HORNER WATER. On National Trust Holnicote Estate, Selworthy TA24 8TJ; upstream from Packhorse Bridge, Horner, to Pool Bridge, approx 2½m; fly fishing, small wild trout; dt £1, wt £4 (4 fish limit) from Horner Tea Garden (tel: 01643 862380) or Estate Office (tel: 01643 862452).

LITTON LAKES, Litton, BA3 4PW, fly fishing for rainbow and brown trout, (tel: 01275 332339).

SILVER SPRINGS FISHERY, Silver Street, Congresbury, BS49 5EY, consists of 2 lakes, a 4.5 acre coarse lake, and a 2.5 acre carp lake, dt on site, coarse lake £7 or £5 conc, £5 half day (from 2pm), carp lake £10 for 2 rods, £7 conc, £7 half day (from 2pm), (tel: 01934 877073; web: www.silverspringsfishery.com).

TRINITY WATERS, Straight Drove, Bridgwater, TA5 2BQ, 4 lake complex, £6 per day for one rod, £2 for any extra rod. conc £4 a day, £1 any extra rod, night fishing £20 per 24hrs, £30 for 48hrs, (booking only), (tel: 01278 450880; see website for more info: www.trinitywaters.co.uk).

WALL EDEN FARM, East Huntspill, Highbridge, TA9 3PU, small pond for trout, £10 (2 fish), also fishing for coarse fish on the **River Brue**, dt £5, (tel: 01278 786488; see website for more: www.walledenfarm.co.uk).

WIMBLEBALL LAKE, Dulverton. 374 acres. South West Lakes Trust, fly only, well-known stocked rainbow trout fishery; season Mar - Oct, boats bookable in advance; dt £20, boats £13, (Wheelyboat for disabled), conc, from self-service kiosk at Hill Farm Barn; ranger (tel: 01398 371372). Tackle shop: Lance Nicholson, 9 & 11 High St, Dulverton TA22 9HB (tel: 01398 323409; see website for more info: www.lancenich.f9.co.uk). Hotel:

B&B at lake: Gillian Payne, Lower Holworthy Farm, Brompton Regis, Dulverton TA22 9NY (tel: 01398 371244). There is a campsite at lake.

YEO. Fishing station: **Congresbury**. Tidal, good fly water for trout; a few coarse fish.

STOUR (Dorset)

Rises in Wiltshire Downs and flows through Dorset, joining Hampshire Avon at its mouth at Christchurch. Noted coarse fishery throughout year (large barbel, chub, roach, dace, bream and pike). Sea trout and salmon in lower reaches.

Christchurch (Dorset). Avon and Stour. Pike, perch, chub, roach, tench, dace. Christchurch AC has many miles of Stour, Avon, plus numerous gravel pits, lakes and ponds; Lifelands stretch of Hants Avon, Ringwood, from local tackle shops; club membership, £140 pa + £20 joining fee, conc, juv and OAP; under-12s £10. **Hordle Lakes**, 1m from New Milton; 7 lakes of total 11 acres, coarse fishing; dt £6 - £10 (tel: 01590 672300). Mixed fishing can be had on **Royalty Fishery** waters; 1½m double bank fishing; dt £12.50, conc £8; from Davis Fishing Tackle(below);, Sea fishing from Mudeford in Christchurch Bay is now excellent, particularly for bass and mullet. Tackle shops: Davis Fishing Tackle, 71-75 Bargates, Christchurch BH23 1QE (tel: 01202 485169; web: www.davistackle.co.uk). Hotel: King's Arms, Christchurch.

Throop (Dorset). Throop fisheries; 5½m of top quality coarse fishing; now Ringwood AC water; dt & wt available from Christchurch tackleists, including Davis Fishing Tackle (above).

STOUR (Dorset) - Tributaries

Wimborne (Dorset). Good chub, roach, bream, barbel, dace and pike. Some trout in Stour, also in R Allen. Small runs of salmon and sea trout. Salisbury & DAC has 2 adjoining stretches; apply Sec; members only; club also has 2 categories of fishing (game and mixed) all in Salisbury area; game: chalk stream dry fly and nymph on Upper Hampshire Avon and tribs (Nadder, Wylie, Ebble and Bourne (25m in all)), and 4 still water trout fisheries; coarse: 5 lakes; dt on two (Waldens at West Grimstead, and Witherington Farm, Downton) £10 on bank; also rivers upper Avon at Amesbury, trout at Durrington, Avon and Nadder near Salisbury; 2 fisheries on Hampshire Avon at Fordingbridge. Wimborne & Dist AC has approx 10m of Stour in Wimborne, Longham to Child Okeford; 11 coarse lakes (from Wareham to Ringwood) and 4 trout lakes (from High Ansty to Winterbourne Zelston); 10m of Stour (from Gains Cross to Longham) and 1m stretch of Avon at Fordingbridge; mainly members + guests only; membership £102; conc £77 contact Hon Sec; (see website for more info: www.wimborneanglingclub.co.uk).

Wessex Water own **Little Canford Ponds**, Wimborne, coarse fishery with good access for disabled; leaflet from Kay Harvey, Wessex Water (tel: 01823 225326). Tackle shops: Minster Sports & Fishing, 8 West St, Wimborne BH21 1JP (tel: 01202 882240; see website for more info: www.minstersports.co.uk); Wessex

Angling Centre, 321 Wimborne Rd, Poole BH15 3DH (tel: 01202 668244; web: www.wessexangling.co.uk; web: www.minstersports.co.uk). Hotels: King's Head, Three Lions.

Sturminster Marshall (Dorset). Southampton PS has about 2m here. Coarse, a few trout; contact Minster Sports & Fishing, 8 West St, Wimborne BH21 1JP (tel: 01202 882240; see website for more info: www.minstersports.co.uk)and local tackle shops.

Shapwick (Dorset). Coarse fish. Southampton PS has several miles of fishing here; dt, conc, from Minster Sports, 8 West St, Wimborne BH21 1JP (tel: 01202 882240; web: www.minstersports.co.uk).

Blandford Forum (Dorset). Roach, chub, dace, perch, bream, carp, grayling, eels, and pike; good all year. Some tench. Dorchester & Dist AS has 600 yards south bank and 1100 yards north bank near **Shillingstone** (Child Okeford); also water at **Little Hanford** (Chesil Farm), and Hanford Farm; enquire Hon Sec; no dt; membership £50, conc available. Blandford & Dist AC has Stour fishing from Durweston Bridge d/s to Charlton Marshall; membership £35; conc; dt £4. Tackle shop: Todber Manor Fisheries Shop, Todber, Sturminster Newton DT10 1JB (tel: 01258 820384; see website for more info: www.todbermanor.co.uk); Arthur Conyers, 3 West Str, Blandford Forum DT11 7AW (tel: 01258 452307).

Sturminster Newton (Dorset). Chub, roach, dace, pike, perch, tench, bream; fishing very good. Dorchester & Dist AS has Factory Farm, near **Marnhull**, u/s from Red Bridge (both banks) and d/s (north bank only); apply Hon Sec; no dt; st £50, conc. Sturminster & Hinton AA has 9m

above and below town; members only; st £35; for wt £12 and dt £5, conc, apply to Todber Manor Fisheries Shop, Todber, Sturminster Newton DT10 1JB (tel: 01258 820384; see website for more info: www.todbermanor.co.uk); Bull Inn; Candy's Newsagent; Marsh's Electrical. Hotel: White Hart.

Stalbridge (Dorset). Chub, roach, tench, dace, pike. Stalbridge AS has 2m of Stour, 2m on **Lydden**; dt £5, conc, from C C Moore & Co, Church Hill, DT10 2LR (tel: 01963 362234; web: www.ccmoore.com).

Gillingham (Dorset). Trout and coarse fish. Dorchester & Dist AS has fishing at Marnhull (Factory Farm): Contact Hon Sec. St £50, conc (no dt). Gillingham & Dist AA has 7m fishing from Gillingham to Marnhull, various beats; **Turner's Paddock Lake**, Stourton (dt £5), and **Mappowder Lakes**, (dt £4) from tackle shops or club treasurer; **Loddon Lakes**, members only. Turners Paddock; dt £5; st £30, conc. Tackle shops: Todber Manor Fisheries Shop, Todber, Sturminster Newton DT10 1JB (tel: 01258 820384; see website for more info: www.todbermanor.co.uk).

Stourton (Wilts). **Stourhead**: Stourhead (Western) Estate at Stourton, near Mere has brown trout fishing on a number of ponds, st £100, wt £30; rods from April to September; contact Sally Monkhouse (tel: 01747 840643). National Trust have leased to Gillingham & DAA Stourhead's Turners Paddock Lake; coarse; members, & dt from Todber Manor Fisheries (tel: 01258 820384); Mere PO.

MOORS:

Verwood (Dorset). Trout in parts, otherwise mainly roach; Ringwood club has water.

STOUR (Kent)

Rises in two arms north-west and south-east of Ashford, where they join. From junction river flows about 30m north-east and east to sea beyond Sandwich. Below Canterbury, good roach fishing with fish to 2lb common, bream to 6lb and pike over 20lb. Trout fishing restricted to club members in upper reaches.

Sandwich (Kent). River fast-flowing from Minster to Sandwich (Vigo Sluice); good fishing for bream and roach; few perch and tench; sea trout and grey mullet. Free fishing from quay and from Ropewalk; bream, rudd, roach. Private fishing from Richborough Road, upstream. Sandwich & Dist AA has Reed Pond at Sandwich, Belle Isle and Wagtail Lake at St Nicholas and Swallowbrook Water at Ash; and North and South Streams at Worth; guest tickets only. **Lydden**; members and guests only. **Stonar Lake** (stocked, carp and rudd) is Canterbury & DAA water; members only. **Canterbury** (Kent). Trout, tench, bream, roach, rudd, pike, etc. Free within city boundary for residents, except for municipal gardens stretch. Canterbury & Dist AA hold water from city boundary d/s to Plucks Gutter, 9m both banks; brown trout stocked, run of sea trout; members only; st £30 joining memb £60, conc; Assn also has Stour and Trenley Lakes, fine coarse fishing, and **Fordwich Lake**, trout pool, members only; Assn also has new water Minster, nr Ramsgate; 2 mixed coarse lakes; and at **Littlebourne Lakes** (3 lakes); carp, tench and perch; all lakes members only; for more information, contact Hon Sec (tel:01227 710830; web: www.cdaa.co.uk). **Longshaw Fishery**, Calcott Hill, Sturry CT3 4ND (tel: 01227 710263); carp, tench, perch, roach; dt £8 (1 rod), £10 (2 rods), conc; bait in lodge. **Tyler Hill Coarse Fishery** (tel: 01227 764048) is open all year; for prices please phone; mixed coarse. Tackle shop: Sandwich Bait & Tackle, South East Water Gardens, Dover Rd, Sandwich CT13

0DG (tel: 01304 613752). Hotels: County; Falstaff; George and Dragon.

Ashford (Kent). Ashford AS holds **River Stour** between **Ashford** and **Wye** (members only), also Rother; and Royal Military Canal from Appledore Dam to Iden Dam, also at Kenardington to Warehorne; also Ham Street to Ruckinge; dt £5, conc, on bank; also 3 lakes at Surrenden Manor Road (members and guests); mixed coarse (incl 1 match lake with silver fish: match bookings, 48 pegs); also Singleton Lake (dt from bailiff on bank or Singleton PO; and pond at Smarden (members only st £55 + £10 joining, conc (children under 12 free), (£5 for key to Surrenden)). Cinque Ports AS controls 4½m of Royal Military Canal from Seabrook Outfall to West Hythe (7m); from West Hythe to Giggers Green, Ashford (4m); also 2 ponds at Beachborough (members only), Etchinghall near Folkestone; and 4 ponds at Fittenden; st £55 (+ entrance fee £10) (husband and wife £75), conc; canal dt £5, conc, from bailiff on bank. Ashford Working Men's Club has a pit; good tench, carp, rudd; members only; no dt. At **Bethersden** is Chequer Tree Trout & Coarse Fishery, Chequer Tree Lane TN26 3JR (tel: 01233 820078; web: www.chequertreefishery.co.uk); dt £20 (3 trout) (evng £10, 1 fish); to £7 1-rod, £10 2-rod, £5 evening (coarse), conc; tuition, tackle hire and camping facilities on site; no boats; carp to 32lb. Mid Kent Fisheries, Chilham Water Mill, Ashford Rd, Chilham CT4 8EE (tel: 01227 730668) have 18 acre Conningbrook among 20 lakes in total; carp, pike, perch; one dt match lake, £6 on bank. Tackle shops: Ashford Tackle Shop, Unit 94, Ellingham Way Ind Est, Ashford

TN23 6LZ (tel: 01233 630914; web: www.ashfordtackle.co.uk); Dens Tackle, 73 Dymchurch Rd, Hythe CT21 6JN (tel: 01303 267053; web: www.denstackle.com); Micks Tackle, 1 Thirlestane Dymchurch Rd, Hythe CT21 6LB (tel: 01303 266334). Hotels: County, Kent Arms.

LITTLE STOUR: Same fish as main river but overgrown in places. Most fishing now private.

WANTSUM. Tench, bream, perch, roach, gudgeon, chub, dace, eels and some pike. Wantsum AA controls 120 peg stretch (90 pegs of which available for dt) from 'Chambers Wall' area of St Nicholas-at-Wade and continues to the north where it meets the sea wall; dt £5, juv £1 from bailiff on bank; on R Stour, at Pucks Gutter, the club controls 32 pegs on south bank d/s from 'Dog & Duck'; roach, bream, perch, gudgeon and chub; dt £5, juv £1 from bailiff on bank; st £30 plus £5 joining fee, jnr £18 plus £5 joining fee, conc £20 plus £5 joining fee; for futher information contact Hon Sec (See clubs). Tackle shop: Kingfisheries, 34 King Str, Margate CT9 1DA (tel: 01843 223866; see website for more info: www.kingfisheries.co.uk).

STOUR (Suffolk)

Coarse fish river forming border between Suffolk and Essex. Enters sea at Harwich via large estuary. Some sea trout in semi-tidal waters below Flatford. Environment Agency are regularly stocking the river with barbel.

Harwich (Essex). Harwich AC has several coarse fisheries in area: Dock River; Bradfield Hall Lakes with roach, rudd, pike, perch, carp, eels, bream; members only; (web: www.harwichac.co.uk).

Manningtree (Essex). Tidal; roach, dace, perch, pike and occasional sea trout (fish of 9lb caught). Lawford AC has stretch at **Cattlewade** (A137 bridge); dt on bank. Dt from bailiff, Mr Tripp, for Elm Park & Hornchurch Dist AS stretch between club notices at **Flatford Mill**; also contact bailiff at The Granary, Flatford, East Bergholt, Colchester CO7 6UL (tel: 01206 298111). Hotel: White Hart.

Nayland (Suffolk). Bream, chub, dace, perch, pike, roach, tench. Colchester APS has water here and at **Wiston, Boxted, Langham, Wormingford** and **Stratford St Mary**; new membership £85, to 29 Lodge Road, Braintree CM7 1JA; no dt, (web: www.colchesteraps.org). Colnes AS has stretches at **Little Horkesley**; members and guests only.

Bures (Essex). Colnes AS has 5 stretches; members only, who can take guests. London AA controls a good deal of water at **Bures Lake** and river. **Henny Bridge** (Essex). Great Cornard AC fishes from Henny Bridge to Henny Weir; book a month in advance, dt water. **Sudbury** (Suffolk). Bream, roach, chub, dace, tench, carp, perch, pike, gudgeon. Sudbury & Long Melford DAA has 7 stretches of Stour (dt £10 on bank, conc; £5 from local tackle shops); membership £55, conc, from Sudbury Angling Centre; also for club's **Rushbrook Farm Lake**, and **Starfield Pits**; also **Butchers Lane**, Boxford, small mixed coarse; dt tackle shops only. Tackleist also sells tickets for Colchester APS water, **Doneylands Lake (Snake Pit Lake).** Hadleigh & Dist AS have various stretches on Stour, R Brett and 6 local stillwaters; restricted membership, guest tickets offered on rivers; contact Hon Sec. Sudbury & Long Melford DAA also has water from Clare to Sudbury, with coarse species incl large chub, bream, roach, pike to 37lbs; and Suffolk Glem; also stillwater at Long Melford, Starfield

Pits, dt from tackle shops only; membership from tackle shops or Hon Sec. Tackle shops: Sudbury Angling Centre, 40 North Str, Sudbury CO10 1RD (tel: 01787 312118); Tackle Up, 49a St Johns Str, Bury St Edmunds

IP33 1SP (tel: 01284 755022; web: www.tackle-up.com).

Cavendish and **Clare** (Suffolk). London AA controls water here. At **Glemsford**, the Assn has 3 lakes near the river on the Essex/Suffolk border; membership £43.

SURREY (lakes)

BURY HILL FISHERIES. Nr Dorking. Well known coarse fishery of four lakes, the largest of which is 12 ½ acres. Particularly known for its tench, roach, carp, bream, pike and zander fishing, all of which run to specimen size; also good stocks of rudd, perch and crucian carp; open all year, bank and boat fishing; tuition courses, full facilities include sit down cafe, all of which are suitable for disabled anglers; dt £11.50, one rod, second rod £5.50 extra; boat: £5.50 per person; evening £5.50 per rod; concessions to jun, OAP; match bookings and corporate days organised; tackle shop on site; further details from Fishery Manager, Estate Office, Old Bury Hill, Surrey RH4 3JU (tel: 01306 883621; web: www.buryhillfisheries.com).

FRENSHAM PONDS. Farnham (4m). 60 acres and 30 acres. Farnham AS has rights on Great Pond, and Little Pond; coarse fishing, tench, with carp, roach, pike, perch etc; members of Farnham AS only; season 16 June to 14 March; apply to memb sec (tel: 01252 320 871; see website for more info: www.farnhamanglingsociety.com).

Halliford Mere Lakes, Chertsey Road, Shepperton, Surrey, TW17 9NN, 4 spring fed lakes for rainbow trout fishing, dt & st available, closed on Mondays but st holders are able to fish only, for more info, (tel: 01932 248547; see website for more info: www.hallifordmere.co.uk).

RIPLEY. **Papercourt** fishery, Sendmarsh; large carp to over 40lb, pike, bream, tench to 11lb, chub,

perch, eels, roach; a Cemex (formerly RMC) Angling Silver Water fishery; st; (For Cemex (formerly RMC) Angling, see Chertsey.)

YATELEY COMPLEX, Yateley. This Cemex (formerly RMC) complex consists of 14 lakes and a stretch of R Blackwater; Gold Venue: **Car Park** lake: Car Park Lake holds carp to 52lbs; £585 pa 2-rods summer/autumn, 3-rods winter; waiting list; night tickets allow fishing on all the Yateley lakes (except Car Park lake and the dt South, North, Pads and Sandhurst lakes); st £110 2-rods day and night, £65 conc on Yateley complex, with exception of the day ticket waters; **South Lake** and **Sandhurst Lake**, both heavily stocked with carp to 35lb: dt for South Lake (2 rods) £17 or 24-hour £22 from Yateley Angling Centre, 16 The Parade GU46 7UN (tel: 01252 873123 (agent Cemex (formerly RMC)); **South Lake**: dt (2 rods) £15 or 24-hour £20 (2 rods); **Pads Lake** is of 4 acres; famous carp water and up to 10 anglers can book the lake for the day: contact Cemex Angling; bookings £135 24-hrs; £800 7-days; (For Cemex Angling, see Chertsey.) Farnham AS has River Blackwater at Yateley, and River Valley Lakes (mixed coarse, 20 acres); and Mill Lane; mixed coarse, 8 acres, specimen; no dt; (tel: 01252 320 871).

SWAN VALLEY, Pond Farm Lane, **Yateley**. Four lakes with carp to 38lbs, tench to 8lbs, pike to 27lbs; syndicate lakes.Tackle shop: Yateley Angling Centre, 16 The Parade, Reading Road,

Yateley GU46 7UN (tel: 01252 861955; see website for more info: www.yateleyanglingcentre.co.uk).

TRILAKES, Yateley Road, **Sandhurst,** Berks GU47 8JQ (tel: 01252 873191): mixed fishery; well stocked with tench, very large carp (common, mirror, crucian, ghost), bream, roach, perch, pike, eels; open 9.30am to 6.00pm or sunset if earlier; open all year; purchase dt on entry, £9.80 (up to 2 rods), £5 half day, (conc); car park, cafe, access for disabled. Tackle shop: Yateley Angling Centre, 16 The Parade, Reading Road, Yateley GU46 7UN (tel: 01252 861955; web: www.yateleyanglingcentre.co.uk).

VIRGINIA WATER. Virginia Water, Johnson Pond and Obelisk Pond, Windsor Great Park fishable by season ticket only; coarse fish; st £67 (incl VAT); early application advised in writing, to Crown Estate Office, The Great Park, Windsor, Berks SL4

2HT (tel: 01753 860222; web: www.thecrownestate.co.uk)(sae).

WILLOW PARK FISHERIES, Youngs Drive, Ash, nr Aldershot GU12 6RE (tel: 01252 325867; web: www.willowparkfisherys.co.uk); three lakes of 13 acres, mixed fishery stocked with a variety of species: carp (to 33lb), tench and other coarse fish; 120 pegs; bait and refreshments on site; dt on site £10 1 rod, £15 2 rods, and £24 for 24-hours, conc for jun; conc for OAP/disabled mid week; disabled facilities now on all 3 lakes.

WINKWORTH ARBORETUM LAKE. Winkworth, nr Godalming. National Trust property. Trout fishery (fly fishing and boats only) managed by Godalming AS; st £280, plus entry fee of £20; details from Hon Sec or (tel: 01483 423205).

WIREMILL POOL, nr **Lingfield.** Coarse fish include tench up to 6lb, bream up to 7lb, roach up to 3lb, carp up to 6lb.

SUSSEX (lakes and streams)

ARDINGLY RESERVOIR. Ardingly Activity Centre, nr Haywards Heath. 198 acre coarse fishery with excellent pike, fish to 30lbs, also good stocks of bream, roach, tench etc; coarse season 1st June-31st May; pike season 1 Oct-1 May; (only very experienced specialist pike anglers allowed, 18+); enq to The Lodge, Ardingly Reservoir, Ardingly, W Sussex RH17 6SQ (tel: 01444 892549; web: www.ardinglyactivitycentre.co.uk).

ARLINGTON RESERVOIR, South East Water, Fishing Lodge, Berwick, Polegate BN26 6TF (tel: 01323 870810); excellent rainbow trout fishery; dt and members tickets from self-service lodge on site (tackle for sale/hire); special membership rates on request; boats and engines for hire (best to book); disabled (wheelyboat) boat and platform.

BARCOMBE RESERVOIR, Barcombe, Lewes, BN8 5BY. 40 acres, South East Water, fly fishing for rainbow trout only; information from Fishing Lodge (tel: 01273 814819); dt from self-service lodge; tuition available.

BLACKWOOL FARM, Colhook Common, Petworth, GU28 9ND, 2 lakes for rainbow & brown trout, various dt prices, (tel: 01428 707 258; web: www.blackwoolfarm.co.uk).

BORINGWHEEL TROUT FISHERY, Cackle Street, Nutley, TN22 3DU, 6 acre trout fishing lake for rainbow & brown trout, various dt prices available, (tel: 01825 712629; web: www.boringwheel.co.uk).

BRICK FARM LAKES, Windmill Hill, Herstmonceux, BN27 4RS, 2 lakes (3rd lake planned) for rainbow trout fishing, dt, 2 fish limit £15, 3 fish limit £20, 4 fish limit £25 & 6 fish limit £35, (tel: 01323 832615; web: www.brickfarmlakes.co.uk).

BUXTED. Uckfield. Oast Farm, Lephams Bridge, TN22 4AU (tel: 01825 733446): coarse pond of quarter acre, with carp (to nearly 20lb), roach, tench; dt £5 weekdays (£6 w/e), conc, at farm shop; cafe on site: Mr Greenland. Boringwheel Trout Fishery, Cackle St, Nutley, Uckfield TN22 3DU **Nutley** (tel: 01825 712629); brown and rainbow; dt 8am to dusk from fishery. Tackle shop: Uckfield Angling Centre, 212A High St, Uckfield TN22 1RD (tel: 01825 760300; see website for more info: www.uckfieldangling.com).

CHALK SPRINGS FISHERY, Park Bottom, Arundel, West Sussex, BN18 0AA (tel: 01903 883742; web: www.chalksprings.com); four lakes, clear water, stocked with brown, rainbow, and blue rainbow trout of 2-20lb; dt £45 (5 fish), £39 (4 fish); part-day £34, £26; lodge on lakes, tuition, tackle.

CHICHESTER CANAL. Chichester (W Sussex). Chichester Ship Canal Trust has 2½m from Chichester to Donnington Bridge, with roach, rudd, perch, carp, tench, bream, pike, eels; no fish to be removed; st £45, wt £9, dt £3.80, conc, from bailiffs on bank. Chichester & DAA have canal fishing; also 6 lakes in Chichester; mixed coarse; members only; prices on application to Hon Sec, (web: www.chichester-as.co.uk). Petworth & Bognor AC has stretch from Chichester Basin to Donnington; dt available from bailiff. Mixed fishery at Lakeside Village, Vinnetrow Road, PO20 1QH (tel: 01243 787715); 11 lakes; carp, perch, pike, rudd, roach, bream, tench; dt £10 from office, or on bank (24hrs); no boats. Tackle shops: Southern Angling Specialists, 2 Stockbridge Place, Stockbridge Rd, Chichester PO19 2QH (tel: 01243 531669); Shore Line Angling, 7 Shore Rd, East Wittering, Chichester PO20 8DY (tel: 01243 673353). Selsey tackle shop: Raycrafts, 119 High Str, Selsey PO20 0QB (tel: 01243 606039; web: www.raycrafts.co.uk).

LAKEDOWN TROUT FISHERY, Swife Lane, Broad Oak, Near Heathfield, TN21 8UX, 4 trout lakes various dt available, (tel: 01435 883 449; see website for more info: www.lakedowntroutfishery.co.uk).

LAKE VIEW FISHERIES, Old Hollow, Worth, Crawley RH10 4TA (tel: 01293 521186; see website: www.lakeview-fisheries.co.uk). 10 acre lake; carp to 25lb, tench, crucians, perch to 4lb; on-site shop; dt from bailiff or Jack Frost Tackle House, Reynolds Place, West Green, Crawley RH11 7HB (tel: 01293 521186; web: www.real-tackle.com).

DARWELL WATER. At Mountfield, **Robertsbridge** TN32 5DR (mobile 07917 307942; see website for more: www.cranbrookanglingclub.co.uk); Cranbrook & DAC water: coarse fish; 158 acres; members only; apply bailiff above; pike, roach, perch, eels, carp, tench); boats to be booked in advance from bailiff; take care over approach route down small lanes; club also fishes Springwood Fishery at Flimwell, members only; mixed coarse incl catfish to 57lb; Park Farm at Frittenden; carp to 36lb, tench; also Pattenden Lane at Marden; mixed match water; Burntwood at Frittenden; mixed coarse; Lamberhurst Lakes; carp; and 2 stretches of Medway at East Peckham and East Farleigh; the club is affiliated to Rother Fisheries Assn.

FRAMFIELD PARK FISHERY, Brookhouse Rd, Framfield, nr Uckfield TN22 5QJ (tel: 01825 890948); three coarse fishing lakes totalling over 7 acres; good match weights, with large tench, bream and carp; shop on site; bailiff will give instruction free to juniors.

POWDERMILL WATER. **Sedlescombe**. 52 acres, wild brown and rainbow trout to 20lb; dt £26 6 fish; boats available; for membership, contact Hon Sec, Hastings Flyfishers Club Ltd; bookings: (tel: 01424 870498, between 9.30 and 10.30am; web: www.hastingsflyfishers.co.uk).

MILTON MOUNT LAKE. **Three Bridges** (W Sussex), Crawley AS water st,carp; members only. Club also has; Ballast Hole, Pound Hill, Crawley; New Pond, Pease Pottage (carp and crucian carp, tench); the Mill Pond, Gossops Green; Buchan Park lakes, nr **Crawley**, carp, pike etc; Hon Sec, (tel: 01923 467064; web: www.crawleyanglingsociety.co.uk).

CLIVE VALE RESERVOIRS. **Harold Road**: mixed coarse fishery, Clive Vale AC; st £40, junior £22, conc £24 (see website for more info: www.clivevaleac.co.uk).

ECCLESBOURNE RESERVOIR. **Hastings**. Good carp, tench, roach, bream pike and rudd; now privately fished: no tickets, as of July 2010 up for sale. **PEVENSEY LEVELS**. Marshland drained by various streams into **Pevensey Haven** and **Wallers Haven**; good coarse fishing on large streams (pike, roach, rudd, perch, bream, carp and tench), most of best waters rented by clubs. Fishing stations: **Eastbourne**, **Hailsham**, **Pevensey**. Southdown AA has major stretches of Pevensey Haven between Pevensey and Rickney, also Railland's Ditch and Chilley Stream (tench, bream, rudd, perch, carp and eels); both banks of Wallers Haven (renowned pike, tench and bream); water on **R Cuckmere** on both banks between Horsebridge and Alfriston, and the association has six sites on still waters; tickets, st £65 + £10 joining fee,jun, & conc; no dt, from Hon Sec & Tackle shops: Polegate Angling Centre, 101 Station Road, Polegate BN26 6EB (tel: 01323 486379); or from Anglers Den, 6 North Rd, Pevensey Bay BN24 6AY (tel: 01323 460441).

SCARLETTS LAKE. 3 acres, between E Grinstead and **Tunbridge Wells**. Good coarse fishing, members only. **WEIR WOOD RESERVOIR**, Priory Road, Forest Row, RH18 5HT, dt 8 trout £28.50, 4 trout £17.50 all tickets between 8am and 8pm; coarse dt 8am to 8pm with 2 rods £15 (limited area and rules apply), boats available, dt pike fishing only on specified days, st also available for coarse & trout fishing, (tel: 01342 820650; see website for more info: www.weirwoodreservoir.co.uk).

YEW TREE TROUT FISHERY, Yew Tree Lane, Rotherfield, TN6 3QP, 3 lakes for rainbow & brown trout, various dt available, (tel: 01892 852430; see website for more info: www.yewtreetroutfishery.com).

TAMAR

Rises in Cornwall and follows boundary between Devon and Cornwall for good part of course, emptying finally into Plymouth Sound. Holds salmon, sea trout, sometimes brown trout, and a few grayling.

Milton Abbot (Devon). Endsleigh Fishing Club has 12m both banks, salmon and sea trout; dt £30 to £60 depending on months; average salmon catch 71; over 90% taken on fly; good car access to pools; tuition on site; (tel: 01822 860520; web: www.endsleigh-fishing-club.com).

Lifton (Devon). Tamar, **Lyd**, **Thrushel**, **Carey**, **Wolf** and **Ottery**; trout, sea trout (late June to end Sept), salmon (May, to mid-October). Hotel: Arundell Arms, Lifton, Devon PL16 0AA (tel: 01566 784666; fax: 01566 784494; see website for more info: www.arundellarms.com), has 20m of excellent water in lovely surroundings; 23 individual beats, also 3-acre trout lake, brown and rainbow trout to 9lb; licences and tackle at hotel, fly fishing courses (beginners and semi-advanced) by two resident instructors; dt (when there are vacancies) for S & st £25-£32 according to date; lake trout £31 (residents only), brown trout £25.

Launceston (Cornwall). Salmon, sea trout, trout and grayling. Permits can be obtained for seven miles of Tamar, **Inney** and **Carey** from Launceston AA, Hon Sec, Colin Hookway (tel: 01822 855053); dt waters, about 13m of fishing in all. Lakes and ponds: **Stone Lake**, 4½ acres coarse fishing. **Hidden Valley Lakes** PL15 8SJ, dt available, conc; mixed coarse, carp to 24lb (tel: 01566 86463). **Alder Quarry Pond**, Lewdown, Okehampton EX20 4PJ (tel: 01566 783444), 4½ acres, coarse, dt £5 water. **Dutson Water**, coarse fishing dt from Holmleigh Garden Centre. Tackle shop: Homeleigh Garden Centre, Homeleigh, Dutson, Launceston PL15 9SP (tel: 01566 773147; web: www.homeleighgardencentre.co.uk); Launceston Sports, 1 Market Street, Launceston PL8 8EP (tel: 01566 774127; see website for more info: www.launcestonsports.co.uk) for Launceston AA tickets. Hotels: White Hart; Eagle House; Race Horse Inn, North Hill.

Bridgerule (Devon). **Tamar Lakes** here: South West Lakes Trust waters for which tickets are issued, (See Cornwall lakes). 18 lakes (total 45 acres); coarse fishing lakes, with various carp species, orfe, tench, and others; contact J Ray, Clawford Vineyard, Clawton, Holsworthy EX22 6PN (tel: 01409 254177; web: www.clawford.co.uk). Hotel: Court Barn, Clawton, Holsworthy.

Tributaries of the Tamar

TAVY: A moorland spate river, rises in Cranmere Pool on Dartmoor and flows about 17m before entering Tamar estuary at Bere Ferrers. Salmon and sea-trout river.

Tavistock (Devon). Tavy, Walkham & Plym FC; salmon, sea trout and brown trout permits for visitors on main river, **Meavy**, **Plym** and **Walkham**; spinning allowed but no natural baits; salmon and sea trout st £140, wt £55, dt £20; brown trout st £55, mt £25, wt £15, no dt, from Yelverton Garage, 1 Moorland Villas PL20 6DT (tel: 01822 853339); there is also associate membership for reserve waters on Tavy; apply Hon Sec. **Tavistock Trout Fishery**, Parkwood Rd, Mount Tavy PL19 9JW (tel: 01822 615441; www.tavistocktroutfishery.co.uk): 1m from A386 towards Oakhampton, nr Trout 'n' Tipple pub; fishing on five lakes beside R Tavy; dt available 7 days a week; rods for hire, plus permit; well stocked children's fishing lake; fly tackle shop. **Mary Tavy** (Devon). Brown trout; run of salmon and sea trout. Fishing mostly privately owned. Plymouth & Dist Freshwater AA has rights at **Peter Tavy** (members only, st available from Hon Sec.

Yelverton (Devon). Good centre for Tavy, Walkham & Plym FC waters; salmon, sea trout; ticket suppliers listed under Tavistock. **Coombe Fisheries**, Miltoncombe PL20 6EZ, adjacent to Buckland Abbey: two 1 acre lakes with rudd, roach, tench, bream, ghost carp in top lake; various carp in bottom lake; open all year, dawn till dusk, barbless hooks only; contact S Horn (tel: 01822 616624).

WALKHAM (tributary of Tavy): rises north-west of Princetown, and joins the Tavy below Tavistock. Upper reaches rocky and overhung, but downstream from Horrabridge there are many fishable pools. Peal run from July onwards.

INNY: Trout, sea trout.

LYD: Trout, sea trout, some salmon.

Lifton (Devon). Arundell Arms has fishing for salmon, sea trout and brown trout, also on main river and other tributaries.

TAW

Rises on Dartmoor and flows 50m to Barnstaple Bay, where it forms estuary. Salmon with sea trout (peal) from May onwards. Excellent brown trout always available and good coarse fishing in places nearby: links with local fisheries.

Barnstaple (Devon). Bass and mullet in estuary. Salmon, sea trout, peal, trout, roach and dace. Peal best July, August. Barnstaple & Dist AA has water immediately below New Bridge; members only; membership/st £30 from local tackle shop or apply Hon Sec; mixed ticket for game and coarse £45 (£30 game or coarse only) as above; club also has water at **Venn** and **South Aller**; mixed coarse. Riverton House and Lakes, **Swimbridge**, EX32 0QX (tel: 01271 830009), has coarse fishing on two lakes of over 2 acres with large carp, bream, tench, roach, perch, rudd; night fishing by prior arrangement: 24-hours £16 (2 rods), dt £8 on specimen lake and £7 on match lake, evening (after 4.30pm) £6 (£5); self-catering cottages. At **Braunton**, coarse fishing at Little Comfort Farm, EX33 2NJ (tel: 01271 812414; see website for more info: www.littlecomfortfarm.co.uk) with carp over 16lbs; dt on site £6–£3; self catering cottages; apply Mr & Mrs Milsom. C L and Mrs Hartnoll, Little Bray House, **Brayford** EX32 7QG (tel: 01598 710295); who also have about 1m (both banks) of Bray; small trout only; dt £5. For other trout fishing see tributary Yeo. East and West Lyns, Badgeworthy Water and Heddon are accessible, as well as fishing on Wistlandpound and Slade Reservoirs. Tackle shop: North Devon Angling Centre, 48 Boutport Street EX31 1SE, tel: 01271 321399; www.northdevonanglingcentre.co.uk

Umberleigh (Devon). Salmon, peal, trout; preserved. Rising Sun, EX37 9DU (tel: 01769 560447; web: www.risingsuninn. com) rents rods to give access to over 2m of water (eight beats) for residents; fly only after March 30; sunday fishing is allowed; salmon best March, April, May, August and September; sea trout June, July, August and September; brochure, giving charges, etc, on request; dt £40 per rod for non-residents; £25 per rod for residents. Other hotel: Northcote Manor, Burrington.

South Molton (Devon). **Oaktree Fishery**, Bottreaux Mill, EX36 3PU (tel: 01398 341568; web: www.oaktreefishery.co.uk), has three well-stocked lakes: two match, one specimen; large carp, tench, roach; open all year; various dt prices at fishery; tackle hire, refreshments, toilet facilities, fisherman's cottages, disabled access, open all year.

Eggesford, Chulmleigh (Devon). Fox & Hounds Country Hotel, EX18 7JZ, has 5m of private salmon, sea trout and brown trout fishing on Taw for more info contact hotel, (tel: 01769 580345; see website for more info: www.foxandhoundshotel.co.uk).

Coldridge (Devon). Taw Fishing Club has 3¼m from Brushford Bridge to Hawkridge Bridge; very good trout fishing; complimentary for members' guests only; st £60 + joining fee £60; limited to 50. Also Crediton FFC has access: contact Hon Sec for dt £15.

North Tawton (Devon). Trout. K Dunn, The Barton EX20 2BB (tel: 01837 82129) also issues dt for about 1m.

YEO (Barnstaple): Sea and brown trout; salmon, sea trout run.

BRAY (tributary of Mole):

South Molton (Devon). South Molton AC has right bank from Brayly Bridge u/s to Newton Bridge, with salmon,

trout and peal, fly only; members only. Tackle shop: Sports Centre, 130 East St, South Molton, EX36 3BU (tel: 01769 572080). Hotels: The George; The Tiverton.

TEES

Rises below Cross Fell in Pennines, flows eastward between Durham and Yorkshire and empties into North Sea near Middlesbrough. The Tees Barrage was completed in June 1995, and has already created a much cleaner river upstream. Fish are being caught throughout all previously tidal stretches, from the new Princess of Wales Bridge to Thornaby and above. Well stocked from Middleton-in-Teesdale down to Croft.

Middlesbrough (Co Durham). NW reservoirs Lockwood and Scaling Dam in vicinity; stocked with trout; dt on site. Middlesbrough AA have R Tees at Over Dinsdale, Thornaby, Stockton; trout, salmon and usual coarse fish, 6 stretches of R Swale at Ainderby, Gatenby, Maunby, Holme Top and Holme Bottom; Marske Reservoir, dt from tackle shop, £3.50, (mixed coarse; stocked with carp); and ponds at Hutton Rudby, all good coarse fishing. West House Trout Lakes at Stillington, 4 lakes, various dt prices, (tel: 07836 330157; web: www.westhouse-troutlakes.co.uk).
Local tackle shops: Anglers Choice, 98 Cumberland Rd, Middlesbrough TS5 6BH (tel: 01642 850428; web: www.anglerschoiceonline.co.uk), who has st £32 (+ £10 entry), conc, for Middlesbrough AA waters; Cleveland Angling Centre, Unit 22a Westbury St, Thornaby, Stockton on Tees TS17 6PG (tel: 01642 677000.

Stockton (Co Durham). Trout; grayling, coarse fish on one of best stretches of river. Stockton AL has over 10m at Gainford, Winston, Middleton-one -Row, nr Darlington, Aislaby and Worsall (good barbel) nr Yarm, and on Swale, nr Ainderby (Morton-on-Swale) and above Great Langton, where the company also has Kiplin Beck. Free stretches in the Stockton town area; fish well for silver fish (roach, perch and bream). Lower

Tees AC has good stretch from Bowesfield Lane upstream to Thornaby; bream; tickets from Tackle Box, who also sell tickets for Charlton's Pond, Billingham (carp to 20lb, tench and bream to 6lb; 6 acres). Hart Reservoir is coarse fishery run by Hartlepool & Dist AC; contact Hon Sec; members only; st £70, conc; club also has 2½m of Lower River Tees. At Middleton St George Ferryhill & DAC has reservoirs; carp and coarse; 6 acres; dt from village shop; enquire Membership Secretary. Tackle shop: Tackle Box, 46 Station Rd, Billingham TS23 1AB (tel: 01642 532034). Stockton Tees permits are sold at Anglers Choice, 53 Clive Rd, Middlesbrough TS5 6BH (tel: 01642 899288; see website for more info: www.anglerschoiceonline.co.uk).

Eaglescliffe, (Co Durham). Yorkshire bank in Yarm free fishing. Leven joins just below Yarm. Trout and coarse fish. Middlesbrough AC to above falls; Thornaby AA and Yarm A Ltd together up to Hutton Rudby; excellent brown trout fishing; occasional sea trout; Middlesbrough AC also have Locke Park, Redcar; mixed coarse; dt on bank £3.

Yarm (Co Durham). Tidal good coarse fishing; chub, dace, roach, occasional trout. Some free fishing inside of loop surrounding town, ½m, on EA licence. Mixed fishery, deep, slow moving water. Yarm A Ltd, strong team club with 15m of Tees fishing at Low Middleton, Yarm, Over Dinsdale, Sockburn and Piercebridge; members of Assn. of Teeside & Dist Angling Clubs, with 10m water.

Neasham (Durham). Free fishing for 300 yards behind Fox and Hounds pub (mixed fishery).

Sockburn (Durham) and **Dinsdale**. Chub, dace, roach. Approx 3m controlled by Association of Teesside & Dist Angling Clubs, which consists of Thornaby AA, Yarm A Ltd, Darlington Brown Trout Anglers and Stockton AL; no dt.

Croft (Durham). Fair head of trout, grayling and coarse fish. Free fishing for 200 yds upstream of road bridge. 5 ½m miles controlled by Thornaby AA, members only, application forms from Darlington Angling Centre or W P Adams (see Darlington).

Darlington (Durham). Trout, grayling, coarse fish; occasional salmon. Council water free to residents. Darlington AC fish 10½m between Croft, Darlington and High Coniscliffe, and 1m of **Clow Beck**, 3m S of Darlington; north bank; strictly for members only. Darlington Brown Trout AA has water at Middleton One Row, also on **Swale**; dt for members' guests only. Stockton AL has water at **Winston**, and **Gainford**; mainly game; members only. Hartlepool & Dist AC fishes 1¼m single bank; excellent pike and barbel; members only; st; contact Hon Sec. Tackle shops: W P Adams Fishing Tackle & Country Pursuits, 42 Duke Str, DL3 7AJ (tel: 01325 468069; web: www.wpadams.com) (has permits for several small coarse ponds in vicinity, and for R Tees fishing); Darlington Angling Centre, 341 North Rd, DL1 3BL (tel: 01325 481818); Eastbourne Fishing Tackle, 1 Belgrave Street, Darlington DL1 4AN (tel: 01325 355156).

Piercebridge (Durham). Trout, grayling, dace, chub, gudgeon; for

Raby Estates water, st £65 trout, dt £12, combined salmon/trout st £125; Estate Office, Staindrop, Darlington DL2 3NF (tel: 01833 660207) or J Raine & Son, 25 Market Place DL12 0QA (tel: 01833 640406). Otherwise preserved. Hotel: George.

Gainford (Durham). Trout, grayling, few sea trout and salmon, coarse fish. Up to Ovington, most of the water held by Stockton AL; no tickets. Alwent Beck, 1m W; trout; private.

Barnard Castle (Durham). Trout, grayling. Free fishing on south bank d/s from stone bridge to Thorngate footbridge. Taking of salmon prohibited. At **Eggleston** Bishop Auckland & DAC has 3½m of Tees; dt from Hon Treasurer or lodge at Witton Castle lakes; salmon and sea trout may be taken; st + joining fee. Barnard Castle FFC has water from Tees Viaduct to Baxton Gill, near **Cotherstone**, private club water; stretch above Abbey Bridge to beyond Tees Viaduct on south bank, and from Lendings caravan park to Tees Viaduct on south bank. Barnard Castle AC has from a point below Abbey Bridge to Tees Viaduct on north bank; private club water, but some dt to visitors staying locally. Darlington FFC has 2½m above and below Abbey Bridge, 1m below Barnard Castle; water holds trout and grayling; members only; club also has 2m one bank of River Greta; 2 beats; members only. **Grassholme** (dt £22 8 fish; family £29 12 fish; dt £20 8 fish conc), **Selset** and **Balderhead** (dt £10 8 fish, conc), **Blackton** (dt £22 8 fish; family £29 12 fish; dt £20 8 fish, conc) and **Hury**, dt obtainable for all, from Grassholme Fishing Lodge (tel: 01833 641121, 8am to 4pm; see website: www.nwl.co.uk/leisure); Northumbrian Water Ltd waters (NW) (see Tees Valley Reservoirs). **Middleton in Teesdale** (Durham). Trout (plentiful but small), a few late salmon. Several miles open to dt on Raby Estate water (tel: 01833 640209, office hours); dt from J Raine & Son (below), or Estate Office. Strathmore Estate water, for salmon/trout, south bank between Cronkley Bridge and County Bridge in Middleton in Teesdale; tackle shop: F E Wilkinson of Barnard Castle, 40 Horsemarket, Barnard Castle DL12 8NA, (tel: 01833 631118; see website for more: www.wilkinsonofbarnardcastle.co.uk).

GRETA: Trout. **Bowes** (Co Durham). All private fishing.

TEIGN

Rises from two sources high on Dartmoor, which form the North and South Teign, joining west of Chagford while still small streams. Between Chagford and Steps Bridge river runs through a wooded gorge, which is best fished around Fingle bridge. Upper Teign contains trout, sea trout and salmon. Principal tributary is Bovey. Salmon, sea trout (peal) and brown trout. Teign usually fishes best for salmon from late May to September. River flows to sea through an estuary beginning below Newton Abbot. For the whole river there is a salmon kill limit of one salmon per angler per year; after one fish is killed bait fishing prohibited, and barbless hooks recommended.

Newton Abbot (Devon). Salmon, sea trout, trout; preserved by Lower Teign FA from Sowton Weir to Teignbridge (stretch from New Bridge to Preston Footbridge members only); three separate beats; dt (3 per beat) £20, valid for 24 hrs from sunrise; spinning by day, at night fly only; Assn also has 3m on Bovey, members only (see Bovey). Newton Abbot FA has six lakes at **Rackerhayes**; 1 for junior preference; full members only on **Dores Pond**; four at **Kingsteignton**, five ponds at **Coombe-in-Teignhead** (good dt water); one full members water (Bradley Pond) at **Bovey Tracey**; newly acquired pond beside Stover Canal, West Golds; fisheries contain carp to 36lbs, pike to 20lbs, large tench to 11lb, roach, rudd, perch, bream; 24-hrs £10, dt £6, conc, on some of these waters; senior full membership £75, conc. Decoy Lake, small coarse lake open all year, stocked; tickets on bank. Tackle shop: Tackle Trader, 2 Wharf House, Wharf Road, Newton Abbot TQ12 2DA (tel: 01626 331613).

Chudleigh (Devon). Salmon, sea trout, trout; Lower Teign FA has water (see Newton Abbot). $2\frac{1}{2}$ acre coarse lake at Finlake Woodland Village; dt water in winter; residents only in summer 31 Mar to 31 Oct. Newton Abbot FA has Wapperwell Pond here; dt, juniors must be accompanied by adult 21+.

Chagford (Devon). Salmon, sea trout, brown trout; Upper Teign FA preserves about 8m in all, on left and right bank; fly only whole season; full annual sub £185, trout membership £80, juv conc; apply Hon Sec; brown trout, wt £45, dt £12.50; from PO Drewsteignton; Bowdens, The Square, Chagford TQ13 8AH (tel: 01647 433271); tickets also from Fingle Bridge Inn, Drewsteignton, Exeter EX6 6PW (tel: 01647 281287).

Tributary of the Teign.

BOVEY: Salmon, sea trout, trout.

Bovey (Devon). On Bovey and Teign. Fishing above Bovey preserved by landowners and below by Lower Teign FA; no tickets. Lakes: Tottiford (coarse, currently closed) and Kennick Reservoirs (stocked rainbows), South West Lakes Trust waters; (see Devon lakes, streams, etc). Hotels: Bovey Castle TQ13 8AA (tel: 01647 445000), one mile from North Bovey (water on Bovey and Bowden, and salmon and trout fisheries on Teign); Glebe House, North Bovey.

TEST

Rises from springs in the chalk near Overton, above Whitchurch and flows via Stockbridge and Romsey to enter Southampton Water. Brown and rainbow trout, salmon and sea trout run most of the system. The Test & Itchen Association represents virtually all riparian owners and many who wish to fish these rivers and their tributaries. The Association has a register of owners who let fishing (see clubs list). Roxton Bailey Robinson let beats on a daily, weekly and seasonal basis: 25 High St, Hungerford, RG17 0NF (tel: 01488 683222).

Romsey (Hants). Trout and grayling fishing good; salmon fishing good below the town, all preserved by the different landowners. Test Valley Angling Club has various lakes and river stretches in vicinity, and also water from Eastleigh across to Romsey, covering Marchwood and Totton; subscriptions are £88 + £20 joining fee, £34 + £5 joining jun, £56 + £10 joining fee OAP; contact Hon Sec. **Broadlands Estates** offers, salmon, sea trout & brown trout fishing, the fishing takes place on three dedicated beats located on the upper stretches of the fishery, for more info on rod availability, (tel: 0208 749 4175; web: www.broadlandsfishing.com). Also there is **Longbridge Carp and Coarse Fishery**,Lee Lane, Lee, Nr Romsey,SO51 9LG, 2 lakes for carp and coarse fishing web: www.longbridgelakes.com, night fishing via app only tel: 07973 523 358, dt tickets must be purchased either on the bank from the bailiff or from Poingdestres Tackle Shop www.poingdestres.co.uk, tel: 02830 510077,

Good trout fishing at **Two Lakes**, near Romsey (see Hampshire, streams, lakes, etc).

Stockbridge (Hants). Greyhound Hotel has water stocked with brown and rainbow trout; dry fly and nymph only; fish average 3lb; dt £83 to £112 from Fishing Breaks (see below). Tackle from Orvis, Bridge House, High Str, Stockbridge SO20 6HB (tel: 01264 810017).

Awbridge (Hants). Fishing Breaks Ltd, The Mill, Heathman Street, Netherwallop, Stockbridge, Hants SO20 8EW (tel: 01264 781988; web: www.fishingbreaks.com) has rods here; also on **Rivers Itchen**, and **Rivers Dever**, **Wallop Brook**, **R Nadder**, **R Kennet**, **R Piddle** and **R Frome**.

Fullerton Bridge (Hants). Trout (av 2lb 8oz). Season mid-April to end of Sept. Strutt and Parker has fishing. Contact Mark Merison (tel: 01635 576905; mark.merison@struttandparker.com).

Tributaries of the Test

WALLOP BROOK:

Nether Wallop (Hants). Fishing Breaks Ltd, The Mill, Heathman Street, Netherwallop, Stockbridge, Hants SO20 8EW (tel: 01264 781988; web: www.fishingbreaks.com) has day rods.

ANTON: Trout, grayling.

Andover (Hants). Anton joins Test at Testcombe Bridge. Trout and grayling. Strutt and Parker has fishing. Contact Mark Merison (tel: +44 (0)1635 576905; email: mark.merison@struttandparker.com). Andover AC owns Foxcotte Lake at **Charlton**, 45 pegs; usual coarse species; st £25 + joining fee £10, conc, dt £5 1 rod, £7 2 rods; from tackle shop John Eadie or Challis (below). **Dever Springs Trout Fishery**, Barton Stacey, Nr

Winchester, SO21 3NP: 2 lakes, 7 acres and River Dever (tel: 01264 720592). Tackle shop: John Eadie Ltd, 5B Union Str, Andover SP10 1PA (tel: 01264 351469); Challis Tackle, 60 Mylen Road, Andover SP10 3HA (tel: 01264 361103). Hotels: White Hart, Junction, George Inn, Anton Arms.

PILL HILL BROOK: Trout, grayling.

Amport and Monxton (Hants). Trout and grayling. Nearly as long as Anton, but pure chalk-stream. Monxton Mill reach greatly improved and contains full head of locally bred brown trout averaging 14oz, with occasional heavier fish. Fishing preserved by landowners. Dry-fly only.

DEVER: Trout, grayling. Dever joins Test at Newton Stacey.

Bullington. Fishing Breaks Ltd, The Mill, Heathman Street, Netherwallop, Stockbridge, Hants SO20 8EW (tel: 01264 781988; see website for more info: www.fishingbreaks.com) has rods here.

BOURNE:

St Mary Bourne (Hants). Bourne joins Test above Longparish.

John Clark on the Compton beat on the River Test

Photo: Neil Nice

THAMES

Second longest river in England. Tidal reaches much recovered from pollution and fish returning in considerable numbers. The river is now considered the cleanest metropolitan estuary in the world. Salmon and sea trout in river, together with dace, roach, flounder, bream, perch, carp and smelt; rainbow trout are caught quite regularly in the freshwater tideway. River worth fishing from Southwark Bridge upstream. Downstream of this point, estuarine species such as eel, flounder, bass and even whiting may be caught. Above Teddington Lock boat traffic can be busy in summer, except in weir pools, but fishing can be good early and late. River fishes well from October to March. Holds good stock of coarse fish, with excellent bream and barbel in some stretches. Perch seem to be making a welcome return to the river throughout its length. Dace fishing in recent years has been good in certain areas. Bream, roach and perch now dominate the lower river, above Teddington, with chub becoming more numerous the further up the river one goes. Among famous tributaries are Kennet, which comes in at Reading and is one of best mixed fisheries in England. Trout and coarse fish run large. Higher up, Coln, Leach and Windrush are noted trout streams, but for most part can be strictly preserved and fishing difficult to obtain, although clubs do allow a degree of public access. Fishing on Thames open up to City Stone at Staines. Above, permission often necessary and lock-keepers and local tackle shops should be consulted. Thames Environment Agency issues annual permits on eighteen locks and weirs, and these are entered below, in the appropriate section of the text. The Thames Angling Preservation Society, founded in 1838, has restocked seven tributaries - now keeps close watch on water quality and fish stocks in whole Thames basin. It is not a fishing club, but a fishery preservation society supported by anglers, membership details from secretary, A E Hodges, The Pines, 32 Tile Kiln Lane, Bexley, Kent DA5 2BB (tel: 01322 5255. London Anglers Association (LAA, Izaak Walton House, 2A Hervey Park Road, London E17 6LJ (020 8520 7477)) still has Eton Wick.

London Docklands. Redevelopment has led to increased angling facilities at **Shadwell**, **Millwall**, **Royal Docks** and **Southwark**, each locality with its own angling society.

Isleworth to **London Bridge** (G London). Tidal. Dace, flounder, eel, roach, perch, with some carp and bream. Juvenile bass common at seaward end of this stretch; free from towpath or boats and foreshore throughout Central London 2 hrs each side of low tide. Reach down past Chiswick Eyot can be good for roach, dace; towpath only; free. **Richmond** (G London). Tidal below Teddington Lock, non-tidal above. Down to Isleworth is fishing for roach, dace, bream, perch, eel, the odd chub; free from towpath or boats. Barnes and Mortlake APS are local club, with water on Grand Union Canal at Brentford from Brentford Lock to Thames Lock (dt on bank) (difficult parking), and **Clockhouse Pool** at Bedfont Country Park; society main water is Shadwells Pool behind Wetlands Centre, Barnes; members only; st £78 incl joining fee, husband & wife £68, conc; (web: www.bmaps.co.uk). In Richmond Park **Pen Ponds** hold pike, carp (leather, mirror, common, ghost), eel, roach, tench and perch; open 16 Jun to 14 Mar; st, conc (I.D. required); fishing permits available from park office (tel: 020 8948 3209; fax: 020 8332 2730; or contact via email: richmond@royalparks.gsi.gov.uk).

For coarse fishing in Potomac Lake, Gunnersbury Park; predominently carp, also pike. Near Epsom CALPAC has Stew Ponds on the Epsom Common; mixed coarse; dt on bank £5; night fishing on this water £30; closed during close season: 15

Mar to 15 June; no ground bait; no keep nets; barless hooks. Tackle shop: Surbiton Angling Centre, 177 Hook Rd, Surbiton KT6 5AR (tel: 020 8391 4110).

Twickenham (G London). Coarse fishing; free from boats and towpath. Deeps hold barbel, roach, bream, eel, carp. Corporation allow fishing from Radnor, Orleans and Terrace Gardens. Syon Park Trout Fishery, Brentford; fly only, dt £19 2 fish, £32 4 fish; managed by Albury Estate Fisheries (see Guildford), Estate Office, Albury, Guildford GU5 9AF (tel: 01483 202323). Tackle shop: Guns and Tackle, 81 High Str, Whitton, Twickenham TW2 7LD (tel: 020 8898 3129). Hotels: Bird's Nest, White Swan.

Teddington (G London). Thames holds dace, roach, bream, eel, perch; free fishing from towpath. **Molesey Lock** is fishable on special Environment Agency annual permit, which covers 18 locks and weirs; contact Kings Meadow House, Kings Meadow Rd, Reading, Berks RG1 8DQ (tel: 08708 506 506; see website for more info: www.visitthames.co.uk, permits £28.50, conc £18.90.

Kingston (G London). Canbury Gardens is very popular stretch and has yielded large carp, bream, perch and roach.

Hampton Court (G London). Thames, Mole; coarse fish. Hampton Court Palace Gardens, Surrey KT8 9AU (tel: 0870 752 7777): contact Ticketing Office, The Barrack Block at palace; postal applications only. **Long Water** and **Rick Pond**, also **Bushy Park**: **Diana Pond**, **Heron Pond** and **Leg of Mutton Pond**; coarse fish; st (conc) waters (prices subject to annual review); no night fishing; tickets from tackle shop. Tackle shop: Fishing Unlimited, 70 Bridge Road, East Molesey KT8 9HF (tel: 020 8941 6633).

Hampton (G London). Hampton Deeps hold bream, pike, perch and sometimes a good trout; free fishing from towpath and boats.

Sunbury (Surrey). Excellent for all-round angling; free. Fine weir and weir shallows fishable; limited access; barbel, chub, dace, bream and occasional trout and salmon may be taken. Most fishing is from creek on Sunbury side; punts from Wilsons; EA licence. Feltham Piscatorial has water on 'The Creek'; apply Hon Sec. Hotel: Magpie.

Walton-on-Thames (Surrey). Bream, perch, dace, chub, carp and pike; perch and pike in backwater. Tackle shop: The Tackle Exchange, 97A Terrace Rd, Walton-on-Thames KT12 2SG (tel: 01932 245453).

Shepperton (Surrey). Pike, barbel, perch, bream and carp; free; boats for hire. Shepperton Lock is Environment Agency fishery; contact Kings Meadow House, Kings Meadow Rd, Reading, Berks RG1 8DQ (tel: 08708 506 506) for permit details. Sheepwalk Lakes: 2 lakes, 7 acres, with carp to 30lbs, tench to 9lbs, bream to 11lbs, good pike fishing; access for disabled; apply to Feltham Piscatorials (see website for more info: www.felthampiscatorials.co.uk). Tackle shop: Tackle Tarts Angling (see Chertsey). Hotel: Anchor.

Weybridge (Surrey). There is local free fishing in Thames and **R Mole**. Members of Weybridge AC and other clubs have fishing on 6 sections of **Wey Navigation** Canal between Town Lock and Walsham Lock and have formed Wey Navigation Angling Amalgamation; st £22, dt £4 from bailiff or from local tackle shops; Weybridge AC also fishes 1,000 yards d/s and 1,000 yards u/s of Wey Bridge on R Wey; st from tackle Shop: Weybridge Guns & Tackle, 137 Oatlands Drive, Weybridge KT13 9LB (tel: 01932 842675). Hotels: Ship, Thames St; Lincoln Arms, Thames Street; Oatlands Park; Blue Anchor.

Chertsey (Surrey). Pike, perch, chub, roach, bream, occasional trout; free fishing from boats and towpath. Between Chertsey Weir and Penton Hook, Staines, good nets of bream caught all year, also perch. Chertsey Bridge is very popular for piking, with fish to 25lbs. Cemex (formerly RMC) Angling (see below) have 6 acre gravel pits; excellent tench, bream, carp to 25lb, roach and pike in pit; chub, roach, dace and perch in river; Gold Venue water. Cemex (formerly RMC) Angling have a stretch of River Wey at Addlestone, 1500m total, with pike, barbel, chub to over 6lb, carp, roach, bream, dace, perch; Silver Venue water; st; Cemex (formerly RMC) Angling (see Miscellaneous Fisheries in Clubs List) run many fisheries throughout southern England, and they may be contacted at Cemex Angling, Coldharbour Lane, Thorpe, Surrey TW20 8RA (tel: 01932 583630; see website for more info: www.cemexangling.com). Free fishing on Shortwood Common, Ashford: 3 acre lake with carp to 20lbs, tench, etc. Ashford Lakes: three lakes of 1 acre each, with large carp, tench, bream, good head of roach and pike; disabled access; dt on bank. Tackle shop: Tackle Tarts Angling, 357 Staines Rd West, Ashford, Middlesex TW15 1RP (tel: 01784 240013; see website for more info: www.tackletartsangling.com).

Staines (Surrey). Good coarse fishing; free from boats and towpath. Environment Agency fisheries at Penton Hook Lock, and Bell Weir Lock, **Egham**; all free fishing d/s from Staines; contact Kings Meadow House, Kings Meadow Rd, Reading, Berks RG1 8DQ (tel: 08708 506 506) for permit details. 18 acre lake **Thorpe Lea Fishery**; dt £12 adult, jun/OAP £9, 24 hr £24, rod limit is 2 rods, (tel: 01784 492182; web: www.thorpeleafishery.co.uk). At **Twynersh** are 8 lakes, mixed fish, dt on site, night fishing. Cemex

(formerly RMC) has **Longfield Road Lake** st £420 (2 rods summer/autumn, 3 rods winter); Gold venue; waiting list; Cemex also has **Fox Pool**, well known for its carp; Gold venue; st £340 (2 rods summer/autumn, 3 rods winter); (For Cemex (formerly RMC) Angling, see Chertsey). Tackle shop: Davies Angling, 47/49 Church Str, Staines TW18 4EN (tel: 01784 461831; see website for more info: www.davies-angling.co.uk).

Wraysbury (Berks). Cemex (formerly RMC) Angling **Kingsmead Island Lake**, at Horton: a Gold Venue lake of 50 acres with carp to 40lbs, and other coarse species; st 3-rods £175, no conc; **Kingsmead One** is a Cemex Gold Venue Water coarse lake of 30 acres; carp to over 40lb, other coarse fish; st (2 rods) £300; Cemex Angling also has Gold Venue water fishing at **Horton** nr Wraysbury, including **Horton Church Lake**, 14 acres with carp to 44lb; st £680, waiting list; max 2 rods summer/autumn, 3 winter; also **Horton Boat Pool**, 6 acres: catfish to 74lb, and other coarse fish; st 3-rod £245; waiting list; Cemex also has **Crayfish Pool**, Park Lane, Horton, a 2 acre lake; carp over 30lb; st £290; rod limit: 2 in summer/autumn, 3 winter; **Wraysbury 1**, home of former British Record carp of 56lb 6oz, is a Gold Venue water, with carp to 48lb; st £215, 4 rods; boat £25; **Wraysbury 2** is a Silver Water fishery, best suited to the specialist; tench, bream, pike over 30lb, carp to over 40lb; st (2 rods) £50, conc £30; 3 rod limit; (For Cemex (formerly RMC) Angling, see Chertsey.) Blenheim AS fishes **Watts Pool**; mixed coarse; members only (see clubs). Berkshire Fisheries Assoc has Slough Arm of G Union Canal from **Cowley** to Slough Basin, approx 5m, excellent fishery in summer, very little boat traffic; specimen tench and other species, and good pike fishing in winter; dt from bailiff.

Windsor (Berks). Chub, barbel, bream, roach, dace, perch, pike. Fishing from south bank below Windsor Bridge and north bank to Eton-Windsor road bridge, by EA licence only. Dt issued for club waters near Maidenhead; enq tackle shops. Salt Hill AC has Clewer Meadow, Windsor, dt on bank. Old Windsor AC has **Romney Island** (no night fishing) and **Meadow** fishing to east of Windsor; all river species; junior trophies and tuition available; st £34, conc, dt £5, conc, at Romney on bank. Free public fishing on right bank from Victoria Bridge u/s to railway bridge; night fishing; presently very productive; water known as Home Park. Royal Berkshire Fishery, North St, Winkfield SL4 4TE (tel: 01344 891101; web: www.rbf.co.uk)): 3 small lakes with coarse fish; dt on bank; cafe and facilities. Fishing can be had in Windsor Great Park ponds and Virginia Water (see Surrey lakes). Tackle shop: Windsor Angling Centre, 153 St Leonard's Rd, Windsor SL4 3DW (tel: 01753 867210).

Boveney (Bucks). Coarse fish. Backwater good for pike, and weir pool for trout and barbel. Towpath free. London AA fish Eton Wick. Hotels: Clarence, Royal Windsor.

Bray (Berks). Weir pool good for coarse fish and a few trout, and free from boat or punt. Bray Mill tail from 1m above lock to lock cut private. Towpath free. Environment Agency fishery at Bray Lock; contact Kings Meadow House, Kings Meadow Rd, Reading, Berks RG1 8DQ (tel: 08708 506 506) for permit details.

Maidenhead (Berks). Roach, pike, perch, barbel, dace, chance of trout. Some free fishing right bank, Maidenhead Bridge to Boulter's Lock. Hurley Lock, Environment Agency fishery; contact Kings Meadow House, Kings Meadow Rd, Reading, Berks RG1 8DQ (tel: 08708 506 506) for permit details. Thames Valley AA has Left bank u/s from Boveney Lock to gardens at Dorney Reach; permits from Hon Sec; also Jubilee River from M4 bridge u/s to Amerden Lane

bridge; dt £3 from tackle shops below; dt for clubs stretch from My Lady Ferry to gardens at Maidenhead from bailiff. Tackle shops: Kings of Maidenhead, 18 Ray Street, Maidenhead SL6 8PW (tel: 01628 629283; see website for more info: www.kingsfishing.com); Maidenhead Bait & Tackle, 11-13 Station Parade, Station Hill, Cookham SL6 9BR (tel: 01628 530500; see website for more info: www.maidenheadbait.co.uk).

Cookham (Berks). Cookham & Dist AC has towpath bank u/s of Cookham road bridge to Bourne End Railway Bridge; chub, bream, barbel, roach, dace, perch, carp; membership & dt purchased before fishing from tackle shop. Tackle shop: Maidenhead Bait & Tackle, 11-13 Station Parade, Station Hill, Cookham, SL6 9BR (tel: 01628 530500; see website for more info: www.maidenheadbait.co.uk). Free fishing on **Odney Island**. **Bourne End** (Bucks). Wide, open water with some shallow stretches, good for fly fishing. London AA has water here; stretch also open to associates. Marlow AC has Spade Oak Pit near Little Marlow; mixed coarse; members only; apply Hon Sec.

Marlow (Bucks). Usual coarse fish, including barbel. Free fishing d/s from Marlow Lock to end of the bend, $\frac{1}{2}$m stretch. Marlow AC has water from Riverswood Drive to opp first islands and left bank u/s from Marlow Bridge opp Temple Island, and pits; club also has a stretch at Medmenham and a backwater; members only; club also has Ski Lake; specimen lake; members only; also Westhorpe Park Lake; specimen lake; Spade Oak; mixed coarse; 80 acres near Little Marlow; and Hillwood and Holloway Pond at Beaconsfield; carp, silver fish respectively; members only, st £49, conc. Tickets from Kings Fishing Tackle, 18 Ray St, Maidenhead SL6 8PW (tel: 01628 629283); Marsh Tackle, Abbey Barn Road, Downley, High Wycombe HP13 5UW (tel:

01494 437035). At West Wycombe Park, 5m north, National Trust has fly-only brown and rainbow trout lake; synicate-managed; for st (subject to availability) contact Estate Office (not NT) (tel: 01494 524411).

Hurley (Berks). Hurley Lock, Environment Agency fishery; contact Kings Meadow House, Kings Meadow Rd, Reading, Berks RG1 8DQ (tel: 08708 506 506) for permit details. Reading & DAA has 800m single (northern) bank; excellent fishing; dt from tackle shops; Mill End (between Hurley and Henley).

Henley (Oxon). Pike, chubb, roach, perch, tench, bream, eels. Free fishing u/s from Promenade to Cold Bath Ditch. Environment Agency fishery at Marsh Lock; contact Kings Meadow House, Kings Meadow Rd, Reading, Berks RG1 8DQ (tel: 08708 506 506) for permit details. Oxon and Bucks bank water controlled by society for members only; also from end of Henley Promenade upstream to Marsh Lock, bridges and meadows upstream from Marsh Lock. Boats: Hobbs.

Wargrave (Berks). Thames and Loddon; good coarse fishing.

Sonning (Berks). Much fishing from **Shiplake** to Sonning Bridge on Oxfordshire bank controlled by Shiplake and Binfield Heath AS; members only. Guests at White Hart can fish private stretch of ½m on Berkshire bank towards Shiplake. Reading & Dist AA has Sonning Eye fishery (lake and river); members only. Environment Agency fishery at Shiplake Lock; contact Kings Meadow House, Kings Meadow Rd, Reading, Berks RG1 8DQ (tel: 08708 506 506) for permit details.

Reading (Berks). Most coarse fish. Reading Borough Council controls length from opposite Caversham Court Gazebo to 1½m u/s of Caversham Bridge. The fishing from Thames-side Promenade to Scours Lane is controlled by Thames Water. There is some free water on the **Kennet** from Horseshoe Bridge to County Weir (adjacent to Inner Distribution Road). Reading & Dist AA, comprising about forty affiliated clubs, control twenty eight miles of river and canal, plus fourteen lakes in Berkshire and Oxfordshire; subscription £60, with concessions; supplementary permits on six specimen waters, £25-£80; £10 dt offered for Wylies Lake and 20 other venues, stocked, with coarse and specimen fishing in Reading vicinity; dt available from tackle shops (all other Reading & Dist AA waters are members only plus guests). Farnborough & DAS has good trout and coarse fishing on **Whitewater** at Heckfield to Bramshill (3m), also 2m fly only stretch; trout membership on application to Hon Sec; web: www.fadas.org. At Bradfield, **The Barn Elms Trout Fishery**, Dark Lane RG7 6DF (tel:0118 9744744 web: www.barnelmsfishery.co.uk), approx 6 acres, stocked with rainbow trout; dt £24 - £34, on bank. Blenheim AS have 1m of Kennet and Avon Canal at Woolhampton; mixed coarse; members only, £70; apply Hon Sec. Cemex (formerly RMC) Angling has coarse fisheries on permit at **St Patrick's Stream**, **Twyford**; and **Theale** (2 lakes, total 52 acres); coarse; St Patrick's Stream: st (2 rods) £45, conc £28; Theale: st £55, £33 conc; their **Woolwich Green** lake has bream, tench, carp, roach, rudd and perch; dt £10 2 rods; tickets from Reading Angling Centre (tel: 01189 872216) or Cemex (tel: 01932 583630); (For Cemex (formerly RMC) Angling, see Chertsey). Twyford, managed by BBONT, has 34-acre lake and 900 yard section of R Loddon; coarse Silver Water; st £40, conc £36. At Theale is Haywards Farm Fishery, Station Rd, RG7 4AS (tel: 01189 323422); 2 lakes totalling 18 acres; rainbows and browns; 1 Mar to 30 Nov; dt on site £37 (4 fish) half day £24 (2 fish); 3-hours £13 (beginners); c&r £20; sporting ticket £32; (see website for more info: www.haywardsfarmfishery.co.uk). Tackle shops: Sportfish, Reading, Haywards Farm, Station Rd, Theale, RG7 4AS. (tel: 0118 930 3860; web: www.sportfish.co.uk). Reading Angling Centre, 69 North'land Avenue RG2 7PS (tel: 0118 987 2216); Thames Valley Angling, 258 Kentwood Hill, Tilehurst, Reading RG31 6DR (tel: 0118 942 8249); Tadley Angling, Padworth Common Rd, Padworth Common, Reading RG7 4QG (tel: 0118 970 1533; web: www.tadleyangling.com). Hotels: Thameside.

Tilehurst (Berks). Purley (now free fishing water); Reading & DAA have Mapledurham on the Oxfordshire bank. Free fishing from towpath to Caversham on town-side (see restrictions under Reading). Tackle shop: Thames Valley Angling, 258 Kentwood Hill, Tilehurst, Reading RG31 6DR (tel: 0118 942 8249); tickets for Reading FC. Hotel: Roebuck Hotel.

Goring (Oxon). Pike, bream, roach, chub, perch and (in weir pool especially) barbel and a few trout. Fishing can be had from towpath above and below lock.

Pangbourne and **Whitchurch** (Berks). Thames and **Pang**. Trout, perch, pike, roach, bream, chub, dace. River fishes well in winter; free fishing 1½m above and below Whitchurch Bridge; good coarse fishing; boats for hire. Weir pool private. Pang holds trout, especially near Tidmarsh, but is strictly preserved; trout at its mouth. Pangbourne and Whitchurch AS is affiliated with Reading & Dist AA, and fishes in a number of localities, including 3m of R Kennet with good chub, barbel, roach and dace; st from Hon Sec; (web: www.rdaa.co.uk).

Moulsford (Berks). All coarse fish. London AA has water at Cholsey; members only. Hotel: Beetle and Wedge.

South Stoke (Oxon). London AA controls the water from footbridge above railway bridge down to Beetle and Wedge ferry; members only, membership £43, conc.

Wallingford (Oxon). Reading & Dist AA has Severals Farm fishing: two sections, above and below Benson Lock. Jolly Anglers have several miles u/s and d/s of Wallingford; roach, dace, chub, barbel, perch, bream, pike, carp and eels; dt £5 available on the bank (for above town road bridge only; members only). Tackle shops: Rides on Air, 45 St Mary's Str, Wallingford OX10 0ER (tel: 01491 836289; web: www.ridesonair.com); for Jolly Anglers tickets, Feet First, 21 St Mary's St (tel: 01491 825224).

Cleeve (Oxon). Usual coarse fish. London AA: for Gatehampton Farm details; ¾m fishing good for bream; some perch, roach, chub; members only; membership £43, conc (open to associates).

Benson (Oxon). Usual coarse fish. Benson & DAC has water for ¾m u/s from the Marina in Benson; st £12, dt £2.50 from Benson Marina and bailiffs on bank; access by footpath only; some Sundays reserved for matches (dates recorded at Marina). Benson Lock is Environment Agency lock and weir fishery; contact Kings Meadow House, Kings Meadow Rd, Reading, Berks RG1 8DQ (tel: 08708 506 506) for permit details.

Shillingford (Oxon). Wallingford AA has water upstream; dt from Hon Sec. Shillingford Bridge Hotel, Shillingford Hill, Wallingford OX10 8LZ (tel: 01865 858567), has good pike fishing with trout, tench, dace, etc, on ¼m (both banks) reserved for guests and members of High Wycombe AC.

Little Wittenham (Oxon). Thames comes in here.

Clifton Hampden (Oxon). Oxford & DAA has water here, d/s from the bridge for four fields; bream, chub and roach, also large barbel; dt £5 on part of this water from tackle shops; £8 on bank; no night fishing. Clifton Lock is Environment Agency fishery; contact Kings Meadow House, Kings Meadow Rd, Reading, Berks RG1 8DQ (tel: 08708 506 506) for permit details. Inn: The Barley Mow.

Appleford (Berks). London AA controls from just above the railway bridge down to beginning of Clifton Hampden cutting; right bank only; members only; membership £41, conc.

Culham (Oxon). Sutton Courtenay AC has pits; no day tickets.

Abingdon (Oxon). Bream, chub, pike and barbel good. Free fishing for residents. Permits from Town Clerk's office for the 1½m controlled by Council, from Nuneham railway bridge to notice-board 200 yds u/s from Culham footbridge; details from Old Abbey House, Abbey Close, Abingdon OX14 3JD (tel: 01235 522642); fishery includes weir, but must be fished from bank. Abingdon & Oxford Anglers Alliance has much local fishing; the Alliance trout section has lake at **Standlake**, Oxon, st £75, entrance fee £30; members and their guests only: contact Hon Sec; Alliance also has water at Bablock Hythe.

Sandford-on-Thames (Oxon). Pike, bream, roach, perch, etc. Abingdon A & RA have 3½m from Sandford lock to Nuneham railway bridge; access from Sandford Lane and Radley village. Environment Agency lock and weir fishery at Sandford Lock; contact Kings Meadow House, Kings Meadow Rd, Reading, Berks RG1 8DQ (tel: 08708 506 506) for permit details.

Iffley (Oxon). Thames (or Isis). From Botley Road Bridge d/s to Folly Bridge is Oxford & DAA water; large shoals of roach, perch and chub; dt from tackle shops £5, or £8 on bank. Inn: Isis Tavern.

Oxford (Oxon). Thames (Isis), **Cherwell** and **Oxford Canal**. All coarse fish. Milton Keynes has access to 1m of R Thames at **Oxford.** North Oxford AS, with regular matches on variety of venues once a fortnight, has water on Thames, at **Carrot's Ham**, Cherwell, canal, and carp and tench fishing in **Dukes Lake**; their best water is **Seacourt Stream** at Carrot's Ham, with many species; club offers dt on water between Godstow and Seacourt Overspill, and Seacourt Stream (members only) from Overspill to A420; st, conc, dt , from tackle shops. **Donnington** and **Iffley** water held by Oxford & DAA; good roach fishing, also chub; Heavy boat traffic here; assn is an affiliation of clubs local to Oxford; it has excellent coarse fishing on Thames at **Medley** (one of the main match stretches), and **Clifton**, and elsewhere, with dt £5 from tackle shop (£8 bank). (4½m W of Oxford, **Farmoor Reservoirs**, Cumnor Rd, Farmoor OX2 9NS; dt £20;. Reservoir No.2, Cumnor Rd, is 240 acre trout fishery, stocked with brown and rainbow, fly only from boat or bank; various dt prices and st from gatehouse; facilities for disabled; (tel: 07747 640 707) for advance bookings. Tackle shops: Fat Phil's Angling Centre, 334-336 Abingdon Rd, Oxford OX1 4TQ (tel: 01865 201020; more on website: www.fatphilsangling.com). Hotels: The Swan Inn, Islip.

Eynsham (Oxon). Good coarse fishing; large bream. Oxford Angling & Pres Soc has water (see Oxford). Eynsham Lock fishing open to holders of Environment Agency lock permits; contact Kings Meadow House, Kings Meadow Rd, Reading, Berks RG1 8DQ (tel: 08708 506 506) for permit details. Hotels: The Talbot Inn, Railway, Red Lion.

Northmoor (Oxon). Reading & Dist AC water, 1½m adjacent u/s of Ferryman Inn; members only. For Hardwicke Fishing Lakes (2m) and Farmoor (5m); trout; special rates for anglers.

Newbridge (Oxon). Near Witney. Good coarse fishing (bream increasing), few trout in the **Windrush**. Shifford Lock is one of Environment Agency's fisheries (long walk necessary); contact Kings Meadow House, Kings Meadow Rd, Reading, Berks RG1 8DQ (tel: 08708 506 506) for permit details. Newland AC has water from **Shifford** to within 600 yds of Newbridge; and Heyford Lakes, with specimen fish; st, dt for lakes only from State Fishing (below). Hotels: Rose Revived Hotel, Newbridge OX8 7QD (tel: 01865 300221). Phoenix AA have 1m of Thames; dt available. Tackle shop: State Fishing Tackle, 23 Fettiplace Rd, Witney OX28 5AP (tel: 01993 702587), who can give further information; Fat Phil's Angling Centre, 334 Abingdon Rd, Oxford OX1 4TQ (tel: 01865 201020; web: www.fatphilsangling.com).

Radcot (Oxon). Bream, chub, barbel, roach, perch, pike, occasional trout. Swan Hotel, OX18 2SX (tel: 01367 810220), has ½m, dt available. Radcot AC and Clanfield AC have 5m, st only, £17.50, conc; apply Hon Sec, or Turner's Tackle. South Cerney AC have Duxford Farm stretch near Hinton Waldrist; members only. Clanfield AC also has left bank, Radcot Lock to Rushey Lock, st only; membership apply Hon Sec. Three Environment Agency lock fisheries, at Rushey; Grafton Lock; and Buscot Lock; contact Kings Meadow House, Kings Meadow Rd, Reading, Berks RG1 8DQ (tel: 08708 506 506) for permit details. Permits for stretch from **Buscot** to Grafton Lock, season cards for Radcot AC and Clanfield AC, from Turner's Tackle and Bait, 4A Station Rd, Faringdon, SN7 7BN (tel: 01367 241044). National Trust has dt for Little Lake, Buscot Park; mixed coarse fishing: bream, carp, roach, skimmers, tench; contact, Cotswold Angling Tackle Warehouse, Unit 1, Aspen Close, Kembrey Trade Centre, Swindon SN2 8AJ (tel: 01793 522922).

Lechlade (Glos). For Thames, Cole and Leach. Phoenix AA controls 2m of Thames at Lechlade upstream from Trout Inn to Murdoch Ditch. Permits for weir pool only, from Trout Inn, GL7 3HA (tel: 01367 252313); dt £5. For Highworth AC water from Trout Inn, nr Lechlade 1.5m d/s towards Kelmsford (western beat); club also has National Trust Coleshill Estate River Cole water; st. For South Cerney AC water (eastern beat) contact M Vines of South Cerney AC; 2m of bank; dt water (tickets on bank). Phoenix AA controls 2m Thames at Lechlade. Tackle shop: Turner's Tackle and Bait, 4A Station Rd, Faringdon, SN7 7BN (tel: 01367 241044).

Cricklade (Wilts). Thames known here as Isis. Isis AC has No 1 Lake at **South Cerney** (Glos), carp to 30lb; membership, dt from tackle shops; dt allows angling on stretch of Avon at Sutton Benger. South Cerney AC has river off A419, and several lakes in Cotswold area including **Ham Pool, Wick Main Lake, Gillman's Lake** and **Stait Lake,** the last two of which are dt waters (£7); membership £50, conc; they also fish the **River Ray** here.

Tributaries of the Thames

MOLE: Coarse fish.

Esher (Surrey). Pike, roach, perch the odd big chub. Epsom AS has ½m at Wayne Flete and ½m on Wey at **Weybridge**; apply Hon Sec. Tackle shop: Weybridge Guns & Tackle, 137

Oatlands Drive, Weybridge KT13 9LB (tel: 01932 842675).

Cobham (Surrey). Central Association of London and Provincial Angling Clubs (CALPAC) has 1½m of Mole here, various coarse species; and Manor Pond (night fishing £30), holding pike, carp, roach, tench and bream; members only; closed 15 Mar to 15 June. Further CALPAC stretch, 1½ miles at **Hersham**: chub, perch, roach, dace, eels, pike, dt £5, conc, sold on bank. Cobham Court AC have water adjacent and above, 4½m (not continuous: large chub, pike, very big perch and eels, and barbel to double figures; some rainbows stocked; dt £6 from Natures World.

Leatherhead (Surrey). Leatherhead & Dist AS have waters above A246 road bridge. Cobham Court AC has water at Norbury Park, Leatherhead, with chub, roach, dace, perch, together with carp and pike to double figures. Tackle shop: S C Fuller, 32 South St, Dorking RH4 2HQ (tel: 01306 882177; web: www.scfuller.co.uk).

Dorking (Surrey). Coarse fish. Dorking & Dist AS has about 4m of Mole and three lakes; large stocks of carp, tench, bream, roach and barbel; members only; contact A Fuller, Fullers Tackle (below). **Furze Farm Fishery**, Knowle Lane, nr Cranleigh; 3½ acre mixed fishery; dt £8 (1 rod) £10 (2 rods) on bankside; contact Fishery, Stone Cottage, Ridgeway Rd, Dorking RH4 3EY (tel: 01306 882708). Tackle shop: S C Fuller, 32 South St, Dorking RH4 2HQ (tel: 01306 882177; see website for more info: www.scfuller.co.uk). Hotels: White Horse; Pilgrim.

Brockham (Surrey). Chub, roach, carp and bream. Brockham AS water; members only.

Betchworth (Surrey). Chub dominate below weir, anything can, and does appear above weir.

Sidlow (Surrey). Roach dominate, together with perch, carp, chub.

Horley PS fish much of this water, including Kinnersley Manor, Meath Green Farm and Court Lodge Playing Fields; also 2 lakes, at Earlswood Common, mainly large tench to 7lb, and Riverside Park, Horley, mixed coarse; members only, £30; apply The Carp Shop, 2 South Parade, Horley RH6 8BH (tel: 01293 407687).

WEY: Coarse fish, trout higher up.

Weybridge (Surrey). Wey Amalgamation have water here (see Thames), tickets from bailiff.

Woking (Surrey). Roach, chub, pike, etc. Woking & Dist AS has rights on 23 miles of river bank and four ponds (perch, carp and tench) at Send; dt for members' guests only; the society also fishes (through affiliation) the Wey Navigation Canal; and exchange permits with other local clubs, thus extending fishings further; new members welcome; details from Hon Sec; (web: www.wadaa.co.uk). Tackle shop: Weybridge Guns & Tackle, 137 Oatlands Drive, Weybridge KT13 9LB (tel: 01932 842675).

Wisley (Surrey); ns Ripley. Ponds: Wisley Mere, Hut Pond, and several other ponds on Ripley Common and Ockham Common; carp, pike, perch, roach.

Guildford (Surrey). Guildford AS, www.guildfordanglingsociety.com) has about 9½m R Wey; lakes at Broad Str, and Whitmoor Common (carp to 19lb in Brittens Pond); dt on bank. At Shamley Green **Willinghurst Fisheries**, Shamley Green GU5 0SU (tel: 07774 188760): 9 lakes, all coarse; dt £11 (1 rod), £15 (2 rods), conc; barbless hooks; night fishing £5 (after 4pm), £25 (24-hours) by appointment only. **Albury Estate Fisheries**, Estate Office, Albury, Guildford GU5 9AF (tel: 01483 202323); 8 lakes, totalling 16 acres, of brown and rainbow trout fishing; 3 dt waters: **Powdermills** (5lbs av), **Weston** (2½lbs) and **Vale End**

(2½lbs); one syndicated: **Park** (2lbs av); dt waters £32 (4 fish) £19 (2 fish) plus £12 membership; instruction, if required. **Brittens Pond**, Salt Box Lane, Jacobs Well; Guildford AS water; big carp, perch, roach, etc; dt on bank. Tackle shops: Guildford Angling Centre, 92 Haydon Place GU1 4LR (tel: 01483 506333); Peter Cockwill, Albury Game Angling, Stream Cottage, The Street, Albury, Guildford GU5 9AG (tel: 01483 205196; see website for more info: www.alburygameangling.co.uk). Hotel: Drummond Arms, Albury.

Shalford (Surrey). Wey; bream, roach, pike, etc. **Tillingbourne**; trout; preserved. Inns: Parrot, Queen Victoria, Seahorse, Percy Arms, Chilworth.

Godalming (Surrey). Godalming AS has Wey from old A3 bridge, just above Stag Inn, Eashing, to Guildford Rowing Club in Guildford (about 8m); coarse fish incl barbel; some grayling and trout on upper reaches; society also has **Broadwater Lake** (10 acres) which holds carp, roach, tench and perch; **Busbridge Lake** (4 acres), coarse; **Johnsons Lake** at Enton (21 acres), coarse; and **Bramley Park Lake** (3 acres), coarse; **Marsh Farm, Milford**, adjacent to Johnsons Lake; 2 3-acre lakes; mixed coarse; no carp; no waiting list: entry fee £65, st £70, conc. **Wintershall Waters**, Bramley GU5 0LS, is 3 acre trout fishery; st only (tel: 01483 275019). Tackle shop: Guildford Angling Centre, 92/94 Haydon Place, Guildford GU1 4LR (tel: 01483 506333). Hotels: Kings Arms, Royal Hotel, Red Lion.

Frensham (Surrey). Farnham AS has Frensham Trout Fishery; **Frensham, Great** and **Little Ponds,** roach, perch, carp, etc; open membership for coarse fishing; st from Hon Sec, The Creel, 36 Station Road, Aldershot, Hants GU11 1HT (tel: 01252 320871).

Haslemere (Surrey). Coarse fish. At St Patricks Lane, **Liss**, is coarse fishing on 2 lakes, plus 5 ponds at **Rake** for matches only.

Farnham (Surrey). Farnham AS offers extensive local fishing, for members only; club coarse fishing waters include 1m R Wey at **Dockenfield** and **Elstead; Frensham Ponds; Badshot Lea** Ponds; **Lodge Pond**; **Stockbridge Pond**, **Tarn Pond** and **Warren Pond** at Puttenham, **Loddon** at **Winnersh**, lakes at **Yateley**, incl specimen water; **R Whitewater** nr Riseley, small stream with chub, perch and roach; no day tickets; st £97, incl joining fee, conc; apply Membership Sec for details. Note: all waters heavily fished early in season.

COLNE: Coarse fish, some trout.

Wraysbury (Berks). Blenheim AS has **Colnebrook** from Coppermill Road down to the Staines Road at Hythe End.; coarse fish and occasional trout; also Cargill Lake; members only; (website: www.blenheimas.co.uk). Twickenham PS and Staines AC have gravel pits; no tickets.

West Drayton (G London). Trout, pike, perch, bream, dace, roach, tench, chub. Grand Union Canal is near. CALPAC has 2¾m of canal Hayes to West Drayton; no keepnets, barbless hooks; dt £5 on bank; open all year. **Lizard Fisheries**, Trout Rd, West Drayton (tel: 07931 255897): all species of carp to 35lbs; coarse fishing; dt from pay and display machine on site; £8, one rod dawn to dusk (£10 2 rods); contact Dave Brett.

Uxbridge (G London). Pike, perch, roach, dace and bream. Fishing free on Uxbridge Moor. London AA holds long stretches of **Grand Union Canal**, on which dt is issued on bank, £4. National Trust **Osterley Park Lake** holds bream, tench, pike, roach, carp; limited st, conc; no night fishing; enquiries to Estate Warden, Osterley Park, Jersey Rd, Isleworth, Middx TW7 4RB (tel: 020 8232 5064). **Farlows Pit, Iver**, holds roach, tench, carp, bream, pike; some st.

Denham (Bucks). Colne; coarse fish. Blenheim AS has 6½m of **Grand Union Canal** from Denham Lock 87 to Batchworth Lock 81; bream, roach, carp, perch, chub, pike; st £40, conc; dt £3, conc, on bank from bailiff on stretches lock 81-83, and lock 85-87. Tackle shops: Harefield Tackle, 2-4 High St, Harefield, Uxbridge UB9 6BX (tel: 01895 822900; web: www.harefieldtackleonline.co.uk); Fishermans Cabin, 795 Field End Rd, Ruislip HA4 0QL (tel: 0208 422 9546).

Harefield (G London). **Savay Lake**, Moorhall Road: 52 acre gravel pit stocked with specimen fish; st from Fishery Manager (tel: 0171 969 6980). **Willows Lakes**, London Colney, **St Albans**: three lakes, two of which have 40 and 110 pegs, with large bream, large carp and catfish; tickets: enquiries to bailiff, (tel: 01727 822106).

Rickmansworth (Herts). Trout, chub, dace, roach, pike, perch. Blenheim AS has 6½m of **Grand Union Canal** between Denham Lock 87 and Batchworth Lock 81 (good roach and bream); dt £3 from bailiff on Pounds Lock 81-83 and Lock 85-87; limited st from Harefield Tackle; (note: no dt on section between Springwell Lock No 83 and Black Jacks Lock No 85; members only); annual £70 + £10 entrance, conc, (canals annual, £40, conc); dt £3, conc, on bank and from tackle shops. Watford Piscators have 6m of canal; also two stretches of **R Gade**, with barbel, large roach, shoals of bream and chub, good perch; three stretches of R Colne; and six coarse lakes, incl Tolpits, Castles, Stanleys, Thurlows, and Rouseburn Lakes, Cassiobury Park; club also has 12 to 16 jun section; all waters members only, except four sections of canal, dt £4 on bank; membership £110 plus joining fee £20, conc. Kings Langley AS has 2m of canal at Hunton Bridge, also short stretch of R Gade. **Chess**; trout, preserved. **Gaywoods Fishery**

Home Park Link Rd, **Kings Langley** WD4 8DZ: 4 acre dug-out pond with carp to 24lbs, tench, roach, perch, etc; dt £10, two rods, juv £6. Tingrith Coarse Fishery, **Tingrith** (tel: 01525 714012): three pools with carp, tench, bream etc.

Watford (Herts). Boxmoor & DAS has stretch of river here, members only; apply to Hon Sec; (see website for more: www.cullumpublishing.co.uk). **Gade** at Cassiobury is free fishing for approx 1m. Ticket waters: Elstree and Tring reservoirs and Grand Union Canal. London AA issues dt £4 on towpath for canal from Hunton Bridge to Tring. Free fishing in Gade in Cassiobury Park. Watford Piscators have fishing in Rivers Gade and Colne, lakes, and dt water on Grand Union Canal (see Rickmansworth). Tackle shops: Tackle Carrier, 157 St Albans Rd, Watford WD24 5BD (tel: 01923 232393); Oxhey Angling Centre, 28 Pinner Road, Oxhey Village, Watford WD19 4ED (tel: 01923 226849). Hotels: Ramada, Hilton, Wellington Arms.

CHESS: Brown and rainbow trout - one of few British streams where rainbows spawn naturally. There is free public fishing at Scotts Bridge Playing Fields, Rickmansworth.

Chorleywood (Bucks). Chess; trout.

GADE: coarse fish.

Boxmoor (Herts). Boxmoor & DAS has private water at Westbrook Mere, with large carp, bream, tench, pike, roach, rudd and perch; club also has Upper Ouse at **Stoney Stratford**, and Colne at Watford, all mixed fishing, matches throughout year; apply Hon secretary. (see website for more info: www.cullumpublishing.co.uk); Assn also has **Durrants Hill** in Apsley, Hemel Hempstead. Harlow District Council, Parks and Landscapes Service, Mead Park Depot, River Way, Harlow CM20 2SE (tel: 01279 446425) also has parts of Stort Navigation; enquiries to Harlow DC.

Boxmoor Trout Fishery, 3 acres of converted water cress farm (tel: 01442 385212).

Berkhamsted (Herts). Visitors can fish London AA water on Grand Union Canal; coarse fish, dt £4, juv £2 from fishery keeper. No free water. **LODDON**: coarse fish, barbel abundant, trout improving in numbers.

Twyford (Berks). St Patrick's stream (fine barbel), held by Cemex (formerly RMC) Angling; st £45, conc £38; (for Cemex (formerly RMC) Angling, see Chertsey).

Hurst (Berks) Reading & DAA has 1m at Whistley Mill; members & guests; good barbel and chub.

Arborfield Cross (Berks). Farnham AS has a stretch at Sindlesham Mill, Winnersh; coarse fish, barbel in faster stretches (see Wey - Farnham). Cove AS also has water near here at **Shinfield** and on **Hart** and **Whitewater**; and Theale Waters; members only (see also Fleet). Farnham AS also has ½m stretch of Whitewater below Riseley Mill. Farnborough & DAS has 2½m R Loddon at **Winnersh**, 3m R Whitewater at Heckfield, Basingstoke Canal and Shawfields Lake and Hollybush Pits; fine mixed coarse fishing, fly fishing, membership on application; (web: www.fadas.org). Felix Farm Trout Fishery, Howe Lane, **Binfield**, RG42 5QL (tel: 01189 345527); 8 acre lake, stocked with brown and rainbows between 2-10 lb; dt £30, 4 fish, £20 2 fish, conc £15; boats for hire, (tel: 0118 934 5527; www.felixfarmtroutfishery.co.uk).

KENNET: One of England's finest mixed coarse fisheries; upper reaches noted for trout and grayling.

Theale (Berks), Water west of point 1m upstream of Bridge House (Wide Mead Lock) strictly preserved; few trout and coarse fish. Englefield Lake, 2m; pike, and fine tench and carp (private). Reading & Dist AA has much water on lower **Kennet** at Theale, Rushey Meadow, Calcot, Lower and Upper Benyons, Ufton, Padworth Mill and elsewhere, the **Holybrook** and backwaters, together with 9 local gravel pits, 120 acres; dt (£10) on a few venues from tackle shops. At **Burghfield** (Cottage Lane, RG20 3UW), Cemex (formerly RMC) Burghfield Blue Pool is dt water of 3 acres with big carp to over 40lb and other species; dt 2-rods £135 24-hours; Burghfield Main Lake is a Silver Venue water; good carp to 53lb, tench, bream, pike, perch, eels; st £70 (2 rods), £42 conc from Reading Angling Centre (tel: 01189 872216) or Cemex (tel: 01932 583630), where tickets are also sold for the 30-peg Burghfield Match Lake (temporarily closed); Cemex also have Gold Water to include 1m R Kennet; mixed fishing, large carp and barbel to over 15lb; st £210 (waiting list); (For Cemex (formerly RMC) Angling, see Chertsey.)

Aldermaston (Berks). Coarse fish and few trout. Old Mill, Aldermaston RG7 4LB, issues permits for about ½m of water with four weirs, and small lake with carp to 30lbs; dt £12 at door, £14 on bank. CALPAC has 750 yard stretch of Kennet at **Padworth**, with large barbel, tench, bream, pike, etc; night fishing £30 on this stretch; members only; key (£6) required for parking off-road; barbless hooks; no keepnets; closed 15 Mar to 15 June incl; rota bookings. London AA has 2m of narrow winding stream, **Fisherman's Brook**, a tributary of the R Kennet; chub, dace, roach; members only; membership £43, conc.

Thatcham (Berks). Fishing between Reading and Thatcham controlled chiefly by Reading & Dist AA; members only on river and Hambridge Lake, but dt £10 on site for Wylies Lake, Thatcham; details from Hon Sec (see clubs list). Thatcham AA has water on canal, R Kennet plus lakes; members only, price of membership on application; contact Hon Sec or tackle shop below. Tackle shop: Thatcham Angling Centre, Unit 4, 156 Sagecroft Road, Thatcham RG18 3BQ (tel: 01635 871450; web: www.thatchamanglingcentre.co.uk).

Newbury (Berks). On Rivers Kennet and **Lambourn** and **Kennet and Avon Canal**; trout and coarse fishing. Newbury & Dist AA, Thatcham AA and Reading & Dist AA, Civil Service AS hold water in this area. Kintbury AC owns canal and river fishing; members only. For these and other local clubs contact local tackle shops. CALPAC has Kennet fishery at Bulls Lock, with large barbel and other coarse species; some brown and rainbow trout have been caught; large pike; members only; closed 15 March to 15 June incl; no keepnets; barbless hooks; web: www.calpac.info.

Hungerford (Berks). Kennet and **Dunn**; trout, grayling; preserved. **Hungerford Canal** fishing in hands of Hungerford Canal AA (3m) (tickets from Thatcham Angling Centre - see Thatcham). CALPAC has fishery at **Sulhampstead**, 750 yds of river, followed by 700 yds of canal, with large barbel and other coarse species; no night fishing; st £48 plus joining fee £20, conc; closed 15 March to 15 June incl; no keepnets; barbless hooks. Reading & Dist AA has water (Froxfield); members only. Accommodation at Pincents Manor, Old Lamb Hotel.

Lockinge (Oxon). Lockinge Fishery, Ian Hockley, West Lake Fly Fishing, 78 Grove Street, Wantage OX12 7BG (tel: 01235 227228; see website: www.westlakeflyfishing.co.uk); stocked trout fishing on lakes and streams, running through Ardington and Lockinge, nr Wantage; av brown and rainbow, 2lb; st £730; half-rods (every other week) £530, max 4 fish per wk taken + return further 4 fish.

Marlborough (Wilts). Trout at Axford. Marlborough & District AA has fishing rights in **Kennet and Avon Canal** from Milkhouse Water to Little Bedwyn; dt water, contact Hon Sec; st £35 + £5 entry, conc; also Heron Lake; mixed coarse; 34 pegs; members only. Wroughton AC fish **Wroughton Reservoir**, Overtown Hill, Wroughton, Swindon; members only; club also fishes Avon and Marden; no dt; st £25, conc. Amalgamated Fisheries Ltd (formerly BB&WAA) has **Tockenham Reservoir**, near Swindon; members only, st £45 from House of Angling (below); no dt. Tackle shop: Cotswold Angling, 1 Kembrey Trade Centre, Kembrey St, Swindon SN2 8AJ (tel: 01793 522922; see website for more info: www.cotswoldangling.com); House of Angling, 59/60 Commercial Rd, Swindon SN1 5NX (tel: 01793 693460). Hotels: Castle and Ball, Crown (Marlborough AA HQ).

THAME: Coarse fish.

Dorchester (Oxon). Thames and Thame. Coarse fish; good chub and dace, and carp quite numerous. Dorchester AS has water where river joins Thames to Dorchester; also Thames itself at Shillingford; st, conc, restricted dt, from Hon Sec. Oxford & Abingdon AA has a lake here; dt on bank £5. Tackle shop: Didcot Angling, 36 Wantage Road, Didcot OX11 0BT (tel: 01235 817005).

Eythrope (Bucks). Roach, bream, perch, chub, good dace. Aylesbury Dist and Izaak Walton AA has water (4m from Aylesbury), members and friends only.

CHERWELL: Coarse fish.

Islip (Oxon). Cherwell and Ray; good chub, roach, perch and pike fishing may be had in the Cherwell. The Bicester & DAA has ½ acre carp pool, 2m Bicester; st from tackle shops. Oxford & DAA has Cherwell at Enslow, Kirtlington and Northbrook; dt from tackle shops. Tackle shops: J & K Tackle, 62/64 Sheep St, Bicester OX26 6LG (tel: 01869 242589; web:

www.jktackle.co.uk). Inns: Red Lion, Swan.

Heyford (Oxon). Oxford & DAA has South Oxford Canal from Enslow Bridge to Heyford Wharf; dt from Oxford tackle shops (£5, or £8 on bank).

Banbury (Oxon). Banbury & DAA has much local water on R Cherwell; and canal fishing, incl stretches at Cropedy, Nell Bridge, Clifton, Somerton, Heyford and Bletchington, also **Clattercote** (BWW) and **Grimsbury Reservoirs**; also **Spital Farm**, Grimsbury; also **Slinket Lake**, Aynho; dt £5, conc; for reservoirs only from tackle shops; **Farnborough Hall Lake** is leased to Banbury & DAA. **Cheyney Manor Fishery**, Manor House, **Barford St Michael** OX15 0RJ; the moat and fishpond contain carp, rudd, roach, tench, chub, bream, perch; tickets (dt £5, conc) from bailiff (tel: 01869 338207). Castle AA fishes two lakes, 6 acres, at **Canons Ashby**: carp to 25lb, bream, tench, barbel and roach; dt £6 on bank, conc. **The Goldfish Bowl**, Boulderdyke Farm, off Chapel Close, Clifton, nr Deddington OX15 0PF (tel: 01869 338539): carp lake, 18 pegs, dt at car park, disabled access. **Nellbridge Coarse Fishery**, Aynho OX17 3NY (tel: 01295 811227; web: www.nellbridgefishery.com): 3 lakes stocked with tench, roach, carp, perch, bream, pike, rudd; dt £5 (2 rods), conc; specimen lake dt £10 (2 rods); disabled access; 100 pegs plus, open 6am till dusk; toilets. Tackle shops: Castaway Fishing Tackle, 86 Warwick Rd OX16 2AJ (tel: 01295 254274; see website for more info: www.castawayfishing.co.uk); Banbury Gunsmiths, 47A Broad St, OX16 5BT (tel: 01295 265819; web: www.banburygunsmiths.co.uk); K & M Fishing Tackle, 23 West St, Chipping Norton OX7 5EU (tel: 01608 645435).

EVENLODE: Trout, coarse fish (roach and dace especially).

Long Hanborough (Oxon). **Salford Trout Lakes**; 5 and 3½ acres stocked with rainbow and brown trout; dt £28 (4 fish limit), ½ day and evening, £20; st £265 also offered; contact Nigel Colston, Rectory Farm, Salford, Chipping Norton OX7 5YZ (tel: 01608 643209; see website for more info: www.salfordtroutlakes.co.uk).

WINDRUSH: Trout, grayling, coarse fish (dace up to 1lb and 2lb roach not rare).

Witney (Oxon). Large trout; preserved below; leave must be obtained from the Proprietors; good hatch of mayfly. Witney AS (HQ Eagle Vaults) has water; no dt and membership restricted to county as a rule, but outside applications considered; apply Hon Sec. Vauxhall AC has Stanton Harcourt; good carp, up to 40lb, members only. Newland AC has Windrush from Witney d/s, and Heyford Lakes Fishery, dt £6. **Richworth Linear Fisheries** have seven dt pools near **Stanton Harcourt** on B4449 road; fishery records incl pike to 30lbs, carp to 42lbs; lakes include **Hunts Corner Lake**, **Hardwick Lake**, **Smiths Pool**, **Manor Farm Lake, Brasenose 1, Brasenose 2, St Johns Lake**, and **Oxlease**; dt on banks; bailiff (mob: 07885 327708); the fisheries also have **Guy Lakes (Gaunts, Unity, Yeomans)** and **River Windrush**; members only; also **Elstow** (35 acres); contact Fishery Manager, 7 Crow Lane, Lower End, Wavendon, Bucks MK17 8AR (tel: 01865 731395; web: www.linear-fisheries.co.uk). **Linch Hill Leisure Park**, Stanton Harcourt OX29 5BB; Stoneacres Lake mixed coarse and carp fishing; dt £20 (24 hrs); dt £7 per rod, conc, (tel: 01865 882215). Tackle shop: State Tackle (see Witney above). Hotel: Old Swan Inn.

Burford (Oxon). Cotswold Flyfishers have 10m at **Swinbrook** and **Stanton Harcourt**; trout (restocked yearly), fly only; all waters within 20m of town; club also fishes Coln, Leach, Glym and Dickler; and 3 stillwaters; membership limited; no dt. Burford AC holds approx 1m, with brown and rainbow trout to 5lbs, grayling, large roach, perch, chub, dace, gudgeon, and pike to 9lbs; all grayling to be returned; club is affiliated with Oxford & DAA. Tackle shop: K & M Fishing Tackle, 23 West St, Chipping Norton OX7 5EU (tel: 01608 645435). Hotels include Cotswold; Mill House; Lamb; Highway.

COLN: notable dry fly fishing for trout of good average size; grayling.

Fairford (Glos). Trout; excellent; April 1 to Sept 30; grayling Oct-Mar; dry fly only upstream; not stocked; tickets can be had for 1½m from Bull Hotel, Market Place, GL7 4AA (tel: 01285 712535); catch/return; trout of 1-1½lb plentiful; dt £38, half day £25 (reduction for residents). **Whelford Pools Fishery**, Welford Rd, Fairford GL7 4DT (tel: 01285 713649; web: www.whelfordpools.co.uk); dt waters, 3 lakes joined by 2 channels; 4 acres in total; carp to 33lb, tench to 12lb; dt £9 (£17 24 hrs); £3 evening (from 5-9 pm), conc; on site or bankside; syndicate lake, waiting list.

Bibury (Glos). Coln: trout. Swan Hotel GL7 5NW (tel: 01285 740695) has 300 yds facing hotel, day tickets from hotel: dry fly only, 3 rods on offer.

TORRIDGE

Rises on Cornwall Devonshire border, but is also fed from Dartmoor via a tributary, the River Okement. It flows into Bideford/Barnstaple Estuary. Salmon, sea trout, peal and brown trout.

Bideford (Devon). River for 2m on east side, and two reservoirs, at **Gammaton**, stocked with brown and rainbow trout, leased by Torridge Fly Fishing Club; st from Hon Sec, written application only; Torridge Fly Fishing Club Gammaton Reservoirs Gammaton Bideford EX39 9QD.

Weare Giffard, 1m right bank, salmon, sea trout, brown trout; dt £30 (salmon and sea trout), residents £26; browns £20 (£17) from Half Moon Inn, Sheepwash, Beaworthy, N Devon EX21 5NE (tel: 01409 231376). Hotels: Royal, New Inn, Tanton's.

Torrington (Devon). Salmon, sea trout, brown trout. Fishing lodge and day rods on **Beaford** stretch; contact, Little Warham, Beaford, Winkleigh EX19 8AB (tel: 01805 603317). The Clinton Arms, Frithelstock, nr Torrington EX38 8JH (tel: 01805 623279) has 1½m both banks; dt £20 per rod, max 3 rods. Coarse fishing at **Darracott Reservoir**, Torrington; 3 acres is South West Lakes Trust water, open all the year, 24 hr day; st

£140 (day and night), £100 st (day), 24-hour £10, dt £5.50, conc £4.50 from Summerlands Tackle, 16-20 Nelson Rd, Westward Ho! EX39 1LF (tel: 01237 471291; see website for more: www.summerlands.co.uk); see above. Tackle shop: Whiskers Pet Centre, 20 South St, Torrington, EX38 8AA (tel: 01805 622859).

Shebbear (Devon). Devil's Stone Inn, EX21 5RU (tel: 01409 281210), can arrange with local farmers for 2½m of salmon, sea trout and brown trout fishing on Torridge; fly and spinning; excellent dry-fly trout water; nearest beat 1m.

Sheepwash (Devon). Half Moon Inn, Sheepwash, Beaworthy, N Devon EX21 5NE (tel: 01409 231376), has 12m of private salmon, sea trout and brown trout fishing on Torridge; season 1 Mar to 30 Sept, spinning allowed in Mar, otherwise fly only; fishing available for non-residents but guests have priority; must be booked in advance; dt for non-residents £30 salmon and sea trout, residents £26;

£10 brown trout; brochure on request; tackle shop at hotel, also tackle for hire, tuition available on request, and rod licences available.

Hatherleigh (Devon). Torridge, Lew, Okement; salmon, sea trout, brown trout. 4 coarse lakes at **Halwill**, '**Anglers Eldorado**'; specimen fish: carp, golden tench, golden orfe, golden rudd, koi, grass carp, all on £5 dt per rod, conc: The Gables, Winsford, Halwill Junction EX21 5XT (tel: 01409 221559), who also offers fishing and fishing holidays as follows: Anglers Paradise: luxury accom and 12 lakes, with coarse fish incl carp to 30lbs, unusual species such as golden orfe, golden rudd, golden tench, for residents only; Anglers Eldorado, four coarse lakes on dt; Anglers Shangri-La, three lakes of up to 240 pegs for match fishing; Anglers Utopia, three villas, purpose built for disabled, with lake fishing; also Anglers Nirvana, 4 dt lakes, incl trout lake (night fishing on Nirvana coarse lakes); tackle shop on site. Hotel: New Inn, Meeth (½m on Torridge; dts for salmon and trout).

Tributaries of the Torridge

LEW: Sea trout, trout.

OKEMENT:

Okehampton (Devon). Salmon, sea trout, trout to 2lb; whole length. **Highampton Trout Fishery** is accessible from Oakhampton (tel: 01409 231216; see website for more info: www.fishdevon.co.uk); 2 trout lakes, dt £24 (4 fish) and large coarse lake, dt £6. Tackle shop: C P Angling, 7 The Arcade, Fore Str, Okehampton EX20 1EX (tel: 01837 53911; web: www.cpangling.co.uk).

WALDON: Principal tributary of Upper Torridge.

Mill Leat Fishery, Thornbury, Holsworthy EX22 7AY (tel: 01409 261426), offers dt on ½m stretch with brown trout, and 3 acre stillwater, with rainbows; self-catering accom at same address.

TRENT

Largest river system in England. Rising in Staffordshire, Trent drains much of Derbyshire, Nottinghamshire and Lincolnshire, and empties into Humber. A hundred years ago, one of England's principal fisheries; now recovering its status following massive effort at water quality improvement. The tidal water, in particular, now fishing excellently. Some famous trout-holding tributaries, notably Dove, Wye and Derwent.

Gainsborough (Lincoln). Pike, perch, roach, carp, barbel, chub. There are a few fish to 3m below Gainsborough. Tidal. Scunthorpe & DAA has 1m at South Clifton, east bank; dt on bank; also 1m at Girton, plus 1m at Besthorpe; dt on bank; also Dunham Bridge. Lincoln & Dist AA has water south of Gainsborough at North Clifton and Laughterton; enquiries, dt £4 from bailiff, D Ellerker, Mill Hill House, North Clifton NG23 7AZ (tel: 01777 228133); or Mike Wright (tel: 01522 703765). Good local carp fishery: Daiwa Manton Pool, nr Scunthorpe; two lakes of 10 and 34 acres, with carp to 39lbs, catfish 45lbs; syndicate only; contact N J Fickling, 27 Lodge Lane, Upton, Gainsborough DN21 5NW (tel: 01427 838731). Tackle shop: The Tackle Shop, 9 King Str, Gainsborough DN21 1JS (tel: 01427 613002; see website for more info: www.thetackle-shop.co.uk).

Marton (Lincoln). Tidal water. Free fishing at Littleborough. Excellent catches of roach.

Torksey (Lincoln). Chub, roach. Lincoln & Dist has fishing east bank at Laughterton and North Clifton; dt £4, conc (annual membership £25, conc £15) from bailiff D Ellerker, Mill Hill House, North Clifton NG23 7AZ or Mike Wright (tel: 01522 703765). White Swan AC has 37 pegs of natural bank and 15 pegs off platforms, between Lincoln and Gainsborough; dt £3 on bank. B&B at White Swan Hotel, 400yds from bank. Scunthorpe & DAA has Dunham Bridge. Worksop & DAA fishes 12 pegs of Torksey Arm, and 4 pegs on opp bank below lock up to White Swan fishery, with chub, roach, bream, skimmer; dt £3 on bank, open from 1 Oct (bailiff, Ken Bradshaw, (tel: 01427 717492).

Dunham (Notts). Rotherham & Dist AA offers dt for its fishing on right bank, u/s and d/s of Dunham.

High Marnham (Notts). Worksop & DAA has water above the Mansfield stretch at **Normanton-on-Trent** (30 pegs); dt on bank, £3, conc.

Sutton-on-Trent (Notts). Tidal water. Pike, roach, dace, chub. Lincoln & Dist AA has fishing at **North Clifton** and **Laughterton**; dt £4, conc £3 (annual membership £25, conc £15, children under 12 £7) from match sec, D Ellerker, Mill Hill House, North Clifton NG23 7AZ; or bailiff, Mike Wright (tel: 01522 703765). Scunthorpe & DAA has **South Clifton** fishing; dt on bank or from bailiff above.

Collingham (Notts). Club water. Trent 2m W; pike, carp, barbel, roach, dace, chub, perch, bream. Collingham AA has 4m from Cromwell Weir to Besthorpe parish boundary; match bookings per peg; dt from bailiff on bank; all round coarse fishing, (tel: 01636 892700). Worksop & DAA waters are from immediately above the weir to just below Winthorpe Lake (over 100 pegs); also 40 pegs above lake to Winthorpe rail crossing; also waters on opp bank at Ness Farm (40 pegs): report to farm for dt for this stretch; also Footits Marsh (30 pegs);

otherwise dt on bank, £3, conc. Hotel: Royal Oak.

Muskham (Notts). Nottingham Piscatorial Society preserves from Fir Tree Corner (Kelham boundary) to Crankley Point, both sides, including gravel pits; members only.

Averham, Kelham (Notts). Very good coarse fishing. Preserved by Nottingham Piscatorial Society for members only; roach, dace, chub (excellent fly water) - from weirs at Staythorpe to South Muskham boundary on both sides of the river, apart from one short stretch.

Newark-on-Trent (Notts). Roach, dace, pike, chub, bream, barbel, gudgeon, perch, eels. Newark & Dist Piscatorial Federation has Trent at Rolleston, East Stoke, Winthorpe, Kelham Hall; tidal Trent at Girton and Cottam, and **Newark Dyke** at three sections; dt £4 on most waters, on bank except for Kelham Hall (which are obtained by post from N Wells, 42 Beacon Hill Road, Newark NG24 1NU (tel: 01636 683461). Nottingham AA fishes from Farndon Ferry to Newark Dyke; dt £3 from bailiff on bank. Other dt stretches: Worksop & DAA controls from above the weir to Winthorpe Lake (Weirfield/Holme Marsh) over 100 pegs; then from Winthorpe Lake to Winthorpe Crossing, 40 pegs; Ness Farm, 40 pegs; Footits Marsh 25 pegs; dt on bank £3, conc; or contact Hon Sec; for matches, contact Richard Brunt (tel: 01909 489109). Newark & Dist PF controls water from Crankly Point to Winthorpe Crossing; dt £4 on bank. Trent Lane, **Collingham**, Collingham AA water; tickets on bank; access to weir via Westfield Lane. Tackle shop: Newark Angling Centre, 29 Albert St, Newark NG24 4BJ (tel: 01636 686212).

Farndon (Notts). South bank let to Nottingham AA; dt £3 issued.

Rolleston (Notts). Newark & Dist PF have fishing here, members only.

Greet, trout; preserved. Nottingham AA has water at **Farndon Ferry** (opp Rolleston); dt from bailiff; matches can be arranged in advance.

Fiskerton (Notts). Good roach, chub and excellent barbel fishing. Nottingham Piscatorial Society water from Greet mouth (Fiskerton) to Farndon, (excluding members field and car park); good roach, barbel and chub; dt £4 from Fiskerton PO; Nottingham tackle shops; no permits on bank. Barnsley & Dist AAS have one mile of left bank; dt £3 from PO shop; conc, st £25; pegs 1 to 85. The Greet enters Trent at Fiskerton; preserved.

Hoveringham (Notts). Dt £3 on bank for Nottingham AA stretch from old Star and Garter 1 field u/s. Midland AS has stretch to Caythorpe, barbel, roach, chub, bream, gudgeon, etc; 146 pegs, dt £3, conc, on bank, matches bookable, apply Hon Sec.

Gunthorpe (Notts). Good coarse fishing; roach, dace, chub. Nottingham & DFAS has north bank water u/s and d/s of Gunthorpe; dt £3 on bank. Good pub near water, The Anchor.

Burton Joyce (Notts). Chub, roach (mainly), dace. Nottingham & DFAS has good north bank stretch for which dt (£3) issued (matches arranged, booked in advance after Nov 1 for following season); tickets from bailiff.

Shelford (Notts). Stoke Weir to Gunthorpe Bridge, Nottingham AA water; members only.

Radcliffe-on-Trent (Notts). Roach, chub, dace and gudgeon, with perch, pike and tench in Lily Ponds. North Bank from Stoke Weir down to **Gunthorpe**, Nottingham & DFAS; dt £3; From Stoke Weir up to Radcliffe Ferry, including Lily Ponds, Nottingham & DFAS; dt £3; Fedn also holds from Radcliffe Ferry upstream (members only) and water below Radcliffe railway bridge (see Burton Joyce); u/s southbank to rowing course at Holme Pierrepont.

Colwick (Notts). Colwick Country Park, River Road, off Mile End Rd, Colwick, NG4 2DW (tel: 0115 987 0785), is operated by Nottingham City Council; and includes a 65 acre trout fishery, and coarse waters on River Trent (with 40 bookable match pegs), and lake of 48 acres (mainly carp and bream); permits and information from Fishing Lodge at above address. Nottingham AA has fishing rights for 1 field from Viaduct downstream; dt £3 on bank; access through Industrial Estate u/s of viaduct. **Nottingham** (Notts). Good mixed fishing. Several miles in city free. Nottingham AA (tel: 0115 9199500) has **Beeston,** north bank; **Colwick,** viaduct d/s 600 yds; East Bridgford below weir (members only d/s for 1,530 yds); assn also has 5 lake complex at Papplewick; mixed coarse; members only; also Old Moor Pond, Strelley Village; mixed coarse; members only; and Sowbrook Lake at Kirk Hallam; single lake; mixed coarse; members only; also 4-lake complex, Newlands Ponds, nr Mansfield; mixed coarse, members only; also Kodak Lakes, near Annesley; mixed coarse; members only. Nottingham PS has fishing at Rolleston and **Fiskerton**, dt from tackle shops only; also East Stoke Fishery from 1m below Hazleford Weir to East Stoke Hall; members only. Long Eaton Victoria AS has 30 pegs below Colwick sluices, left bank; members only, no dt. Nottingham & DFAS have dt at Clifton Bridge; other clubs with Trent fishing near town are Nottingham Waltonians (Clifton Grove), Nottingham AA, (several stretches on both banks, south of town). Nottingham & DFAS comprises upwards of 68 clubs, with water at **Burton Joyce**, **Thrumpton**, **Gunthorpe**, **Carlton**, **Hazelford**, **Clifton Grove**, and **Holme Pierrepont** and River Derwent at Borrowash; also **Erewash Canal** at **Ilkeston**; dt £3 on bank; **Nottingham-Beeston Canal** from

Meadow Lane to Chain Bridge; dt £3 on bank. Midland AS has 146 pegs at Hoveringham and Caythorpe; dt , conc, on bank. Parkside FC has **Grantham Canal**, and **Castle Marina**, both near Nottingham; dt £3 on bank on all waters, except Marina which is members only; club has 60 pegs on Trent at West Bridgford; dt £3. Lake in **Wollaton Park** may be fished by dt from Parks Superintendent, Wollaton Park. Long Eaton Victoria AS has left bank below sluice at Colwick; members only no dt. National Watersports Centre, Holme Pierrepont NG12 2LU (tel: 0115 9821212), offer angling on 62 acre coarse lake with roach, perch, dt from boathouse. Tackle shops: Netherfield Tackle Centre, 75 Victoria Road, Netherfield, Nottingham, NG4 2NN (tel: 0115 987 0525); Matchman Supplies Fishing Tackle, 4 Ella Road, West Bridgford, Nottingham NG2 5GW (tel: 0115 981 3834; see website for more info: www.matchmansupplies.co.uk); and many others.

Beeston (Notts). Chub, roach, dace, bleak, gudgeon; preserved by Nottingham AA; dt for stretch from N Bank Lock from bailiff; assn also has water on **Beeston Canal**; assn also has 250 acre Attenborough Gravel Pits, members only (st £39); mixed coarse. Tackle shops: see Nottingham. Hotels: Brackley House; Hylands.

Thrumpton and Long Eaton (Notts). Roach, bream, dace, chub, perch, barbel. Long Eaton Victoria AS has 2 meadows d/s of Cranfleet Lock; full membership £24, conc £18, juniors £8, dt on bank; the society also has 2 stillwaters here; members only: Fletcher's Pond, specimen pool, carp to 30lb; Grange Pond, carp, tench, roach, bream, no dt. Soldiers & Sailors AC have Trent Lock to railway bridge, dt on bank; contact Mr Walker (tel: 0115 9721478). **Erewash Canal**; roach, gudgeon, bream, carp,

perch, chub. Nottingham AA has canal from Sandiacre bridge to Stanton lock; dt on bank. Long Eaton Victoria AS has **Soar**, at Kegworth, and also a section at Ratcliffe, members only, no dt, u/s of A453, chub, barbel, bream and roach; canal fishing, on Cranfleet Canal (Trent Lock), Erewash Canal dt available, (Long Eaton Lock to Trent Lock), also 2 ponds in Long Eaton, members only. Long Eaton & Dist AF has 120 pegs on **Erewash Canal** from Long Eaton to Sandiacre Lock; dt; apply bailiff local or tackle shops. Tackle shops: Bridge Tackle Shop, 30 Derby Road, Long Eaton, Nottingham NG10 1PD (tel: 0115 972 8338). Hotels; Elms; Europa; Sleep Inn.

Sawley (Notts). Above moorings, Olympic AC offer day tickets, purchased in advance. Pride of Derby AA has fishing on both banks above and below M1 motorway bridge, from Marina down to R Derwent, and 1m at Willington on Repton bank; also 5 lakes (including Redhouse Lake) and ponds of 60 acres total (including Ully Gully); st, conc from Hon Sec.

Barrow-upon-Trent (Derbys). Manor House Fishery: 20 pegs designed for disabled anglers, most with vehicle access, open Monday to Sunday; excellent chub, roach, barbel and perch; details of fishery, contact Barry Poxon, Chairman, Practical Angling for the Disabled AC; also for dt (which are not issued on bank) but may be issued to non-disabled anglers; membership applicants must be in receipt of DLA, mobility allowance or war pensions equivalent; disabled toilets. The fishing is available for matches hire.

Burton-upon-Trent (Staffs). Free fishing for Burton residents either side of St Peters Bridge (Stapenhill Pleasure Gardens and Waterside). Burton-upon-Trent Mutual AA have fishing which includes **Dove** at **Tutbury** to confluence with Trent; Trent between Willington and Cuttle

Brook (Swarkestone); gravel pit at **Kings Bromley**; Branstone Water Park; and other waters; these inclde Oddstone Gravel Pit, and put & take fly-only water between **Barton-under-Needwood** and **Walton upon Trent**; also stretch of **Trent and Mersey Canal** between Clay Mills and **Wychnor**; members only; also Caldwell Pool; mixed coarse; also **Kingstanding Pools**, near Newborough; also **Staunton Harold Reservoir**. **Hartshorne Dams**, 2 coarse lakes, are 2 min off A50 at Woodville; enquire Mr David Burchell, Manor Farm, Hartshorne DE11 7ER (tel: 01283 215769). Pride of Derby AA has 12m of **Trent and Mersey Canal** in vicinity; also water on Dove at Scropton; st, conc from Hon Sec. Stoke-on-Trent AS also fishes at Scropton and Fauld; members only. Willesley Lake, Moira, has dt for carp to 30lbs, good stocks of bream, etc; tickets on bank. Tickets for canals, various stretches on the R Trent and eight local trout and coarse venues from tackle shops. Tackle shop: Burton Angling Supplies, 31 Borough Rd, Burton on Trent DE14 2DA (tel: 01283 548540); Trent Angling, Unit 2, Horninglow St, Burton on Trent DE14 1NG (tel: 01283 564865). Hotels: Three Queens, Station and Midland.

Alrewas (Staffs). Chub, dace, roach. Warrington AA controls 1500 yards of fishing, one mile north of Alrewas, at Willow Brook Farm and Caravan Park; members only; apply Hon Sec. Prince Albert AS has fishing on both banks, north of Alrewas, below Alrewas AC water on right bank; all three clubs, members only. Fenton & Dist AS has 300 yards right bank on the weir; also Trent and Mersey Canal at confluence; members only. **Trent and Mersey Canal**, dt from keeper. **Fisherwick Lakes**, Chris Sheldon, Fisherwick Wood Lane, Whittington, Lichfield, Staffs WS13 8QQ (tel: 01543 433606; see website for more: www.fisheries.co.uk/fisherwick);

seven lakes, 32 acres, 12 acres of trout fishery, all other pools coarse, between Lichfield and Tamworth, all year-round fishing.

Rugeley (Staffs). Usual species. Armitage to Rugeley, and Wolseley Bridge to Colwich are all BW direct managed. Bridge 69 to Wolseley Bridge is Hednesford AC water on **Trent and Mersey Canal** from Armitage to Wolseley Bridge. From here to Colwich held by British Waterways; dt from them; roach, pike, perch. **Blithfield Reservoir**, 4m NE; trout; Blithfield Anglers allows fishing on season permit £620, and dt £20; boats, £15 per day engine included; enquiries to Fishery Office, **Blithfield Reservoir**, Abbots Bromley, Rugeley, Staffs WS15 3DU (tel: 01283 840284; see website for more: www.blithfield.com/anglers).

Stone (Staffs). Stone & Dist AS fishes 750m Trent left bank here. Hanley AS has a stretch of double bank between Sandon and Burston. Crown AC has pools at Eccleshall and Market Drayton, as well as Shropshire Union Canal; dt.

Stoke-on-Trent (Staffs). Stoke-on-Trent AS has fishing on **Stanley Reservoir** (famous for pike), Knypersley and **Rudyard Reservoirs**; members only. Fenton & Dist AS has fishing on **R Dove** (barbel, chub and grayling); **R Churnet**, trout and coarse; **Stoke Overflow**, with large carp; **Knypersley Reservoir**; **Trent & Mersey Canal** fishing (Stoke-on-Trent to Barlaston); **Sutton Brook**, Hilton; 2 pools at **Cheadle**; **Black Lake** at Meir Heath; mixed coarse, for Trent & Mersey Canal stretch, as for **Smith Pool** and **Longton Park Lake**, from Dolphin Discount (below), and other tackle shops. At **Newcastle-under-Lyme**: Cudmore Fishery, twenty pools with carp, barbel, bream, tench, chub, incl specimen pool; tickets from the Lodge, Pleck Lane, Whitmore ST5

5HW (tel: 01782 680919; web: www.browningcudmorefisheries.com).

Tackle shops: Pickerings, 38 Moorland Road, Biddulph, Stoke-on-Trent ST8 6EW. (tel: 01782 790143; see website for more info: www.pickeringsfishingtackle.co.uk); Abbey Pet Stores, 1493 Leek Road, Abbey Hulton, Stoke on Trent ST2 8DA (tel: 01782 534667); Dolphin Boats, Old Whieldon Road, Stoke-on-Trent ST4 4HW (tel: 01782 849390; see website for more info: www.dolphin-discount.co.uk); Mellors Tackle, 30/32 Brunswick St,

Hanley, Stoke-on-Trent ST1 1DR (tel: 01782 266742); and many others.

Trentham (Staffs). Village about 3m from Stoke-on-Trent on main road London to Manchester. Lake of 80 acres at Trentham Gardens Coarse Fishery, Stone Rd, Trentham ST4 8AX; bream, carp, roach, rudd, pike and perch; st from Estates Office Reception (tel: 01782 657341).

Weston-on-Trent (Staffs). Coarse fishing in **Trent and Mersey Canal**; chub, roach, bream, perch.

Tributaries of the Trent

IDLE: Excellent coarse fishing in parts, with bream, roach, chub, predominating.

Bawtry (Notts). Chub, roach main species. Environment Agency has 500 yds of left bank free to licence holders (tel: 08708 506506). Tackle shop: R & R Sports, 40 High Str, Bawtry, DN10 6JE (tel: 01302 711130).

Retford (Notts. Derbyshire County AC has water in the area, with chub, roach, dace, bream, barbel, pike; members only,

miles of excellent fishing on the rivers Derwent, Trent and Idle and the Chesterfield Canal at Retford along with a superb lake near Sawley and another 20 acre lake at Willington; www.derbyshirecountyac.org.uk

Hallcroft Coarse Fisheries, Hallcroft Rd, Retford DN 22 7RA (tel: 01777 710448; see website for more info: www.hallcroftfishery.co.uk): six lakes with bream, roach, carp, tench, perch, chub, and river fishing on the River**River Idle**; dt £5 , conc £4.50, jnr £4 at tackle shop on site.

TORNE and NEW IDLE. Doncaster & Dist AA has 5m from Epworth Road Bridge to Pilfrey Bridge; dt £3 from bank.. Scunthorpe & DAA has water on the Three Rivers from Pilfrey Bridge to the half way point to

the outflow at Keadby; known for its tench, pike and bream; dt on bank; and water on **Stainforth and Keadby Canal**.

Althorpe (S Humberside). **Stainforth & Keadby Canal;** coarse fish; about 14m of water above and down to Trent; good fishing; rights held by Scunthorpe & DAA. Other fishing stations for canal are **Thorne** and **Crowle**. **Lindholme Lakes**, **Sandtoft**, Doncaster DN9 1LF (tel: 01427 872905; see website for more info: www.lindholmelakes.co.uk), mixed fishery on 8 lakes: all general coarse and match lakes; dt £6, match dt £6, under 16s and disabled £5; conc.

Crowle (S Humberside). Excellent centre for coarse fishing. **Stainforth and Keadby Canal**, and **Torne** are ½m from Crowle Central Station; Scunthorpe & DAA; roach, tench, bream, perch, carp, pike; Three Drains on A18. Tackle shops: many in Doncaster and Scunthorpe. Hotels: Friendship Inn, Keadby. Tackle shops in Doncaster (17m) or Scunthorpe (10m).

RYTON (tributary of Idle); Coarse fish.

Worksop (Notts). On Ryton and **Chesterfield Canal**; coarse fish. Worksop & DAA has 10½m of canal from W Retford Bridge to Drakeholes Tunnel. **Clumber Park Lake** (National Trust 100 acre lake), where dt and st can be had from Estate Office, Clumber Park S80 3AZ (tel: 01909 476592) or from bailiff on bank; 7am to dusk; st, dt, both conc. **Woodsetts Quarry Pond**, 8 acres; and **Sandhill Lake**; coarse fish; dt on all waters; Worksop & DAA waters. Grafton AA (tel: 0114 287 3110) fishes 4m of Chesterfield Canal (from Bracebridge Lock to Shireoaks Bridge) in and around town; predominantly large bream (stocked), chub, rudd, ruffe, carp, skimmer, gudgeon, plenty of (stocked) roach and tench. For **Langold Lakes**, 14 acres with bream and carp, north of Worksop; £4.01, conc (under 14s £1.03), contact Site Office (tel: 01909 730189). Tackle shops: Angling Supplies, 49 Retford Rd, Worksop S80 2PU (tel: 01909 482974); Ken Ward Sports, 6 Carlton Rd, Worksop S80 1PH (tel: 01909 472904); Gateford Angling Supplies, 155 Gateford Rd, Worksop S80 1UD (tel: 01909 531115).

MAUN (tributary of Idle): Improving fish stocks: chub, dace, roach. Little formal access; apply to local landowners.

Mansfield (Notts). Field Mill Dam (now owned by Mansfield District Council); coarse fish, dt £3 on bank. Vicar Water, Clipstone; coarse fish, dt. **Kings Mill Reservoir**, Sutton Rd: Nottingham AA water, with carp, roach, bream, dt £3 on bank. Permits for local coarse ponds also from Mansfield Angling, 20 Byron Street, Shirebrook, Mansfield NG18 5PR (tel: 01623 633790).

Sutton-in-Ashfield (Notts). Lakes: Lawn, Dam. King's Mill Reservoir, 1m NE; tickets on bank. **Hardwick Lakes**, Hardwick Hall, are 6m W; National Trust water, all coarse ponds: **Carr Ponds** is members only club water (tel: 01246 850242); **Great Pond**, and **Millers Pond**; mixed coarse fish (no pike) are st (£50 per rod), and dt £5 per rod (on bank) waters (tel: 01246 851787); **Row Ponds** (5 in all) club members only; mixed coarse; contact Ken Hardy (01623 407265). Tackle shop: Tackle Shack Ltd, 50 Mansfield Road, Clipstone Village, NG21 9EQ (tel: 01623 627422). Hotels: Twin Oaks, Holiday Inn.

DEVON: Coarse fish.

Bottesford (Notts). Smite, 3m NW at Orston. Car Dyke, 5m NW. Bottesford & DAA preserves 5m of **Grantham Canal** at Bottesford, Muston Bridge and Woolsthorpe-by-Belvoir; st £20, conc, and dt £3 from Hon Sec and from bailiffs on bank; good coarse fishing, with pike over 27lb; other Assn waters are **River Witham** at Westborough, members only. Tackle shop: Roger Hurst Rods & Tackle, Old Forge, Saltby Road, Croxton Kerrial, Grantham NG32 1QG (tel: 01476 870707).

Belvoir Castle (Leics). Between Melton Mowbray and Grantham, Belvoir Lakes and Knipton Reservoir (coarse fish); open all year; st £60, $\frac{1}{2}$ st £40, dt £7 on bank, conc £5, enquiries to bailiff, Anthony Silvester, Rookery Farm, Gorse Lane, Hungerton, Grantham NG32 1AJ (tel: 01476 870647). **Nottingham and Grantham Canal**: Bottesford & DAA has water; dt £3 on bank. Other stations on canal are **Long Clawson**, **Harby**, **Hose** and **Stathern**.

GREET: Trout; coarse fish; preserved.

Southwell (Notts). River private. Trent, 3m SE at Fiskerton. At Oxton, 5m SW, Nottingham Fly Fishers' Club has a trout lake at Gibsmere; strictly members only, long waiting list. Greet FC, too, has trout fishing. Derbyshire County AC has Coneygre and Widgeon Lakes; brown and rainbow; fly only; pike also in winter; members only.

West Hallam (Derby). Lakes: **Mapperley Reservoir**, 2m N, **Shipley**

Park Lakes, Loscoe Dam and stretch of Erewash Canal all NCB waters; st, conc, from Hon Sec; dt from park rangers for some waters (max 2 rods).

SOAR: Very popular coarse fishery with anglers in the Leicester area. Environment Agency fishery at **Thurmaston**, nearly 1,000 yds right bank free to licence holders, west of A46 road.

Radcliffe (Derby); Good coarse fishing. Long Eaton & Dist AF administer between Kegworth and Radcliffe Flood Locks; dt from tackle dealers and Anchor Inn at Kegworth. Soldiers & Sailors AC have Trent Lock fishing; also Derwent at Draycott, and Barkers Pond, Long Eaton; mixed coarse; dt £3 on bank; contact W Walker, 41 Hawthorne Ave, Long Eaton NG10 3NG (tel: 0115 9721478).

Kegworth (Derby). Roach, dace, bream, tench, chub, perch. Two meadows u/s of Kegworth Bridge held by Long Eaton Victoria AS; no dt, members only. Nottingham AA has from Kingston Dyke one field u/s to boatyard (members only); also 1 field d/s of Kingston Dyke; members only. Long Eaton AF has good 2m stretch from Kegworth Shallow to Ratcliffe Lock, 90 pegs; coarse; dt £2 from Anchor Inn, Station Rd DE74 2FR, (tel: 01509 672722); tackle shops at Long Eaton and Borrowash. Soar AS has water here. Kegworth AS has approx 400 mtrs.

Normanton-on-Soar (Leics), Good coarse fishing. Loughborough Soar AS water, 2 fields: first and third; st from Hon Sec (sae).

Loughborough (Leics). Loughborough Soar AS has fishing near here with large carp, chub, bream, roach, perch, plus dace and barbel on two stretches; st contact Hon Sec. **Proctor's Pleasure Park**, Barrow-on-Soar LE12 8QF (tel: 0150 9412434): lake and river fishing, mainly carp, bream, tench, perch; dt £3 (3x£1 coins) from

machine on site; lake open during close season. **Charnwood Water**: 11 acre lake with carp, pike; council fishery; dt £3.40 per rod, conc £1.70 from Bennett's. Tackle shops: Bennett's Angling Store, 9 Market Place, Mountsorrel LE12 7BA (tel: 0116 2302818) who also sell Wreake AC tickets for fishing the Wreake; good perch and roach, few trout.

Quorn (Leics). Roach, bream. Quorn AS has rights on stretches of river and 1m of canal. River fishes best in autumn and winter.

Barrow-upon-Soar (Leics). About 3m river and canal fishing; good roach and bream; recently restocked. Fishes best autumn and winter. Loughborough Soar AS has water, Osiers stretch; st only, contact Hon Sec. (See Loughborough), also Quorn AC. Proctor's Park has about 1m fishing (see Loughborough). Leicester & DASA has 2m; one bank; dt £4 on bank; st £15 from Hon Sec or local tackle shops; assn also has stillwater at Walton on the Wolds (Fishpool Lake), well-stocked with carp, roach, skimmers; st £30, dt £4, in advance from local tackle shop in Syston: Match Catch, 14 The Green, Syston LE7 1HQ (tel: 0116 2600850).

Leicester (Leics). Coarse fish. 6,000m between Leicester and Barrow on Soar, towpath side, held by Leicester & DASA; also **Nene** at Ironbridge, and canals; membership £15; no dt. Wreake AC has 4,500m 1 bank **Wreake** at **Brooksby**. Wigston AC: Soar and canal; dt and st. **Leicester Canal**; some good coarse fish but boat traffic ruins summer sport. Very high quality stillwater fishing in twelve lakes totalling 22 acres in **Mallory Park** (tel: 0116 2774131; web: www.malloryparkfisheries.co.uk), 8m from Leicester; st £250, conc £160, (covering all twelve lakes). Broome AS (the largest club in Leicestershire with over 750 members) fishes 6 coarse lakes at

Asfordby; 2 lakes at **Frolesworth** with carp to 20lbs, and mixed coarse;

2 acre lake at **Syston** with large carp, and good head of small fish, and stretches of **Soar** between Narborough & Croft Quarry; membership £46 p/a + £10 joining fee, conc, from Hon secretary. Tackle shops: The Angling Man, 228 Melton Rd, LE4 7PG (tel: 0116 2665579); Match Catch, 14 The Green, Syston LE7 1HQ (tel: 0116 2600850); Angling Corner, 3 Denton St LE3 6DD (tel: 0116 2230008). Hotels: Grand, Royal, Hermitage Park (Oadby).

Narborough (Leics). Hinckley & Dist AA has water here containing trout and grayling; permits from permits sec. Broome AS has a stretch; members only.

WREAKE (tributary of Soar): An attractive coarse fishery on which Wreake AC and Asfordby & Melton Society of Anglers have extensive coarse fishing rights between Thrussington and Melton Mowbray; all members only.

Asfordby (Leics). Roach, perch, dace, pike, chub. Asfordby & Melton Society of Anglers has water on Wreake and pits at **Frisby** (1m); members only, no dt. Broome AS also has water between Frisby and Ashfordby (5 lakes); members only.

Melton Mowbray (Leics). Local club: Asfordby and Melton Society of Anglers have Hoby, Frisby, Ashfordby and Sysonby; members only. **Kala Lakes**, Hoby Rd, Ashfordby, has carp to double figures, dt (conc) on bank. **Eye Kettleby Lakes**, off Leicester Rd, 7 dt coarse lakes with large carp, etc, dt on bank. Disabled swims at both these fisheries (tel: 01664 565900). Tackle shop: Roger Hurst Rods & Tackle, Old Forge, Saltby Road, Croxton Kerrial, Grantham NG32 1QG (tel: 01476 870707).

DERWENT: Noted trout and grayling water in upper reaches; downstream coarse fish come into their own. Derbyshire County AC have several stretches (9 miles) upstream and downstream of Derby.

Sawley (Derby). Coarse fish. Pride of Derby AA has one mile of **R Dove** at **Scropton** and 12m of Trent and Mersey Canal between Shardlow and Burton upon Trent; and several ponds (including Grimleys Ponds); members only; also Pride Lake and Olvers Lake, carp (exclusive day & night fishing st £200 + 2 passport photos), st £50 + £20 joining, conc from Hon Sec. Soldiers & Sailors AC has Derwent fishing nearby at **Draycott**, members only; contact W Walker (tel: 0115 9721478).

Borrowash (Derby). Coarse fish. Earl of Harrington AC waters (see Derby). Derbyshire County AC has 6½m stretch, mainly double bank, Borrowash to Sawley with barbel, chub, roach, bream, carp, tench, perch and pike; (see website for more info: www.derbyshirecountyac.org.uk). Nottingham & DFAS has fishing rights at Riverside Farm Estates, on Derwent, mill streams and lake; strictly members only.

Spondon (Derby). Coarse fish; preserved by Earl of Harrington AC. Chaddesden Brook, 1m NW, and Locko Park, 2m N. Private.

Derby (Derby). Coarse fish, Earl of Harrington AC has Derwent from Borrowash Road Bridge u/s to Darley Park, and from Borrowash u/s to Railway Bridge, st £22, No Day Tickets sold in outlets between March15th 2009 - March14th 2010 (Closed Season), all other tickets are available from tackle shops below. and from Borrowash u/s to Railway Bridge. DCC, Derby City Parks, 15 Stores St, Derby DE21 4BD (tel: 01332 367800); dt £4.30/rod, conc £2.15/rod, from ranger on bank. Corp issues tickets for coarse fishing at **Alvaston Lake**, **Markeaton Park Lake**, **Allestree Park Lake** and

Derwent in **Darley Abbey Park**. Locko Park Lake and Chaddesden Brook private. Other clubs: Pride of Derby AA; Derby RIFC (water on Derwent, **Trent**, **Dove**, **Ecclesbourne**; canals). Earl of Harrington AC (Derwent, 1m of **Big Shrine** at Borrowash, dt); Derbyshire County AC has fishing on Derwent at Allestree, 1½m; fly fishing for trout and grayling; also coarse; the club also has Hoon Hay Farm Lake, 6 acres; fly only for browns and rainbows; members only; st ; also Willington Fisheries: 2m of River Trent, a 20 acre coarse lake and 20 acre trout lake, both members only. Fenton & DAS has Colley Croft Lake near Etwall; members only. At Kedleston Hall, National Trust has 2 coarse lakes; good winter fishing; carp, pike, tench; contact Head Warden (tel: 01332 844052). Tackle shops: Nathans Tackle, Edgeware Road, Mackworth, Derby (tel: 01332 523630). Derby, Angling Centre, 33 Nightingale Road, Derby DE24 8BG (tel: 01332 380605) (Earl of Harrington AC tickets).

Duffield (Derby). Coarse fish, trout and grayling. Derbyshire Angling Federation has 3m from Milford Bridge to Little Eaton, trout and coarse fish, also R **Ecclesbourne** from Duffield to Derwent confluence; st, conc, from Federation. Tackle shop: Belper Tackle, 37 Bridge St, Belper DE56 1AY (tel: 01773 822525; see website for more info: www.belpertackle.com).

Belper (Derby). Chub, roach, bream, perch, barbel, pike, grayling, trout; Belper & DAC: 6m covered by st, dt, conc, incl 2½ acre **Wyver Lane Pond**, carp to 30lb, double figure barbel etc, st only for pond, conc, from Belper Tackle, 37 Bridge St, Belper DE56 1AY (tel: 01773 822525; web: www.belpertackle.com), which also issues dt £6, conc, for **Possey Ponds**; carp, tench, roach etc.

Ambergate (Derby). Few trout, pike, coarse fish. Derbyshire County AC has water; coarse; members only. **Butterley Reservoir**, Coppice Lake; roach, bream, tench, carp, pike; Ripley & Dist AA waters, who also fish River Derwent between the Green Bus lay-by and Whatstandwell on the roadside bank (Coppice Lake and river, members only), st, dt only for Butterley Res. Tackle shop: Rod & Line Tackle Shop, 17 Nottingham Road, Ripley DE5 3DJ (tel: 01773 749545). Hotel: Hurt Arms.

Whatstandwell (Derby). Mostly grayling, brown and rainbow trout, with chub, barbel, some dace and odd perch. Derwent Hotel, Derby Rd, Whatstandwell, Matlock DE4 5HG, (tel: 01773 856616), has ¼m fishing; rather overhung with trees, but plenty of fish and good wading in low water; car park on bank; dt for visitors, free fishing to hotel guests. Derbyshire County AC has 2m of Derwent. At **Hartington**, Charles Cotton Hotel SK17 0AL (tel: 01298 84229) has 400m double banks of River **Manifold** at Hulme End, 1½m from hotel, fishing via token system. **Cromford** (Derby). Trout; fly only; preserved below road bridge (both banks), as far as and including Homesford Meadows, by Cromford Fly Fishers; members only, no tickets; waiting list. Above bridge, Derbyshire County AC water, 1m; fly only in trout season; coarse in winter; members only; st. Hotel: Greyhound.

Matlock (Derby). Trout (some rainbows), grayling and coarse fish. Matlock AC issue dt; water at Matlock and Matlock Bath; trout and coarse; about 1m. Derbyshire County AC has water at Darley Dale, 800 metres; fly only in trout season; grayling in winter; members only. **Press Manor Fishery**, Birkin Lane, **Wingerworth**, nr Chesterfield, off Matlock-Chesterfield A632 Road. Trout & Coarse fishery, various dt prices available, (tel: 07976 306073 web: www.pressmanorfishery.co.uk), nearest tackle shop Leegem Angling Chesterfield phone 01246-559480 **Rowsley** (Derby). Haddon Estate, Bakewell DE45 1LA (tel (the agent): 01629 812855) owns **River Wye** from Rowsley to just north of Bakewell, together with Rivers Lathkill and **Bradford** (latter syndicate only, no dt); for most of their length. Wye has pure wild rainbows, and is one of the few rivers in which they breed; and fine head of natural browns (all c&r); dt £35 low season, £65 high season: dry fly only; for information contact Head River Keeper, Warren Slaney (mob: 07801 457225); dt are also obtainable from main outlet, the Peacock Hotel, Rowsley, DE4 2EB (tel: 01629 733518) to residents and non-residents; who also have fishing for residents on Derwent. Darley Dale FFC has 3m both banks; members only; st & dt for guests with members; apply Hon Sec; web: http://ddffc.net. Warrington AA has fishing at Darley Abbey; members only.

Baslow (Derby); nr Bakewell, 4m. The Cavendish Hotel, DE45 1SP (tel: 01246 582311), originally the famous Peacock, has unique sporting rights over Derwent and Wye, unavailable any other way; 6 rods on the **Chatsworth Fishery**, from Old Bridge at Baslow to Smelting Mill Brook at Rowsley (brown and rainbow trout, grayling). For **Monsal Dale Fishery** on R Wye, from boundary of Chatsworth Estate below Cressbrook Mill to New Bridge at Ashford Marble Works (brown and rainbow trout) (courtesy of Chatsworth Estate), contact Stephen Moores (Keeper) (tel: 01629 640159). For annual membership of Chatsworth Fishery (Derwent fishing river keeper mob: 0775 4175557) and Monsal Dale Fisheries apply to Estate Office, Edensor, Bakewell DE45 1PJ (tel: 01246 565300).

Hathersage (Derby). Trout, grayling; preserved by the Derwent FFC; also at Bamford and Grindleford (members only).

Bamford (Derby). Trout, grayling. Derwent FFC has water below Bamford Mill; and from Bamford Mill to Yorkshire Bridge; members only. Peak Forest AC has **River Noe** upstream from Derwent confluence to Edale; fly fishing for brown and rainbow trout and grayling; also Bradwell Brook and Castleton Brook, Hope, trout and grayling; members only; subscriptions £275; contact Hon Sec.

Ladybower. Centre for **Ladybower and Derwent Reservoirs;** trout; fly only (see Midlands reservoirs and lakes). Hotels: Ladybower Inn, Yorkshire Bridge Inn, Ye Derwent Hotel, Bamford (1m), Anglers' Rest (1m), Rising Sun, Bamford (2m).

AMBER (tributary of Derwent): trout, coarse fish.

Alfreton (Derby). St & dt from Ripley AC for reservoir at **Butterley**: pike, perch, roach, tench, bream, and carp. Sheffield Trout Anglers have water on Amber at Wingfield. Tackle shop: Alfreton Angling, 11 Park St, Alfreton DE55 7JE (tel: 01773 832611). Hotels: George. Also fair fishing in Derwent at Ambergate, 5m SW.

WYE (tributary of Derwent): One of few rivers in which rainbow trout breed. Also holds good brown trout.

Bakewell (Derby). Trout. Fishing preserved by Haddon Estate. Details are to be found under **Rowsley**, above.

Monsal Dale (Derby). The Chatsworth Estate has excellent trout fishing on ¾m double bank; 4 rods per day only; apply for day tickets at £35 or £30 depending on season, to River Keeper (tel: 01629 640159; see website for more info: www.chatsworth.org).

Buxton (Derby). River private. Brown and rainbow trout fly fishing in **Lightwood** and **Stanley Moor** reservoirs.

DOVE. Dovedale waters, where Izaak Walton and Charles Cotton fished, are preserved, no tickets. Good sport with trout and grayling elsewhere; a few salmon recently. In lower reaches, where Churnet enters Dove, angling is improving. Stretches below Uttoxeter, Doveridge, Marchington, Sudbury, etc, also improving: barbel, chub, grayling, pike present. Very limited opportunities for day tickets.

Uttoxeter (Staffs). Trout, grayling. Uttoxer AA preserves good deal of water between Rocester and Uttoxeter; no permits. Leek & Moorlands FC has water here (also **Crakemarsh Pool**); membership £30 + £10 joining fee, conc; half mile l bank. Fenton & Dist AS has water on Dove, members only. **Ashbourne** (Derby). Several miles of **R Henmore** and **Bentley Brook**, both tributaries stocked with trout and grayling, and two small lakes controlled by Ashbourne Fly Fishers' Club; st only; no dt. National Trust has South Peak Estate, including Dovedale; fly only; Leek & Dist FFC water; anglers must obtain info about procedures to guard against infection by Signal Crayfish. In **Dovedale** 3m of good trout and grayling fishing can be had by guests only; at Izaak Walton Hotel, Dovedale DE6 2AY (tel: 01335 350555; see website for more info: www.izaakwaltonhotel.com). Yeaveley Estate nr Ashbourne DE6 2DT (tel: 01335 330247; web: www.yeaveley-estate.co.uk), has fly fishing for rainbow and brown trout on 1½ acre lake, open all year; membership available, dt £25, all browns to be returned; tuition by appointment, flies for sale. Hotel in Ashbourne; Green Man; hotel at Mayfield, 2m SW (Staffs); Royal Oak.

Hartington (Derby). Trout. Derbyshire County AC has 2m and 25 weirs double bank at Wolfscote Dale; fly for wild and stocked browns and grayling; members only. Charles

Cotton Hotel has about 250 yds of the River Dove; token system. Proprietor will give data about stretches permitted by farmers.

CHURNET (tributary of Dove): Mixed fishery: trout, grayling, coarse.

Leek (Staffs). Trout, coarse fish; preserved above Leek town by landowners. Fishing improving. Leek & Moorlands FC has coarse fishing on Leek Arm of Caldon **Caldon Canal**; **Deep Hayes Country Park**, Longsdon; **Heron Marsh Pool**, Rudyard; **Crakemarsh Pool**, nr Uttoxeter; also Larkhall Pool, nr Bradnot; mixed coarse, members + wt for visitors from Leek Pet and Anglers (see below); also **R Dove** and **R Churnet**; tickets for Deep Hayes Country Park from Leek Pet and Fishing Centre (see below), otherwise members only; membership £30 + £10 joining fee, conc. **Turners Pool**, Swythamley, nr Rushton Spencer SK11 0SL; coarse fish, dt £7: contact Olive or Kenneth Wilshaw (tel: 01260 227225). **Rudyard Lake** is 3m NW, 168 acre reservoir; very good bream, with roach, perch, and pike to 30lb; dt £4 (bank); boats on half and full day from water bailiff (tel: 01538 306280); 3 match lengths pegged. Basford Coarse Fishery, Turners Croft, **Basford** ST13 7ET (tel: 01538 360616); carp and other coarse fish, dt, conc, at poolside, 4 pools. **Tittesworth Reservoir**: 189-acre Severn-Trent W trout fishery; enquire visitor centre. (See Midlands reservoirs and lakes). Tackle shops: Leek Pet and Fishing Centre, 33 St Edward St ST13 5DN (tel: 01538 398958; Moorland Tackle, 32 Russell St ST13 5JF (tel: 01538 372288).

MANIFOLD (tributary of Dove): Offers visitors few opportunities.

Longnor (Staffs). Buxton, 7m; trout. Dove, 1m E; trout, grayling. 7m stretch in Manifold valley, Derbyshire County AC; members only. Part of Hoo Brook and Manifold is National

Trust property; trout restocked; anglers must obtain info about procedures to guard against infection by Signal Crayfish.

MEASE. Coarse fish. Fishing stations are: **Measham** (Leics); **Snarestone** (Leics); and **Ashby-de-la-Zouch** (Leics); **Netherseal** (Derby); **Edingale** and **Harlaston** (Staffs); Birmingham AA has water at last three; dt £5 from tackle shops. Hotels: Queen's Head, Royal.

SEAL BROOK (tributary of Mease): a small watercourse with few fish.

Over Seal (Leics). Lakes: Ashby Wolds Reservoir, 1m N.

TAME: After a long history of pollution, much recovered under the care of the Severn-Trent W. Fish now present in many stretches. Further improvement scheduled.

Tamworth (Staffs). Tributary Anker holds roach, pike and perch. Town waters are all let to clubs, tickets from bailiff on bank. Mease; roach, chub, dace; Haunton, **Harleston**; dt from W T Ward and Harleston Mill. Local clubs: Lamb AC; Fazeley Victory AC; Birch Coppice AC; Tamworth WMC, Polesworth AC; which fishes Coventry and Birmingham Canals; some tickets on offer. Tackle shops: Tamworth Fishing Tackle, 23 Lichfield St, Tamworth B79 7QE (tel: 01827 66701); Hambry's, 8 Tamworth Rd, Polesworth (tel: 01827 895011).

Kingsbury (Warwicks). Kingsbury Water Park, Bodymoor Heath Lane, Sutton Coldfield, B76 0DY (tel: 01827 872660); nr Tamworth, 2m from Junction 9 of M42; 13 fishing lakes, with specimen carp to 32lb, tench to 8lb, large bream, roach, perch and pike; some pegs suitable for disabled; a variety of season and day permits offered, from a family st at £150, to dt £2.50 to £4.50, some conc; car park fee £3; buy dt from machine in fishing lodge preferably (no change); contact Information Centre at above address.

Sutton Coldfield (W Midlands). Lakes at Visitors Centre, Sutton Park, Park Rd, Sutton Coldfield B74 2YT (tel 0121 3556370): Bracebridge Pool, Blackroot Pool, Powell's Pool, Keepers; fishing includes carp to 30lb, bream, roach, pike, and other species; st (for all Birmingham waters), dt on bank. Penns Carp Fishery, Penns Hall, Wylde Green; dt from tackle shop, or on bank. Local club: Sutton Coldfield AS has fishing on rivers and lakes. Tackle shop: Fosters of Birmingham, Unit K, Moor Lane, B'ham B6 7HH (tel: 0121 344 3333; web: www.fostersofbirmingham.co.uk). Hotel: Penns Hall, beside fishery.

ANKER (tributary of Tame): coarse fish; best sport in winter.

SENCE (tributary of Anker): small stream, but good trout and grayling in places, as well as chub, roach and dace.

BOSWORTH BROOK (tributary of Sence): Trout; preserved.

Market Bosworth (Leics). Bosworth Brook, 1m North; trout; preserved by owner of Bosworth Hall. Sence, 3m W. Tweed, 3m SW. Lakes: The Duckery, Bosworth Park, 1m S; pike, etc. Gabriel Pool, 3m NE.

BOURNE BROOK (tributary of Bourne). Fishing station: Plough Inn, **Shustoke**, Warwicks. Trout fishing in Avon Division STW Shustoke Reservoir.

BLYTH (tributary of Tame): Coarse fish. Centres: **Coleshill** (Warwicks). Chub, perch, pike, roach. **Hampton-in-Arden** (Warwicks). Chub, dace, roach. **Solihull** (Warwicks). Earlswood Lakes, 6m SW; ticket for three coarse lakes on bank from bailiff. **Olton Mere** coarse fishing; apply to sec, Olton Mere Club.

REA (tributary of Tame): Urban river with poor access. Poor habitat and water quality result in poor fish stocks.

Birmingham (W Midlands). Birmingham AA, formed from a number of local clubs, controls extensive water on river, canal and lake throughout the Midlands and into Wales. The club-card gives details of all fishing rights, which include numerous fisheries on **Severn and tributaries, Trent and tributaries,** canals, lakes and ponds. A detailed guide with excellent maps is issued from Assn HQ, (web: www.baa.uk.com) (see clubs list); members only st various prices. White Swan Piscatorials (web: www.whiteswanpiscatorials.org.uk) own or rent waters on the **Severn, Avon, Teme, Mease, Rea, Lugg, Ithon, Herefordshire, Aran, Wye** and numerous pools and a streth on the South Stratford Canal; st limited. Reservoir at **Edgbaston** fishable on permit. **Park Lakes**: coarse fishing on 14 lakes and pools in city; dt from park keepers; special st for pensioners. Tackle shop: Fosters of Birmingham, Unit K, Moor Lane, B'ham (tel: 0121 344 3333; web: www.fostersofbirmingham.co.uk); and many others. Many hotels.

Lifford (Birmingham). Lifford Reservoir. Good coarse fishing; dt from park keeper.

FORD BROOK (tributary of Tame). Fishing stations : **Pelsall** and **Walsall** (W Midlands). Brook polluted. Lake: Hatherton Lake; pike. Swan AC leases **Sneyd Pool**, Bloxwich, **Essington Wyrley Canal** (now from Walsall to Wolverhampton) st £5, conc, coarse fishing; dt £3 on bank; match booking. Walsall & Dist AS has **Hatherton Canal**. **Park Lime Pits**; carp, bream, roach, perch, pike; dt and st for small charge. **Aboretum Lake**; bream, tench, roach, perch, pike; dt; fishing 6am to dusk.

SOWE: Coarse fish, some trout.

Stafford (Staffs). Upstream of town; perch, pike, dace, roach, chub. Downstream; perch, roach, bream, chub, occasional trout. Free for about ½m upstream of town on left bank only; remainder preserved by Izaak Walton (Stafford) AA. This association has fisheries on the Sowe, **Trent & Mersey Canal, Shropshire Union Canal** and **Hopton Pools**, carp, tench and other coarse fish; apply Hon Sec for annual membership, wt and dt and Holts. Tackle shop: Holts Fishing Tackle, 122 Marston Rd, ST16 3BX (tel: 01785 251073). Hotels: Swan, Station, Vine, Royal Oak, Tillington Hall.

Eccleshall (Staffs); Trout; preserved. Stoke-on-Trent AS has 1m river at Great Bridgeford; members only; also Ellenhall Pools (Ellenhall Park Farm); mixed coarse; no night fishing; members only; apply Hon Sec.

PENK (tributary of Sowe):

Penkridge (Staffs). Coarse fish. **Staffordshire and Worcestershire Canal.** Stafford AA has water (see Stafford); Radford Bridge (Staffs). Izaak Walton (Stafford) AA has water here d/s from Roseford Bridge at Acton Trussell to Milford Aquaduct; members only, st from Archline Tackle (below). **Gailey Upper Reservoir**, Cannock, 35 acres, trout fishery, run by anglers for anglers; stocked rainbows, browns, blue trout; open all year, pike fishing Nov-Mar; day tickets, 4 and 6 hour tickets, sporting tickets, season tickets available, boats & café, apply to Gailey Trout Fishery, Gailey Lea Lane, Penkridge, Staffs ST19 5PT (tel: 01785 715848; web: www.gaileytrout.co.uk). Further tackle shop: Archline Tackle, Unit 6, Lakeside Plaza, Bridgtown, Cannock WS11 0XE (tel: 01922 411205; web: www.archlineangling.co.uk).

TYNE

Formed by junction of North Tyne and South Tyne at Hexham, and empties into North Sea at Tynemouth. Since recovering from pollution this river is now the best salmon river in England; trout fishing fair. Chub and roach are increasing in lower reaches and dace in the lower North and South Tyne. Much of the fishing is controlled by private fishing clubs where day tickets are mainly issued to members' guests only. The website FishTyne (www.fishtyne.co.uk) operated by the Tyne Rivers Trust (www.tyneriverstrust.org) is, however, making access easier by pulling together fishing opportunities into one online location and encouraging the local clubs to make their waters more accessible to visitors. Their Tyne Angling Passport is also a welcome scheme offering great-value trout fishing on various beats on Tyne and tributaries—see www.fishtyne.co.uk for details.

Newcastle upon Tyne (North'land). Whittle Dene Reservoirs, nr Stamfordham, 17 acres; coarse fishery; dt from fishing lodge at reservoir (tel: 01207 255250) a Northumbrian Water coarse fishery, dt £6; general NW enquiries (tel: 0870 240 3549). Free fishing at Killingworth Pond, N Tyneside. Killingworth Lake is dt coarse fishery. Tackle shops: Bagnall & Kirkwood, 28 Grey St, Newcastle upon Tyne NE1 6AE (tel: 0191 2325873; web: www.bagnallandkirkwood.com).

Ryton (Tyne and Wear). Salmon, trout, coarse fish. Northumbrian Anglers' Federation have a stretch also Tyneside Anglers Syndicate.

Wylam (North'land). Wylam Angling Club; trout day-tickets only and North East Railways Angling Club (NERAC); members' guests only. Upstream Northumbrian Anglers' Federation water. Salmon, trout, coarse fish. (See below).

Prudhoe (North'land). Trout, coarse fish; salmon; water here and at Ovingham and Ryton preserved by the Northumbrian Anglers' Federation; also Coquet at Warkworth, Felton and Rothbury; st £95 (combined permit), dt £30 salmon, sea trout, brown trout, conc, from Head Bailiff, 15 Woodlands, Rothbury, Morpeth, Northumberland, NE65 7XZ (tel: 01669 620984) (see website for more: www.northumbriananglersfed.co.uk) £65 trout; coarse fish st £27 only from head bailiff. Mickley (North'land). Trout, coarse fish, salmon; Federation water (See Prudhoe). **Eltringham** 1.6 miles of south bank. Salmon, sea trout and trout. Day tickets through; (web: www.fishtyne.co.uk).

Bywell (North'land). Major salmon beat 2.5 miles with 12 named pools. One of the few Tyne beats with a full time ghillie. Bookings through Bywell Estate Office, (tel: 01661 843296; web: www.allendale-estates.co.uk). Day tickets also through (web: www.fishtyne.co.uk).

Corbridge (North'land). Trout and dace; trout plentiful but small with runs of sea trout and salmon. Corbridge Riverside Sports Club has 3m on south bank; membership restricted to persons living locally; dt to members' guests only.

Hexham (North'land). Trout (av ¾lb), coarse fish; salmon improving. Tynedale Council, Prospect House, Hexham NE46 3NH (tel: 01434 652121), owns ½m on south bank off Tyne Green from Hexham bridge upstream to old railway bridge; st, dt available; most other salmon water, club beats for member's and their guests only. Fishing is also available where the North & South Tyne meet, known as the **Tyne Waters Meet**, Sept – Oct 2010 dt prices are £130, early season prices are cheaper, available via www.fishtyne.co.uk only. **Langley Dam**, 8m west of Hexham: 14 acre lake stocked weekly with rainbow trout; fly only; sporting c&r £16 (8 hours), £10 (4 hours); dt £20 (8 hours) 5 fish; £12, 4hour, 3 fish (apply tel: 01434 688846, 8am to 9pm). **Derwent Reservoir**, 10m east, 1,000 acres; dt for brown and rainbow trout, £22 (8 fish), conc £20; north bank fly only, south bank and dam wall fly and multibait, spinning (tel: 01207 255250). Club: Hexham AA has water; guests tickets only. Westwater Angling Ltd has water at **Hallington Reservoir**, nr Hexham; members only, st £530, conc, dt to guests only; contact Hon Sec, (tel: 01434 681405; see website for more info: www.westwaterangling.co.uk).

Tributaries of the Tyne

DERWENT: Stocked brown trout, average about 1lb, with fish to 3lb, some grayling.

Consett, just south of Consett is Knitsley Mill Fishery, 3 lakes, dt.

Swalwell (Durham). Derwent Haugh to Lintzford is now pollution free, held by Axwell Park and Derwent Valley AA; dt for brown trout, no spinning at any time, a spinning reel may not be used at any time or for any purpose. Shotley Bridge (Durham). Derwent, 1m W; trout and grayling. Derwent AA preserves about 14m of river from Lintzford to Derwent Reservoir (see Durham reservoirs) and one bank above reservoir to Baybridge; open membership; dt £6. Licences from Post Office, Shotley Bridge (tel: 01207 502084), Allensford Caravan Park, Frasers Angling, Gateshead, and AMH Angling Ltd, Front Street, Annfield Plain; (see website for more info: www.derwentangling.co.uk).

NORTH TYNE: trout, sea trout & salmon. One or two clubs issue tickets for trout, sea trout and salmon fishing and the website: www.fishtyne.co.uk has details and availability of fishing at Chollerton, Haughton Castle, Chipchase, Nunwick, Chesters, Broadbank & other small tributaries.

Chollerford (North'land). Salmon, sea trout trout, coarse fish. The George Hotel, Chollerford NE46 4EW (tel: 01434 681611), has ¾m bank fishing upstream of bridge for residents and nonresidents; trout average ½lb; dt £12.

Bellingham (North'land). Trout, salmon, sea trout; best July-Oct. Felling Fly Fishing Club has approx 5 ½m from Low Carriteth u/s of Bellingham to Tail of the Eals pool d/s several excellent named pools. Ferryhill and District Angling Club have stretch east bank. **Riverdale Hall Hotel**, Bellingham, NE48 2JT, has salmon and sea trout fishing for residents, 7 beats on North Tyne, (tel: 01434 220254; see website for more info: www.riverdalehallhotel.co.uk).

Falstone (North'land). Forest Enterprise offers dt £3, wt £15, st £25, for stretch between Butteryhaugh and Deadwater; the permit also covers Akenshaw, Lewis, and Kielder, and is sold at Kielder Castle Forest Centre (tel: 01434 250209); who also issue tickets for River Rede. Falstone FC issues permits for 2m of North Tyne, £10 per day, £30 between Sept-Oct, from Blackcock Inn NE48 1AA (tel: 01434 240200), or from Alan Banks, 5 Hawkhope Rd, Falstone NE48 1BD (tel: 01434 240158).

Kielder (North'land). Major Northumbrian Water (NW) reservoir of 2,700 acres; stocked with browns and rainbows, also contains a good head of wild brown trout; dt £22 8 fish, conc £20 8 fish; family tickets, boats for hire £23; fly, trolling and worm; tickets on site (tel: 01434 250312). Hotels: Riverdale Hall, Bellingham; Percy Arms, Otterburn.

REDE: Trout and pike, with autumn salmon & sea trout. West Woodburn, Felling Fly Fishing Club, has 3 mile stretch; (see website for more info: www.fellingflyfishers.co.uk);

Otterburn (North'land). Otterburn Tower Hotel, NE19 1NS (tel: 01830 520620), has 3½m on Rede, south of Mill Bridge; trout, sea trout & salmon. Sweethope Loughs, Lough House, Sweethope, Harle NE19 2PN (tel: 01830 540349): trout fishing for natural browns, stocked rainbows; split into 4 hour sessions from 8.45am, 1pm, 5pm (£17 each, 3 fish); £34 for 8hrs (6 fish) or £22 for 3 fish; £17 all day c&r; boats £6 to £12 per session.

SOUTH TYNE: An excellent spate river, usually fishes well by Jun-Jul, best Sep-Oct for salmon. One or two clubs issue tickets for trout, sea trout and salmon fishing. Most beats for club members and their guests only.

Warden (North'land)., Three salmon & sea trout beats shared with local club, contact The Boatside Inn, Warden, Hexham, Northumberland, NE46 4SQ, (tel: 01434 602233, 2010 dt price £33.)

Fourstones, Haydon Bridge, Bardon Mill (North'land). Salmon, sea trout & trout, most beats (if not all) run by private angling clubs, the possibility of guest dt via club members only.

Melkridge (North'Land) North East Railways Angling Club (NERAC) offer beat north bank. All proceeds to support Tyne Rivers Trust, dt only, £25 to £35 from www.fishtyne.co.uk, max 2 rods per day, salmon, sea trout

& brown trout (Hen salmon to be returned and all brown trout).

Haltwhistle (North'land), Brown trout, sea trout, salmon. Haltwhistle & DAA has visitors wt from £20, for approx 10m around Haltwhistle, contact Mr David Stobbart, (tel: 01434 321858). Bellister Estate National Trust water is 1½m of double and single bank fishing; no bait fishing; members only (apply Hon Sec); Day and week tickets available Feb-Aug only from Mags newsagents, Market Square, Haltwhistle, NE49 0AZ, (tel: 01434 320381), junior season permits available £15. No day tickets issued after end Sept. 3m NE of Haltwhistle is National Trust Crag Lough, syndicate managed by Felling Fly Fishers; browns and rainbows; members only, (see website for more info: www.fellingflyfishers.co.uk).

Lambley Farm Estate (North'Land), Lambley, CA8 7LQ. Private and secluded ¾ mile double-bank beat. Trout best: Apr, May, Jun. Salmon and sea trout: summer onwards — peaking in the rains of Sep and Oct. Fishing available with cottages on estate, (tel: 01434 322121; see website for more info: www.tynesalmonfishing.com). Spare day tickets available from (web: www.fishtyne.co.uk).

Alston (Cumbria). Salmon, sea trout, trout. Alston & Dist AA has 10m of water with various beats between Lambley Viaduct and Alston, to 31 Jul dt £11 up to June 15th, £20 onwards, tickets from Alston PO.

WANSBECK

Northumberland trout stream which fishes well under favourable conditions of water, but opportunities for visitors are few.

Ponteland (North'land). Higham Lakes Trout Fishery, 3 lakes, various priced dt on site, (tel: 07950428159; web: www.highamlakes.com). Also **Bolam Lake**, just off A696 at Bolam, north of Belsay, coarse fishing for perch &

pike, dt from Belsay PO, (tel: 01661 881207).

Morpeth (North'land). Brown trout; Water in town free to licence holders. **South Lindon Fishery** at Longhorsley is approx 7 miles north of

Morpeth, 2 lakes, trout only, dt on site, (tel: 01670 788366; See website: www.southlindenfishery.co.uk).

Fontburn Reservoir, NW fishery of 87 acres, with stocked rainbow (to 26lb 8oz) and wild brown trout (to 9lb 4oz) and blues; family permit £25 (2 adults + any number of their children under 17); dt £25 12 fish; £22 8 fish, £20 conc 8 fish, dt on site; permits from lodge (tel: 01669 621368). Also **Felton Fence Fisheries**, between Morpeth & Alnwick, follow A697 to Long Framlington, fishery off the B6345, (tel: 01665 570205 or 07714 152967; see website for more info: www.feltonfence.co.uk), dt on-site, tackle and bait shop, species: Carp, Perch, Roach, Rudd, Tench. Tackle shop: Amble Angling Centre, 4 Newburgh St, Amble, Morpeth NE65 0AQ (tel: 01665 711200). Hotels: Waterford Lodge, Queen's Head, Angler's Arms, Weldon Bridge.

Tributary of the Wansbeck

BROOKER BURN: **Longhirst** (North'land). Wansbeck, 2m S; trout. Lyne, 2m N.

WAVENEY

(see Norfolk and Suffolk Broads)

The Wheelyboat Trust is a small national charity dedicated to providing disabled people with the opportunity and freedom to participate in waterborne activities all over the UK. Its main role is to help public waters acquire Wheelyboats for the benefit of their disabled visitors who use them for angling, pleasure boating and nature watching. So far, 144 Wheelyboats of various design have been supplied by the Trust and the majority of them are used by disabled anglers for game, coarse and even sea fishing.

We provide help and advice to fisheries wishing to acquire Wheelyboats and, with help from organisations like charitable trusts and the Environment Agency, funds can be made available to help with the cost. There is a list of fisheries with Wheelyboats near the start of this book.

We are funded entirely by voluntary donations and receive no statutory funding. Please support our work with a donation – Gift Aid forms are available via post or download. For more information, please contact Andy or visit our website.

Andy Beadsley, Director. North Lodge, Burton Park, Petworh, West Sussex GU28 OJT. Tel/fax 01798 342222, info@wheelyboats.org
www.wheelyboats.org

WEAR

Rises on Kilhope Moors in extreme west of Co Durham and enters North Sea at Wearmouth. River now contains salmon, excellent sea trout, grayling, brown trout; in lower reaches: dace, chub, roach and barbel, perch and bream. Tributaries Browney and Rookhope are improving, with Browney sustaining a run of sea trout. Bedburn preserved.

Chester-le-Street (Co. Durham). Salmon, sea trout, brown trout (stocked by club) excellent coarse fish. Chester-le-Street & DAC has 10m good water with the above species plus, dace, chub, barbel, eels, roach; membership £100, conc, dt available from District Council. Hartlepool & Dist AC fishes 1m single bank; members only, contact Hon secretary.

Finchale Abbey (Co Durham). 2 mile beat, west bank, beside the ancient ruined abbey in lovely setting. Caravans welcome (no children) and popular with holiday makers and day trippers. Good varied water suitable for all methods. Salmon, sea trout, trout, chub and barbel. Season £45, and day tickets at £9 & £5 (child) available. Finchale Abbey Touring Park (tel: 0191 3866528; see website: www.finchaleabbey.co.uk).

Angel of the North Fishing Lakes, just north of Chester-le-Street, Bassetts Lookout, Northside, Birtley, DH3 1RF, 3 lakes (2 coarse, 1 carp), for more info (tel: 0191 4100449; web: www.angelnorthlakes.com), booking advised before turning up.

Sharpley Springs, trout, dt, (tel: 0191 5818045; see website for more info: www.sharpleywaters.co.uk).

Durham (Co. Durham). Trout, sea trout. Free fishing on EA licence from Ice Rink to Sewage Works, also Ice Rink to Kepier Farm Boundary. Last stretch to Orchard Wall is strictly private. Durham City AC has more than 2½m on river, and stillwater fisheries stocked with coarse fish; one specimen lake lake and three mixed coarse; st £50, conc; dt for guests only; enquiries to Hon Secretary; (web: www.durhamanglers.co.uk) Grange AC has stretch of river at Kepier Woods, migratory fish, good head of brown trout, grayling, chub, dace, large pike; and Brasside Pond; dt water. Bear Park, Cornsay and New Branspeth Assns all have water on **Browney**, 4m W of Durham; limited dt; restocking. Ferryhill & DAC have Wear fishing, also Browney, both banks to Wear junction, and R Gaunless, 1½m from West Auckland, with brown trout; with 2000 yards of excellent Wear salmon and sea trout pools and specimen coarse fish (Brockbank stretch); the Club also has access to Association waters in the Croxdale area; apply Hon Sec for dt waters (not rivers) availability. 9m SE, Hartlepool & Dist AC have 4½ acre Tilery Lake at Wingate; and Kenny's Pond at Hutton Henry (2 acres), both mixed coarse; members only; contact Hon Sec; st £70. Near Stanley are **South Causey Lakes** (used to be Beamish Lakes), a trout fishery; dt on site. Tackle shop: Bagnall & Kirkwood, 28 Grey St, Newcastle upon Tyne NE1 6AE (tel: 0191 2325873; see website for more info: www.bagnallandkirkwood.com).

Approx 3M west of Durham at Bearpark is **Aldin Grange Lakes**, mixed fishery, 3 coarse lakes, (1 lake match only) 2 trout lakes (fly only). Coarse dt £7, trout dt from £11 - £23, c&r £9 - £13. Tackle shop on site plus café. Great farm shop. (tel: 07901 538 587 Mick the bailiff; (web: www.aldingrangelakes.co.uk). Near to Wingate are **Eden Meadows Fishery**, coarse fishing on 3 lakes, dt £7, conc £5, eve £4, (tel: 01429 835836; see website for more info: www.edenmeadows.webeden.co.uk).

Willington (Co. Durham). Willington & Dist AC has fishing at Sunnybrow to Page Bank; dt £7 trout, £15 salmon/sea trout; coarse ponds £5, conc; club also has 3m of river at Eastgate; 4m at Willington and 2m further down; membership available from £25 (ponds); membership otherwise from £55, sea trout and salmon; from Sheldons Newsagents in High Street. Tackle shop: Reid Fishing Tackle and Sports, 33 Hope Street, Crook DL15 9HU (tel: 01388 763867); Sheldon Newsagents.

Bishop Auckland (Co. Durham). Sea trout, brown trout, grayling, salmon. Bishop Auckland & DAC controls some 20m of water on Wear, between Witton le Wear and Croxdale; dt £20 from Hon Treasurer; also stretch of Tees at Eggleston; membership £120 + £40 joining fee; also Witton Castle Lakes (tel: 01388 488691), trout stillwater; dt at lodge; 3 fish dt £24, £15 for sporting ticket (c&r), conc, details from Hon Sec; club has the Angling and Conservation Centre at Witton Park as HQ (DL14 0DY). Get Hooked on Fishing has Wadsworth Lake; specimen carp fishery and 2 mixed coarse lakes; dt and st at the Get Hooked Centre DL14 0DY (tel: 01388 664789). **West Auckland** (Durham). **Jubilee Lakes** approx 3 miles south at Redworth, various dt on site, (tel: 01388 772611; web: www.jubileelakes.co.uk). Ferryhill & DAC has fishing at **Croxdale**, **Tudhoe**, **Witworth Estates**; also **Newfield** and **Page Bank**; club waters also include Rivers **Browney**, **Tees**, **Swale**, **Skern**, **Gaunless**, North Tyne at Bellingham and various coarse fishing ponds; some dt waters; membership + entrance fee, conc. Hotel: Manor House, West Auckland. Tackle Shop: Deltaflash Fishing Tackle, 40 Broom Road, Ferryhill DL17 8AF (tel: 01740 652360).

Witton le Wear (Co. Durham). Bishop Auckland & DAC (see above).

Wolsingham (Co. Durham). Trout, sea trout (good). Wolsingham AA has water; members only (limited st plus joining fee for visitors); long waiting list; no dt. At Hagbridge, **Eastgate** (about 8m W), Northumbrian Environment Agency has leased stretch to Weardale FFC; st £25 from Hon Sec, dt £10 from The Paper Shop, Front Str, in Stanhope. NWL has trout fishing on **Hisehope**, **Waskerley** and **Smiddy Shaw Reservoirs**. **Tunstall Reservoir** is a NWL fishery, leased to Weardale FFC, jointly run with Ferry Hill AC; a limited number of day permits are available to the public. Please call 01388 818945 for further information. **Frosterley** (Durham). Trout, sea trout. About 1½m water belongs to Frosterley AC; members only, who must reside in area.

Stanhope (Co. Durham). Trout, sea trout and salmon. About 2m water (both banks) belongs to Stanhope AA; members only, limited membership £30, when available; no limit for juniors; sea trout June onwards. Weardale Flyfishers has 2½m u/s from Stanhope; dt £10 from newsagent. Hotel: Bonny Moorhen.

Upper Weardale (Co. Durham). Trout, sea trout (Sept and Oct), occasional salmon. Upper Weardale AA has 6m in total of Wear and tributaries from Westgate to Cowshill; st £35, wt £12 (not available Sept/Oct), dt £6 (Sept/Oct £8), conc, from The Post Office, St John's Chapel (tel: 01388 537214); water re-stocked during season with 12in brown trout. Hotels: Cowshill, Cowshill; Golden Lion.

Tributary of the Wear

BROWNEY: now free of pollution; trout and sea trout.

Langley Park (Co. Durham). Langley Park AA lease river here; assn also has coarse ponds: Edmondsley, near Sacriston; Esh Pond (good crucians) near Esh village; and Tursdale Pond near Durham. Tackle shop: Turners

Tackle, 25 Front Street, Sacriston DH7 6JS (tel: 0191 371 1804).

Burn Hill (Co. Durham). Waskerley, Tunstall Hisehope and Smiddy Shaw Reservoirs close together on moors between Stanhope and Consett. (See above and under Durham Reservoirs).

WEAVER

Rises south-west of Cheshire and flows into Mersey estuary. Most species of coarse fish, trout in the upper reaches. British Waterways have a cooperative scheme, the Weaver Waiters, which invites fishing clubs to partake in the management of the River Weaver Navigation between Saltisford and Weston, and represents a long-term strategy of improvement and development of the lower reaches of the river. Contact Regional Manager for further details.

Northwich (Cheshire). Good coarse fishing held by Northwich AA; water on **Weaver, Dane, Trent and Mersey Canal** (about 17m); **Billinge Green Pools**; **Great Budworth Mere**; **Petty Pool Mere** (limited access); **Pickmere Lake**; comprehensive st (all waters); st £40 + joining fee £20 from tackle shop; no dt; exceptional concessions to OAP and juv, from Box 18, Northwich; no tickets sold on bank. Lymm AC has carp complex (specimen fish) at Belmont Estate, 4m north; members only. Tackle shop: Vale Royal Angling Centre, 84 Station Rd, Northwich CW9 5RB (tel: 01606 46060; see website for more info: www.valeroyalangling.co.uk); Dave's of Middlewich, Lewin Street, Middlewich CW10 9AS (tel: 01606 833853; see website for more info: www.daves-fishing.co.uk). Hotel: Mayfield Guest House, London Rd.

Winsford (Cheshire). Roach, bream, perch, carp. Winsford & Dist AA have stretch from New Bridge upstream to Church Minshull, several pools around Winsford and R Dane at Middlewich, with barbel and chub; large restocking in past two years, dt available to fish the River Weaver from the end of Bottom Flash down to Newbridge, dt fishing is also available

for Newbridge Pool again at a cost of £5 and also from the bailiff on bank; no dt on upper Weaver. Lymm AC has 7 acre lake at Marton, Lymm Vale; mixed coarse, many specimen; members only. Crewe LMR Sports AS has Sandhole Pool (coarse fish) and good tench water at **Warmingham** ($\frac{1}{2}$m).

Crewe (Cheshire). Weaver $2\frac{1}{2}$m W. No fishing in Crewe, but Crewe LMR Sports and Social Centre, Goddard Str, CW1 3HL, has 3m of Weaver near Nantwich (4m away) on Batherton Estate; **Sandhole Pool** (1m), rights on **Shropshire Union Canal** and stretches of **Severn**, **Weaver** and **Dane**; as well as good bream, tench and pike fishing on **Hortons Flash**; guest tickets are not issued for any of these waters; dt on bank for Macclesfield Canal; coarse fish (see also Congleton). Tackle shop: Crewe's Carp 'n' Match Angling Centre, 122 West Street, CW1 3HG (tel: 01270 588466; see website for more info: www.crewecarpin.co.uk).

Nantwich (Cheshire). Trout, grayling, dace, roach, chub. Nantwich AS controls nearly all Weaver near Nantwich; st only; water starts in town and stretches SE of town for 7m mainly on both banks, broken at

Batherton Mill; society also has stretch on **Severn** at Leighton Bridge near Welshpool; also Dee at Holt and Farndon. Other clubs with water near Nantwich are Pioneer AA, Amalgamated Anglers and LMR Sports (all Crewe) and Wyche Anglers; Winsford and Dist AA control **Weaver**, from Newbridge to Church Minshull; flashes; pools; st from Hon Sec. Winsford Club's pools contain fine tench, carp, bream and pike. **Shropshire Union Canal** dt from bank ranger; st from tackle shop. Other waters within 10m of Nantwich are: Big Mere, Osmere, Blakemere (boats), Combermere (boats). Egerton Lake, Mitchells Fruit Farm, Cholmondely (tel: 01829 720206); carp water of 50 pegs, dt from bailiff. Apply tackle shop also for Lakemore

Fisheries, one mixed coarse, 2 carp & catfish. Also **Hampton Springs Fishery**, Hampton Springs, Shay Lane, Hampton, Malpas SY14 8AD (tel: 01948 820789; see website for more: www.hamptonsprings.co.uk), mixed fishery; 8 lakes; cafe on site; toilet facilities for disabled. Tackle shop: Stapeley Angling Centre, Stapeley Water Gardens, London Rd, CW5 7LH (tel: 01270 611500; web: www.stapeleywg.com); tickets Nantwich AS; licences. Hotel: Crown.

Audlem (Cheshire). Adderley Brook. Birchall Brook, 2m NE. Lake: Woolfall Pool, 2m NE. Hotels: Lamb, Crown. (for club water see Nantwich).

Wrenbury (Cheshire). Marbury Brook. Sale Brook, 2m S. Baddiley Brook, 2m N. Hotel: Combermere Arms, Burleydam, Whitchurch.

Tributaries of the Weaver

DANE: Grayling, wild brown trout, coarse fishing.

Northwich (Cheshire). Chub, dace, pike to 20lb, bream, double-figure barbel and roach. Northwich AA have fishing from town centre to weir, no dt offered, but holiday permit £14 seven days, by post (POBox 18, Northwich CW9 5SE); Assn also fishes Rookery Pool, Canal Pit, Vale Royal Pool, Eyres Pit, and 3 lakes, Dane Valley Fisheries; members only.

Davenham (Cheshire). Trout, barbel, roach. Davenham AC have fishing, members only, Davenham to Leftwich; also Davenham Pits.

Middlewich (Cheshire). Dace, roach, chub. Winsford & Dist AA have fishing, 65 pegs running from below the canal bridge in Middlewich down to Bulls Wood, no dt. Middlewich Joint Anglers have Trent and Mersey Canal stretches, and pool and river fishing, which includes **R Dane**, left bank u/s from Byley Bridge, approx 2m; right bank u/s approx ½m, both banks between Byley and Ravenscroft

Bridge, and from Wheelock confluence on left bank d/s; also **R Wheelock**, right bank u/s from R Dane confluence; grayling, wild brown trout, chub, dace, roach, gudgeon, barbel, and other species; also **Tetton** and **Sparrow Grove** lakes: coarse; st £40, conc; dt £5 in advance at some waters, £10 on bank. Tackle shop: Dave's of Middlewich, Lewin St, CW10 9AS (tel: 01606 833853; see website for more info: www.daves-fishing.co.uk). (Middlewich JA cards). Hotel: Boars Head.

Swettenham (Cheshire). Prince Albert AS has much of R Dane; here, and at Allgreave, Congleton, Byley, and Wincle, members only.

Congleton (Cheshire). Dace, roach, chub, gudgeon and occasional grayling and perch. Prolific water in and around Congleton controlled by Congleton AS, plus excellent carp and coarse fishing in **Goodwins Pool**; disabled pegs; society also has Knypersley Reservoir, Macclesfield

Canal, Trent & Mersey Canal at The Romping Donkey; coarse; membership £28, conc £12; (web: www.apcr33.dsl.pipex.com). From Radnor Bridge towards Holmes Chapel partly controlled by Prince Albert AA, Grove and Whitnall AA and Warrington AA. Stoke-on-Trent AS has Astbury Mere; 43 acre lake; mixed coarse, incl carp to 25lb; contact Hon Sec. St for Prince Albert AA stretch at **Somerfordbooths** from secretary or tackle shops; Assn also has water on Severn. Eaton Flyfishers have fly only water from Eaton to North Road; members and guests only (web: www.eatonflyfishers.co.uk). **Moreton Coarse Fisheries**, New Rd, Astbury, nr Congleton CW12 4RY (tel: 01260 272839): fishing on 3 lakes, dt £7 (1 or 2 rods), conc (except w/e), from manager in office; carp to 28lb, large bream and tench; barbless hooks only, bays for disabled. **Westlow Mere Trout Fisheries**, Giantswood Lane CW12 2JJ (tel: 01260 270012; see website for more info: www.westlowmere.co.uk); dt £20 4 fish, £15 2 fish, £10 c&r, conc £8, c&r; boat £8 day (48hrs notice required). **Macclesfield Canal**: Warrington AA; roach, perch, tench, bream, pike. Lymm AC has stretches of Dane at Sproston near Holmes Chapel, members only. Astbury Meadow Garden Centre, Newcastle Rd, has coarse fishery on site. Tackle shop: Terrys of Congleton, 47 Lawton St CW12 1RU (tel: 01260 273770), has club memberships for Congleton AS, Mow Cop Anglers, Biddulph Anglers.

Bosley nr **Macclesfield** (Cheshire). Roach, chub, carp, bream, pike; private. Lake: **Bosley Reservoir**; Prince Albert AS water, members only.

Macclesfield (Cheshire). Extensive fishing controlled by Prince Albert AS, a nationally famous club with many rivers, lakes and reservoirs in the NW of England and in Wales.

These include many stretches on the R **Dane**, the **Severn**, the **Ribble**, **Wye**, **Wenning**, **Wharfe**, **Towy**, **Teifi**, **Cothi**, **Banwy**, **Twymyn**, **Trent**, **Dove**, **Winster**, **Vyrnwy**, **Lledr**, **Dulas**, **Dysinni**, **Dee**, **Dovey**, **Mawddach** and **Lune**; **Marbury Mere**, Whitchurch, **Isle Lake**, Shrewsbury, **Langley Bottoms** and **Lamaload Reservoirs,** Macclesfield and others; long waiting list for membership; dt issued for a few of their waters. **Danebridge Fisheries**, Pingle Cottage, Wincle, Macclesfield SK11 0QE (tel: 01260 227293), has small (2 acre) trout lake at Wincle, fish to 16lb, sporting ticket £14 (5 hours), £20 (2 fish, 5 hours), dt £26 (3 fish, 9 hours); instruction can be arranged . Marton Heath Trout Pools, Pikelow Farm, School Lane, Marton SK11 9HD (tel: 01260 224231); seven acres of stocked trout fishing, rainbow and brown; tuition; barbless hooks only; coarse pool on site well stocked with common, mirror and crucian carp, roach, etc; tackle available. Macclesfield Waltonians A.S (website: www.waltonians.co.uk) has **Teggsnose Reservoir**, coarse fish, carp to 20lb; st forms from Barlows (below). Other clubs: Macclesfield FC (12m on Dane and **Clough Brook**, preserved; no tickets). **Macclesfield Canal**; good carp, pike, roach, etc. Prince Albert AS has approx 6m, from Buxton Rd Bridge to Robin Hood Bridge. **Redesmere** and **Capesthorne**; roach, bream, tench, perch, pike, mirror and crucian carp; dt as guest of member from bailiff; Stoke AS water. East Lodge, Capesthorne (see Cheshire lakes, meres, etc). Other waters in area: **South Park Pool**; carp, roach, perch, pike; dt from pavilion. **Knypersley Reservoir**; no night fishing. Tackle shop: Barlows of Bond Street, 47 Bond St, Macclesfield SK11 6QS (tel: 01625 619935).

WHEELOCK (tributary of Dane):

Sandbach (Cheshire). Club with fishing in vicinity are Wheelock AC,

Middlewich Joint Anglers. Congleton AS has ½m here of Trent & Mersey

Canal; see website for more info: www.apcr33.dsl.pipex.com).

WELLAND

Rises near Market Harborough and flows through Lincolnshire Fens to The Wash. Coarse fishing very good, much of it controlled by clubs. Upstream of Market Deeping river is renowned for large winter catches of chub and roach. Downstream, river is much wider, with regular banks and excellent access, and slow flowing with bream, roach, tench and eels, also a popular match and pike venue. Fen Drains hold roach, bream, tench and pike, North and South Drove Drains improving, especially in winter.

Spalding (Lincs). Four Mile Bar to Spalding Centre, good fishing for pike, perch, chub, roach, dace, bream and tench; controlled by Spalding AC; dt local tackle shops. Deeping St James AC has Market Deeping, Perkins Meadow to Four Mile Bar, dt local tackle shops, in Market Deeping.

Lincolnshire Drains; good coarse fishing. At South Holland Drain, Foreman's Bridge Caravan Park, Sutton Rd, Sutton St James PE12 0HU (tel: 01945 440346; web: www.foremans-bridge.co.uk). Holbeach & Dist AC water in **South Holland** and **Little Holland Main Drains**; dt from local tackle shops. Spalding FC preserves Counter, North, South Drains; pike, perch, roach, carp, rudd, bream, tench. Deeping St James controls **Vernatts Drain** through East Midlands Anglers Federation. Tackle shop: Tidswells Tackle & Guns, New Bungalow, Burr Lane, Spalding PE12 6AZ (tel: 01775 723640).

Cowbit (Lincs). Pike, perch, dace. Spalding FC water (see Spalding).

Crowland (Lincs). Pike, perch, dace. Nene, 2m SE at Black Horse Mills. New River from Spalding to Crowland preserved by Spalding FC; pike, roach, perch, dace, rudd, bream, tench.

Deeping St James (Lincs). Chub, dace, roach, bream, rudd, pike. Deeping St James AC controls much water in vicinity, including Several Fishery, above town at junction of old river;

Welland at Market Deeping; **Nene** fishing; the **Bourne Eau**; **R Glen**; all mixed fisheries, dt £3.50 obtainable. **Market Deeping** (Lincs). Several Fishery controlled by Deeping St James AC; it extends 6½m from Market Deeping to Kennulph's Stone, on Deeping high bank; also a new double bank fishing from Wards Farm to Four Mile Bar, along about 5m; notice boards erected; dt £3.50 on most club waters, from bailiffs. **Stamford** (Lincs). Chub, dace, roach, pike, perch; fishing free to licence holders on N bank between Town and Broadend Bridges; approx 1¼m. Elsewhere preserved by Stamford Welland AAA; approx 18m of water, stretching from Barrowden to confluence of R Gwash and w bank of **Gwash** to Newstead road bridge, eight stretches in all; chub to 5lb; bream to 7lb; st £15, jun £5, OAP £5, from Hon Sec or tackle shop. **Burghley Park Lake**, 1m SE (bream and tench, some rudd), Monday to Saturdays; dt to fish island side of Burghley Lake from Burghley Estate Office, 61 St Martins, Stamford, PE9 2LQ (tel: 01780 752075; web: www.burghley.co.uk). Tackle shop: Stamford Tackle, 13a Foundry Rd, Stamford PE9 2PY (tel: 01780 754541).

Ketton (Leics). Oakham AS has water here and on **River Chater**; members only; coarse fish.

Rockingham (Northants). 400 acre Eyebrook Reservoir is only 2m distant, just south of Caldecott; good trout fishing (see Midlands reservoirs and lakes). At **Corby**, coarse fishing on Corby Boating Lake (tel: 01536 464674), with carp, chub, perch, roach, rudd. Hotels: Elizabeth Rockingham; Hampton by Hilton, Corby.

Market Harborough (Leics). **Saddington Reservoir**; 45 acres, mainly bream; contact Harry Bosworth, bailiff (mob: 0790 4493417) is Saddington AA water; enquiries regarding membership £50, conc. Broughton and Dunton AC has members only lake at Liere. Wellingborough Nene AC have 5m of Grand Union Canal between Foxton Locks and Theddingworth; apply Hon Sec. **CJ's Fishery**, Saddington Rd, Shearsby LE17 6PX (tel: 0116 2478101); 3 lakes; carp and match; 4m NW; dt on bank. **Mill Farm Fishery**, Gilmorton, nr Lutterworth; 2 lakes totalling 6 acres; carp, tench and others; additional 8 peg lake containing mixed coarse (tel: 01455 552392; see website for more info: www.millfarmfishery.co.uk); dt £6 on bank (1 rod) (£8 2 rods), conc; also **Holly Farm Fisheries**, Ashby Magna; 3 lakes, carp (tel: 01455 202391; web: www.hollyfarmfishery.com); tickets on site. Tackle shop: Rugby Tackle Mail Order, 155a Bilton Rd, Rugby CV22 7DS (tel: 01788 570645; web: www.rugbytackle.co.uk); Oadby Angling, 89 London Rd, Oadby, Leicester LE2 5DN (tel: 01162 710789). Hotels: Angel, Premier Inn.

Tributaries of the Welland

GLEN: River free from Surfleet village to reservoir, coarse fish; trout above Bourne.

Surfleet (Lincs). Glen free below village. Preserved above by Spalding FC.

Pinchbeck (Lincs). Permits issued by Welland and Nene RD. River Welland, 2m SE at Spalding; also Coronation Channel.

Counter Drain (Lincs). Counter Drain; coarse fish; Spalding FC.

Bourne (Lincs). Glen holds trout upstream.

GWASH: Fair trout and grayling stream. Private fishing. Stamford Welland AAA have confluence with Welland to Newstead road bridge, west bank.

CHATER:

Ketton (Leics). Roach and dace. Stamford Welland AAA has stretch from junction with Welland to Ketton road bridge, both banks.

EYE BROOK: Good head of roach, dace and chub; trout upstream.

Smart Carping. *Photo: Ian Gemson*

WITHAM

Rises south of Grantham and flows northward to Lincoln, then south-eastward to Boston, where it enters the Wash. Above Grantham noted mainly for trout and grayling, mainly private. Between Grantham and Lincoln it is a good mixed coarse fishery, with chub, dace and barbel, mainly private clubs. Winter areas include Kirkstead and Tattershall Bridge sections. From Lincoln to Boston it is entirely embanked with excellent roach and bream fishing. The fishing rights for the majority of this length are leased to the Witham & District Joint Anglers' Federation. Members of the following affiliated associations have free fishing: Boston & DAA; Lincoln & Dist AA; Newark PF. Otherwise, temporary members, day-permits from their bailiffs on the bankside or local tackle shops. Main fishing accesses are **Washingborough**, **Bardney**, **Southrey**, **Stixwold**, **Kirkstead Bridge** to **Tattershall Bridge** (road alongside), **Chapel Hill**, **Langrick Bridge** and **Boston**. **Woodhall Spa** is another good centre for Witham angling, with several hotels catering for anglers, including Kings Arms.

Boston (Lincs). Angling facilities exceptionally good; at least 100 miles of good coarse fishing (pike, perch, dace, tench, roach and bream) in Witham; Witham & Dist JAF holds 26m between Lincoln and Boston, also tributaries. Boston & DAA waters: **South Forty Foot Drain**, (full disabled facilities at Wyberton Chain Bridge), **Sibsey Trader** (carp to 25lb), **Bargate Drain** (Horncastle Rd), **River Glen** at Guthrum and Tongue End, the **Bourne Eau**, and **East and West Fen Catchwaters**; disabled pegs on Trader Drain; st £17, conc, dt £5 on bank; £3.50 in advance; free fishing on Hob Hole Drain, Kelsey Drain and West Fen System, on each of which Boston & DAA have the match rights (tel Mrs Mallett on 01205 871815). Tackle shop: Boston Angling Centre, 11 Horncastle Rd, Boston PE21 9BN (tel: 01205 353436). Accom at Fairfield Guest House, 101 London Rd; Kings Arms, Horncastle Rd.

Lincoln (Lincs). Good coarse fishing. Witham fishes best from Aug to Oct with bream predominant. Witham & Dist JAF has Witham from Stamp End Lock to Boston West on right bank, with exception of a few short stretches, Witham left bank, Lincoln 1,500 yds d/s of Stamp End Lock to Bardney, with exception of 1,200 yds in Willingham Fen, Witham at Stixwould to Kirkstead Bridge; **Sincil Drain/South Delph** between Stamp End Lock and point 630 yds u/s of Bardney Lock; **North Delph**, **Branston Delph**, **Sandhill Beck**, **Timberland Delph**, **Billinghay Skerth**; dt £4 from bailiffs on bank. Lincoln & Dist AA has excellent coarse fishing on **Trent**; **Till** at Lincoln, **Saxilby** and **Sturton by Stow**; drains, dykes, **Boultham Park**, and **Starmers Pit** (good bream, eels, pike, carp and others species). Saxilby is Witham & Dist JAF waters; membership books available from tackle shops, concessions to jun, OAP; dt £3.50 on banks; 11m **Fossdyke Canal** between Torksey and Lincoln, mainly roach, rudd, perch and bream; also Witham & Dist JAF managed. **North Hykeham**; Cemex. **Richmond Lakes**, 40 acres, coarse; dt on bank. Tackle shops: G Harrison & Son, 55 Croft Str, Lincoln LN2 5AZ (tel: 01522 523834); Feed'n'Weed, 22 Birchwood Centre, Jasmin Rd, Lincoln LN6 0PY (tel: 01522 695528). Hotels: Barbican, many others.

Grantham (Lincs). Grantham AA has good coarse fishing on Witham, **Grantham Canal,** and **Denton Reservoir**; membership from Hon Sec; membership £22, conc £11; assn is a member of the federation of Midlands clubs, which includes

Boston, Oakham, Newark, Asfordby and Deeping St James clubs, and has been established to protect fisheries in area and leases waters on **Bourne Eau** and the **Glen**; membership: apply Hon Sec; assn also has **Queen Elizabeth Pond**, Queen Elizabeth Park for disabled and OAP's only; tench, crucian, rudd. **Woodland Waters,** Willoughby Rd, Ancaster, Grantham

NG32 3RT (tel: 01400 230888), has match lake, with large head of tench, and specimen lake, with carp over 30lbs; dt £5 (£8 carp, 1 rod), conc; holiday camping on site. Tackle shops: Roger Hurst Rods & Tackle, Old Forge, Saltby Road, Croxton Kerrial, Grantham NG32 1QG (tel: 01476 870707).

Tributaries of the Witham

SOUTH FORTY FOOT DRAIN: Good coarse fishing. From Boston to Little Hale Drove, Boston & DAA; matches booked through Hon Sec. Centres are **Boston, Wyberton, Hubberts Bridge, Swineshead, Donington**.

RIVER BAIN:

Tattershall (Lincs). Good stretch of river with large chub, occasional barbel, also good bream, roach, perch, and pike to 25lbs; Boston & DAA water; no dt on bank, but books available from Hon Sec and tackle shops.

Horncastle (Lincs). Rivers Bain and Waring; trout, roach; preserved. Some good chub water, free fishing. Tupholme Brook 7m NW. Horncastle AA had Bell Yard Pit but currently closed while building works take place; enquiries to Hon Sec. **Revesby Reservoir**, 35 acres, coarse fish; contains big pike, roach, tench, bream, perch, eels; members only; apply to Estate Office, Revesby, Boston PE22 7NB (tel: 01507 568395). Hotels: Bull, Red Lion, Rodney.

FOSSDYKE NAVIGATION: Fossdyke held by Witham & Dist JAF. Centres: **Lincoln, Saxilby** and **Torksey**. Good coarse fishing, especially noted for bream. Match bookings (Witham & District JAF) to David Ellerker (tel: 01777 228133); or Mike Wright (tel: 01522 703765).

HOBHOLE DRAIN, EAST AND WEST FEN DRAINS: Each canalised lengths of river forming part of the fen drainage system. Hold good stock of coarse fish (bream, roach, perch, pike, tench); area includes following waters: **Maud Foster, Sibsey Trader, East Fen Catchwater drains, West Fen**; also **Kelsey** and **Bellwater drains**. St and dt from Boston tackle shops; match pegs. Hobhole, Kelsey and West Fen drains may be fished free on EA licence only. St covers also fishing on **Witham, Steeping Relief Channel, Bourne Eau, Coronation Channel, Vernats Drain, Fossdyke Canal** and **South Forty Foot**.

SLEA: Rises west of Sleaford and enters Witham at Chapel Hill. Trout in upper reaches. Coarse fish, particularly roach, elsewhere. Private fishing throughout length. Hotel: Carre Arms.

Details changed or missing? Please let us know, so we can update in the next reprint or Edition; contact *Where to Fish* by email: editor@wheretofish.co.uk

WYE

This most famous of English salmon rivers, rises on the south side of the Plynlimon mountains in Mid Wales, very close to the source of the Severn, and flows about 160 miles to enter the Severn estuary near Chepstow. The river flows through England for a substantial part of its course from Hay-on-Wye down to the sea.

The Wye was justly famous for its run of very large spring salmon with several 50lb fish recorded, the most recent in 1963. Today, these fine spring salmon are sadly much fewer in number and great efforts are being made to restore the salmon runs of the Wye to their former glory. Unlike most rivers in England and Wales the peak months for salmon fishing on the Wye are May and June. The Wye is also a top class coarse fishery in the middle and lower reaches and the upper reaches provide excellent grayling and brown trout fishing in season. The middle and lower river and its tributaries have chub, barbel, dace, eels, roach, perch, grayling and pike all of which grow to a very good, if not record, sizes. Below Hereford there are also increasing numbers of carp and a few very localised tench and bream; flounders are also relatively abundant, surprisingly far from the sea, and run to well over 1lb in weight. Although now protected, the river also hosts one of the largest UK populations of twaite shad which enter the river in May, ascend as far as about Builth Wells, stay for about six weeks and are a nuisance to salmon anglers as they will take almost any fly or spinner.

A substantial amount of the fishing on the main river and its tributaries is administered by the Wye and Usk Foundation through their Passport scheme. (tel: 01982 560788; web: www.wyeuskfoundation.org).

Bigsweir (Glos.) The Bigsweir Fishery provides salmon fishing close to the tide, above and below Bigsweir Bridge, and is one of the most prolific salmon fisheries on the river. For salmon fishing contact Charles Hopkinson (tel: 01594 530073). The Winter fishing is controlled by Newport AA but members only, no day tickets. Contact Hon. Sec: G. Locke (tel: 01633 852601). Newport AA also have further Wye fishing at Symonds Yat and on the River Ebbw as well as stillwaters.

Redbrook (Glos.). Chub, dace, pike, perch, salmon. Contact the Post Office, Redbrook. At **Fairoak Fishery**, The Cot, St Arvans, Chepstow, Monmouth NP16 6HQ (tel: 01291 689711;), fly only fishing for trout on three waters; various tickets on site, incl £30, 5 fish, £17, 2 fish; lodge on site, with good facilities for anglers; expert tuition, with a purpose built novice pool. The Big Well Trout Fishery at Tinmans Green near Redbrook offers stillwater fishing for rainbow and blue trout in 4 small pools. Catch and Release tickets available. Contact: Colin and Liz Evans (tel: 01600 772904).

Wyesham (Monmouthshire.) Roger Stokes, Springfield, Peterchurch HR2 0RT (tel: 01981 550540) is responsible for letting 2½m double bank on Lower Wyesham and The Duke's Water which has excellent fly water; ghillie available; let by season £1365 per rod one day per week; reputedly one of best Wye fishings.

Monmouth (Monmouthshire). Wye holds salmon, pike, trout, grayling, chub, barbel, roach, perch, dace and bleak; preserved. Town water is a short stretch above the road bridge, free for coarse or small fee for salmon: Monmouth District Council Offices, Monmouth NP5 3DY (tel: 01633 644541). Monmouth Dist AS own or rent part of three rivers: 4m of Wye, including the Duke's and Wyastone Leys fisheries, winter coarse fishing, the Duke's is downstream from Wye Bridge to mouth of Trothy. (1200 yds), Wyastone Leys is both banks upstream from the inflow of the Malley Brook to Vaga House at river bend; **Monnow**, with trout, grayling, chub, dace, carp, 3m of single or double bank fishing; **Trothy**, at Dingestow and Wonastow, 5 miles fly & worm fishing for brown trout, dt in advance only from Bridge Cycles in Monmouth, 9–13 St Thomas's Square. NP25 5ES. (tel: 01600 719942; web: www.bridgecycles.co.uk). Glamorgan AC have about 0.75 mile of coarse fishing upstream of Monmouth between Wyastone Leys and the Monmouth 'free' water, starting at Malley Brook and running downstream on both banks to the fence just upstream of Monmouth Rowing Club. Glamorgan AC also have coarse fishing at the Biblins upstream of Wyestone Leys, this is a noted barbel stretch and is accessed by a long drive on forestry roads, tickets and keys from Gary Evans Fishing Tackle, 109 Whitchurch Road, Cardiff. (web: www.garryevans.co.uk). GAC also have a short stretch of the Trothy at Monmouth and other fishing on the Usk, Taff, and various stillwateres in South Wales. The GAC Wye fishing is not 'winter only' and is available all year except during the coarse fishing close season.

Symonds Yat (Hereford). Salmon, trout and coarse fishing all preserved. $1\frac{1}{2}$m both banks between **Goodrich** and Symonds Yat controlled by Newport AA; members only; no dt. Prince Albert AS has two beats at Huntsham Bridge near Symonds Yat, members only, waiting list, no dt.

Kerne Bridge (Hereford). Chub, dace, pike, perch, salmon, trout; preserved. Castle Brook, Garron, 2m; trout. Luke Brook, 2m. Lammerch Brook, 5m.

Ross-on-Wye (Hereford). Salmon, trout, barbel, bleak, carp, bream, roach, large pike, chub and good dace.

Ross-on-Wye AC has fishing on Town Water, Weir End and Benhall, approx 5m; membership £40 (waiting list) plus joining fee £10, conc, wt £18, dt £6 for town water, on bank or from G B Sports (below); club also has a salmon section st £125 (who must be club members); club also has waters outside salmon season at Sallack, 5m u/s. Ebbw Vale Welfare AC has $2\frac{1}{2}$m at **Foy**, with chub, dace, roach, barbel; members only, membership open to application. Hotels: Royal, Radcliffe Guest House. G B Sports sells tickets for 15 acre mixed coarse fishing at Upton Bishop, Drummonds Dub. **Foy Bridge Fishery**, Lyndor HR9 7JW (tel: 01989 563833) has 250 metres double bank, spinning and fly fishing; boat for hire; caravan club site with electric. Wye Lea Country Manor, **Bridstow**, HR9 6PZ (tel: 01989 562880; web: www.wyelea.co.uk), has 1m single bank from Backney to Wye Lea; salmon (4 rods); mixed coarse is included; ghillie can be provided. Licences and tackle from G & B Sports, 10 Broad St, Ross HR9 7EA (tel: 01989 563723; web: www.gb-sports.co.uk); Wye Angling, 5 Croft Court, Hill Street HR9 7AD (tel: 01989 566986).

Hereford (Hereford). Salmon, trout, grayling, other coarse fish incl big chub, and more recently barbel. Hereford & Dist AA holds $11\frac{1}{2}$m bank on Wye and 8m **Lugg**, dt £15 salmon, £5 trout and coarse; in addition, three stillwater fisheries, one trout and two coarse fish; members only; three types of membership offered; salmon members may fish some 18 named pools, fishable at various heights; membership applications to Hon Sec; also apply Woody's (below). For 20 pegs at Luggs Mouth to Shipley, Holme Lacy nr Hereford; contact Monty Bishop (tel: 01432 354309); tickets from Mordiford PO. Letton Court, Hereford HR3 6DJ, has salmon fishing on $1\frac{1}{2}$m of Wye, dt £25-£35; trout £10; also coarse fishing on $1\frac{1}{2}$m of river and stillwater, (tel: 01531 890 455). 3m from Kington is **Bollingham Pools**; brown and rainbow trout, fly only; dt £7, c&r also available (extra fish may be purchased at cost); contact R F Pennington, Bollingham Pools, nr Eardisley HR5 3LE (tel: 01497 831665). Birmingham AA has water on Lugg at Dinmore and Moreton; dt £5 from tackle shops. For Byford fishing on Garnons Estate, Bridge Sollars, who sometimes have salmon dt, in advance only, also coarse dt; phone bailiff, Phil Jordan (tel: 01981 590270 before 9pm); and Red Lion, Bredwardine. Local tackle shop: Woody's Angling Centre, 67 Whitecross Road, Hereford HR4 0DQ (tel: 01432 344644). Hotels: Green Dragon; Pilgrim; Kilverts; Booth Hall. Red House Farm, Eaton Bishop, caters for anglers.

Bredwardine (Hereford). Red Lion Hotel, HR3 6BU (tel: 01981 500303; web: www.redlion-hotel.com), has 4m (Moccas Fishery), tickets; salmon, trout, coarse fishing; season is from 16 June to 14 March.

Hay-on-Wye (Hereford). Salmon, trout, pike, perch, chub. Hay-on-Wye Fishermans Assn has local fishing, with trout, grayling and coarse, not salmon. EA licences from post office. Permits for Hay Town Council water from Post Office. Hotel: Swan Hotel, Church St HR3 5DQ (tel: 01497 821188). Tackle shop: Sportfish, Winforton, nr Hay-on-Wye HR3 6SP (tel: 01544 327111; see website for more info: www.sportfish.co.uk); F W Golesworthy & Sons, 17 Broad St, HR3 5DB (tel: 01497 820491). Hotel: Rose and Crown.

Glasbury-on-Wye (Powys). Salmon, trout, chub, dace, grayling, pike. Fishing in Wye and Llynfi preserved. Llangorse lake is accessible.

Builth Wells (Powys). Salmon (best April, May, June and Oct); good head of grayling, wild brown trout. Groe

Park & Irfon AC has 2m on Wye incl ½m double bank, 1m on Irfon, incl ½m double bank, with 9 salmon catches on Wye and 4 late season catches on **Irfon**; fly fishing only during trout season on Irfon and 2 sections of Wye; club stocks heavily with brown trout; 3-day salmon permit £25, trout £18, trout dt £10, juv £3, coarse dt between 1 Oct-end Feb dt £5, conc, from T D Niblett & Co, 43 High St LD2 3AB (tel: 01982 553624); or M Morgan, The Beeches, 10 Cae Llewellyn, Cilmery, Builth Wells (tel: 01982 552759); Conti's Newsagent, High Street (open Sundays); no keep nets for grayling on club waters, prawn and shrimp for salmon banned; club also owns Llyn Alarch, 1½ acres, nr Builth, stocked rainbows; platforms for disabled anglers; 4 fish limit, dt £16, conc, contact Brian Haycock (tel: 01982 551396); a few country memberships available, salmon £64, trout £32, contact Hon Sec. **Elan Estate Reservoirs** accessible (see Rhayader). Cueiddon, Duhonw, Baili and Edw preserved. Tackle shop: Rods & Reels, 1 Kings Head Lane, Builth Wells LD2 3DP (tel: 01982 551706). Hotels: Park Hotel; Lion; Caer Beris Manor Hotel.

Newbridge-on-Wye (Powys). Salmon, trout, grayling, chub, dace, pike, roach; preserved, Ithon; trout; preserved.

Rhayader (Powys). Wye; trout (av ½lb; Wye record, 10½lb, caught at Rhayader Bridge), salmon. Rhayader & DAA has 4m on **Wye**, 3m on **R Marteg** to St Harmon, 1½m on **R Elan**, and 16-acre lake **Llyngwyn** at Nant Glas, boats £6/day; rainbow trout to 10lbs and browns; fly only; river dt £5, lake dt £18, st £100 (lake) (river £25), conc, from John and Les Price, Nant-y-Mynach Farm, Nantmel, Llandrindod Wells, LD1 6EW (tel: 01597 810491), or Mrs Daisy Powell (all tickets), newsagent, West Street, Rhyader (tel: 01597 810451); brown trout fishing in **Elan**

Valley, (Caban Coch, Garreg Ddu, Pen-y-Garreg and Craig Goch), all fly only, st £65, dt £8.50, conc, from Visitors' Centre below Caban Coch dam (10am-6pm), and Mrs Powell (above); lakes fly only; 6 fish limit per day; minimum size 10in. **Claerwen Reservoir** (650 acres), controlled by WW dt from Mrs Powell. Elan Valley Hotel, LD6 5HN (tel: 01597 810448; web: www.elanvalleyhotel.co.uk), caters for anglers. Mr and Mrs C Easton, Glanrhos, Llanwrthwl,

Llandridod Wells LD1 6NT (tel: 01597 810277), have accom for anglers, and ¾m west bank of Wye north of Llanwrthwl Bridge, 7 pools, with plentiful trout and grayling, salmon late season, fly only; dt £6, longer term permits available at discounted rates; fishing by arrangement. Hotels: Crown Inn, North St; Lamb & Flag, North St; Bear, East St; Elan Valley Hotel, Elan Valley, nr Rhayader.

Tributaries of the Wye

TROTHY (TRODDI): Trout, some assn water. Small stream running barely 12 miles from near Llanvertherine to enter the Wye about a mile below Monmouth. It is a good trout stream but narrow in many places. It has an excellent mayfly hatch, but the river has high banks and overhanging trees making fly fishing challenging at times. **Dingestow** (Mon.). Trout; preserved. Monmouth & Dist AS has 5m, mostly double bank. Trout and eels only.

MONNOW: Good trout and grayling stream with excellent coarse fishing in the lower reaches. It meets the Wye at Monmouth. The Monnow Fisheries Association is undertaking major habitat improvement work on the Monnow catchment and has opened up a significant amount of wild trout and grayling fishing on the Monnow, Honddu, Esceley, Dore and Worm Brook. www.monnow.org The fishing can be booked through the MFA website or the Wye and Usk Foundation website. The Gamefishers Club has water on **Lugg**, **Rea**, **Monnow**, **Honddu** and several brooks; trout and grayling; day permits to members' guests only; contact Hon Sec. **Monmouth:** Monmouth & Dist AS has 3m of Monnow, some trout and grayling but good coarse fishing with chub, dace,

roach and eels the main species with increasing numbers of barbel and some carp, bleak, perch, pike, flounders, and occasional tench and bream. Contact Hon. Sec Peter Brundrett 01989 770667. Tregate AC have 3m mostly double bank near Maypole; members only, waiting list, no dt.

Skenfrith (Hereford). Trout, chub, dace.

Pandy (Gwent). Trout, grayling; preserved. Honddu: trout; preserved. Hotel: Old Pandy Inn.

HONDDU (tributary of Monnow): Trout.

Llanfihangel Crucorney (Gwent). Permits for trout fishing here may be purchased at local post office.

LUGG: Trout and grayling, with coarse fish in some stretches.

Mordiford (Hereford). Trout, grayling, etc. Birmingham AA also has good stretch here, also water at Dinmore, Marden and Moreton; dt £6, must be booked in advance; (web: www.baa.uk.com) or from tackle shops. The Moon Inn, HR1 4LW (tel: 01432 873067) has permits for Wye at Holme Lacey; tickets for Holme Lacy also from Post Office & Stores, Mordiford HR1 4LN (tel: 01432 870235).

Lugwardine (Hereford). 8½m preserved by Hereford & District AA; dt for right bank d/s starting some 150 yds below the Worcester Rd (see clubs list).

Leominster (Hereford). Trout, grayling, pike, perch, dace. Above town Lugg preserved by landowners. White Swan Piscatorials also have water; otherwise preserved by landowners. **Pinsley Brook**; trout, grayling; landowners sometimes give permission. Mr T Brooke, Nicholson Farm, Docklow HR6 0SL (tel: 01568 760346; see website for more info: www.nicholsonfarm.co.uk), has coarse pools at Docklow: dt £6; accom available. **Kingsland** (Hereford). Lugg. Arrow, and Pinsley Brook; trout, grayling. Fishing generally preserved by landowners. 2m from Kingsland is River Arrow at Eardisland. Accommodation: Angel and Mortimer Cross.

Presteigne (Powys). Lugg, Arrow and Teme afford excellent trout and grayling fishing, generally dry fly; preserved. The Gamefishers Club has Lugg here, as well as Honddu near Pontrilas; Rea, Cradley Brook and Leigh Brook near Worcester; and Severn tributaries Tanat and Cound Brook near Shrewsbury; all brown trout waters, fly only, members only: apply Hon Sec. Near Presteigne, B&B in Georgian farmhouse, with fly fishing for trout on 4-acre Hindwell Lake (once fished by Wordsworth!); stocked annually with 300-400 rainbows; boat on water; details from Mrs A Goodwin, Hindwell Farm, Walton, Presteigne LD8 2NU (tel: 01544 350252).

FROME (tributary of Lugg). Trout, preserved.

Ashperton (Hereford). Frome, 2½m Leddon, 2½m. Devereux Park Lakes, 4m.

ARROW (tributary of Lugg): Trout, grayling, dace; but few opportunities for visitors.

Pembridge (Hereford). Trout, grayling, dace; preserved by landowners. White

Swan Piscatorials have a stretch at Ivington; no tickets. Inn: New Inn.

Kington (Hereford). Trout; preserved. Inns: Swan, Royal Oak.

LLYNFI: Trout, grayling, etc; preserved.

Glasbury-on-Wye (Hereford). Lynfi enters Wye here. Trout, grayling, chub. Fishing good, but mostly preserved.

Talgarth (Powys). Llynfi. Dulais brook. Rhiangoll; trout. Treffrwd, 2m. **Llangorse Lake** (pike, perch) can be fished from here (4m); boats for hire. Hotel: Castle, Talgarth. Visitors' tickets from local association.

IRFON: limited salmon, trout few unless stocked; good grayling.

Llangammarch Wells (Powys). Lake Country House Hotel, LD4 4BS (tel: 01591 620202) has about 5m of Irfon and nearby streams (**Garth Dulas**, **Chwefri**, etc), and some rods for salmon fishing on Wye available via ghillie (enquire hotel); also 2½ acre trout lake in grounds, brown and rainbow; fish to 3½lb; lake and rivers restocked annually; fly only, wading sometimes essential; wt and dt offered: salmon dt £30, trout and grayling £25; limit 2 brace from lake, £3.25 per lb caught; seasons on Irfon: trout 3 Mar-30 Sept; salmon 26 Jan-25 Oct; grayling 16 Jun-14 Mar; lake open all year.

Llanwrtyd Wells (Powys). Trout. 3m of Association water. Lakes.

ITHON: Trout, chub, few salmon. Good hotel and assn water.

Llandrindod Wells (Powys). Trout, grayling, chub, some eels and salmon. Llandrindod Wells AA controls 4m of trout fishing close to town, mainly between Disserth and Llanyre Bridges; limit 2 brace per day; Sunday fishing; no spinning for trout allowed, 9" size limit; waders essential. Accom with private fishing at Disserth Caravan and Camping Park, LD1 6NL (tel: 01597 860277; web:

www.disserth.biz) who sell assoc tickets; private fishing free to residents. Hotels: The Bell; Llanerch Inn.

Penybont (Powys). Trout, grayling; chub, dace, eels, pike. Hotel: Severn Arms LD1 5UA (tel: 01597

851224/344), has trout fishing on Ithon, free to residents, otherwise dt £7.50; fish run to 3lb average. Tackle from Wayfarers at Llandrindod Wells.

Llanbadarn Fynydd (Powys). Upper Ithon. New Inn, LD1 6YA (tel: 01597 840378), for 3½m trout fishing.

WYRE

From Churchtown downstream coarse fish and brown trout. Above Churchtown limited amount of salmon, sea trout and brown trout fishing.

Fleetwood (Lancs). Sport in estuary improving as water quality improves; flatfish mostly.

St Michael's (Lancs). Mainly brown trout and coarse fish. Ribble and Wyre FA have fishing at St Michaels, some sea trout. **Churchtown** (Lancs). Salmon, sea trout, trout and coarse

fish. Warrington AA has fishing here; members only.

Garstang (Lancs). Salmon, sea trout, trout and coarse fish. Garstang AA preserves 3m both banks; fly only; no dt, members only. **Scorton** (Lancs). Salmon, sea trout, trout, coarse fish. Wyresdale Anglers have 7m water; no tickets.

YARE

(See Norfolk and Suffolk Broads)

YORKSHIRE (lakes, reservoirs, canals and streams)

BRANDESBURTON PONDS. Several ponds offering varied sport to leisure anglers and specialists. Hull & DAA, membership from local tackle shop or Secretary. No dt.

BURTON CONSTABLE LAKES. 25 acres, at caravan park in grounds of Burton Constable Hall; excellent coarse fishing for roach, bream, perch, tench, carp and pike; st £70, wt £20, dt £6 (£7 2 rods), conc, from Warden, Old Lodges, Sproatley, nr Hull HU11 4LN (tel: 01964 562508); or on bank; season 1 Mar-1 Jan; entry for dt 8am.

CASTLE HOWARD GREAT LAKE. Near **Malton**. 78 acres, formerly noted for specimen pike over 40lb, perch, tench to 10lb, bream to 14lb, roach, and eels to 8lb+. Season 31 March-1 June inc. No night fishing. However due to over-fishing in the North Sea, cormorants have significantly reduced

lake stocks. It is not intended to re-stock, nor to close the fishing which, for the time being will be free to customers of the touring park.

CHELKER, SILSDEN, LEESHAW, WINTERBURN RESERVOIRS. Trout; waiting list for the local club. No tickets. Near Silsden and Ilkley.

DAMFLASK and **UNDERBANK RESERVOIRS**. YW Services Ltd. Damflask Coarse Fisheries (tel: 01274 372742), 5m from Sheffield. Underbank, near Stocksbridge now let to Hadfield Anglers; dt on bank. Both coarse fisheries, bank fishing only; disabled access at high water (with caution); Damflask day and monthly tickets sold from machines at reservoirs; further enquiries to Yorkshire Water, PO Box 500, Western House, Western Way, Halifax Rd, Bradford BD6 2LZ (tel:

01274 691111); for Damflask, contact bailiff (mob 07952 485798).

DOE PARK RESERVOIR,
Denholme. 20 acres. Coarse fish; formerly Bradford City AA water; currently closed.

EMBSAY, and WHINNYGILL RESERVOIR. Let by YW to Skipton AA; open all year round (2 fish trout limit); st £61 + £10 entrance fee, conc; dt £12 (Embsay, trout), £6 (Whinnygill, trout, roach, bream and perch); £5 winter coarse fishing; assn also has fishing on R Aire, dt £5; tickets obtainable from Paper Shop, 1a Sun Moor Drive, Skipton BD23 2JS (tel: 01756 793557), and Jacksons of Earby (tackle shop).

FEWSTON, SWINSTY and **THRUSCROSS** (wild browns only) **RESERVOIRS**. YWS Ltd trout fishery, ranging from 142 to 156 acres, fly only for Fewston and Thruscross, spinning (Swinsty only Oct-Nov), barbless hooks; regular stocking, 1lb 6oz av, 3lb+ rainbows; dt (limit 4 eve2 fish), from machine at Fishing Office at Swinsty Moor car park; contact Colin Winterburn (tel: 01943 880658); area for disabled bank anglers only, at Swinsty Lagoon where worm or fly may be used; to fish Thruscross; av catches 3 fish per rod. Near **Harrogate** and **Otley**.

HORNSEA MERE. **Hornsea** HU18 1AX. Yorkshire's largest inland water (350 acres); very good pike, carp, bream, rudd, perch, roach, tench; Hornsea Mere Marine Co (tel: 01964 533277); dt £5, junior £2.50, punts £7 day + £5 per person fishing (limited boat and bank fishing).

LEIGHTON RESERVOIR. Masham, N Yorks. 105 acre water-supply reservoir on the Swinton Estate stocked with rainbow trout (some very large); day ticket fishing; block booking (discount applies); barbless hooks; dt £18 (4 fish), evening £12, (2 fish), conc £15 (3 fish), from fishing hut in car park; catch and return allowed after limit reached; Swinton Estate Office, Swinton, Masham, Ripon, N Yorks HG4 4JR. Phone 01765 689224 for further details.

LEVEN CANAL. Beverley 6m. 3m of good coarse fishing.

LINDHOLME LAKE FISHERIES, Epworth. 8 match & pleasure coarse lakes, dt on site. Enquiries to Lindholme Leisure Lakes Ltd, Don Farm House, West Carr, Epworth, Doncaster DN9 1LF (tel: 01427 872905; see website for more info: www.lindholmelakes.co.uk).

MALHAM TARN. 6m from **Settle**. A Nature Reserve owned by the National Trust; boat fishing only, for trout with fly; barbless hooks only; c&r only; no keepnets; no bank fishing; fish may run large; bookings and detailed information from Warden or Secretary (tel: 01729 830331); phone bookings recommended; seasons May 1 to 30 Sept; accommodation locally.

MARKET WEIGHTON CANAL.
Fishing stations: **Newport** and **Broomfleet**. 6m long; bream, perch, roach, pike. Match fishing leased from Environment Agency. Dt sold locally.

MORE HALL RESERVOIR.
Sheffield 7m. YW Services Ltd water now leased to More Hall FF; trout, fly only; contact David Watson, Hon Sec on 07989 918812; dt available; barbless hooks; members only.
SCOUT DIKE, Penistone. 16m from Sheffield. YW water now leased to Barnsley TC (tel: 01484 866231; web: www.barnsleytroutclub.co.uk); dt £12 trout on bank.

SHIPTON LAKE. Shipton- by-Beningbrough. Tench, perch, roach, pike. Bradford City AA water, members only.

STAINFORTH AND KEADBY CANAL. Controlled by joint committee including following clubs:

Worksop, Doncaster, Scunthorpe, and British Railways. Usual Coarse fish.

THORNTON STEWARD
RESERVOIR, Bedale. 35 acre Felling Flyfishing Club (see below) trout fishery known as **Thornton Steward Game Fishery**, 4m E of Leyburn; fly only, barbless hooks; regularly stocked with rainbows, 1lb 6oz to 4lb; also contains wild brown; open all year to members; season for tickets is 1 March-31 Nov; 4 or 2 fish limit; no boats; dt £18, conc, from Joan Hainsworth, Hargill House, Finghall, Leyburn DL8 5ND (tel: 01677 450245).

TILERY LAKE, Faxfleet, nr Goole; 30 acres of water with carp to 30lb, bream, pike and roach; controlled by Hull & DAA, st from Hon Sec or tackle shops in Hull and Goole locality; only fishable with valid night permit; from Night Permit Sec; bream to double figures, pike to 25lb plus, good head of carp.

ULLEY COUNTRY PARK, nr **Sheffield.** Rotherham MBC. 33 acre coarse fishery with bream, roach, perch, pike, rudd. Disabled platform; ticket machine at fishery; tackle shop on site; enquiries to Ulley C P, Pleasley Road, Ulley S26 3XL (tel: 01709 365332); currently closed until Spring 2010 owing to flood damage; contact Thrybergh Country Park on 01709 850353 for further information.

WORSBROUGH RESERVOIR,
Barnsley. Coarse fish, all species, open all year. Barnsley & Dist AAS has rights; season book £25, conc £12.50; dt £3 from bailiffs walking the bank; keep nets allowed (except for carp), bloodworm (not allowed except from Oct), hempseed now allowed.

NORTHUMBERLAND, Co DURHAM, and CLEVELAND RESERVOIRS. These groups of

reservoirs, managed or leased by Northumbrian Water, include both stocked and wild trout fishing. **Fontburn**; family dt £29 12 fish; dt £22 8 fish, conc £20 8 fish; credit cruncher after 2.30pm £15; **Whittle Dene** (3 small lakes near Harlow Hill off B6318; coarse); **Grassholme** (140 acres) (see Barnard Castle); Cow Green wild brown trout, dt 12 fish £10, conc £8; honesty box); **Scaling Dam** (105 acres); family dt £29 12 fish; dt £22 8 fish, conc £20 8 fish; credit cruncher after 2.30pm £15; **Blackton** (66 acres), fly only (see Barnard Castle); **Hury** (125 acres coarse fishery: roach); **Derwent**; family dt £29 12 fish; dt £22 8 fish, conc £20 8 fish; credit cruncher after 2.30pm £15; **Hanningfield** managed by Essex and Suffolk Water; dt £24 8 fish, conc £22, from lodge (explorer ticket valid); for **Kielder** (see North Tyne); brown trout seasons: Kielder & Derwent 1 May to 3 Oct; Grassholme, Fontburn and Scaling 22 Mar to 30 Sept; prices are as follows: **'Explorer'** £765 (24 fish per week, max 8 per day, conc £655); covers all NW waters; available from fishing lodges, or self-service; bank fishing only, except Kielder which also has boat hire: £23; for information: Kielder: (tel: 01434 250312); Fontburn: (tel: 01669 621368); Grassholme, Blackton and Hury (tel: 01833 641121); Scaling Dam: (tel: 01287 644032); Hanningfield (tel: 01245 212034; see websites for info: www.nwl.co.uk and www.eswater.co.uk), Derwent: (tel: 01207 255250). **Lockwood Beck Trout Fishery**, is situated directly off the A171 Guisborough to Whitby Road. 60 acre fly fishery for rainbow & brown trout, dt & st available at various prices. Wheelyboat for disabled anglers, (tel: 01287 660501; web: www.lockwoodfishery.co.uk).

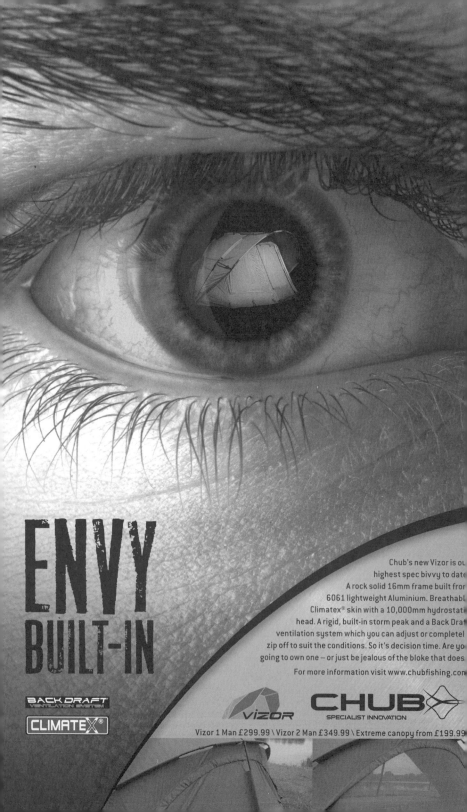

CANAL FISHING IN ENGLAND

British Waterways own over 1,200 miles of canal, and 89 operational supply reservoirs. The large majority of these fisheries are licensed to fishing clubs, but the BW retains direct control of fishing on a number of canal sections, and several reservoirs (shown below) or in the appropriate geographical section of the book, with season or day tickets easily obtainable.

Up to 100,000 anglers fish British Waterways fisheries regularly. They form an important part of the coarse fishing on offer in England, Scotland and Wales. Roach, perch, bream, gudgeon, eels, pike, dace, chub, and other coarse fish are to be found. Carp to 48lb have been reported from the Grand Union Canal, and in some lightly boated sections, a good head of tench, larger bream and crucian carp are present. Stocking levels are extremely good and surpass the EIFAC designated standard. The fishing is governed, as elsewhere, by water quality and natural food supply. Facilities for anglers in wheelchairs have been introduced in places; competitions can be arranged on directly controlled waters on application to the local Fisheries Manager.

The North West area has introduced various schemes, which include the Waterways Anglers Together, by which a number of fishing clubs share the leasing of a large mileage of canal fishing, not only in the North West area but also in the Wales and Border Counties area. In the North West area, these include 45m of Leeds and Liverpool Canal, 55m of Lancaster Canal, Ashton Canal, Huddersfield Narrow Canal, Peak Forest Canal and Rochdale Canal: members of participating clubs are able to fish anywhere on participating fisheries included in the scheme as often as they like at no extra charge (a whole year at less than half the day ticket charge). The Wales and Border Counties fishings are very extensive and include the Caldon Canal, Llangollen Canal, Macclesfield Canal, Middlewich Branch, Monmouth and Brecon Canal, Shropshire Union, Trent and Mersey Canal and Weaver Navigation. Clubs wishing to join the scheme should contact BW for prices.

The Waterway Wanderers Permit is valid on the same waters; the latter offer st £20 adult, £10 conc, £5 juniors (under 17), dt £5;

Individual members of the Angling Trust are also entitled to the £10 concessionary rate upon receipt of a photocopy of their membership card.

Season permits for angling clubs: Any bona fida angling club registering in advance with the Waterway Wanderers Administrator may join the Waterway Wanderers club scheme. Registration is free of charge but all clubs registering must hold third party public liability insurance. Registered clubs with 10 or more joining members could purchase season permits at the concessionary rate of £10. All club permits would be bought in blocks of 5 with a minimum purchase of 10. This also entitles the registered club to a certain number of free matches (a £10 booking fee is required but no peg fees) on any fishery within the Waterway Wanderers Scheme

Before fishing anywhere in England or Wales, it is necessary to have an Environment Agency Rod Licence, obtainable from most Post Offices.

Anglers should take special care to avoid overhead power lines on all canals. Do not assemble tackle near power lines and do not carry assembled tackle from peg to peg.

There are thirteen administrative areas of waterways fisheries administered by British Waterways: (see map on: www.waterscape.com)

Fisheries Units (areas):

Scottish Highlands

British Waterways Scotland Highlands, Canal Office, Seaport Marina, Muirtown Wharf, Inverness IV3 5LS (tel: 01463 725500; email: enquiries.scotland@ britishwaterways.co.uk)

All fish to be returned to the water alive and unharmed; maximum 2 rods (3 for pike fishing); no fishing within 25 ft of a lock or swingbridge:

- Caledonian Canal
- Loch Ness
- Loch Oich
- Loch Lochy

Scottish Lowlands

British Waterways Scotland Lowlands, Canal House, Applecross Street, Glasgow. G4 9SP (tel: 0141 332 6936: email: enquiries.scotland@ britishwaterways.co.uk)

All fish to be returned to the water alive and unharmed; maximum 2 rods (3 for pike fishing); no fishing within 25 ft of a lock or swingbridge:

- Crinan Canal
- Forth & Clyde Canal
- Monkland Canal
- Union Canal
- Loch Lomond*

North West

British Waterways North West, Waterside House, Waterside Drive, Wigan WN3 5AZ (tel: 01942 405700; fax: 01942 405710; email: enquiries.northwest@ britishwaterways.co.uk)

- Lancaster Canal
- Leeds & Liverpool Canal
- St Helens (Sankey) Canal

North East

British Waterways North East, Fearns Wharf, Neptune Street, Leeds LS9 8PB (tel: 0113 281 6800; email: enquiries.northeast@ britishwaterways.co.uk)

- Tees Navigation & Barrage
- River Ure
- Ripon Canal
- River Ouse
- Pocklington Canal
- River Hull
- Aire & Calder Navigation
- River Derwent
- Selby Canal
- Stainforth & Keadby Canal
- New Junction Canal
- Calder & Hebble Navigation
- South Yorkshire Navigation
- Huddersfield Broad Canal
- Driffield Navigation*
- Market Weighton Canal*

Manchester & Pennine

British Waterways Manchester & Pennine, Red Bull Yard, Congleton Road South, Church Lawton, Stoke-on-Trent ST7 3AP (tel: 01782 785703; email: enquiries.manchesterpennine@ britishwaterways.co.uk)

- Rochdale Canal
- Ashton Canal
- Peak Forest Canal
- Macclesfield Canal
- Manchester Ship Canal*
- Bridgewater Canal*

North Wales & Borders

British Waterways North Wales & Borders, Navigation House, Navigation Road, Northwich CW8 1BH (tel: 01606 723800; email: enquiries.northwalesborders@ britishwaterways.co.uk)

- Weaver Navigation
- River Dee
- Middlewich Branch
- Shropshire Union Canal
- Llangollen Canal
- Montgomery Canal

West Midlands

West Midlands Waterways, Peels Wharf, Lichfield Street, Fazeley, Tamworth, Staffordshire B78 3QZ (tel: 01827 252000; email: enquiries.westmidlands@ britishwaterways.co.uk)

- Birmingham Canal Navigations
- Staffordshire & Worcestershire Canal
- Stourbridge Canal
- Stratford-upon-Avon Canal
- Birmingham & Fazeley Canal

Central Shires

British Waterways Central Shires, Peel's Wharf, Lichfield Street, Fazeley, Tamworth B78 3QZ (tel: 01827 252000; email: enquiries.centralshires@britishwaterways.co.uk)

- Trent & Mersey Canal
- Caldon Canal
- Coventry Canal
- Ashby Canal
- River Soar

East Midlands

British Waterways East Midlands, The Kiln, Mather Road, Newark, Nottinghamshire NG24 1FB (tel: 01636 704481; fax: 01636 705584; email: enquiries.eastmidlands@ britishwaterways.co.uk)

- Sheffield & Tinsley Canal
- Chesterfield Canal
- Fossdyke Navigation
- Trent Navigation
- Witham Navigation
- Erewash Canal
- Nottingham & Beeston Canal
- Grantham Canal
- River Ancholme*
- Louth Navigation*
- Sleaford Navigation*

South Wales & Severn

British Waterways South Wales & Severn, The Dock Office, Commercial Road, Gloucester GL1 2EB (tel: 01452 318000; email:enquiries.southwalessevern@ britishwaterways.co.uk)

- Swansea Canal
- Monmouthshire & Brecon Canal
- River Severn
- Sharpness Docks
- Droitwich Canals
- Worcester & Birmingham Canal
- Neath & Tennam Canal*
- River Wye*
- Lyndey Harbour*
- Herefordshire & Gloucestershire Canal*
- Lower Avon Navigation*
- Upper Avon Navigation*
- River Thames*

South East

British Waterways South East, 510-524 Elder House, Elder Gate, Central Milton Keynes MK9 1BW (tel: 01908 302500; fax: 01908 302510; email: enquiries.southeast@ britishwaterways.co.uk)

- Oxford Canal
- Grand Union Canal Leicester Line
- Market Harborough Arm
- Grand Union Canal
- Grand Union Canal Aylesbury Arm
- Grand Union Canal Wendover Arm

South West

British Waterways Kennet & Avon, The Locks, Bath Road, Devizes SN10 1QR (tel: 01380 722859; email: enquiries.kennetavon@ britishwaterways.co.uk)

- Kennet & Avon Canal
- River Avon
- River Parrett
- Bridgwater & Taunton Canal

London & South

British Waterways London, 1 Sheldon Square, Paddington Central, London W2 6TT (tel: 020 7985 7200; fax: 020 7985 7201; email: enquiries.london@ britishwaterways.co.uk)

- River Stort Navigation
- River Lee Navigation
- Regent's Canal
- Hertford Union Canal
- Limehouse Cut
- Slough Arm
- Paddington Branch

* Waters within BW Units (areas) managed by AINI (see below)

Association of Inland Navigation Authorities (AINI) waters

North

- Bassenthwaite
- Ullswater
- Windermere

East

- River Stour
- Great Ouse
- River Nene
- Middle Level Navigations
- Twenty Foot Drain
- Old Bedford River
- Old West River
- Ely Ouse
- River Cam
- New Bedford River
- Sixteen Foot Drain
- Ten Mile Ouse
- River Lark

- Little River Ouse
- River Wissey
- Old River Nene
- River Glen
- River Welland
- The Broads
- Chelmer & Blackwater Navigation

South

- Basingstoke Canal
- River Wey
- Wey & Arun Canal
- River Arun
- River Medway

South West

- Bude Canal
- Exeter Ship Canal
- Great Western Canal

The following waters are covered by the Waterway Wanderers scheme.

Ashby Canal

- Marston Junction – Bridge 44 (Market Bosworth)

Ashton Canal

- Ducie Street Junction – Lock 17
- Lock 18 – ASDA Tunnel

BCN – Daw End Canal

- Catshill Junction – Rushall Junction (Brownhills – Great Barr)

BCN – Main Line Canal

- Coseley Tunnel – Factory Junction Bridge
- Factory Junction Bridge – Spon Lane Junction
- Netherton Branch
- Netherton Branch Canal (Dudley Port Junction) - Bromford Junction
- Gower Branch
- Spon Lane Junction - St Vincent Street Bridge
- Bromford Junction - Smethwick Junction

BCN – Stourbridge Canal

- Stourbridge Town Arm
- Brettle Lane Bridge to Leys Road Bridge(Brierley Hill)
- Wordesley Junction – Fens Pool
- Stourton Top Lock – Wordesley Aqueduct

BCN – Tame Valley Canal

- Balls Hill Bridge – Gorse Farm Bridge
- Piercy Aqueduct – Walsall Road Bridge

Coventry Canal

- Bridge 10a – Bridge 34
- Bridge 40 – Bridge 43 (Atherstone)
- Bridge 54 – Bridge 55
- Bridge 59 – Bridge 63
- Bridge 69 – Bridge 71 (Amington)
- Bridge 74 – New A5 Bridge
- Fazeley Junction – Sutton Road Bridge (Fazeley)
- Balls Bridge – Tamhorn House Bridge
- Hademore House Bridge – Whittington Bridge
- Bridge 80 – Huddlesford Junction (Wittington – Huddlesford)
- Bridge 86 – Bridge 89
- Bridge 90 – Fradley Junction

Grand Union Canal Mainline

- Clitheroes Lock Number 99 (Brentford) to Bridge 200 (Hayes)
- Braunston Tunnel – Bridge 21 Stockton
- Bridge 24 – Bridge 51
- Bridge 70 – Bridge 71
- Bridge 77 – Bridge 78
- Bridge 79 – Bridge 83
- Bridge 86 – Bridge 89
- Bridge 98 – Bridge 109

Grand Union Canal Leicester Line

- Bridge 23 – Bridge 36
- Bridge 38 – 47
- Bridge 60 – top of Foxton Locks
- North portal of Saddington Tunnel – Bridge 84
- Welford Arm

Grand Union Paddington Arm

- Bulls Bridge Junction to Bridge 6 (Kensal Green)

Hertford Union

- Whole length from junction of Regents Canal to junction with River Lee Navigation

Huddersfield Narrow Canal

- ASDA Tunnel – Lock 19W

Lancaster Canal

- Ashton Basin – Kendal
- Glasson Branch

Leeds & Liverpool Canal

- (Leigh Branch) Wigan Junction – B
- Bridge 8 (Plank Lane Swing Bridge)
- Bridge 80 (Moss Lane) – Bridge 87 (Jackson's Bridge)
- Bridge 91b (Finnington Bridge) – Bridge 178
- Bridge 183a – Bridge 191
- Bridge 192 – Bridge 194
- Bridge 210 – Lock 16
- Bridge 214b – Bridge 215a
- Bridge 217 to Lock 1

Limehouse Cut

- Limehouse Basin to Blackwall Tunnel Approach Road

Llangollen Canal

- Hurleston Junction – Bridge 13
- Bridge 22 – Bridge 25
- Bridge 33 – Bridge 50
- Bridge 51 – Bridge 55
- Bridge 59 – Bridge 70
- Bridge 70 – Br 49aW (Kings Bridge)

Manchester, Bolton and Bury Canal

No waters available

Monmouthshire & Brecon Canal

- Bridge 45 – Bridge 51
- Bridge 53 – Bridge 95a (Tods Bridge)
- Bridge 96 – Ashford Tunnel

Montgomery Canal

- Frankton Junction – Bridge 83 (Redwith Bridge)
- Bridge 91 –Bridge 92
- Bridge 134 – Bridge 153

Oxford Canal

- Bridge 136 at Fenny Compton to Hawkesbury Junction

Peak Forest Canal

- Dukinfield Junction – Bridge 38 (Whaley Bridge)
- Bugsworth Arm

Regents Canal

- Maida Vale Tunnel to Commercial Road Lock

Rochdale Canal

- Castle Street Bridge – Bridge 64 (Manchester Road Bridge)

Shropshire Union Canal

- (Middlewich Branch) Barbridge
- Junction – Bridge 14
- (Middlewich Branch) Bridge 15 – Bridge 32
- Bridge 13 – Stretton Aqueduct A5
- Bridge 17 – Bridge 20
- Bridge 59 – Bridge 82
- Bridge 83 – Bridge 88
- Bridge 113 – Bridge 117
- Bridge 120 – Bridge 147

Stratford upon Avon Canal

- Kings Norton Junction – Brandwood End Tunnel (Kings Norton)
- Bridge 3 – Bridge 19
- Bridge 36 – Bridge 47 (Lowsonford)

Trent & Mersey Canal

- Bridge 52 to Woodend Turn (Fradley)
- Bridge 58 – Bridge 71 (Armatage, Rugeley)
- Bridge 74 – Bridge 75
- Bridge 77 – Bridge 79
- Lock 25 (Sandon Lock) – Lock 26
- Bridge 111 – Lock 36
- Lock 36 to Lock 37 (from 29.9.10)
- Lock 37 (Cockshutts Lock) – Bridge 117
- Bridge 126 – Harecastle Tunnel (South)

- Harecastle Tunnel (North) – Bridge 139
- Bridge 141 – Bridge 145
- Bridge 147 – Bridge 150
- Bridge 156 – Bridge 158
- Bridge 161 – Lock 67
- Bridge 163 – Lock 69

Weaver Navigation

- Witton Brook
- Saltersford Locks No 3 (nr Barnton) – Sutton Swing Bridge (Sutton Weaver) 1000m near to Acton Bridge, but includes the River Weaver at Dunton Locks

Worcester & Birmingham Canal

- Bridge 70 Kings Norton Tunnel – Bridge 75

Waters NOT covered by the Waterway Wanderers Scheme

- Aire & Calder Navigation
- Bridgwater & Taunton Canal
- Calder & Hebble Navigation
- Chesterfield Canal
- Cromford Canal
- Erewash Canal
- Fosdyke Canal
- Gloucester & Sharpness Canal
- Grantham Canal
- Huddersfield Broad Canal
- Kennet & Avon Canal
- Macclesfield Canal
- Manchester, Bury & Bolton Canal
- New Junction Canal
- Nottingham & Beeston Canal
- Pocklington Canal
- Ripon Canal

- River Aire
- River Calder
- River Lee Navigation
- River Ouse Yorkshire
- River Severn Navigation
- River Soar
- River Stort Navigation
- River Trent
- River Witham
- St Helen's Canal
- Selby Canal
- Sheffield & Tinsley Canal
- South Yorkshire Navigation
- Staffordshire & Worcestershire Canal
- Stainforth & Keadby Canal
- Stourbridge Canal
- Stroudwater Canal
- Ure Navigation

EAST MIDLANDS:

Erewash Canal: Langley Mill Lock to Shipley Lock NCB No 5 Area Fishing. Shipley Lock to Barkers Cotmanhay AC. Barkers to Bridge 20 Pride of Derby AA. Bridge 20 to Stanton Lock Nottingham & DFAS. Stanton Lock to B5010 road bridge Nottingham AA. Derby Road to Sandiacre Lock The West End Angling Club. Sandiacre Lock to Long Eaton Lock Long Eaton & DAF. Long Eaton Lock to Trent Lock Long Eaton & DAF. Trent Lock to Cranfleet Cut Long Eaton & DAF. **Butterly Reservoir** Ripley & District AC.

Chesterfield Canal: **Harthill Reservoir** Harthill Carp & Coarse AC. West Retford Lock to Thunder Bridge, and Old Barracks at Ranby Retford Canal AS. Bottoms Lock at Cinder Hill to Toplock at Shireoaks Low Lock Station Hotel. Chequer House Bridge to Bracebridge Lock Worksop United AA. Bracebridge Lock to Shireoaks Low Lock Grafton AA. West Stockwith to Drakeholes Low Wharf Sheffield & DAA. Clayworth Church Lane Bridge to Retford Bridge Worksop & DAA. Norwood Tunnels to Thorpe Top Lock Treble Lock Wales & Kiverton AC.

Trent & Mersey Canal: Weston Parish Derby Railway AC. **Findern Crossing Pond** Derby Railway AC. Shardlow to Bridge 28 (except Weston Parish) Pride of Derby AA.

River Soar and **Grand Union Canal** at Leicester. Pillings Flood Lock to North Lock Leicester & DAS. Kegworth Flood Lock to Ratcliffe Lock Long Eaton & DAF. Pillings Flood Lock to Loughborough Lock Quorn AS. Bridge 84 to North Lock Wigston AS. Loughborough Lock to Kegworth Deep Loughborough Soar AS.

Cromford Canal: Codnor Park Reservoir: Torksey Lock Footbridge to Brayford New Bridge Witham & DJAF. Brayford New Bridge to Kirk-stead Witham & DJAF. Fossdyke Arm Torksey: Worksop & DJAF.

Upper Trent: Beeston Lock to Lenton Chain Bridge Nottingham AA. Lenton Chain Bridge to Meadow Lock Nottingham & DFAS. **River Trent:** Stoke Weir Ashfield AA. **Newark Dyke** (various lengths)**:** Newark & DPF. Gunthorpe Weir d/s (except weir) Nottingham & DFAS. Gunthorpe Weir u/s (right bank) Nottingham AA. Right bank d/s Cromwell Weir Kingfisher AA. Right bank d/s Cromwell Weir Collingham AA. D/s Cromwell Lock (lock side) Ashfield AA.

Grantham Canal: Bridge 54-53 Ropsley AC. Bridge 53-51 Barnstone AC. Bridge 39-37 Nottingham AA. Smite Aqueduct to Bridge 33 (Jason Scarborough). Bridge 27-26 Parkside AC. Bridge 12-15 Nottingham AA. Bridge 7-12 Nottingham AA. Bridge 7-2 Nottingham AA.

LONDON

River Stort Navigation: R Stort at Roydon from Bridge 6 to Bridge 7 Two Bridges AS. Bridge 7 to Hunsdon Lock Globe AS. Burnt Mill Lock to Parndon Lock Stort Valley AA. R Stort as shown on BW plan Sawbridgeworth AS. Backwater at Spellbrook (privately fished). End of navigation at Bishops Stortford to A11 road bridge Bishops Stortford & DAS. Cattle Bridge to Spellbrook Lock Bishops Stortford & DAS.

Slough Arm (Grand Union Canal): Whole of Arm from Junction with main line at Cowley to Slough Gerrards Cross & Uxbridge DAS.

Hertford Union & Paddington Arm (Grand Union Canal): Paddington Arm Bridge 5A-6 Ladbroke Rovers AC.

Grand Union Canal: Road bridge below Brentford Lock to Thames Lock Barnes & Mortlake A&PS. Bridge

200-191 CALPAC. Bridge 191-187 London AA. Lock 87-81 Blenheim AA.

River Lee Navigation: The Bow Back Rivers Lee Anglers. Bow Lock to 300 metres south of Aqueduct Lock Lee Anglers. River Lee at Cheshunt (offside) plus Cadmore Lane Gravel Pit Metropolitan Police AS. Above King's Weir to 300 metres south of Aqueduct Lock London AA. Old River Lee Aqueduct Lock to BW boundary London AA. West bank of Old Lee River from northern point of King's Weir including west bank of Weir Pool (privately fished). King's Weir (privately fished). Island Bank Carthagena Weir Carthagena Lock AC. Dobbs Weir Lee Valley Regional Park Authority. Weir Pools at Fieldes Weir (one bank only) Lee Anglers. Fieldes Weir Lock to Rye House Station Bridge Lee Anglers. Rye House Bridge for 1020 metres u/s London AA. Point 1020 metres u/s of Rye House Bridge to end of navigation at Hertford Lee Anglers. Offside bank u/s of Hardmeade Lock to north end of Lee and Stort Cruising Club premises Ware AC.

NORTH WEST

Fisheries available to **Waterways Anglers Together/Waterways Wanderer**s permit-holders (subject to change as clubs take up waters):

Ashton Canal: Junction with Rochdale to Fairfield Bottom Lock. Fairfield Top Lock to Whitelands Road Bridge.

Huddersfield Narrow Canal: Caroline Street Stalybridge to Lock 1.

Lancaster Canal: Stocks Bridge Preston to Stainton.

Leeds and Liverpool Canal: Johnsons Hillock Bottom Lock to Bridge 82. Bridge 84-93B. Bridge 94-153.

Peak Forest Canal: Dukinfield Junction to Canal Terminus Whaleybridge.

Rochdale Canal: Lock 55-92.

Club Waters:

Huddersfield Narrow Canal: Brunclough Reservoir: Saddleworth & DAS. Lock 20W-19W Border Anglers.

Rochdale Canal: Lock 51-55 Castleton AA. Lock 36 to Manchester Road Bridge Castleton Todmorden AS. Lock 13-36 Todmorden AS. Junction Calder and Hebble to Lock 13 Hebden Bridge AS.

Leeds and Liverpool: Liverpool to Bridge 25 Liverpool & DAA. **Lower Foulridge Reservoir** Pendle Borough. Bridge 25-80 Wigan & DAA. Plank Lane swingbridge to Leigh Wharf Leigh & DAA. **Rishton Reservoir** Hyndburn & Blackburn AA. **Upper Foulridge Reservoir** Colne AA.

Manchester, Bolton & Bury Canal: Hall Lane to Nob End Bolton & DAA.

St Helens Canal: Carr Mill End to Old Double Locks St Helens AA.

Ashton Canal: Fairfield Bottom Lock to Top Lock Watersport Adventure Centre.

SOUTH EAST

Northampton Arm (Grand Union Canal): Junction with Grand Union Main Line to Bridge 3 Britannia AC. Bridge 3 to Lock 17 plus stretch of River Nene at Cotton End Northampton Nene AC.

Leicester Line (Grand Union Canal): Norton Junction to A5 road bridge Towcester & DAC. A5 road bridge to south end of Crick Tunnel Am-Pro Long Buckby AC. North end of Crick Tunnel to Bridge 20 Old Kings Head AC. Bridge 28-29 Finedon AC. Bridge 36-38 Lutterworth & DAC. Bridge 47-51 Fox Match Black Horse AC. Bridge 51-60 Wellingborough & District Nene AC. Bridge 65 to southern portal of Saddington Tunnel Wreake AC. Bridge 87 to Lock 38 Wigston AS.

Market Harborough Arm (Grand Union Canal): Sign far end of Union Basin to Debdale Wharf Wreake AC.

Grand Union Canal - Main Line: Bridge 191 to Lock 87 London AA. Lock 87-81 Blenheim AA. Sabeys Pool and **River Chess** from swingbridge to lock West Hampstead AS. From railway bridge south of Lock 80 to Bridge 166 Watford Piscators. **River Gade** by Lock 80 Watford Piscators. Lock 81-80 Watford Piscators. Bridge 166 to Lock 72 Kings Langley AS. Lock 72 to Bridge 135 London AA. Bridge 135-126 Tring Anglers. Bridge 126-102 Luton AC. Bridge 102-81 Milton Keynes AA. River Great Ouse stretch Milton Keynes AA. Bridge 81-76 Linford AC. Bridge 76-68 Milton Keynes AA. Bridge 68 to aqueduct crossing River Ouse plus part offside bank Galleon AC. Lock 21 to Bridge 64 Deanshanger & the Stratfords AC. Bridge 64-62 Britannia AC. Bridge 62-22 Northampton Nene AC. Bridge 22-18 Flore & Weedon AC. Bridge 18-15 Daventry AC. Bridge 15 to southern portal of Braunston Tunnel Am-Pro UK AC.

Oxford Canal: R Thames at Oxford John Radcliffe Hospital AC. The Dukes Cut North Oxford AS. Wolvercote Pool North Oxford AS. Terminus at Oxford to Bridge 227 North Oxford AS. Bridge 227-224 Kidlington AS. Bridge 224-221 Banbury & DAA. End of Thrupp Moorings to Bridge 216 Banbury & DAA. Stretch of R Cherwell Oxford & DAA. Bridge 216-206 Oxford & DAA. R Cherwell at Kirtlington Oxford & DAA. R Cherwell at Thrupp Kidlington AS. R Cherwell at Northbrook Oxford & DAA. Bridge 206-152 Banbury & DAA. R Cherwell Lower Heyford and other stretches Banbury & DAA. Bridge 148-144 Stoneleigh AC. Bridge 144-141 Ford Leamington AC.

Wendover Arm (Grand Union Canal): Junction with main line to Tringford Pumping Station Tring Anglers.

Aylesbury Arm (Grand Union Canal): Junction with main line to Red House Lock near Aston Clinton Tring Anglers. Red House Lock to footbridge u/s of Aylesbury Basin Aylesbury & DAF.

Reservoirs: Boddington Reservoir: BW intensively managed. **Clattercote Reservoir** BW intensively managed. **Wormleighton Reservoir** Wormleighton FC.

SOUTH WEST

Gloucester and Sharpness Canal: Llanthony Bridge to site of former railway bridge at Sharpness Winget AC. D/s of Tanker Bay Ravern AC. Opp Borros Silos (offside bank) Babcock AC. Ryalls Farm to Stone at Frampton-on-Severn (offside bank) Frampton & DAA. Permitted length on canal Sharpness Dockers AC. Sims Bridge to bay beyond new road bridge (offside) Gloucester UAA.

Bridgwater & Taunton Canal: Firepool Lock to Higher Maunsell Lock Taunton AA. Higher Maunsell Locks to Bridgwater Docks Bridgwater AA.

Kennet and Avon Canal: Bear Wharf near Lock 106 at Reading to start of Fobney Meadow at Rose Kiln Lane Reading & DAA. Fobney Lock to confluence with R Kennet d/s of Bridge 11 Reading & DAA. Lock 104-103 Reading & DAA. Lock 102-101 Reading & DAA. Theale swing bridge to approx 100 metres d/s of Lock 100 Reading & DAA. Stretches near Sulhampstead Lock CALPAC. Lock 99 to confluence with R Kennet Reading & DAA. Lock 98-96 Reading & DAA. Lock 95 to head of Salmons Cut and Marina Reading & DAA. Lock 94-93 Blenheim AS. Offside bank from approx 350 metres east of Oxlease swing bridge to Old Heales Lock Blenheim AS. Lock 93 to Midgham Bridge Reading & DAA. Lock 92 to east side of Aldershot Water foot bridge Reed Thatcham AA. Lock 92 to cross fence by Floorco factory Reed Thatcham AA. Thatcham swing bridge to Lock 90 Thatcham AA. Lock 90-89 Thatcham AA. Bulls Lock to Ham Lock Newbury AA. White House Turnover Bridge to Lock 86 Thatcham AA. Lock 86 to Greenham Island Newbury AA. Junction with River Kennet at Northcroft to Guyers Bridge Newbury AA. Lock 81 to confluence with R Kennet Abbey Cross AS. Two sections at Kintbury Civil Service AS. Bridge 104-112 Marlborough AC. Bruce Tunnel to Bridge 94 Marlborough AC. Bridge 112-120 Pewsey & DAA. Bridge 120-161 Devizes AA. Bridge 161-163 Avon AC. Bridge 166-170 Airsprung AC. Bridge 170 to Avoncliffe Aqueduct Airsprung AC. Bridge 175 to confluence with R Avon at Bath (excluding basin area) Bathampton AA.

Stroudwater Canal: Whitminster stretch Frampton-on-Severn AC. Ryeford double lock to Westfield Lock Association Phoenix. Ebley to Thrupp Stroud & DAC.

River Severn: Upper Lode - Lock Island Upper Lode AC. D/s of Diglis Weir (Mr Garry Hunt). Diglis Weir (Lock Island) Diglis Anglers Salmon Society. Bevere Lock (offside) (Mr N Gwillam). Bevere Lock (Colin Russell). Holt Fleet Birmingham AA. Lincomb Weir (Martin Charles). Lincomb Weir salmon fishing (Mr Peter Gough). Lincomb Weir coarse fishing (offside) Sabrina Products.

WALES & BORDER COUNTIES

Fisheries available to **Waterways Anglers Together/Waterways Wanderers** permit-holders (subject to change as clubs take up waters):

Caldon Canal: Planet Lock 3 to Caldon Road Bridge 6. Lichfield Bridge 8 to Bridge 10. Bridge 11 to Bridge 25. Bridge 26 to Hazlehurst Junction. Hazlehurst Bottom Lock to Willow Cottage No 47. Bridge 48 for approx 600 metres d/s past Bridge 48. Bridge 54 to Bridge 55. Hazlehurst Junction to Bridge 6.

Llangollen Canal: Hurleston Locks to Bridge 50. Bridge 51 to Bridge 55. Bridge 59 to Bridge 68. Bridge 2 to Bridge 49A.

Macclesfield Canal: Bridge 61-66.

Middlewich Branch: Barbridge Junction to Lock 4. Bridge 5A-32.

Monmouth and Brecon Canal: Bridge 45-51. Bridge 53-84. Bridge 84-141. Ashford Tunnel to Theatre Basin Brecon.

Montgomery Canal: Bridge 70-83. Bridge 93-109. Bridge 123-153.

Shropshire Union Canal: Bridge 7-8. Bridge 10-11. Bridge 12 to Stretton Aqueduct. Bridge 17-18. Bridge 45-47. Bridge 56-57. Bridge 60-65. Bridge 66-74. Bridge 74-82. Bridge 83-147.

Trent and Mersey Canal: Lock 25 to Bridge 87. Whieldon Road to Lock 37. Lock 39 to Bridge 120. Bridge 126-127. Bridge 127-128. Bridge 128A-129. A500 link Chatterley to Harecastle Tunnel (south). Harecastle Tunnel (north) to Lock 50. Lock 52 to Bridge 145. Bridge 156-161. Saltersford Locks to Sutton Weaver.

Club Waters:

Caldon Canal: Bridge 6-8 Caldon AC. Bridge 10-11 Goms Mill Juniors. Bridge 47-48 Embreys Bakeries AC. Bridge 49-54 Potteries AS. Bridge 55 to Canal Terminus Froghall Wharf (Leek branch of canal). Bridge 6 to Canal end, near Leek, Leek & Moorlands AC. **Stanley Reservoir:** dt on site/Stoke-on-Trent AS. **Rudyard Reservoir:** dt on site. **Knypersley Reservoir:** (Cheshire AA).

Llangollen Canal: Bridge 50-51 Fernwood FC.

Macclesfield Canal: Bridge 1-37 (Northern AA). Bridge 37-61 (Prince Albert AS). Bridge 66-68 Congleton AS. Bridge 68-72 Warrington AA. Bridge 72-77 Warrington AA. Bridge

77-80 Victoria & Biddulph AS. Bridge 80-85 Warrington AA. Bridge 85-86 Middleport AC. Bridge 86-93 Warrington AA. Lock 93 to Hardingswood Junction Kidsgrove & DAA. **Sutton Reservoir:** (Macclesfield Victoria AS). **Bosley Reservoir:** (Prince Albert AS).

Middlewich Branch: Lock 4 to Railway Bridge 5A Venetian Marine AC.

Monmouth and Brecon Canal: Bridge 51-53 Pontypool AA. Bridge 95A to Llanfoist Beacon Park boats. Ashford Tunnel to Bridge 162 Brecon Coarse AC.

Montgomery Canal: Bridge 109-115 (Montgomery AA). Bridge 115 to 119A Montgomeryshire AA. Bridge 119A-123 (Montgomery AA). Montgomery River Severn: Penarth Weir Point A to Penarth Weir Point B Potteries AS.

Shropshire Union Canal: Bridge 2-6 Wolverhampton AA. Bridge 6-7 MidLeisure AC. Bridge 8-10 Dawley AC. Bridge 8-10 Dawley AC. A5 to Bridge 17 Brewood AC. Bridge 19-20 Chubb AC. Bridge 20-21 Albrighton Anglers. Bridge 21-23 Goodyear AS. Bridge 23-25 Izaac Walton AA. Bridge 25 to Cowley Tunnel Viscount Newport's 2000 settlement. Bridge 35-41 Stoke City AC. Bridge 41-42 (Mrs E Cliff). Bridge 42-45 (Mr P Galbraith). Bridge 47-48 Wyche Anglers. Bridge 48-51 Wyche Anglers. Bridge 51-55 Hodnet AS. Bridge 55-56 Market Drayton Anglers. Bridge 58-59 Hanley AS. Bridge 65 to 220 metres past towards Audlem Lock Goms Mill Juniors. Bridge 82-83 Wybunbury AA. Junction D branch and River Dee Elver Fishing. **Trench Pool:** Telford AA.

Trent and Mersey Canal: Lock 23 to Bridge 77 Izaac Walton AA. Bridge 77-78 Stafford Post Office. Bridge 78-79 Creda AC. Bridge 81-85 Saracens Head AC. Bridge 82 to Lock 25 Goms Mill Juniors. Lock 26 to Bridge 91 Wedgewood AS. Bridge 91 to

Lock 33 Stone & DAS. Lock 33-35 Fenton & DAS. Trentham Lock to Winkles Works Stoke Basin Fenton & DAS. Lock 38-39 Goms Mill Juniors. Bridge 126 Middleport AC. Bridge 128-128A Red Lion Anglers. Bridge 145-147 Congleton AS. Bridge 147-156 Crewe Pioneers AC. Bridge 161-163 Middlewich JA. Lock 69-71 Cheshire Match Group. Middlewich Junction to Preston Brook Tunnel Trent & Mersey Canal AA.

Weaver Navigation: Winsford Town Bridge to Newbridge Winsford & DAA. Newbridge to Bostock Works Meadow Bank Sports & Social Club. Newbridge to Saltersford Northwich AA.

Weaver Valley: Sutton Pool Warrington AA. **Eton Bank Pool:** vacant. **Witton Brook:** vacant. **Weaver River at Frodsham:** vacant. Frodsham Cut Warrington AA.

WEST MIDLANDS:

Ashby Canal; Bridge 44-45 is Measham AC water. Green Lane to Snarestone Tunnel, Measham FC. Snarestone Tunnel to Terminus Swadlincote AA. Bridge 42-44 Bridge Tackle water. Marston Junction to Bridge 30 Bracadale AC.

Birmingham and Fazeley Canal; Curdworth Tunnel to Balk Bridge Stirrup Cup Lounge AC. Curdworth Tunnel to Bayliss Bridge Stirrup Cup to Lounge AC. Dunton Wharf to Fazeley Junction, Birmingham AA. Holly Lane to Wood Lane Smithswood AC. Brace Factory Bridge (Holly Lane) to Broad Bulk Bridge Dams and Lock AC. Wood Lane to Spaghetti Junction Kingsbury & DAC. Aston Church Road to Nechells Lock Barford AA.

Birmingham Canal Navigation (BCN), Wyreley and Essington Canal: Deans Road Bridge to New Bentley Bridge (New Cross Avenue) Bentley Bridge Residents Association. Leamore Lane to Broad Lane North Swan AC. Sneyd Pool (J M Stanhope). Litchfield Road to Hollands Bridge Green Rivers AC. Yorks Bridge to Freeths Bridge Cashmores AC. Anglesey Branch Coopers Bridge to Catshill Junction Community AC. **Cannock Extension. BCN Main Line;** (Mr S Megson). **BCN Dudley Canal,** Howne Basin to Barratts Lane Bridge Bull FC. Northfield Road to Stoney Lane Old Hill AC. Griffin Bridge (Northfield Road) to Bullfield Bridge (Blackberry Lane) Old Hill Legion AC. Peartree Lane to Stoney Lane (Netherton) Mosella Black Country. Peartre Road to Waterfront Bridge Woodside AA.

Birmingham Canal Navigation (BCN), Main Line: Dixon Street to Horseleyfields Junction Hankat AS. Coseley Tunnel to Walbrook Bridge Bramford AC. Ivy House Lane to Dixon Street Hankat AS. Railway Bridge Wellington Road to Dudley Road Bridge **Soho Loop** (Mr C Gregg). Tipton Locks to Netherton Branch Canal Sportsman AC. Titford Pools to Engine Street Lock Langley Conservative Club.

Birmingham Canal Navigation (BCN), Stourbridge: Town Arm Halesowen Royal British Legion.

Birmingham Canal Navigation (BCN), Tame Valley: Junction to Balls Hill Bridge Hankat AS. Crankhall Lane Bridge to Friar Park Farm Bridge Friends of Tame Valley. Old Walsall Road Aqueduct to Gorse Farm Bridge Beacon.

Birmingham Canal Navigation (BCN), Walsall Canal: Bull Lane to Ryders Green Locks Hankat AS. Bridgeman Street to Rollingmill Street, Walsall Town Arm, M6 to Midland Road Boat AC.

Coventry Canal: Sutton Road to Balls Bridge to Lamb AC. Balls Bridge to Hopwas Wood Bridge Tamworth Tackle AC. Tamhorn Farm Bridge to Whittington Bridge Barford AA Whit-

tington Bridge to Bridge 80 Whittington & Fisherwich PC. Fazeley Junction to Sutton Road Bridge (Mr P Mortimer). Coventry Basin to the M6 Alex AC. Bridge 10a-20 Bracadale AC. Bridge 20 (Boot Bridge) to Bridge 24 Browning Team Central. Bridge 26-31 Coventry Canal Junior Anglers. Bridge 34-40 Mail of the Mill FC. Bridge 45 to Atherstone Bottom Lock Kingsbury & DAC. Atherstone Bottom Lock to Bridge 48. Bridge 50-54 Birchmore AC. Bridge 43-44 Atherstone Canal Juniors. Bridge 55-57 Polesworth WMC. Bridge 59-63 Bulls Head AC. Bridge 63-69 Lamb AC. Bridge 71-74 Kettlebrook AC. New A5 Bridge to Tame Aqueduct Glascote WMC AC. Tame Aqueduct to Fazeley Junction Belgrave SSH AC. Huddlesford Junction to Bridge 85. Bridge 85-86 Streethay Wharf AC. Bridge 87-88 Walsall Education. Bridge 88-89 PERLS. Bridge 89-90 Pirelli AC.

Grand Union Canal, Main Line: Bridge 89 to Camphill Bottom Locks Cornerstone AC. Bridge 77-78 Banbury Social FC. Bridge 77 to M42 and Bridge 78-79Lode Mill Angling Syndicate. Bridge 73-75 Commercial Cleaners. Bridge 72-73 Barford AA. Bridge 71-72 Warwick DAS. Bridge 1 62-67 Stoneleigh Park FC. Bridge 51-52 Oaklands Farm AC. Hatton Side Ponds Warwick DAS. Stockton Lock Area Blue Lais. Bridge 84-86 Studley Road AC.

North Statford: Brandwood End to Bridge 3 Studley Road AC. Bridge 19-22 Redditch Federation.Bridge 25 to Lock 2 Swallow Cruisers.

Oxford Canal: Hawksbury Junction to Bridge 9 (Mr Allibone).

South Stratford: Lapworth Top Pool PERLS. Calf Heath Reservoir Blackfords Progressive AS. Bridge 54 to Dimmingsdale Lock Sedgley WMC. Bridge 56-59 Wightwick Lock AC. Bridge 63-64 Brewood & DAC. Bridge 63 to Compton Lock Bilston

Angling Centre. Bridge 65 to Auther-ley Junction Oxley AC. Bridge 68-69 Bilston Angling Centre. Bridge 79-82 Jubilee AC. Bridge 69-70 Chubb AC. Bridge 70-74 Goodyear AS. Bridge 74-75 Shifnal & Telford AC. Bridge 75-77 (Four Ashes) Chubb AC. Bridge 77-78 Schenectady Europe AC. Bridge 78 to First Bend Chubb AC. Bridge 82-94 Wolverhampton AA. Bridge 94 to Milford Aqueduct Izaac Walton AA. Dimmingsdale Lock to Botherham Lock Wolver-hampton AA. Pond at 4 Crosses and canal road bridge east to next bridge Great Wyreley AC. Claypit Pools (Ms J Bannister). **Dimmingsdale Reservoir** GKN Sankey AC. Gailey Lower Reservoir Bailey AC. **Gailey Upper Reservoir** Bailey FF. York Street to Botherham Lock (except Hyde Lock to Kinver Lock) Mr J Williams. Great Haywood Junction to Milford Aque-duct Potteries AS. Bridge 28 to Wychnor Lock Burton Mutual. Wychnor Lock to Alrewas Lock Kingsbury & DAC. Alrewas Lock to Bridge 50 Birmingham AA. Bridge 58-62 Bass AC. Bridge 67-68 Pear Tree AC. **Tardebigge Reservoir** Tar-debigge Anglers. Mill Street Worces-ter to Blackpole Worcester & DAA. Blackpole to Kings Norton (Mr J Wil-liams). Bridge 75-Bridge 78 Get Hooked on Fishing.

YORKSHIRE:

Aire & Calder Navigation: Woodles-ford Bridge to Fleet Bridge, plus 120 metres north bank, Allerton Bywater Colliery AC. Bridge 4 for 135 metres u/s, Birkwood (offside only) Birk-wood Farm Fisheries. Heck Bridge to concrete works Goole Boothferry JAC. River Calder near Castleford Bradford No1 AA. Whitley Old Bridge to M62 motorway bridge Bradford No1 AA. River Calder d/s of Woodnook Lock BWB Castleford AC. **Woodnook Lock Reservoir** BWB Castleford AC. 175 metres u/s of Knostrop Lock/right bank from

Knostrop Lock to Thwaite Mills Leeds & DASA. Goodman Street to Woodlesford Lock (towpath side) Leeds & DASA. Castleford Cut from castleford Lock to Bulholme Lock Lock Side AC. Off-side by Great Heck Basin South Yorkshire Boat Club. Kings Road to Arm leading to Altofts Lock (except Marina Arm) Walton AC. Woodlesford Lock to Woodlesford Bridge (right bank) Wortley AC.

South Yorkshire Navigation: Barnby Dun Bridge to Old Bridge Kirk San-dall Barnby Dun Bridge SAC. Long Sandall to Sprotborough Doncaster & DAA. Kilnhurst to Swinton Kilnhurst & DAA. Sheffield & South Yorkshire Navigation Canal between Mexbor-ough Top Lock and railway bridge Kilnhurst & DAA. Old Bridge Kirk Sandall to railway bridge (Long San-dall) Pilkington AC. Overflow Weir at Eastwood to Swing Bridge Rother-ham & DUAF. Jordans Lock to Hol-mes Lock Rotherham & DUAF. **Burcroft Ponds** Rotherham & DUAF. Holmes Lock to Ickles Lock Rotherham & DUAF. Strotborough to Mexborough Top Lock Rotherham & DUAF. Kilnhurst Bridge to Eastwood Top Lock Rotherham & DUAF. Raw-marsh Road swingbridge to Raw-marsh Road Bridge Rotherham & DUAF. Stainforth Bridge to Bram-with Lock Stainforth AA. Dunston Hill Bridge to Stainforth Bridge Stain-forth AA. Mexborough New Cut opp Community Park (8 pegs) Swinton Lock Activity Centre.

Leeds and Liverpool Canal: Dowley Gap Top Lock to Swine Lane Bridge Bingley AC. Idle Swing Bridge to Bridge 214B Idle & Thackley AA. Belmont Bridge 178 to Farnhill Bridge 183A Keighley AC. Bridge 194-196 Keighley AC. Bridge 191-192 Keighley AC. Bridge 217-218 Leeds & DASA. Bridge 216A-215A Listerhills Old Boys. Bridge 197A-198 Marsden Star AS. Bridge 196-197A Marsden Star AS.

Bridge 216A-217 Rodley Boats AC. Dowley Gap Bottom Lock to Dock swing bridge 209 Saltaire. Bridge 209-210 Saltaire.

Calder and Hebble Navigation: Kirkless Cut R Calder Kirkless and Brighouse Bradford No1 AA. River Calder to u/s Elland Lock Bradford No1 AA. River Calder to u/s Ganny Lock Brighouse AA. Stainland Road to Bridge 8 Brighouse AA. Forge Lane Bridge to Thornhill Double Locks Dewsbury AC. River Calder (right bank) Battye Ford Flood Gates to 250 metres d/s Holme Valley PA. Kirkless Park Brook to Wood Lane Bridge Holme Valley PA. New Cut Top Lock to Bridge 8 Mirfield AC (who also fish various other waters: Huddersfield Broad, Apsley Basin to Lock 1, HNC Bridge 21 to Lock 11E, C&H Greenwood Bridge to Greenwood A6026 road bridge to 'Stopway'). A6026 road bridge to 'Stopway' Nestlé AC. Battye Ford cut and right bank of R Calder from Bridge 4 to 450 metres u/s Old Bank AC. Mirfield Cut Old1 Bank AC. Salterhebble Top Lock to Chain Bridge Ryburn AS. R Calder at Copley Ryburn AS. Dewsbury Cut and to Figure of Three Locks Thornhill AA. Five Stretches Wakefield AC. Figure of Three Locks to Broad Cut road bridge Wakefield AC. Horbury road bridge to Bridge 31 Wakefield AC. R Calder by Broad Cut Top Lock u/s for 250 metres Wakefield AC.

Southfield Reservoir: Doncaster & DAA.

New Junction Canal: New Junction Canal Barnby Dun and Aire and Calder Doncaster & DAA.

Selby Canal: West Haddlesy Flood Lock to Burn Bridge Fishing Tackle Direct. Burn Bridge to Brayton Bridge Selby & DAA. Brayton Bridge to Selby Canal Basin York & DAA.

Sheffield and Tinsley Canal: Coleridge Road to Darnall Road Fox House Social. Lock 3-5 Outokumpu Stainless Sports and Social Club. Broughton Lane to Lock 3 Tinsley & DAC. Lock 12 to Lock 8 (incl pond on Flight) Tinsley & DAC. Sheffield South Yorkshire Navigation at Lock 5-7 Tinsley Wire AC.

River Ure: Milby Cut to Milby Lock Harrogate & Claro CAA. From Boroughbridge Unity AC.

River Aire: Haddlesey Bridge 350 metres u/s (south bank) Leeds & DASA. At Ferry Bridge Leeds & DASA.

Ripon Canal: Ripon PA.

Stainforth and Keadby Canal: Keadby Basin to Maud's Bridge Scunthorpe & DAA.

Sparth Reservoir: Slaithwaite & DAC.

Slaithwaite Reservoir: Hill Top Slaithwaite & DAC.

Huddersfield Narrow Canal: West Slaithwaite Road Bridge to Lock 34E. Lock 17E-21 and Lock 11E Slaithwaite & DAC.

Pocklington Canal: York & DAA water.

RESERVOIRS AND LAKES in ENGLISH CANAL SYSTEM:

Butterly Reservoir, Ripley & Dist AC.

Caldon Canal Reservoirs. Stanley, dt on site/ Stoke-on-Trent AS. **Rudyard**, dt on site. **Knypersley**, Cheshire AA.

Calf Heath Reservoir, nr **Wolverhampton**. Good coarse fishery with carp, tench, big bream; leased to Blackford Progressive AS.

PEAK FOREST CANAL: **Combs Reservoir**.

Earlswood Lakes. BW direct managed fishery. Three Lakes totalling 85 acres. Engine Pool, commercial carp fishery; Windmill Pool, stocked with roach, perch, bream, pike; Terry's Pool, roach, bream. Dt on bank from bailiff. Match booking enquiries (tel: 01827 252066).

Elton Reservoir, Greater Manchester.

AIRE & CALDER (& R AIRE). **Ferry Bridge Ponds**, Leeds & Dist ASA. **Southfield Reservoir**, Doncaster & DAA.

Gailey Lower Reservoir, nr **Wolverhampton**. 64 acre coarse fishery.

Gayton Pool, Gayton, nr Northampton. Carp fishery.

Halton Reservoir, Wendover. Coarse fishery.

Harthill, nr **Worksop**. Coarse fishing leased by Harthill Carp & Coarse AC.

Himley Hall Lake, Himley. Trout, coarse fish.

HUDDERSFIELD NARROW CANAL Reservoirs: **Brunclough**, Saddleworth & DAS; **Tunnel End**; **Redbrook**; **March Haigh**; **Black Moss**; **Swellands**; **Slaithwaithe**, Hill Top Slaithwaite & DAC; **Sparth**, Slaithwaite & DAC. **Diggle**, Pennine Shooting & Sports AS.

Lifford Reservoir. Birmingham Parks; dt from park keeper.

Lodge Farm Reservoir, Dudley. Coarse fishery. Enquiries to Dudley Corporation.

LEEDS & LIVERPOOL CANAL Reservoirs: **Barrowford Reservoir**. **Lower Foulridge Reservoir**, Borough of Pendle Council, Town Hall Pendle BB8 0AQ (tel: 01282 865500 xtn 401). **Rishton Reservoir**, Hyndburn & Blackburn AA. **Slipperhill Reservoir** Barrowford Angling. **Upper Foulridge Reservoir** Colne AA. **Whitemoor Reservoir**.

GRAND UNION CANAL: Weston Turville Reservoir, Prestwood & DAC. **Tring Reservoirs** (Startops, Marsworth, Wilston, Tringford) BW. **Drayton Reservoir,** BW. **Daventry Reservoir,** Daventry DC. **Naseby Reservoir,** BW. **Welford Reservoir,** BW. **Sulby Reservoir**, Northants, MEM Fisheries.

Saddington Reservoir, Saddington AC.

Stockton Reservoir. BW, excellent coarse fishery, tickets on the bank. Match booking enquiries (tel: 01827 252066).

Sneyd Pool, Walsall. Excellent carp and tench fishing, privately let.

WORCESTER AND BIRMINGHAM CANAL: Tardebigge Reservoir, Bromsgrove, specimen carp fishery, Tardebigge Anglers.

Upper and Lower Bittell Reservoirs (nr **Bromsgrove**). Rights owned by Barnt Green FC, who stock Lower Bittell and adjacent Arrow Pools with trout; other pools hold coarse fish, including pike and bream. Tickets for coarse fishing to members' personal guests only.

Trench Pool, Telford. 16 acres, coarse fishing. Telford AA. Dt on bank.

Welford Reservoir, Northants. BW. Bream, tench and pike to 20lb plus.

Wormleighton Reservoir, nr **Banbury**. Tench to 9lb. Wormleighton AC.

Wern Clay Pits, Montgomery.

LEEDS AND LIVERPOOL CANAL: Winterburn Reservoir.

CALDER AND HEBBLE NAVIGATION: Woodnook Lock Reservoir, Castleford AC.

Capturing the grandson's catch for the memory book.
Fish caught from canal dug out at Heronbrook Fisheries, Staffordshire.
Photo: Graham Marsden

Fishing the Shropshire union canal in spring
Photo: Graham Marsden

Sea fishing at Saltburn
Photo: Dave Marshall

SEA FISHING LOCATIONS IN ENGLAND

In the following list the principal stations are arranged in order from north east to south west and then to north west. Sea fishing can, of course, be had at many other places, but most of those mentioned cater especially for the sea angler. Clubs secretaries and tackle shops are usually willing to help visiting anglers either personally or by post on receipt of a stamped and addressed envelope. Details of accommodation, etc, can generally be had from the local authority amenities officer or information bureau of the town concerned. Those fishing the Devon and Cornwall estuaries should be aware of prohibitions on the taking of bass in some areas.

Seaham (Co Durham). Cod, whiting, flounder (winter); coalfish, plaice, dab, mackerel, cod. Excellent fishing from North Pier, open only to members of Seaham AC, George Tully House, South Terrace, SR7 7HN (tel: 0191 581 0321). Club has 500 members, and well equipped HQ; promotes annual competitions and active junior section; membership £25.50, conc; keys to all locks; further information from George Hope, Competition Sec. There is disabled access only on north pier, and promenade. Tackle shop: Tackle Supplies, 72 Church Str, SR7 7HE (tel: 0191 581 7915).

Sunderland (Co Durham). Fishing from river, pier, beaches and rocks, for codling (best Oct-Apr), whiting (best Sept-Feb), mackerel (best June-Sept), coalfish, flounders, eels, throughout year. Roker Pier provides good sport with cod and flatfish. North Pier is free of charge to anglers, good access for disabled. Several small boat owners at North Dock can arrange fishing parties, but there are also good beaches. R Wear banks at entrance good for flounders throughout year. Bait can be dug in Whitburn Bay and bought from tackle shops. Clubs: Sunderland Sea AA, membership £10 per year; Ryhope Sea AA. Tackle shops: Rutherfords Angling, 125 Roker Ave, Sunderland SR6 0HL

(tel: 0191 5654183; see website for more: www.rutherfordsangling.co.uk) Fishing Republic, Woodbine Street, Hendon, Sunderland SR1 2NL. (tel: 0191 5679770). Many B&Bs.

Saltburn (Cleveland). Flatfish, coalfish, codling, whiting, mackerel, few gurnard, some bass in summer and haddock (in boats) late autumn. Floatfishing from pier in summer gives good sport (mackerel); good codling fishing Oct to March. Tackle Shop: Keith's Sports, 31 Milton Str, TS12 1DN (tel: 01287 624296; web: www.keithssports.co.uk). Tourist Information: 3 Station Buildings, Station Square, TS12 1AQ (tel: 01287 622422).

Redcar (Cleveland). Five miles of fishing off rock and sand. Principal fish caught: Jan-April, codling; April-June, flatfish; -summer months, coalfish (billet), whiting, bass, mackerel, gurnard. Larger codling arrive latter part of August and remain all winter. Local anglers say fishing best at night. South Gare breakwater (4m away); good fishing, but hard on tackle, spinning for mackerel successful in summer. Good fishing from beach two hours before and after low tide. Competitions throughout year. Club: Redcar Navy & Gentlemen's SAC (Tel: 01642 503049); Tackle shop: Redcar Angling Centre, 159 High St, Redcar,

TS10 3AN (tel: 01642 474006; web: www.redcarangling.com).

Whitby (N Yorks). A popular centre for boat fishing on hard ground and wrecks, with charter boats travelling up to 60 miles from Whitby. Cod taken from boats, British record cod, 58lb 6oz caught here, as well as catches of haddock, coalfish, whiting, flatfish, sea bream, catfish, ling, mackerel, etc. Boat festival in July. West Pier: fishing only from lower part of pier extension. Mainly sandy bottom, but weeds and rock towards end. Billet, codling, flatfish, mackerel and whiting in season. East Pier: mainly on rocky bottom, weed off pier extension. More and bigger codling off this pier. Beach fishing from the sands either to Sandsend or Saltwick: billet, codling, flatfish, whiting, mackerel, a few bass. Small area at end of New Quay Rd for children only. No fishing allowed in harbour entrance. Best baits are lugworm', mussel, peeler crab, crab cart. Local assn: Whitby Sea Anglers, meets in winter only, at The Fleece, Church St. Boats to accommodate 8 to 12 persons on hire at quays: Chieftain (tel: 01642 273822) and others (enquire tackle shop). Tackle shop: Rods & Reels, 67 Church Str, Whitby YO22 4AS (tel: 01947 825079); Whitby Angling Supplies, 65 Haggersgate, Whitby YO21 3PP (tel: 01947 603855).

Scarborough (N Yorks). Sea fishing good from boat or harbour piers most of year. Autumn whiting very good in bay. West Pier fishes on sandy bottom, East Pier on rock, with better chances of bigger codling. Codling most plentiful Aug onwards. Winter codling fishing from First or Second Points to south of Scarborough and the Marine Drive. Mackerel, June-Sept, float or spinning. A boats take out parties; large bags of cod in 12hr sessions sometimes taken; many over 20lb, ling also, 20lb plus from wrecks. Festival in Sept. Charter boat for hire, taking 812 anglers. Charge:

approx £5 per person per hour; longish trips to fish reefs and wrecks now popular. Tackle shops: GB Angling, 119 Victoria Rd, YO11 1SP (tel: 01723 365000); Bill Costin, Unit 9, Quay St YO11 1PL (tel: 01723 507501). Harbour Master: Harbour Dept, 18 West Pier, YO11 1PD (tel: 01723 360684).

Filey (Yorks). Codling, dabs, coalfish, ling, mackerel, flatfish, bass, pollack. Famous Filey Brigg, ridge of rocks from which baits can be cast into deep water, is fishable in most weathers and tides. Ledgering with crab and mussel baits (summer), worm and mussel (winter) can produce good catches of cod, coalfish and wrasse. Use of a sliding float with mussel, and mackerel bait is effective technique for coalfish, pollack and mackerel (Jul-Sept). At Reighton Sands, ledgering with mussel, rag, lug and mackerel baits can produce flounders, some dabs, and occasional plaice or bass (flyfishing possible). Preferred method for bass is spinning. Local bait digging prohibited, good supplies from Scarborough tackle shop. Launching site for small privately owned boats. Local clubs: Filey Brigg AS organises fishing festival every year (first week of Sept), with 6 boating and 8 shore events. Good flyfishing for coalfish (billet) from Brigg. Tide tables from Tourist Information: Evron Centre, John Str, YO14 9DW (tel: 01723 518000). Tackle shop: Filey's Fishing Tackle Supplies, Household Stores, 4-8 Bellevue Street YO14 9HY (tel: 01723 512217).

Bridlington (N Humberside). South Pier may be fished free all year and North Pier in winter only. Sport in summer only fair small whiting, billet, flatfish mainly but good codling and whiting from Dec-March; fledgling area for tope. Launches and cobles sail daily from Harbour at 0730, 0930, 1330, 1800 during summer. They operate from 3 to 60 mile radius around Flamborough Head, or wrecks. Catches include cod, haddock, mackerel, plaice, ling and skate. Rock fishing from shore at Thornwick Bay. Bait: lugworm may be dug in South Bay and small sand eels caught by raking and digging on edge of tide. Sea angling festival Sept. Boats: many charter boats; enquire tackle shops. Tackle shops: North Bay Angling Centre, 84 Promenade, Bridlington YO15 2QL (tel: 01262 401144); Linford's Fishing Tackle, 12 Hilderthorpe Rd, Bridlington YO15 3BB (tel: 01262 678045). Hotels: Windsor, Londesborough and others.

Hornsea (N Humberside). Skate, flounders, spotted dogfish, occasional bass from shore; cod, haddock, plaice, dabs, tope, skate, mackerel (June-Sept) from boats. May to Oct. Whiting, dabs, codling, Oct to May. Tackle shop: East Coast Fishing Tackle, 1b Willows Drive, HU18 1DA (tel: 01964 535064; see website for more info: www.ect.fishermen.co.uk).

Grimsby (NE Lincs). Sea fishing along Humber bank free, wall from Immingham to Grimsby free, and along foreshore to Tetney Lock; dover sole, plaice, codling and whiting (Sept-March), dabs, flounders, eels. Good centre for fens and broads. Clubs: Humber SAC. Tackle shops: Sparkes Bros Fishing Tackle & Bait, 43a Cromwell Avenue DN31 2DR (tel: 01472 342613). Many hotels and B&B.

Mablethorpe (Lincs). Good sea fishing from Mablethorpe to Sutton-on-Sea. Beach all sand; mainly flatfish, but some bass, skate, mackerel, tope from boats. Cod in winter. Sept-Dec best. Boat fishing limited by surf and open beach. Good flounders in Saltfleet Haven; also sea trout in Sept. Tackle shop: Bela's Sport and Toy Shop, 54 High Str, LN12 1AD (tel: 01507 473328). Mablethorpe TIC, High Street LN12 1AF (Tel: 01507 474939). Hotels at Mablethorpe, Trusthorpe, Sutton-on-Sea.

Skegness (Lincs). Beach fishing for cod, dab and whiting in winter; silver eels, dabs and bass in summer; whiting and dab in Sept and Oct. Chapel Point (producing many cod over 4lbs; smoothhounds (May-Aug), Huttoft Bank and Ingoldmells the best beaches in winter, 3 hrs before high tide until 2 hours after. Lugworm best bait and mackerel, frozen crab for smoothhounds. No charter boats operate in Lincolnshire, other than one boat from Boston (20 miles away). Club: Skegness Pier SAC. Tackle and bait from Tackle 4 U, 155 Roman Bank PE25 1RY (tel: 01754 611172); Tackle 4 U, 2 Midland Buildings, Skegness Rd, Ingoldmells PE25 1NP (tel: 01754 874950).

Salthouse, near Sheringham (Norfolk). Sea here is deep quite close in shore, and fishing considered good. Good flatfish, Oct-Jan. Occasional bass and mackerel in summer.

Sheringham (Norfolk). Flatfish and bass all year; cod autumn and winter, mackerel June-Sept, sometimes earlier. Beaches good all year, best months April and May. Best sport west of lifeboat shed towards Weybourne or extreme east towards Cromer. Centre beaches too crowded in season. Bait can be ordered from tackle shops. Boat fishing best well off shore. Tope to 40lb and thornbacks to 20lb; plenty of mackerel. Blakeney: good launching ramps. Tackle shop: Brights The Outdoor Man, 8 Wyndham Str, NR26 8BA (tel: 01263 825858; see website for more info: www.brightsfishing.com). Tourist Information: Station Approach, (tel: 01263 824329).

Cromer (Norfolk). Good all year fishing; winter months: codling, whiting and dabs; summer: bass, flounder, dabs, mullet and mackerel. Around the third breakwater east of the pier the water is deeper, last two hours of flood tide best time. Mackerel and occasional bass from end of pier. Fresh lugworm, frozen baits from tackle shop: Team Sabre Fishing Tackle, 21 New St, Cromer, NR27 9HP (tel: 01263 513676) open Sundays during holidays. Hotels: Cliftonville; Ye Olde Red Lion; Western House, recommended for anglers.

Great Yarmouth, (Norfolk). All styles of sea fishing catered for, including two piers, several miles of perfect shore line for beach angler, two miles of well-wharved river from harbour's mouth to Haven Bridge, and boat angling. To north are Caister, Scratby, Hemsby, Winterton, Horsey, Sea Palling, Weybourne etc, and to south, Gorleston-on-Sea and Corton. The riverside at Gorleston from the lifeboat shed leading to the harbour entrance, and Gorleston Pier are popular venues. Sport very similar in all these places; Sept-Jan, whiting, dabs, flounders, eels, bass, cod from latter end of Oct. From Apr-Sept, Winterton known for good bass fishing. Most successful baits are lugworm, ragworm, herring or mackerel; lug, peeler crab and squid for bass, flatfish etc, Apr-Sept. Boats: Dybles; John Temple (tel: 01493 858523), Richard Green (tel: 01493 601008); Dybles: (below). Tackle shops: Gorleston Tackle Centre, 7/8 Pier Walk, Gorleston, Great Yarmouth NR31 6DA (tel: 01493 662448; see website for more info: www.gorlestontackle.co.uk); Dyble Fishing Trips, Hemsby Rd, Scratby, NR29 3PQ (tel: 01493 731305).

Gorleston-on-Sea (Norfolk). Whiting, cod, dabs and flounders from beaches and in estuary (best Oct to March); good run of bass Sept-Dec. Sport good in these periods from boats, pier or at Harbour Bend in river and on beaches. Baits: lugworm, crab and ragworm. Freshwater fishing (coarse fish) within easy reach on rivers and broads. Boats: John Temple (tel: 01493 858523), Richard Green (tel: 01493 601008). Tackle shop: Gorleston Tackle Centre, 7/8 Pier

Walk, Gorleston, Great Yarmouth NR31 6DA (tel: 01493 662448; web: www.gorlestontackle.co.uk).

Lowestoft (Suffolk). Noted centre for cod, autumn-May. Also whiting, flatfish, pollack and coalfish, with bass, tope, ray from charter boats and mullet in warmer months. Lugworm best bait. Good sloping beaches to north and south. Hopton, Pakefield, Kessingland are best. North best on flood, south on ebb. Club: Lowestoft SAS. Frozen baits from tackle shop: Oulton Broad Fishing Tackle, Unit 6 & 7 Yacht Station, Bridge Rd, Lowestoft, Suffolk NR33 9JS (tel: 01502 539593). Further information from Tourist Information: East Point Pavilion NR33 0AP (tel: 01502 533600).

Southwold (Suffolk); ns Halesworth. Good codling, whiting, bass, plaice, flounder, dab, pollack, mackerel, mullet fishing from river Blyth, October to March. Bass main species in summer from harbour or shore, starting May; soles and silver eels also provide sport May to Sept. Reydon Lake is local freshwater fishery. Licences from Purdy's Newsagents, 37 High Str, IP18 6AB (tel: 01502 724250). Tackle shop: Southwold Angling Centre, 9 Station Rd, IP18 6AX (tel: 01502 722085). Hotels: Swan, Crown, Blythe.

Felixstowe (Suffolk). Fishing in autumn and winter for cod and whiting. Excellent bass fishing in recent years, with fish well into double figures from sea front and Rivers Orwell and Deben; garfish by day and sole at night, and with eels in the estuaries, May-Sept; flounders from Oct-Jan from the Orwell towards Ipswich. Skate fishing good in May, June and July, especially in harbour. Other species: pouting, plaice, tope. Good sport from boats, good fishing in evenings from Manor Terrace to Landguard Point, Sept onwards. Pier closed, pending restoration. Wrecking trips obtainable locally. Felixstowe

SAS organises matches, beach festivals, and cater for the needs of boat anglers, with a compound of 50 dinghies adjacent to club HQ. Tackle shop: Castaway Tackle, 20 Undercliffe Rd West, IP11 2AW (tel: 01394 278316).

Harwich and Dovercourt (Essex). Bass (from Halfpenny Pier), mullet, eels, garfish, flatfish, stingray, thornback, soles (all May to Sept), whiting, pouting, codling (Sept to March). Best fishing from boats, but Stone Breakwater, Dovercourt is good (covered by water in high tide). Several good boat marks in estuary of Stour and Orwell and in harbour approaches. Best baits: lug, king rag when available, soft and peeler crabs. Club: Harwich AC (freshwater). Bait: Homecraft, 461463 Main Road, Dovercourt CO12 4HB (tel: 01255 502540). Tourist Information: Harwich Connexions TIC, Iconfield Park, Parkeston, Harwich, CO12 4EN (tel: 01255 506139).

Walton on the Naze (Essex). Cod, skate, bass, whiting (Sept to March) dab are species most commonly caught, best fishing is from pier, Frinton Wall and Frinton Sea Front. Cod fishing begins about second week in Sept and runs to end of March. Club: Walton on the Naze Sea AC. Boats may be chartered in Walton: Terry Woodrow, 2 Florence Rd, CO14 8HP (tel: 01255 675664). Tackle shop: Metcalfe Fish & Tackle, 15 Newgate Str, CO14 8DT (tel: 01255 675680). Hotels: Queens Head; Regency.

Clacton-on-Sea (Essex). Mainly autumn and winter fishing for whiting, codling and cod. Summer fishing from beach, pier and boats for dabs, plaice, bass, eels, thornback, dogfish, tope, sting ray to 50lb. Matches arranged by Clacton Sea AC. Tackle shop: Brian Dean Fishing Tackle, 43 Pallister Rd, CO15 1PG (tel: 01255 425992) baits, permits and information. Hotels: Kingscliff, many others, from Tourist Information: Town Hall, Station Road, CO15 1SE (tel: 01255 686633).

Southend-on-Sea (Essex). Mullet, bass, mackerel, scad, garfish, plaice and flounders are the main catches from the pier during the summer, with cod, codling, whiting and flounders in the winter. Boats operate from various moorings. Thornback, stingray, smoothhound, bass, tope, plaice and cod can be caught. Pier: st day £47, night £45 (must be a member of an affiliated club); dt £4, conc; application form from Southend Borough Council, Directorate of Leisure Services, Civic Centre, Victoria Ave, SS1 3PY; also from Tourist Information Centre, Western Esplanade, Southend Pier SS1 1EE (tel: 01702 215120) at Pier entrance. Off season shore fishing in vicinity, with all year round facilities at the Thorpe Bay and Westcliff bastions, also the river Crouch. Numerous open, pier, shore events organised. Tackle shops: Southend Angling Centre, 5/6 Pier Approach, SS1 2EH (tel: 01702 603303); Jetty Anglers, 47 Eastern Esplanade, SS1 2ES (tel: 01702 301777; see website for more info: www.jettyanglers.co.uk).

Sheerness (Kent). Popular marks around Sheerness are Bartons Point; New Sea Wall, Garison; East Church Gap; cod and whiting plentiful from beaches in autumn, flounders, eels (Mar-Nov); thornback ray (late Feb-April). Tackle shop: Island Bait & Tackle Shop, 68 Halfway Rd, ME12 3AT (tel: 01795 668506); fresh bait always obtainable.

Whitstable and Tankerton (Kent). Good fishing in spring and summer on shore between Swale and Whitstable. Dabs, plaice, bass, skate, flounders, eels, etc. Lugworm and white ragworm are to be found in shallow areas. Peeler crabs are plentiful in Swale estuary. Cod in winter from Tankerton beach. Freshwater fishing on Seasalter Marshes, near Whitstable; roach, rudd, tench, pike, eels. Harbour Master: (tel: 01227

274086). Tourist Information: 7 Oxford Str, Whitstable, CT5 1DB (tel: 01227 275482). Tackle shop: Keith's Angling, 1 St John's Road CT5 2QT (tel: 01227 794806).

Herne Bay (Kent). Excellent spring fishing for flounders, bass and eels, bags of up to 20lb may be expected on peeler crab bait, which can be collected locally or bought at tackle shops in April and May. In June, bass move into the shallow warm water of the estuary. These may be caught with the last of the peeler crab, ragworm, and by spinning. In July and August bass are plentiful, lesser spotted dogfish, smoothhound and stingray may be caught with ragworm on beaches between Bishopstone and Reculver. Local record stingray, over 40lb. Whiting in autumn and winter on main beaches: just after dark is the best time to fish for them. Excellent facilities for anglers with own dinghies to launch and recover from 60 ft wide slipway. Local information on best marks, etc, from tackle shop. Club: Herne Bay AA, (HQ) 59/60 Central Parade, CT6 5JG (tel: 01227 362127). Tackle, bait and licences: Ron Edwards Fishing Tackle, 50 High Str, CT6 5LH (tel: 01227 372517). Hotels: Victoria, Adelaide and Beauville Guest Houses, all Central Parade.

Margate (Kent). Noted for mixed catches. Plentiful bass often taken from shore and boat on paternoster or spinning. Stone pier bass, dogfish and thornback ray in summer, and plentiful whiting in winter. Larger bass from rocks at low water from April onwards. Most popular rock marks are at Foreness, Botany Bay, Kingsgate, Dumpton Gap. Thornback ray at Minnis Bay, Birchington. Also dogfish and thornback ray from boats. Tackle shop: Kingfisheries, 34 King Str, CT9 1DA (tel: 01843 223866).

Broadstairs (Kent). Bass, plaice, flounders, eels, from beaches or stone jetty. Best in winter months.

Lugworm usual bait, dug in Pegwell Bay. Tackle shop, see Margate. Tourist Information: Dickens House Museum, 2 Victoria Road, Broadstairs CT20 1QS (tel: 0870 2646111).

Ramsgate (Kent). Good sport along 2m of shore, harbour piers (free fishing), and Eastern and Western Chines. East Pier gives ample scope, best in winter. Beaches crowded in summer, so night fishing best. In spring and summer good bass fishing (from shore), also soles, flounders, dabs and limited thornbacks. In autumn and winter; whiting and codling. Foreness and Dumpton Gap are good boat marks for mackerel, bass. Six boats operate at Harbour. Goodwin Sands produce skate, bass, dogfish, spurdog, tope and plaice. Wreck fishing very prolific from May onwards. Lugworm may be dug in Pegwell Bay. Licences available from all Post Offices. Bait, fishing trips and freshwater angling information from tackle shops. Charter boat for wreck fishing: A Booth, 6 St Augustines Park, CT11 0DE (tel: 01843 595042) and others (consult Fisherman's Corner). Tackle shop: Bruce Sales at Fisherman's Corner, 6 Kent Place, CT11 8LT (tel: 01843 582174). Hotels in Thanet too many to list.

Sandwich (Kent). Bass at Pegwell Bay; sea trout and mullet run up the river; flounders, grey mullet, plaice, dabs, codling and pouting more seaward. Entry to Sandwich Bay by toll road, 9am to 5pm. For winter cod fishing, deep water off yacht club end of bay is best. Local club: Sandwich & Dist AS. Tackle shop: Sandwich Bait & Tackle, 14 Cattle Market, CT13 9AF (tel: 01304 620913); boats from Ramsgate; stillwaters: Anglers Kabin, Cottington Lakes, Sholden CT14 0AR (tel: 01304 380691). Hotels: Bell; Haven Guest House (for freshwater fishing see Stour (Kent)).

Deal and Walmer (Kent). Excellent sea fishing throughout the year from beaches and Deal Pier, open 8 am to 10 pm, all night Friday and Saturday. Winter cod fishing, from Sandown Castle, Deal Castle, Walmer Castle. Charter boats take anglers to the Goodwin Sands and the prolific waters of the Downs. Cod (Oct-Mar), whiting (Oct-Mar) and dabs (Oct-Mar), skate in summer from Apr-Jul; plaice, bass, sole, mackerel, eels, flounders, garfish throughout summer, dogfish all year. Strong tidal currents. Tide tables from local tackle shops. Clubs: Deal & Walmer AA; Deal 1919 AC. Only 1 charter boat for fishing: Dave Lawrance (tel: 01304 364616). Tackle shops: Channel Angling, Deal Pier, Beach Str, Deal CT14 6HZ (tel: 01304 373104). Tourist Information: High Str, Deal CT14 6BB (tel: 01304 369576).

Dover (Kent). Excellent boat and beach fishing in the area; cod taken from wrecks and sand banks; good fishing for bass, codling, whiting and flatfish. Good beach fishing from Shakespeare Beach. Prince of Wales Pier suitable for all anglers, incl junior and handicapped. Admiralty Pier controlled by Dover Sea AA: open 8am to 4pm (winter) to 9pm (summer) and all day and night Fri and Sat. £6 dt, conc. Access to Sandwich Bay is by toll road, £4. Boat: Dover Motor Boat Co (tel: 01304 206809) to fish Southern Breakwater departs 8 am from Dump Head, Wellington Dock, £11 fishing charge. Tackle shops: Bill's Bait & Tackle, 121 Snargate Str, CT17 9DA (tel: 01304 204542); K J Brazil, Anglers Dent, 162 Snargate Str, CT17 9BZ (tel: 01304 201457). Hotels: many.

Folkestone (Kent). Good boat, beach and pier fishing. Conger, cod, bass, bream, flatfish, whiting, pouting and pollack, with mackerel in midsummer. Pier open to anglers, £4 per day, £2 conc. Cod caught from boats on the Varne Bank all through the year, but from the shore, Oct-Feb only. Beach fishing best dusk onwards for bass and conger. The Warren produces good catches of cod in winter and bass in summer. Good sport from pier. Some good offshore marks. Popular rock spots are Rotunda Beach, Mermaid Point, Sandgate Riviera. For tickets, boats and bait apply: Folkestone Angling, 12 Tontine Str, CT20 1JU (tel: 01303 253881). Hotels: Burlington and others.

Sandgate (Kent). Very good fishing from beach and boats. There is a ridge of rock extending for over a mile 20 yds out from lowwater mark. Bass good July-October; codling, flounder, dabs and whiting October onwards, pouting, conger March-May, August-Nov; mackerel July-Sept good plaice taken May-June, especially from boats. Best months for boat fishing, Sept-Dec. Tackle at Folkestone.

Hythe (Kent). Fishing from boat and shore for bass, codling, pouting, whiting, conger and flats. Princes Parade, Seabrook, is popular for cod fishing, between Sept and Jan, lugworm is the best bait. Open storm beach, giving pouting, whiting, bass, mackerel, sole, dab and flounder in summer and cod (up to 25lb), whiting and pouting in winter. Clubs: Seabrook Sea AA. The Fountain SAC. Tackle shops: Dens Tackle, 73 Dymchurch Rd, CT21 6JN (tel: 01303 267053; see website for more info: www.denstackle.co.uk); Micks Tackle, 1 Thirlstane Terrace, CT21 6LB (tel: 01303 266334; web: www.seabrooksaa.co.uk). Hotels: Fern Lodge; Romney Bay House, New Romney; Imperial.

Dungeness (Kent). Cod fishing around the lighthouse, with whiting, and dab in winter; pout, bass, dab, eels and sole in summer. Best bait is black lugworm. Denge Marsh is a top venue for sole; marks are at Diamond and towards Galloways, lugworm for bait. Best months: good boat fishing all year, at wrecks in summer; Oct to end-Jan for cod; Oct to Feb for shore fishing. Tackle shop: The Point Tackle Shop, Allendale, Dungeness TN29 9ND (tel: 01797 320049).

Hastings (Sussex). Sea fishing from pier (currently closed) and boats. Tope, bass, conger, plaice, codling, whiting, etc. Boats from local fishing clubs. Hastings and St Leonards SAA has its own boats on beach opposite headquarters; club boundary, Beachy Head to R Rother at Rye. Winching facilities. Annual International Festivals: boat in June/July; shore in October/Nov. Bait, tackle: Steve's Tackle Shop, 38 White Rock, TN34 1JL (tel: 01424 433404; web: www.stevestackle.co.uk); Hastings Angling Centre, 33/35 The Bourne, TN34 3AY (tel: 01424 432178; web: www.hastingsangling.co.uk).

St Leonards (Sussex). Good sea fishing all the year round from boats and beach for flatfish, bass, mackerel, conger, tope, whiting, cod, bull huss, turbot. Tackle shops, see Hastings.

Bexhill (Sussex). Boat and shore fishing. Cod, conger, whiting (Sept to end Dec). Dabs, plaice, mackerel, tope (July-Sept). Bass, best months May-July and Oct-Dec. Club: Bexhill SAC (Hon Sec will help visitors, enclose sae). Freshwater fishing in Pevensey Sluice, Pevensey Haven and dykes; coarse fish. Hastings, Bexhill & DFAA have 3 miles of Wallers Haven, one bank, coarse, members only; Bexhill SAC (enquire Hook, Line & Sinker). Tackle shop: Hook Line & Sinker, 54 Sackville Rd, TN39 3JE (tel: 01424 733211) (web: www.hls-fishing-tackle.co.uk). Hotel: Jarvis Cooden Beach.

Eastbourne (Sussex). Boat, pier and shore fishing. Dabs, huss, pouting and conger (all year), cod in winter and skate (May to Dec). Best for plaice and bream from April to Oct. Also soles, whiting, flounders, mullet. Good bass and mullet in warmer months. A good tope centre; June and July best. Some of the best beach fishing for bass around Beachy Head (up to 17lb). Pollack from rocks. Flatfish off Langney Point and from landing stages of pier. Best marks for beach fishing are on east side of pier. West side can be rocky in places. Club: Eastbourne AA, Club House, Royal Parade, BN22 7AA (tel: 01323 723442); membership £38; full-time boatman; boats available to members. Tackle shops: Anglers Den, 6 North Rd, Pevensey Bay, BN24 6AY (tel: 01323 460441).

Seaford (Sussex). Beach and boat fishing. Bass, cod, codling, flats, huss, mackerel and few ling and pollack. Good night fishing off beach. Catches of tope few miles offshore. Seaford AC has freshwater fishing on local waters, members only; apply tackle shop. Tackle shop: Peacehaven Angler, 135a South Coast Rd, Peacehaven, BN10 8PA (tel: 01273 586000). Tourist Information Centre: 37 Church Street BN25 1HG (tel: 01323 897426).

Newhaven (Sussex). Centre for deep sea fishing. Beach fishing for bass excellent May-Oct, mackerel and garfish. Flounders from Tide Mills Beach. Good cod fishing from beaches between Seaford Head and Newhaven's East Pier, late Oct to early March. Breakwater gives good all-round sport, with bass, and cod all running large. Boat fishing excellent for cod in winter, large Channel whiting also give good sport. Club: Newhaven Deep Sea AC, Denton Island, BN9 9BA (tel: 01273 517330) and at Piddinghoe (tel: 01273 517428). Tackle shop: The Newhaven Angler, Unit 2, Villandry, West Quay, Newhaven, BN9 9GB. (tel: 01273 512186). Hotel: Harbourside.

Brighton and Hove (Sussex). Very good bass fishing from boats, trolling with variety of plug baits, Apr-Oct. Charter boats operate from Shoreham, Newhaven and Brighton Marina, for deep sea and wreck fishing. In spring and summer boat fishing produces bream, bass, conger, tope, plaice and dabs; shore fishing: mackerel off marina wall, bass at night or l/w surf, mullet. Winter boat fishing for large cod, whiting, bull huss; shore for whiting, flounders and cod. Most dealers supply bait. Hove Deep Sea AC members launch boats from beach, and generally fish inshore marks; membership £60 plus joining (£20 for associate memb), allows free use of boats, equipment, car park; active social club (tel: 01273 413000 for details). Marina arms for mackerel, garfish, pollack, occasional bass, fishing fee, £3 per rod per day. Tackle shop: Lagoon Bait & Tackle, 327 Kingsway, Hove BN3 4LD (tel: 01273 415879); The Tackle Box, Brighton Marina Village BN2 5UF (tel: 01273 696477).

Shoreham and Southwick (Sussex). Boat and harbour fishing. Bass (July and August); grey mullet, skate and huss (June to Sept); cod and whiting (Sept to end Jan); dabs, plaice, pouting, black bream, mackerel and flounders (May onwards). Mullet fishing in River Adur near Lancing College very good July-August; light paternoster tackle and red ragworm recommended. Baits: white rag, red rag and lugworms may be dug from beach and mud banks of river. Mussels and other baits can also be obtained. Tackle shop: Squires Fishing Tackle, 25 Southwick Square, Southwick, Brighton, BN42 4FP (tel: 01273 592903).

Worthing (Sussex). Beach and pier fishing. Flounder, bass, whiting, codling, plaice, mullet, eels. Mixed catches from boats. River Adur, east of Worthing, noted for flounders, mullet and eels. Bait digging in Adur restricted to between toll bridge and harbour. Local association: Worthing & Dist Sea AA. Boats from harbours at Shoreham and Littlehampton. Numerous club competitions held on pier. Tackle shops: Prime Angling, 74 Brighton Rd, Worthing, BN11 2EN (tel: 01903 821594).

Littlehampton (Sussex). Noted for black bream, which are taken in large numbers during May and early June, but wide variety, including skate, smoothound (spring), whiting and cod (winter best) and plaice. Mid channel wrecking for cod, pollack, ling and conger (spring onwards). Well known marks are Kingmere Rocks for black bream, West Ditch for smoothound, Hooe Bank for conger. A large fleet of boats caters for sea anglers, and there is good fishing from beaches and in harbour. Boats list from Harbour Master, Harbour Office, Pier Rd, BN17 5LR (tel: 01903 721215). Tackle shop: Tropicana, 5&6 Pier Rd, BN17 5BA (tel: 01903 715190); Arun Angling Centre, Old Blacksmith Yard, Water Lane, Angmering, BN16 4EP (tel: 01903 770099; see website for more info: www.arunangling.co.uk).

Bognor Regis (Sussex). Good sea fishing at several marks off Bognor. Tope, bass, pollack, mackerel, whiting, wrasse. From May to July bream are plentiful. The conger, skate and sole fishing is very good. Grey mullet abound in the shallow water between Felpham and Littlehampton Harbour. Good cod fishing between September and November. Bass weighing 5 10lb and more caught from pier and shore. Good shore fishing for bass, mackerel, cod, smooth hounds off East and West Beaches at Selsey. Club: Selsey Angling & Tope Club. Tackle shops: Aldwick Angling, 25 Nyewood Lane, PO21 2QB (tel: 01243 829054; see website for more info: www.aldwickangling.com); Raycrafts Angling Centre, 119 High St, Selsey, Chichester PO20 0QB (tel: 01243 606039; see website for more info: www.raycrafts.co.uk), who has tickets for Chichester Canal fishing.

Hayling Island (Hants). From the South Beach of Hayling Island good fishing can be had with a rod and line for bass, plaice, flounders, dabs, whiting, etc, according to season. Fishing from boats in Hayling Bay for tope, skate, bass, mackerel, etc, is popular and a much favoured area is in the vicinity of the Church Rocks and in Chichester Harbour. Portsmouth & DAS has coarse lake in area. Tackle shop: Paige's Fishing Tackle, 36 Station Rd, Hayling Island, PO11 0EQ (tel: 02392 463500; see website for more info: www.paigestackle.com), (open Sundays).

Southsea (Hants). Over 4m of beach from Eastney to Portsmouth Harbour provide good sport all year. Bass fishing especially good from spring to September. Flatfish and rays numerous, large mackerel shoals in midsummer. Best sport from boats. Boom defence line from Southsea to IoW, although navigational hazard, is probably one of the best bass fishing marks on the South Coast. Vicinity of forts yields good bags of pollack, bass, black bream, skate, etc. Tope fishing good during summer. Portsmouth, Langstone and Chichester within easy reach and provide good sheltered water in rough weather. Boats can be hired from Portsmouth boatmen; large charter boat fleet in Langstone harbour. Club: Southsea Sea Angling Club; Eastleigh Cruising Assn. Tackle shops: Solent Tackle, 147 Winter Rd, Southsea, PO4 8DR (tel: 023 92739116; web: www.solenttackle.co.uk); Allan's Marine, 143 Twyford Ave, Portsmouth, PO2 8HU (tel: 023 92671833; see website for more info: www.allansmarine.co.uk).

Southampton (Hants). Fishing in Southampton Water really estuary fishing; thus not so varied as at some coastal stations. However, flounders abound (float and/or baited spoon fishing recommended), and whiting, pouting, silver eels, conger, bass, grey mullet, soles, dogfish, thornback, skate, stingray, plaice, dabs, scad, shad, mackerel have all been caught. At the entrance to Southampton Water, in Stokes Bay and the Solent generally, excellent tope fishing may be had. Angling from Hythe Pier, and from Netley and Hamble shores, but best fishing from boats. Southampton Water is rarely un-fishable. Good sport in power station outflow. Tackle shops: Sammy's Tackle & Bait, Cabin Boatyard, Bridge Road, Bursledon SO31 8AW (tel: 023 8040 6378).

Lymington (Hants). Stingray, smoothound, bass, eels in summer; cod, whiting, flounder, rockling, in winter; also short run of gilthead bream. Hurst Castle and Shingle Bank good fishing all year round for bass, cod, garfish, mackerel, rays; Shingle Bank also for black bream and occasional large flatfish; Lymington and Pennington sea walls for flounders, eels, bass, mullet. Lymington and Dist SFC fishes areas from Eastern boundary of Emsworth to western side of Lyme Regis, including Solent and all round Isle of Wight. Charter skippers operate from Lymington and Keyhaven. Around Needles area, good fishing for black bream, tope, smoothound and bass in summer months; large cod, OctFeb. Tackle shops: Loni's Angling Centre, 119 & 123 Old Milton Road, New Milton BH25 6DP (tel: 01425 616323); Ashley Angling & Pet Centre, 9 The Parade, Ashley Road, New Milton BH25 5BS (tel: 01425 638628).

Mudeford (Dorset). Christchurch Harbour at Stanpit is good for bass and grey mullet. All-round sea fishing in Christchurch and Poole Bay, the vicinity of the Ledge Rocks and farther afield on the Dolphin Banks. Tope, dogfish, conger, bream, pout, pollack, whiting and good sport spinning for mackerel and bass. Plaice off Southbourne; flounders, dabs, skate and sole off beaches at Highcliffe, Barton and Southbourne; flatfish, bass, whiting, etc, from quay, beach, groyne or shore at Hengistbury Head; large tope, stingray, skate and occasional thresher shark and turbot off The Dolphins. Fairly good cod fishing in winter, Needles-Christchurch Ledge, Pout Hole and Avon Beach (off Hengistbury Head). Whole squid favourite bait, but large baited spoons and jigs also successful. Good sole from Taddiford and Highcliffe Castle (best after dark). Groyne at Hengistbury good for bass in summer; sand eels by day and squid by night. Best months for general sport, mid-June to mid or late Sept. Most local fishermen now take parties out mackerel fishing in summer. Flounders, eels, bass and mullet taken inside the harbour. Tackle shop: Davis Fishing Tackle, 71-75 Bargates, Christchurch, BH23 1QE (tel: 01202 485169; see website for more info: www.davistackle.co.uk). Hotels: Christchurch Harbour Hotel, Waterford Lodge, The Pines Guest House.

Bournemouth (Dorset). Fishing good at times from the pier yielding bass, grey mullet, plaice, dabs, etc. Excellent catches of plaice, dabs, codling, silver whiting, mackerel (spinning), tope up to 40lb, conger, skate, from boats. Shore fishing, when sea is suitable, for bass and other usual sea fish. Bait supplies fairly good. Club: Christchurch & Dist FC. Tackle shops: Christchurch Angling Centre, 7 Castle Parade, Bournemouth, BH7 6SH (tel: 01202 480520); Bournemouth Fishing Lodge, 904 Wimborne Rd, Moordown, BH9 2DW (01202 514345; see website for more: www.bournemouthfishinglodge.co.uk (For freshwater fishing, see Avon (Wiltshire) and Stour (Dorset)). Accommodation: Royalty View Guesthouse.

Poole (Dorset). Boat, beach and quay fishing in vast natural harbour. Great variety of fish, but now noted for deep-sea boat angling and bass fishing. Conger, tope, bream, etc, are caught within three miles of the shore. Bass, plaice, flounders, etc, caught inside the harbour at Sandbanks and Hamworthy Park in their seasons. Local tackle shops should be consulted for up-to-the-minute information. For boat fishing facilities contact Poole Sea Angling Centre. Sea Fishing (Poole) Ltd, Fisherman's Dock, The Quay, BH15 1HJ (tel: 01202 679666), also cater for bass and deepsea angling. Baits favoured locally: mackerel, squid, sand eel and ragworm. Tackle shop: Poole Sea Angling Centre, 5 High Str, BH15 1AB (tel: 01202 676597) (web: www.pooleseaanglingcentre.co.uk).

Swanage (Dorset). Double high tide in Swanage and Poole Harbour. Species taken from pier and beach incl bass, mullet, pollack, mackerel, flounder, wrasse and pouting. Beach here too crowded for daytime fishing, but boat fishing is very good, with skate, conger, bream, huss, dogfish, pollack, large wrasse, tope and other species. Good cod fishing in winter, a few miles offshore, and boats are on hire at Poole and Weymouth. In summer, boats operate from Swanage Angling Centre, just off quay. Local knowledge is essential as tides and races are very dangerous for small boats. Several open angling competitions are held each year. Tourist Information is at The White House, Shore Rd, Swanage, BH19 1LB (tel: 01929 422885). Tackle and boat hire from tackle shop: Swanage Angling Centre, 6 High St, BH19 2NT (tel: 01929 424989; see website for more: www.swanageangling.com). Many hotels.

Weymouth (Dorset). Centre for the famous Chesil Beach, Shambles Bank, Portland and Lulworth Ledges. The steeply sloping Chesil Beach provides year-round sport for many species, but autumn and winter best for codling, whiting, bream and dogfish; and summertime best for garfish, triggerfish and various visiting Mediterranean species; beach fishes best at night; fairly heavy tackle required. Good conger fishing at the Chesil Cove end, Ringstead Bay, Redcliffe and round the piers. Piers yield good sport all year round. Good bass from Greenhill beach in heavy surf, with variety of flatfish at most times. Ferrybridge and the Fleet noted for bass, mullet and flounders. Boat fishing: In the area around Portland Bill some blonde and thornback rays, skate give good sport, while the notable Shambles Bank continues to yield turbot and skate, etc. Lulworth Ledges have a large variety of fish including tope, blue shark, conger, skate, dogfish, black bream, pollack, whiting, etc. Best baits are lugworm, ragworm, soft crab, mackerel and squid. No boats from Chesil Bank, but 20 boatmen operate from Weymouth throughout year. Tackle shop: Weymouth Angling Centre, Old Harbour House, 24 Trinity Road DT4 8TJ (tel: 01305 777771; see web for info: www.weymouthangling.com); Denning Tackle & Guns, 114 Portland Rd, Wyke Regis, DT4 9AD (tel: 01305 783145).

Portland (Dorset). Good bass fishing in harbour; live prawns for bait. Mullet, mackerel, whiting and conger are plentiful. No longer charter boats from fishermen at Castletown (for the harbour). Shore fishing from Church Ope Cove, The Bill and on the beach. Near the breakwater is a good spot. Weymouth tackle shops.

Bridport (Dorset). Beach, now a World Heritage site and famous for its Jurassic coastline, fishing yields bass, pouting, flatfish, thornback rays and conger, with whiting and cod in winter and large numbers of mackerel in summer. From boats: black bream, conger, pollack, whiting, pout, dogfish, bull huss, rays, cod, wrasse and other species. West Bay is the angling centre. Burton Bradstock, Cogden, West Bexington and Abbotsbury are popular venues on Chesil Beach. Eype and Seatown favoured to west. Bait: lugworm, sand

eel, ragworm, squid, mackerel favoured. For boat charter from West Bay for offshore wreck fishing trips enquire at tackle shops. Club: West Bay Sea AC, has brilliant junior section with special competitions, etc. Tackle shops: West Bay Water Sports, 10a West Bay, DT6 4EL (tel: 01308 421800; web: www.fishto.net); The Tackle Shop, 9e West Bay, DT6 4EN (tel: 01308 428226). Hotel: The George, West Bay.

Lyme Regis (Dorset). Bass may be caught from the shore. Best baits are fresh mackerel, (sometimes obtainable from motorboats in harbour), or ragworm from tackle shop. Mackerel may be caught from May to October. Pollack plentiful in spring months. Conger and skate can be caught from boats about 2m from shore. Deep sea day and half day trips from Charter boats bookable. Self drive motor boats are on hire at the Cobb Harbour, also tackle, mackerel lines free of charge, salted bait available. Information from Harbour Master, The Cobb, Lyme Regis, DT7 3JJ (tel: 01297 442137). Tackle shop: The Tackle Box, 20 Marine Parade, Lyme Regis DT7 3JF (tel: 01297 443373; web: www.lymetackle.com).

Seaton (Devon). Boat fishing. Pollack, pouting, conger, wrasse (March to Sept), bass (virtually all year, but best Sept-Nov), bream, mackerel, dabs, skate, plaice, dogfish. Axe estuary good for bass, mullet and sea trout: dt water. Tackle shops: Seaton Tackle Shop, The Harbour, Axmouth EX12 4AA (tel: 01297 625511; web: www.britishtackle.com); Sports & Leisure, Fosseway Court, Seaton EX12 2LP; (tel: 01297 21874) (web: www.stcstores.co.uk). Tourist Information: (tel: 01297 21660).

Sidmouth (Devon). Sea fishing in Sidmouth Bay. Mackerel (May to Oct), pollack (excellent sport spring and summer east and west of town), bass (to 13lb in surf at Jacob's Ladder beach during summer), wrasse, large winter whiting (July-Oct on rocky bottom), skate to 105lb and conger to 44lb have been taken; bull huss to 19lb, and tope. Also plaice, dabs, flounders and occasional turbot. Club: Sidmouth SAC, Port Royal, Esplanade, EX10 8BG (tel: 01395 512286). At Budleigh Salterton, a few grey mullet in river, but fairly un-catchable; beach best fished at night for flatfish. Tackle Shop: Sidmouth Tackle and Pet Supplies, Shopping Centre, High Str, EX10 8LD (tel: 01395 512626).

Exmouth (Devon). Main species caught here in summer are pollack, wrasse, pout, bass, garfish and mackerel. Favourite baits are lugworm, ragworm, peeler crab and sand eel. Pollack are caught on artificial sand eels. Popular places are: car park near Beach Hotel, docks area, estuary beaches, where flounders are caught, mid Sept to Jan. Deep Sea and wreck fishing trips can be booked in the area, with chances of conger eel &c. Tackle shop: Exmouth Tackle Shop, 20 The Strand, EX8 1AF (tel: 01395 274918).

Dawlish (Devon). Dabs and whiting in bay off Parson and Clerk Rock and between Smugglers' Gap and Sprey Point. Mackerel good in summer. Conger eels and dogfish about ¾m from shore between Parson and Clerk Rock and Shell Cove. Good fishing sometimes off breakwater by station and from wall of Boat Cove. Boats from Boat Cove. Tackle shop; see Teignmouth.

Teignmouth (Devon). Sea fishing ideal (especially for light spool casting with sandeels for bass). Bass, pollack, flounders in estuary. Mackerel, dabs and whiting in the bay. Good flounder fishing from the shore. Deep sea, wreck and offshore trips are possible. The town has an annual sea fishing flounder festival. Club: Teignmouth SAS (HQ: River Beach). Tackle shop: Fairweather News, 52 Northumberland Place, TQ14 8DE (tel: 01626 773380; see website for more: www.fairweathernews.co.uk) (bait for sea angling, information). Boats and bait obtainable on river beach. Details of accommodation from Tourist Information Centre, The Den. It should be noted that the estuary is a bass nursery area between May and October.

Torcross; nr Kingsbridge (Devon). The sea fishing is very good, especially the bass fishing with summer mackerel. Tackle shop: Devon Angling Centre, Unit 4/5 Orchard Meadow, Orchard Way, Chillington, Kingsbridge TQ7 2LB (tel: 01548 580888) (web: www.anglingcentre.net).

Torquay (Devon). Excellent centre for sea fishing, most species found. Base for famous Skerries Bank and Torbay wrecks; conger, cod, pollack, turbot, flatfish, whiting, etc. Hope's Nose peninsula provides best venue for shore angler, with bass and plaice mainly sought. Other species caught are dabs, wrasse, mullet, flounder, gurnard. Babbacombe Pier good for mackerel. Bass and pollack off the rocks. Natural bait hard to come by, but tackle dealers can supply. Local association: Torbay & Babbacombe ASA. Tackle shops: Tidal Tackle, 23 Victoria Parade, TQ1 2BD (tel: 01803 292080; web: www.tidaltackle.co.uk). (For freshwater fishing, including Torquay Corporation reservoirs, see Teign and Dart).

Paignton (Devon). Summer and autumn best. Bass, mackerel and garfish can be taken from beaches between Preston and Broadsands and from harbour, promenade and pier respectively. Mullet also present, but very shy. Fishing from rock marks too. Club: Paignton Sea AA, who have information service and social centre for anglers at HQ: Ravenswood, 26 Cliff Rd, The Harbour (open 7.30 pm onwards); annual membership available. Tackle shops: Torbay Angling, 7 Dartmouth Rd, Paignton TQ4 5AA (tel: 01803 552496).

Brixham (Devon). Boat fishing in bay for plaice, dabs, mackerel. Good pollack off East and West Cod rocks of Berry Head. Neap tides best; baits: worms or prawn. Farther out is Mudstone Ridge, a deep area, strong tide run, but good general fishing with big conger. Local boats take visitors out to deep water marks (wreck fishing) or to Skerries Bank, off Dartmouth, for turbot (occasional), plaice, etc; advance bookings (at harbour) advisable. Shore fishing: bass, pollack, wrasse, conger, mackerel from Fishcombe Point, Shoalstone and the long Breakwater. Grey mullet abound in the harbour area (bait, bread or whiting flesh). Bass from St Mary's Beach (best after dark) and south side of Berry Head (bottom of cliffs) for flat fishing. Sharkham Point good for mackerel and bass (float with mackerel, strip bait or prawn for bass). Mansands Point good for bass and pollack (float). Night fishing from Elbury or Broadsands beach for bass, flatfish or conger (use thigh boots). Club: Brixham SAA. Tackle shop: Brixham Bait & Tackle, 10 The Quay, TQ5 8AW (tel: 01803 853390; web: www.brixhambaitandtackle.co.uk). Hotel: Quayside Hotel.

Dartmouth (Devon). River holds large conger, record around 60lb; thornback ray to 17lb: best bait, prawn; also dabs, flounder, mullet, pollack, pouting. Baits, squid, ragworm, peeler crab, prawns. Shore angling is best from late Sept. Good marks are Warfleet Creek, mullet; rocks at castle, with garfish, mackerel, scad, wrasse, bass and other species caught; Leonards Cove, bass, mullet, wrasse, pollack in summer, whiting and codling in winter; Combe Rocks, boat fishing for wrasse, pollack, dogfish, bass, garfish, mackerel, rock pouting, ling, conger; Western Black Stone, best at night for bass: Homestone Ledge and Mewstone are boat locations. Charter boats available.

Association Club House is at 5 Oxford St. Tackle shop: nearest Brixham. Hotels: Castle, Dart Marina. (For freshwater fishing, see Dart).

Salcombe (Devon). Mackerel June to Sept and turbot, dabs, flounders, plaice, skate and rays rest of year. Entire estuary is a bass nursery area, and it is illegal to land boat caught bass. Plenty of natural bait. Beaches crowded in summer, but fishable in winter. Wreck fishing for conger, bream, etc. April-Oct. Good turbot. Boats: Whitestrand Boat Hire, Whitestrand Quay, TQ8 8ET (tel: 01548 843818); Salcombe Boat Hire (tel: 01548 844475). Club: Salcombe & Dist SAA (HQ: Victoria Inn); annual membership £10 (conc); annual summer festival; special prizes and trophies for visitors throughout season.

Newton Ferrers (Devon). Noted station on Yealm Estuary. All-year bottom fishing; bass, flounders, pollack (from rocks), with mullet, conger, mackerel and flat fish from boats; shark June-Oct. Good base for trips to Eddystone. Boats available. Abundant bait in estuary. Hotels: River Yealm and others.

Plymouth (Devon). One of finest stations in country for offshore deep water fishing at such marks as East & West Rutts, Hands Deep and, of course, famous Eddystone Reef. Specimen pollack, conger, ling, whiting, pouting, cod, bream and mackerel plentiful. Fishing vessels for charter are Decca and Sounder equipped fast exploring numerous wrecks within easy steaming of port; outstanding specimens taken. Inshore fishing for same species off Stoke Point, The Mewstone, Penlee, Rame and The Ledges. Sheltered boat and shore fishing in deep water harbour and extensive estuary network at its best in autumn for bass, pollack, flounders, thornback and mullet. Shore fishing from rocks at Hilsea, Stoke, Gara Point, Rame Head,

Penlee and Queeners for bass, pollack and wrasse, etc. Beach (surf) fishing at Whitsands and sand bar estuaries of Yealm, Erme and Avon rivers for bass, flounder and ray. All angling associations in city British Conger Club (affiliated with ninety seven sea angling clubs), Plymouth Federation Sea AC and Plymouth SAC now under one roof, on waterfront, at Mountbatten Water Sports Centre. Visiting anglers cordially welcomed. Tackle shops: Tackle & Bait Shop, 93 Victoria Rd, PL5 1RX (tel: 01752 361294) (see website for more info: www.plymouthangling.com); Clive's Tackle & Bait, 182 Exeter Str, PL4 0NQ (tel: 01752 228940). Charter boats are all moored on Sea Angling Centre Marina, Vauxhall Quay. Plymouth Angling Boatman's Assn (tel: 01752 666576).

Looe (Cornwall). Important centre for all-round sport. Bass, pollack and mullet from 'Banjo Pier' breakwater, October to March. Excellent bass fishing in Looe River when fish are running, and mullet. Good rock fishing from White Rock, Hannafore, and westwards to Talland Bay, where pollack, bass, conger and wrasse can be taken. Eastwards, flatfish from beaches at Millendreath, Downderry and Whitsand Bay. Bass, flounders, eels, pollack and mullet from river at quayside and upriver. Excellent sport from boats on deepsea marks; porbeagle, mako, blue and some thresher shark taken, and wide variety of other fish. Clubs: Looe is HQ of Shark AC of Gt Britain (tel/fax: 01503 262642) and is official weighing-in station for British Conger Club. Local club: Looe AC. Deep sea boats, tackle and information from Looe Chandlery, Millpool Boatyard, West Looe, PL13 2AE (tel: 01503 264355). Looe Information Bureau is at The Guildhall, Fore St, PL13 1AA (tel: 01503 262072).

Polperro (Cornwall). Few boats, shore fishing weedy. Bass, whiting, pollack,

mackerel are most likely catches. Tackle shops: see Looe. Hotels: Claremont, Noughts & Crosses, Ship, Three Pilchards; also farm accommodation.

Fowey (Cornwall). Excellent sport with bass (June to Oct) in estuary and local bays from Udder to Cannis. Pollack numerous and heavy (20lb and more). Good bream, cod, conger, dogfish, ling, mullet, mackerel, wrasse, whiting and flatfish (big flounders and turbot). Bass, mullet and flounders taken from river. Par Beach to west also good for bass. Rock fishing at Polruan, Gribben Head and Pencarrow. Sandeel, rag and lugworm obtainable. Clubs: Polruan Sea AC, Lugger Inn, The Quay, Polruan PL23 1PA (tel: 01726 870007). Boats: Fowey River Boat Hire, Mill Pool Yard, Passage Lane PL23 1JS (tel: 01726 832874); Red Admiral Fishing Trips, Polruan (tel: (mob) 0779 2738270). Tourist Information: 5 South Str, PL23 1AR (tel: 01726 833616). Fowey River Fishing Tackle, 19 Station Rd, Caffa Mill PL23 1DF (tel: 01726 833327).

Mevagissey (Cornwall). Excellent sea fishing, boat and shore, especially in summer. Shark boats are based here (local club affiliated to the Shark AC of Great Britain). Mevagissey Shark Angling Centre will make arrangements for shark and deepsea trips; £50 per day, £30 half day, incl rod and reel use. Shore fishing quite productive, especially bass from beach. Good night fishing at Pendower and Carne beaches, near Veryan, in Gerrans Bay area; best on falling tide and at low water, best bait squid and lug worm. Rock fishing productive at Blackhead near St Austell, dogfish, pollack, wrasse, gurnard, garfish, plaice, flounder. Good pollack off Dodman Point and from marks out to sea. Bass in large numbers again owing to bass nursery in Foy estuary. Excellent sport with large mackerel at Gwinges and close to Dodman from late Aug. Sport from the pier can be very good at times, especially with mullet; weights in excess of 2oz must use a shock leader. Club: Mevagissey SAC (HQ: The Porthpean Golf Club; meet 1st Mon of month; chairman tel: 01726 844100; visitors welcome). Tackle shop: Mevagissey Shark Angling Centre, West Wharf, St Austell, PL26 6UJ (tel: 01726 843430).

Gorran Haven (Cornwall). Same marks fished as at Mevagissey. Rock fishing in area. Bass from sand beach. The Gorran Haven fishermen offer some facilities for visitors wishing a day's fishing. Excellent pollack fishing from boat with rubber sandeel off Dodman Point.

Falmouth (Cornwall). Excellent estuary, harbour (pier, shore and boat) and offshore fishing, especially over Manacles Rocks. Noted for big bass and pollack, latter taken off wreck and rock marks. Pendennis Point for wrasse and pollack; St Anthonys Head for wrasse, black bream at night in autumn. Porthallow for coalfish and conger; Lizard for wrasse, mackerel, and conger at night. Bait in estuary or from tackle shops. For boats, enquire at Tackle Box. Tackle shop: Tackle Box, Swanpool Str, TR11 3HU (tel: 01326 315849). Details of hotel accom from Tourist Information: 11 Market Strand, Prince of Wales Pier, TR11 3DF (tel: 01326 312300). (For freshwater fishing, see River Fal).

Porthleven (Cornwall). Bass are plentiful. Best bass fishing from Loe Bar, 1½ m E, but be beware of dangerously strong currents (no swimming) and not to be fished in a south westerly or westerly gale; ask local advice. Good pollack and mackerel fishing outside the rocks. Nearly all fishing is done from the Mount's Bay type of boat in deep water. For charter boats, contact tackle shop: Porthleven Angling Centre, 8 Celtic House, Harbour Head, Porthleven, Helston TR13 9JY (tel: 01326 561885).

Penzance (Cornwall). Excellent boat, pier, rock and shore fishing for pollack, mackerel (March-Nov), mullet, bass (May-Dec), whiting and codling (Nov-Jan), flounders (Nov-Jan), trigger fish (July-Sept). Long Rock beach recommended, best Jun-Nov; bass, ray, flatfish. Marazion beaches offer flatfish and ray. Pier at Lamorna, turbot, gurnard and dogfish (care over car clamping). Breakwater and beach at Sennen, the same. Praa Sands excellent for bass, smalleyed ray and turbot. Boat trips can be arranged with Newtown Angling. Shark fishing also possible (catch & release preferred); best months: Easter-Nov. Best baits: live sand eel in daylight (April to Oct), lugworm and ragworm at night, frozen sand eel as substitute. Club: Mount's Bay AS (HQ: Bath Inn, Penzance). Annual fishing festival, three weeks, Aug-Sept. Tackle shop: Newtown Angling Centre, Newton Germoe, TR20 9AE (tel: 01736 763721) (web: www.newtownangling.com).

Mousehole, via Penzance (Cornwall). Good station for fishing Mount's Bay. Excellent mackerel, bream, pollack, conger, whiting, bass close to harbour according to season. Sheltered from west. Rock fishing in rough weather. Bell Rock between Newlyn and Mousehole has produced record catches. Between Mousehole and Lamorna, Penza Point, Kemyell Point and Carn Dhu are marks. Best grounds: Longships and Runnel Stone. Good results with sharks. Hotels: Old Coastguard.

Isles of Scilly. From shores and small boats around islands, wrasse, pollack, mackerel, dogfish, bullhuss, rockling, mullet (thick lipped), dab, codling, garfish, conger and plaice; farther off in deep sea, particularly on The Powl, southwest of St Agnes, big catches made of cod, ling, conger, pollack, etc. Mullet pay periodical visits inshore, but usually caught by net; bass very rare in these waters. Some shark fishing July-Sept, all tackle provided. Peninnis Head and Deep Point on St Mary's are good rock marks for pollack, wrasse and mackerel. Boating can be dangerous, so experience essential. Accommodation limited, early bookings advisable between May and Sept. For boats enquire of Sports Mode. Tackle shop: Sports Mode, The Parade, St Mary's TR21 0LP (tel: 01720 422293) (see website for info: www.sportsmode-ios.co.uk). Other information from Tourist Information: Hugh Str, St Mary's, TR21 0LL (tel: 01720 422536).

St Ives (Cornwall). Bass, flounder, turbot, plaice, mackerel and garfish plentiful in St Ives area. Surf fishing from shore, especially from island, Aire Point (can be very dangerous), Cape Cornwall, Portheras, Besigrau, Man's Head, Clodgy Point; Godrevy Point offers mackerel, pollack and wrasse, which are also found at Navax Point (the latter two of which can also be dangerous in swells). Chapel Porth good for ray and turbot. Boat fishing gives sport with mackerel (summer months) and large pollack (off reef from Godrevy Island). For boats contact Harbourmaster (tel: 01736 795018). Bass, tope, mullet, flatfish and occasional sea trout taken in Hayle river estuary. Trout fishing on Drift Reservoir, Penzance and St Erth Stream (4m). Tackle shop: The Fisherman's Co-operative Society, The Wharf TR26 1PU (tel: 01736 796276).

Newquay (Cornwall). Boat, beach; rock and estuary fishing. Mackerel (April to Oct); school bass (June-Sept); larger fish July onwards, including winter; pollack (May-Nov); flatfish, wrasse (May-Sept). Mullet good from June-Sept. Beach fishing at Perranporth, Holywell Bay, Crantock and Watergate Bay: ray, turbot and plaice rare. Off-peak times only. Shark

and deep sea fishing possible. For boats, contact Boatmans Assn, Kiosk 4, South Quay (tel: 01637 876352, mob: 07772 196845); or Anchor Sea Angling Centre, South Quay TR7 1HR (tel: 01637 877613). Tackle Shop: Atlantic Angling, 9b Cliff Rd, TR7 2NE (tel: 01637 850777). Numerous hotels.

Padstow (Cornwall). Trevose Head, Park Head and Stepper Point are good marks in summer for float fishing and spinning for mackerel, pollack; garfish, bass, wrasse, dog fish, plaice, turbot, occ. tope, and in winter for whiting, codling, dogfish, conger. Carneweather Point nr Polzeath is recommended for all-year-round fishing with cod in winter, but beware of dangerous ocean swells; ask local advice. The beaches at Trevone, Harlyn, Mother Ivys, Boobys, Constantine, Treyarnon, Porthcothan, Mawgan Porth, provide surf casting for bass, plaice, turbot, rays. The estuary has good flounder fishing in winter. Club: Grenville Fishing Club, Social Club, St Dennis; Padstow & District Sea Angling Association (can join at Padstow Angling Centre) or contact tackle shop: Padstow Angling Centre, Strand House, South Quay, Padstow PL28 8BL (tel: 01841 532762) (for Padstow SAC).

Bude (Cornwall). Codling, flatfish, mackerel, cod, whiting and dogfish from breakwater, Crackington Haven and Clovelly. Northcott Mouth Crooklets, Maer, for skate, bass and flatfish. Widemouth Bay is good venue for rays which may be taken from shore in late summer and autumn; also bass and cod on high tide. Rock fishing is to be had from Upton, Wanson and Millock. Several boats work from Port Isaac in summer. Tackle shop: Waterfront Fishing & Shooting, Lower Wharf Centre, The Wharf, Bude, Cornwall EX23 8LG. (tel: 01288 359606; see website: www.waterfront-fishing.com).

Hartland (Devon); ns Barnstaple, 24m. Good all-round sea fishing, especially for bass at times with india-rubber sandeel, prawn or limpet from beach or rocks according to tide (bass up to 11½lb have been caught); whiting, mullet, conger and pouting also taken. Tackle shop: Summerlands Tackle (see Westward Ho!). Hotels: Hartland Quay, New Inn, King's Arms.

Lundy (Bristol Channel). Good mackerel, conger, pollack and wrasse inshore. Ray, plaice, dabs, tope and bass at East Bank. 1¼ to 2½m E. Good anchorage at Lundy, but no harbour. Boats occasionally on hire for 8 persons fishing. For accommodation write to The Agent, Lundy, Bristol Channel, N Devon EX39 2LY.

Clovelly (Devon). W of Bideford. Whiting, cod, conger, bull huss, dogfish and the occasional plaice caught all the year round; ray in spring, bass and mackerel in summer. Few inshore boats; fishing from the breakwater forbidden in summer. Hotels: New Inn; Red Lion.

Bideford (Devon). Bass (from the bridge, in summer) flounders, mullet higher up the river. Tackle Shop: Summerlands Tackle, 1620 Nelson Rd, Westward Ho! EX39 1LF (tel: 01237 471291).

Westward Ho! (Devon). Extensive beach and rocks from which bass, dogfish, smoothhounds, bull huss, tope and mackerel may be taken in summer; codling to 10lbs in winter. Tackle Shop: Summerlands Tackle, 1620 Nelson Rd, Westward Ho! EX39 1LF (tel: 01237 471291) (web: www.summerlands.co.uk); baits, and advice offered to anglers; information on all fishing trips. Appledore, north of Bideford in Torridge estuary, in summer has good bass fishing from rocks by the lifeboat slip or the main quay. Cod and whiting in winter. Lugworm beds at Appledore and Instow. Few boats.

Ilfracombe (Devon). From pier: conger, pollack, whiting, dabs. Capstone Point, bass, wrasse. Capstone Rocks, similar species; Watermouth Cove, mixed bag: pollack, coalfish, wrasse, bass, a few flatfish. From boat, conger, skate, ray; mackerel Jun-Sept. Cod Dec-Feb. Bait: mackerel, squid, sand eel. Reservoir trout fishing (see freshwater section). Tackle and bait from Variety Sports, 23 Broad Str, EX34 9EE (tel: 01271 862039). Details of accom from Tourist Information Centre: The Landmark Theatre, The Seafront EX34 9BX (tel: 01271 863001).

Lynmouth (Devon). Good harbour and boat fishing. Grey mullet and bass from harbour arm. Drift fishing for pollack and mackerel. Tope, skate and conger in Lynmouth Bay and off Sand Ridge, 1m. Best months: June to Oct. Tackle shop: Churchill House, Church Hill, Lynton EX35 6HY (tel: 01598 752557). Several hotels in Lynton and Lynmouth; details from Lynton & Lynmouth Tourist Office, Town Hall, Lee Rd, Lynton, EX35 6BT (tel: 01598 752225) (tickets for Watersmeet and Glenthorne Fisheries, East Lyn River). (For freshwater fishing see Lyn).

Minehead (Som). Beach, boat and rock fishing, principally for tope, skate, ling, thornback ray, conger, cod, bass and flatfish (Dunster to Porlock good for bass from beaches). Dogfish in bay. Mackerel in summer. Harbour and promenade walls provide sport with mullet, codling and some bass. Boats from kiosk in harbour. Bait from sands at low water. Club: Minehead & Dist SAC. Tackle shops: Minehead Sports, 55 The Avenue, TA24 5BB (tel: 01643 703423); Westcoast Tackle, The Quay, Minehead TA24 5UL (tel: 01643 705745; see website for more info: www.westcoastangling.co.uk).

Watchet (Som). Watchet and Dist Sea Angling Society fishes all the year round, covering coast from St Audries

Bay to Porlock Wier. Monthly competitions from piers and shore. Codling, bass, whiting, conger and skate, according to season. Good boat fishing. New members welcomed by AS. Charter boats, enquire tackle shop: Westcoast Angling Centre, 53 Swain Str, TA23 0AG (tel: 01984 634807; see website for more info: www.westcoastangling.co.uk).

Weston-super-Mare (Avon). Record list of the Weston-super-Mare Sea AA includes conger at 25lb, sole at 2lb 8oz, bass 13lb, skate 16lb 8oz, cod at 22lb, silver eel at 4lb, whiting and flounder at 2lb. Best venues 2 hours either side of low tide are Brean Down, conger, skate; Weston Beach, whiting, flatfish; Knightstone now closed. Woodspring is fishable throughout year, best at autumn. For baits, beds of lugworms are to be found along the low water mark of the town beach and off Kewstoke Rocks. Also from Tackle shop: Weston Angling Centre, 25A Locking Rd, Weston-super-Mare, BS23 3BY (tel: 01934 631140).

Southport (Merseyside). Dabs and flounders, with plentiful whiting and cod (Oct Feb), chief fish caught here; also skate, mullet, dogfish, sole, a lot of tope, plaice, conger, gurnard and some bass. Shore flat and sandy, and fishing from pier limited to pier closing times. Local clubs: Southport SAC. Good coarse fishing on River Crossens run by Southport & DAS. Tackle shops: Tight Lines Angling Centre, 2 Hampton Rd, PR8 6SS (tel: 01704 541014); Catch 22 Fishing Tackle, Unit 39, Birkdale Trdg Est, Liverpool Rd, Southport PR8 4PZ (tel: 01704 568450). At **Liverpool**, Mersey is cleaner nowadays, and cod, bass and whiting are taken from both sides of river; dock fishing very restricted.

Blackpool (Lancs). Seven miles of beach, but boat fishing is the best option, although only one boat are now operating. Tickets for certain parts of Wyre from tackle shops. Coarse fishing in Stanley Park Lake; for membership and dt apply boat office in Stanley Park. Tackle shop: Blackpool Angling Centre, 328330 Church Str, Blackpool, FY1 3QH (tel: 01253 290961); Chris Webb Bait & Tackle, 52a St Annes Rd, FY4 2AN (tel: 01253 470004). Many hotels.

Morecambe and Heysham (Lancs). Beach and stone jetty fishing throughout year. Beaches yield plaice, flounders, dabs, bass and eels from June to October, and dabs, codling, whiting and flounders in winter. Estuary catches up to 100 flounders to 2lb weight at Arnside. Stone jetty has been extended, angling free; good catches of plaice, flounders, codling, whiting. At Heysham Harbour and North Wall whiting, cod, flounders, dabs, pouting, conger and mullet can be taken; dogfish (Sept-Oct) mainly off North Wall. Storm Groynes is producing good flatfish. Tackle shops: Morecambe Angling Centre, Grand Gar, Thornton Rd, Morecambe LA4 5PB (tel: 01524 832332).

Fleetwood (Lancs). Plaice, whiting, skate, codling, tope, etc, from boats and shore. Club: Fleetwood & District AC. Tackle shop: Blackpool Angling Centre, 328 Church Str, Blackpool FY1 3QH (tel: 01253 290961).

Barrow-in-Furness (Cumbria). Boat and shore fishing for tope, bass, cod, plaice, whiting, thornback skate. Good marks include Foulney Island, Roa Island, Piel Island, Scarth Hole and Black Tower (Walney Island) and Roanhead. Good beach areas are Priory Point to Canal Foot, bait may be dug here, also, and Greenodd from sea wall alongside A590 and from car park. Tackle shop: Angling and Hiking Centre, 275277 Rawlinson Str, LA14 1DH (tel: 01229 829661; web: www.anglingandhikingcentre.co.uk).

ISLE OF WIGHT

The Island provides a wealth of shore and boat fishing, and sheltered conditions can always be found, Bass are the main quarry for beach anglers, but pollack, conger, mackerel, pouting, thornback rays, flatfish and wrasse, with occasional tope, are also taken. Black bream, skate and shark are caught by boat anglers as well as the species already mentioned. Cod run regularly to 20lb in autumn. Due to strong tides on the north coast and lack of harbours on the south coast, the visiting angler would be best advised to arrange boat trips with one of the local charter skippers working out of Yarmouth or Bembridge. Strong tides also mean heavy leads and sometimes, wire line. There are a large number of fishing clubs on the island. T I centres provide information about them.

Alum Bay. This necessitates a steep descent from the car park down the steps provided. From March to October there is a chair lift in operation. Fishes well after dark for large conger, bass, rays and sole, especially when rough. From the old pier remains to the white cliffs is the main area, although the rocks to the east, towards Totland, make a good station from which to spin for bass in the tide race, or to light ledger with squid or mackerel. Deep water at all states of tide.

Atherfield. A number of record fish have been taken from this stretch. The beach is of shingle with scattered rock, easily reached via path alongside holiday camp. Bass, rays, pout, etc after dark, to mackerel, squid and cuttle baits. Crab bait produces smooth hounds. Ragworm fished over the drying ledge to the left of this mark produces large wrasse and bass, day or night. Large cod in late autumn.

Bembridge. Species to be caught include bass, pout, conger, ling, bream, dogfish, turbot, brill, pollack, skate and ray. The shore from Whitecliff to Bembridge is mainly rock formation with stretches of shingle and is good ground for bass and conger although not fished a great deal. Bass, mullet, eels, among the rocks. Here, the beach turns to fine flat sand and flatfish and bass are taken. Bembridge Harbour is a wide inlet with St Helens on the opposite bank. Shark fishing, July-August, drifting from St Catherines Light to Nab Tower. Boats and bait obtainable on shore. A sand gully near the 'Crab and Lobster' can be fished from the rocks. Fine bream may be taken from boats on Bembridge Ledge, early May to June, plenty of mackerel, also. A good number of fish are taken in the harbour: flounders, eels, bass. Many large mullet can be seen but are seldom fished for. Very strong tide in narrowest part of entrance. Kingrag and lugworm are good baits for ledgering and small mud ragworm on light float tackle is successful. Baited spoon or wander tackle works well for flounder and plaice. Sea wall at St Helens is a convenient place to park and fish over the top of the tide. Club: Bembridge AC, holds 12 competitions p.a., open to non-members. The Club has 50 moorings let to members.

Bonchurch. Bass, conger, wrasse and pout from beach. Good fishing in gulleys between the extensive rocks at flood tide, after dark, especially after a south westerly gale.

Brooke. A shallow water mark that fishes well when the sea is coloured. Expect conger, bass, pout, plus cod in late autumn. One good spot is to be found in front of easy cliff path, 200 yds to left of point.

Chale. Best beach for rays on island, reached by steep cliff path. Specimen small eyed rays are taken on frozen sand eel, day or night, from Mar-Sept, when sea is coloured after a storm.

Some bass and conger, plus mackerel in summer.

Colwell Bay. A shallow sandy beach with easy access. Bass, sole, wrasse after dark, when crowds have gone home.

Totland Bay. Next to Colwell Bay, deeper water. More chance of bass, especially when rough. It's possible to fish straight from a car on the sea wall. Fishing is good beside the disused pier.

Compton Bay. 1m west of Brooke. Long flat sandy beach with patches of flat rock. Occasional bass when the sea is rough. Avoid the rocks under the cliff at the west end, where there is a danger of major cliff falls.

Cowes. The River Medina runs from Newport to Cowes Harbour and offers flounder fishing throughout the year with the best sport from the late summer to autumn. The shoals move about the river with the tide and location is often a matter of local knowledge. As a general guide the fish may be expected further upstream on the stronger spring tides. Weights average up to a pound. Bass also move into the river and have been taken to 4lbs, often on flounder tackle. Rowing boats may be launched from the Folly Inn on the East bank, reached by turning off the main Newport to East Cowes road. Kingston power station about a mile down from Folly is a good boat mark for school bass, plaice, sole. Mullet and silver eels may be caught anywhere. Ragworm is usually used in preference to lugworm.

Cowes Harbour. Bass, flounder, plaice and sole may be taken by the boat angler from either side of the fairway above and below the floating bridge and during the summer there are many large mullet within the harbour. Inside the breakwater to the east, flounder and plaice are taken on the bottom from along the edge of the hovercraft channel to inshore towards the East Cowes Esplanade. Flounder and plaice are also taken from the mudflats outside the East Cowes breakwater.

West Cowes Esplanade to Gurnard. Float fishing and spinning from the slipways and jetties for bass and mullet. Along the Princes Green to Egypt Light, bass and conger can be found and in late summer bass often venture close in under the walls in search of prawns and may be taken by trailing a worm over the balustrade and walking it quietly along. At Egypt Light, the shingle slopes steeply so long casting is unnecessary, and tope have occasionally been landed here as well as bass to 8lb, and cod to 20lb in late autumn. The sandy patches among the rocks may yield sole and plaice in season. Car parking here.

Freshwater Bay. Pouting, bass, small pollack and few conger. Fish from middle of beach when rough. Survey at low tide, then fish after dark. Very easy access.

Newport. Nearest sea fishing in River Medina; flounders, school bass, mullet, plaice, eels. Tackle/boat hire information from Scotties, branch at 11 Lugley Str, PO30 9HD (tel: 01983 522115).

Newtown. Bass and flounders in Newtown River. Clamerkin reach is best, using light gear and ragworm. Limited access, as large area is nature reserve.

Ventnor to St Catherines. Series of rocky ledges and gullies, best surveyed at low water. Bass, conger, pout, wrasse etc after dark and some mullet during calm days.

Yarmouth. Flounder and mullet and school bass in harbour. Bass, rays and mackerel from pier in summer. Notable cod venue in late autumn but strong tides prevail.

Ryde. A very shallow, sandy beech, popular with holiday makers. Bass, small pollack, plaice, flounders, eels, bream and grey mullet from pier. Conger, dogfish, dabs, skate, mackerel from deep water marks, and plaice, flounder, bass and sole fishing inshore. Cod up to 24lb taken in autumn. Sheltered resort giving ideal fishing conditions all year. All beaches fishable. King rag and lugworm plentiful. Boats can be hired along shore.

Sandown. Fishing from end of pier (daytime only) produces plaice, rays, garfish, bass and bream on sandy ground. Float fishing produces mackerel, scad, small pollack and mullet. Local club: Sandown and Lake AS, organising frequent competitions. Visitors welcome. Membership £15 annually (£7.50 juveniles) dt £2 from pier from Easter to end-Sept. Boat hire, tickets and tackle; Scotties, 22 Fitzroy Str, PO36 8HZ (tel: 01983 404555; www. isleofwight-fishing.com/018.htm).

Seaview. From St Helens to Seaview the coast is a mixture of rocks and sand and shingle. Priory Bay is reached by boat and provides very good mackerel and bass fishing. Plaice may be taken to 3lb from early April, with lugworm. During the summer months bream can

also be taken from this spot. From June onwards, bass and mackerel are shoaling and large catches from boats are common. Cod are also taken late in the year.

Shanklin. Pier has been demolished. Various other venues exist which fish well for specific species, such as congers, bass, wrasse, but require very detailed directions re access, times to fish, etc. Contact Scotties of Newport for such details, and to obtain a wide variety of suitable baits.

Totland. Bass off shingle bank from boat. Bass, conger from shore. Fishing from beach only. Hotels: Sentrymead.

Ventnor. The western end of the beach is good for bass, skate, pout and conger and harbour and the sea wall in front of the canoe lake is a good bass spot. Club: Ventnor AC (associate members welcome). Beach fishing (see also Bonchurch).

Wootton. School bass and flounders.

Yarmouth. Bass, small pollack; pier fishing.

CHANNEL ISLANDS

Wide variety of sport from beaches, rocky headlands and boats. Many specimen fish landed from deepsea marks. Shark fishing growing in popularity. Boats easy to come by.

Guernsey. No fewer than 76 different species are recorded in Bailiwick of Guernsey rodcaught record lists. Guernsey is 15 miles from the Hurd Deep, near major shipping lanes, and hundreds of wrecks yield high catches. In-shore, many headlands offer first-class spinning, and a flat, sandy, west coast gives good surfcasting for bass and a few flatfish. Several Guernsey fish accepted as new British records.

The most common species are bass, bream, conger, dogfish, garfish, mackerel, mullet, plaice, pollack and wrasse. Anglers may fish anywhere

from the shore except for marinas, the fishermans quay, and the land reclamation to the south of St Sampson's Harbour. Bottom fishing is productive in spring, late autumn and winter; spinning in summer. Long casting is no advantage, on westerly rocks. Baits: ragworm is found in the rocky bays on west coast (and can also be bought, as can sand eels): Grand Havre, Bordeaux North, to Beaucette Marina, Bellgreve Bay; lugworm in sandy bays, especially, Grand Havre, Cobo and Vazon. Crabs, prawns and white rag can also be obtained. In north east, Fort Doyle is one of the best marks; south east, Soldiers Bay.

South west cliffs are fishable but dangerous. There are many different fishing competitions between June and December. Local clubs: Guernsey SAC; Guernsey Freshwater AS; Guernsey Mullet Club; West Coast SAC, and others, including two bass clubs; for records contact The Bailiwick of Guernsey Record (Rock Caught) Fish Committee, c/o Pinewood, Jerbourg Rd, St Martins (tel: 01481 237755). Tackle shops: Western Tackle Supplies, Rue de la Hougue, Castel GY5 7EB (tel: 01481 256080); Mick's Fishing Supplies, Unit 6, Les Canus Rd GY2 4UJ. (tel: 01481 700390; see website for more: www.micksfishing.co.uk); Tackle and Accessories Centre, Rue de l'Eglise, Castel GY99 9ZZ (tel: 01481 251844); Quayside Ltd, North Side, St Sampsons Harbour GY1 3ET (tel: 01481 245881). Baits, rod hire; Boatworks Plus, St Peter Port, GY1 1AU (tel: 01481 726071). For further information about Guernsey fisheries contact States of Guernsey Sea Fisheries, Raymond Fala House, PO Box 459, Longue Rue, St Martins, Guernsey GY1 6AF (tel: 01481 235741; web: www.gov.gg). Tourist Information, Visit Guernsey (tel: 01481 234567).

Alderney. Alderney has become a notable centre for good sport. Turbot, brill, bass and good tope within 34 miles of shore; good pollack and cod wreck fishing; shore noted for mullet, and in autumn and winter exceptional range of species and quality of fish. Contact Alderney Angling & Sports, 32 Victoria Street, St Anne's GY9 3TA (tel: 01481 824884; web: www.alderneyangling.com); bait and can arrange a charter boat, and has good guide for anglers.

Jersey. Winter fishing yields pollack, ray and other flatfish, conger, a few bass, cod fishing can be good. Spring: garfish, early mackerel shore fishing) off such points as Sorel and La Moye; grey mullet and other species. Summer is good for all forms of fishing, by boat on offshore reefs, which is 80% of charter angling. Excellent fishing for bream commences in May and continues to Oct, fish up to 5lb. Rays (incl blonde rays, over 30lb) are caught in good quantities on inshore sandbanks, as well as brill and turbot, especially early and late season. In autumn, whitebait concentrates at places such as Belle Hougue and bring in large mackerel and bass, and flatfish move into shallow waters in the Islands bays.

Venues: St Helier's harbour heads; Noirmont Point; St Brelade's Bay; La Corbiere; L'Etacq; Plemont; Greve de Lecq; Bonne Nuit Bay harbour; Bouley Bay harbour; Rozel Bay harbour; St Catherine's breakwater; St Aubin's Bay. Charter boats: 'Anna II', from La Collette Marina, contact Tony Heart, The Coach House, 7 Clarendon Rd, JE2 3YW (tel: 01534 888552; mob: 07797 725301); 'Theseus', D Nuth (tel: 01534 858046; mob: 07797 728316). Local club: Jersey SFC. Jersey Freshwater AA, has coarse and trout dt from all tackle shops or: R A Mallet (tel: 01534 723882). Tackle shops: Iron Stores Marine and Leisure, 15/16 Commercial Buildings, JE2 3NB (tel: 01534 850090; web: www.ismarine.je); JFS Sport, The Fish Market, 7 Beresford Str, JE2 4WN (tel: 01534 874875); Mick Ward, Mr Fish Ltd, La Route de St Aubin, JE2 3SH (tel: 01534 618886; mob: 07797 822818; website: www.mrfishjersey.net); St Ouens Motor Works, La Grande Route de St Ouen JE3 2HY (tel: 01534 481870); all St Helier.

ISLE OF MAN

The Island's coastline is extremely varied. The long, flat, surf beaches of the North contrast sharply with the sheer faces of the South. Similarly, its fishing methods and species of fish are equally diverse. Despite the Island's location, coastline and clean waters, saltwater angling from both shore and boat remains unexploited and largely undiscovered. Information is obtainable from Isle of Man Tourist and Leisure Department, Information Bureau, Sea Terminal, Douglas, IM1 2RG (tel: 01624 686766).

Castletown. Conger, pollack, cod, wrasse, tope, flatfish from beach and boat; best months, June to Oct. Big skate from boats 600 yds off Langness; best Aug-Sept. Boats for hire locally.

Douglas. Plaice, sole (British record lemon sole), coalfish, pollack, flounder from Victoria Pier; best months, May to Oct, coalfish, wrasse, cod, plaice, dabs, sole from boats in Douglas Bay. Rock fishing off Douglas Head; float or spinner (good pollack). Cod, wrasse, red gurnard, plaice, Little Ness Head to Douglas Head; skate from boats 2m out, and large tope, conger, cod, etc. Club: Douglas (IOM) & District AC (membership includes trout fishing rights in R Glass); contact Hon Sec for further information and applications for membership; st, wt, dt enquire Hobbytime. 12 Castle St, Douglas IM1 2EU (tel: 01624 625720); The Roland Westcott Tackle Company, 1 The Shops, Ballaquayle Rd, Douglas IM2 5DF (tel: 01624 629599). Hotels: Devonian.

Kirk Michael. Beach fishing from here to Point of Ayre is excellent for bass, flatfish, dogfish.

Laxey. Plaice, dabs and bass from March to Oct from beach. Cod, mackerel, flatfish, offshore from boats at Garwick Bay. Tackle shop (see Douglas). Hotel: Bridge Inn.

Peel. Breakwater: cod, coalfish, dogfish plentiful all year round; mackerel, dogfish, coalfish, plaice, flounder, dabs (July to Oct). Beach: similar. Rock fishing: from Castle rocks and

headlands plenty of pollack. Sand eel best bait all season. Limited lugworm on beach. Boat fishing, but hire limited: cod and haddock in winter. In spring and summer spur dogfish common. Rock fishing off St Patrick's Isle for mackerel, wrasse, coalfish; float and spinner. Local club; Peel Angling Club.

Port Erin. Good sport from pier and breakwater for pollack, mackerel, wrasse, grey mullet, coalfish, angler fish and conger. The bay yields flatfish and mackerel, with cod in the colder months. Hotels: Balmoral; Falcons Nest.

Port St Mary. Probably best centre on island. Pollack, coalfish, wrasse from rocks, pier, boats (most of year). Flatfish and mackerel offshore and pier during herring season. Tope, skate, cod, conger, ling from boats. Several competitions. Enquiries to Hon Sec, Southern AC. Visitors welcome. Tackle shop (see Douglas). Hotels: Bay View.

Ramsey. No fishing from iron pier. Dogfish, codling, whiting, flounder, dab, coalfish, plaice, mackerel, rockling; from Ramsey beach to Point of Ayre, plus bass (Aug-Sept), tope, bull huss. Pollack also taken by spinning with artificial sandeel. For help with bait and boats, contact C Culshaw of Ramsey AC (tel: 01624 812279, after 6pm; 07624 300173; web: www.ramseyanglingclub.com); annual membership fee £15, conc. Tackle shop: The Ramsey Warehouse, 37 Parliament Str, IM8 1AT (tel: 01624 813092). Hotels: Sulby Glen.

FISHING CLUBS & ASSOCIATIONS IN ENGLAND

The English fishing clubs and associations listed below are by no means the total number of those existing. Club secretaries retire or change address, often after a comparatively short term of office, making it all too probable that the address list is out of date by the time it is issued. This regrettable fact also applies to the club lists in the others national sections of the book. Please advise the publishers (address at the front of the book) of any changed details for the next edition.

NATIONAL BODIES

Angling Trust Ltd
Eastwood House
6 Rainbow Street
Leominster
Herefordshire HR6 8DQ
Tel: 0844 7700616
Tel: 01568 620447 (Fish Legal)
www.anglingtrust.net
admin@anglingtrust.net

Angling Trades Assn
Federation House
Stoneleigh Park
Warwickshire CV8 2RF
Tel: 02476 414999
Fax: 02476 414990
www.anglingtradesassociation.com
ata@sportsandplay.com

Association of Rivers Trusts
Rain-Charm House
Kyl Cober Parc
Stoke Climsland
Callington, Cornwall
PL17 8PH
T: +44 (0)1579 372 142
info@associationofriverstrusts.org.uk
www.associationofriverstrusts.org.uk
Registered Charity No: 1107144

Atlantic Salmon Trust
Director: Tony Andrews
King James VI Centre
Friarton Road, Perth
Perthshire PH2 8DG
Tel: 01738 472032
Fax: 01738 472033
www.atlanticsalmontrust.org
director@atlanticsalmontrust.org

Barbel Society
Membership Secretary
1 Larchwood, Castlegate,
Scotforth, Lancaster LA1 4QG
www.barbelsociety.co.uk

Bass Anglers' Sportfishing Society (BASS)
Frank Whittingham
Shawe Cottage
Shawe
Kingsley Holt
Cheadle
Staffordshire ST10 2DL
www.ukbass.com

British Conger Club
Mrs Diana Byrne
2 Drake Court
264 Citadel Road
Plymouth
Devon PL1 2PY
Tel: 01752 223815
www.britishcongerclub.org.uk
(Affiliated with ninety eight sea
angling clubs)

British Disabled Angling Association
Terry Moseley
9 Yew Tree Road
Delves, Walsall
West Midlands WS5 4NQ
Tel: 01922 860 912
terry@bdaa.co.uk
www.bdaa.co.uk

British Record (rodcaught)
Fish Committee
Secretary: David Rowe
BRFC
Eastwood House
6 Rainbow Street
Leominster
Herefordshire HR6 8DQ
www.anglingtrust.net
brfc@anglingtrust.net

British Trout Assn
The Rural Centre
West Mains, Ingliston
Midlothian EH28 8NZ
Scotland
Tel: +44 (0)0131 472 4080
Fax: +44 (0)0131 472 4083
www.britishtrout.co.uk
Office@britishtrout.co.uk

English Youth Flyfishing Association
Bobbie Worker
EYFA Secretary
www.eyfa.co.uk

British Waterways HQ
Fisheries Department
510-524 Elder House
Elder Gate, Central Milton Keynes
MK9 1BW
Tel: 01908 302556
Fax: 01908 302510
www.fisheries.co.uk
www.waterscape.com
enquiries.southeast@
britishwaterways.co.uk

Fish Health Inspectorate
Cefas Weymouth Laboratory
The Nothe
Barrack Road
Weymouth
Dorset DT4 8UB
Tel: 01305 206700
fhi@cefas.co.uk
www.cefas.co.uk

Confederation of English Fly Fishers
(recognised authority on competitive
flyfishing in England)
Hon Sec: Malcolm Price
23 Smithson Close
Talbot Village
Poole
Dorset BH12 5EY
Tel: 01202 537321
Mob: 07754 091923
www.ceff.org.uk

Countryside Alliance
Robert Gray
367 Kennington Road
London SE11 4PT
Tel: 0207 840 9200
Fax: 0207 793 8899
www.countrysidealliance.org.uk
info@countrysidealliance.org

English Carp Heritage Organisation
16 The Parade
Reading Road
Yateley
Hampshire GU46 7UN
Tel: 01252 861955
echocarp@hotmail.com
www.echocarp.co.uk

European Fishing Tackle Trade Association
Unit 2i Ashley Works,
25 Ashley Road,
Tottenham Hale,
London N17 9LJ
Tel: 020 8365 0405
info@eftta.com
www.eftta.com

The Flydressers Guild
A. Middleton
Chairman
Wor Yem
Blackgate Lane
Henfield BN5 9HA
Tel: 0796 4961834
www.the-fdg.org

Freshwater Biological Assn
The Director
The Ferry Landing
Far Sawrey, Ambleside
Cumbria LA22 0LP
Tel: 015394 42468
Fax: 015394 46914
www.fba.org.uk
info@fba.org.uk

Grayling Society
Mike Tebbs, Membership Secretary
Tel: 01985 841192
miketebbs@btinternet.com
www.graylingsociety.net

Game & Wildlife Conservation Trust
Burgate Manor
Fordingbridge
Hampshire SP6 1EF
Tel: 01425 652381
info@gwct.org.uk
www.gwct.org.uk

Pike Fly Fishing Association
PFFA Membership Secretary
401 Fordgreen Road, Norton
Stoke on Trent
Staffs ST6 8LX
www.pffa.co.uk

International Fly Fishing Assn
Ian Campbell, Secretary & Treasurer
Cruachan
16 Marindin Park
Glenfarg
Perth & Kinross PH2 9NQ
Tel: 01577 830582
iffa@glenfarg.com
www.iffa.net

Marine Biological Assn of the United Kingdom
The Secretary
The Laboratory
Citadel Hill
Plymouth PL1 2PB
Tel: 01752 633100
Fax: 01752 633102
www.mba.ac.uk
sec@mba.ac.uk

Pike Anglers' Club of Great Britain
memberships@pacgb.co.uk
www.pacgb.co.uk

The River Restoration Centre
Cranfield University
Building 53
Cranfield
Bedfordshire MK43 0AL
Tel: 01234 752979
rrc@therrc.co.uk
www.therrc.co.uk

Riverfly Partnership
Fishmongers' Hall
London Bridge
London
EC4R 9EL
Tel: 020 7929 6966
info@riverflies.org
www.riverflies.org

Salmon & Trout Assn
Paul Knight, CEO
Fishmongers' Hall
London Bridge
London EC4R 9EL
Tel: 020 7283 5838
www.salmon-trout.org
hq@salmon-trout.org

Shark Angling Club of Great Britain
Linda Reynolds
Middletons Corner
The Quay
East Looe
Cornwall PL13 1AH
Tel: 01503 262642
sharkanglingclubofgreatbritain.org.uk

**Stillwater Trout
Fisheries' Association**
Packington Fisheries
Meriden
Coventry
West Midlands CV7 7HR
Tel/Fax: 01676 522754
www.troutfisheries.co.uk

Wheelyboat Trust (The)
Director: Andy Beadsley
North Lodge
Burton Park
Petworth
West Sussex GU28 0JT
Tel/Fax: 01798 342222
www.wheelyboats.org

Wild Trout Trust (The)
P O Box 120
Waterlooville
Hants PO8 0WZ
Tel/fax: 023 9257 0985
office@wildtrout.org
www.wildtrout.org

Young James Lavell with a 25lb 5oz carp
Photo: Ian Gemson

FISHING CLUBS

Abingdon & Oxford Anglers Alliance
(alliance of Abingdon & Dist ARA,
Clifton Hampden & Dist PS and
Oxford APS)
R Bateman
16 The Gap
Marcham
Oxon OX13 6NJ
Tel: 01865 391809

Accrington New Anglers
Brian Stevens
15 Windsor Avenue
Church
nr Accrington
Lancashire BB5 6LN
Tel: 01254 871370

Addingham Angling Assn
M Rowe
120 Main Street
Addingham LS29 0NS
Tel: 01943 830153

Aln Angling Assn
Les Jobson
2 Queens Road
Alnwick NE66 1RB
Tel: 01665 605083

Alston & District Angling Assn
Ken Little
Treasurer
Angel Inn
Alston CA9 3HU
Tel: 01434 381363

Altrincham & District Angling Club
John Deas
111 Hoylake Rd
Sale
Cheshire M33 2XJ
Tel: 0161 969 7475
www.bagup.org.uk

Alveston Village Angling Club
Mark Pitcher
62 Avon Crescent
Stratford upon Avon CV37 7EZ
Tel: 01789 268110
www.avaac.co.uk

**Amalgamated Fisheries Ltd
(formerly BB&WAA)**
John and Pat Leonard
48 Abbots Road
Hanham
Bristol BS15 3NG
Tel: 0117 9603378
www.amalgamatedfisheriesltd.co.uk

**Ampthill Angling & Fish
Preservation Society**
Dick Ward
15 Kingfisher Road
Flitwick
Beds MK45 1RA
Tel: 01525 751850
www.ampthillac.org

Amwell Magna Fishery
Est 1841.
(The Oldest Fishing Club in Britain)
River Lea
Hertfordshire
www.amwellmagnafishery.org

**Appletreewick, Barden & Burnsall
Angling Club**
Bryan Ayton
8 Park Crescent
Embsay
Skipton
North Yorkshire BD23 6PB
Tel: 01756 791625

**Army and Navy Club Fly Fishers
Association**
Col Charles Bone
Tel: 01962 864921
charles.bone@ntlworld.com

Ashford Angling Society
  Memb Sec: Mick Ladley
  46 Alfred Road
  Ashford TN24 0PH
  Tel: 01233 627813

**Association of Teesside & District
Angling Clubs**
  (Thornaby AA, Yarm AA,
  Darlington Brown Trout Anglers and
  Stockton AL)
  George Coulson
  5 Grange Avenue
  Hurworth Place
  Darlington
  Co Durham DL2 2HE
  Tel: 01325 720 246

Astwood Bank Angling Club
  Nigel Hill
  Tel: 01527 458081
  www.astwoodbankac.co.uk

Avon Angling Club
  Percy Edwards
  56 Addison Road
  Melksham
  Wilts SN12 8DR
  Tel: 01225 705036

Avon Fishing Assn (Devon)
  Brian Dent
  Aune Bank
  Avonwick
  South Brent TQ10 9NB
  Tel: 01364 73274

Avon & Tributaries Angling Assn
  Rob Whish
  Membership Secretary
  robwhish@yahoo.co.uk
  www.ataafishing.net

Aylsham & District Angling Club
  K Sutton
  17 Town Lane
  Aylsham
  Norfolk NR11 6HH
  Tel: 01263 732433

Banbury & District Angling Assn
  Brian Syde: Treasurer
  17 Timms Road
  Banbury
  Oxon OX16 9DL
  Tel: 01295 253068
  or
  Brian Clarke (bookings)
  Tel: 01295 265212

**Barnsley & District
AmalgamatedAnglers' Society**
  Tony Eaton
  60 Walton Street
  Gawber, Barnsley
  Yorks S75 2PD
  Tel: 01226 203090

Barnstaple & District Angling Assn
  S Toms
  Upcott Farm
  Brayford
  N Devon EX32 7QA
  Tel: 01598 710857

Barnt Green Fishing Club
  Hon Sec
  c/o The Keeper
  Keeper's Cottage
  Cofton Church Lane
  Barnt Green
  Worcs B45 8BW
  Tel: 0121 445 1226

Barrow Angling Assn
  Keith Rodger
  25 Thorncliffe Road
  Barrow-in-Furness
  Cumbria LA14 5PZ
  Tel: 01229 836986

Basingstoke Canal Angling Assn
  Jeff Bunch
  2 Wentworth Close
  Ash Vale
  Aldershot GU12 5NB
  Tel: 01252 326421
  www.basingstokecanalaa.co.uk

Bathampton Angling Assn
D Crookes
25 Otago Terrace
Larkhall
Bath
Avon BA1 6SX
Tel: 01225 427164
www.bathampton.org

Bay Malton Angling Club
Stewart Godber
Secretary
P.O. Box 646
Broadheath
Altrincham WA14 5YZ
www.baymaltonanglingclub.org.uk

Bedford Angling Club
Mrs M E Appleton
18 Moriston Road
Bedford
Beds MK41 7UG
Tel: 01234 354708

Bedlington & Blagdon Angling Assn
D Symons, Chairman
26 Ridley Ave
Blyth NE24 3BB
Tel: 01670 356539

Belper & District Angling Club
Paul Spencer
35 Field Lane
Belper
Derbys
Tel: 01773 825197

Bembridge (IOW) Angling Club
Peter Knight
North Quay
St Helens
Isle of Wight PO35 1YU
Tel: 01983 875030 (club)
Tel: 07966 538319 (Hon Sec)

Benson & District Angling Club
D Cook
24 The Cedars
Benson
Wallingford
Oxon OX10 6LL
Tel: 01491 834540

Berkhamsted & District Angling Society
P Welling
1 South Park Gardens
Berkhamsted
Herts HP4 1JA
Mob: 07907 022290
Tel: 01442 875106
www.berkhamstedangling.co.uk

Bewl Bridge Flyfishers Club
John Hancock
Trodgers Way
Little Trodgers Lane
Mayfield
TN20 6PN
Tel: 01435 872171
www.bewlbridgeflyfishers.co uk

Biggleswade, Hitchin Angling Assn Ltd
Anthony Pogmore, membership sec
147 Mead End
Biggleswade SG18 8JX
Tel: 01767 223147
www.bighitaa.co.uk

Billericay and District Angling Club
Fred Barnes
General secretary
Tel: 0844 335 3978 (9 to 9pm only)
secretary@bdac.co.uk
www.bdac.co.uk

Billingshurst Angling Society
Peter Stockwood
School House
Billingshurst
W Sussex RH14 9RX
Tel: 01403 782160
www.billingshurstas.co.uk

Birmingham Anglers' Assn Ltd
John Williams
106 Icknield Port Road
Rotton Park
Birmingham B16 0AA
Tel: 0121 454 9111
www.baa.uk.com
baajnw@btinternet.com
(9.30am to 2pm Monday to Friday)

**Bishop Auckland & District Angling
Club Ltd**
Don Lodge
6 Redworth Grove
Bishop Auckland DL14 8QP
Tel: 01388 603158
www.bishopaucklanddistrictanglingc
lub.co.uk

Blackmoss Fishing Assn
John Dateson
23 Grove Street
Barrowford
Lancs BB9 8PW
Tel: 01282 697500

Blandford & District Angling Club
Peter Brundish
10 Windmill Road
Blandford
Dorset DT11 7HG
Tel: 01258 453545

Blenheim Angling Society
F W Lancaster
Briarwood, Burtons Lane
Chalfont St Giles
Bucks HP8 4BB
Tel: 01494 764977
www.blenheimas.co.uk

Blunham & District Angling Club
(affiliated to the Ivel Protection
Association)
Graham Palmer
5 Brockwell
Oakley
Beds MK43 7TD
Tel: 01234 823959
www.blunhamac.co.uk

Bodmin Anglers' Assn
Hon Sec: Ivan Lyne
Ivy Cottage
Dunmere
Bodmin PL31 2RD
or
Roger's Tackle Shop
Stan May's Store
Higher Bore Str
Bodmin PL31 1DZ
Tel: 01208 78006
www.bodminaa.bravehost.com

Bolton & District Angling Assn
Terence A McKee
1 Lever Edge Lane
Great Lever
Bolton, Lancs BL3 3BU
Tel: 01204 393726

**Boroughbridge & District Angling
Club**
c/o M Burgess
No 1 Bungalow
Littlethorpe Rd
Ripon
N Yorks HG4 1TZ
Tel: 01765 690715

Boston Spa Angling Club
Dennis Fish
284 High Street
Boston Spa
Wetherby LS23 6AS
Tel: 01937 849624

Bottesford & District Angling Assn
Brian Cross
12 The Square
Bottesford
Notts NG13 0EY
Tel: 01949 843164

Bowland Game Fishing Assn
David Pilling
Mob: 0781 5504162
or
Roy Freeman
Membership Secretary
Tel: 01253 882156

Boston & District Angling Assn
(Affiliated local clubs: Lincolnshire
Disabled Anglers, Fishtoft AC,
Fenland Pike Club, Louth & Dist AC,
RAF Coningsby AC, Sibsey AC,
Stickney AC)
Mrs Barbara Clifton
13 Brand End Road
Butterwick
Boston
Lincs PE22 0ET
Tel: 01205 760666
or
Barry Mallet
Match Secretary
Tel: 01205 871815
www.bostonanglingassoc.co.uk

Boxmoor & District Angling Society
Mike Heylin
41 Crofts Path
Leverstock Green
Hemel Hempstead
Herts HP3 8HB
Tel: 01442 398022
www.bdas.org

Bradford No 1 Angling Assn
Ticket & Licence
John Sparks
14 Raglan St
Queensbury
Bradford BD13 1AG
Tel: 01274 421786
or
Hon Sec. H M Foster
8 Micklethwaite Drive
Queensbury
Bradford BD13 2JZ
Tel: 01274 881851
www.bradfordno1.com

Bradford City Angling Assn
M Briggs
4 Brownhill Close
Birkinshaw BD11 2AS
Tel: 01274 684906
www.bradfordcityaa.co.uk

Brampton (Cambs) Angling Society
Kevin Medlock
1 Stanch Hill Rd
Sawtry, Huntingdon
Cambs PE28 5XG
Tel: 01487 830984

Brampton Angling Society
Bill Candeland
The Beeches
Moorthwaite
Cumwhitton
Brampton
Cumbria CA8 9HB
Tel: 01228 560916
www.bramptonangling.plus.com

Brandon & District Angling Club
Paul Macloughlin
43 The Paddocks
Brandon
Suffolk IP27 0DY
01842 812979

Bridgwater Angling Assn
Andy Danahy
127 Old Basin
Somerset Bridge
Bridgwater
Somerset TA6 6LJ
Tel: 01278 457022
www.bridgwaterangling.co.uk

Brighouse Angling Assn
Clive Milson
Mob: 0775 968 2526
www.brighouseangling.co.uk
or (tickets)
c/o Calder Anglers Supplies
39a Rastrick Common
Rastrick
Brighouse
Huddersfield HD6 3DW
Tel: 01484 711063
www.calderanglerssupplies.co.uk

Bristol & West of England Federation of Anglers
B Lloyd
386 Speedwell Road
By Kingswood
Bristol BS15 1ES
Tel: 0117 9676030
brianlloyd386@btinternet.com

Brixham Sea Anglers' Society
Mike Bailey
5 Deep Dene Close
Brixham
Devon TQ5 0DZ
Tel: 01803 853252

Broome Angling Society
A Smith
10 Lords Avenue
Benskins Croft
Leicester LE4 2HX
Tel: 0116 2357210
alan.smith@broomeanglingsociety.co.uk
www.broomeanglingsociety.co.uk

Brunswick Brothers Angling Society
Terry Taylor
40 St Andrews Road
Cranbrook
Ilford IG1 3PF
Tel: 020 8554 4600

Buckingham & District AnglingAssn
Bernard Lewis
38 Queen Catherine Road
Steeple Claydon
Buckingham MK18 2PY
Tel: 01296 730702
www.bdaafishing.org.uk

Bude Canal Angling Assn
Brian Powell
B R Auto Spares
The Strand
Bude
Cornwall EX23 8RA
Tel: 01288 352755

Burnley Angling Society
Hon Sec: Alan Bell
5 Hill Crest Avenue
Burnley BB10 4JA
Tel: 01282 424178
or
via Roggerham Gate Inn
Todmorden Road
Brierclisse
Burnley BB10 3PQ
Tel: 01282 422039

Burton-upon-Trent Mutual Angling Assn
D J Clark
7 Denton Rise
BurtononTrent
Staffordshire DE13 0QB
Tel: 01283 544734
www.burtonmutual.co.uk

Burwash Fishing Club
J Deeley
Red Tiles
Straight Mile
Etchingham TN19 7BA
Tel: 01580 819298

Bury St Edmunds Angling Assn
David Plampin
Brooklyn House
1 Mill Road
Honington
Bury St Edmunds
Suffolk
Tel: 01359 269163

Caersws Angling Assn
Secretary
Mr Rob Davis
Tel: 01686 688843
www.caersws-aa.co.uk

Calne Angling Assn
Miss J M Knowler
c/o T K Tackle
123A London Road
Calne
Wiltshire SN11 0AQ
Tel: 01249 812003

Cambridge Albion Angling Society
Mr Terry Easey
Secretary
9 Fairbairn Road
Cambridge
CB4 1UG
Tel: 01223 424248
www.cambridgealbionas.moonfruit.com

Cambridge Fish Preservation and Angling Society
G Tweed
27A Villa Road
Impington
Cambridge
Cambs CB4 9NZ
Tel: 01223 234616 (before 8pm).
www.cambridge-fpas.co.uk

Cambridge Izaak Walton Society
T J Sawyer
6 Pump Lane
Hardwick
Cambs CB3 7QW

Canterbury & District Angling Assn
R D Barton
Riversdale
14 Mill Road
Sturry, Canterbury
Kent CT2 0AF
Tel: 01227 710830
www.cdaa.co.uk
enquiries@cdaa.co.uk

Carlisle Angling Assn
David Altham
13 Punton Road
Carlisle CA3 9BB
Tel: 01228 532666
www.carlisleanglingassociation.org

Castle Angling Assn
Sharon Tansley
4 Hereward Road
Far Cotton
Northampton NN4 8NP
Tel: 01604 764497

Central Assn of London & Provincial Angling Clubs (CALPAC)
Malcolm MilfordScott
316 Old Lodge Lane
Purley
Surrey CR8 4AQ
Tel: 020 8645 6820 (not after 8pm)
www.calpac.info

Chard & District Angling Assn
Alan Gage
Secretary
C/o Barrons Tackle
2 Holyrood Street
Chard
Somerset
Tel: 01460 63593
www.chardanddistrictanglingclub.co.uk

Cheddar Angling Club
Mr R Heard
P O Box 1183
Cheddar,
Somerset
BS27 3LT
Tel: 07796 990205
www.cheddaranglingclub.co.uk

Chelmsford Angling Assn
Membership Secretary
11 Barbrook Lane
Tiptree
Essex CO5 0EE
Mob: 07840 881970
www.chelmsfordaa.co.uk

Chester-le-Street & District Angling Club
G Curry
62 Newcastle Road
ChesterleStreet
Co Durham DH3 3UF
Tel: 0191 388 7072
www.chester-le-streetanglingclub.co.uk

Chichester & District Angling Society
Mr Patrick Loten
07712 581696
www.chichester-as.co.uk

Chichester Ship Canal Trust
Linda Wilkinson1
Chidham Lane
Chidham
Chichester
West Sussex PO18 8TL
Tel: 01243 576701
www.chichestercanal.org.uk

Chippenham Angling Club
S. Wade
c/o Premier Angling
19, New Road
Chippenham
Wiltshire SN15 1HT
www.chippenhamac.org.uk

Christchurch Angling Club
Graham Newton, Secretary
21D Magnolia House
19-21 Stour Road
Christchurch
Hants BH23 1PL
Tel: 01202 480009
www.christchurchac.org.uk

Clanfield Angling Club
Doug Foreshew
117 Farmers Close
Witney
Oxon OX28 1NR
Tel: 01993 200371

Clevedon & District Freshwater Angling Club
Bob Newton
clevedon-fwac@virginmedia.com
www.clevedon-fwac.webs.com
(see North Somerset AA)

Clitheroe Angling Assn
David Rawkins
The Spinney
Grindleton
Clitheroe BB7 4QE
Tel: 01200 440870

Clive Vale Angling Club
Kevin Thornley
Hastings
East Sussex
www.clivevaleac.co.uk

Cobham Court Angling Club
R.G. Billingham
Secretary
www.cobhamcourtac.co.uk

Cockermouth Angling Assn
Sue Moses
8 Riverdale Drive
Cockermouth CA13 9EL
Tel: 01900 824798

Colchester Angling Preservation Society
Mr Mick Turner
29 Lodge Road
Braintree
Essex CM7 1JA
membership@Colchesteraps.org
www.colchesteraps.org

Colchester Piscatorial Society
R J Moore
66 The Willows
Colchester
Essex CO2 8PX

Collingham Angling Assn
June Wilson
93 Breamer Road
Collingham
nr Newark
Notts NG23 7PN
Tel: 01636 892700
www.collinghamaa.co.uk

Colnes Angling Society
Paul Empson
16 Station Road
Earls Colne
Colne Engaine
Colchester
Essex CO6 2ES
Tel: 01787 223331

Colne Water Angling Club
Membership Secretary
Mrs Janis Counsell
Tel: 01254-883395
www.colnewaterangling.club.officeli
ve.com

Colwick Flyfishers
Rob Haywood
The Hollies
PO Box 6226
Nottingham NG5 4WZ
www.colwickffc.org

Congleton Angling Society
c/o Smith's Bait & Tackle
44 Lawton Street
Congleton
Cheshire CW12 1RU
Tel: (01260) 273770
www.congleton-anglers.co.uk

Coopers Angling Club
John Dickens
2 Witchford Rd
Ely
Cambs CB6 3DP
Tel: 01353 663398

Copthorne & District Angling Society
General Secretary
40 Fairfield Avenue
Horley
Surrey RH6 7PD
Richamp@aol.com
www.copthorneangling.co.uk

Cotterstock Angling Assn
Mrs Margaret Wing
Manor Farm Cottage
Cotterstock
Peterborough PE8 5HD
Tel: 01832 226340

Coventry & District Angling Assn
A Hyde
1 Oak Tree Avenue
Green Lane
Coventry CV3 6DG

**Cranbrook & District Angling Club
(affiliated to Rother Fisheries Assn)**
Dave Sherwood
P O Box 18
Cranbrook
Kent TN17 3ZL
Tel: 07917 307942
www.cranbrookanglingclub.co.uk

Crediton Fly Fishing Club
Mike Willis
mikewillis@fly-fishing-club.co.uk
www.fly-fishing-club.co.uk

Danby Angling Club
F Farrow
11 Dale End
Danby
Whitby
N Yorkshire YO21 2JF

Darley Dale Fly Fishers Club
www.ddffc.net

Darlington Anglers Club
John Leighton
44 Low Coniscliffe
Darlington DL2 2JY
Tel: 01325 287307
www.darlingtonac.co.uk

Darlington Brown Trout Angling Assn
E Willans
28 Dundee Street
Darlington DL1 JTX
Tel: 07960 999441

Darlington Fly Fishers' Club
R. Watson
Stone House
Vicar's Lane
Manfield
Darlington DL2 2RF
www.darlingtonflyfishers.com

Dart Angling Assn
Philip Prowse
2 School Cottages
StokeinTeignhead
Newton Abbot
Devon TQ12 4QE
Tel: 01626 872434
www.dartaa.org.uk

**Dartford & District Angling &
Preservation Society**
Darren Fellows
Lake House
2 Walnut Tree Avenue
Wilmington
Kent DA1 1LJ
Tel: 01322 270397
www.ddaps.org

Dartmouth Angling & BoatingAssn
Mrs Joan Porter
Flat 6
Thomas Newcomen Court
Dartmouth
Devon TQ6 9FT
Tel: 01803 835830

Darwen Anglers' Assn
F W Kendall
45 Holden Fold
Darwen
Lancashire BB3 3AU
Tel: 01254 775501

Deal & Walmer Angling Assn
Mrs D Pettit
108 Blenheim Road
Deal CT14 7EY
Tel: 01304 365617

**Deal & Walmer Inshore Fishermen's
Assn**
Dave Harris
Tel: 01304 362703

**Deanshanger & The Stratfords
Angling Assn**
T Valentine
34 Mallets Close
Stony Stratford
Milton Keynes MK11 1DQ
Tel: 01908 565446

Deeping St James Angling Club
Ray Gregory, Match Angling Sec
Tel: 01780 721936

Derbyshire Angling Federation
Steve Clifton
8 Damside, Belper
Derbys DE56 1HZ
Tel: 01773 821582
or
P O Box 5602
Ripley DE5 3ZR

Derby Railway Angling Club
Mr R. Anderson
22, Shirley Park
Aston on Trent
Derby
DE72 2AP
Tel: 01332 792807
secretary@drac.org.uk
www.drac.org.uk

Derbyshire County Angling Club
David T Holmes
12 Bakers Hill
Heage, Belper
Derbys DE56 2BL
Tel: 07790 825347
www.derbyshirecountyac.org.uk

Dereham & District Angling Club
Mr J. Mills
Club Secretary
Tel: 07876 563378
www.ddac.info

Doncaster & District Angling Assn
Martin Warne
59 Broughton Avenue
Bentley
Doncaster DN5 9QS
Mob: 07771 986849
www.ddaa.co.uk

Dorchester & District Angling Society
Mr Steve Crowford
Membership Secretary
40 Melcombe Ave
Greenhill
Weymouth
Dorset DT4 7TF
www.d-das.com

Dorchester Fishing Club
Richard Miller
richard@grhe.co.uk
www.grhe.co.uk

Dorking & District Angling Soc
Brian Burgess
secretary@dorkingas.co.uk
c/o S C Fuller Fishing Tackle
28/32 South St
Dorking RH4 2HQ
Tel: 01306 882177
www.dorkingas.co.uk

Dulverton Angling Association
Lance Nicholson
9 High Str
Dulverton TA22 9HB
Tel: 01398 323409
www.lancenich.co.uk

Durham City Angling Club
Mr J Hepworth
Membership Sec.
PO Box No 508
Durham City DH1 9BP
Tel: 0191 386 6000
www.durhamanglers.co.uk

Earl Manvers Angling Assn
G R Dennis
11 First Avenue
Carlton
Nottingham NG4 1PH
Tel: 0115 987 9994

Earls Barton Angling Club
R Line, Treasurer
9 New Street
Earls Barton
Northampton NN6 0NN
Tel: 01604 812059

East Hastings Sea Angling Association
The Stade
Hastings
East Sussex TN34 3PZ
Tel: 01424 430230

Eastbourne Angling Assn
The Club House
Royal Parade
Eastbourne
East Sussex BN22 7AA
Tel: 01323 723442
www.eastbourneanglingclub.com

Eastleigh & District Angling Club
c/o Home Stores Tackle
68 High Road
Swaythling
Southampton SO16 2HZ
Tel: 023 8055 1974
www.edac.org.uk
jgc@ecs.soton.ac.uk

Edenbridge Angling Society
H Fennell
22 Church Lane
Copthorne
W Sussex RH10 3PT
Tel: 01342 713519
www.edenbridge-angling.co.uk

Egremont & District Angling Assn
Permit Sec: Neil Thompson
The Hatchery
Little Mill
Egremont
Cumbria CA22 2PR
Tel: 01946 823778

Ellesmere Angling Club
Kevan Busby
7 Penda's Park
Penley
Wrexham LL13 0NN
Tel: 01948 830695
Or Comrades Club (1st Thur of
month from 8pm)
8 Victoria Street
Ellesmere SY12 0AB
Tel: 01691 622419

Elm Park & Hornchurch District Angling Society
Mr. P. Anderson
23 Becket Close
Warley Brentwood
Essex CM13 3BU
Tel: 01277 210024
www.ephdas.co.uk

Ely Beet Sports & Social Club Angling Club
Dave Newman
Lynn Rd
Ely
Cambs. CB6 1DD
Tel: 01353 662029

Errwood Fly Fishing Club
Ian Gould
Honorary Secretary
7 New Market Street
Buxton
Derbyshire
SK17 6LP
Tel: 07798 906 701
www.effc.co.uk

Evesham & District Angling Assn
Howard Norledge
50 Coronation Street
Evesham
Worcs WR11 3DB
Tel: 01386 47776

Exeter & District Angling Assn
Roly Palmer
4 Diamond Road
City Industrial
Exeter EX2 8DN
Tel: 01392 668935
www.exeteranglingassociation.co.uk

Fakenham Angling Club
G Twite
16 Back Street
Hempton, Fakenham
Norfolk NR21 7LR

Farnborough & District Angling Society
Dave Cassell
102 Park Road
Farnborough
Hants GU14 6LT
Tel: 01252 511533
Mob: 0784 0627 986
www.fadas.org

Farnham Angling Society
M J Borra
The Creel
36 Station Road
Aldershot
Hants GU11 1HT
Tel: 01252 320871
www.farnhamanglingsociety.com

Faversham Angling Club
Nick Prior
1C St Nicholas Road
Faversham
Kent ME13 7PG
Tel: 01795 590824
www.favershamanglingclub.com

Felixstowe Sea Angling Society
End Manor Terrace
Felixstowe
Suffolk IP11 8EL
secretary@fsas.org.uk
www.fsas.org.uk

Feltham Piscatorials
Membership Secretary
kevin.compton@btconnect.com
www.felthampiscatorials.co.uk

Fenton & District Angling Society
Clifford Yates
5 Gatley Grove
Meir Park
Stoke-on-Trent
Staffs ST3 7SH
Tel: 01782 396913

Ferryhill & District Angling Club
A Lowery
P O Box 87
Ferryhill DL16 9AE
Tel: c/o 01740 652360
admin@ferryhillangling.co.uk
www.ferryhillangling.co.uk

Filey Brigg Angling Society
President: Mr Pete Watson
Chairman: Mr Adrian Colling
Hon Treasurer: Mr James Haxby
www.fileybrigganglingsociety. co.uk

Fishing For Everyone
Lucy Bowden
Po Box 82
Alnwick
Northumberland NE66 9AD
Tel: 07890519392
info@fishingforeveryone.com
www.fishingforeveryone.com

Flyfishers' Club
Antony Pinsent
President
69 Brook Street
London WIK 4ER
Tel: 020 7629 5958
www.flyfishersclub.org.uk
(Private members club, no fishery)

Framlingham & District Angling Club
Mrs M Wood
34 Simons Cross
Wickham Market
Woodbridge
Suffolk IP13 0ST
Tel: 01728 746929
margaretwood34@yahoo.co.uk

Gillingham & District Angling Assn
Simon Hebditch
8 Maple Way
Gillingham
Dorset SP8 4RR
Tel: 01747 821218
www.theanglingclub.net

Gipping Angling Preservation Society
Richard Young
126 Valley Road
Ipswich
Suffolk IP1 4PA
Tel: 01473 222240
www.gippingaps.co.uk

Godalming Angling Society
M R Richardson
87 Summers Road
Farncombe, Godalming
Surrey GU7 3BE
Tel: 01483 422791
www.godalminganglingsociety. co.uk

Godmanchester Angling & Fish Preservation Society
S J Binge, Match Secretary
7 Old Court Hall
Godmanchester PE29 2HS
Tel: 01480 453303

Gosforth Angler's Club
G Thomas
11 Fell View Park
Gosforth
Seascale
Cumbria CA20 1HY
Tel: 019467 25367

Gloucester Angling Club
 Richard Mander
 Secretary
 171 Tuffley Avenue
 Gloucester GL1 5NR
 Tel: 0771 5326568
 richmander@blueyonder.co.uk
 www.gloucesteranglingclub.co.uk

Grafton Angling Assn
 G D Williams
 9 Edward Street
 Worksop
 Notts S80 1QP

Grantham Angling Assn
 (a member of East Midlands Angling
 Federation that includes Boston,
 Oakham, Newark, Ashfordby,
 Deeping St James)
 J. Mawhood
 Tel: 01476 568533
 www.granthamaa.co.uk
 jeff@granthamaa.co.uk

Great Yarmouth & Norfolk County Angling Assn
 K Ford
 2 Parana Road
 Sprowston
 Norwich NR7 8BG
 Tel: 01603 483923

Guernsey Mullet Club
 M Weysom
 La Cachette
 6 Clos des Caches
 St Martin
 Guernsey GY4 6PL
 Tel: 01481 237678

Hadleigh & District Angling Society
 D George
 10 Garrards Rd
 Elmsett
 Ipswich
 Suffolk IP7 6NB

Haltwhistle & District Angling Assn
 David Stobbart
 Heatherlea
 Park Road
 Haltwhistle
 Northumberland NE49 9BP
 Tel: 01434 321858

Harleston, Wortwell & District Angling Club
 Nigel Poll: Match Secretary
 Tel: 01379 853571
 www.harlestonanglingclub.co.uk

Hartlepool & Dist Angling Club
 P L Arrowsmith
 c/o Anglers Services Fishing Tackle
 27 Park Road
 Hartlepool TS24 7PW
 Tel: 01429 274844
 www.hadac.co.uk

Harwich Angling Club
 Laurie Snell
 The Old Thatched Cottage
 Stones Green Road
 Tendring
 Essex CO16 0DD
 Tel: 01255 870312
 Mob: 07791 752315
 www.harwichac.co.uk

Haslingden & District Fly Fishing Club
 W Monk
 6 Ryde Close
 Haslingden
 Rossendale BB4 6QR
 Tel: 01706 211724

Hastings & St Leonards AnglingAssn
 Marine Parade
 Hastings
 East Sussex TN34 3AG
 Tel: 01424 431923/430120

Hastings, Bexhill & District Freshwater Angling Assn
Alan Carter
156 Ninfield Road
Bexhill-on-Sea TN39 5BD
Tel: 01424 223234

Hastings Flyfishers' Club Ltd
Mrs Mary Stacey
3 Valleyside Road
Hastings TN23 5AD
Tel: 01424 439 633
www.hastingsflyfishers.co.uk

Hawes & High Abbotside Angling Assn
Jennifer Dinsdale
Brough Side
Bainbridge
North Yorks DL8 3EG
Tel: 01969 650304

Hawkshead Angling Club
Emma Macintosh on 015394 36116
email alex@garishglobes.co.uk
Residents only
Limited to 100 members; 20 juniors)

Hay-on-Wye Fishermen's Assn
B Wigington
Flat 2, Pembertons
4 High Town
Hay-on-Wye
Herefords HR3 5AE

Haywards Heath & District Angling Society
Jim Ford
8 Newton Close
Lindfield
West Sussex RH16 2NE
Tel: 0794 757 1699
www.hhdas.com

Hebden Bridge Angling Club
Keith Marshall, Membership
Secretary
62 Mixenden Road
Mixenden
Tel: 01422 243331
john.marshall63@btinternet.com

Helperby & Brafferton Angling Club
F Marrison
Gardener's Cottage
Helperby, York
North Yorks YO6 2PQ
Tel: 01423 360632

Hereford & District Angling Assn
P O Box 35
Hereford
or
Woody's Angling Centre
67 Whitecross Road
Hereford HR4 0DQ
Tel: 01432 344644

Herne Bay Angling Assn
Honorary Secretary
c/o HQ, 59 Central Parade
Herne Bay
Kent CT6 5JG
Tel: 01227 362127
www.herne-bay-angling.com

Hertford Angling Club
Chris Bite
12 Stafford Drive
Broxbourne
Herts EN10 7JT
Tel: 01992 467585

Histon & District Angling Society
Colin Dodd
122 Rampton Road
Willingham
Cambs CB4 5JF
Tel: 07773 719330
www.histonangling.org.uk

Holmesdale Angling & ConservationSociety
David Payne
98 Homefield Drive
Orpington
Kent BR6 0RW
Mob: 07802 157631
www.holmesdale.acs.btinternet.co.uk

Holme Valley Piscatorial Assn
c/o Chris Roberts Fishing Tackle
22 Chapel Hill
Huddersfield HD1 3EB
Tel: 01484 545032

Horncastle Angling Club
Lorraine Hassall
21 Low Toynton Road
Horncastle
Lincs LN9 5LL
Tel: 01507 527420

Horsham & District Angling Assn
PO Box 22
Horsham
West Sussex RH12 2YT
www.hdaa.co.uk
or
G Hillman (address as above)
Tel: 01403 271885

Horwich & District Fly Fishing Club
Patricia Unsworth
4 Old Swan Close
Egerton
Bolton
Lancs BL7 9UW
Tel: 01204 591905

Hove Deep Sea Anglers
Western Esplanade
Portslade
Hove BN41 1WE
Tel: 01273 413000
www.hovedeepseaanglers.co.uk

Hull & District Anglers' Assn
Jason Dickinson
3 Fairfax Drive
Hedon
Hull HU12 8PF
Mob: 079385 61245
www.hdaafishing.co.uk

Huntingdon Angling & Fish Preservation Society
Miss Anne M Wallis
8 Clayton's Way
Huntingdon
Cambs PE29 1UT
Tel: 01480 458935

Huttons Ambo Angling Club
Paul Thompson
Firby Hall
Firby
Yorks YO6 7LH

Idle & Thackley AnglingAssn
Charles Taylor Hardaker
24 Park Avenue
Thackley
Bradford
West Yorks BD10 0RJ
Tel: 01274 615016
www.idleandthackaa.supanet.com

Ilkley & Dist Angling Assn
B Moore
6 North Croft Grove
Ilkley LS29 9BB
Tel: 01943 604653
www.ilkleyanglingassociation.co uk

Invicta Fly Fishing Club
Alan Prevost
5 Willingham Road.
Over Cambridge CB24 5PD
Tel: 01954 230678
alan@prevost.net
www.invictaffc.org.uk

Isle of Man Fly Fishers
Ray Caley: President
Sulby Stores
Sulby
Isle of Man IM7 2HR
www.iomff.co.uk

Isle of Wight Freshwater Angling Assn

R J Kirby
125 Furlongs
Newport
Isle of Wight PO30 2BD
Tel: 01983 529617
www.isleofwight-fishing.com

Jolly Anglers

Jeremy Denton
6 Trenchard Close
Wallingford
Oxon. OX10 9BA
Tel: 01491 834769

Keighley Angling Club

D Freeman
Treasurer/Secretary
62 Eel Holme
View Street
Beechcliffe
Keighley
West Yorks BD20 6AY
Tel: 01535 663695
www.keighleyanglingclub.co.uk

Kelvedon & District Angling Assn

Brian Pike
11 Keene Way
Galleywood
Chelmsford CM2 8NT
Tel: 01245 262545
www.kdaa.co.uk

Kempston Angling Club (now merged with Vauxhall AC)

www.vauxhallanglingclub.co.uk
VauxAC@yahoo.co.uk

Kent (Westmorland) Angling Assn

C T Preston
Green Court
Main Street
Arkholme LA6 1AU
Tel: 015242 21670
www.kentangling.co.uk

Keswick Anglers Assn

Mike Tinnion
50 Latrigg Close
Keswick
Cumbria CA12 4LG
Tel: 017687 72127
www.keswickanglers.co.uk

Kettering, Thrapston & District Angling Assn

Mike Cardy
Tel: 01536 518178
www.ketteringthrapstonangling.webs
.com

Kidderminster & District Angling Assn

M Millinchip
246 Marlpool Lane
Kidderminster
Worces DY11 5DD
Tel: 01562 753471

Kilnsey Angling Club

Edward Wood
Moorside House
Union Lane
Ogden
Halifax, W Yorks HX2 8XP
Tel: 01422 244720

King's Lynn Angling Assn

www.klaa.co.uk

Kirkby Fleetham Angling Club

M L Smith
26 Eden Grove
Middridge
Newton Aycliffe
Co Durham DL5 7JG
Tel: 01325 312843

Kirkby Lonsdale & District Angling Assn

David Halton
77 Fairgarth Drive
Kirkby Lonsdale
Carnforth LA6 2FB
Tel: 015242 71069

Kirkby Stephen & District Angling Assn
  John Garner
  Ghyll House
  Great Ormside
  Appleby
  Westmorland
  Cumbria CA16 6EJ
  Tel: 017683 51552
  www.kirkbystephen.net

Kirkham & District Fly Fishers'Club
  kirkhamanddistrictflyfishersclub.org.uk

Knaresborough Piscatorials
  Martin Lofthouse
  13 Roseville Road
  Harrogate
  N Yorks HG1 4TD
  Tel: 01423 885947

Lamorbey Angling Society
  Membership Officer
  PO Box 56
  Sidcup
  DA15 7AR
  www.lamorbeyas.org
  lamorbeyas@aol.com

Langport & District Angling Assn
  D Jolly
  30 King Street
  Yeovil
  BA21 4DN
  Tel: 01935 420836
  www.langportaa.com

Lanhydrock Angling Assn
  B Muelaner
  The National Trust Estate Office
  Lanhydrock Park
  Bodmin
  Cornwall PL30 4DE
  Tel: 01208 265211

Lark Angling Preservation Society
  Rodger Pigerham
  Tel: 01638 510995
  www.lark-angling.co.uk
  rpigerham@aol.com

Launceston Anglers Association
  Hon Sec, Colin Hookway
  7 Grenville Park
  Yelverton
  Devon DL20 6DQ
  Tel: 01822 855053

Lees & Hey Angling Club
  Nigel Bunn
  4 Hey Crescent
  Lees
  Oldham
  Lancs OL4 3LJ
  Tel: 0161 626 9183

Lee Anglers' Consortium (LAC)
  Memb Sec: Dennis Meadhurst CPFA
  P O Box 19426
  London
  E4 8UZ
  Tel: 020 8524 7270
  Hertford to Feildes Weir: Bailiff
  Denis Cavanagh; Martin Phipps
  Cheshunt to Bow Lock: Bailiff
  Tom Rowley
  www.lee-anglers-consortium.co.uk

Leeds & District Amalgamated Society of Anglers
  75 Stoney Rock Lane
  Beckett Street
  Leeds
  West Yorks LS9 7TB
  Tel/fax: 0113 225 3366
  Mob: 07765 075582
  www.leedsdasa.co.uk

Leek & Moorlands Angling Club
  Roy BirchMachin
  53 Novi Lane
  Leek
  Staffs ST13 6NX
  Tel: 01538 371128

Leicester & District Amalgamated Society of Anglers
  Dave Tasker
  2 Curlew Close
  Syston
  Leicester LE7 1XA
  Tel: 0116 2607525

Leigh & District Angling Association
(see also Pennington Flash)
Ken Buxton
22 Hope Carr Lane
Leigh WN7 3XA
Tel: 01942 517610

Leighton Buzzard Angling Club
Brian Smalley
102 Heath Rd
Leighton Buzzard
Beds LU7 3AD
Tel: 01525 379099
www.lbac.co.uk

Letchworth Garden City Angling Assn
Memb Sec: Len Leroux
Tel: 01462 631994
www.letchworthangling.org.uk

Lewisham Piscatorials Assn
D J Head
75 Riverview Park
Catford
London SE6 4PL
Tel: 020 8690 4603

Lincoln & District Angling Assn
David Ellerker
Mill Hill House
North Clifton
Notts NG23 7AZ
Tel: 01777 228133
for
Juniors Organiser:
Kevin Martin
Mob: 07966 450155
for
Veterans Organiser
Jim Bradshaw
Tel: 01522 808943

Linton, Threshfield and Grassington AC
S Binns
Secretary
Tel: 01756 753510

Liskeard & District Angling Club
W H Eliot
64 Portbyhan Road
West Looe
Cornwall PL13 2QN
Tel: 01503 264173
www.ldac.org.uk
ticket_enquiries@ldac.org.uk

Littlehampton & Dist Angling Club
Fisherman's Quay
Littlehampton BN17 5BL
Tel: 01903 722769
www.ldac.co.uk

Littleport Angling Club
Secretary: Phil Houghton
Tel: 01353 862167
info@littleportanglingclub.co.uk
www.littleportanglingclub.co.uk

Liverpool & District AnglingAssn
Hon Sec: Jo Farrell
Tel: 07764 926643

Llandrindod Wells AnglingAssn
B D Price
The Cedars
Llanyre
Llandrindod Wells
Powys LD1 6DY
Tel: 01597 823539

Lloyd's Fly Fishing Society
Brian Fitzsimmons
"Windmolen"
White Horse Road
East Bergholt
Suffolk CO7 6TU
Tel: 01206 299400
www.lloydsflyfishers.org

London Anglers' Assn
A E Hodges, FIFM
Izaak Walton House
2A Hervey Park Road
Walthamstow
London E17 6LJ
Tel/Fax: 020 8520 7477
www.londonanglers.net
admin@londonanglers.net

Long Buckby Angling Club
Michael Hill
33 South Close
Long Buckby
Northants NN6 7PX
Tel: 01327 843091

**Long Eaton & District Angling
Federation**
W Parker
75 College Street
Long Eaton
Notts

Long Eaton Victoria Angling Society
Mr P Richardson
81 Stafford Street
Long Eaton
Nottingham
Tel: 0115 972 8547
www.levas.co.uk

Lonsdale Angling Club
David Mason
15 Lambert Road
Lancaster LA1 2NA
Tel: 07989 761369
www.lonsdaleac.blogspot.com
davidmason080@btinternet.com
No day tickets

Looe Angling Club
The Quay
E Looe
Cornwall PL13 1DX
Tel: 01503 263337

Lostwithiel Fishing Assn
J H Hooper
4 Reeds Park
Lostwithiel
Cornwall PL22 0HF

Loughborough Soar Angling Society
Contact Brian Hull

Lowestoft Sea Angling Society
57 Lorne Park Road
Lowestoft
Suffolk NR33 0RB
Tel: 01502 581943

Lune & Wyre Fisheries Assn
Bill Arnold
Higher Broadwood
Wray
Lancaster LA2 8QT
Tel: tel: 01524 222324
bill@arnold.net

Luton Angling Club
Chairman: D W Edwards
4 Stratton Gardens
Luton
Beds LU2 7DS
Tel: 01582 728114
www.lutonac.org

**Lymington & District Sea Fishing
Club**
Mrs G Moody
'GinaMia'
Hundred Lane, Portmore
Lymington
Hants SO41 5RG
Tel: 01590 674962

Lymm Angling Club
Neil Jupp
P O Box 350
Warrington WA2 9FB
Tel: 01925 411774
www.lymmanglersclub.com
Secretary@lymmanglersclub.com

Macclesfield Flyfishers' Club
W F Williams
1 Westwood Drive
Brooklands
Sale
Cheshire M33 3QW

Macclesfield Waltonian AnglingSociety
Alastair Pirrie: Treasurer
1 Marsden Terrace
Macclesfield
Cheshire SK11 6QB
Tel: 01625 431694
www.waltonians.co.uk

Maidstone Victory Angling & Medway Preservation Society
Membership Secretary
19a Turketel Road
Folkstone
Kent CT20 2PA
Tel: 01303 255221
www.maidstonevictory.co.uk

Maldon Angling Society
David Spalding
Rustling Oaks
Field View Drive
Little Totham
Essex CM9 8ND
Tel: 01621 892197
www.maldonas.co.uk

Malton & Norton Angling Club
S Peel
19 Leahurst Close
Norton, Malton
Yorks YO17 9DF
Tel: 01653 692824

Mansfield & District Angling Assn
John Smith
16 Holmwood Road
Rainworth
Mansfield NG21 0HT
Tel: 01623 400790

Manx Game Fishing Club
P O Box 95
2A Lord Street
Douglas
Isle of Man

Marazion Angling Club
Newtown Angling Centre
Newtown
Germoe
Penzance TR20 9AE
Tel: 01736 763721
www.marazionanglingclub.co.uk

March & District Angling Association
Bob Fitzjohn
64 Hereward Street
March
Cambs PE15 8LZ
Tel: 01354 653223

Marlborough & District AnglingAssn
Malcolm Ellis
Failte Elcot Close
Marlborough SN8 2BB
Tel: 01672 512922
www.marlboroughangling.co.uk

Marlow Angling Club
Jeff Brown, Chairman and
Membership Secretary
12 Johnson Road
Lane End
High Wycombe HP14 3DG
Tel: 01494 882565
www.marlowac.co.uk

Marsden Star Angling Society
Jeff Hartley
3 Duerden Street
Nelson
Lancs BB9 9BJ
Tel 01282 603362

Martham & District Angling Club
Treasurer: Mick Bensley
Tel: 01493 732661

Matlock Angling Club
Mr R Cantrill
8 Turnpike Close
Matlock
Derbyshire DE4 3DR
Tel: 01629 57268
www.matlockanglingclub.co.uk

Medlock Bridge Angling Club
Charlie Webb, Chairman
15 Waterworks Road
Waterhead
Oldham OL4 2JH
Mob: 0798 0716337
Tel: 01616 261636

Mid Ribble Angling Society
J W Whitham, Secretary
Pendleside
58 Lingmoor Drive
Burnley BB12 8UY
Tel: 01282 411340
www.midribble.co.uk

Middlesbrough Angling Club
R Thompson
30 Greenland Avenue
Whinneybanks, Middlesbrough
Cleveland TS5 4JW
Tel: 01642 893461

Middlewich Joint Anglers
Barbara Bennion
Brynlow Drive
Middlewich
Cheshire CW10 0TD
Tel: 01606 836401

Midland Angling Society
Jack Bradbury
19 Ethel Avenue
Hucknall
Notts NG15 8DB
Tel: 0115 9634487

Mildenhall Angling Club
M Hampshire
63 Downing Close
Mildenhall
Suffolk IP28 7PB
Tel: 01638 718205

Millom & District Angling Assn
Brian Crawford
16 Lancashire Road
Millom
Cumbria LA18 4AW
Tel: 01229 777648

Milnthorpe Angling Assn
Peter Moreton
Tel: 01524 762043
www.milnthorpeaa.co.uk

Milton Keynes Angling Assn
Trevor Johnson
52 Jenkinson Road
Towcester NN12 6AW
Tel: 01908 270000
www.mkaa.co.uk

Mitre Angling Club
Denis Halstead
Membership Secretary
Tel: 01282 692261
enquires@mitreanglingclub.net
www.mitreanglingclub.net

Montgomeryshire Angling Assn
Andrew Jones
53 Llwyn Perthy
Arddleen
Llanymynech
Powys SY22 6QX
Tel: 01938 590129
www.montgomeryshireanglingassoci
ation.co.uk

Moor Hall & Belhus Angling Society
Ray Smith
25 Annalee Gdns
South Ockendon
Essex RM15 5DE
Tel: 01708 859405

Nantwich Angling Society
Janet Wilson
Mob: 0776 4760410
www.nantwichangling.co.uk

National Anguilla Angling Club
Ade Lees
Hillview Cottage
359 Rawnsley Road, Cannock
Staffordshire WS12 1RD
secretary@nationalanguillaclub.co.u
k
www.nationalanguillaclub.co.uk

National Coal Board No5 Area FC
Andrew Kowalski
157 Roper Avenue
Marlpool Heanor
Derbys DE75 7BE
Tel: 01773 769363
www.ncbno5fishingclub.com

Newark & District Piscatorial Federation
J N Garland
58 Riverside Road
Newark
Notts NG24 4RJ
Tel: 01636 702962
www.newarkpiscatorial.co.uk

Newhaven Deep Sea Angling Club
Denton Island
Newhaven
East Sussex BN9 9BA
Tel: 01273 517330

Newport Pagnell Fishing Assn
R D Dorrill
7 Bury Street
Newport Pagnell
Milton Keynes MK16 0DS
Tel: 01908 610639
www.npfa.org.uk

Newton Abbot Fishing Assn
Ian Donaldson
P O Box 229
Totnes
Devon TQ9 6EY

Nidderdale Angling Club
Membership Secretary
P O Box 7
Pateley Bridge, nr Harrogate
North Yorks HG3 5XB
www.nidderdaleac.co.uk

Northallerton Angling Club
Rex Dale
The Garth
Danby Wiske
Northallerton
North Yorks DL7 0NA
Tel: 01609 771117
www.nadac.org.uk

Northampton Nene Angling Club
Secretary: Maggie Petch
Tel: 01604 705205
www.northamptonneneangling
club.co.uk

Northern Anglers' Assn
Gerry Wilson
11 Guildford Avenue
Chorley
Lancs PR6 8TG
Tel: 01257 249372

North Oxford Angling Society
Andrew Crisp
4 Grove Street
Summertown
Oxford OX2 7JT
Tel: 01865 553800

North Somerset Assn of Anglers
(Embracing Highbridge & Clevedon clubs)
R Newton
64 Clevedon Road
Tickenham
Clevedon
Somerset BS21 6RD
Tel: 01275 856107

Northumbrian Anglers' Federation
W Farndale
15 Woodlands
Rothbury
Morpeth
Northumberland NE65 7XZ
Tel: 01669 620984
www.northumbriananglersfed.co. uk

NorthWest Durham Angling Assn
Graham Robinson
Hon Treasurer
Tel: 07759 431731
www.nwdaa.btik.com

Northwich Anglers Assn
P O Box 18
Northwich
Cheshire CW9 5SE
Tel: 01606 786787
www.northwich-anglers.org.uk

Norwich & District Anglers Assn
Malcolm Major
Tumble Weed
Flaxlands
Carleton Rode
NR16 1AD
Tel: 01953 789541
www.ndaa.org uk

**North Eastern Railways
Angling Club**
Stephen Hutchinson
Chairman
Tel: 07931 298532
www.nerac.co.uk (Members only)

Nottingham Anglers' Assn
David Turner
3a Beckhampton Road
Bestwood Park
Nottingham NG5 5SP
Tel: 0115 9199500
www.nottinghamanglers.co.uk

**Nottingham & District Federation of
Angling Societies**
William Belshaw
17 Spring Green
Clifton Estate
Nottingham NG11 9EF
Tel: 0115 9216645

Nottingham Piscatorial Society
Tony Farrar
9 Columbia Close
Selston
Notts NG16 6GP
Mob: 07831 469160

Offord & Buckden Angling Society
Val Jolly
24 Perry Road
Buckden
St Neots
Cambs PE19 5XG
Tel: 01480 811125

Old Kings Head Angling Club
Fiona Dennett
Hollywood Cottage
Wood Farm
London Road
Daventry NN11 4ND
Tel: 07811 245567
www.btinternet.com/~fishing.club

Oldham Fly Fishers Club
Chris Bradshaw
The Cottage
Higher Ogden
Newhey
Rochdale OL16 3TD
Tel: 01706 849016

Oldham United Anglers
Secretary, Wyngate
Higher Hartshead
Ashton-under-Lyne
OL6 9AF
Tel: 01457 833148
www.oldham-chronicle.co.uk/sites/o
ua

Old Windsor Angling Club
Alan Beaven
88 St Andrews Way
Slough
Berks SL1 5LJ
Tel: 01628 602537 (after 6pm)

Oundle Angling Assn
Mark Cunnington
1 New Road
Oundle
Peterborough PE8 4LA
Tel: 01832 272995

Ouse Valley (Sussex) FlyFishers Club
Meetings at the Royal Oak
Barcombe
ovsf@live.co.uk
www.ovsf.freeuk.com

Ouse Angling Preservation Society
Permit Sec: Andrew Woolley
14 The Martlets
Mill Lane
South Chailey
E Sussex BN8 4QG
Tel: 01273 891312
www.ouseaps.co.uk

Oxford & District Anglers Assn
President: Miss Janet Moores
6 Evans Lane
Kidlington OX5 2HX
Tel: 01865 373545

Paddock Wood Angling & Conservation Society
George Haynes
23 Bramley Gardens
Paddock Wood
Kent TN12 6BD
Tel: 01892 832730

Padstow Sea Angling Club
c/o Padstow Angling Centre
Strand House
South Quay
Padstow, PL28 8BL
Tel: 01841 532762

Paignton Sea Anglers' Assn
Hon Sec: Les Harding
Clubhouse "Ravenswood"
26 Cliff Rd
Paignton
Devon TQ4 6DH
Tel: 01803 553118
www.psaa.org.uk

Parkside Fishing Club
D Fallows
27 Woodstock Avenue
Radford
Nottingham NG7 5QP
Tel: 01159 787350

Peak Forest Angling Club (Derbyshire)
Colin Jones
1 Willow Croft
Hope Road
Bamford
Hope Valley
Derbys S33 0AL
Tel: 01433 659909

Pennington Flash Angling Assn
(now Leigh & District AA)
Ken Buxton
22 Hope Carr Lane
Leigh WN7 3XA
Tel: 01942 517610

Penrith Angling Assn
Andrew Dixon
3 Newtown Cottages
Skirwith
Penrith, Cumbria CA10 1RJ
Tel: 01768 88294
www.penrithanglers.co.uk

Peterborough & District Angling Assn
Jon Means (Head Bailiff)
101B Peterborough Road
Ailsworth
Peterborough
PE5 7AJ
Tel: 01733 380768
peterboroughdaa.yuku.com

Petersfield & District Angling Club
Mr Geoff Grimes
10 York Close
Petersfield
Hants GU32 3YR
Tel: 01730 260686 (after 6pm only)
www.thepdac.com

Petworth & Bognor Angling Club
Tim Nudd
Arun Angling Centre
The Old Blacksmiths Yard
Water Lane
Angmering BN16 4EP
Tel: 01903 770099
www.sussexangling.co.uk

Pewsey & District Angling Club
Jim Broomham
85 Broadfields
Pewsey
Wilts SN9 5DU
Tel: 01672 563690

Plymouth & District Freshwater Angling Assn
David Bickell
2 Boundary Road
Dousland
Yelverton
Plymouth PL20 6NQ
Tel: 01822 854241
www.pdfaa.org.uk

Portsmouth & District Angling Society
Dave Coombs
122 Stebbington Avenue
North End
Portsmouth PO2 0JL
Tel: 02392 792461
www.portsmouthdas.co.uk

Practical Angling for Disabled Club (PAD Angling Club)
Barry Poxon
4 Lyndhurst Grove
Cherrytree Hill
Chaddesden
Derby DE21 6RX
Tel: 01332 665730
www.padanglingclub.co.uk

Pride of Derby Angling Assn Ltd
Alan Miller
16 Mercia Drive
Willington
Derby DE65 6DA
Tel: 01283 702701
www.prideofderby.co.uk

Prince Albert Angling Society
Hon Sec
P O Box 151
Macclesfield
Cheshire SK10 2HR
www.paas.co.uk

Pulborough Angling Society
Mick Booth
5 South Lane
Houghton
Arundel
W Sussex BN18 9LN
Tel: 01798 831525
www.pulboroughas.com

Radcot Angling Club
Steve Heath
Mob: 07711 326171

Ramsey & District Angling Society (Cambs)
Mr A Parnell
62 Blenheim Road
Ramsey
Cambs PE26 1AW
Tel: 01487 815437
or
Match Sec: Keith Rayment
27 Princes Street
Ramsey
Cambs PE26 1JW
Tel: 01487 814077

Ramsey Angling Club (I.O.M.)
Chairman: Chris Culshaw
Parkhill
Coburg Road
Ramsey
Isle of Man IM8 3EH
Tel: 01624 812279
www.ramseyanglingclub.com

Raychem Fishing Club
Trevor Humphrey
Raychem
Darby Close
Swindon
SN2 2DU
Tel: 07989 276189
www.raychemfishingclub.co.uk

Reading & District Angling Assn
A C Hughes
217 Beech Lane
Earley
Reading RG6 5UP
Tel 0118 9867 430
www.rdaa.co.uk

Red Spinner Angling Society
R Keys
226 Churchgate Road
Cheshunt
Herts EN8 9EQ
Tel: 01992 622131

Rhayader & District Angling Assn
Alan Lewis
Hafod Hardware
East Street
Rhayader
Powys LD6 5DS
Tel: 01597 810383
www.rhayaderangling.co.uk

Ribblesdale Angling Assn
Fred Higham
99 Waddington Road
Clitheroe BB7 2HN
Tel: 01200 423314
www.ribblesdaleangling.co.uk

Ribchester & District Angling Club
D Harwood
The Fold
15 Smithy Row
Hurst Green
Clitheroe BB7 9QA
Tel: 01254 826252
or
HQ: Ribchester Sports & Social Club
Church St
Ribchester
Lancs
www.radac.org.uk

Richmond (Yorks) & District Angling Society
P Bennett
1 Theakston Lane
Richmond
N Yorks DL10 4LL
Tel: 01748 824894.

Ringwood & District Anglers Club
Peter Hutchinson
Cornerways Cottage
Gorley Road, Poulner
Ringwood
Hants BH24 3RB
Tel: 01425 476415
www.ringwoodfishing.co.uk

Ripon Angling Club
Roger Trees
43 College Road
Ripon
N Yorks HG4 2HE
Tel: 01765 602277

Ripon Fly Fishers
C J Clarke
6 Church Close
Sharow
Ripon
N Yorks HG4 5BL
Tel: 01765 601677
www.riponflyfishers.co.uk

Ripon Piscatorial Assn
K Hunt
Rosedale
46 Hillshaw Park Way
Ripon HG4 1JT
Tel: 01765 600011
www.ripon-piscatorial.co.uk

Rochdale Walton Angling Society
Mr B Watkins
26 Somerset Grove
Cutgate
Rochdale
Lancashire OL11 5YS
www.rochdalewalton.co.uk

Ross-on-Wye Angling Club
Terry Gibson
10 Redwood Close
RossonWye
Herefordshire HR9 5UD
Tel: 01989 567775
www.rossanglingclub.co.uk

Rother Angling Club
Ivor Osborne
20 Common View
Stedham
Midhurst GU29 0NX
Tel: 01730 814361
Mob: 0777 240 6770
www.rotherac.co.uk

Rother Fishery Assn
Vince Gould
13 Park Cottages
Hawkhurst
Kent TN18 4HN
Tel: 01580 754898
www.fishingkent.com

Royal Leamington Spa Angling Assn
Hon Sec: 01926 312319
www.leamingtonangling.co.uk

Rudgwick Angling Society
Robbie Gaiger
32 Glebe Road
Cranleigh
Surrey GU6 7AS
Tel: 01483 275944

Rushden & Higham Ferrers Irchester Angling Assn
John Boswell
49 Washbrook Road
Rushden
Northants NN10 9UY
Tel: 01933 313039

Royal Tunbridge Wells Angling Society
www.rtwas.co.uk

Ryburn & Halifax Angling Society (prev. Dean Clough & Ryburn AS)
T Hooson
Croft Bank
238 Rochdale Road
Willowfield
Halifax
West Yorks HX2 7NL
Tel: 01422 344223 (evenings)

St Helens Angling Assn
Les Bramilow
4 Bassenthwaite Avenue
St Helens
Merseyside WA11 7AB
Tel: 01744 601287
www.sthelensaa.co.uk

St Helens Ramblers Angling Society
Alec Twiss
18 The Beeches
Sutton Leach
St Helens
WA9 4SU
Tel: 01744 851815

St Ives & District Fish Preservation & Angling Society
Chris Geeson
12 Enderbys Wharf
St Ives
Cambs PE27 5GT
Tel: 01480 496667
www.stivesanglingsociety.co.uk

St Mawgan Angling Club
Chairman: Peter Parkinson
Tel: 01637 860517

St Neots & District Angling & Fish Preservation Society
Mrs D Linger
Skewbridge Cottage
Great Paxton
St Neots
Huntingdon
Cambs PE19 4RA
Tel: 01480 216730

Salcombe & District Sea Anglers' Assn
Kings Arms
Salcombe
Devon TQ8 8BU
Tel: 01548 842202

Salisbury & District Angling Club
Secretary
The Car Shed
New Bottom Road
StratfordsubCastle
Salisbury
Wilts SP4 6AB
Tel: 01722 321164
www.salisburydistrictac.co.uk

Saltaire Angling Club
D P Brazendale
General Secretary
19 St Aidans Road, Baildon
Shipley BD17 6AJ
Tel: 01274 214441
www.saltaire-aa.org

Sandwich & District Angling Assn
Mike Edgar
49 Pegwell Road
Ramsgate CT11 0NP
Tel: 01843 596668
www.sandwichangling.net

Sawbridgeworth Angling Society
David Spears
20 Ladywell Prospect
Sawbridgeworth
Herts CM21 9PT
Tel: 01279 832622
www.sawbo.co.uk

Saxmundham Angling Club
Saxmundham Angling Centre
Bakery Yard
rear of Market Place
Saxmundham IP17 1AH
Tel: 01728 603443

Scunthorpe & District Angling Assn
M Storey
12 Mill Close
Scawby Brook
Brigg
North Lincs
DN20 9LL
Tel (mob): 077 177 48523

Sedbergh & District Angling Assn
Dr David Wright
East Backstonegill Farm
Dent
Sedbergh LA10 5TE
Mob: 077333 11322
or
Hon Visitors Sec: C S Dandy
Tel: 015396 21920
www.sedberghanglers.org.uk

Selby Angling Club
J Waterhouse
20 Pinfold Street
Howden
Goole DN14 7DD
Tel: 01430 432225

Selsey Angling & Tope Club
Mike Bell: Secretary
19 Littlefield Close
Selsey
West Sussex PO20 0DZ
Tel: 01243 607998

Seven Angling Club
John Horsman
2 Manor Park
Broughton
Malton YO17 6QL
Tel: 01653 693659

Severnside Angling Club
Steven Potts
902 Falcon Court
Newtown SY16 1LQ
Tel: 01686 624871

Sheffield & District Anglers' Assn Ltd
53 Seagrave Crescent
Sheffield
South Yorks S12 2JL
Tel: 0114 239 3465

Shefford & District Angling Assn Ltd
Chris Mayes
4 Brookmead
Meppershall
Beds SG17 5SA
Mob: 07762 103791
www.shefforddaa.org.uk

Skipton Angling Assn
M L Mawson
6 Lytham Close
Skipton
N Yorks BD23 2LF
Tel: 01756 794022
www.skiptonangling.co.uk

Slaithwaite & District Angling Club
David German
Mob: 07734 220794
or
David Jones
16 Malvern Road
Newsome
Huddersfield HD4 6BY
Tel: 01484 308948

Soldiers & Sailors Angling Club
W Walker
41 Hawthorne Ave
Long Eaton NG10 3NG
Tel: 0115 9721478

South Cerney Angling Club
M Vines, Hon Sec
Fishermans Rest
Broadway Lane
South Cerney
Cirencester GL7 5UH
or
Treasurer
Francine Garner
Tel: 01285 861876
www.scac.org.uk

Southdown Angling Assn
(amalgamation of Compleat Angler FC and Hailsham AA)
Hon Sec: Mike Richardson
c/o Polegate Angling Centre
101 Station Road
Polegate
East Sussex BN26 6EB
Tel: 01435 812854
www.southdown-angling.org

Southsea Sea Angling Club
c/o 42 Granada Road
Southsea
Hants PO4 0RG
Tel: 023 92825508

Stamford Welland Amalgamated Anglers Assn
G E Bates
16a Austin Street
Stamford
Lincs PE9 2QP
Tel: 01780 751060

Stanhope Angling Assn
David Reay
Bondisle Way
Stanhope
Bishop Auckland
Co Durham DL13 2YU
Tel: 01388 526267

Stockport & District Anglers Federation
John Murphy
3 Kelsall Close
Bridgehall Estate
Adswood
Stockport SK3 8NS
Tel: 0161 477 4536

Stockton Angling Ltd
S R Targett
19 Tofts Close
Low Worsall
Yarm
TS15 9QA
Tel: 01642 781825
www.stocktonangling.co.uk

Stoke-on-Trent Angling Society
A Perkins
Muirhearlich
Fowlers Lane
Light Oaks
Stoke on Trent ST2 7NB
Tel: 01782 541500
www.sotangling.co.uk

Stoke-sub-Hamdon & District Angling Society
Derek Goad
2 Windsor Lane
StokesubHamdon
Somerset

Stort Valley Angling Society
Bob Groom
28 Park Mead
Harlow
Essex CM20 1RJ
Tel: 01279 437888
Mob: 0787 652 13636
www.stortvalleyanglingsociety.org

Stratford-upon-Avon Angling Assn
Chris Green
74 Lodge Road
StratfordonAvon
Warwickshire CV37 9DN
Tel: 01789 552012

Sturminster & Hinton Angling Assn
Dave Rigby
Penny Gates
Penny Street
Sturminster Newton
Dorset DT10 1DE
Tel: 01258 472068
www.s-haa.co.uk

Sudbury & Long Melford District Angling Assn
Hugh Smith
3 Stanley Road
Sudbury CO10 1NH
Tel: 01787 881955

Sunderland Sea Angling Assn
c/o Andrew Rutherford
125 Roker Avenue
Roker
Sunderland SR6 0HL
Tel: 0191 565 4183
www.rutherfordsangling.co.uk

Sutton Coldfield Angling Society
Steve Russell
or
Gary Poulton
7 Wheatmoor Rise
Sutton Coldfield
West Midlands B75 6AW
Tel: 0121 378 2152
www.suttoncoldfieldangling.co.uk

Swan Angling Club
J Stanhope
4 High Road
Lane Head
Willenhall
West Midlands WV12 4JQ
Tel: 01902 630110

Swanage & District Angling Club
Mike Blonfield
Peveril Slipway
Swanage
Dorset BH19 2AY

Taunton Angling Assn
Matthew Hawkins
70 Tone Hill
Wellington TA21 0AY
Tel: 01823 664388
www.taunton-angling.co.uk

Taunton Fly Fishing Club
J Connolley
35 Manor Road
Taunton TA1 5BG
Tel: 01823 274272
www.tauntonflyfishing.co.uk

Tavy, Walkham & Plym Fishing Club
Roger Round
7 Buena Vista Close
Glenholt
Plymouth PL6 7JH
Tel: 01752 701945
www.twpfishing.net

Taw Fishing Club
Nick Payne
Honorary Secretary
Tel: 01837 840442

Tebay Anglers Assn
Graham Cave
1 Highfield
Tebay
via Penrith
Cumbria CA10 3TJ
Tel: 01539 624321
www.tebayanglers.com

Teignmouth Sea Angling Society
Luke Stewart
32 Gilbert Avenue
Teignmouth TQ14 9NN
Tel: 01626 778666

Teise Anglers' and Owners' Assn
C J Turpin
Weald Barn House
Weirton Hill
Boughton Monchelsea
Kent ME17 4JS
Tel: 01622 746549
www.teiseangling.co.uk

Telford Angling Assn
Stan Harris
1 Grange Close
Stirchley
Telford
Salop TF3 1EX
Tel: 01952 590605

Temple Steelheads Fly Fishing Club
Temple Trout Fishery
Temple Rd
Temple PL30 4HW
Tel: 01208 821730

Tenbury Fishing Assn
Mrs L M Rickett
The Post House
Berrington Road
Tenbury Wells
Worcs WR15 8EN
Tel: 01584 810695

Test & Itchen Assn Ltd
Tom Davis, Executive Director
Kimbridge Lane
Kimbridge
Romsey SO51 0LE

Test Valley Angling Club (amalg. with Southampton Piscatorial Soc)
Mrs Pat Hogben
1A Rumbridge Street
Totton
Southampton
Hants SO40 9DQ
Tel: 02380 863068/868007
www.tvacspsangling.co.uk

Tewkesbury Popular Angling Assn
Robert Danter
31 Barton Street
Tewkesbury
Glos GL20 5PR
Tel: 01684 293234

The Thames Angling Preservation Society
Secretary, A E Hodges
The Pines
32 Tile Kiln Lane
Bexley
Kent DA5 2BB
Tel: 01322 525575

Thames Valley Angling Assn
(amal of 14 Thames Valley clubs)
Jeff Woodhouse
Conifers
Ash Road
Booker
High Wycombe
Bucks HP12 4QW
Mob: 07921 311443

Thirsk Angling Club
Colin Weaver
2 Garden Cottages
South Crescent
Sowerby
Thirsk YO7 1RA
Tel: 01845 524633

Thornaby Angling Assn
Graham Jeavons
38 Briardene Court
Bishopsgarth
StocktononTees
Co Durham TS19 8UX
Tel: 01642 585770
www.thornaby-angling-association.co.uk

Three Lakes Angling
Paul Herford
15 Juniper Road
Boreham
Chelmsford CM3 3DX
Mob: 077253 49397
www.threelakesangling.pwp.
blueyonder.co.uk

Tisbury Angling Club
Treasurer:
E J Stevens
Knapp Cottage
Fovant
Salisbury SP3 5JW
Tel: 01722 714245
or
Subscript Sec: B Broom
28 The Hollows
Wilton
Salisbury SP2 0JD
Tel: 01722 743255

Tiverton & District Angling Club
Eric Priest
Crantock
Blundells Road
Tiverton EX16 4NA
Tel: 01884 243454

Todmorden Angling Society
R Barber
4 The Coppice
Burnley
Lancs BB11 2LT
Mob: 07970 897849
www.todangling.org

Tonbridge & District Angling and Fish Preservation Society
Alex Heggie
POBox 131
Tonbridge TN11 8WB
Mob: 07503 111551
www.tonbridge-angling.co.uk

Torbay & Babbacombe Association of Sea Anglers
Dave Stevens
Westerly
Small Lane
Broadclyst
Exeter EX5 3HP
Tel: 01392 461747
www.tbasa.org.uk

Towcester & District Angling Club
Membership Sec: Steve Jackson
26 Primrose Road
Bradwell Village
Milton Keynes MK13 9AT
Tel: 01908 319678

Trimpley Anglers Association Ltd
Donald Smart
3 Ribbesford House
Bewdley
Worcs DY12 2TG
Tel: 01299 402299

The Tring Anglers
Memb Sec: Neil Williams
35 Tring Rd
Wilstone
Tring
Herts HP23 4PE
Tel: 01442 823579
www.tringanglers.org.uk
email. info@tringanglers.org.uk

Ulverston Angling Assn
David Anderson
4 Hoad Terrace
Ulverston
Cumbria LA12 7DJ
Tel: 01229 586221
www.ulverstonangling.org

Upper Teign Fishing Assn
Membership Secretary
Chris Hall
Higher Sticklepath Farm
Belstone
Okehampton
Devon EX20 1RD
www.upper-teign-fishing.org.uk

Upper Thames Fisheries Consultative
R Knowles
360 Banbury Road
Oxford OX2 7PP
Tel: 01865 552451

Upper Weardale Angling Assn
H C Lee
7 Westfall
Wearhead
Co Durham DL13 1JD
Tel: 01388 537482

Vauxhall Angling Club
Dave Maple
Chairman
P O Box 232
Baldock
SG7 6XY
www.vauxhallanglingclub.co.uk

Verulam Angling Club
PO Box 2295,
Leagrave,
Luton LU3 3WF
Tel: 01582 593798 - before 9pm only
www.verulam-angling.demon.co.uk

Victoria & Biddulph Angling Society
A Armstrong
12 Lagonda Close
Knypersley
Stoke on Trent
Staffs ST8 6PZ
Tel: 01782 518212

Wadebridge & District Angling Assn
Jon Evans
Polgeel
Polbrock
Wadebridge PL30 3AN
Tel: 01208 812447

Wainfleet Angling Club
c/o Storr's
37/38 High St
Wainfleet
Skegness PE24 4BJ
Tel: 01754 880378

Wantsum Angling Assn
Hon Sec: Mark Ellcock
P O Box 314
Margate
Kent CT7 9BQ
Tel: 01843 841360
Mob: 07966 262338
www.wantsumangling.co.uk

Ware Angling Club
David Fussell
30 Kennedy Avenue
Hoddesdon
Herts
Mob: 07768 746059

Wareham & District Angling Society
Dave Cave
9 Shore Gardens
Upton
Poole
Dorset BH16 5DX
Tel: 01202 624182

Warmington Angling Club
R Bosworth
2 Buntings Lane
Warmington
Peterborough PE8 6TT
Tel: 01832 280360

Warrington Angling Assn
Hon Sec: Frank Lythgoe
Tel: 01928 716238
Headquarters52 Parker St
Warrington
Cheshire WA1 1LT
Tel: 01928 716238
www.warrington-anglers.org.uk
(Open every Friday 7pm 9.30pm)

Waterbeach Angling Club
Mrs Pam Day
10 Northfields Lode
Cambridge CB5 9EU
Tel: 01223 812050
www.waterbeachac.co.uk

Wath Brow & Ennerdale Angling Assn
(see Ennerdale Lake Fisheries)
Sam Laird
5 Churchill Drive
Moresby Park
Whitehaven
Cumbria CA28 8UZ
Tel: 01946 694820

Watford Piscators
Press & Public Relations Officer
Peter Hadwin
54 Hagden Lane
Watford WD18 0HE
Mob: 07746 571771
www.watfordpiscators.co.uk

Weardale Fly Fishers Club
Eddie Forster
16 Paragon Street
Stanhope
Bishop Aukland DL13 2NN
Tel: 01388 528712

Welney Angling Club
Shaun Booth.
Chairman & Secretary
Cambridgeshire
Tel: 01354 638638
sw@edenfab.co.uk
www.welneyanglingclub.co.uk

Wellingborough & District Nene Angling Club
R Blenkharn
66 Redland Drive
Kingsthorpe
Northampton NN2 8TU
Tel: 01604 820380
Mob: 07949 246662
www.wdnac.org.uk

Wellington Angling Assn
Graham Woodward
1 Waterloo Road
Wellington
Somerset TA21 8HU
Tel: 01823 663236

Wensleydale Angling Assn
Chairman: L Mason Scarr
Cravenholme
Bainbridge
Leyburn
N Yorks DL8 3EG
Tel: 01969 650488

West Bay Sea Angling Club
Richard Daw
56a Crock Lane
Bridport
Dorset DT6 4DF
Tel: 01308 421272
www.west-bay-sea-angling-club.co.uk

Weston-super-Mare & District Angling Assn
Rob Stark
Weston Angling Centre
25a Locking Road
WestonsuperMare
Somerset BS23 3BY
Tel: 01934 631140

Westwater Angling Ltd
John Rodger
Fishing Lodge
Hallington Reservoir
Hexham
Northumberland NE46 4TT
Tel: 01434 681405
www.westwaterangling.co.uk

**Wey Navigation Angling
Amalgamation**
Secretary
c/o Village Hall
Byfleet
Surrey

Weybridge Angling Club
Howard Whiting
79 Gaston Way
Shepperton
TW17 8EZ
Tel: 01932 242978
Membership from:
Weybridge Guns & Tackle
137 Oatlands Drive
Oatlands Village, Weybridge
Surrey KT13 9LB
Tel: 01932 842675

Weymouth Angling Society
Ron Paterson
Commercial Road
Weymouth, Dorset DT4 8NF
Tel: 01305 785032
www.weymouthanglingsociety.co.uk

Whitby Sea Anglers Assn
D Perrett
29 Westbourne Road
Whitby
Yorks YO21 3NE
Tel: 01947 601686
www.whitbyseaanglers.co.uk

White Swan Angling Club
N Barratt
Three Trees
Newark Road
Torksey Lock
Lincoln LN1 2EJ
Tel: 01427 718342

Whittlesey Angling Assn
J Warren
55 Bellmans Road
Whittlesey
Cambs PE7 1TY
Tel: 01733 203800
www.whittleseyaa.org.uk

Wigan & District Angling Assn
Memb Sec: Ken Hogg
95 Holme Terrace
Wigan W1N 2HF
Tel: 01942 492376

**Willington & District Angling
Association**
Eric Clegg
7 Vicarage Gardens
Willington
Crook
Co Durham DL15 0UZ
Tel: 01388 747110

Wimborne & District Angling Club
Membership Secretary: Dan Jenner
WDAC
P.O.Box No. 6632
Poole
Dorset BH12 4AH
www.wimborneanglingclub.co.uk

**Windermere, Ambleside & District
Angling Assn (WADAA)**
Neil Birkinshaw
Rosedean
46 Kirkhead Road
Grange-over-Sands LA11 7DD
Tel: 015395 35630
www.lakedistrictfishing.net

Winsford & District Angling Assn
Steve Beech
WDAA
PO Box 262
Middlewich
CW7 9FG
Tel: 07814 877275
www.winsford-anglers.org.uk

Wirral Angling Clubs (Assn of)
Chairman: Malcolm Gillies
17 Rockville Street
Rock Ferry
Birkenhead CH42 3XY
Tel: 0151 645 3396
or
Hon Sec: S Ross
18 Orchard Grange
Moreton
Birkenhead CH46 6DZ

Witham & District Joint Anglers Federation
Stewart Oxborough
6 Ormsby Close
Cleethorpes
South Humberside DN35 9PE
Tel: 01472 508639

Withnell Angling Club
www.withnell-angling-club.co.uk

Wolverhampton Angling Assn
Bill Turner
37 Prole Street
Park Village
Wolverhampton WV10 9AD
Tel: 01902 457906

Woodbridge & District Angling Club
D Ward
c/o Saxmundham Angling Centre
Bakery Yard, rear of Market Place
Saxmundham IP17 1AH
Tel: 01728 603443

Worcester & District United Angling Assn
Colin Pettifer
11 Shrubbery Road
Worcester
Worcs WR1 1QR
Tel: 01905 25193

Worksop & District Anglers Assn
Derek Brown
4 Dove Close
Worksop
Notts S81 7LG
Tel: 01909 486350
www.worksopanglers.com

Worthing & District Piscatorial Society
Ray Baker
19 Brendon Road
Worthing
BN13 2PS
Tel: 01903 265899
www.wdps.org.uk

Wroxham & District Anglers Assn
R Westgate
31 The Paddocks
Old Catton
Norwich
Norfolk NR6 7HF
Tel: 01603 401062

Yarm Angling Ltd
Secretary: Richard Sidgwick
c/o 4 Blenavon Court
Yarm
Teesside TS15 9AN
Tel: 01642 786444
www.yarm-anglingclub.co.uk

Yaxley Farcet Holme and Dist Angling Assn
Paul Marriott
72 Portchester Close
Park Farm
Peterborough PE2 8UP
Tel: 01733 893804

Yeldington Piscatorial Society
Hon. Secretary
Rectory Cottage
Stoke Abbott
Beaminster DT8 3JT

Yeovil & Sherborne Angling Assn
Richard Cattle, Treasurer
14 Milford Road
Yeovil
Somerset BA21 4QE
www.ysaa-online.co.uk

York Angling Assn
Dave Carr
36 Garth End
Pocklington
York YO42 2JA
Tel: 01759 304176

York & District Amalgamation of Anglers
Bob Hutchinson
16 Manor Park Close
York YO30 5UZ
Tel: 01904 651346
www.ydaa.org.uk

Action stations at the FishingMagic Keith Culley Memorial Match
Photo: Richard Fisk

MISCELLANEOUS

Anglian Water Services
Recreation Department: Wing WTW
Morcott Road
Wing
Oakham LE15 8SA
Tel: 01572 653021
www.anglianwater.co.uk/leisure
fishing@anglianwater.co.uk

Bristol Water Plc
Recreations Department
Woodford Lodge
Chew Stoke
Bristol BS40 8XH
Tel: 01275 332339
www.bristolwater.co.uk
woodford.lodge@bristolwater.co.uk)

Cemex Angling (formerly RMC)
CEMEX House
Coldharbour Lane
Thorpe
Surrey TW20 8RA
Tel: 01932 583630
www.cemexangling.com

Lee Valley Regional Park Authority
Lee Valley Park Fisheries
Hollyfield Hall Farm
Stubbins Hall Lane
Crooked Mile
Waltham Abbey
Essex EN9 2EG
Tel: 01992 892291
www.leevalleyangling.com

North Atlantic Salmon Fund
Skipholti 35
105 Reykjavik
Iceland
nasf@vortex.is

The National Trust
PO Box 39
Warrington
WA5 7WD
Tel: 0844 800 1895
Holiday booking: 0844 8002070
www.nationaltrust.org.uk

Northumbrian Water plc
Abbey Road
Pity Me
Durham DH1 5FJ
Tel: 0845 604 7468
www.nwl.co.uk

Ribble Fisheries Consultative Association
(amalgamation of 26 local clubs and 17 riperian owners)
J W Whitham, Secretary
Pendleside
58 Lingmoor Drive
Burnley BB12 8UY
Tel: 01282 411340
www.ribblefisheriesca.co.uk

South West Lakes Trust
Lidn Park,
Quarry Crescent
Pennygillam Industrial Estate
Launceston
Cornwall PL15 7PF
Tel: 01566 771930
www.swlakestrust.org.uk
Info@swlakes.org.uk

Wessex Water
Claverton Down Road
Bath, BA2 7WW
Tel: 0845 6004600
www.wessexwater.co.uk

Lake Vyrnwy, providing spectacular brown trout fishing in the heart of Wales
Photo: Colin Bradshaw

Visit Wales
www.fishing.visitwales.com

FISHING LOCATIONS IN WALES

In the pages that follow, the catchment areas of Wales, are given in alphabetical order, being interspersed with the streams and the lakes under headings such as 'Powys (streams)'; 'Gwynedd (lakes)', etc. The whole of the Wye and the Severn, it should be remembered, are included in the section on England, while the whole of the Dee is listed among the Welsh rivers.

Note: *Sea trout are commonly referred to as 'sewin' in South Wales although some associations in mid and North Wales define sewin as small sea trout returning to the river after only a couple of months in the sea.*

AERON

Rises in Llyn Eiddwen, 7m north-west of Tregaron, and flows about 17m to sea at Aberaeron. Excellent run of sewin from June onwards with smaller salmon run. Brown trout plentiful but small. Spate river fishes well on a retreating flood.

Aberaeron (Ceredigion). Salmon, sea trout and brown trout. Aberaeron Town AC has a 2½m stretch on R Aeron; 3m on **Arth**, a beautiful stream to the north, which holds the occasional brown trout and has a sporadic run of sea trout; and 2 stretches on **Teifi**, north of Lampeter. A further 1½m of private fishing available upstream of club waters; Llanerchaeron Estate, National Trust; contact Property Office (tel: 01545 570200); tickets from Aber Fishing Tackle Shop; st £45, wt £20, dt £10. Tackle shop: Aber Fishing Tackle, 3 Terrace Road, Aberystwyth SY23 1NY (tel: 01970 611200; web: www.flymail.com); and Aeron Sports & Fishing Tackle, 2 Bridge Street, Aberaeron SA46 0AP (tel: 01545 571209).

ANGLESEY (streams)

ALAW. Llanfachraeth (Anglesey). Rises above Cors y Bol bog and flows some 7m to sea beyond Llanfachraeth, opposite Holyhead. Fishes well (trout) for first three months of season and again in September when good run of small sea trout expected; usually too low in summer. Permission of farmers.

BRAINT. Llangeinwen (Anglesey). Small stream which flows almost whole width of the island, parallel with Menai Straits, to sea at Aber Menai, beyond Llangeinwen. Trout, some sea trout, but usually fishable only first three months of season. Permission of farmers.

CEFNI. Llangefni (Anglesey). Rises above Llangwyllog, flows through Llyn Frogwy, on to Llangefni and Cefni Reservoir, and then to sea in 6m. Lower reaches canalised. Only fair-sized river in island. Brown trout and chance of late salmon or sea trout. Permission of farmers.

CEINT. Pentraeth (Anglesey). Small stream entering sea at Red Wharf Bay; some trout; permission of farmers; summer conditions difficult.

FFRAW or GWNA. Bodorgan (Anglesey). Under the name of Gwna rises 4m above Bodorgan and waters Llyn Coron just below village. Stream then takes name of Ffraw and runs to sea at Aberffraw in 2m. Little more than brook. One or two pools fishable early on, but overgrown June onwards. Trout, some sea trout.

WYGYR. Cemaes (Anglesey). Small stream falling into sea at Cemaes Bay. Trout; restocked. Good sea fishing in bay. Hotels: Harbour, Cemaes Bay, Gwynedd LL67 0NN (tel: 01407 710273); Cefn Glas Hotel,

Llanfechell, Amlwch, Gwynedd LL68 0PT (tel: 01407 710526).

ANGLESEY (lakes)

Bodafon Lake. Llanallgo (Anglesey). Rudd and tench; contact Trescawen Estate, Anglesey, Gwynedd.

Cefni Reservoir. Llangefni (Anglesey), 172 acres: wild brown (especially) and rainbow trout, fly only; good wading; boats; leased by Welsh Water plc to Cefni AA; permits from D G Evans (Treasurer), Wenllys, Capel Coch, Llangefni LL77 7UR (tel: 01248 470306); dt and wt from Peter Rowe, Jewellers, above Mon Properties, Glanhwfa Rd, Llangefni and Anglesey Bait Centre, Gallows Point, Beaumaris; st adults £190, sen citizens £160, student (18-21) £95, juniors £30, dt £16, evng £12, wt £45. Hotels: Tre Ysgawen Hall, Capel Coch LL77 7UR (tel: 01248 750750).

Cwn Reservoir. Holyhead (Anglesey). Coarse fishing on 2 acre reservoir; carp, rudd, bream, roach and tench; open all year round.

Holyhead (Anglesey). Ynys Mon AA has 20 pegs at **Breakwater Park** (3 pegs for wheelchair anglers) dt £5 on bank or from cafe on site (summer), conc.

Llyn Alaw. Llantrisant (Anglesey). Situated in open lowland countryside this productive 777 acre reservoir offers fly fishing, spinning and worming, for brown and rainbow trout; season 25 Mar - 17 Oct for brown; 21 Mar - 26 Oct for rainbow (variable annually); dt £16, concessions £15, evening £14, junior (2 fish) £9, st £467.50 (concession £424), from Visitor Centre at reservoir (dt and evening from machine in car park); worms, flies, weights, spinners and a wide variety of other tackle for sale at Visitor Centre; further information from Llyn Alaw Visitor Centre, Llyn Alaw

Reservoir, Llantrisant, Holyhead, Anglesey LL65 4TW (tel: 01407 730762). Accommodation: caravans and camping at Bodnolwyn Wen Farm, Llantrisant, Holyhead, Anglesey LL65 4TW (tel: 01407 730298); B&B at Lastra Farm Hotel, Amlwch, LL68 9TF (tel: 01407 830906); and caravans and camping at The Ring (Public House), Rhosgoch, Anglesey LL66 0AB (tel: 01407 830720).

Llyn Bryntirion. Dwyran (Anglesey). Carp, tench, roach and perch fishing on 3 ponds (3 acres of water); all year; no barbed hooks or keepnets; only one rod per angler; dt from J Naylor, Bryntirion Working Farm, Dwyran, Anglesey LL61 6BQ (tel: 01248 430232).

Llyn Coron. Bodorgan (Anglesey). Brown trout and sea trout; controlled by syndicate (max 40 members), £150 per season; dt £10 (4 fish limit); contact bailiff, Mr Gerald Richardson (tel: 01248 810297); permits also available from the fishing lodge at lakeside, Aberffraw PO and Llanfaelog PO.

Llyn Dewi. Llandeusant (Anglesey). Coarse fishing on 1 acre lake; carp, roach and rudd; open all year. Ynys Mon AA has **Nant Anog Lake** 40 pegs, 5 for wheelchair anglers; recently stocked with chubb; dt £5, conc, on bank; ring Hon Sec first.

Llanerchymedd (Anglesey). Coarse and game fishing on $\frac{1}{2}$ acre lake; rudd and brown trout; fishing is only available for guests at Llwydiarth Fawr (guest house); contact R & M L Hughes, Llwydiarth Fawr, Llanerchymedd, Anglesey LL71 8DF (tel: 01248 470321). Ynys Mon AA has 40 pegs on Llyn Nant Anog at

Carmel; dt £5, conc; also 16 pegs (2 disabled) on Llyn Tacan at Carna Farm, Llanfair-yn-Neubwll; dt £5, conc; obtainable from Cymryan Hotel across road from water; members night fishing only on any assn water.

Llyn Maelog. Rhosneigr (Anglesey). Roach, perch, rudd, bream, eels, pike. Permission to fish from various landowners; dt £5, conc, for whole of right hand bank (looking at lake from the road) of Ynys Mon AA water from Wayside Shop, Llanfaelog, Rhosneigr. Hotels: Maelog Lake and Glan Neigr.

Llyn y Gors. Llandegfan (Anglesey). 30 acres coarse fishery, seven lakes including 3 specimen carp lakes: specimen carp; mixed lake with carp, tench, roach, rudd and perch; one carp lake with carp to 30lb; pike and catfish; second carp lake, carp to 35lb, catfish to 35lb; match lake and beginner's lake; permits, large tackle shop and bait on site; self-catering cottages, tents and tourers; further information from tackle shop: Fishing Warehouse Shop, Llyn y Gors, Llandegfan, Menai Bridge, Anglesey, LL59 5PN (tel: 01248 713410; web: www.llynygors.co.uk).

Llyn Edna Trout Fishery. Llanerchymedd (Anglesey). Llyn Edna is 5 acre, man-made lake; stocked with rainbow and blue trout; tickets from the lodge at the water; contact Neil Johnson, Medora House, Llanddeusant, LL65 4AD (tel: 01248 470838); accommodation in self-catering cottages: contact Andrew Gannon, Parc Newydd, Carmel, nr Llanerchymedd LL71 7BT (tel: 01248 470700) which also has 2 coarse fishing lakes.

Tyddyn Sargent. Benllech (Anglesey). Coarse fishing on 1¾ acre lake and small lake; common carp, ghost carp, crucian carp, perch, roach, rudd, tench and bream; barbless hooks only; accommodation and tickets: contact K Twist, Tyddyn Sargent, Tynygongl, nr Benllech, Anglesey LL74 8NT (tel: 01248 853024; see website for more info: www.angleseyfishery.co.uk).

CLEDDAU (Eastern and Western)

East Cleddau rises on the east side of Prescelly Mountains and flows 15m south-west, partly along old Carmarthenshire border, to north branch of Milford Haven. West Cleddau rises in the hills and valleys south-west of Mathry and flows east towards Castle Morris. It is joined by streams such as the Afon Cleddau and Nant-y-Bugail and then flows south-east to Wolf's Castle. Here it is joined by the Afon Anghof and Afon Glan Rhyd. It then flows south to Haverfordwest and on to join the E Cleddau in a creek in the Haven. Fishing for sewin and trout is mainly in June, July and August; for salmon in August.

WESTERN CLEDDAU: Salmon, sewin and trout.

Haverfordwest (Pembrokeshire). Pembrokeshire AA has 15m stretch along A40, Haverfordwest to Fishguard, (Wolf's Castle); salmon, sea trout, brown trout; visitors: wt £45 (8 consecutive days), dt £15, juv (under 12) £5; members: st £70 + £15 joining fee; wheelchair anglers, conc; permits from County Sports, 3 Old Bridge, Haverfordwest SA61 2EZ (tel: 01437 763740; see website for more: www.county-sports.co.uk); the assn also has a sea trout stocking programme in place. Pembrokeshire AA have a purpose-built disabled fishing facility at Treffgarne, which includes concreted surface, safety barrier and parking for 3 cars; also a picnic table with wheelchair access. Accommodation: The Rising Sun Inn, Pelcomb Bridge, Haverfordwest SA62 6EA (tel: 01437 765171); Caravan and

Camp Site, St David's Road, Haverfordwest, SA62 6EA (tel: 01437 765171). United Utilities manages 2 reservoirs in the area on behalf of Welsh Water plc. **Llys-y-Fran Reservoir** (212 acres), rainbow trout reared in cages within the reservoir and brown trout; season Mar - 31 Oct; limited winter fishing only until early Dec; catch limit 6 fish (half-day 4 fish); size limit 10"; boats; permits and tackle from Llys-y-Fran Visitor Centre Shop (below). **Rosebush Reservoir** (33 acres) brown trout fishery in Prescelly Hills; now operated by local syndicate but bank and boat rods from Llys-y-Fran Reservoir; advanced booking advisable; for further information contact, Visitor Centre, Llys-y-Fran Reservoir, Clarbeston Road, nr Haverfordwest, Pembs SA63 4RR (tel: 01437 532732/532694). Riparian owners may give permission elsewhere. Sewin fishing good June to August. Tackle shop: County Sports, 3 Old Bridge, Haverfordwest SA61 2EZ (tel: 01437 763740; web: www.county-sports.co.uk); tickets Pembrokeshire AA, Llangwarren Trout Lake, E & W Cleddau. Hotels: Mariners, Mariners Square SA61 2DU.

EASTERN CLEDDAU. Trout in all rivers and tributaries in E Cleddau area; stocks mostly small fish under 7 $\frac{1}{2}$". Trout, sewin and salmon in **Syfynwy**, a tributary of E Cleddau. Picton Waters AC has 3m; right bank from Gelly Bridge downstream to Holgan Farm and several stretches on left bank d/s from Penlan Farm to Llawhaden Bridge; limited st; wt details on application; contact Hon Sec.

Llanycefn (Dyfed). Fishing in E Cleddau controlled largely by individual syndicates as far as the ford at Llandissilio; day tickets are sold by T & P J Murphy, Llangwm Farm, Llanycefn, Clynderwen, SA66 7LN (tel/fax: 01437 563604). U/s seek farmers permission; d/s fishing is expensive and it is necessary to join syndicates. Glancleddau Farm, Felinfach and Landre Egremont have holiday caravan parks where visitors enjoy some of the best fishing in the area. Rod licences from Post Office, Felinfach, Ceredigion SA48 8AE (tel: 01570 470321).

Fishing spiders on the river Wye in early summer. *Photo: Andrew Cartwright*

CLWYD

A celebrated sea trout and salmon river which has its source in the high ground to the north of Corwen and runs down through Ruthin, passes Denbigh, St Asaph and Rhuddlan and finally enters the Irish Sea at Rhyl. Best fished for sea trout from June onwards as these fish tend to run during latter part of the month although some large fish run as early as May. The native brown trout population is mostly composed of small fish, though stocking of larger specimens is undertaken annually in the upper reaches by one of the angling clubs. There are no coarse fish species in this area but occasional rainbow trout drop down from the commercial fisheries on the catchment.

Rhyl (Denbighshire). Salmon, sea trout, brown trout. No permits needed for stretch from sea to railway bridge, however, no holding pools, therefore salmon and sea trout tend to run straight through; for salmon, trout and eels, rod licence needed; close season 17 Oct-1 March. Rhyl & St Asaph AA is one of the oldest fishing clubs in the Vale of Clwyd; the majority of its waters are rented, but the club is fortunate in owning the fishing rights on 6 beats, some substantial, on the **R Elwy** including Maes Elwy, Pont y Ddol and Maes Elwy Woods; it rents 3 further stretches including **Pentre Isaf** and **Bron Heulog** and the assn also fishes St Asaph Town Water; all beats on the **R Clwyd** (Bryn Clwyd, Wern Ddu and Bryn Polyn, and Bodfair) are rented, except one owned stretch, **Ysgubor-y-Coed**; about 20m fishing in total; all stretches (17 beats) contain pools which give good fishing, holding salmon, sea trout and trout; members only, limited membership; st £105 + joining fee £50; apply to Hon Sec; short waiting list; conc for juv. **Tan-y-Mynydd Lakes**; rainbow, brown and brook trout from 1½ to 15lb; 5 purpose-built trout lakes, total 4 acres; contact Bryn and Neil Roberts, **Tan-Y-Mynydd Trout Fishery**, (Tan-y-Mynydd Trout & Leisure), Moelfre, Abergele, Clwyd LL22 9RF (tel: 01745 826722); prices 1 fish (4 hrs) £11, all day 4 fish £25; sporting tickets: 4 hours £9.00; 6 hours £12.00.

St Asaph (Denbighshire). Salmon, sea trout to 14lb and brown trout. Rhyl & St Asaph AA has excellent and various fishing: 6 beats on **Clwyd**; 10 beats on **Elwy**, 18m in St Asaph area; a beat on **Aled**, 1½m double bank at **Llansannan**; trout lake at Prion; st £105 (conc) + £50 joining fee (no joining fee for juniors); day permits for Elwy; and limited dt £20 on all waters, from Foxon's Tackle, Lower Denbigh Rd, St Asaph LL17 0ED (tel: 01745 583583; see website for more info: www.foxons.co.uk), which, in addition to a comprehensive range of tackle, sells various permits (Rhyl & St Asaph AA; Denbigh & Clwyd AC), and offers expert advice on all aspects of fishing both game and coarse. Hotel: Oriel House, Upper Denbigh Road LL17 0LW (tel: 01745 582716). Wirral Game FC has about 1m of single bank near St. Asaph, members only, no dt, waiting list.

Denbigh (Denbighshire). Clwyd, 2m E; salmon, sea trout, brown trout. Denbigh & Clwyd AC has extentive water on Clwyd, **Ystrad**, **Elwy**, **Wheeler**, and also on small stocked trout lake; members only + visitors; dt available on line or from Foxon's (see above); membership from Hon Sec or on line. **Llyn Brenig** (2 wheelyboats) and **Alwen Reservoir**, 11m SW; trout. **Llyn Aled**, 11m SW; coarse; permits for Llyn Brenig, Alwen Reservoir and Llyn Aled from Llyn Brenig Visitor Centre, Cerrigydrudion, Corwen, Conwy LL21 9TT (tel: 01490 420463) where tackle shop and cafe available. Rhyl & St Asaph AA has fishing on **Lake Prion** at Denbigh; brown and rainbow trout; no dt. Bodelwyddan Game Anglers has ½m on River Clwyd near Bodfari. Hotel: Fron Haul.

Ruthin (Denbighshire). Trout, salmon, sea trout. Denbigh & Clwyd AC has water on Clwyd and on **River Clywedog**; dt £16 from Foxon's Tackle, Lower Denbigh Rd, St Asaph LL17 0ED (tel: 01745 583583; web: www.foxons.co.uk) or online (see clubs). Hotel: Ruthin Castle.

Tributaries of the Clwyd

ELWY: Brown trout, sea trout (June onwards), salmon. No coarse fish.

St Asaph (Denbighshire). Capenhurst AC has water; salmon, sea trout and trout; members only (£60 p/year). Wirral Game FC has access to several beats on the middle Elwy, members only, no dt, waiting list. Rhyl & St Asaph AA has Gypsy Lane Waters; no dt. Tackle shop: Foxon's Tackle, Lower Denbigh Rd, St Asaph LL17 0ED (tel: 01745 583583; web: www.foxons.co.uk).

Bodelwyddan (Denbighshire). Bodelwyddan Game Anglers controls three stretches on the Elwy, 1m of which is double bank; and ½m on River Clwyd near Bodfari; also some lake fishing, notably Tai Lake, browns and rainbows; no day tickets available; contact Hon Sec for membership *(see Clubs)*. Tackle shop: Foxon's Tackle, Lower Denbigh Rd, St Asaph LL17 0ED (tel: 01745 583583; web: www.foxons.co.uk).

Llansannan (Denbighshire). Rhyl & St Asaph AA has 1½m double bank on **Aled**; dt from Foxon's. At Llannefydd is **Dolwen**, now leased out to independent club, well stocked with rainbow trout. Tackle shop: Foxon's Tackle, Lower Denbigh Rd, St Asaph LL17 0ED (tel: 01745 583583; web: www.foxons.co.uk); for Dolwen, enquire Llyn Brenig Visitor Centre, Cerrigydrudion, Corwen, Conwy LL21 9TT (tel: 01490 420463).

WHEELER: Trout.

Afonwen (Flintshire). Denbigh & Clwyd AC has 2m; fly only; dt from tackle shop: Foxon's (see above) or on-line.

CLYWEDOG: Salmon and sea trout (very late), trout. Much water strictly preserved.

Ruthin (Denbighshire). Denbigh & Clwyd AC has stretch from confluence with Clwyd to Rhewl; and has water in Llanrhaeadr area; dt £16 from Foxon's Tackle, Lower Denbigh Rd, St Asaph LL17 0ED (tel: 01745 583583; web: www.foxons.co.uk), or on-line. Capenhurst AC has stretch at Bontuchel; salmon, sea trout and trout; members only (£60/year); members children (under 18) may fish free of charge, but must be accompanied by adult.

CONWY

Rises on Migneint, in the County of Conwy and flows between the old Caernarfonshire and Denbighshire boundaries for much of its course, emptying into the Irish Sea near Conwy. The upper part of its valley is noted for its beauty. Spate river with salmon runs throughout season (best from mid-August); grilse from early July; sea trout runs from June to the end of season.

Conwy (Caernarfonshire). Tidal; sea fishing only. Codling, dabs, plaice, bass and mullet above and below suspension bridge; boats for hire. Salmon and sea trout; Prince Albert AS has Belmont fishery, at Maenan Abbey. **Bodelwyddan Game Anglers** have 7 acre lake, **Llyn Syberi**, of coarse fishing on the Bodnant Estate; dt £6 from the garden centre or Post Office in village. **Llyn Gwern Engan**, a small lake on Sychnant Pass Common; rudd, tench, carp, gudgeon; also free fishing, contact Snowdonia National Park Committee, Penrhydeudraeth, Gwynedd LL48 6LF (tel: 01766 770274). **Llyn Nant-y-Cerrig**, Brynymaen, 1½ acres; carp, bream, tench, perch; tickets at lakeside or local tackle shops; for further information contact Llandullas AC (Ian Randle (tel: 01492 516756); or c/o Goleugell, Eglwysbach, Colwyn Bay, Clwyd LL28 5UH (tel: 01492 650314). **Clobryn Pool**, Clobryn Rd, Colwyn Bay; tench, crucian carp, roach, rudd, perch. **Glas Coed Pools**, Bodelwyddan, set in grounds of Bodelwyddan Castle, carp, tench, roach, rudd; no dt. **Trefnant Pool**; stocked with tench, carp, roach, rudd and perch; dt £4 from Foxon's Tackle, Lower Denbigh Rd, St Asaph LL17 0ED (tel: 01745 583583; web: www.foxons.co.uk). Permits for Llyn Nant-y-Cerrig, Clobryn Pool, Glas Coed Pools and Trefant Pool from tackle shops. Tackle shop: Paddy's Bait & Tackle, Unit 4, Happy Valley Road, Llandudno LL30 2LP (tel: 01492 877678).

Dolgarrog (Caernarfonshire). Salmon, sea trout and brown trout; deep tidal pools. Dolgarrog FC has 1½m of tidal water; club also has brown trout fishing on **Llyn Coedty**, **Llyn Eigiau**, **Llyn Melynllyn** and **Llyn Dulyn**, (no boats on these lakes); permits from Hon Sec. **Llyn Cowlyd** (5m W Llanwrst), trout reservoir belongs to Welsh Water plc; st £10 from office at Llyn Brenig Visitor Centre, Cerrigdrudion, Corwen, Conwy LL21 9TT (tel: 01490 420463).

Llanrwst (Denbighshire). Salmon and good sea trout; brown trout poor. Llanrwst AC has various beats on R Conwy at Llanrwst and Trefriw; some sections members only; limited wt and dt from Hon Sec; Sunday fishing allowed. Permits from National Trust, for left bank of **Machno** from junction with Conwy and portion of right bank; dt from Ysbyty Estate Office (tel: 01690 710636). Hotels: Maenan Abbey Hotel, The Priory Hotel LL26 0UL (tel: 01492 660734) (has salmon and trout); and Eagles Hotel.

Betws-y-Coed (Caernarfonshire). Salmon, sea trout, brown trout. Bodelwyddan Game Anglers have right hand bank of Conwy above Waterloo Bridge; members only; apply Hon Sec. Betws-y-Coed AC has 4½m of salmon, sea trout and brown trout fishing on Conwy and **Llugwy**; on the Conwy, from the Waterloo Bridge (left bank) downstream to the confluence of the **Llugwy**; the club also has three trout lakes: **Elsi Lake**, stocked with some American brook trout, brown trout and rainbows; **Llyn Goddionduon** (brown trout); free boat for members; **Llyn Bychan** (brown trout); st £140 (£75 for partially disabled), juv st £20, from Hon Sec; dt from £18 (river), and £15 (lake) from Hon Sec or Pendyffryn Stores (Newsagents), Pendyffryn, Betws-y-Coed LL24 0AN (tel: 01690 710436), which has started to sell tackle and worms. Gwydyr Hotel has 12m of salmon and sea trout fishing; season 20 Mar - 17 Oct; priority tickets for residents; dt subject to availability; for further information contact Owen Wainwright, Gwydyr Hotel, Betws-y-Coed LL24 0AB (tel: 01690 710777). Other hotels: Waterloo; Glan Aber; B&B Tyn-y-Bryn.

Ysbyty Ifan (Caernarfonshire). Brown trout. National Trust has stretch at Ysbyty Ifan and Dinas Water on upper Conwy; fly, worm and spinning; permits from National Trust, Ysbyty Estate Office, Betws y Coed LL24 0HF (tel: 01690 710636); and Robin O Ellis, Bron Ryffydd, Padog, Betws-y-Coed, Conwy LL24 0HF (tel: 01690 710567).

Tributaries of the Conwy

ROE: Trout.

Rowen (Caernarfonshire). **Conwy Water Gardens & Aquatic Centre & Coarse Fishery**, Glyn Isa, Rowen, nr Conwy LL32 8TP (tel: 01492 650063; see website for more info: www.conwywatergardens.co.uk) has 3 lakes stocked with carp, bream, tench, golden orfe, roach, rudd, barbel and chub; dt and half-dt available from shop; bank: 7.30 am to dusk, Tues-Sun, all year (closed Mondays except Bank Holidays); dt £8, 4-hrs £5.50, under-14's £5.50; good access for disabled.

DULYN: Brown trout.

Dolgarrog FC has fishing; dt £12.50, conc, contact Hon Sec.

PORTH-LLWYD: Brown trout; Dolgarrog FC has fishing; dt £12.50 contact Hon. Sec.

DDU: Brown trout.

Pont Dolgarrog (Caernarfonshire). Trout. Ddu enters Conwy ½m below village; drains Llyn Cowlyd. **Llyn Cowlyd**, brown trout and Arctic char; fly only; £10 st from Welsh Water plc. Dolgarrog FC has fishing on **Afon Ddu**; dt £12.50, contact Hon. Secretary.

CRAFNANT: Trout.

Trefriw (Caernarfonshire). Trout fishing on Llyn Crafnant, one of the most beautiful lakes in Wales, 63 acres, stocked rainbow trout supplementing wild brown trout; Sunday fishing; day tickets, boats, cafe, self-catering accommodation, toilets, car parking and information from Mr or Mrs J Collins, Lakeside Café, Llyn Crafnant, Trefriw LL27 0JZ (tel: 01492 640818). Hotel: Princes Arms.

LLUGWY: Salmon, sea trout, brown trout.

Betws-y-Coed (Caernarfonshire). Betws-y-Coed AC has a stretch, both banks, from Swallow Falls downstream to the confluence of Conwy on right bank and to railway bridge on left bank; permits from Hon Sec or Pendyffryn Stores (Newsagents), Pendyffryn, Betws-y-Coed LL24 0AN (tel: 01690 710436).

LLEDR: Trout, sewin, salmon. Both salmon and sewin can enter the Lledr early, from May onwards, but need a 2m flood on the Conwy to run in numbers. Fish move through quickly so timing is critical. Wirral Game FC has 3m of single bank above confluence with Conwy. Members only, no dt, waiting list. Enquire Hon Sec.

Dolwyddelan (Caernarfonshire). Dolwyddelan FA fishing on River Lledr both below the village, and at Pont y Pant; salmon, brown trout and sea trout; good late season salmon runs; sea trout from 1st July; wt (Mon-Fri) and dt for visitors, although wt only for visitors resident in village; permits from Siop-Y-Llan, Church Str, Dolwyddelan, Gwynedd LL25 0NZ (tel: 01690 750237). Prince Albert AS has two stretches, at Bertheos and Hendre; enquire Hon Sec. Hotel: Elen's Castle Hotel, Dolwyddelan.

MACHNO: Trout.

Penmachno (Caernarfonshire). National Trust has water on Machno; also Dinas and Ysbyty at Ifan on same permit; dt available; fly or worm depending on season; no salmon fishing above Conwy Falls; brown trout only; permits from National Trust, Ysbyty Estate Office, Betws y Coed LL24 0HF (tel: 01690 710636); and Robin O Ellis, Bron Ryffydd, Padog, Betws-y-Coed, Conwy LL24 0HF (tel: 01690 710567).

DEE (Welsh)

Usually has a small spring run of fish up to 30lb. Grilse enter in June and there is a run of grilse and summer fish until the end of the season as a rule; with a good mixture of 10-20lb fish Sept/Oct. In spring most fish are taken from Bangor to Corwen. Sewin, including some very large specimens, also run the Dee system in good numbers but catches sometimes do not reflect the numbers running. Trout and grayling from Bangor upstream; best grayling from Newbridge to Corwen. Coarse fish best downstream of Bangor. River holds good bream, roach, chub, barbel, dace, perch and pike.

Holywell (Flintshire). **Forest Hill Trout Farm**, Mostyn, nr Holywell, CH8 9EQ (tel: 01745 560151): fishing on 3 lakes fed by spring water, stocked with home reared rainbow and brown trout; fly and bait; tea, coffee, facilities for disabled. **Seven Springs Fisheries**, Caerwys, nr Mold, Flintshire CH7 5EZ (tel: 01352 720511; web: www.seven-springs.co.uk); 3 pools (newly renovated) over 1 acre, containing rainbow trout; fly and bait; tackle hire; cafe; tickets at fisheries. Coarse fishing at **Gyrn Castle Fishery**, Llanasa, Holywell, Flintshire CH8 9BQ; 2 lakes: 3 acres and 1 acre; well stocked with carp, rudd and tench; heaviest carp to date - 30 lbs; barbless hooks only; open all days of week; dt £15 (large lake £18), accompanied juv £7.50; only 12 permits per day allowed; disabled access; permits from Mr Partington, Gyrn Castle Estate, South Lodge, Glan-yr-Afon (tel: 01745 561672). **Flour Mill Pool** is a 4 acre fishery situated in Greenfield Valley Heritage Park (Admin Centre), Basingwerk House, Greenfield Valley, Holywell, Flintshire CH8 7GH (tel: 01352 714172); crucian carp, tench, perch, bream, ghost, common and mirror carp, gudgeon, roach; permits from Admin Centre; st, dt available.

Connah's Quay (Flintshire). Connah's Quay & Dist AC water; club has coarse fishing at **Wepre Pool**, dt available; **Warren Pool** (Broughton), members only, conc; also **Bala Lake**, members only; st and dt from Deeside Fishing Tackle, 28 Chester Rd East, Shotton, Deeside CH5 1QA (tel: 01244 813674) who provide Dee fishing at Farndon, approx 10 miles.

Chester (Cheshire). Coarse fish. Little permit-free fishing. No licence for coarse fishing in tidal waters. Lymm AC has 2 stretches close to Chester, at Farndon, and Churton, single bank; members only. Free fishing, on Eaton Estate from public footpath that adjoins river. **River Gowy**, which runs into Mersey, passing by Mickle Trafford about 3m from Chester; Warrington AA has water; members only. **Meadow Fishery**, Mickle Trafford CH2 4EB (tel: 01244 300236), rainbow and brown trout; 10 acres; st and dt. Stoke-on-Trent AS has Bolesworth Castle Lake, 12 acres (1m long); float fishing venue; mixed coarse incl rudd, carp and eels; contact Hon Sec. Tackle shops: Henry Monk (Gunmakers) Ltd, 8 Queen Str, CH1 3LG (tel: 01244 320988); Chester Tackle Locker, 140 Tarvin Rd, Boughton CH3 5EE (tel: 01244 345069; see website for more info: www.tacklelocker.co.uk) (Warrington AA tickets).

Holt (Denbighshire). Salmon,sewin, trout, pike, bream. Dee AA rent approx 10m of Dee in the Farndon and Sutton Green area; maps can be obtained from Hon Sec, price 50p plus SAE; assn issues salmon permits (limited) for Sutton Green stretch; separate trout and coarse fish permits; permits from Andy Davies (tel: 01244 545148). Warrington AA has Shocklach Water and stretch at Almere; members only. Prince Albert AS has stretch at Shocklach; members only, no dt. Lavister AC has 1m stretch (left bank) upstream from

Almere Ferry; bream, dace, roach, perch, pike; members only st £10, apply Hon Sec. Waters on the **Grosvenor Estates** at Churton and Aldford downstream to Chester; free freelance fishing but matches must be booked with the Eaton Estate Office, Eccleston, Chester CH4 9ET (tel: 01244 684400). Chester Tackle Locker, 140 Tarvin Rd, Boughton CH3 5EE (tel: 01244 345069; web: www.tacklelocker.co.uk).

Bangor-on-Dee (Denbighshire). Salmon, sewin, trout, coarse fish. Bangor-on-Dee Salmon AA has 5 stretches totalling 6 miles; membership £70 + £35 joining; dt coarse £5; trout £9; salmon and sea trout £16; waters: one downstream from town; one near Shocklach; also Pickhill; Isycoed (3 beats); members only but membership available; permits from the Middle Shop (tel: 01978 780073). Corwen & DAC has 1 ½m single bank at Isycoed; all species; any legal method; members only; apply membership secretary (tel: 01824 710609). Warrington AA has water on Worthenbury Brook; members only. Tackle shops: Deggy's Fishing Tackle, 2 Ruabon Road, Wrexham LL13 7PB (tel: 01978 351815). Hotel: The Buck House Hotel.

Overton (Denbighshire). Bryn-y-Pys AA has 7m on R Dee between Overton Bridge and Bangor-on-Dee; rainbow (stocked) and brown trout, grayling and coarse fish; st £30 + £10 entry fee, £27 (OAP) and free for juniors accompanied by member; dt £10 (trout season) and £4, from Deggy's Fishing Tackle, 2 Ruabon Road, Wrexham LL13 7PB (tel: 01978 351815). Prince Albert AS has a beat at the Boat Inn, Erbistock LL13 0DL (tel: 01978 780666) with salmon, sewin, trout and grayling. **Trench Farm** has 3 pools (3 acres) with carp up to 35lb, tench, rudd, roach and crucian carp; day tickets only £6, conc (under 16's must be accompanied by adult); contact Mr or Mrs M A Huntbach, Trench Farm, Redhall Lane, Penley, Wrexham LL13 0NA (tel: 01978 710098; web: www.trenchfarmfisheries.co.uk).

Cefn Mawr (Denbighshire). Trout, salmon, sewin, coarse fish (including pike and excellent grayling fishing); world fly-fishing championships have been held on this water; and site of Commonwealth Fly Fishing championships 2002 and 2006, plus 5 river internationals and 4 European grayling championships; also World Youth Fly Fishing championships; Maelor Angling Ltd has 6½m, with good salmon fishing from late spring onwards, particularly mid-summer to autumn, on 2 beats, coarse fishing, stocked brown trout, and very good winter grayling; st £230 salmon, st trout/grayling £60, dt £10, 2 fish per day limit; contact Managing Director (tel: 01978 820608) or Derek's *(below);* coarse fishing good September onwards. Newbridge AA has Wynnstay Estate Waters from Newbridge Old Bridge downstream on wooded bank, approx 3m; salmon, trout, grayling, dace and pike fishing; members only, except for salmon rods on top beat; members to reside within local radius of 5m; salmon permits from Hon Sec, membership £45 per annum; salmon rods £60, one named day throughout season for non-members. Tackle shop: Derek's Cycles, London House, Well St, Cefn Mawr, Wrexham LL14 3AE (tel: 01978 821841). Hotel: Wynnstay Arms, Ruabon; Greenbank, Victoria Sq, Llangollen LL20 8EU (tel: 01978 861835). Prince Albert AS has about 1m single bank at Dee Lodge upstream of Newbridge bridge, members only, no dt. Wirral Game FC owns a short beat downstream of bridge, members only, no dt. Waiting list, enquire Hon Sec.

Llangollen (Denbighshire). Salmon, sea trout, brown trout, grayling. Llangollen AA has 14m of bank fishing in and around the town; all waters have good access and parking provided; downstream from Horseshoe Falls, all methods for salmon and trout; above Horseshoe Falls, all methods for salmon, fly only for trout and grayling; trout water stocked with 5,500 trout per season, averaging 12" with larger fish up to 3lbs; both trout and grayling fishing excellent and near best on River Dee; salmon fishing good from May to end of season, average catch for club is 65 fish; permits from Watkin & Williams Hardware, 6 Berwyn St, LL20 8ND (tel: 01978 860652); open Sunday. Hand Hotel, Bridge St, Llangollen, Denbighshire LL20 8PL (tel: 01978 860303), has own stretch of water below the bridge on right bank; fishing on hotel stretch of river for hotel residents only.

Glyndyfrdwy (Denbighshire). Salmon, sewin, trout and grayling. Corwen & Dist AC has 1¼m (mainly single bank) on Berwyn Arms Water; 5 named salmon pools; fly only for trout and grayling; contact Membership Sec (tel: 01824 710609). Midland Flyfishers has 3m of trout fishing on the Dee from Groeslwyd to Glyndyfrdwy; dt £10; D Jones, Llanon, Twynedd (tel: 01490 430363); Watkin & Williams Hardware, 6 Berwyn St, Llangollen, LL20 8ND (tel: 01978 861531); Berwyn Arms Hotel, Glyndyfrdwy, Corwen LL21 9EY (tel: 01490 430210). Wirral Game FC has over a mile of single bank between Carrog and Corwen. Waiting list, no dt. Enquire Hon Sec.

Corwen (Denbighshire). Corwen & Dist AC has **Rhug Estate** Trust, approx 2½m mostly double bank, trout and grayling, fly only except winter grayling; 200 metres stretch at **Cynwyd** including large holding pool, salmon, sewin, trout and grayling; ¾m stretch at **Carrog**, 3 named pools and runs, salmon, sewin, trout and grayling; 1½m stretch at Glyndyfrdwy; 2 stretches, 1m (double bank) and ¾m (double bank), between Cynwyd and Llandrillo, salmon, sewin, trout and grayling; and Chain Pool at Bonwm; five stretches varying in length, mostly in Corwen area; salmon, sewin, trout and grayling; club also has several miles of water on **Rivers Alwen** and **Ceirw** at Bettws Gwerfil Goch and Maerdy; salmon and sea trout, mid to late season; and good trout early and late; bait fishing for winter grayling allowed on most club waters; no dt; members only; joining fee £25-£50; various categories of ticket £10-£140; apply to Membership Sec (tel: 01824 710609). Capenhurst AC has stretch at Carrog; salmon, sea trout, trout and grayling; members only (£60 p/year). **Gwyddelwern Pool**, Corwen, ¾ acre lake, stocked with coarse fish (large carp and tench); permits from D M Lewis, Maes-y-Llyn, Gwyddelwern, Corwen, Wrexham LL21 9DG (tel: 01490 412761). Rod licences from Corwen Post Office. Hotels: Owain Glyndwr, Central, both Corwen; and ; Berwyn Arms Hotel, Glyndyfrdwy, Corwen LL21 9EY (tel: 01490 430210).

Cynwyd (Denbighshire). Trout, grayling, salmon, sewin. Corwen & Dist AC has stretch on Dee at Glascoed; plus 1¾m double bank (salmon, sewin, trout and grayling) above Cynwyd Bridge; Sunday fishing, fly only; members only; st available, contact membership secretary (tel: 01824 710609). Crown Inn, Llanfihangel, Glyn Myfyr LL21 9UL (tel: 01490 420209), has free fishing for guests. Prince Albert AS has a short beat at Cynwyd, members only, no dt.

Llandrillo (Denbighshire). Salmon, sewin, trout, grayling, perch and pike. Corwen & DAC has water at Cillan Bridge, 1m single bank below and 1½m above bridge double bank; members only; st at various prices, apply membership secretary (tel: 01824 710609).

Llandderfel (Merioneth). Salmon, sewin, trout, grayling. Corwen & DAC has ¾m single bank below village; members only; apply membership secretary (tel: 01824 710609). Pale Hall Country House Hotel, Llandderfel, nr Bala, Gwynedd LL23 7PS (tel: 01678 530285; web: www.palehall.co.uk), has prime salmon and trout fishing during game season; permits free for hotel residents; excellent grayling fishing provides ideal winter sport with specimens reaching 3lbs; fishing is based on 6m of **River Dee** with access to brown trout in mountain lake. Prince Albert AS has 1m right bank above Llandderfel bridge. Members only, no dt.

Bala (Merioneth). Salmon, trout, perch, pike and grayling. Bala & Dist AA has water, including from confluence with Tryweryn to outlet Bala Lake and fishing on Bala Lake (members only); also **Rivers Tryweryn** (both banks between weir and Tryweryn Bridge; both banks above and below Bont Tyn-Ddol); **Lliw** (upper and lower reaches near Llanuwchllyn); **Llafar** (left bank d/stream from road bridge; both banks u/stream from road bridge); **Lynn Tryweryn** (trout, fly only); flyfishing only during game fishing season; st £50 (residents), £60 (non-residents), conc £20 (residents), £35 (non-residents), dt water (Bala outflow only), conc; available from Derwen Stores, 6 Stryd Fawr, LL23 7AG (tel: 01678 521084); Post Office, High Str, Bala (tel: 01678 520317); Tourist Information Centre, Penllyn Pensarn Rd, Bala, Gwynedd LL23 7SR (tel: 01678 521021). **Bala Lake** or **Llyn Tegid**; trout, roach, perch, pike, grayling, eel; owned by Snowdonia National Park Authority; permits from Lake Warden, Warden's Office, 24 Ffordd Pensarn, Bala LL23 7SR (tel: 01678 520626); or on bank or pay-and-display machines in car park. Hotels and accommodation: White Lion; Royal; Plas Coch.

Llanuwchllyn (Merioneth). Trout and grayling. Prince Albert AS has trout and grayling fishing on nine stretches of Dee, here and elsewhere and Twrch; members only; waiting list. Dolhendre Uchaf Caravan Park, Llanuwchllyn, Bala LL23 7TD (tel: 01678 540629), has private fishing for owners of caravans on site only, on the River Lliw (brown trout and coarse fish).

Tributaries of the Dee

ALYN: Trout. Drains hills to west of Clwydian Range, runs past Mold towards Wrexham and finally opens into lower part of Dee on Cheshire Plains near Farndon at Almere.

Rossett (Denbighshire). Trout. Rossett & Gresford FF has wild brown trout fishing on 2½m stretch (both banks) on well maintained and stocked section of R Alyn between Rossett and Gresford, nr Wrexham; members only; fly only; bag limit; st £45 and £5 (juniors); permits from Hon Sec. Warrington AA have water lower down and stretch on Dee, at Almere. Tackle shop: David Gibson, 13 Pepper Row, Pepper Str, Chester CH1 1EA (tel: 01244 316132). Hotel: Trevor Arms Hotel.

Wrexham (Denbighshire). Wrexham & Dist FA has water on Alyn; brown trout fishing, fly only; permits issued to guests of members only. Dee Valley Water plc, Packsaddle, Wrexham Rd, Rhostyllen, Wrexham, Clwyd LL14 4DS (tel: 01978 846946), manage 3 local reservoirs: **Ty Mawr Reservoir** (20 acres), **Penycae Upper Reservoir** (7 acres) and **Penycae Lower Reservoir** (5 acres); the fishing is quiet and secluded with very clear water; possible to locate and stalk individual fish (stocked up to 6 lbs); brown and rainbow trout; fly fishing only; st £300, dt £24, half-day £15; at least 12 hrs notice must be given in order to reserve a rod; number of rods limited; contact the bailiff (tel: 01978 840116). Ponciau AS has **Ponciau Pool**, 2½m from Wrexham; roach, bream, tench, carp; members only. Rhostyllen AC (affiliated to Dee AA) has coarse fishing at pool near Sontley; club also has access to extensive game and coarse fisheries on **Dee**, **Severn**. Tackle shops: Deggy's Fishing Tackle, 2 Ruabon Road, Wrexham, Clwyd LL13 7PB (tel: 01978 351815); Derek's Cycles, London House, Well St, Cefn Mawr, Wrexham LL14 3AE (tel: 01978 821841). Hotel: Trevor Arms Hotel, Marford, Wrexham.

Llay (Denbighshire). Llay AA has good coarse fishing on **Llay Reservoir** (tench, carp, rudd, perch); and **Cymau Pool** (carp, rudd, tench, perch, roach, crucian carp and gudgeon) at Caergwrle; members only; st £12 (jun £6 and OAP £6) from Hon Sec, local shops or bailiff on bank; no dt; village residents have preference; st entitles angler to fish 14m of River Dee around Holt and Farndon area. Hotels: Crown Inn.

Hope (Flintshire). Wrexham & Dist FA has trout fishing from Pontblyddyn to Hope; fly only; permits issued to members' guests only. Rainbow trout fishing at **Tree Tops Fly Fishery**; eight lakes stocked with rainbow; rods for hire and basic tuition by arrangement; cafe, tackle shop and accommodation; for further details contact Joy or Peter Price, Tree Tops Fly Fishery, Llanfynydd, nr Wrexham LL11 5HR (tel: 01352 770648; web: www.walesselfcatering.co.uk).

Mold (Flintshire). Mold FF has fishing on **New Lake**, Llanferres; fishery stocked with brown and rainbow trout; they also have trout fishing on **Pistyll Pool** at Nercwys, 1½ acres (stocked brown and rainbow trout); members only; day tickets if accompanied by member, conc for juv; enquire about

River Dee fishing. **Pen-y-Ffrith Carp & Coarse Fishery**, Llandegla Rd, Llanarmon-yn-Ial, Mold, CH7 4QX (tel: 01824 780501; also see website: www.pen-y-ffrithcoarsefishery.co.uk) ; 3 spring fed lakes well stocked; dt £6, conc; night fishing on specimen lake with carp to 30lb, £15 per evening (incldes next day fishing); book in at lodge. Buckley AA has **Trap Pool**, a 4 ½ acre good mixed fishery of varying depths; dt £6 (1 rod), conc; juv must be accompanied by adult; permits from Lionel's Tackle Shop, 11a Ewloe Place, Buckley CH11 3NJ (tel: 01244 543191; web: www.fish-in-the.net); also membership for Warrington AA; and for Llay coarse fishery. Coarse fishing at **Gweryd Lakes**, Gweryd Lodge, Plas Lane, Llanarmon-yn-lal, nr Mold CH7 4QJ (tel: 01824 780230) (web: www.gwerydlakes.co.uk); 12½ acre lake with specimen carp; 1¼ acre lake with silver fish, crucian carp, perch and tench, etc; dt from £5, from £6 Fri/Sun, conc for juv; tackle shop; cafe; accom on site.

Cilcain (Flintshire). Cilcain FFA has four trout reservoirs nearby (largest is 4 acres); stocked monthly with rainbow trout; fly only; dt £14, 2 brace limit; permits from the village Post Office (please book, tel: 01352 740184). **Nant-y-Gain Fishery**, 2 pools stocked with brown and rainbow trout, fly only; access and facilities for disabled anglers; tickets and refreshments available on site; contact Glyn or Judy Jones, Nant-y-Gain Fishery, Cilcain, Flintshire, CH7 5PE (tel: 01352 740936).

Nannerch (Denbighshire). **Sarn Mill Fly and Coarse Fisheries**, Denbigh Road, Nannerch, nr Mold CH7 5RH (tel: 01352 720854), 4 pools; 2 pools fly only, stocked with wild browns and rainbow trout; 2 pools coarse fishing, roach, rudd, tench and carp; open all year; disabled access; dt on bank. **Wal Goch Fly Fishing**; 2 lakes (2½ and ½ acre); brown and rainbow trout; open all year; fly only; max 20 rods; c&r,

trickle stocked; contact Philip Robinson, Wal Goch Fly Fishing, Wal Goch Farm, CH7 5RP (tel: 01352 741378).

CEIRIOG: Trout, grayling and sea trout.

Chirk (Denbighshire). Ceiriog Fly Fishers have 8m, both banks, from Dee Junction to Chirk, and from Chirk Aquaduct to Pontfadog Village; good fishing, trout and grayling, and recent runs of sea trout Aug to Oct; fly only; keepered and stocked with browns; no tickets; strictly members and guests only; st £125 plus joining fee from to Hon Sec, conc. **Chirk Trout Fishery**, LL14 5BL (tel: 01691 772420); two small lakes for fly only, plus a children's lake; stocked with rainbow, brown, and American brook trout; dt available. Hotel: The Hand Hotel, Chirk; Golden Pheasant, Pontfadog, Llwyn Mawr.

Glyn Ceiriog (Denbighshire). Glyn Ceiriog FC has trout fishing on **River Teirw** at Pandy, nr Glyn Ceiriog; dt from The Cross Grocery Shop, Glyn Ceiriog.

Llanarmon Dyffryn Ceiriog (Denbighshire). Ceiriog, 2½m, brown trout. The West Arms Hotel, Llanarmon D C, Llangollen LL20 7LD (tel: 01691 600665), has 1½m (both banks) trout fishing; shallow clear water with some deep pools; free to hotel residents; dt for non-residents; limit 2 rods per day; fly only. Hand at Llanarmon, Llanarmon DC, Ceiriog Valley, nr Llangollen, LL20 7LD (tel: 01691 600666; www.thehandhotel.co.uk) can arrange trout and coarse fishing for guests.

ALWEN: Flows out of large reservoir (trout, perch) on Denbigh Moors and enters Dee near Corwen. Very good trout fishing and some salmon.

Cerrig-y-Drudion (Denbighshire). Cerrig-y-Drudion AA has river fishing on Alwen and on **R Ceirw**,

parallel with A5 road. Crown Inn, Llanfihangel Glyn Myfyr, has fishing on ¼m of bank for small wild brown trout; fly and worm; permits (free to hotel residents). Dwr Cymru Welsh Water plc manage three reservoirs north of village. **Llyn Brenig**, 919-acre reservoir amid heather moorland and forest; fly only, brown and rainbow trout; increasing numbers of pike have resulted in winter pike fishing now being available; Llyn Brenig was the venue for 1990 World Fly Fishing Championship and regular Home Fly Fishing Internationals; st £499, dt £17, evening £15, boats £19.50 w/ends, weekdays £17.50 per day, subject to review; Wheelyboat £6 (wheelchair users only); season: Mar-Nov; concessions OAP & jun; block bookings offered; contact Llyn Brenig Visitor Centre, Cerrigdrudion, Corwen, Conwy LL21 9TT (tel: 01490 420463). **Alwen Reservoir** (368 acre), moorland reservoir stocked with rainbows, although also natural population of brown trout and perch; dt £13, conc; fly fishing, spinning and worming permitted; catch limit 6 trout; season Mar-Oct incl, apply Llyn Brenig Visitor Centre (above); **Llyn Aled Reservoir** (110 acres), holds large numbers of roach, perch and pike and is a good match venue; occasional wild brown trout; no close season for coarse fish; concessions OAP and jun; tickets (dt £4.50, conc) and further information from Llyn Brenig Visitor Centre, Cerrigdrudion, Corwen, Conwy LL21 9TT (tel: 01490 420463); where there is also a café and well-stocked tackle shop. Fly fishing at **Dragonfly Fisheries**, on the A5, Cerrig-y-Drudion, Corwen, Clwyd LL21 0RU (tel: 01490 420530); blue trout (2001 Welsh record at 10¾lb), tiger (to 12lb), rainbow and brown trout; stocked daily with fish from 3lb min to 28lb; dt £25, plus variants, conc; min 2 hours £10 (c&r), 4 hours

£17 (2 fish); 6 hours £20 (2 fish), 8 hours £25 (3 fish).

TRYWERYN: Joins Dee below Lake Bala. Good trout fishing but extensively used for whitewater rafting and caneoing.

Bala (Merioneth). Bala & DAA has stretch on Tryweryn, **Llyn Celyn** and mountain lake **Cwm Prysor**; also Dee outflow; Dee below sluice gates; Dee at Llandderfel; tickets from Hon Sec, tackle shop (below) or Tourist Information, Penllyn Pensarn Rd, LL23 7YE (tel: 01678 521021). Tackle shop: Rowlands Spanner-a-Hanner, 9-11 Tegid Str LL23 7UR (tel: 01678 520382).

DYFI (DOVEY)

Rises on east side of Aran Fawddwy and flows 30m south and south-west to Cardigan Bay at Aberdovey. Has long estuary and provides splendid sport with sewin (sea trout) and salmon. Many large sea trout taken. Salmon run in from July to October; sea trout from May on. Best months: July, August, September. Small tributaries hold some little trout, and permission can generally be obtained from owners.

Aberdyfi (Ceredigion). At estuary mouth; surf and estuary fishing. Free trout fishing in Happy Valley on permission of farmers; stream; trout small.

Machynlleth (Powys). Sea trout and salmon. The New Dovey Fishery Association controls 15m (both banks) of river between Llyfnant stream and Nant Ty-Mawr and left bank, from opposite Llyfnant mouth to Abergwybedyn brook; season rods available when vacancies occur (long waiting list - contact Hon Sec); upper reaches st £163 from Hon Sec; limited visitors wt £184 from Mrs L Humphreys, Post Office, Cemmaes Rd, Machynlleth, Powys SY20 8JZ (tel: 01650 511422); and Hon Sec (tel/fax: 01654 702721); Reads Petrol Station at Machynlleth (tel: 01654 703360); dt £16 for upper reaches, juv dt £4 (when accompanied by adult); no Sunday fishing. Prince Albert AS has fishing on single bank Dulas North, tributary of Dyfi E1/2m upstream. Corris Caravan Park SY20 9HD has fishing for caravan owners only (tel: 01654 761220). Permission from farmers for **Pennal Stream**; rapid water; trout small. Hotels: Wynnstay Arms, White Lion.

Llanbrynmair (Powys). On **River Twymyn**, a tributary of **Dyfi**; sewin, salmon. Llanbrynmair & Dist AC has water on Twymyn from village to confluence with Dyfi (apart from one stretch held by Prince Albert AS); and wild brown trout fishing on **Lakes Gwyddior** and **Coch-Hwyad**, both lakes 25 acres with boats on each; best months Jul-Oct for river; lakes mid-April to Sept; dt water, conc available from Mrs D R Lewis, Bryn-Llugwy, Llanbrynmair, Powys SY19 7AA (tel: 01650 521385). Prince Albert AS control 3m of Twymyn (members only), and Dyfi at **Aberangell** and **Dinas Mawddwy**; enquiries to Hon Sec.

Dinas Mawddwy (Powys). Sewin, salmon, trout; fishing good. The Dolbrodmaeth Riverside Hotel, Dinas Mawddwy, Machynlleth, Powys SY20 9LP (tel: 01650 531333), has ½m stretch on Dyfi in grounds of hotel; sewin, salmon, trout; free to hotel residents; tickets available. Dolgellau AA issues tickets for approx 12m-13m of Rivers **Mawddach** and **Wnion**, and **Llyn Cynwch**, which club is stocking with additional large fish (all in vicinity of Dolgellau). Prince Albert AS has 2½m stretch of Dyfi at Gwastad Coed, Gwerhefin; members only.

DWYRYD

Rises in small, nameless pool 3m above Tanygrisiau and flows into Cardigan Bay through estuary north of Harlech. A classic spate river with deep pools which hold good numbers of fish following a spate. Sea trout enter the river towards the end of May: these tend to be large fish with the 1-3lbs following in June. Fresh sea trout still enter the river in October. The first run of salmon appear in July with increasing numbers in August, September and October.

Maentwrog (Denbighshire). Dwyryd Anglers Ltd has fishing at **Tan-y-Bwlch Fishery** on River Dwryrd (north bank only), 1¾m downstream from Maentwrog Bridge; st £60 (limited), wt £30 (any 7 consecutive days) and dt £10; concessions for juniors and OAPs; disabled platform on river; permits from Gareth Price, Hafan, Fford Peniel, Ffestiniog, Gwynedd LL41 4LP (tel: 01766 762451); Dwyryd Anglers Ltd also have 3½m (double bank) of private water on Dwyryd; a very limited number of season rods may become available, contact Gareth Price for information.

Blaenau Ffestiniog (Merioneth). Principal trout lakes controlled by Cambrian AA as follows: **Dubach**, well stocked with brown trout; **Manod**, fishing can be rather rough due to rocky shore conditions, holds plenty of fish; **Morwynion**, most easily accessible, average weight 12ozs; special area of conservation; stocked with rainbows twice yearly; **Cwmorthin**, well stocked with brown trout 8-9ozs; other Cambrian AA lakes: **Dubach-y-Bont**, fish to 2½lbs no rarity, and up to 4lb, **Barlwyd**, **Cwm Foel** and **Cwm Corsiog**; st £50, wt £30, dt £10, conc. **Tanygrisiau Reservoir** (2m NW), 95 acres, stocked with brown and rainbow trout; controlled by local syndicate; spinning and bait fishing allowed. Permits for Cambrian AA waters and for Tanygrisiau from PO Llan Ffestiniog; Newsagents, Siop Cynan, 34 High Street, Blaenau Ffestiniog (tel: 01766 830910); Penrhyn Guns, 7 High Street, Penrhyndeudraeth LL48 6BN (tel: 01766 770339; web: www.ukgunroom.com). Hotels: Pengwern Arms, Blaenau Ffestiniog.

Tributaries of the Dwyryd

PRYSOR:

Trawsfynydd (Merioneth). Prysor AA controls 5m on **Prysor River**, which provides good fishing towards the end of the season when late trout run upstream; season 1 Apr-30 Sep; also 3m on upper **Eden**: salmon and sea trout July onwards; Assn also manages **Trawsfynydd Lake**, 1200 acres; brown and rainbow trout (average 1lb 10oz), perch and rudd; season: rainbow trout 1 Feb-31 Dec; brown trout 3 April-30 Sept; coarse fish 1 Feb-31 Dec; fly fishing, bottom fishing and spinning; boats with motors for daily hire; fly only from boats; st £250, dt £16; boats with motors per day £45 (pair) £36 (single); fly only from boats; regular trout stocking; membership and permit enquiries to Hon Sec. Tickets J & J Newsagents, Manchester House, Trawsfynydd LL41 4UB (tel: 01766 540234). Hotels: Cross Foxes, Blaenau Ffestiniog; Grapes, Maentwrog. Accommodation at Old Mill Farmhouse, Fron Oleu Farm LL41 4UN (tel/fax: 01766 540397); and in self-catering chalets at Trawsfynydd Holiday Village.

DYSYNNI

Rises in Llyn Cau, on steep southern side of Cader Idris, then falls rather rapidly via Dol-y-Cau. Falls into Talyllyn Valley about half a mile above well known Talyllyn Lake. Emerging from lake, flows westwards as typical upland stream to Abergynolwyn where, joined by the Gwernol, it turns north through narrow valley until it enters upper end of broad Dysynni Valley. At Peniarth it becomes deep and sluggish and finally enters Cardigan Bay 1½m north of Tywyn. Trout along whole length and tributaries, and sea trout (sewin) and salmon travel beyond Talyllyn Lake and up to Dolgoch on Afon Fathew. In lower reaches good sport may be had, early and late in season, with trout and sewin; July and August generally best. Salmon are in very low numbers in the Dysynni and sewin are the primary migratory fish in the system. Also excellent grey mullet and bass in estuary.

Tywyn (Merioneth). Salmon, sewin, trout, eels, with grey mullet in tidal parts and excellent bass fishing at mouth and from adjacent beaches. Rod licence only needed for fishing on estuary. Tywyn Post Office, Garnedd High St LL36 9AD (tel: 01654 710444) issues permits for several beats on River Dysynni and EA rod licences and permits for Peniarth. **Penowern Water**, ½m left bank from confluence with Afon Fathew; private waters; contact Richard Jones, Ysguborlau, Bryncrug LL36 9RY. **Peniarth Estate** has 3½m of double bank, either side of the Dysynni Bridge; st, wt, dt available; contact the Estate Office, Peniarth, Llanegryn LL36 9UD (tel: 01654 710101); tickets from Siop-y-Bont, Brycrug; Middle Peniarth Estate beat is private. Ystumaner AA water near Abergynolwyn upstream towards Cedris Bridge, 2m, st, dt £7, from Railway Inn, Abergynolwyn. Prince Albert AA has Upper Peniarth Estate beat; members only. Peniarth Estate also has caravan park, 3m from Tywyn (retains 5 rods). Tackle shop: Barry's Fishing Tackle, 6 College Green, Tywyn LL36 9BS (tel: 01654 710357; web: www.barrysfishingtackle.com).

Abergynolwyn (Merioneth). Salmon, sea trout, brown trout. Ystumaner AA has 2m on Dysynni; bag limit 4 trout, 2 salmon, 2 sea trout; membership for local residents only; visitors permits: st £25, wt £12, dt £7 (conc for jun), from Railway Inn, Abergynolwyn (tel: 01654 782279). Hotel: Tyn-y-Cornel *(see below)*.

Talyllyn (Merioneth). Salmon, sea trout, brown trout. Tyn-y-Cornel Hotel and Talyllyn Fishery, Talyllyn, Tywyn, Gwynedd LL36 9AJ (tel: 01654 782282); issues permits for **River Dysynni**, 1½m of all double bank fishing; **Talyllyn Lake**, 220 acres; flies and leader material from fishery office *(see above)*; ghillies and fishing tuition by prior arrangement, boat hire (with engine) and tackle hire; day tickets available; Talyllyn: dt £15, half-dt £13.50; boat permit additional full day £18, part day £13; hotel also sells permits for Ystumaner AA; **Llyn Bugeilyn**, 45 acres; first rate brown trout fishing; dt £11; + £11 for boat. The Wye and Usk Foundation now adminster the fishing on Llyn Bugeilyn.

GLASLYN

Rises in Llyn Glaslyn, 3m south-west of Pen-y-Gwyrd, and flows through three lakes to Beddgelert then along Pass of Aberglaslyn to lower reaches and Porthmadog, where it enters the sea. Noted sea trout river and efforts are being made to increase salmon run. Best trout fishing in upper reaches, mountain lakes and tributaries. Best spots for salmon and sewin are: Glaslyn Hotel Bridge; Verlas; and above the pass. A fast-flowing river: steep access to best pools. The Glaslyn is one of the earliest sea trout rivers in Wales with fish running from April onwards.

Porthmadog (Caernarfonshire). Glaslyn AA has most of 8m both banks of R Glaslyn between Porthmadog and Beddgelert, and far bank of **Dinas Lake**; trout, sea trout and salmon; no prawn fishing; no maggot fishing; bait permitted, worm & shrimp; boat fishing (not for visitors at present); st, wt and dt available: enquire Hon Sec; conc for OAPs, dis and juv; tickets from Pikes Newsagent, 63 High Street LL49 9LR (tel: 01766 512578); K Owen, Llyndu Farm, Nantgwynant, Beddgelert, Gwynedd LL55 4NL; Penrhyn Guns *(below)*; P O Beddgelert. **Llyn Cwmystradllyn**, Caernarfon Rd, wild brown trout fishery and rainbows, 95 acres, 6 bag limit; dt £14; conc; permits from D & E Hughes, Walsall Stores, 24 Penlan St, Pwllheli, LL53 5DE (tel: 01758 613291; web: www.llynangling.net). **Llyn Glan Morfa Mawr Fishery**, Glan Morfa Farm, Porthmadog LL54 5TP; 5 acre lake, rainbow trout; contact Justin Roberts (tel: 01766 514980/513333); rainbow (av 2lb - any method) 8 bag limit, dt £15; father & son ticket (4 fish each) £17, from Fishery; camping field adjacent. **Bron Eifion** Fishing Lakes and Lodges, Criccieth, Gwynedd LL52 0SA (tel: 01766 523512; see website for more info: www.broneifion.com); 6 acre coarse lake; centre of excellence for Wales. Penrhyn Guns, 7 High Street, Penrhyndeudraeth LL48 6BN (tel: 01766 770339; web: www.ukgunroom.com), who also sell permits for Artro & Talsarnau FA

waters; st £40, dt £8, conc (coarse fishing lake dt £6); at Llangecwn society has Tecwyn Isaf and Tecwyn Uchaf; lower lake is mixed coarse; upper lake wild browns up to 6lb; both dt from tackle shop; also at Llanbedr, Cook's Dam, 2 acre lake stocked during season with rainbows; dt. Tackle shop: Angling Wales, Sheffield House, 41-43 High St, Criccieth LL52 0EY (tel: 01766 522805; see website for more info: www.anglingwales.co.uk). Hotels: Royal Sportsman, High St, Porthmadog; Royal Madog Arms Hotel, Tremadog.

Beddgelert (Caernarfonshire). Sea trout and salmon. Best for sea trout mid-May to early Sept; salmon May-Oct. Glaslyn AA has Glaslyn from Beddgelert to Porthmadog; and **Llyn Dinas**, 2m NE, sea trout and salmon; season starts 20 March to 17 Oct (browns start 31 May in lower regions); an early sea trout river; wt; left (far) bank (only) on Llyn Dinas, no boats yet; concessions jun & OAP; permits from Beddgelert Post Office, Llys Buckley, Caernarfon Road, Beddgelert LL55 4UY (tel: 01766 890201). National Trust has fishing here let to Glaslyn AA, **Nantgwynant**; information from North West Wales Area Office (tel: 01690 713300); National Trust also water at **Aberglaslyn**; Glaslyn AA fishing; dt available; apply Hon Sec Enid Edwards (tel: 01766 770339). Many good hotels, guest houses, and B&B.

GWYNEDD (rivers and streams)

ABER. **Aber**, nr Llanfairfechan (Caernarfonshire). Aber rises in Llyn Anafon, runs to Aber and sea in 2m. Trout (average 7-8 in). Now a Nature Reserve. No fishing.

ARTRO. Rises in Llyn Cwm Bychan, 6m E of Harlech, and enters sea 1m below Llanbedr. Good bass fishing in tidal waters. Noted for night fishing for sea trout. Good fly pools below village and above Dol-y-Bebin.

Llanbedr (Caernarfonshire). Artro & Talsarnau FA has salmon and sea trout fishing on Artro; assn also has water on **River Nantcol**, brown trout; **Cooke's Dam**, rainbow trout; **Llyn Tecwyn Uchaf** (wild brown trout up to 5lb) and **Llyn Tecwyn Isaf** (stocked with carp to 15lb, roach, rudd, tench, perch) at Talsarnau; **River Glyn** at Talsarnau, sea trout and salmon; and **Llyn Fedw** at Harlech, brown trout; assn also has **Lake Bodlyn**, 5 acres; brown trout; st £45, wt £20, dt £8 (coarse £5); concessions for OAP and junior; permits from Spar The Old Bakery, Newsagent & General Stores, Llanbedr LL45 2LE (tel: 01341 241380); and tackle shops in Penrhyndeudraeth and Barmouth. Tackle shop: Beachcaster, St Annes Chambers, High Street, Barmouth LL42 1AR (tel: 01341 281537). Hotels: Victoria.

DARON. **Aberdaron** (Caernarfonshire). Daron and Cyll-y-Felin run down two valleys and join at Aberdaron; restocked and hold good sized trout. Sea fishing for mackerel, pollack, lobster, crab, etc., from rocks or boat. Tackle and bait from GW & AG Jones, Eleri Stores, Aberdaron LL53 8BG (tel: 01758 760233).

DWYFOR. Best part of river lies 1m W of Criccieth, where there is length of 12m unobstructed and good for fly fishing. Salmon fishing has greatly improved owing to restrictions on netting. Sewin very good; late June to Oct; night fishing best.

Criccieth (Caernarfonshire). Sea trout and salmon. Criccieth, Llanystumdwy & Dist AA controls about 10m both banks; assn also has about 2m on **Dwyfach**; shorter river than Dwyfor (about 10m) and rather heavily wooded; st £110, wt £55, 72-hrs £33, dt £16.50, from Angling Wales, Sheffield House, 41-43 High St, Criccieth LL52 0EY (tel: 01766 522805; see website for more info: www.anglingwales.co.uk). Rod licences from Post Office. **Eisteddfa Fisheries**, Eisteddfa Uchaf, Pentrefelin LL52 0PT (tel: 01766 523425; see website for more info: www.eisteddfa-fisheries.com); 5 lakes, one mixed coarse lake and one carp; one trout; one family coarse; fly only trout lake; tickets on bank. Good sea fishing in this area. Hotels: Glyn y Coed; Lion; George IV; Caerwylan.

ERCH. **Pwllheli** (Caernarfonshire). Pwllheli & Dist AA has brown trout, sea trout and salmon fishing on **Rivers Erch** and **Rhydhir**; Assn also has brown and rainbow trout fishing on **Llyn Cwmystradllyn**; approx 10m NW; 95-acre lake holding wild brown trout and stocked rainbows; an upland fishery, situated in the heart of the rugged foothills of Snowdonia; bag limit 6 trout per day; st £70, wt £35, dt £14 (includes two rivers); concessions for juniors and OAPs; permits from D & E Hughes, Walsall Stores, 24 Penlan St, LL53 5DE (tel: 01758 613291; web: www.llynangling.net); Angling Wales, Sheffield House, 41-43 High St, Criccieth LL52 0EY (tel: 01766 522805; see website for more info: www.anglingwales.co.uk).

GEIRCH. **Nefyn** (Caernarfonshire). Geirch, 2m W, 5m long; good sea fishing at Morfa Nefyn.

GWYRFAI. Issues from Llyn Cwellyn, near Snowdon, and flows into Menai

Strait through Betws Garmon and Llanwnda. Salmon, sea trout, trout.

Betws Garmon (Caernarfonshire). Seiont, Gwyrfai and Llyfni AS controls much of Gwyrfai; salmon, sea trout and brown trout; wt £80, dt £17; the society provides top quality self-catering accommodation in Old Corn Mill, on banks of Llyfni at Pantllyfni; contact Hon Sec for details (tel: 01248 670666); society permits and accommodation from Cwellyn Arms Hotel, Rhyd-ddu, LL54 6TL (tel: 01766 890321; see website for more info: www.snowdoninn.co.uk). **Bontnewydd Fishery**, salmon, sea and brown trout; dt from G J M Wills, Bryn Mafon, Caethro, Caernarfon LL55 2TE (tel: 01286 673379 - after 6pm) or his Bangor office, Treborth Leisure; (tel: 01248 364399).

Rhyd-Ddu (Caernarfonshire). Seiont, Gwyrfai and Llyfni AS offers boat fishing on **Llyn Nantlle**, salmon and sea trout fishing; **Llyn Cwm Dwythwch**, Llanbers, and **Llyn Cwm Silyn**, Nantlle all have excellent wild brown trout; **Llyn Cwellyn**, brown trout, char, salmon and sea trout; **Llyn-y-Dywarchen**, regularly restocked with rainbow and brown trout, fly only, bag limit 4; wt £80, dt £17 (Llyn Cwellyn £10 and Llyn-y-Dywarchen £17); permits from Cwellyn Arms, Rhyd-ddu LL54 6TL (tel/fax: 01766 890321; web:

www.snowdoninn.co.uk); boat packages available, enquiries to Hon Sec (tel: 01248 670666).

LLYFNI. Penygroes (Caernarfonshire). Rises in Drws-y-Coed, 4m E of town and runs through Nantlle Lake; salmon, sea trout (good), trout. Seiont, Gwyrfai and Llyfni AS controls most of river; wt £80, dt £17; permits from A D Griffiths, Newsagent, Snowdon St; society also has fishing on **Llyn Nantlle**; boat bookings (only) for salmon and trout; apply to Cwellyn Arms (below); the society provides top quality self-catering accommodation in Old Corn Mill, on banks of Lllyfni at Pantllyfni; contact Hon Sec for details; accommodation and boat bookings: Cwellyn Arms, Rhyd-ddu LL54 6TL (tel/fax: 01766 890321; see website for more info: www.snowdoninn.co.uk).

SOCH. Llangian (Caernarfonshire). Trout and rudd; an early stream; dry fly useful; weeds troublesome later; some sewin, late; plenty of sea fishing, bass, pollack, whiting, flatfish, at Abersoch, from which this stream can be fished. Accommodation: Rhydolion Farm, Llangian, Abersoch, Pwllheli LL53 7LE (tel: 01758 712342); own fishing.

YSGETHIN. River rises in **Llyn Bodlyn**. Brown trout, Arctic char.

GWYNEDD (lakes)

Bala Lake or **Llyn Tegid**. **Bala** (Merioneth). Owned by Snowdonia National Park Authority, Penrhydeudraeth. Permits from Lake Warden, Warden's Office, 24 Ffordd Pensarn, Bala LL23 7SR (tel: 01678 520626); dt also avail from pay and display machines in car park; trout early in season; pike, perch, roach, grayling, eels; Bala is largest natural lake in Wales, 4m long, ¾m wide; here, too, is found that rare and interesting fish called the gwyniad, a land-locked whitefish; coarse fishermen will find all their wants more than provided for; pike up to 30lb; perch and good roach; rod licence required.

Llyn Celyn. **Bala** (Merioneth). Situated in the Snowdonia National Park at the foot of the Arenig Mountains; rainbow trout and wild brown trout. Reservoir managed by Welsh Water. Sunday fishing.

Cwm Bychan Lake. **Llanbedr** (Merioneth). Brown trout and "the red bellied char"; good fishing. For permission to fish, apply to Farm Manager, Cwm Bychan Farm, Cwm Bychan. For **Gloywlyn Lake** apply Cwmrafon Farm. **Llyn Perfeddau**, trout, good fishing; free.

Maentwrog (Merioneth). **Y-Garnedd**, 1m N (trout) and **Hafod-y-Llyn**, 1m

NW (pike, coarse fish) are both private. Cambrian AA lakes in area: **Morwynion, Cwmorthin, Manod, Barlwyd, Dubach, Dubach-y-Bont, Cwm Foel, Cwm Corsiog, Llyn Gamallt**, one of the best wild brown fisheries in North Wales; **Llyn yr Adar**, lies just below 2000ft and well worth a visit, wild browns, one hour's walking; **Llyn Ffridd y Bwlch**, wild browns, stocked with rainbows throughout season, 3 acres, 5 minutes from town (car park); disabled access; also Llyn Llagy, 2 hours walk (well worth it!) from Tanygrisiau; and Llyn Conlog, largest of Welsh lakes, lying over 2000 feet, also 2 hours walk (also well worth it!) from Tanygrisiau, both wild browns; dt from suppliers: PO Llan Ffestiniog; Newsagents, Siop Cynan, 34 High Street, Blaenau Ffestiniog (tel: 01766 830910); Penrhyn Guns, 7 High Street, Penrhyndeudraeth LL48 6BN (tel: 01766 770339; see website for more info: www.ukgunroom.com).

Talsarnau (Merioneth). Artro & Talsarnau FA has water on **Llyn Tecwyn Uchaf** and **Llyn Tecwyn Isaf**, brown trout; and on **River Glyn**, sea trout and salmon; st £45, wt £20, dt £8; permits from Post Office. Hotels: Ship Aground; Motel.

LLWCHWR (or LOUGHOR)

Rises some 3m east of Llandybie on Taircarn Mountain and flows 15m south-west through Ammanford and Pontardulais to Burry Inlet, north of Gower Peninsula. Fishing very good for sewin, and some brown trout and salmon (Jun-July; Aug-Oct best). Salmon and sewin runs reported to be increasing. Most fishing controlled by clubs, from whom tickets are available.

Llanelli (Carmarthenshire). Carmarthenshire County Council controls fishing on **Upper** and **Lower Lliedi Reservoirs**; with game fishing only on Upper Lliedi; fly only; rainbows and browns

(browns c&r only); 4 fish limit; dt £15; boat hire is available for members of Llanelli AA at £6 per day; the bottom Lliedi Reservoir is now a coarse fishery of 32 acres.

The council also has fishing at **Furnace Pond** and **Old Castle Pond** (carp, bream and pike), and **Cwmoernant Reservoirs, Carmarthen**. Within Council's jurisdiction is **Gwellian Pool**, nr Kidwelly, with trout, sewin and salmon; st and dt from Tourism and Leisure Office, Trostre Depot, Trostre Rd, Llanelli, SA14 9RA (tel: 01554 747500). Tackle shop: Anglers Corner, 80 Station Rd, SA15 1AN (tel: 01554 773981; web: www.thinkinganglers.co.uk); Fly Shack (Mr Holborn), 38 Swansea Road SA15 3YT (tel: 01554 776001; web: www.flyshack.co.uk) tickets for Cross Hands & DAA, Llanelli AA.

Llangennech (Carmarthenshire). 4m on **River Gwendraeth Fach** between Llandyfaelog and Llangendeirne Bridge near Kidwelly; mainly brown trout with good runs of sea trout; permission of farmers. Tackle Shop: Anglers Corner, 80 Station Rd, SA15 1AN (tel: 01554 773981; web: www.thinkinganglers.co.uk). Club offers fresh water and occasional sea fishing competitions; and, during the close season, runs fly-tying classes.

Pontardulais (Glamorgan). Trout and a run of sea trout; some salmon.

Pontardulais & Dist AA has 6m good fishing; wt £45, dt £15, conc for OAP and jun; Assn also has 1m single bank on River Teifi near Lampeter. Gwaun-Cae-Gurwen AA has 1¾ miles double bank (access left bank); members only; apply Hon Sec. **White Springs Lakes**, Holiday Complex, Garnswllt Rd, Pontardulais, Swansea SA4 8QG (tel: 01792 885699; web: www.whitespringsfishery.co.uk); 6 coarse lakes with large carp, tench, golden orfe, etc; 1 specimen carp lake; night-fishing and tents allowed; small caravan park; lakeside parking; tickets on site in shop, also maggots, ground bait, tackle and rods for sale; licensed lodge; accommodation in holiday apartments.

Ammanford (Carmarthenshire). Ammanford & Dist AA has water on middle and upper reaches of Llwchwr and tributaries; dt from tackleist below. Welsh Water have water at **Llys-y-Fran Reservoir**, rainbow (up to 6lb) and brown; contact Visitor Centre (tel: 01437 5322730. Permits for these and other local waters from Tightlines Direct, 72-74 Wind St, Ammanford, Carmarthenshire SA18 3DR (tel: 01269 592380; web: www.tightlines.co.uk).

Tributaries of the Llwchwr

AMMAN. Trout, sewin, few salmon. Very fast running; fishes well in spate.

Ammanford (Carmarthenshire). Ammanford & Dist AA has water on **Llwchwr**, 5m; **Amman**, 3m; **Lash**, 1m; **Marlais**, 1m; ½m; **Gwili**, 1½m; sea trout run from May onwards; concessions for juniors, youths; instruction, fly-tying classes and competitions; dt from Tightlines

Direct, 72-74 Wind St, Ammanford, Carmarthenshire SA18 3DR (tel: 01269 592380; see website for more info: www.tightlines.co.uk); and Hon Sec. Hotel: Glynhir Mansion.

MARLAIS BROOK. **Llandybie** (Dyfed). Sewin, July onwards. **Llwchwr**, 3m. **Gwendraeth Fawr,** 5m W. **Llyn Lechowen**, 5m W.

MAWDDACH

Rises in hills between Bala and Trawsfynydd Lakes and flows 10m south to confluence with Wnion, 2m below Dolgellau, and thence through long estuary to sea at Barmouth. One of the best rivers in Wales for salmon and sea trout fishing, also brown trout, and is all preserved, although permits can be had for some stretches. Successful stocking with locally hatched salmon and sea trout. Salmon and sea trout may be taken up to Pistyll Mawddach.

Barmouth (Merioneth). Rivers Mawddach and **Wnion**; lower reaches of Wnion have excellent night fly fishing for sewin and sea trout, in various named pools; Lower beats of Mawddach; bass have been caught. Dolgellau AA has fishing on both rivers; permits, *see Dolgellau*; run of sea trout and salmon is from beginning of June to end of season; stocked by Mawddach Hatchery; there have recently been bass on the lower beat. Trout fishing on **Cregennan Lakes**, Emlyn Lloyd, Fridd Boedel Farm, Arthog, nr Fairbourne LL39 1LJ (tel: 01341 250468); 2 natural lakes owned by the National Trust, situated on northern slopes of Cader Idris overlooking beautiful Mawddach Estuary; 27 acre lake with island, wild brown trout only, fly, spin or worm; dt £12 and evening £6; conc; 13 acre lake, regularly stocked with rainbows, plus a good head of wild brown trout, fly only; dt £20 and evening £12; boat for hire but booking advisable. Permits from Fishtails, Bridge St, Dolgellau OL40 1AU (tel: 01341 421080); or at Fridd Boedel Farm *(see above)*. **Penmaenpool** (Gwynedd). Salmon, sea trout. Dolgellau AA waters; salmon and sea trout fishing on lower beats of Mawddach. National Trust has Dolmelynllyn Estate, Afon Mawddach; dt water; spin, worm or fly depending on season; fishing permits available to residents and non-residents of Hotel Tyn-y-Groes (tel: 01341 440275; see website for more info: www.tynygroes.com) and Dolmelynllyn Hotel (tel: 01341 440273).

Ganllwyd (Merioneth). Salmon, sea trout. Dolgellau AA has left bank of upper beat from Ganllwyd to Tyn-y-Groes Pool; tickets from Fishtails, Bridge St, Dolgellau OL40 1AU (tel: 01341 421080); Plas Dolmelynllyn Hall; and Mile End Garage near Little Chef *(see below)* *(see Dolgellau)*. Hotels: Tyn-y-Groes, Ganllwyd, (tel: 01341 440275); (1¼m salmon and sea trout fishing on river); Plas Dolmelynllyn Hall, Ganllwyd, LL40 2HP (tel: 01341 440273) has 1½m salmon and sea trout fishing on Mawddach right bank, priority given to guests.

Tributaries of Mawddach.

WNION: Salmon, sewin, sea trout. The Rivers Mawddach and Wnion are well known for the excellent salmon and sea trout fishing. Dry weather only affects the upper reaches of the two rivers, as lower beats cover tidal waters.

Dolgellau (Merioneth). Salmon and sea trout. Wnion runs past Dolgellau and joins Mawddach 2m below town. Best months for salmon and sea trout: May-Oct. Sewin fishing: Jul-Oct. The Dolgellau AA owns 13m of salmon and sea trout fishing on Mawddach and Wnion, situated in and around Dolgellau; both stocked with salmon and sea trout each year from the local Mawddach Hatchery; excellent evening and night fishing for sea trout on lower beats of Wnion; assn also has wild brown trout and rainbow trout fishing on **Llyn Cynwch**, near well-known Precipice Walk (wonderful views); largest rainbow

2007 7lb 8oz; bait or fly (fly c&r after 3 fish); permits from Mile-End Garage (next to the Little Chef); Llion James, Newsagent, Eldon Square; Beachcaster Fishing Tackle *(below)*; st £75, wt £45, rivers dt £20, juv st £20 (allows fishing on the two rivers and Llyn Cynwch), lake dt £12; also from Fishtails. Tackle shops: Fishtails, Bridge St, Dolgellau OL40 1AU (tel: 01341 421080); Beachcaster Fishing Tackle, High St, Barmouth LL42 1DS (tel: 01341 281537). Hotels: Fronoleu Farm Hotel, Tabor, Dolgellau LL40 2PS (tel: 01341 422361); Plas Dolmelynllyn Hall, Ganllwyd, LL40 2HP (tel: 01341 440273) (both Dolgellau AA tickets) (with private fishing, *(see Ganllwyd)*; Tynygroes Hotel, Ganllwyd.

OGWEN

Rises in Ogwen Lake, halfway between Bethesda and Capel Curig, with tributaries running in from Ffynnon Lloer and Bochlwyd Lakes, and runs from lake to outlet at Menai Straits, near Bangor, about 10m in all. Excellent trout fishing; leased by Ogwen Valley AA from Penrhyn Estate. Trout, sea trout (sewin) and salmon. Autumn good for salmon.

Bangor (Caernarfonshire). **Ogwen**, 2m E; salmon, sewin, trout. Sea trout run starts about mid-June. Salmon best Aug-Oct. Parts of river leased by Ogwen Valley AA; visitors permits, wt £35, dt £14, conc for juv. Tackle shop: Bangor Angling Supply Stores, 21 The High St, Bangor LL57 1NP (tel: 01248 355518). Hotels: British; Garden.

Bethesda (Caernarfonshire). Ogwen Valley AA has approx 5m of River Ogwen and tributaries near Bethesda; sea trout and salmon from July onwards; assn also has brown trout fishing on four lakes: **Ogwen**, **Idwal**, **Ffynon Lloer** and **Bochlwyd**; Lake Ogwen stocked regularly with rainbows; wt £35 and dt £14; concessions for juniors; permits from W Edwin (Grocer), opp Victoria Hotel, High St; Ogwen Bank Caravan Park, Gwernydd LL57 3LQ (tel: 01248 600486); or Ogwen Falls Cafe, nr Ogwen Cottage, Ogwen Lake; Lorne House (Newsagent), 82 High Str.

POWYS (lakes)

Gludy Lake, Cradoc, **Brecon**, LD3 9PA (tel: 01874 610427): fly fishing for brown and rainbow trout to 14lbs, with boats, full self-catering lodge sleeps up to nine; dt for exclusive use of whole lake (up to 6 anglers, max 8) £260 for 6, then £45 extra per angler, (various prices for other combinations: apply Lake House); all c&r (av catch rate is 10 fish per angler per day.

Llyn Clywedog. Llanidloes (Powys). NW 3m; Llanidloes & Dist AA; 615 acres; small part of reservoir used by sailing club; western half is fishery area; well stocked with brown and rainbow trout averaging 1¾lb; fly only; season 18 Mar to 7 Oct (browns) (30 Nov for rainbows); boat hire; fishing and boat permits from Woosnam & Davies (newsagents), Longbridge St, Llanidloes (tel: 01686 412263); rod licence required is supplied by Post Office (in Spar), Longbridge St, Llanidloes (tel: 01686 412889) **Dol-llys Farm** has free fishing for their caravan users; bunk barn accommodation and campers kitchen; contact O S Evans, Dol-llys Farm, Llanidloes, Powys SY18 6JA (tel: 01686 412694). Hotels: Mount Inn; Unicorn; Lloyds.

Llangorse Lake. **Llangorse** (Powys). Holds good pike, good bream, perch, roach, eels. Fishing from boats only; can be hired. Permit needed to launch privately owned boats. Caravans for hire from Apr-Oct; some tackle from lakeside shop; permits and boats from Ray Davies, Lakeside Caravan and Camping Park, Llangorse Lake, Brecon, Powys LD3 7TR (tel: 01874 658226). Llynfi runs from lake to Wye at Glasbury and holds a few trout; overgrown in places; requires short rod. Hotel: Red Lion.

Talybont Reservoir. **Brecon** (Powys). Reservoir in Brecon Beacons National Park, 318 acres, good wild brown trout fishery; season 20 Mar-17 Oct; fly only; catch limit 6 fish; size limit 9 inches; tickets from machine at the Aber camp site below dam; further information from Richard Poole, Area Manager, United Utilities Operational Services Ltd., Sluvad Treatment Works, Llandegfedd Reservoir, New Inn, Pontypool, Monmouthshire NP4 0TA (tel: 01291 673722). Hotels: White Hart; Usk.

Lake Vyrnwy (Powys). Lake (1,100 acres) stocked with rainbow and brown trout, also a strong wild brown population; annual catch 3000 to 3500 averaging ¾lb; by fly and from boat only; dt and half-dt from hotel only; ghillies and instructors can be arranged who may hire out rods; disabled fishing from bank by special arrangement; apply to Lake Vyrnwy Hotel, Lake Vyrnwy, Llanwddyn, Powys SY10 0LY (tel: 01691 870692; web: www.lakevyrnwy.com). Ceiriog FF also has river fishing; members and guests only.

SEIONT

Rises in two tarns in Cwm-glas, under crest of Snowdon, and runs to Llanberis, 3m, where it enters the Llanberis Lakes and Llyn Padarn. Flows thence into Menai Straits at Caernarfon. Attractive river with long flats, nice runs and excellent pools holding salmon (May onwards), sea trout (June onwards), and brown trout. Trout rather small, but in faster water can give good account of themselves.

Caernarfon (Caernarfonshire). Salmon, sea trout, trout. Seiont, Gwyrfai and Llyfni AS has 40m of salmon, sea trout and brown trout fishing on **Rivers Seiont**, **Gwyrfai** and **Llyfni**; assn also has boat and bank fishing on **Llyn Padarn**, brown trout, char, salmon, sea trout; **Llyn Cwellyn**, brown trout, char, salmon, sea trout; **Llyn-y-Dwarchen**, 35 acres, rainbow trout and brown trout, fly only; season ticket on application only; wt £80, dt £17 (£10 Llyn Padarn and Llyn Cwellyn; £17 Llyn-y-Dywarchen), from Post Bach Newsagent, 55 Pool St; A D Griffiths, Newsagent, Penygroes; Post Office, High St, Llanberis; Cwellyn Arms Hotel, Rhyd-ddu, LL54 6TL (tel: 01766 890321; see website for more info: www.snowdoninn.co.uk) who also provide accommodation and boat bookings; maps and information from Hon Sec (see clubs). Seiont Manor Hotel, Llanrug, Caernarfon, Gwynedd LL55 2AQ (tel: 01286 673366), offers fishing for guests on all club waters; on lake: £6 for 2 hrs (c&r), £12 for 4 hours (catch & keep 2 fish); on river: £10 dt; tuition £20 per hour (tackle supplied). Accommodation: Lakeview Hotel, Tan-Y-Pant LL55 4EL (tel: 01286 870422).

Llanberis (Caernarfonshire). Brown trout, Arctic char, salmon, sea trout. Seiont, Gwyrfai and Llyfai AS has bank and boat fishing on almost the whole of **Llyn Padarn**; dt £10 from Garth Maelog *(below);* Beran Garage, Deiniolen; special boat permits allow fishing on Lakes Padarn, Cwellyn, Dywarchen, and Nantlle, by booking only (tel: 01248 670666). Hotels: Lakeview Hotel, Tan-Y-Pant LL55 4EL (tel: 01286 870422); Dolbadarn,

High St, Caernarvon, LL55 4SU (tel/fax: 01286 870277).

SOUTH EAST WALES

AFAN. Aberavon (Glamorgan). Small trout stream (with sewin on lower reaches) on which Afan Valley AC has water from Aberavon to Cymmer; assn has improved sport; 3 salmon caught in 1991 season; tremendous runs of sewin in last few years; regular stocking; fly only in March; worming allowed rest of season; spinning June-Sept at certain water levels. **River Nedd** 4m away; trout, sewin. Hotels: The Twelve Knights, Port Talbot; Aberavon Hotel.

CADOXTON STREAM. Cadoxton (South Glamorgan). Cadoxton Stream rises 6½m from Cardiff and enters the sea 2m below Cadoxton. Small trout; permission from farmers (Glamorgan RD).

Eglwys Nunydd Reservoir. Margam (West Glamorgan). Corus (Port Talbot) reservoir; excellent trout fishing, brown, blue and rainbow; open all year; good stocking levels; good benefits for members; 3 boats for members; fishing lodge for anglers; dt £20 (3 fish with c&r (then barbless hooks must be used and no buoyant flies on sunken lines)); apply Corus Sports Club, Corus plc, Groes, Margam, Port Talbot (tel: 01639 871111 extn 3368); during day Stephen Gale (Hon Sec) (mob: 077914 29672).

NEATH. Rises in the Brecon Beacons and flows 27m to sea. Salmon, sewin, brown trout. Tributaries of the Neath include **Dulais** and **Pyrddin**.

Neath (Glamorgan). Neath & Dulais AC has fishing on **River Neath** from Rehola to the estuary except for a short private beat; both banks; trout, sea trout and salmon; assn also has both banks on **River Dulais** above Aberdulais Falls to the treatment

works at Crynant; st £45, wt £55; dt £20; limit of 100 members out of area; concessions for juniors and OAPs; apply Hon Sec. Skewen AC has fishing on: **Tennant Canal**, Aberdulais to Jersey Marine (all species); **Neath Canal**, Tonna to Briton Ferry (all species including pike); **Square Pond** at Briton Ferry (carp, roach, rudd, tench, bream, perch, eels, grass carp); 2 rods only on all waters except Square Pond where 3 rods allowed; also Lower Gnoll Pond and Fishpond at Gnoll Country Park, both mixed coarse; st from tackle shops; permits available from Membership Secretary (tel: 01639 639657); Tackle and Bait, 149 Windsor Road, Neath SA11 1NU (tel: 01639 634148); and Mainwarings, 44 Vivian Road, Sketty, Swansea SA2 0UH (tel: 01792 202245; web: www.mainwaringsfishing.co.uk). Hotel: Castle.

Glynneath (Glamorgan). Glynneath & Dist AA has salmon, sea trout and brown trout waters on Neath and its tributaries, **Pyrddin**, **Nedd Fach**, **Mellte**, **Hepste** and **Sychryd**; fly, worm and spinning from July only; junior (under 12s) competition in June; joining fee £20 for full and OAP's; st £40, OAP £30, 12-18 yrs £15; under 12's £7.50; wt £20; OAP £15; 12-18's £10; dts £8, £4 and £2.50 respectively; coarse fishing on canal, between Tonna and Neath, also from Assn; membership and joining fee from Hon Sec; daily and weekly permits from Hon Sec; Dave Pitman's Hair-Stylist, 3 Heathfield Avenue, Glynneath, which also sells a selection of fishing tackle. In headwaters of the Neath is Ystradfellte Reservoir. Tackle shop:

Tackle and Bait, 149 Windsor Road, Neath SA11 1NU (tel: 01639 634148).

OGMORE. Porthcawl (Glamorgan). Porthcawl AA has coarse fishing on **Wilderness Lake** and **Pwll-y-Waem Lake** (known as the Meadow Lake); carp, bream, tench, crucian carp, roach, few perch and eels; dt £5, conc for juv (must be accompanied at all times by adult) (EA licence must be produced); permits from Ewenny Angling *(below);* Parc Stores, Cilparc, Porthcawl. Tackle shop: Ewenny Angling, 21 Coychurch Rd, Bridgend CF31 3AP (tel: 01656 662691; web: www.reelfishing.co.uk); Ewenny Angling has application forms for Glamorgan AC. Keens Angling Store, Bridgend Road, Upper Aberkenfig. Hotels: Brentwood; Ewenny Farm Guesthouse.

Bridgend (Glamorgan). Ogmore AA has 6m of Ogmore and tributaries **Ewenny**, **Llynfi** and **Garw**; salmon, sea trout and brown trout; membership is restricted but weekly tickets are available from secretary; dt £15 to end-August, then £20, from tackle shops; competitions for juniors; and fly-tying. Garw Valley AA has water on Ogmore and Garw; membership restricted to residents but weekly tickets £40 for visitors, conc for juniors and OAPs; contact Hon Sec. Tackle shops: Ewenny Angling, 21 Coychurch Rd, Bridgend CF31 3AP (tel: 01656 662691; see website for more info: www.reelfishing.co.uk); Keens Tackle, 119 Bridgend Rd, Aberkenfig, Bridgend, CF32 9AP (tel: 01656 722448; see website for more info: www.keenstackleandguns.co.uk. Hotel: Heronston.

Maesteg (Glamorgan). **River Llynfi**, a tributary of Ogmore; trout and sea trout. Llynfi Valley AA has 8m (Maesteg to Tondu); trout, sea trout and salmon; flyfishing-only stretch and no spinning until 1 Jul; members only; st £30 + £25 joining fee from Hon Sec.

RHYMNEY. Rhymney (Monmouthshire). About 30m long, rises above town. Excellent grayling, chub, roach and dace fishing run by Caerphilly AC; further information from Green's Fishing Tackle; dt water. Upstream at Llanbradach, Royal Oak AC have water; members only; memb £10, conc; enquire Green's Fishing Tackle (below). Rhymney & Dist AS has rights on Butetown Pond, Rhymney, and Bryn Brith Pond (The Pem), **Pontlottyn**; also **Cwm-Darren Lake**; Rhos-las, nr **Dowlias**; with fishing on **Wye** between Oct and Feb at Boughwood, near Lyswen. All well stocked with coarse fish of usual species; pike in Rhos-las, all fish to be returned to water; dt on all waters; matches run most Saturdays for juniors and Sundays for seniors most of the year, plus aggregate awards; st £15, conc, dt £3. Other tackle shops: Green's Fishing Tackle, Bryn Road, Pontllanfraith, Blackwood NP12 2BU (tel: 01495 221881)sells Rhymney & Dist AS tickets.

TAWE. Lower tidal reach now impounded by a barrage. Salmon and sewin runs have increased in recent years and they can be caught from Abercraf to Morriston. Upper reaches noted for scenery. Fishing controlled by clubs in all but tidal reaches.

Swansea (Glamorgan). Swansea Amateur AA has salmon and sea trout fishing on the upper reaches of **Cothi** and a section of **Towy** at Llanwrda; assn is a private company with a limited membership with a limited allocation of tickets for members' guests. Swansea AC has coarse fishing at Gower on **Fairwood Lake**, pike, bream, carp, perch, tench, roach, rudd, eels; also **Gelli Hir**, Tir Mynydd Road, Three Crosses; 3 lakes; carp to 20lb, good head of tench to 7lb; dt from Mainwaring's or Country Stores, Gowerton. City and County of Swansea has coarse fishing on 2 lakes: **Singleton Boating Lake**, Singleton

Park, 2 acres; carp, tench, rudd, perch, crucian carp, eels; angling permitted when boats not in use; **Clyne Valley Pond**, small, very deep lake; perch, rudd, eels, trout; **Pluck Pond**, Lower Swansea Valley, 1 acre; perch, rudd; The Fendrod, 18 acres, carp to 30lb, bream to 13lb, others; **The Half Round Pond**, mixed coarse; plus small pond, **Swiss Cottage**; permit covers all six waters: from Mainwarings (below). Brynmill & Dist AC have coarse fishing at **Fendrod Lake**, 15 acres, 82 pegs, with fairly good head of fish from carp up to 31lb and bream up to 13lb, with an extra bonus of attractive surroundings; and at Half Round Ponds, two ponds of one acre each, with rudd, perch, tench; st £25.80; dt £4, juveniles/OAP/disabled £2.80 on bank; from Mainwaring's (below); or from Leisure Services Dept, The Guildhall, Swansea SA1 4PE (tel: 01792 635411). **Shimano Felindre Trout Fishery**; rainbow, brown and golden trout; fly only; tackle for hire; casting lessons; contact Jud Hamblin, Manager, Shimano Felindre Trout Fishery, Blaen-Nant Ddu, Felindre, Swansea SA5 7ND (tel: 01792 796584; see website for more info: www.shimanofelindre.co.uk).

Riverside Caravan Park has 1½m private stretch on Tawe; st £30, dt £3; touring caravan park with all facilities; for further information contact Riverside Caravan Park, Ynysforgan Farm, Morriston, Swansea SA6 6QL (tel: 01792 775587); excellent 2009 salmon & sewin runs. Tackle shops: Mainwaring's Angling Centre, 44 Vivian Road, Sketty, Swansea SA2 0UH (tel: 01792 202245; web: www.mainwaringsfishing.co.uk), has permits for a number of lake and river fisheries within range of Swansea, both coarse and game; Siop-y-Pentres, 600 Clydach Road, Ynystawe, Swansea SA6 5AY (tel: 01792 842533): full and day permits on sale.

Pontardawe (Glamorgan). Pontardawe & Swansea AS has stretch on R Tawe from **Ynysmeudwy** to **Morriston**; brown trout, sea trout and salmon; new adult members £80 (£57 renewal), OAP's £15, seriously disabled £15, 11-17's £10, under 11's £5; tickets available by post from secretary or from Mainwaring's *(see below)* (new members only); or H R Jones, Clydach (tel: 01792 842202) ; Siop-y-Pentref, 600 Clydach Road, Ynystawe, Swansea SA6 5AY (tel: 01792 842533), or H R Jones (Ironmongers), 68 High Street, Clydach SA6 5LN (tel: 01792 842202). Tackle shop: Mainwaring's Angling Centre, 44 Vivian Road, Sketty, Swansea SA2 0UH (tel: 01792 202245; see website for more info: www.mainwaringsfishing.co.uk).

Ystradgynlais (Glamorgan). Tawe & Tributaries AA has 25m on **Tawe** and tributaries **Twrch**, **Gwys**, **Llynfell**, **Giedd**, **Lech**, **Gurlais** and **Cwn Du**, above Pontardawe; salmon, sea trout, brown trout and eels; trout stocked regularly up to 3lbs; assn runs its own brown trout hatchery and rearing pond complex (stocked waters 2007 with over 3,000 brown trout measuring from 9-14in); membership restricted to local residents but permits available to non members; st, wt, and dt (24 hours) available; concessions for juniors and OAPs; junior river competition held annually; fly-tying and casting tuition during close season; permits from local shops. Hotels: Abercrave Inn and others.

SOUTH WEST WALES (lakes)

Lake Berwyn. **Tregaron** (Ceredigion), 4m SE. Liming has taken place and as a result it holds excellent brown trout up to 1-2lbs; stocked periodically. Tregaron AA hold fishing rights; Assn also has wild brown trout fishing on R Teifi, and Teifi Pools, three remote mountain lakes with plenty of wild browns; st £120, river only £60, Teifi Pools only £60, Lllyn Berwyn only £60; wt (all waters) £60; dt (river & Berwyn) £10, Teifi Pool £10; concessions for OAP's, juveniles; permits: Medical Hall, Tregaron; Post Office, Pontrhydfendigaid; Post Office, Llanddewi Brefi; Post Office, Llanfair Clydogau; Alan Williams, Lampeter Angling, 57 Bridge Str, Lampeter SA48 7AB (tel: 01570 422985 (evngs: 01570 434313)). Tackle shop: Aber Fishing Tackle, 3 Terrace Road, Aberystwyth SY23 1NY (tel: 01970 611200; web: www.flymail.com).

Devil's Bridge (Ceredigion). Aberystwyth AA has the Penrhyncoch lakes in the hills near Devil's Bridge, (**Llyn Craig-y-Pistyll, Llyn Rhosgoch, Llyn Syfydrin, Llyn Blaenmelindwr**; the Trisant Lakes 2m SW of Devil's Bridge, (**Llyn Frongoch** and **Llyn Rhosrhydd)**; and ownership of **Llyn Oerfa** and **Llyn Glandwgan**; some are stocked, others self-stocking; several contain trout up to 6lb; fly only on Rhosgoch, Frongoch and Rhosrhydd; spinning and fly only on Craig-y-Pistyll and Oerfa; permits: Aber Fishing Tackle, st husband & wife £145; st £95, dt £20, conc. Tackle shop: Aber Fishing Tackle, 3 Terrace Road, Aberystwyth SY23 1NY (tel: 01970 611200; web: www.flymail.com), who sell Tregaron AC tickets; also Llanilar AA. Hotel: Hafod Hotel, Devil's Bridge SY23 3JL.

Nant-y-Moch and **Dinas Reservoirs**. **Ponterwyd** (Ceredigion). These waters are set in the hills 12m E of Aberystwyth: Dinas, 38 acres, stocked weekly with brown and rainbow trout; fly, spinning and worming; Nant-y-Moch, 600 acres, native brown trout, fly only; **Cwm Rheidol Dam**, native brown trout, salmon and sea trout; fly spinning and worming; permits from the Power Station gate, Capel Bangor; further information from the BP petrol station, Ponterwyd SY23 3AD (tel: 01970 890649).

Pembroke (Pembrokeshire). Pembroke Town Mill Pool; mullet, bass, flatfish; apply Pembroke Tackle (below) for Pembroke & DC water: Decoy Pond; mixed coarse; dt £5. At **Stackpole**, 5m south, National Trust has 74 acres Bosherston Lily Ponds; coarse; fishing from numbered pegs (1-52) only; st £42, conc, dt £6 (in advance) £7 at lakeside; close season 15 Mar to 15 June incl; no night fishing; no live baiting; sea bait only; contact warden (tel: 01646 661359). Hotel: Milton Manor, Tenby. Tackle shop: Pembroke Angling, 31 Meyrick Street, Pembroke Dock SA72 6AL (tel: 01646 622712; web: www.pembsrt.org)

Talybont (Ceredigion). Talybont AA has exclusive rights on **Llyn Conach, Llyn Dwfn, Llyn Nantycagal** and **Llyn Penrhaeadr**; lakes some 7-9m into hills from village; 3 lakes stocked with brown trout; native wild brown in Penrhaeadr; fly only on all lakes except Nantycagal; boat hire on all lakes for holders of season tickets; st £45, dt £10 (bank only); permits from Spar Store, Talybont; Aber Fishing Tackle, 3 Terrace Road, Aberystwyth SY23 1NY (tel: 01970 611200; web: www.flymail.com).

Teifi Lakes. Pontrhydfendigaid (Ceredigion). Lakes at headwaters of Teifi. Permits obtainable from the Post Office, Pontrhydfendigaid.

SOUTH WEST WALES (rivers and streams)

ALUN. St David's (Pembrokeshire). 6m long; 4m suitable for fishing, mostly on private property with owners permission; trout good quality but small. Robert O Evans, Ystwyth Stores, 10 High St, St Davids SA62 6SD (tel: 01437 720399) can arrange boat trips. Rod licences from Post Office, 13 New St.

BRAWDY BROOK. Brawdy (Pembrokeshire). Small trout. Brook, 7m long, is mostly on private property. Licences can be purchased at Post Office, 13 New Dew Str, St David's.

CARNE. Loveston (Pembrokeshire). Carne rises 1½m W of Templeton, runs 3m to Loveston, and 1m down is joined on left bank by **Langden Brook**. Little or no rod fishing interest above Bishop's Bridge; sea trout and brown trout in season below Bishop's Bridge, if adequate flows. From confluence of Carne and Langden Brook into Cresswell, fishing controlled by Cresselly Estate, c/o Owen & Owen, 142 Main St, Pembroke, SA71 4HN (tel: 01646 621500). Coarse fishing reservoir at **Roadside Farm**; common, crucian and mirror carp, bream and roach; well stocked; tranquil surroundings and ample parking; day, week and year permits; contact D A Crowley, Roadside Farm, Templeton, Narberth, Dyfed SA67 8DA (tel: 01834 891313/891283). Carp fishing at West Atherton near Narberth.

CAREW BROOK. Carew (Pembrokeshire). This river, which rises by Redberth, is 4m long, joining sea water at Carew which is an inlet from Milford Haven. Although there is an element of rod fishing effort put into this river and its tributaries, the controlling interest is the farmer and the catchment has been prone to agricultural pollution. The river does support a very small number of sea trout which only seem to appear in the close season.

CLARACH. Good numbers of sea trout can be found in the river late July onwards.

Aberystwyth (Ceredigion). Enters sea 1m N of Aberystwyth. Holds trout, sewin and occasional salmon; preserved. Permission from farmers. Tackle shop: Aber Fishing Tackle, 3 Terrace Road, Aberystwyth SY23 1NY (tel: 01970 611200; web: www.flymail.com).

GWAUN. Fishguard (Pembrokeshire). This 8-9m trout stream rises on lower slopes of Prescelly Mountains, and runs through a beautiful wooded valley. Trout not large but provide excellent sport with fly, and sewin also caught in season. A few salmon. Tackle shop: Goodwick Marine Services, 1 Wern Road, Goodwick SA64 0AA (tel: 01348 873955; Hotel: Glanmoy Country House.

GWENDRAETH FACH. Kidwelly (Carmarthenshire). Carmarthen & Dist AC has 2m fishing about 2m north of town, both banks; very good trout fishing; occasional sea trout; st £75 before 1 April, then £140, conc; contact Andrew Derby, Town & Country Stores, Myrtle Hill, Penfarn (tel: 01267 236794). **Gwendraeth Fawr** runs 1m E from Kidwelly; trouting fair. Hotel: White Lion; Pen-y-Bac Farm (river fishing for trout, sewin and salmon; tuition and equipment).

LLANDILO BROOK. Maenclochog (Carmarthenshire). Small trout. Electro-fishing surveys show very few fish of takeable size. No angling clubs. Seek permission from farmers to fish.

LLETHI. Llanarth (Ceredigion). Llethi Gido rises 3m above Llanarth, and 2m down is joined on left bank by brook 4m long. Llethi runs to Llanina and sea. One mile NE runs Drowy to sea, 4m long. Small rivers that may run dry in summer; small trout. **Llanarth Coarse Fishery** (tel: 01545 580598), ¾m south of Llanarth, 2 acre pool, heavily stocked with carp; mixed silver fish pond (known as The Canal), open 7 days a week; dt £5, conc. **Nine Oaks Trout and Coarse Fishery**: Mr W Baker & Mrs V James, Oakford, nr Aberaeron, SA47 0RW (tel: 01545 580482); fly and coarse fishing, 2m inland between Newquay and Aberaeron; rainbow and brown trout in three pools; 3 coarse: carp to 25lbs, tench and bream; tackle hire, beginners tuition; accommodation; trout dt £24 4 fish, 3 fish £18, 2 fish £14, £10 c&r; £7 (1 rod), £9 2 rods, £18 hight fishing for 24 hours, coarse; tackle shop on site; also hire.

MARLAIS. **Narberth** (Pembrokeshire). Gwaithnoak, 2m. Eastern Cleddau, 2m. Taf, 5m. Small trout. NW of Narberth is Glandwr Trout Fishery, Pontygaffel Farm, Glandwr, Whitland, Pembs SA34 0YD (tel: 07967 516431), rainbow, brown, blue trout; dt 3 for £25, 4 for £30, 6 for £35, worming pond: 3 for £12, 6 for £20; booking advisable; disabled access.

MULLOCK BROOK. St Ishmael's (Pembrokeshire). Small trout, 6m long, joining the sea at Dale Road.

NEVERN: Nevern (Pembrokeshire). River rises near Crymych and flows to sea at Newport; fast-flowing, densely wooded, deep holding pools. Nevern AA has salmon, sea trout and brown trout fishing; 6m on **Nevern**, nr Newport; st apply Hon Sec, juveniles £10; wt £35 and dt £18, available from Chairman, Viv Owen (see Clubs) and Trewern Arms, Nevern SA42 0NB (tel: 01239 820395). Hotels: Trewern Arms; Cnapan, Newport; Salutation Inn, Felindre Farchog. Guest House, Llys Meddyg, East St, Newport.

PERIS. Llanon (Ceredigion). Peris is 6m long. Llanon, 4m long, runs ½m.

Small trout. Hotel: Plas Morfa, Llanon.

RHEIDOL. **Aberystwyth** (Ceredigion). Salmon, sea trout. Hydro-electric scheme governs flow. River almost entirely Aberystwyth AA water; assn also has 2m hired stretch on **River Ystwyth**; and trout fishing on 9 lakes; permits Hon Sec or from Aber Fishing Tackle, 3 Terrace Road, Aberystwyth SY23 1NY (tel: 01970 611200; see website for more: www.flymail.com); st £144, dt £20, conc; assn has 2 caravans (sleep six) to let at **Frongoch Lake**, from £190 to £250 per week (tel: 01970 612683 Mr Lewis); includes week's fishing on the whole fishery at half normal visitor rates, and exclusive use of boats (on 3 of the 9 lakes) for 4 days of the week. Coarse fishing at **Capel Bangor Golf Club**; 2½ acre pond; carp, roach and tench; permits from W Evans, Capel Bangor Golf Club, Capel Bangor, Aberystwyth SY23 3LL (tel: 01970 880741). Hotel: Conrah, Chancery.

WYRE. **Llanrhystyd** (Ceredigion). Trout (small), some salmon and sometimes good for sewin. Fishing controlled by a number of riparian owners.

YSTWYTH. A natural, gravel bed spate river. Brown trout stocked in spring; large sea trout run in first spate in June, several runs of smaller sea trout July to Sept. Salmon usually run Mid Aug to early Oct.

Aberystwyth (Ceredigion). Llanilar AA has most of river, approx 15m both banks, from Aberystwyth to Pontrhydygroes; some brown trout in Llanilar area; best sea trout fishing is by fly at night, spinning in high water and with quill minnow as water clears; small fly is also effective during the day when there is a touch of colour in the water; st £50, wt £30, dt £15, conc, from Hon Sec; Aber Fishing Tackle *(see above)*; Llanilar Garage; Blaenplwyf Post Office, nr Aberystwyth SY23 1DS (tel: 01970

612499 (River Ystwyth tickets)); and Royal Oak, Llanfarian SY23 4BS. Ken and Susan Diplock, Fron Farm, **Bont-newydd**, SY23 4JG (tel: 01974 251392), have 3 lakes with rainbow, blue, brown trout, atlantic salmon; fly only; and one coarse fishing lake; tuition (free) by appointment. **Trawscoed Estate Fishery** has over 3m stretch on the central reaches of R Ystwyth, sea trout from June onwards, now let to Llanilar AA; for dt contact Hon Sec. **Birchgrove Reservoir** situated in Forestry Commission woodlands, 1½ acres, invaded by otters; no fish. Tackle Shop: Aber Fishing Tackle, 3 Terrace Road, Aberystwyth SY23 1NY (tel: 01970 611200; see website for more info: www.flymail.com).

TÂF

Rises on Prescelly Mountains and flows about 25 miles south-east to Carmarthen Bay at mouth of Towy. Has good runs of sewin and salmon most years. Brown trout fishing good upstream of Whitland.

St Clears (Carmarthen). Good salmon and sewin; brown trout fair. April, May, Sept best for salmon. Sewin mid-June onwards. Carmarthen & Dist AC have water on Tâf and stretch on **Dewi Fawr**; also tidal water from Carmarthen Bridge. St Clears & District AA has 5m on Tâf, from St Clears to Llanddowror; salmon, sea trout and brown trout. Assn also has salmon, occasional sea trout and brown trout fishing on **R Ginning**, 3m; **R Dewi Fawr**, 1½m; **R Cowin**, 1 ½m; st £50, wt £40, dt £20, conc; contact President/Jenkins Chemist, Pentre Rd, Carmarthen, Dyfed SA33 4AA (tel: 01994 230456). Other waters on these rivers by permission of farmers. Hotels: Black Lion; Gardde Guest House; Picton House, Llanddowror, The Old Board School Guest House, St Clears. Caravan sites at St Clears and Laugharne.

Whitland (Carmarthenshire). Salmon, sewin, brown trout; Whitland AA has approx 5m of fishing, mainly double bank; all legal methods, season 1 Apr-17 Oct; st £60, conc for juv, OAP, dt £15 from Hon Sec (see Clubs list). **White House Mill Trout Fishery**, Barbara Hunt: contact Mrs Hunt at fishery, Lampeter Velfrey, Whitland SA34 0RB (tel: 01834 831304): fly fishing for brown, blue and rainbow trout on 4 acre lake, emphasis on nymph and dry fly; easy access for disabled, tackle for hire, self-catering cottage near lake; dt from £15 (3 fish) then £5 per fish, max 6; closed Mon and Tues. Coarse fishing on **Llyn Carfan**; two lakes of 1½ acres each with good quality water, stocked with carp to 31lbs, grass carp to 29lb, tench, plentiful roach to 3lb, and rudd; dt at house or on bank; rods and tackle for hire; contact Llyn Carfan Course Fishing, Whitland, Pembs. SA34 0NP (tel: 01994 240819; see website for more: www.wwpf.pembrokeshiretourism.net); member of West Wales Premier Fisheries.

TAFF and ELY

Taff has its source in two headstreams on the Brecon Beacons and flows about 40m south-east to enter the Severn Estuary at Cardiff. A short and steep gravel bedded river, heavily polluted in the 18th and 20th centuries by local iron, coal and steel industries. However, by the early 1980's there had been major improvements in the water quality due to economic recession and improved pollution control. Sea trout and some salmon were again entering lower reaches of river, although much of the river remained inaccessible at this time because of large weirs, since cleared. Since then, the Welsh Water Authority, and subsequently the National Rivers Authority and Environment Agency Wales, have been successfully carrying out a strategy for rehabilitating salmon in the Taff; through pollution control, building fish passes, artificial propagation and control of exploitation. The lower reaches of the Taff are now an established sea trout and salmon fishery with declared rod catches for the former exceeding 100 in most recent seasons. Salmon appear in catches less often; typically declared catches vary between 20 and 50 fish. The recently completed Treforest fish pass close to Pontypridd will allow migratory fish to access the vast majority of the catchment. Although too early to be conclusive, it is likely that sea trout will enter upper reaches during the season, providing anglers previously only able to target brown trout, with a new quarry. The Lower Taff, from Cardiff to Pontypridd is also a good coarse fishery, the main species being chub, dace, roach, gudgeon and barbel, the last of which have reached over 115lb. Now that the polluted legacy of the past has largely disappeared, the remainder of the Taff catchment supports good brown trout and excellent grayling. The River Ely joins the mouth of Taff at Penarth. The Ely, like the Taff, has benefitted from substantial improvements in environmental quality such that quality brown trout fishing, chub and roach fishing can be found at reasonable cost. Salmon and sea trout spawn quite regularly in the Ely. Cardiff Bay is now a healthy coarse fishery, with diverse habitats and species: roach, chub, dace, perch bream, carp, rudd and pike; the mainn fishing areas are: Hamadryad Park on River Taff, Grangemoor Park and Sanatorium Park on River Ely, the Barrage Embankment.

Cardiff (Glamorgan). Brown trout (stocked) and run of sea trout and salmon. Glamorgan AC has fishing on **River Taff** (chub, dace, eels, roach, salmon, sea trout, barbel and brown trout); 2 stretches on **River Wye**, at Monmouth (chub, dace, perch, pike, roach, bleak, gudgeon, eels and barbel) and at Clifford (chub, dace, roach, perch, pike, barbel, bleak and grayling); **River Usk** near Abergavenny (chub, dace, brown trout, salmon and sea trout); (**East Dock** (roach, perch, chub, dace, carp and eels) is now run by a private syndicate; **River Ely** at St Fagans (roach, chub and trout); **River Trothy** near Monmouth (chub, dace, trout, grayling, roach and pike; **Troes Pond** at Troes near Bridgend (bream, tench, perch, carp, roach and rudd);

Pysgodlyn Mawr (bream, carp, roach, perch, rudd and tench); **Llantrythyd Lake** (carp, bream, roach, rudd, tench, perch and eels); and **St-y-Nyll Ponds** (pike, rudd, tench, perch and carp). For membership contact M Roberts, Glamorgan AC, 4 Heol Don, Whitchurch, Cardiff CF14 2AU (web: www.glamorgananglersclub.org.uk. Bute AS, Birchgrove (Cardiff) AS and Glamorgan AC share lease of approx 3m fishing on R Taff in city limits; coarse (chub, roach, dace, gudgeon with barbel introduced recently); and game (salmon, sewin and brown trout) under auspices of combined Cardiff clubs known as Taff Fisheries; dt from Garry Evans Ltd, 105/109 Whitchurch Rd, Cardiff CF14 3JQ (tel: 029 2061 9828; web: www.garryevans.co.uk)

(see tackle shop below). Bute AS has fixture list fishing on **R Wye** from Erwood to Builth Wells, and on a private lake within Cardiff's city limits; all venues hold roach, dace, gudgeon, bleak; members only; club membership from secretary. Birchgrove (Cardiff) AS has fishing on **Rivers Ely** and **Taff**; salmon, sea trout, grayling, chub, dace, roach and barbel; through kindness of riparian owners, the society also has coarse fishing on prime stretches on **R Wye** between Glasbury and Builth Wells; chub, dace, eels, grayling, pike, roach and perch; fishing on Wye for members only.

Roath Park Lake (Cardiff Corporation) holds rudd, roach, carp, tench; dt on bank. The recent improvement of **Cardiff Bay** has produced a large freshwater lake. Early indications are that coarse fish populations have flourished, particularly chub. Although as yet under-developed as a fishery, moves are afoot to improve angling access at what could become the premier S Wales coarse fish venue. Tackle shops: A Bale & Son, 166a Richmond Road, Cardiff CF24 3BX (tel: 029 2049 9898; see web: www.arthurbale.co.uk), bait and licences who issue tickets for River Taf and Cardiff Bay; Anglers Supplies, 172 Penarth Rd, Cardiff CF11 6NL (tel: 029 20220723); Tony's Angling, 826 Newport Road, Rumney, Cardiff CF3 4LH (tel: 029 2025 7505); Garry Evans Ltd, 105 Whitchurch Road, Cardiff CF14 3JQ (tel: 029 2061 9828; web: www.garryevans.co.uk). Hotels: Angel; Novotel; Clare Court; Glenmor.

Merthyr Tydfil (Glamorgan). Merthyr Tydfil AA offers a large variety of waters from wild brown trout fishing on the Upper Neuadd Reservoir in the heart of the Brecon Beacons to salmon fishing on the Usk, with ponds and reservoirs for the coarse fishing enthusiasts; the Assn has 17m on **Taff** and **Taf Fechan** at Merthyr Tydfil from Pontsticill Reservoir to Quaker's Yard, brown trout, regularly stocked, size limit 10", bag limit 4 fish; also ¾m both banks (small wild brook trout) on **River Tarrell**; **Upper Neuadd Reservoir**, wild brown trout, very lightly stocked, fly only; **Taf Fechan Reservoirs**, trout (20 Mar - 17 Oct) and coarse all year except pike (16 Jun - 14 Mar); no pike or other coarse fish to be removed; **Penywern Ponds**, coarse fish including carp in excess of 20lb, dt from Merthyr Angling Centre *(below)*; Tony Rees, Treasurer, 13 Alexandra Avenue CF47 9AE (tel: 01685 723520) and Hon Secretary; Assn also has 3 stretches of salmon and trout fishing on **Usk** including at **Mardy Fishery**, 1¼m; and **Kemeys Fishery**, ¾m; day tickets for Usk from A Rees and N Morgan *(see above)*; also **Cyfarthfa Lake**, a popular coarse fishing lake for juveniles. Reservoirs in **Taf Fawr Valley** managed by United Utilities: **Beacons Reservoir** (52 acres) brown trout, fly only; **Cantref Reservoir** (42 acres) rainbow and brown trout, fly only; **Llwyn-On Reservoir** (150 acres) rainbow and brown trout, fly, worm and spinner. All located in Brecon Beacons National Park adjacent to A470 (T) road, 3m north of Merthyr Tydfil and 15m south of Brecon. Cater for disabled. Private boats permitted only on Usk Reservoir; dt from Garwnant Visitor Centre. For further information, contact Richard Poole, Area Manager, United Utilities, Sluvad Treatment Works, Llandegfedd Reservoir, New Inn, Pontypool, Monmouthshire NP4 0TA (tel: 01495 769281). Tackle shops: Merthyr Angling Centre, 185 High St, Cefn Coed, Merthyr Tydfil CF48 2PG (tel: 01685 379809).

Tributaries of Taff

RHONDDA FAWR and RHONDDA FACH:

Pontypridd (Glamorgan). At Junction of Rhondda Fawr and Fach, and Taff.

Tonypandy (Glamorgan). Glyncornel AA has 12m trout fishing on Rhondda from The Stag Hotel in Treorchy to the Barry Sidings Park, Trehafod; restocked annually with brown trout; st £25, conc for juv £16, no dt; competitions for adults and juniors; fly fishing on Glyncornel Lake, 2 fish (c&r until 2nd rainbow killed), brown and rainbow, members only; incl river seniors £125, juv £100 apply Hon Sec. Tickets: Tonypandy Army Surplus & Guns, 10 Dunraven St, Tonypandy CF40 1QE (tel: 01443 432856); Howells Newsagents, 51 Pontypridd Road, Porth, Mid Glam. CF39 9PG (tel: 01443 682507).

Ferndale (Glamorgan). Maerdy & Ferndale AC has water on River Rhondda Fach; and on **Lluest Wen** and **Castell Nos Reservoirs** at Maerdy; all waters are trickle-stocked throughout the season; fly only on Lluest Wen; dt from Graham Bumford, North Road Motors, Morris Terrace, Ferndale, Mid Glamorgan CF43 4ST (tel: 01443 755048); st available *(see above)*.

Ely (Glamorgan). Glamorgan AC has trout fishing on River Ely at St Fagans and coarse fishing in **St-y-Nyll Ponds** at St Brides-super-Ely.

Llantrisant (Glamorgan). **Seven Oaks Fishery**, Talygarn, nr Pontyclun, Mid Glam CF72 9JU (tel: 01446 775474): dt on site for game (dt £12.50-£27 depending on number of fish) and coarse fishing (dt £6.50); also novice pool for trout, dt £6 + £2 per fish (limit 6 fish); tackle hire and some tackle sold on site, bank only, good access for disabled.

TEIFI

Rises in Llyn Teifi, near Strata Florida, in Ceredigion, flows south-west and then west, entering Cardigan Bay below Cardigan Town. Association water provides salmon, sea trout (sewin) and brown trout fishing. April and May are the best months for spring salmon; summer salmon fishing through to October can also be productive given reasonable water levels. Sea trout run from May onwards. Main salmon run September onwards.

Cardigan (Ceredigion). Salmon, sewin, trout. Bass, mullet and flounders below bridge to sea, 2m; boats for hire. Teifi Trout Assn has fishing for salmon, sea trout and brown trout on 20m stretch of lower River Teifi, from a few miles above Cardigan to just beyond Newcastle Emlyn, including fishing at Cenarth; Assn also has stretch, ¾m, above Henllan (salmon, sea trout and brown trout); st £135 plus £30 joining fee from Membership Secretary; concessions for OAPs, disabled and junior; wt £80-£110 until 1 Sept, then £100-£140 (conc), and dt £30-£45 to end August; after £35-£55 (no conc) from tackle shop: The Salmon Leap, Cenarth, Newcastle Emlyn SA38 9JP (tel: 01239 711242), and Cenarth Falls Holiday Park, Cenarth; and Afon Teifi Caravan Park, Pentrecagal.

Llechryd (Ceredigion). Salmon, sea trout. Teifi Trout Assn has ¾m stretches on R Teifi, nr Llechryd; assn water; wt £80-£110 until 1 Sept, then £100-£140 (conc), and dt £30-£45 to end August; after £35-£55 (no conc) from The Salmon Leap, Cenarth, Newcastle Emlyn SA38 9JP (tel: 01239 711242). Tackle shop: County Sports, 3 Old Bridge, Haverfordwest SA61 2EZ (tel: 01437 763740; web: www.county-sports.co.uk). Accomodation: The Trewern Arms, Nevern; The Salutation, Felindre.

Cenarth (Carmarthenshire). Salmon, sewin, trout. Famous falls. Teifi Trout Assn water; permits from The Salmon Leap, Cenarth, Newcastle Emlyn SA38 9JP (tel: 01239 711242), where there is also a comprehensive range of fishing tackle and bait for sale; and Cenarth Caravan Park, Newcastle

Emlyn SA38 9JS (tel: 01239 710344). Tackle shops: Alan Williams, Lampeter Angling, 57 Bridge Str, Lampeter SA48 7AB (tel: 01570 422985 (evngs: 01570 434313)). Accom: The Porth Hotel, Llandysul, Ceredigion SA44 4QS (tel: 01559 362202) for permits, maps and river information for Llandysul AA water.

Newcastle Emlyn (Carmarthenshire). Salmon and sea trout. Good centre for Teifi. Teifi Trout Assn has water; riverside cottages with exclusive private fishing on an adjoining ¾m stretch of Teifi, salmon, sea trout and brown trout; dt (varied prices) from A Jackson, Teifi River Guides, Little Manor, Castle Square, Cilgerran SA43 2SE (tel: 01239 614254; mob: 07770 817602; see website for more info: www.teifiriverguides.co.uk). Hotel: Emlyn Arms.

Llandysul (Ceredigion). Salmon, sewin, brown trout. Popular centre with good fishing. Best April-May and Aug-Oct for salmon; sewin June onwards. Llandysul AA has Middle Teifi from Newcastle Emlyn to above 2m north of Lampeter. For fly fishing courses and casting instruction in the Teifi Valley: weekend courses during the season from April to October, specialising in wild brown trout fishing in the spring, sea trout (sewin) in summer, and salmon in autumn; private beat on **R Teifi**; flyfishing courses and casting instruction in the Teifi Valley; free fishing and conservation lessons for young people during school summer holidays, in conjunction with Llandysul AA: instructors Pat O'Reilly, Sue Parker; contact First Nature, Bwlchgwyn, Rhydlewis, Llandysul, SA44 5RE (tel: 01239 851952; email: enquiries@first-nature.com; web: www.first-nature.com/dreamstreams) Cross Hands & Dist AA has stretch on R Teifi, nr Llandysul; salmon and sea trout; joining fee £20; st £75 (waiting list); dt £20, wt £40, conc for juv. Rainbow trout fishing on a 3-acre lake at **Rhydlewis Trout Fishery**; stocked regularly; fly only; lakeside parking, toilets, tea & coffee-making facilities, smokery and smokery shop; further details from, Ryd-yr-Onnen, Rhydlewis, Llandysul, Ceredigion SA44 5QS (tel: 01239 851224). Tackle shops: Alan Williams, Lampeter Angling, 57 Bridge Str, Lampeter SA48 7AB (tel: 01570 422985 (evngs: 01570 434313)). Hotel: Kings Arms, Llandysul.

Llanybydder (Carmarthenshire). Salmon, sewin, brown trout. Llanybydder AA has approx 5m of Middle Teifi, both banks, above and below Llanybydder Bridge; st £50, wt £35 and £40, dt £10 and £15; concessions for jun; instruction, and challenge cup for best junior angler; permits from Hon Sec and David Morgan, Siop-y-Bont (Londis), Llanybydder (tel: 01570 480980). Hotels: Black Lion; Grannell Hotel, Llannwnen, Ceredigion.

Lampeter (Ceredigion). Salmon, April onwards; sewin, late June, July, August onwards; brown trout, both dry and wet fly. Both Llandysul AA and Tregaron AA have water on Teifi around Lampeter. **Troed-y-Bryn Fisheries**, rainbow and brown trout, privately owned lakes, 3½ acres, fly only; permits from Mrs E E Edwards, Troed-y-Bryn, Cribyn, Lampeter SA48 7QH (tel: 01570 470798). Pontardulais & Dist AA has 1m single bank on Teifi near Lampeter; and also has 6m good fishing on River Llwchwr; wt £45, dt £15, conc for OAP and jun; contact Hon Sec. Tackle shop: Alan Williams, Lampeter Angling, 57 Bridge Str, Lampeter SA48 7AB (tel: 01570 422985 (evngs: 01570 434313)).

Tregaron (Ceredigion). Good fly fishing for brown trout. Salmon fishing also good when conditions right. Tregaron AA has 17m of **R Teifi** from Pontrhydfendigaid to Tregaron and down river to Cellan; **Teifi Pools**, 3 mountain lakes, with wild brown trout; and **Llyn Berwyn**, 50 acres; st £120, river only £60, Teifi Pools only £60, Llyn Berwyn only £60; wt (all waters) £60; dt (river & Berwyn) £10, Teifi Pool £10; concessions for OAP's, juveniles; permits: Medical Hall, Tregaron; Post Office, Pontrhydfendigaid; Post Office, Llanddewi Brefi; Post Office, Llanfair Clydogau, Lampeter, Dyfed SA48 8LA. Tackle shop: Aber Fishing Tackle, 3 Terrace Road, Aberystwyth SY23 1NY (tel: 01970 611200; web: www.flymail.com); Alan Williams, Lampeter Angling, 57 Bridge Str, Lampeter SA48 7AB (tel: 01570 422985 (evngs: 01570 434313)). Other good fishing on Aeron, 6m. Hotel: Talbot. Accommodation: Brynawel Guest House.

TOWY (or TYWI)

Lower reaches near Carmarthen are tidal holding trout, salmon and sewin in season (June to Oct best salmon; sewin Apr to Oct; brown trout very limited); association waters. Above this Towy mostly preserved, but some fishing by leave, ticket or from hotels. Salmon average 12lb and sea trout up to 20lb are taken; brown trout generally small.

Carmarthen (Carmarthenshire). Salmon, sewin, trout. April and May usually good for large sewin. Tidal up to Carmarthen and 3m above. Gwaun-Cae-Gurwen AA has just over 1m one bank; st £80; wt £35; apply Hon Sec. Carmarthen Amateur AA has water at **Llanarthney** with 2 car parks; 3 beats; and on **Towy** at Nantgaredig, White Mill and Abergwili; sewin and salmon; assn arranges 6 competitions a year and has 5 private car parks; weekly permits from Secretary, or Carmarthen & Pumpsaint Farmers Co-op, Pensarn. Carmarthen & Dist AC has water on **Rivers Towy** (incl exclusive tidal access rights), **Cothi** (downstream from The Cothi Bridge Hotel), **Gwili** (at Bronwydd), **Taf** and **Gwendraeth Fach** (near Llandyfaelog and Kidwelly); also White Mill and Nantgaredig; all these waters are within 5-10 miles of Carmarthen; membership before 1 April £75, then £140, conc; dt £35 from (Andrew Derby) Town & Country Stores, Myrtle Hill, Penfarn (tel: 01267 236794); under 16 free; permits are available from Hon Sec. Council has tickets for Cwmoernant Ponds (Carmarthen Town); crucian carp, perch, roach, rudd, tench; tickets on bank and from tackle shops. **Pantybedw Fishery**, Nantgaredig SA32 7LH (tel: 01267 290315): 7½ acre fly fishing lake, catch and release and catch and keep, dt c&r £15; 2 fish c&k £16; 4 fish c&k £25. Hotel: Golden Grove Arms, Llanathne, Carmarthen SA32 8JU (tel: 01558 668551). Accommodation: Capel Dewi Uchaf Country House, Capel Dewi, Carmarthen, Carmarthenshire SA32 8AY (tel: 01267 290799; fax: 01267 290003; see website for more: http://capel-dewi-uchaf-country-hous e.wales.info); Old Priory Guest House, 20 Priory St, Carmarthen, Dyfed SA31 1NE (tel: 01267 237471; www.oldprioryguesthouse.co.uk); Spillman Hotel, Spillman St, SA31 1LQ (tel: 01267 237037).

Nantgaredig (Carmarthenshire). Salmon and sea trout fishing on the Abercothi Estate Fishery (tel: 01494 524411; web: www.abercothi.co.uk); 3 beats on **Towy** and part of **Cothi**; daily letting for up to 5 rods on each beat. Carmarthen Amateur AA has water on **Cothi** and **Gwili**; all-waters wt £90; tributaries-augmented wt £70, from Hon Sec or Farmers Co-op. Cross Hands & Dist AA has stretches on R Towy (6m), Teifi (1½m) and R Cothi (4m) in area; salmon and trout; dt from Ian Jenkins (tel: 01558 668373); dt, wt, conc; The Red Lion, Llangadog (tel: 01550 777357).

Llandeilo (Carmarthenshire). Salmon, sea trout, brown trout. Llandeilo AA preserves 4½m on **Towy**, about 1½m on **Lower Dulais**; season tickets, members only (waiting list), from Hon Sec; wt £75 and dt £25, conc, from Mrs G Morgan, Station House, Cwmifor, Llandeilo SA19 7AH (tel: 01558 822517); concessions for jun; fishing good when water in condition. Gwaun-Cae-Gurwen AA has 1¾m 3m above town, left bank; st £80, wt £35; apply Hon Sec. Cross Hands & Dist AA has several stretches of Towy in vicinity, also water on R Cothi, and **R Teifi** at Llandysul; access for disabled on some waters; membership £75 + joining fee £20, conc; limited dt £20 and wt £40-£50 (see Nantgaredig above). Salmon and sea trout fishing on Golden Grove Estate; 10m stretch on **Towy** from Llandeilo to Nantgaredig, mainly double bank; 5 beats, some available for season rods, others for 3-day, and wt; best months May-Aug; self-catering accommodation for anglers at Sannan Court, Llanfynydd; contact Ian Jenkins, Afallon, Dryslwyn, Camarthen SA32 8QY (tel: 01558 668180 office; 01558 668373 home; web: www.sannan.co.uk). **Cennen** good trout stream. Hotels: Cawdor Arms; Castle; Edwinsford Arms; Plough Inn. Ty-Isaf Fishing Lodge and Country Cottages, Trapp, Llandeilo (game fishing on rivers and reservoirs; tuition).

Llangadog (Carmarthenshire). Salmon, sewin, trout. Llangadog AA Ltd have water 2m of fishing on Towy; limited dt from Eric Jones, 6 Bryniago, Llangadog, Dyfed SA19 9LL (tel: 01550 777645); or local PO. Cross Hands & Dist AA also has water.

Llanwrda (Carmarthenshire). Salmon and sea trout. Swansea Amateur AA rents 1m (both banks), on an annual basis; access south of railway station; fly only; members and guests only;

concessions for juniors. **Springwater Lakes**, **Harford**, Llanwrda, SA19 8DT (tel: 01558 650788): trout lake (fly only); one mixed coarse lake; one specimen carp lake with carp to 32lb; 8am to dusk during summer, dt prices depend on lake; tackle hire, facilities, access for disabled; touring caravans, motorhomes and tents.

Llandovery (Carmarthenshire). Salmon, sewin (best May-Aug), trout. Llandovery AA has 8m on **Towy**, double and single bank, excellent fly water below Llandovery, holding pools with fish (sewin) up to 14lbs, and salmon and grilse in Aug-Sep; and 10m on tributaries **R Gwydderig** and **R Bran**, good head of natural trout and sewin from July onwards; membership occasionally available from Mike Davies, Sec (tel: 01550 720633); dt £25 (or £10 above town) available from Castle Hotel in town or Hon Sec; P&D Co-Op, Llandovery; Castle Hotel, Kings Rd, SA20 0AP (tel: 01550 720343). Accom: Mrs Lewis has self-catering cottage with 2 rods, which overlooks the fishing: Cwmgwyn Farm SA20 0EQ (tel: 01550 720410).

Tributaries of the Towy

GWILI. Small river of 12ft to 16ft in width which joins Towy 1m north of Carmarthen. Sea trout (sewin), fish running from early June onwards, averaging 2lb and attaining 6lb. Brown trout fishing poor. A few salmon caught on Gwili, especially at the end of year.

Llanpumsaint (Carmarthenshire). Sewin, trout, occasional salmon, although salmon stocking will result in improvements. Carmarthen Amateur AA and Carmarthen & Dist AC both have stretches on Gwili. Accommodation: Fferm-y-Felin, Llanpumsaint SA33 6DA (tel: 01267 253498); (18th century farmhouse with 15 acres of countryside for fishing and bird watching).

COTHI. The largest tributary of the Towy, noted for its sewin which run in late summer and early autumn. Salmon, sewin and brown trout.

Carmarthen (Carmarthenshire). Carmarthen Amateur AA and Carmarthen & Dist AC both have stretches on Cothi. The Cothi Bridge Hotel, Pontargothi, Carmarthen, Dyfed SA32 7NG (tel: 01267 290251; web: www.cothibridgehotel.co.uk) has a short stretch of salmon fishing (guests only) and has arrangements for guests to fish on other private and club waters; permits sold for Cross Hands & Dist AA water.

Brechfa (Carmarthenshire). Salmon and sea trout. Swansea Amateur AA has 2m (both banks), between

Abergorlech and Brechfa; members and guests only. Gwaun-Cae-Gurwen AA has 1m left bank some way below village; members only; apply Hon Sec. Hotels: Ty Mawr.

Pumpsaint (Carmarthenshire). **Cothi** and **Twrch**. Trout, sea trout (June onwards); salmon from early July. National Trust has approx 8m of the river; season starts from July to August when the salmon come up; permits from National Trust.

SAWDDE.   **Llanddeusant** (Carmarthenshire).   Trout. Accommodation and fishing at Black Mountain Caravan and Camping Park, Llanddeusant, nr Llangadog, SA19 9YG (tel: 01550 740217; web: www.blackmountainholidays.co.uk); rainbow and brown trout fishing on **Usk Reservoir** (3m), also on Sawdde (3m) and Towy (6m). Licences from Post Office, Llangadog; tickets from machine at Usk Reservoir.

A fine Usk trout for casting instructor, Mark Roberts APGAI

Photo: Mark Roberts

USK and EBBW

The River Usk is a good salmon river and first rate for trout with particularly good early season fishing. Since the mid-1990s there has also been a significant run of sewin. Geological formation is red sandstone, merging into limestone in lower reaches. Trout average about one pound in the main stem with some considerably bigger fish, and from about ¼lb to ½lb in the tributaries. Some tributaries afford good trout fishing: Afon Llwyd, Honddu, Grwyne, Yscir; the best for trout are Cilieni, Honddu and Grywne (April to June). Salmon fishing mostly private in the lower reaches, but several opportunities for trout. The River Ebbw flows into the Severn Estuary between the mouths of the River Rhymney and the River Usk. The Ebbw has recently experienced great improvements in water quality which has been reflected in the fishery improvements, with very good trout and reports of sea trout. The Sirhowy, a tributary of Ebbw, also has good trout fishing. The Wye & Usk Foundation, Dolgarreg North Road, Builth Wells, Powys LD2 3DD (tel: 01982 551520; see website for more info: www.wyeuskfoundation.org) provides detailed information on the fishing and supplies tickets mainly for mid to upper reaches of the river and tributaries (see clubs list).

Newport (Monmouthshire). Newport AA has stretch of **Monmouthshire and Brecon Canal**, **Woodstock Pool**, **Morgans Pool** and **Spytty Lake**; all providing good coarse fishing, including roach, perch, bream, carp and tench; assn also has coarse fishing on **R Wye** at Symonds Yat; roach, dace, chub and excellent pike; day tickets £5 beforehand, or £7 from bailiffs at lakes. Islwyn & Dist AC have 10m trout fishing on **Ebbw**, **Sirhowy** and **Penyfan Pond** (14 acres) near **Oakdale** and **Pant-yr-eos** Reservoir (12 acres) near **Risca**; membership Green's (below); membership £140, incl joining fee of £25, juv £30, dt £15; dt from Green's Fishing Tackle, Bryn Road, Pontllanfraith, Blackwood NP12 2BU (tel: 01495 221881); st from Cwmbran Angling, 39 Richmond Road, Pontnewydd, Cwmbran NP44 1EQ (tel: 01633 868890; web: www.cwmbranangling.co.uk) for Pant-yr-eos, on site; for Penyfan Pond, from Pontllanfraith Leisure Centre, Coed Cae Ddu Rd, Pontllanfraith, Blackwood NP12 2DA (tel: 01495 224562). Newport Reservoirs FFA has fishing on **Ysyfro Reservoir**, High Cross, nr Newport; rainbow and brown trout; day permits for non members can be purchased from hut at reservoir (dt £10 catch and release and kill 2 fish/day); fishing stops after 2nd fish killed. **Wentwood Reservoir**, nr **Chepstow**, brown and rainbow trout; tickets at fishing lodge, for details contact Hon Sec, Wentwood Reservoir FFA (tel: 01291 425158); dt £17 (5 fish), £11 (2 fish), juv conc; 2010 trial period c&r @ £1 (max 2 fish). Rainbow and brown trout fishing on **Cefn Mably Lakes**, a complex of 8 spring-fed lakes on farm land lying beside the River Rhymney; one 6½ acre lake, fly only; two any method; two coarse lakes stocked with carp, roach, rudd, perch, gudgeon, bream, etc, open all year; access for disabled, bait and full facilities on site; apply to John Jones, Cefn Mably Lakes, nr Castleton, Newport CF3 6LP (tel: 01633 681101; web: www.cefnmablylakes.co.uk). **Hendre Lake**, 6 acre coarse fishery at St Mellons; an excellent lake, carp to 20lb, especially in hot and cold weather when other lakes are struggling; dt on bank. Tackle shops: Garry Evans Ltd, 105/109 Whitchurch Rd, Cardiff CF14 3JQ (tel: 029 2061 9828; web: www.garryevans.co.uk); Dave Richards, 73 Church Road, Newport NP19 7EH (tel: 01633 254910); Cwmbran Angling, 39 Richmond Road, Pontnewydd, Cwmbran NP44 1EQ (tel: 01633

868890; see website for more info: www.cwmbranangling.co.uk).

Pontypool (Monmouthshire). Usk private. Tributary **Afon Llwyd**, good trout fishing and regularly stocked by local clubs. Exceptionally fast flowing river in places. Pontypool AA and Cwmbran AA have stretches. Pontypool AA also has **Olway Brook**, nr Usk, trout, dace and chub: and coarse fishing on **Monmouthshire & Brecon Canal** at Pontypool (Bridges 72 to 74), roach, perch, bream, carp and tench; st from Cwmbran Angling, 39 Richmond Road, Pontnewydd, Cwmbran NP44 1EQ (tel: 01633 868890; web: www.cwmbranangling.co.uk).

Llandegfedd Reservoir (435 acres), United Utilities, Sluvad Treatment Works, Llandegfedd Reservoir, Panteg, Pontypool, NP4 0TA (tel: 01291 673722); owned by Welsh Water plc, and a major boat fishery; stocked with 25,000 rainbow trout av 1½lbs-2lbs, small numbers of browns; season 1 Mar-31 Oct (rainbow), 20 Mar-17 Oct (brown); fly only; st available, dt £16, 6 fish, £13, 4 fish, conc OAP and juv; permits from Ranger's waterside office; 32 boats for hire, incl for disabled (wheelyboat), with or without motor, £17-£8, pre-booking is recommended. The British rod caught pike record (46lb 13oz) currently comes from Llandegfedd and there are short seasons for pike fishing in most years. Cwmbran AA has coarse fishing on **Monmouthshire & Brecon Canal**; average depth 4ft; stocked with bream, tench, crucian carp, roach, perch, good eels in parts; strict control on litter; assn also has coarse fishing, for members only, at **Llantarnam Industrial Estates Ponds** (3 ponds stocked with roach, perch and dace, and one stocked with rudd and bream); and excellent mixed fishing on **River Monnow**, trout, grayling, bream, roach, perch, dace, chub and carp. Wye and Usk Foundation has day tickets for trout and grayling on Monnow; £10-£20 depending on beat: contact the Wye and Usk Foundation, Dolgarreg, North Road, Builth Wells, Powys LD2 3DD (tel: 01982 551520); Foundation also has fishing on Lugg and Arrow. Permits for Cwmbran AA water from Cwmbran Angling, 39 Richmond Road, Pontnewydd, Cwmbran NP44 1EQ (tel: 01633 868890; see website for more info: www.cwmbranangling.co.uk); no day tickets on Llantarnam Ponds; members only.

Usk (Monmouthshire). Usk Town Water Fishery Association holds about 2m, mostly above Usk Bridge; trout fishing only; rod licence required; thigh wading only. Merthyr Tydfil AA has water at **Kemeys Commander**. Tackle shop: Sweet's Fishing Tackle, 14 Porthycarne St, Usk, NP15 1RY (tel: 01291 672552). Hotels: Three Salmons; Cross Keys; Glen-yr-Avon; Kings Head.

Abergavenny (Monmouthshire). Salmon, trout. Monmouth DC holds town waters, both banks downstream from Llanfoist Bridge to Sewer Bridge; tickets from Bridge Inn, Llanfoist; Keith Price Garages, Merthyr Road NP7 5DB (Mon-Sat 6.00am to 9.30pm (Sun 7am to 9.30pm)) (tel: 01873 857644). Merthyr Tydfil AA has rights to **Mardy Fishery**, 2¼m above town; also Kemys beat. Crickhowell & Dist AS has approx 1½m u/s of Llanfoist Bridge, on left bank, known as the Red Barn Fishery *(see Crickhowell)* members only, also Glangrwyne Court; also ½m right bank, salmon and trout on **Usk** at Lower Cadvor Farm, Abergavenny; also ½m right bank. Gwent AS has 2½m at Chainbridge and Ty-Mawr; dt from Hon Sec. Tackle shop: Sweet's Fishing Tackle, 14 Porthycarne St, Usk, Monmouthshire NP5 1RY (tel: 01291 672552). Hotel: Wenallt. Information on fishing and accom from TIC,

Monmouth Road, Swan Meadows NP7 5HL (tel: 01873 853254).

Crickhowell (Powys). Salmon, sea trout, wild brown trout. Crickhowell & Dist AS has approx 1m d/s of Crickhowell Bridge on both banks, except for garden of Bridgend Public House on left bank; also approx ½m u/s of bridge on left bank; all waters members only; waiting list; society also has **Glangrwynne Court Fishery** between Crickhowell and Abergavenny; brown trout, sea trout and salmon; also 1½m mainly double bank River **Grwynne** at Glangrwynne; trout and salmon; members only; also ½m single (right) bank of River Usk, the Home Beat at **Pant-y-Goitre**; also ½m right bank, salmon and trout on **Usk** at Lower Cadvor Farm, Abergavenny. Gliffaes Country House Hotel, NP8 1RH (tel: 01874 730 371; see website for more info: www.gliffaeshotel.com), has 1m on Usk adjacent to hotel and a further 1½m upstream; excellent wild brown trout water; salmon improving and some sea trout; primarily for hotel guests but outside rods if space. Bridge End Inn, Bridge St, Crickhowell NP8 1AR (tel: 01873 810338) has short length below bridge; dt £10 for salmon and trout from Inn. **Trecastle** and **Talybont Reservoirs** are within reach. Accom and angling information from Crickhowell Resource & Information Centre, Beaufort St NP8 1BN (tel: 01873 812105).

Brecon (Powys). Brecon AS has water on R Usk from Llanfaes Bridge to Boat House; salmon and trout; left bank (Llanfaes side) members only; Promenade bank (right bank) dt from The Guildhall *(see beklow)*. Brecon Town Council has stretch on Usk from Llanfaes Bridge to Gwennies Lane, on which salmon stones and groynes have been placed, and water is stocked with brown trout; tickets (dt £15, 4 fish) from Town Clerk's Office, Guildhall LD3 7AL (tel: 01874 622884) (web:

www.wyeuskfoundation.org) (open 9am to 1pm) and also from H M Supplies (above); st £40, 3-day ticket £25, dt £15. For salmon and trout fishing day tickets on Wye and Usk in the Brecon and Builth Wells area and also in mid Wales and borders, contact the Wye and Usk Foundation, Dolgarreg, North Road, Builth Wells, Powys LD2 3DD (tel: 01982 551520). Brecon AS has 1m both banks above Llanfaes Bridge; trout; fly only. Coarse fishing in pools on **Dderw Farm, Llyswen**; carp (to 15lbs), roach, tench; permits from Mrs J Eckley, Dderw Farm, Llyswen, Brecon LD3 0UT (tel: 01874 754224). **Llangorse Lake**, 6m from Brecon; pike, perch, roach and bream; boat only; disabled access; dt from lakeside shop. Tackle shop: H M Supplies Ltd, 90 The Watton, Brecon LD3 7EN (tel: 01874 622148; see website for more info: www.hmsupplies.com). Hotels: Griffin Inn, Llangoed Hall, Castle of Brecon; Nythfa House, Brecon.

Sennybridge (Powys). Gwaun-Cae-Gurwen AA has 2 stretches, 1 mile each, left bank, apply Hon Sec, members only; browns and late season salmon. Rods on **Crai Reservoir** (100 acres) owned by Cnewr Estate Ltd, Sennybridge, Brecon LD3 8SP (tel: 01874 636207); wild trout; fly fishing from bank only; day tickets from the Cnewr Farm House (on the A4067); self-catering accommodation available.

Trecastle (Powys). **Usk Reservoir** (280 acres), one of the best trout fisheries in Wales, well stocked with rainbow and brown trout supplementing natural production; fly fishing, spinning and worming; catch limit 6 fish; size limit 9 inches; anglers are permitted to use their own boats by prior arrangement; caters for disabled; permits from machine on site; for further information contact Richard Poole, Area Manager, United Utilities Operational Services Ltd., Sluvad Treatment Works, Llandegfedd

Reservoir, New Inn, Pontypool, Monmouthshire NP4 0TA (tel: 01495 769281). Hotel: Castle.

Ebbw Vale (Monmouthshire). Ebbw Vale Welfare AC has coarse fishing on **River Wye** at Foy, nr Ross-on-Wye, 2½m (chub, dace, roach and barbel), restricted membership; and ponds in the Ebbw Vale area (carp, pike, roach, perch and gudgeon); members only £25 (incl river), conc; membership open to all; from Hon Sec and local pet shop; contact Hon Sec for season tickets for people on holiday; concessions for juniors. Tackle shops: Animal Magic, 56 Bethcar St NP23 6HG (tel: 01495 305353), tickets for Ebbw Vale Welfare AC; Petsville, 52 Bethcar St NP23 6HG (tel: 01495 301292).

WYE

The whole of the river Wye is included in the section on England, although it also flows through Monmouthshire and Powys.

The River Wye from Symonds Yat viewpoint, upstream of Monmouth

SEA FISHING LOCATIONS IN WALES

Those given in the following list are arranged from south to north. Sea fishing is available at other places also, but those mentioned are included because they cater specially for the sea angler. Further information may be had from the tackle shops and club secretaries (whose addresses will be found in the club list). When writing, please enclose stamped addressed envelope for reply. Local tourist information offices will help with accommodation.

Newport (Monmouthshire). Newport and District Sea Anglers operate in Magor, Redwick, Goldcliff, St Brides, Cardiff and Barry, with rover matches from Severn Bridge to Gower in West Wales; matches held every weekend. Tackle shops: Dave Richards, 73 Church Rd, NP19 7EH (tel: 01633 254910). Hotel: Kings.

Cardiff (Glamorgan). Sea fishing is available on the north arm of the new barrage; whiting, cod, bass, flounder, sole, eel, mullet and dogfish; free fishing during barrage opening hours; summer 7am to 10 pm; winter 8am to 8pm. There are now sea fishing trips to Flatholm, an island in the middle of the Bristol Channel, which has camping availability, and other accommodation: a new virgin fishery; contact Flatholm office (tel: 02920 353817; see website for more info: www.flatholmisland.com). Tackle shop: A Bale & Son, 166a Richmond Road, Cardiff CF24 3BX (tel: 029 2049 9898; see website for more info: www.arthurbale.co.uk).

Swansea (Glamorgan). Bass, flatfish from beaches and rocks (Worm's Head). Fish baits cast from Llanmadoc take tope, thornbacks and bass. Mackerel caught in warmer months. Bass, mullet and flounders in estuary at Loughor Bridge. Excellent boat fishing in Carmarthen Bay and off Worm's Head. Charter boats operate from Swansea Marina, for fishing the bay and Pwlldu. Information from Roger's (below). Small bass, mullet, flatfish and mackerel off Mumbles

Pier; night fishing by arrangement. Bait can be dug in Swansea Bay and estuary; squid, herring, sprats and mackerel from Swansea Market or tackle shops. List of clubs available from South West Wales Assn of SAC. Tackle shops: Mainwaring's Angling Centre, 44 Vivian Rd, Sketty, Swansea SA2 0UH (tel: 01792 202245); (web: www.mainwaringsfishing.co.uk); Roger's Tackle, Sea Angling Centre, Pilot House Wharf, Swansea SA1 1UN (tel: 01792 469999); web: www.rogerstackle.co.uk).

Tenby (Pembrokeshire). Good sport from Old Pier; whiting, pollack, bass, codling and grey mullet; good bass fishing from south and north sandy beaches, and spinning from rocks. Fine mackerel fishing most seasons, and tope off Caldey Island. For boats enquire tackle shops. Tackle shops: Morris Bros, Bank House, 16 High St, SA70 7AZ (tel: 01834 844789); Tenby Angling, 10 Old Market Hall, High St, SA70 7EU (tel: 01834 844430), (see website for more info: www.tenbyangling.net).

Milford Haven and **Pembroke** (Pembrokeshire). Fine surf-fishing and spinning from rocks for bass from Freshwater West and Broad Haven (Bosherton); best late summer and autumn. Kilpaison good for bass, flatfish early on; also codling and coalfish. Stone piers and jetties inside Haven provide deep water sport for pollack, skate, rays, whiting, codling, dogfish and coalfish. Hobbs Point (Pembroke Dock) excellent for conger and skate. Mackerel from rocks and boats (Stackpole Quay good). Tope from boats in Barafundle Bay and mackerel and bass from rocks. Other useful venues are Nab Head, Martins Haven and Angle Bay, Thorn, Rat and Sheep Islands and Harbour Rock. Mackerel from boats at harbour entrance. Lugworm and razor fish may be dug in several places, especially mud-flats at Kilpaison and Angle Bay. Pennar Gut and Pembroke River.

Fishguard (Pembrokeshire). Main captures from shore and breakwaters are flatfish, codling, conger, pouting, mackerel, bass, pollack, whiting and some tope. Sea trout and mullet near mouth of Gwaun. Tope, mackerel, conger, skate, etc. from boats. Tackle shop: Goodwick Marine Services, 1 Wern Rd, Goodwick SA64 0AA (tel: 01348 873955).

Aberystwyth (Ceredigion). From the shore, May to November, bass (especially on soft crab bait), pollack, painted ray, mullet, huss, conger, wrasse. From October to January, whiting; July to September, mackerel. Dogfish, dabs and flounder throughout the year, turbot also caught. Fish caught off the rocks, off storm beaches, from the harbour and stone jetty. Borth beach and Leri estuary specially good for flounders, bass with lure spinning; Tan-y-Bwlch beach particularly good for whiting. Bull huss and thornback ray form the backbone of the boat fishing, but dogfish, dabs, gurnard, pollack, tope, bream, turbot, monkfish and porbeagle shark are taken in their seasons. Boat trips are run from the harbour ranging from 2-hour sessions for mackerel to 12 hours out at sea. There are many well-equipped boats commanded by highly experienced skippers. Tackle shops: Aber Fishing Tackle, 3 Terrace Rd, SY23 1NY (tel: 01970 611200; see website for more info: www.flymail.com); Aeron Sports & Fishing Tackle, 2 Bridge St,

Aberaeron SA46 0AP (tel: 01545 571209). Accommodation: many guest houses.

Tywyn (Merioneth). Good beach fishing for bass, plaice, mackerel, rays, turbot, cod and codling. Tope, bass, black bream, bass, mackerel and codling from two charter boats which operate from Aberdovey (summer to October). Tackle shop: Barry's Fishing Tackle, 6 College Green LL36 9BS (tel: 01654 710357; web: www.barrysfishingtackle.com).

Barmouth (Merioneth). Bass (large), flatfish, mullet in Mawddach estuary and from nearby beaches; also codling, mackerel, flatfish, and even tope and skate from boats. Ynys-y-Brawd island good for bass and flounders from shore and boats. Charter boat, Viking II, operates Apr-Oct; 2-hour, 4-hour, 8-hour deep sea or fishing or short mackerel trips; pleasure trips; licensed by the Dept of Trade for up to 12 passengers; a new faster boat capable of longer distances will be available from April; full safety equipment and fishing tackle for hire. Bookings can be made at Viking Tackle, High Street, Barmouth LL42 1DS. tel: 01341 281821; web: www.charteredboatfishingbarmouth.co.uk Tackle shops: Beachcaster Fishing Tackle, St Annes Chambers, High Street, LL42 1AR (tel: 01341 281537); Viking Tackle (see above).

Pwllheli and **Criccieth** (Caernarfonshire). Bass fishing April-October; dogfish, dabs, plaice, skate, pollack and a few sole the year round; mackerel, tope and monkfish from June to September and black bream, gilthead bream now on the increase. October to January; whiting and coalfish. Boat and bait available. Tackle shops: D & E Hughes, Walsall Stores, 24 Penlan Str, Pwllheli LL53 5DE (tel: 01758 613291); Sheffield House, 41-43 High Str, Criccieth LL52 0EY (tel: 01766 522805). Eisteddfa Fishery, Pentrefelin, Criccieth LL52 0PT (tel: 01766

523425; see website for more info: www.eisteddfa-fisheries.com); 1m east of Criccieth; 3 coarse lakes; two trout lakes: one bait and fly, other fly only; dt trout £17 for 5 fish, £11 3 fish; carp lake dt £10; mixed coarse £6.50, conc for coarse only.

Bangor (Caernarfonshire). Centre for Menai Straits and Anglesey. In Menai Straits, good mackerel and skate fishing during summer months, also plaice and flounder; good winter fishing for cod, pollack and whiting. Bait is plentiful along shores, incl crab and lugworm. Best beaches on Anglesey. Good rock marks abound for wrasse, pollack, thornback, smooth hound, mackerel, herring and bull huss. Good cod fishing in winter.

Deganwy (Caernarfonshire). Wide variety of fish taken from boats in Gt Orme, Menai Straits and Puffin Island areas. Bass in estuary and off Benarth, Bodlondeb and Deganwy Points and Beacon Light. Wreck fishing. Bait from shore and estuary. Sea fishing trips on Lady Gwen II, licensed by the Dept of Trade for up to 12 passengers, with tackle for sale or hire from Carl Davies, Pen-y-Berllan, Pentywyn Rd, Deganwy LL31 9TL (tel: 01492 581983; mob: 07710 819747; web: www.sea-fishing-trips.co.uk); specialises in wreck fishing for pollack, conger, cod, etc, and reef fishing for bass, around Anglesey, Conwy Bay and Great Orme area, Llandudno; accom arranged, disabled catered for.

Llandudno (Caernarfonshire). Skate, cod, codling, pollack, bass, mackerel, plaice, whiting, conger, coalfish, etc. Rocky beach at corner of Little Orme good for bass; so is west shore, especially Black Rocks area. Bait plentiful. Fishing from pier (dt £2.50, max 2 rods; st £65, apply at tackle shop) at beach, rocks and boats. Llandudno Tope and mackerel taken by boat fishers. Tackle shop: Rhos Point Pathfinder Sea Fishing Charters,

2 Marine Drive, Rhos on Sea LL28 4NL (tel: 01492 544829), also sells kyaks and operates sea fishing charters. Hotel: Epperstone Hotel, Abbey Rd LL30 2EE (tel: 01492 860681; see website for more info: www.epperstonehotel.co.uk).

Colwyn Bay (Denbighshire). Bass in late summer and autumn from Rhos Point, Penrhyn Bay and Llandulas, over low water. Codling (Nov-Feb). Colwyn Bay promenade over high for whiting, dabs and dogfish. Tan-Lan beach from low water up for the best mixed fishing in the area all year round (best in darkness). Piers at Colwyn Bay and Llandudno fish well over high for a variety of fish, including dabs, whiting and some plaice. Club: Colwyn Bay Victoria SAC, Marine Drive, Rhos-on-Sea. For sea fishing contact Rhos Point Pathfinder Sea Fishing Charters (see above). Hotel: Ashmount Hotel.

Rhyl (Denbighshire). Skate, dabs, codling, whiting, plaice, gurnard, dog-fish, tope. From Foryd Harbour at Rhyl, east towards Dee Estuary at Prestatyn, no licence or permit to fish is required, providing tackle and bait used are for sea fishing and not game fishing. Several boats, fully licensed to take fishing parties and charter booking, are available; contact tackle shop: Geoff's Tackle & Bait, 163b Wellington Rd LL18 1LW (tel: 01745 356236; see website for more info: www.geoffstackle.co.uk).

ANGLESEY

Holyhead and **Holy Island** (Anglesey). Fishing off Holyhead Breakwater, 1¾m long, good on any tide; summer and winter fishing, many species caught. Very good fishing also on Stanley Embankment, at Cymyran, Rhoscolyn, Trearddur Bay, Porthdafarch and Holyhead Mountain. Bull huss, dogfish, pollack, wrasse, mullet, cod, plaice, dab, flounder, conger, whiting, codling, thornback ray and bass all taken in season from the various shore-marks. Boat-fishing, possible in all but the worst of weather, yields also tope, ling and smoothhound. Bait readily available. Excellent boat fishing. Charter boat *Bad Boyz* provides one to one tuition for special needs anglers (licenced for 12); Bad Ladz 2 has side opening door for easy access to special needs anglers; contact Pearl or Mel (tel: 01407 769214; freephone: 0800 0830368; mob: 07711 984952). Bait in harbour or from tackle shop: Trefs Shop, 1 Stanley Terrace LL65 1BY (tel: 01407 769892). Tourist Information, Terminal 1, Stenna Line Port, LL65 1DQ (tel: 01407 762622).

Cemaes Bay and **Amlwch** (Anglesey). Tope taken to 80lb, skate, conger, herring, mackerel, cod, ling, pollack, whiting, tope (all tope to be photographed, weighed, measured and tagged and released from Stingray [below]), huss, bass, plaice, coley, spurdog, from boats; charter boat from Cemaes Bay, wreck and other fishing for up to 8 anglers, *Stingray*, D Williams, The Boathouse, Beach Rd, Cemaes Bay, LL67 0ES, (tel: 01407 710510; mob: 07860 175111; web: www.seafishingtrips.co.uk); rods on board, facilities, bait to order accommodation available if required.

At **Benllech**, the area one mile out to sea has been recommended as good boat fishing for mackerel in summer, pollack, whiting in winter, and dogfish all year round; thornback ray; bull huss off rocks at night. Tackle shop: Lathams, Merainadd Stores, Benllech, Tyng y gongol LL74 8TG (tel: 01248 852555); open during season.

Beaumaris (Anglesey). Big bass, tope, pollack, mullet and mackerel opposite Beaumaris and along the Straits. Cod (in winter), skate, turbot and whiting outside the Straits. Between Menai and The Tubular Bridge fair-sized bass and conger are caught. Wreck fishing up to 60 miles offshore. For boat fishing contact Stan Zalot, Starida Boats, Little Bryn, off Rosemary Lane LL58 8EE (tel: 01248 810251; web: www.starida.co.uk), and Dave Jones, Beaumaris Marine Services, The Anchorage, Rosemary Lane, LL58 8ED (tel: 01248 810746; mob: 07860 811988; see website for more: www.beaumarismarine.com); 'Cerismar Two', fast twin-engined catamaran. Tackle shop: Anglesey Bait Centre, The Shop, Gallows Point, Beaumaris LL58 8YL (tel: 01248 810009). Hotels: White Lion; Liverpool Arms.

FISHING CLUBS & ASSOCIATIONS IN WALES

Included in this list of fishing clubs and associations in Wales are some organisations which have their water on the upper reaches of the Wye or Severn, details of which are contained in the English section of *Where to Fish*. Further information can usually be had from the Secretaries and a courtesy which is appreciated is the inclusion of a stamped addressed envelope with postal inquiries. Please advise the publishers (address at the front of the book) of any changed details for the next edition.

NATIONAL BODIES

Federation of Welsh Anglers
Chris Bond
Angling Development Manager
Riverside
The Pandy
Hirwaun
Aberdare CF44 9SY
Tel: 01685 814899
info@fed-welshanglers.co.uk
crbond2@hotmail.co.uk
www.fed-welshanglers.co.uk

Visit Wales
Fishing Wales
Brunel House
2 Fitzalan Road
Cardiff CF24 0UY
Tel: 08701 211250
www.fishing.visitwales.com

Welsh Federation of Coarse Anglers
Nick Massey
17 Gilbert Street
Holyhead
Anglesea LL65 2NR
Tel: 01407 761055
zandorion@aol.com
www.welshfederationofcoarseanglers
2009.co.uk

Welsh Federation of Sea Anglers
Colin Doyle
23 Park Road
Bargoed
Mid-Glam CF81 8SQ
Tel/fax: 01443 831684
www.wfsa.org.uk
cdoyle0361@aol.com

Welsh Salmon & Trout Angling Assn
M J (Moc) Morgan, OBE
Swyn Teifi
Pontrhydfendigaid
Ystrad Meurig
Ceredigion SY25 6EF
Tel/fax: 01970 624791
www.wstaa.org

Wheelyboat Trust (The)
Director: Andy Beadsley
North Lodge
Burton Park
Petworth
West Sussex GU28 0JT
Tel/Fax: 01798 342222
www.wheelyboats.org

CLUBS

Aberaeron Town Angling Club
Shane Jones
Brynteg
Lampeter Road
Aberaeron
Ceredigion SA46 0ED
Tel: 01545 571335
Mob: 07974 780681
www.aberaeron-angling.org

Aberystwyth Angling Assn
P W Eklund
42 Erwgoch
Waunfawr
Aberystwyth
Dyfed SY23 3AZ
Tel: 01970 623021
www.aber-angling.co.uk

Afan Valley Angling Club
N. Humphreys, Secretary
82, Darren Wen,
Baglan,
Port Talbot SA12 8YN
Tel: 01639 820150
avangling@ntlworld.com
www.afanvalleyangling.com

Ammanford & District Angling Assn
John Jones
8 Florence Rd
Ammanford SA18 2DN
Tel: 01269 595770
www.ammanfordangling.co.uk

Artro & Talsarnau Fishing Assn
B Powell
3 Glandwr Cottages
Llanbedr
Gwynedd LL45 2PB
Tel: 01341 241295

Bala & District Angling Assn
Hon Sec: Trevor Edwards
22 Blaenddol
Bala
Gwynedd LL23 7BB
Tel: 07779 343824
www.balaangling.co.uk

Bangor-on-Dee Salmon Angling Assn
Huw Owen
12 Mayfair Drive
Northwich
Cheshire CW9 8GF
Tel: 01606 40341
www.bodsaa.org.uk

Bargoed Sea Anglers Club
Colin Doyle
Secretary
Meets at Club Lennox, Bargoed
cdoyle0361@aol.com
www.bargoedseaanglers.org.uk

Betws-y-Coed Anglers' Club
Mrs Sian Godbert
3 Bwlch-y-Maen
Betws-y-Coed
Gwynedd LL24 0DN
Tel: 01690 710143
www.betws-y-coed-anglers.org

Birchgrove (Cardiff) Angling Assn
J S Wilmot
4 Clydesmuir Rd
Tremorfa
Cardiff CF24 2QA
Tel: 029 20460697
www.glamorgananglersclub.org.uk

Bodelwyddan Game Anglers
W A Wilkes
30 Roland Avenue
Kinmel Bay
Rhyl
Clwyd LL18 5DN
Tel: 01745 334935
www.gameanglers.co.uk

Brecon Angling Society
D D Harris
66 Coryton Close,
Brecon,
Powys LD3 9HP

Brynmill & District Angling Club
Dave Gough
226 Mynydd Garnllwyd Road
Morriston
Swansea
SA6 7QQ
Tel: 07799 753058 (Before 7.30pm)
www.bdac.ik.com

Bryn-y-Pys Angling Assn
c/o Deggy's Fishing Tackle
2 Ruabon Road
Wrexham LL13 7PB
Tel: 01978 351815

Buckley Angling Assn
Martin Powell
Pensarn
2 Llys-y-Wern
Sychdyn
Flintshire CH7 6BJ
Tel: 01352 757648
www.buckleyaa.co.uk

Bute Angling Society
Bob Williams
19 Clos-y-Cwarra
St Fagans
Cardiff CF5 4QT
Tel: 02920 593540
www.glamorgananglersclub.org.uk

Caersws Angling Assn
Mr Rob Davis
1 Broneirion Cottages,
Llandinam,
Powys
Secretary
Tel: 01686 688843
www.caersws-aa.co.uk

Capenhurst Angling Club
A T Howdon
24 Saughall Hey
Saughall
Chester CH1 6EJ
Tel: 01244 880621

Carmarthen Amateur Angling Assn
Est. 1894. 27 miles of water on the
Tywi, Cothi and Gwili
Timothy Hooper
Summerfield Cottage
Newport Road
Castleton
Cardiff CF3 2UR
Tel: 01633 680223

Carmarthen & District Angling Assn
Tim Coupland
tel: 01267 232457
www.carmarthendistrictac.co.uk

Cambrian Angling Assn
Mel Jones
Ty Saron
Llan Ffestiniog LL41 4LY
Tel: 01766 762401
www.cambrianangling.com

Cefni Angling Assn
(see: Cymdeithas Pysgota)
Hugh Edwards
2 Hen Siop
Gaerwen
Anglesey
Mob: 07912 949319
www.llyncefni.co.uk

Ceiriog Fly Fishers Ltd
Alan Hudson
96 Crogen
Lodgevale Park
Chirk
Wrexham LL14 5BJ
Tel: 01691 773632

Cilcain Fly Fishing Assn
Kim Catherhall
3 Belmont Crescent
Buckley
Flintshire CH7 3NE
Tel: 01244 543972

Colwyn Bay Victoria Sea Angling Club
Steve Tinkler
Club Headquarters & Club House
Rhos Promenade
Rhos on Sea
Conwy
LL28 4NG
Tel: 01492 544403
www.cbvsac.co.uk

Connah's Quay & District Angling Assn
C Hett
Deeside Fishing Tackle
28 Chester Rd East
Shotton
Deeside CH5 1QA
Tel: 01244 813674

Corwen & District Angling Club
Gordon H Smith
Llais-yr-Afon
Bontuchel
Ruthin
Denbighshire LL15 2BE
Tel: 01824 710609
www.cadac.org.uk

Criccieth, Llanystumdwy & District Angling Assn
Geraint Pritchard
8 Dolwar
Four Crosses
Chwilog LL53 6UQ
Tel: 01766 810548

Crickhowell & District Angling Society
Chairman: Paul Bowen
13 Hatherleigh Road
Abergavenny
Monmouth NP7 7RG
Tel: 01873 858440

Cross Hands & District Angling Assn
Hon Sec: Pat Kiernan
48 Waterloo Road
Penygroes
Llanelli
Carmarthen SA14 7NS
Tel: 01269 842083
or
Memb. Sec: G V Davis
6 Close-yr-Hendre
Capel Hendre
Ammanford SA18 3NN
Tel: 01269 843462

Cwmcelyn Angling Club
Kevin Taggart
Brynheulog
Waun Ebbw Road
Nantyglo NP23 4QR
www.cwmcelynanglingclub.webs.com
Tel: 0777 3524418

Cefni Angling Assn
(see: Cymdeithas Pysgota)
Hugh Edwards
2 Hen Siop
Gaerwen
Anglesey
Mob: 07912 949319
www.llyncefni.co.uk

Cwmllynfell Fly Fishing Club
Paul Morris
6 Park Lane
Brynamman
nr Ammanford SA18 1TE
tel: 01269 823646

Cymdeithas Pysgota Talybont (Talybont Angling Assn)
Michael Williams
Llawr-y-Glyn
Lledrod
Ceredigion SY23 4TA
Tel: 01974 251330

Dee Anglers Assn
Martin Powell
Pensarn
2 Llys-y-Wern
Sychdyn
Flintshire CH7 6BJ
Tel: 01352 757648

Denbigh & Clwyd Angling Club
Colin Blythin
Y Fron
Abbey Road
Rhuddlan
Rhyl
Clwyd LL18 5RG
Tel: 01745 591281
www.denbighandclwydac.co.uk

Dolgarrog Fishing Club
W P Jones
12 Hillside
Dolgarrog
Gwynedd LL32 8JP
Tel: 01492 660373

Dolgellau Angling Assn
E Marshall Davies
2 Maescaled
Dolgellau
Gwynedd LL40 1UF
Tel: 01341 422706
www.dolgellauanglingassociation.co.uk

Dwyryd Anglers Ltd
Gareth Ffestin Price
Hafan
Ffordd Peniel
Ffestiniog
Gwynedd LL41 4LP
Tel: 01766 762451

Ebbw Vale Welfare Angling Club
R Satterley
8 Pen-y-lan
Ebbw Vale
Monmouthshire NP23 5LS
Tel: 01495 307613

Estimaner Angling Assn (Ystumaner Angling Assn.)
Hon Sec: John Baxter
11 Tan y Fedw
Abergynolwyn
Gwynedd LL36 9YU
Tel: 01654 782632

Garw Valley Angling Assn
John Weeks
28 Heol Tynton
Llangeinor
Bridgend CF32 8PP
Tel: 01656 872275

Glamorgan Angling Club
M Roberts
4 Heol Don
Whitchurch
Cardiff CF14 2AU
www.glamorgananglersclub.org.uk

Glaslyn Angling Assn
Enid Edwards
Gun & Tackle Shop
7 High Street
Penrhyndeudraeth LL48 6BN
Tel: 01766 770339
www.penrhyndeudraeth.cymru.org

Glyncornel Angling Assn
David Picton-Davies
94 Tylacelyn Road
Penygraig-Tonypandy
Rhondda
Mid Glam. CF40 1JR
Tel: 01443 432289 (2pm to 10pm)
www.glyncornelangling.co.uk

Glynneath & District Angling Assn
Gareth Evans
21 Godfrey Avenue
Glynneath, Neath
West Glamorgan SA11 5HF
Tel: 01639 721301
www.fishingglynneath.co.uk

Groe Park & Irfon Angling Club
J L Burton
Angle House
Pentrosfa Crescent
Llandrindod Wells
Powys LD1 5NW
Tel: 01597 822404 (day)
Tel: 01597 823119

Gwaun-Cae-Gurwen Angling Assn
Lynnford Martinson
16 Waunsterw
Rhydyfro
Pontardawe
Swansea SA8 4NF
Tel: 01792 863828

Gwent Angling Society
Mark Roberts
www.gwentanglingsociety.co.uk

Isca Angling Club
Phil Facey
3 Clipper Close
St Julians
Newport
Monmouth NP19 7LL
Tel: 01633 678790

Islwyn & District Anglers
Hon Sec: J H Otter
10 Penygroes
Parc Derwen
Oakdale
Monmouth NP12 0ER

Lavister Angling Club
G Watkins
Rathgillan
Lache Hall Crescent
Chester
Cheshire CH4 7NE
Tel: 01244 677330

Llanbrynmair & District Angling Club
Richard Evans
Penegoes
Machynlleth
Powys SY20 8NN
Tel (Mr Emyr Lewis): 01650 521385
or
Chairman: Emyr Lewis
Bryn-Llugwy
Llanbrynmair
Powys SY19 7AA
Tel: 01650 521385

Llandeilo Angling Assn
Tony Stevens
Annedd Wen
Milo
Llandybie
Ammanford SA18 3NX
Tel: 01269 832824

Llandovery Angling Assn
Michael Davies
Cwmrhuddan Lodge
Llandovery
Carmarthenshire SA20 0DX
Tel: 01550 720633

Llandysul Angling Assn
Andrew James
The Porth Hotel
Llandysul
Ceredigion SA44 4QS
Tel: 01559 362202
www.fishing-in-wales.com

Llangadog Angling Assn Ltd
Eifion Jones
Waundyrfal
Llangadog
Dyfed SA19 9EL
Tel: 01550 777296
www.llangadogfishing.com

Llangennech Angling Assn
P Holborn
32 Tyisha Rd
Llanelli SA15 1RW
Tel: 01554 753161

Llangollen Angling Assn
W N Elbourn
Bwthyn Bach
2 Green Lane
Llangollen
Denbighshire LL20 8TB

Llanidloes & District Angling Assn
Dalis Davies
Dresden House
Great Oak Street
Llanidloes, Powys SY18 6BW
Tel: 01686 412644 (after 7pm)

Llanilar Angling Assn
John H Astill
Dryslwyn
Llanafan
Aberystwyth
Ceredigion SY23 4AX
Tel: 01974 261237

Llanrwst Anglers' Club
David W P Hughes
36 Station Road
Llanrwst
Gwynedd LL26 0AD

Llanybydder Angling Assn
Andrew Morgan
Dolau View
Neuadd Road
Llanybydder
Dyfed SA40 9UB
Tel: 01570 480998

Llay Angling Assn
John Preston
20 Mold Road Estate
Gwersyllt
Wrexham
Clwyd LL11 4AA
Tel: 01978 758178

Llynfi Valley Angling Assn
Brian Hall
47 Park View Estate
Maesteg
Mid Glamorgan CF34 9HF
Tel: 01656 737995

Maelor Angling Ltd
K Bathers
Sunnyside
11 Hill Street
Cefn Mawr
Wrexham
Clwyd LL14 3AY
Tel: 01978 820608
www.maelorangling.co.uk

Maerdy & Ferndale Angling Club
Hon Sec: Myrddin Hughes
30 Union St
Ferndale
Mid Glamorgan CF43 4HD
Tel: 01443 732048

Merthyr Tydfil Angling Assn
c/o Carl Jones
Merthyr Angling Centre
185 High St
Cefn Coed
Merthyr Tydfil
CF48 2PG
Tel: 01685 379809
www.mtaa.co.uk

Neath & Dulais Angling Assn
Garry Davies
6 Martyns Avenue
Seven Sisters
Neath
SA10 9DP
Tel: 01639 701899
www.nadac.co.uk

Nevern Angling Assn
Viv Owen
Glyn-Deri
Nevern
Newport SA42 0NE
Tel: 01239 820365

Newbridge Angling Assn
Kerry F R Clutton
28 Worsley Avenue
Johnstown
nr Wrexham
Clwyd LL14 2TD
Tel: 01978 840377

The New Dovey Fishery Assn (1929) Ltd
Richard Evans
Y Plas
Aberystwyth Road
Machynlleth
Powys SY20 8ER
Tel/Fax: 01654 702721 (Mon or Fri 10am to noon)

Newport Angling Assn
Looks after fishing in several stillwaters around Newport and 1.5 miles of River Wye.
Chairman: D Ballett
102 Victoria Avenue
Newport
Monmouth NP19 8GG
Tel: 01633 264608

Newport & District Sea Anglers
Karen Davies
18 Gibbs Road
Newport
Monmouth NP19 8AT
Tel: 01633 676561

Newport Reservoirs Flyfishing Assn
Ynysyfro Reservoir
Newport
South Wales
or
Colin Jones
50 Ruskin Avenue
Rogerstone
Newport NP10 0ED
Tel: 01633 776787
www.nrffa.co.uk

Ogmore Angling Assn
Chairman: Adrian Curnock
Tel: 01656 721591
www.ogmoreanglingassociation.com
or
Sec: W Griffiths
secretary@
ogmoreanglingassociation.com

Ogwen Valley Angling Assn
Bryn Evans
Tan y Coed
Bron Arfon
Llanllechid
Bangor
Gwynedd LL57 3LW
Tel: 01248 602309
www.ogwen.net

Pembrokeshire Anglers Assn
Mrs J.A.Batty
14 Tudor Gardens
Merlins Bridge
Haverfordwest
Pembrokeshire
SA61 1LB
www.pembrokeshire-anglers.co.uk

Picton Waters Anglers Club
Hon Sec: Paul Watkins
Glynfada
Maidenwells
Pembroke SA71 5ES
Tel: 01646 683294

Ponciau Angling Society
D K Valentine
Bryn-yr-Owen
Ponciau
Wrexham

Pontardawe & Swansea Angling Society
R H Lockyer
8 Bwllfa Road
Ynystawe
Swansea SA6 5AL
Tel: 01792 844014
ray@rlockyer.wanadoo.co.uk

Pontardulais & District Angling Assn
Membership Sec: A Thomas
1 Lon Yr Ysgol
Llangennech
Llanelli
Carmarthenshire
SA14 8UZ
Tel: 01554 82160
www.pontarddulaisangling.co.uk

Porthcawl Angling Assn
Ray Owen
7 John Street
Nantymoel
Bridgend
Tel: 01656 841827
Mob: 07740 492779
www.porthcawl-angling-association.co.uk

Prince Albert Angling Society
Hon Sec:
PO Box 151
Macclesfield
Cheshire SK10 2HR
secretary@paas.co.uk
www.paas.co.uk

Pwllheli & District Angling Assn
E W Evans
2 Fron-Oleu
Caernarfon Road
Pwllheli
Gwynedd LL53 5LN
Tel: 01758 613444
www.pwllheliangling.co.uk

Prysor Angling Assn
M P Atherton
14 Bro Prysor
Trawsfynydd
Gwynedd LL41 4SS
Tel: 01766 540771
www.trawslake.com

Rhostyllen Angling Club
Bryan Ryley
23 Y-Fron
Nant Parc
Johnstown
Wrexham LL14 1UP
Tel: 01978 842017

Rossett & Gresford Fly Fishers
Mark Pierce
Mob: 07980 530674
www.rossett-flyfishers.co.uk

Rhyl & St Asaph Angling Assn
Martin Fowell
Bon-Amie
28 Ffordd Tanrallt
Meliden
Prestatyn
Denbighshire LL19 8PS
Tel: 01745 854390
www.rhylandstasaphanglers.org

Rhymney & District Angling Society
J Pugh
12 Castlefields
Rhymney
Monmouthshire NP2 5NS
Tel: 01685 840122

St Clears & District Angling Assn
David J Bryan
Madras Cottage
Broadway
Laugharne
Carmarthen SA33 4NU
Tel: 01994 427331

Seiont, Gwyrfai and Llyfni Angling Assn
H P Hughes
Llugwy, Ystad Eryri
Bethel
Caernarfon
Gwynedd LL55 1BX
Tel: 01248 670666
www.sgll.co.uk

Skewen Angling Club
Phil Lewis
Membership Secretary
31 Brookfield
Neath Abbey
Neath
Tel: 01639 639657
www.skewenac.com

Swansea Amateur Angling Assn
J B Wolfe
147 St Helen's Road
Swansea SA1 4DB

Swansea Angling Club
Malcolm Brown
31 Stepney Road
Cockett
Swansea SA2 0FZ
Tel: 01792 582058

Tawe & Tributaries Angling Assn.
Laurence Jones
20 Thomas Street
Pontardawe
Swansea Valley SA8 4HD
Tel: 01792 863522

Teifi Trout Assn
Jez Moore
Secretary
Mob: 07828 229353
www.teifitrout.com

Tregaron Angling Assn
Cheryl Mawson
28 Maesyrawel
Tregaron
Ceredigion SY25 6HJ
www.tregaronangling.com

Upper Tanat Fishing Club
enquiries@tanatfishing.com
www.tanatfishing.com

Warrington Angling Assn
Frank Lythgoe
Hon. Secretary
Tel: 01928 716238
Headquarters
52 Parker St
Warrington
Cheshire WA1 1LT
Tel: 01928 716238
www.warrington-anglers.org.uk
(Open every Friday 7pm - 9.30pm)

Wentwood Reservoir Fly Fishing Assn
D G P Jones
123 Castle Lea
Caldicot
Monmouth NP26 4HS
Tel: 01291 425158

Wirral Game Fishing Club
Fishing on Welsh Dee, Conwy, Lledr, Clwyd and Elwy.
Secretary
Paul King
17 Llys y Tywysog
Tremeirchion
St. Asaph
Denbs. LL17 0UL
Tel: 01745 710560
paullking@gmail.com
www.wirralgame.org.uk

Wrexham & District Fly-fishing Assn
John Grocott
Sandbank
Gresford Road
Hope
Wrexham LL12 9EL
Tel: 01978 761728

Wye & Usk Foundation
Dolgarreg
North Road, Builth Wells
Powys LD2 3DD
Tel: 01982 551520
www.wyeuskfoundation.org

Ynys Mon Angling Assn
Hon Sec: R T Swales
36 Trem-y-Mor
Rhosneigr
Anglesey LL64 5QR
Tel: 01407 810136
www.ynysmonangling.co.uk

Estimaner Angling Assn (Ystumaner Angling Assn)
Hon Sec: John Baxter
11 Tan y Fedw
Abergynolwyn
Gwynedd LL36 9YU
Tel: 01654 782632

FISHING IN SCOTLAND

District Salmon Fishery Boards and Close Season for Salmon and Trout

The annual close season for brown trout in Scotland extends from 7 October to 14 March, both days included (with local variations). Trout may not be sold between the first day of September and the thirty-first day of March, both inclusive, nor at any time if the fish are less than 20cm long.

Visiting anglers are reminded that on Scottish rivers and lochs the owner of the fishing rights for freshwater fish is the riparian proprietor, whose permission to fish should be obtained. The only public right of fishing for brown trout and other freshwater fish is in those portions of the rivers which are both tidal and navigable, but the right must not be exercised so as to interfere with salmon or sea-trout fishing and can be exercised only where there is a right of access to the water from a boat or from the banks. A number of rivers in Scotland including the Aberdeenshire Don are subject to Protection Orders granted by the Secretary of State for Scotland. On rivers where a Protection Order is in force, it is a criminal offence to fish for any freshwater species without the owner's written permission. Anglers visiting Scotland to fish for coarse fish should note that up to four rods can be used, but for trout and salmon only one. Four rods can be used from a boat for all fish types.

No person shall fish for or take salmon and sea trout during Sunday.

Salmon. Provision was made in the Salmon and Freshwater Fisheries (Consolidation)(Scotland) Act 2003, for the formation and amalgamation of District Salmon Fishery Boards, composed of representatives of proprietors of salmon fisheries in each district, and co-opted representatives of anglers and tenant netsmen. These boards, the addresses of which are given on pages below, are responsible for the administration and protection of the salmon fisheries in their districts, and boards have been formed for practically all the important salmon rivers. More recently, the Boards have become increasingly involved in scientifically based management, research and stock enhancement.

Increasingly, the practice of catch and release is being encouraged by boards and proprietors of salmon fishings. Regulations restricting various baits and lures are in force in a number of Salmon Fishery Districts. On 1 October 2002, a ban on the sale in Scotland of rod and line caught salmon and sea-trout was introduced.

In the following list, the days fixing the start and finish of the annual close time for salmon rod fishing are shown. The dates are inclusive.

Add: Nov 1 to Feb 15.

Ailort: Nov 1 to Feb 10.

Aline: Nov 1 to Feb 10.

Annan: Nov 16 to Feb 24.

Applecross: Nov 1 to Feb 10.

Arnisdale: Nov 1 to Feb 10.

Awe: Oct 16 to Feb 10.

Ayr: Nov 1 to Feb 10.

Baa and Goladoir: Nov 1 to Feb 10.

Badachro and Kerry: Nov 1 to Feb 10.

Balgay and Shieldaig. Nov 1 to Feb 10.

Beauly: Oct 16 to Feb 10.

Berriedale: Nov 1 to Feb 10.

Bervie: Nov 1 to Feb 24.

Bladnoch: Nov 1 to Feb 10.

Brora: Oct 16 to Jan 31.

Carradale: Nov 1 to Feb 24.

Carron: Nov 1 to Feb 10.

Clayburn (Western Isles):
Nov 1 to Feb 24.

Clyde and Leven: Nov 1 to Feb 10.

Conon: Oct 1 to Feb 10.

Cowie: Nov 1 to Feb 10.

Cree: Oct 15 to Feb 28.

Creran (Loch Creran): Nov 1 to Feb 10.

Crowe and Shiel: Nov 1 to Feb 10.

Dee (Aberdeenshire): Oct 15 to Jan 31.

Dee (Kirkcudbright.): Nov 1 to Feb 10.

Deveron: Nov 1 to Feb 10.

Don: Nov 1 to Feb 10.

Doon: Nov 1 to Feb 10.

Drummachloy (Bute):
Oct 16 to Feb 15.

Dunbeath: Oct 16 to Feb 10.

Eachaig: Nov 1 to Apr 30.

Earn (Tay): Nov 1 to Jan 31.

East Lewis (Western Isles):
Nov 1 to Feb 10.

Eden (Tay): Nov 1 to Feb 4.

Esk, North: Nov 1 to Feb 15.

Esk, South: Nov 1 to Feb 15.

Ewe: Nov 1 to Feb 10.

Fincastle (Western Isles):
Nov 1 to Feb 24.

Findhorn: Oct 1 to Feb 10.

Fleet (Kirkcudbrightshire):
Nov 1 to Feb 24.

Fleet (Sutherland): Nov 1 to Feb 24.

Forss: Nov 1 to Feb 10.

Forth: Nov 1 to Jan 31.

Garnock: Nov 1 to Feb 24.

Girvan: Nov 1 to Feb 24.

Glenelg: Nov 1 to Feb 10.

Gour: Nov 1 to Feb 10.

Grudie or **Dionard**: Nov 1 to Feb 10.

Gruinard and Little Gruinard:
Nov 1 to Feb 10.

Halladale: Oct 1 to Jan 11.

Helmsdale: Oct 1 to Jan 10.

Hope and Polla: Oct 1 to Jan 11.

Howmore (Western Isles):
Nov 1 to Feb 24.

Inchard: Nov 1 to Feb 10.

Inner (Jura): Nov 1 to Feb 24.

Inver: Nov 1 to Feb 10.

Iorsa (Arran): Nov 1 to Feb 24.

Irvine: Nov 16 to Feb 24.

Kannaird: Nov 1 to Feb 10.

Kilchoan: (Loch Nevis):
Nov 1 to Feb 10.

Kinloch (Kyle of Tongue):
Nov 1 to Feb 10.

Kirkaig: Nov 1 to Feb 10.

Kishorn: Nov 1 to Feb 10.

Kyle of Sutherland: Oct 1 to Jan 10.

Laggan and **Sorn** (Islay):
Nov 1 to Feb 24.

Laxford: Nov 1 to Feb 10.

Leven: Nov 1 to Feb 10.

Little Loch Broom: Nov 1 to Feb 10.

Loch Long: Nov 1 to Feb 10.

Loch Roag (Western Isles):
Oct 17 to Feb 10.

Loch Sunart: Nov 1 to Feb 10.

Lochy: Nov 1 to Feb 10.

Lossie: Nov 1 to Feb 24.

Luce: Nov 1 to Feb 24.

Lussa (Mull): Nov 1 to Feb 10.

Moidart: Nov 1 to Feb 10.

Morar: Nov 1 to Feb 10.

Mullanageren (Western Isles):
Nov 1 to Feb 24.

Nairn: Oct 8 to Feb 10.

Naver and **Borgie**: Oct 1 to Jan 11.

Nell, Feochan and **Euchar**:
Nov 1 to Feb 10.

Ness: Oct 16 to Jan 14.

Nith: Dec 1 to Feb 24.

Orkney Islands: Nov 1 to Feb 24.

Ormsary: Nov 1 to Feb 10.

Pennygowan and **Aros** (Mull):
Nov 1 to Feb 10.

Resort (Western Isles): Nov 1 to Feb 10.

Ruel: Nov 1 to Feb 15.

Sanda: Nov 1 to Feb 10.

Scaddle: Nov 1 to Feb 10.

Shetland Islands: Nov 1 to Feb 24.

Shiel (Loch Shiel): Nov 1 to Feb 10.

Skye, Isle of: Oct 16 to Feb 10.

Spey: Oct 1 to Feb 10.

Stinchar: Nov 1 to Feb 24.

Strathy: Oct 1 to Jan 11.

Tay: Oct 16 to Jan 14.

Thurso: Oct 6 to Jan 10.

Torridon: Nov 1 to Feb 10.

Tweed: Dec 1 to Jan 31.

Ugie: Nov 1 to Feb 9.

Ullapool (Loch Broom):
Nov 1 to Feb 10.

Urr: Dec 1 to Feb 24.

Wick: Nov 1 to Feb 10.

Ythan: Nov 1 to Feb 10.

DISTRICT SALMON FISHERY BOARDS

The names, addresses and telephone numbers of the clerks of the various salmon district fishery boards in Scotland are as follows: Please note that their duties are purely to operate the Acts and that they do not have fishing to let.

Annan District Salmon Fishery Board. Maxine McLoughlin, Fisheries Board Office, Annandale Estates, St Ann's, Lockerbie, Dumfriesshire DG11 1HQ (tel: 01576 470600, web: www.annanfisheryboard.co.uk).

Argyll District Salmon Fishery Board. Jane Wright, Woodbank, Cove, Helensburgh G84 0NU (tel: 01436 842312; e-mail: admin@argyllfisheriestrust.co.uk; web: www.argyllfisheriestrust.co.uk).

Ayr District Salmon Fishery Board. F M Watson, D W Shaw & Company, 34a Sandgate, Ayr KA7 1BG (tel: 01292 265033; fax:01292 284906; e-mail: fwatson@dwshaw.co.uk; web: www.ayrshireriverstrust.org/river-ayr.htm).

Beauly District Salmon Fishery Board. A Campbell, Bidwells, Alder House, Cradlehall Business Park, Inverness IV2 5JH (tel: 01463 796053; web: www.nbft.co.uk).

Bladnoch District Salmon Fishery Board. Peter M Murray, Messrs A B & A Matthews, Bank of Scotland Buildings, Newton Stewart, Wigtownshire DG8 6EG (tel: 01671 404100; web: www.gallowayfisheriestrust.org).

Brora District Salmon Fishery Board. C J Whealing, Sutherland Estates Office, Duke Str, Golspie, Sutherland KW10 6RR (tel: 01408 633268).

Caithness District Salmon Fishery Board. P J W Blackwood, Estate Office, Thurso East, Thurso, Caithness KW14 8HW (tel: 01847 893134).

Cree District Salmon Fishery Board. Peter M Murray, Messrs A B & A Matthews, Solicitors, Bank of Scotland Buildings, Newton Stewart, Wigtownshire DG8 6EG (tel: 01671 404100; web: www.gallowayfisheriestrust.org).

Cromarty District Salmon Fishery Board. Malcolm Younger, CKD Galbraith, Reay House, 17 Old Edinburgh Road, Inverness IV2 3HF. (Tel: 01463 224343).

Dee (Aberdeen) District Salmon Fishery Board. Mr Mark Bilsby (River Director), 4 Mill of Dinnet, Dinnet, Aboyne, Aberdeenshire AB34 5LA (tel: 01339 880411; web: www.riverdee.org.uk).

Dee (Kirkcudbrightshire) District Salmon Fishery Board. Mr I Lindsay, Bridge of Dee, Castle Douglas DG7 1TR (web: www.gallowayfisheriestrust.org).

Deveron District Salmon Fishery Board. John A Christie, Murdoch, McMath and Mitchell, Solicitors, 27-29 Duke Str, Huntly AB54 5DP (tel: 01466 792291; web: www.deveron.org).

Don District Salmon Fishery Board. George Alpine, 15 Golden Sq, Aberdeen AB10 1WF (tel: 01224 644333; web: www.riverdon.org.uk).

Doon District Salmon Fishery Board. Austin M Thomson, 46 Dalblair Rd, Ayr KA7 1UQ (tel: 01292 272603; web: www.ayrshireriverstrust.org/river-doon.htm).

Eachaig District Salmon Fishery Board, Robert C G Teasdale, Quarry Cottage, Rashfield, by Dunoon, Argyll PA23 3QT (tel: 01369 840510).

Esk District Salmon Fishery Board. Dr Marshall M Halliday, Graywalls, Ecclesgreig Rd, St Cyrus, by Montrose DD10 0BH (tel: 07769 850164).

Findhorn District Salmon Fishery Board. Mr W Cowie, R & R Urquhart, 121 High Str, Forres, Morayshire IV36 0AB (tel: 013096 72216; web: www.riverfindhorn.org.uk/).

Fleet (Kirkcudbrightshire) District Salmon Fishery Board. C R Graves, Auchenshiel, Rhonehouse, by Castle Douglas DG7 1SA (tel: 01556 680330; web: www.gallowayfisheriestrust.org).

Forth District Salmon Fishery Board. P Fothringham, The Lagg, Aberfeldy PH15 2EE. (tel: 07788 416788; web: www.fishforth.co.uk/fdsb/).

Girvan District Salmon Fishery Board. Austin M Thomson LLB, 46 Dalblair Rd, Ayr, Ayrshire KA7 1UQ (tel: 01292 272603; web: www.ayrshireriverstrust.org/river-girvan.htm).

Helmsdale District Salmon Fishery Board. N Wright, Arthur and Carmichael, Cathedral Square, Dornoch, IV25 3SW (tel: 01862 810202;).

Kyle of Sutherland District Salmon Fishery Board. Gordon Robertson, Swordale, Evanton, Ross-shire IV16 9XA (tel: 01863 766683; web: www.dsfb.co.uk).

Laggan & Sorn (Islay) District Salmon Fishery Board, Roderick Styles, Walker and Sharp Solicitors, 37 George Street, Dumfries DG1 1EB (tel: 01586 553737).

Lochaber District Salmon Fishery Board. Jon Gibb,5 Lochy Crescent, Inverlochy, Fort William PH33 6NG. (tel and fax: 01397 702784).

Lossie District Salmon Fishery Board. Beth Dunlop, Administrator, Findhorn, Nairn and Lossie Fisheries Trust, Logie Steading, Logie, Forres IV36 2QN. (tel: 01309 611220).

Luce District Salmon Fishery Board. R W Peters, Stair Estates, The Estate Office, Rephad, Stranraer, Wigtownshire, DG9 8BX (web: www.gallowayfisheriestrust.org).

Mull District Salmon Fishery Board. Christopher James, The Estate Office, Torosay Castle, By Craignure, Isle of Mull PA65 6AY. (tel: 01680 812421).

Nairn District Salmon Fishery Board. Peter Loutit, Dalriech, Auchnahillin, Daviot East, Inverness-shire IV2 5XQ (tel: 01463 772369).

Ness District Salmon Fishery Board. N Fraser, Strutt & Parker LLP, 9-11 Bank Lane, Inverness IV1 1WA. (tel: 01463 719171; web: www.nbft.co.uk).

Nith District Salmon Fishery Board. R Styles, Walker and Sharp, Solicitors, 37 George Str, Dumfries DG1 1EB (tel: 01387 267222; web: www.nithfisheryboard.org).

Northern District Salmon Fishery Board. Crispian Cook, Bell Ingram Ltd, Estates Office, Bonar Bridge, Sutherland IV24 3EA (tel: 01863 766683).

Skye District Salmon Fishery Board. Jim Rennie, Ardslane, 1 Clachamish, Skeabost Bridge, Portree, Isle of Skye, IV51 9NY (tel: 01470 582257; web: www.skyedsfb.org.uk).

Spey District Salmon Fishery Board. R Knight, 1 Nether Borlum Cottage, Knockando, Aberlour AB38 7SD (tel: 01340 810841; web: www.speyfisheryboard.com).

Stinchar District Salmon Fishery Board. Austin M Thomson, 46 Dalblair Rd, Ayr, Ayrshire KA7 1UQ (tel: 01292 272603; web: www.stincharfishing.co.uk).

Tay District Salmon Fishery Board. D Summers (Director), Site 6, Cromwellpark, Almondbank, Perth PH1 3LW (tel: 01738 583733; web: www.tdsfb.org).

The North & West District Salmon Fishery Board. Crispian Cook, Bell Ingram Ltd, Estates Office, Bonar Bridge, Sutherland IV24 3EA (tel: 01863 766683).

River Tweed Commissioners. N P Yonge, River Tweed Commissioners, The North Court, Drygrange Steading, by Roxburghshire TD6 9DJ (tel: 01896 848294; web: www.rtc.org.uk).

Ugie District Salmon Fishery Board. Rachael McLean, Masson & Glennie, Solicitors, Broad House, Broad Str, Peterhead AB42 6JA (tel: 01779 474271).

Urr District Salmon Fishery Board. Matthew Pumphrey, Primrose & Gordon, Solicitors & Estate Agents, 92 Irish Str, Dumfries DG1 2PF (tel: 01387 267316).

Wester Ross District Salmon Fishery Board. Tracey Mclachlan, The Harbour Centre, Gairloch, Wester Ross IV21 2BQ (tel: 01445 712899).

Western Isles District Salmon Fishery Board. Carol Mair, The Sawmill, Marybank, Stornoway, Isle of Lewis HS2 0DD. (tel: 01851 703434; e-mail: carol@ohft.org.uk; web: www.ohft.org.uk).

Ythan District Salmon Fishery Board. Mark Andrew, Estate Office, Mains of Haddo, Tarves, Ellon, Aberdeenshire AB41 0LD (tel: 01651 851664; web: www.ythan.co.uk).

SCOTTISH ENVIRONMENT PROTECTION AGENCY

The Scottish Environment Protection Agency (SEPA) is the public body responsible for environmental regulation and improvement in Scotland. It was established under the Environment Act 1995 and became fully operational from 1 April 1996. SEPA's role in protecting the water environment is far-reaching and involves several programmes that provide a comprehensive and robust means of protecting and enhancing the quality, quantity and conservation value of Scotland's waters. In 2000 the Water Framework Directive was introduced, to replace seven existing Directives; Scottish legislation (2003) implements this. Transposed into Scottish law, it drives major improvements to protecting the whole water environment. SEPA uses its water classification schemes to monitor changes in Scotland's water environment, and has delivered a major improvement in the quality of rivers by reducing the length of poor and seriously polluted waters significantly since 1996. A number of European Directives will continue to drive improvements to the water from the main pollutants of sewage and agricultural discharges; and also cover river engineering.

SEPA

Corporate Office
Erskine Court
Castle Business Park
Stirling FK9 4TR
Tel: 01786 457700

Fax: 01786 446885
www.sepa.org.uk
24-hour Pollution Line:
0800 80 70 60
Floodline: 0845 988 1188.

Home of wild browns and charr. Talla Reservoir, Scottish Borders

A good wave on Loch Voshimid, Amhuinnsuidhe Castle Estate, Western Isles

A first ever salmon on! Traquair beat, River Tweed

FISHING LOCATIONS IN SCOTLAND

The nature of Scotland with its many rivers and lochs, especially on the west coast, makes it impracticable in some cases to deal with each river's catchment area separately. Thus some fisheries on the west coast, north of the Firth of Clyde, are grouped under the heading 'West Coast Rivers and Lochs'.

The need again arises to decide whether a river should be included in England or Scotland. The Border Esk is dealt with in the English section, together with the Kirtle and the Sark, which happens to fall within the Esk's catchment area on the map. Tweed and all its tributaries are included in this Scottish section. All the Scottish Islands, including Shetland and Orkney, are considered as within one watershed, viz, 'The Islands', in which, for convenience, Kintyre is included. The exact position in the book of any river or fishing station can, of course, readily be found by reference to the index.

ALNESS and GLASS

Alness drains Loch Morie, then flows 12 miles to enter Cromarty Firth at Alness. Glass drains Loch Glass then flows into Cromarty Firth near Evanton.

Alness (Ross shire). Small, fast flowing river with grilse, salmon, sea trout, and brown trout. Salmon and grilse runs improved over the last decade. Good bank fishing on Loch Morie; fly only; River Alness has 6 beats, 4 rods per beat sold from Salmonquest (see Evanton) (tel: 01349 830606; web: www.salmonquest.co.uk); also on Loch Morie, brown trout, ferox and Arctic charr; also Loch Bad à Bhathaich, brown trout (web: www.troutquest.com). Alness AC has water on estuary of R Alness, salmon, sea trout, brown trout. Permits from Hon secretary.

Evanton (Ross shire). Brown trout fishing on **Loch Glass**; bank fishing; contact Evanton AC which also has salmon, sea trout and brown trout fishing on Rivers Glass and Skiach; and only brown trout fishing on Loch Glass; club also has sea trout fishing on shore of Cromarty Firth; contact Hon Sec; dt on river and lochs. Contact Roger Dowsett (tel: 01349 830606; mob: 07714 983100; web: www.alnessfishing.com) for River Alness fishing; six rotating beats; good salmon, sea tout and browns).

ANNAN

Rises in Moffat Hills and flows about 30 miles to Solway Firth. Strong tidal river. Several good pools on river N of Annan. Some spring salmon, excellent sea trout in June and July, and excellent salmon in late autumn, Oct Nov; a few brown trout in spring and summer.

Ecclefechan (Dumfriesshire). Annan, 2m SW; salmon, herling (late July onwards), brown trout. Hoddom & Kinmount Estates, Estate Office, Hoddom, Lockerbie DG11 1BE (tel: 01576 300244) (water bailiff: 01576 300417; mob: 077116 81507), have Hoddom Castle Water, over 2m stretch on Annan; salmon; grilse late July onwards; sea trout, May Aug; dt available, limited to 15 rods per day; fly only, except when river height is above red line on Hoddom Bridge when spinning is permitted; Hoddom & Kinmount Estates also have trout fishing on **Purdomstone Reservoir**, now let Annan AC; and coarse fishing on **Kelhead Quarry** and **Kinmount Lake,** which has first rate pike fishing; Purdomstone Reservoir, brown trout; Kelhead Quarry; brown and rainbow trout, perch, roach, bream, carp, pike, tench, eels; dt available; suitable for disabled; permits for Hoddom Estates waters may be booked from Water Bailiff, Estate Office, Hoddom, Lockerbie DG11 1BE (booking: 01573 470612 or www.fishannan.co.uk); Kelhead Quarry permits, from Water Bailiff, Kinmount Bungalows, Kinmount, Annan (tel: 01461 700344).

Lockerbie (Dumfriesshire). R Annan 1 ½m W; salmon, sea trout, brown trout. Castle Milk & Corrie Estates DG11 2QX (tel: 01576 510203) has four beats on R Annan and Castle Milk Water (St Mungo Parish); salmon and sea trout, brown trout, graling; 2m, left bank only; fly only; grayling during closed salmon seaon dt £5; limited dt £11.75 (early season to 1 May), 1 May to 31 Aug £23.50, and £47 (late season); the Estate also has the Brocklerigg stretch, also above Shillahill Bridge st only, 1200 yards left bank and 600 yards right bank; Royal Four Towns Water; salmon, grayling, sea trout, brown trout, herling, chub, grilse; 3¾m, both banks; grayling during closed salmon seaon dt £5; dt £10 (early season) and £20 (late season), also wt, £50 £100; contact Castle Milk & Corrie Estates (above) or Mrs Ratcliffe, Kay ar, The High Road, Hightae DT11 1JS (tel: 01387 810220). A tributary of Annan is River Milk, now syndicate water. **Kirkwood water**: 1⅓m single bank with good salmon and sea trout fishing; wt from Castle Milk & Corrie Estates (see above). **Jardine Hall** water: 2½m, some double bank, good sea trout, and late salmon; wt from £50 £160; contact Anthony Steel, Kirkwood Holiday Cottages & Fishings, Kirkwood, Dalton, Lockerbie DG11 1DH (tel: 01576

510200; see website for more info: www.kirkwood-lockerbie.co.uk). Halleaths Water, west bank of Annan, near Lockerbie and Lochmaben; salmon and trout, fly only; three tickets per week in the season, 25 Feb 15 Nov; no dt; permits from McJerrow and Stevenson, Solicitors, 55 High St, Lockerbie DG11 2JJ (tel: 01576 202123). Upper Annandale AA has salmon, sea trout and trout fishing in two beats: upper beat, between **Moffat** and **Johnstonebridge,** 4m double bank from just south of Moffat d/s to Cogries railway viaduct; and Applegarth beat, 4m double bank between Johnstonebridge and Lockerbie which includes 1m of **Kinnel Water**; grayling and chub, also present on Applegarth beat; may be fished from 25 Feb to 15 Nov; there is now also grayling/coarse permit on Applegarth beat from 1 Dec to 31 March: dt both beats £12, wt £60, conc; also £5 grayling ticket: 1 Dec to 31 March (incl Sunday till start of salmon season) (on line only), from Video Sport, 48 High St, Lockerbie DG11 2AA (tel: 01576 202400); Red House Hotel, Wamphray, nr Moffat DG10 9NF (tel: 01576 470470); after 15 Sept, salmon only, wt £90; Gents Hairdressers, Well St, Moffat; Esso Petrol Station, Moffat; or Hon Sec; limited dt £30 available only from Red House Hotel. Tackle shops: D McMillan, 6 Friars Vennel, Dumfries DG1 2RN (tel: 01387 252075); Pattie's of Dumfries, 109 Queensberry St, Dumfries DG1 1BH (tel: 01387 252891; see website info: www.pattiesofdumfries.co.uk).

Lochmaben (Dumfriesshire). Salmon, sea trout, brown trout, chub (good); Royal Four Towns Water, Hightae; salmon season, Feb 25 to Nov 15; brown trout, March 15 to Oct 6; no Sunday fishing, from Sept Nov advance booking advisable; apply The Clerk of the Commissionaires of Fishing for Royal Four Towns, High Rd, Hightae DG11 1JS (tel: 01387

810220). Brown trout fishing on Water of Ae in Forest of Ae; fly, worm; no ground bait; season 15 Mar to 30 Sept; no Sunday fishing; dt £5 + VAT: Forestry Commission Scotland, Ae Village, Dumfries DG1 1QB (tel 01387 860247). Coarse fishing on Castle Loch; dt from Lochmaben PO, High St, Lochmaben, Lockerbie DG11 1NG (tel: 01387 810221); st from water bailiff Bruce Gillie (tel: 07773 658 136). Hotel: The Hightae Inn, Hightae.

Wamphray (Dumfriesshire). Two beats of R Annan controlled by Upper Annandale AA; plus Annandale Estate beat (on line tickets only); permits for these, totalling 13m in all, including from Red House Hotel, Wamphray, nr Moffat DG10 9NF (tel: 01576 470470); for dt contact web: www.fishannan.co.uk; st £70 (25 Feb to 15 Sept), dt £8 16 Nov to 24 Feb; then £10 25 Feb to 15 Sept, then from 16 Sept to 15 Nov £25 dt, book 5 days and get 6th free; afterwards wt £63, dt £25; st £176 (limited to 15 only); grayling 16 Nov to 24 Feb, dt £8, st £50; conc; st only from Annandale Estate Office, St Anns, Lockerbie (tel: 01576 470317); for grayling (Nov Feb) dt £8.

Moffat (Dumfriesshire). Upper Annandale AA has 4m double bank of Annan; with salmon, brown trout, and sea trout fishing; permits (lower beats) obtainable; 25 Feb to 15 Nov: dt £12, wt £60 (after 15 Sept wt only), conc, from Video Sport, 48 High St, Lockerbie DG11 2AA (tel: 01576 202400); Red House Hotel, Wamphray, nr Moffat DG10 9NF (tel: 01576 470470) (after 15 Sept, salmon only, wt £90; limited dt available, only from this hotel); Gents Hairdressers, Well St, Moffat; Esso Petrol Station, Moffat; or Hon secretary.

AWE and LOCH AWE and LOCH ETIVE

A short river, but one of best known salmon streams of west coast. Connects Loch Awe to sea by way of Loch Etive, which it enters at Bonawe. River fishes best from June onwards.

Taynuilt (Argyllshire). Salmon, sea trout, trout. Inverawe Fisheries, Taynuilt, Argyll PA35 1HU (tel: 01866 822777; see website for more info: www.inverawe-fisheries.co.uk), has 1m on River Awe, salmon and sea trout; and three lochs stocked daily with rainbow trout; fly only; half day tickets £18, conc; tuition, tackle for hire (book in advance) and refreshments on site. Salmon and trout fishing also from T L Nelson, Kilmaronaig, Connel, Argyll PA37 1PW (tel: 01631 710223) who has a stretch on R Awe. Loch Etive (salt water), brown, sea trout and sea fish; no permit required. Hotel: Polfearn Hotel. Inverawe Holiday Cottages on estate.

LOCH AWE. Salmon, sea trout, wild brown trout (av. 14oz), ferox, charr, occasional large rainbows, perch and pike. British record for brown trout has been broken here four times in the last decade. The record currently stands at 31lb 11oz, an Awe fish caught in 2002. Pike over 20lb not uncommon. Protected and controlled by Loch Awe Improvement Association, fishing is by permit only, which does not include salmon and sea trout. There is a road right round loch. Salmon are most often caught by trolling. Sea trout are rarely caught and only at north end. Trout can be caught anywhere and average just under 1lb; best months for fly fishing Apr, May and Sep. Charr are caught on a very deep sunk line, ferox generally by trolling at depth. Pike and perch can be taken on a spun lure or dead bait.

Loch Awe (Argyllshire). Loch Awe Improvement Association water (tel: 07867 534707 or 01499 302681) is open to all who buy season tickets £60, weekly (£20), 3 day (£12), and daily (£6) tickets; assn also has trout fishing on **River Avich** and **Loch Avich**; 50% concessions for OAPs and juniors (under 12 accompanied by permit holding adult　free); permits and boats from D Wilson (below); permits and tackle from Loch Awe Stores, Loch Awe, Dalmally, PA33 1AQ (tel: 01838 200200); and many other sales points including tackle shops throughout Scotland (a full list is issued by Sec of Association, tel: 01499 302681). Tackle: D Wilson, Loch Awe Boats, Ardbrecknish, by Dalmally PA33 1BH (tel: 01866 833256; mob: 07703 112422; web: www.loch-awe.com).

Kilchrenan (Argyllshire). Taychreggan Hotel, on lochside, has pike, trout and salmon fishing on Loch Awe; fish run to good size; 2 boats with outboard engines; fishing also arrangeable on River Awe (salmon), and Loch Etive (sea trout); good sea fishing; hotel has own jetty; permits and further information from Taychreggan Hotel, Kilchrenan, by Taynuilt, Argyll PA35 1HQ (tel: 01866 833211; fax: 01866 833244; see website for more info: www.taychregganhotel.co.uk).

Dalavich (Argyllshire). For fishing on Loch Awe (brown trout, rainbow trout, ferox, charr, perch, pike), Loch Avich (brown trout) and River Avich (salmon and brown trout); dt available: permits, boat hire and rod hire, from N D Clark, 11 Dalavich, by Taynuilt PA35 1HN (tel: 01866 844209). Loch Aweside Marine has Loch Avich trout fishing; good beginners' loch; £45 full day with engine, £23 without; see Loch Awe for permit prices and telephone number.

Ford (Argyllshire). Permits for Loch Awe and Loch Avich from Ford House Hotel, Ford, Lochgilphead PA31 8RH (tel: 01546 810273) or Anglers Corner, 112 George Street Oban PA34 5NT (tel: 01631 566374). For pike fishing in Loch Ederline and brown trout fishing in 18 hill lochs contact Angus Wilson, The Big House, Ederline Estate (tel: 01949 850372 or 01546 810284); dt £10, boat £20, half day £15; tickets for L Ederline on bank; 3 self catering cottages.

Tributaries of the Awe

ORCHY: Good salmon.

Dalmally (Argyllshire). River flows into Loch Awe here, excellent salmon fishing in May, June, Sept and Oct. Permits for several beats on Orchy; and pike and trout permits for Loch Awe, and Loch Avich, from Loch Awe Stores, Loch Awe, Dalmally PA33 1AQ(tel: 01838 200200), who can also supply fishing tackle for sale. D Hadley, Ebor Cottage, St Patricks Rd, Hucknall Notts NG15 6LU, has 7m single roadside bank, excellent fly fishing water; permits from Loch Awe Stores; cottage to let, if required. Upper Craig beat, 2m both banks, 14 named pools; fly, spin or worm; return all undamaged fish; dt £20; no Sunday fishing; apply Loch Awe Stores, Loch Awe, Dalmally PA33 1AQ(tel: 01838 200200) Hotels: Glenorchy Lodge; Orchy Bank; Craig Villa. Self catering and B & B accommodation in area.

Bridge of Orchy (Argyllshire). For permits on Orchy beats: Dalmally 1, 2, 3, 4 & 5, Craig Beat and Inveroran, contact Loch Awe Stores, Loch Awe, Dalmally, PA33 1AQ (tel: 01838 200200); permits range from £25 - £45 per rod per day for river; trout season 15 Mar to 6 Oct (pike all year round).

AYR

Rises in Glenbuck and flows into Firth of Clyde through town of Ayr opposite south end of Isle of Arran. Good brown trout and grayling river (av ½lb) with fair runs of salmon and sea trout.

Ayr (Ayrshire). Mostly preserved, but have ¾m Cragie stretch of R Ayr, leased from South Ayrshire Council. Ayr AC has stretch on River Ayr at Ayr and near Annbank (salmon, sea trout, brown trout); and on Loch Shankston (rainbow, blue and brown), Loch Snipe (rainbow trout) and Loch Bradan (brown trout); members only; wading essential for good Lochsport; waters restocked with brown trout; membership from GameSport (below). Tickets for Ayr waters and many others; GameSport of Ayr, 60 Sandgate, Ayr KA7 1BX (tel: 01292 263822; see website for more info: www.gamesportofayr.co.uk).

Belston Loch at Sinclairston, a small rainbow trout fishery, 6m from Ayr; dt available.

Other fisheries: **Springwater Fishery** (tel: 01292 560343; web: www.springwaterfishery.co.uk), nr Dalrymple KA6 6AW, stocked with blue, rainbows, steelhead and brown trout: permits from fishery, also for coarse fishery. Others: Burns Fishery, Tarbolton Loch, Tarbolton KA5 5NT(tel: 01292 540214; web: www.assf.net); Coyle Water, stocked with steelheads and rainbows, permits at fishery; Prestwick Reservoir nr Monkton, stocked brown and rainbow, permits from GameSport and Monkton newsagent; tickets for town and other waters on Rivers Ayr and

Doon may be obtained, and for coarse fishing lochs. For further information contact GameSport of Ayr, 60 Sandgate, Ayr KA7 1BX (tel: 01292 263822; see website for more info: www.gamesportofayr.co.uk). Hotel: Manor Park, Monkton.

Mauchline (Ayrshire). Salmon, sea trout and brown trout fishing on Rivers Ayr, Cessnock and Lugar (tickets from newsagents); and brown and rainbow trout fishing on Loch Belston at Sinclairston, refer to GameSport (see Belston above); boats on Loch Belston; members only.

Muirkirk (Ayrshire). Fish pass has been built at Catrine Dam, allowing fish to run to headwaters at Muirkirk. Muirkirk AA has approx 6m on River Ayr, both banks; salmon, sea trout, brown trout, grayling; assn also has fishing on Greenock Water; fishing (trout and grayling only) allowed till 30 Sept on Greenock W; on R Ayr salmon and sea trout 1 Apr 31 Oct, browns 15 Mar 6 Oct; also on Glenbuck Loch; boats, phone first (tel: 0775 2456393); brown trout restocking program; limited to 4 fish per day; apply to Hon Sec; concessions and 3 competitions per year for juveniles. Limited tackle from Moorheads, 42 Main St KA10 3RA (tel: 01290 661321); Hotel: Coach House Inn.

Tributaries of the Ayr

COYLE. Sea trout, trout, grayling, few salmon.

Drongan (Ayrshire). For Snipe Loch enquire Ayr AC; brown and rainbow;

stocked; fish up to 11lb are being caught.

BEAULY

Beauly is approximately 9m long, and flows from the junction of Glass and Farrar into Beauly Firth and thence into Moray Firth. Salmon, sea trout good from beginning of season. Main grilse runs in July/August. Plentiful food supply in Beauly Firth, hence the presence of bottlenose dolphins, porpoises and seals.

Beauly (Inverness shire). Salmon, sea trout, occasional brown trout. Beauly AA has water below Lovat Bridge, and river mouth to Coulmore Bay, north shore, and Bunchrew Burn on south shore (sea trout and occasional bass); strictly fly only from Lovat bridge to Wester Lovat; tickets from Hon Sec. For river and loch fishing, salmon and trout, enquire Morrison's, Ironmonger, West End, Beauly IV4 7BT (tel: 01463 782213). Sea trout fishing on Beauly Firth at Clachnaharry and North Kessock; permits from J Graham & Co, 37 39 Castle St, Inverness IV2 3EA (tel: 01463 233178); good sea trout from the beginning of the season.

Loch Ruthven, trout fly fishing by boat, 12m from Inverness. Tarvie Lochs Trout Fishery, Inchdrean, Tarvie, Strathpeffer IV14 0EJ (tel: 01997 421250), rainbow, brown and blue trout, fly; boat and bank fishing, 25m from Inverness; tickets for the three lochs from lodge; from £10. Loch Ashie and Loch Duntelchaig, fly and spinning, 10m from Inverness; tickets from Scottish Water. Tickets for 3m double bank of R Ness from J Graham (above). For 7m on R Nairn, Pat Fraser, 41 High St, Nairn IV12 4AG (tel: 01667 453038). Hotels: Lovat; Priory; Caledonian IV4 7BY (tel: 01463 782 278), which can arrange fishing on river and several lochs; all Beauly.

Tributaries of the Beauly.

FARRAR and GLASS:

Tomich (Inverness shire). Salmon and brown trout. For fishing in Guisachan Hill Lochs; brown and rainbow trout; tickets available through Mr K Laidlay, Culbogie Cottage, Tomich, Cannich IV4 7LY (tel: 01456 415352); season: 1 May to 6 Oct.

CANNICH: Tributary of the Glass.

Cannich (Inverness shire). Permits from John and Liz Perkins, Kerrow House, Cannich, Strathglass, Inverness shire IV4 7NA (tel: 01456 415 243; web: www.kerrow-house.co.uk), for 3½m of brown trout fishing on River Glass (fly only); free for guests of Kerrow House (B&B and self catering). Fly fishing on R Farrar and Glass; dt £30 £65 (salmon) and £10 (trout); from F Spencer Nairn, Culligran House, Glen Strathfarrar, Struy, nr Beauly IV4 7JX (tel: 01463 761285;

www.fishpal.com/scotland/beauly/; www.culligrancottages.co.uk); priority given to guests of Culligran Cottages (self catering), brochure issued. Upstream on R Glass dt sometimes available on River Glass syndicate water between Struy and Cannich; contact Alison Fraser (tel: 01463 761205). Dt available for small stretch of River Glass; contact Cnoc Hotel, Struy (tel: 01463 761264; see website: www.thecnochotel.co.uk). At confluence of Cannich and Glass, Strathglass Fishing has boat fishing, fly only, for brown trout on **Loch Benevean**, and Loch **Beannacharan**, and can arrange salmon fishing on River Glass. Reservations direct to Strathglass Fishing, Runivraid Cammich, Inverness IV4 7LS (tel: 01456 415477; mob: 07770 826045; web: www.strathglassfishing.co.uk). Hotel: Kerrow House.

BERVIE

Rises on Glen Farquhar Estate and flows 14m to North Sea near Inverbervie. Essentially an autumn river for finnock, sea trout and salmon although also good for brown trout.

Inverbervie (Angus). Finnock, sea trout, salmon (best Sept Oct). For fishing upstream from Donald's Hole; dt from Inverbervie Sports Centre, Kirkburn, Inverbervie, Montrose DD10 4RS (tel: 01561 361182).

BRORA

After being joined by tributaries Blackwater and Skinsdale, Brora flows through Loch Brora and into sea at Brora.

Brora (Sutherland). **Loch Brora**; salmon, sea trout and brown trout. Hotel: Royal Marine.

CARRON (Grampian)

Rises in Glenbervie and flows about 9m to the North Sea at Stonehaven. Trout.

Stonehaven (Kincardineshire). About 2 ½m brown trout fishing offered to visitors by Stonehaven & Dist AA; permits also issued for River Cowie (about 1¼m), sea trout, salmon and brown trout; best July, August and Sept; permits from David's Sports & Leisure, 31 Market Sq AB39 2BA (tel: 01569 762239). Good sea fishing. Hotels: many B&Bs.

CLYDE

Rises near watershed of Tweed and Annan, and flows about 50m to the Atlantic by way of Glasgow. Once a famous salmon river, then spoiled by pollution. Now, river has improved, with salmon and sea trout returning annually. Controls are in force, to conserve stocks. Trout and grayling fishing, especially in higher reaches. The Clyde's most famous tributary, the Leven, which connects with Loch Lomond, has run of salmon and sea trout. In north west corner of Renfrewshire is Loch Thom, linked by water spill with Loch Compensation, which, when water is high, drains into River Kip in Shielhill Burn. United Clyde Angling Protective Association Ltd, controls much of Clyde and tributaries upstream of Motherwell Bridge to Daer Reservoir, in three sections, the Upper, Middle and Lower Reaches, and restocks periodically. The Clyde is covered by a Protection Order: anglers must have a permit before approaching the water. Permits and prices as follows: st £30, dt £10, salmon st £60, OAP £10, juv conc. These are obtainable from various tackle dealers and sports shops in Lanarkshire and Glasgow. Accommodation can be arranged through Greater Glasgow and Clyde Valley Tourist Board.

Greenock (Renfrewshire). On the estuary of Clyde. Greenock & Dist AC preserves Loch Thom (365 acres, trout), and has rights on Yetts, No. 8 and No. 6 (Spring Dam), good trout; permits from Brian Peterson, The Fishing Shop (below); club membership restricted to persons resident in Greenock and district, but permits sold to visitors; Sunday fishing; no parties; fly only; bank fishing only. Largs & DAC has

Muirhead Reservoir on A760 10m S; brown & rainbow; club also has Crosbie Reservoir at West Kilbride, browns and rainbows, dt available; also Outerwards Reservoir 3m S of Greenock, brown trout, dt water; also 2 burns (Gogo and Nodsdale Water ('Noddle')) which flow into sea at Largs, very occasional salmon and sea trout, dt; tickets from Hastie of Largs Ltd (Tackle Shop), 109 Main St, Largs KA30 8JJ (tel: 01475 673104; web: www.hasties.com); and R T Cycles, 73 Main Rd, Glengarnock, Beith KA14 3AA (tel: 01505 682191). Tickets for trout fisheries in vicinity; Lawfield Trout Fishery, Houston Rd, Kilmacolm PA13 4NY (tel: 01505 874182), brown trout, rainbow and blues, permits and instruction at fishery; disabled access; refreshments on site. New Haylie Fishing Loch, Bray, Largs KA30 8JA (tel: 01475 676005) (4 acres), has rainbows, browns, blues, gold, tiger, cut throat and bronze trout; atlantic charr, dt £12 2 fish; £16 3 fish; £20 4 fish; £24 5 fish; £26 6 fish ; refreshments and tackle available; fishing lodge. Tackle shop: The Fishing Shop, 24 Union Str, Greenock, PA16 8DD (tel: 01475 888085); dt for Greenock & DAC, Port Glasgow AC and Largs AC. Good sea fishing for cod, skate, dogfish, conger, haddock and plaice. Hotel: Tontine.

Glasgow (Lanarkshire). Glasgow has excellent trout, sea trout and salmon fishing within a radius of 60m. Lochs Lomond, Dochart, Awe, Tay, Ard, Leven, Lubnaig, Venachar, Lake of Menteith, etc, and Rivers Annan, Goil, Cur (head of Loch Eck), Clyde (trout and grayling only), Teith, Tweed, Allan, Dochart, Leven, Kinglass etc, all accessible from here. Coarse fishing on whole of Forth and Clyde Canal; pike, perch, roach, tench, eels, mirror carp on 35 miles of canal; no close season; for further details apply to British Waterways,

Lowland Canals, New Port Downie, Lime Road, Tamfourhill, Falkirk FK1 4RA (tel: 01324 671217; web: www.britishwaterways.co.uk/scotland). For coarse fishing in Glasgow at **Auchinstarry Basin**, Kilsyth (tench, roach, perch and rudd), dt first from Anglers Rendezvous. Kilmadinny Loch, Bearsden; Bardowie Loch, Balmore; Mugdock Park Pond, Milgavie; Tench Pool, Milgavie; Carp Pond, Seafar; and Hogganfield Loch, Glasgow all free. United Clyde Angling Protective Association, issues annual tickets for stretches on Clyde and R Douglas near Motherwell, Lanark, Carstairs, Roberton and Thankerton; brown trout and grayling fishing; permits from Hon Sec or tackle shops. Kilsyth FC controls Townhead Reservoir; apply to Hon Sec. Tackle shop: Anglers Rendezvous, 18 Saltmarket, G1 5LD (tel: 0141 552 4662; web: www.anglersrendezvous.co.uk) issues many permits; non members welcome.

Airdrie (Lanarkshire). Airdrie & DAC has Hillend Reservoir; brown and rainbow trout 1lb 12lb stocked weekly; pike to 32lb and perch; all legal methods; bag limit 4 fish; boat and bank fishing, good access for disabled; no ground bait; permits at water £10 (£8 from lodge), 4 fish limit; st £75, juv £55, conc; boats for hire; disabled Wheelyboat; there is an associate membership scheme: enquire Hon Sec. Clarkston AC has Lilly Loch at Calderdruix; rainbow and brown trout; season 1 Mar 31 Oct for rainbows; any legal method (fly only from boats); dt from bailiffs on site (tel chairman Sam Armstrong: 01236 769221). Hotel: Owl & Trout, Caldercruix, By Airdrie.

Motherwell (Lanarkshire). United Clyde APA has water on Clyde and Douglas; brown trout and grayling; permits from local tackle shops. Coarse fishing on Strathclyde Country Park Loch and adjacent R

Clyde; carp, bream, roach, pike, perch; no close season; no fly fishing; no boat fishing; lead free weights only; also limited trout and grayling fishing on Clyde; permits from Booking Office, Watersports Centre, 366 Hamilton Rd, Motherwell ML1 3ED (tel: 01698 402060).

Strathaven (Lanarkshire). Avon; trout and grayling. Avon AC has water; contact Hon Sec.

Lanark (Lanarkshire). Trout and grayling. United Clyde APA water on Clyde and Douglas; permits from local tourist information. Coarse fishing on Lanark Loch; carp and tench; no close season. Tackle shop: Fishing & Survival, 35 Bannatyne St ML11 7JR (tel: 01555 660097). Hotel: Cartland Bridge.

Carstairs (Lanarkshire). Trout and grayling. United Clyde APA water on Clyde and Douglas; permits from local tackle shops.

Thankerton (Lanarkshire). Lamington & DAIA has 9m of water from Thankerton to Roberton; trout and grayling st £40, wt £18, dt £8, (no conc); no trout under 10"; no spinning or minnow fishing on main river at any time; 4 fish limit; permits from Hon Sec; W P Bryden Newsagent, 153 High St, Biggar ML12 6DL (tel: 01899 220069); no Sunday fishing; also from Visit Scotland in Lanark and Abington. United Clyde APA water below Thankerton.

Biggar (Lanarkshire). Lamington & DAIA fish from Roberton Burn mouth to Thankerton boat bridge, approx 9m, both banks, with brown trout and grayling; good wading; prices (see above). Tackle shop: W P Bryden Newsagent, 153 High St, Biggar ML12 6DL (tel: 01899 220069). Hotel: Cornhill House Hotel.

Abington (Lanarkshire). Trout and grayling; United Clyde APA water; permits from Abington PO, 85 Carlisle Rd, Abnington, Biggar ML12 6SD (tel: 01864 502374). Other assn water at Crawford and Elvanfoot. Hotel: Abington.

Tributaries of the Clyde

LEVEN and LOCH LOMOND: Salmon, sea trout, pike and perch.

Loch Lomond (Dunbartonshire). Loch has the largest surface area of any freshwater body in Britain, being 22.6 miles long and up to 5 miles wide, and has over forty islands on it. The powan, a member of the salmon family, is found in only one other loch in Scotland (Loch Eck); the loch held the record for Britain's largest pike, and there are 17 other fish species present. Good sea trout and salmon fishing (best July to Oct) (also perch, roach and pike) can be had from various centres on loch; under control of Loch Lomond Angling Improvement Assn; fishing reserved for full members only on Fruin and most stretches of Endrick; day permits are joint for River Leven and/or Loch Lomond, available at most local tackle shops, boat hirers; children's permits available; no Sunday fishing for salmon or sea trout; late April and May earliest for fly on Loch Lomond (sea trout and salmon); boat hire; dt £15 (east side of loch); coarse permits also available £2.50 dt, st £25 (loch only): McFarlane & Son, The Boatyard, Balmaha G63 0JQ (tel: 01360 870214); permits also from local tourist office; also at Luss (the village shop); also Ardlui Hotel. Tackle shop: O'Brien, Newsagent, 225 Bank St, Alexandria G83 0WJ (tel: 01389 752037). Balloch Tourist Information Centre, Old Station Building, Balloch Rd, Balloch G83 8LQ (tel: 01389 753533) can provide information fishing Loch Lomond. For Carbeth Fishery, Stockiemuir Rd, carbeth G63 9AY, just off A809 Milngavie/Drymen road; (tel: 01360 771006; see website for more info: www.carbethfishery.com); rainbow and brown trout; 3 ponds; dt £12 2 fish (four hours); £13 2-fish on fly pond; disabled facilities.

Rowardennan, By Drymen (Lanarkshire). Convenient for Loch Lomond; permits and boats. Hotel: Rowardennan.

Balloch (Lanarkshire). Good sea trout and salmon fishing on River Leven and Loch Lomond; large perch and pike in loch; fishing controlled by Loch Lomond AIA. Vale of Leven & Dist AC issues permits for brown trout fishing on Loch Sloy; fly only, dt water; apply to Hon Sec.

KELVIN: (tributary of R Clyde). River Kelvin AC has 20m both banks; salmon, trout, sea trout; st from tackle shop: Anglers Rendezvous, 18 Saltmarket, G1 5LD (tel: 0141 552 4662; see website for more info: www.anglersrendezvous.co.uk).

FRUIN: (tributary of Loch Lomond).

Helensburgh (Dunbartonshire). Salmon, sea trout and brown trout; fly only; permits issued by Loch Lomond AIA; full members only.

Ardlui (Dumbartonshire). Sea trout and salmon fishing in Loch Lomond. Hotel: Ardlui.

ENDRICK: (tributary of Loch Lomond).

Killearn, Balfron and **Fintry**. Good trout, sea trout and salmon fishing. Loch Lomond AIA has water; fly only; no Sunday fishing; accommodation arranged; ghillie, boat hire for Loch Lomond available (mainly Balmaha); full members only.

GRYFE (or GRYFFE): Brown trout, salmon, sea trout, grayling.

Bridge of Weir (Renfrewshire). Bridge of Weir River AC has 3m of water. Trout: 15 Mar 6 Oct; salmon: 15 Mar 31 Oct; st (locals only) from Hon Sec (60 associate members); day tickets from Sarwar in Main Street in village and also Rods 'n' Reels, 17 High St, Johnstone PA5 8JU (tel: 01505 337601).

Kilmacolm (Renfrewshire). Strathgryfe AA has water on R Gryfe and tributaries Green Water, Blackety Water and Burnbank Water; approx. 25m in all, with brown trout and grayling; st £15 plus £10 entrance, with concessions; permits from Hon Sec, or from butcher's shop (Blackwood), Kilmacolm; no day tickets on a Sunday. Two fisheries with rainbow trout in Kilmacolm area: Lawfield and Pinewoods.

CALDER and **BLACK CART**:

Lochwinnoch (Renfrewshire). St Winnoch AC has stretch of Calder (brown trout); and Castle Semple Loch, pike, perch, roach and eels. Club also has IBarr LochBarr Loch (coarse) and Queenside Muir Loch (browns, fly only); st holders only; permits from Rods 'n' Reels, 17 High St, Johnstone PA5 8JU (tel: 01505 337601) who also sell Castle AC tickets for Black Cart Water, salmon, sea trout, and brown trout; Castle Semple Loch, coarse; tackle shop also issues tickets for Rowbank AC water and Loch Awe AC water.

AVON:

Strathaven (Lanarkshire). Avon AC fishes approx 14m of excellent brown trout and grayling water, with additional salmon and sea trout, near Strathaven Stonehouse and Larkhall; restocked annually; members only.

CONON (including Blackwater)

Drains Loch Luichart and is joined by Orrin and Blackwater before entering the Moray Firth and North Sea by way of Cromarty Firth. Spring fishing has declined and main salmon runs now take place from July to September. Sport then among best in Highlands.

Dingwall (Ross shire). Salmon, sea trout and brown trout. Dingwall & District AC has lower beat on R Conon; fly only for salmon, sea trout and brown trout; thigh or waist waders only; season: 10 Feb to 30 Sept, best months Apr to Sept; dt £15 £20, wt £60 from Hon Sec and Sports & Model Shop, 66 High Street, Dingwall IV15 9RY (tel: 01349 862346; see website for more: www.sportsandmodelshop.co.uk).; also salmon and trout fishing on River Balnagowan. Brahan Estate IV7 8EE has Loch Ussie; at Brahan there are 3 beats of brown trout fishing on R Conon and a stocked brown and rainbow trout pond; tickets from estate office; dt available (river from £7/day; pond £8 for 4 hours) (tel: 01349 861150). Coarse fishing on Loch Ussie, pike and eels; permits from Seaforth Highland Estates, Brahan, by Dingwall IV7 8EE (tel: 01349 861150). Tackle shop: Sports & Model Shop, 66 High Street, Dingwall IV15 9RY (tel: 01349 862346; web: www.sportsandmodelshop.co.uk). Hotels: Conon Bridge Hotel at Conon Bridge; Craigdarroch, both Contin; also Coul House Hotel, Contin, by Strathpeffer IV14 9ES (tel: 01997 421487; see website for more info: www.coulhousehotel.com).

Strathpeffer (Ross shire). R Conon, above Loch Achonachie, salmon and brown trout; fly or spinning. River Blackwater above Rogie Falls, salmon, brown trout and pike. Loch Achonachie, brown trout, perch, pike and salmon; bank (very limited) and boat fishing; use of a boat produces best results; fly or spinning; Loch Achonachie AC has water here and also fishes Loch Meig (84 salmon up to 13lb, 1240 brown trout up to 11lb caught 2009) and Loch Scardroy;

(Wheelyboat on Loch Meig; av trout 1 $\frac{1}{4}$lb, largest 7lb): contact Hon Sec; dt from Contin Filling Station (tel: 01997 421948); members (£45 joining, st £60, conc) have access to many other locations through exchange tickets with other clubs (incl Spey, L Ailsh, Assynt, Oykel, Thurso, L Shin, Skye and many others). Coul House Hotel books permits for beats on Rivers Conon and Blackwater (salmon, sea trout, brown trout); and for Lochs Tarvie (rainbow trout), Achonachie (brown trout), Meig (brown trout), Morie (brown trout, arctic charr), Glascarnoch, Chullin, Achanalt, Scardroy or **Beannacharain** (all brown trout); apply to Coul House Hotel, Contin, by Strathpeffer IV14 9ES (tel: 01997 421487; fax 01997 421945; see website for more info: www.coulhousehotel.com); the hotel arranges its fishing through Roger Dowsett, Salmonquest; web: www.salmonquest.co.uk; hotel provides full angling service, including rod racks, guest freezer, drying room and fish smoking arranged.

Garve (Ross shire). Garve Hotel IV23 2PR (tel: 01997 414205) has excellent fishing on Loch Garve, which holds large trout (fish up to 12lb taken) also pike to 30lb and perch; brown trout fishing on 1$\frac{1}{2}$m of River Blackwater within hotel grounds; free fishing for hotel patrons. Loch an Eich Bhain (The Tarvie Loch), 25 acres, Ross shire's first Troutmaster water; stocked with rainbow and blue trout to 20lbs and brown trout to 8lbs, blues to 6lb; fly only; fly fishing exclusively by boat; Loch Ruith a Phuill, 17 acres; wild brown trout, stocked rainbow and blue to 10lb; coarse and fly fishing tackle allowed; third loch, 11 acres, stocked browns to 6lbs, fly only, with boat; permits from Tarvie Lochs Trout Fishery, Tarvie, by Contin IV14 9EJ (tel: 01997 421250). Loch Glascarnoch, is a hydro-scheme loch and provides free fishing for brown trout, pike and perch.

CREE and BLADNOCH

Cree drains Loch Moan and flows about 25m to sea at Wigtown Bay. Runs of salmon and sea trout in summer and early autumn. Minnoch, tributary of Cree, is also a salmon river, joining Cree about six miles from Newton Stewart. Bladnoch, a strong tidal river, flows into Cree Estuary at Wigtown. Salmon in season. Good pools.

Newton Stewart (Wigtownshire). Salmon, sea trout; best early in season. Newton Stewart & DAA has fishing on Cree, salmon and sea trout; and Bruntis Loch, brown and rainbow trout, bank fishing only; Kirriereoch Loch, brown trout, bank fishing, fly only, Clatteringshaws Loch, browns, pike and perch; plus other waters including Loch Ochiltree, rainbows and browns; Loch Dee, brown trout; assn spends between £10,000 £15,000 annually restocking 6 stillwaters with trout; dt lochs £15, dt rivers £20, salmon weekly £120, from A J Dickinson, Galloway Guns & Tackle, 36 Arthur St, Newton Stewart DG8 6DE (tel: 01671 403404), who supply all game, coarse and sea fishing tackle together with frozen and live bait. Forestry Commission Scotland has fishing on **Palnure Burn**, salmon, sea trout, brown trout; dt £8, juv £4; R Minnoch above Kirriereoch bridge: brown trout only Mar Jun, salmon and brown trout Jul to end Sept: dt Mar Jun £8 (juv £4); dt Jul end Sept £10 (juv £5); Black Loch, brown trout, fly only; dt £8, juv £4; Loch of Lowes, brown trout, fly only; dt £8, juv £4; Lilies Loch, brown trout; dt £8, juv £4; Lochs Spectacle and Garwachie, pike, perch, tench, roach, rudd; Loch Eldrig, pike, perch, roach; dt for each £6, juv £3; and Stroan Loch, mainly pike but also perch, roach and trout; dt £6; permits from Forestry Commission Scotland, Galloway Forest District, Creebridge, Newton Stewart DG8 6AJ (tel: 01671 402420). Creebridge House Hotel, Newton Stewart DG8 6NP (tel: 01671 402121; fax: 01671 403258; web: www.creebridge.co.uk; email: info@ creebridge.co.uk), can arrange fishing on R Bladnoch, good spring run of grilse, Feb Oct, 2m for up to 4 rods; R Minnoch, a tributary of Cree fed by Glentrool Loch, 4m for up to 12 rods, spawning pools; 22 pools in all; hotel has excellent food and accommodation, can store rods in a lockable room and has freezer and drying facilities; permits from hotel or A J Dickinson (see above); hotel has assn water on stretch of Cree which runs through town to estuary mouth. Trout fishing on **Black Loch**, and excellent bream fishing on **Lochs Heron** and **Ronald**; permit and boat hire from Three Lochs Caravan Park, nr Kirkcowan, Newton Stewart DG8 0EP (tel: 01671 830304; web: 3lochs.co.uk). Cree and Bladnoch fishing holidays, and information on all fishing in the area, can be resourced from J Haley, Oak Cottage, Mochrum Park, Kirkcowan, Newton Stewart DG8 0DA (tel: 01671 830471; see website for more info: www.mochrumpark.co.uk). Galloway Angling, 1 Queen Street, Newton Stewart DG8 6JR (tel: 01671 401333), covering coast, has game and pike fishing in private loch; permits on application; stock of various baits; open 7 days a week.

CROSS WATER OF LUCE

Depends on flood water for good salmon fishing, but very good for sea trout after dark. Best July onwards.

Stranraer (Wigtownshire). Excellent centre for river, loch and sea fishing. Stranraer & Dist AA has Soulseat Loch, rainbow and brown trout, fly and bait; Dindinnie Reservoir, brown and rainbow trout, fly only; Knockquassan Reservoir, brown trout, fly only; and Penwhirn Reservoir, brown trout, fly only; all these waters are near Stranraer; dt £13, £70 weekly, conc, from The Sports Shop, 86 George St DG9 7JS (tel: 01776 702705); who also sell tickets for Glenluce AA water: Whitefield Loch, coarse (pike); dt £5. Torwood House Hotel, Gass, Glenluce DG8 0PB (tel/fax: 01581 300469; email: torwoodglenluce@aol.com) issues permits for Torwood Lochs, dt £5.50, trout £12 (c&r); trout, bream, tench, carp, roach, rudd, perch. Dunskey Estate, Portpatrick, Stranraer DG9 8TJ, has 2 lochs with stocked brown and rainbow trout: contact Keeper, P Hoyer (tel: 01776 810364; web: www.dunskey.com). Whitefield Loch (part), pike and perch, apply to Cock Inn, Auchenmalg, Glenluce DG8 0JT (tel: 01581 500224). Sea fishing in Loch Ryan, Irish Sea and Luce Bay; charter boats and bait obtainable locally. Hotel: Ruddicot.

Spring salmon fishing on the Aberdeenshire Dee at Brig o'Dee
Photo: Dr W Pacynko

DEE (Aberdeenshire)

One of the most famous salmon rivers of Scotland; for fly fishing probably the best. Also holds sea trout and brown trout. Rises in Cairngorms and flows into North Sea at Aberdeen. Best months for salmon: April, May, June but good all season. Best for sea trout: June and July. Tackle shops: Bains Fishing Tackle, 419 George Street AB25 1ER (tel: 01224 625161); Somers Fishing Tackle, 13 15 Bon Accord Terrace AB11 6DP (tel: 01224 210008). Orvis, 2-8 Bridge Street, Banchory, AB31 5SX (tel: 01330 824319).

Aberdeen. Salmon, sea trout, brown trout; sea fishing. Many owners let for whole or part of season, but some good stretches held by hotels. Some hotel waters free to guests during summer. Lower reaches give good finnock fishing. Sea fishing is good in vicinity of Aberdeen. Hotel: Cults.

Banchory (Aberdeenshire). Strutt and Parker has fishing. Contact Mark Merison (tel: +44 (0)1635 576905; email: mark.merison@struttandparker.com); Middle Blackhall beat: 1m single bank just u/s of town; 3 rods; ghillie included; accom also available for up to 6 people in Glenbogle Lodge in middle of beat. Salmon and sea trout. Banchory Lodge Hotel by river can arrange salmon and trout fishing on Dee for four rods, fly only; c&r; ghillie, Mr Walter Rait, and tuition on site: apply to Mrs Margaret Jaffray, Banchory Lodge Hotel, Banchory AB31 5HS (tel: 0133 082 2625). Feughside Inn, Strachan, by Banchory AB31 6NS (tel: 01330 850 225), issues Aberdeen & DAA permits for 1½m on River Feugh, salmon and sea trout. Hotels: Raemoir House.

Aboyne (Aberdeenshire). Dee: salmon and sea trout; Glen Tanar Loch: rainbow trout, stocked, fly only fishing (boats only); and 2 beats on the river (no Sunday fishing on Dee) apply for permits from Glen Tanar Estate, Brooks House, Glen Tanar AB34 5EU (tel: 013398 86451). Aboyne Loch: Coarse fishing on Aboyne Loch; pike, roach, carp, tench and perch; permits from the Office, Aboyne Loch Caravan Park AB34 5BR (tel: 013398 86244). Pronie Loch AB34 4XX, brown trout, fly only; permits: dt £18, £10 half day; boat available; contact Lee Williams (tel: 013398 81332). Hotels: Birse Lodge; Huntly Arms.

Ballater (Aberdeenshire). Balmoral, Mar, Glenmuick and Invercauld Estates preserve most of Upper River Dee salmon fishings. Contact Ian Murray (tel: 013397 55459) for Lower Invercauld (8m left bank) and Monaltrie (3m left bank) fishings; also Glenmuick (2m right bank) fishing on Dee. Ballater AA has fishing on five lochs with brown and rainbow trout, beats of Rivers Muick and Gairn by Ballater, with brown trout; Dee at Mar Estate and Deveron at Banff, with salmon and sea trout; these waters are mostly for members only, but permits for Loch Vrotichan, with brown trout, fly only, are obtainable from Hon Sec and Countrywear (below); information for Mar Estate water also available from Countrywear (see below); Hon Sec, Ballater AA has information on fishing on other waters. Tackle shop: Countrywear, 15 Bridge St, Ballater AB35 5QP (tel: 01339 755453). Many hotels and guest houses in vicinity.

Braemar (Aberdeenshire). Salmon fishing: Invercauld Estate lets Crathie beat and private water, details from The Factor, Invercauld Estates Office, 4 The Keiloch, Braemar, by Ballater AB35 5TW (tel: 013397 41224); brown trout fishing on Rivers $IGairn,

RiverGairn and Clunie: permits from Invercauld Estates Office; Tourist Office, Braemar; Lochs Bainnie and Nan Ean, brown trout, fly only; permits also from Invercauld Estates

Office. Hotels: Inver Hotel, Crathie; B&B: Craiglea, Hillside Drive, Braemar AB35 5YU (tel: 013397 41641).

DEE (Dumfries & Galloway), (including Lochs Dee and Ken)

Flows through Loch Ken about 16m to Solway. Salmon, sea trout and brown trout. Netting reduced and river stocked with salmon fry. An area in which acidification problems have been reported. Some lochs affected.

Castle Douglas (Kirkcudbrightshire). Forestry Commission Scotland has fishing on Loch Dee, brown trout, fly only; dt on application from Clatteringshaws Visitor Centre (tel: 01644 420285), or forest district office (tel: 01671 402420). Woodhall Loch, best known as pike water but also roach, perch and few trout; good winter venue with big pike catches, including 20lb plus fish; brown trout in River Blackwater of Dee; dt from Mossdale PO DG7 2NF (tel: 01644 450281). Castle Douglas & Dist AA has 7m stretch on River Urr; salmon, sea trout and brown trout; re stocked annually; good runs of sea trout and grilse starting in June; dt £10 and £25 (Sept, Oct, Nov); wt £40 and £100; Assn also has brown and rainbow trout fishing on Loch Roan; 4 boats; dt £25 per boat for 2 rods; permits from McCowan & Son (see below). Loch Ken, pike and perch; open all year for coarse fish; permits from local hotels, Mossdale PO, Mossdale, Castle Douglas, Kirkcudbrightshire, DG7 2NF; tel: 01644 450281; Loch Ken Holiday Park, Loch Ken Marina. Tackle shop: McCowan & Son, 50/52 King St, Castle Douglas DG7 1AD (tel: 01556 502009) (branch also in Dalbeattie); Dalbeattie AA tickets. Hotels: Douglas Arms; Imperial; Urr Valley Country House.

Crossmichael (Kirkcudbrightshire). Boats for Loch Ken from Crossmichael Marina, which has been upgraded and re equipped, boats for hire all year round. Loch Ken, pike,

perch, roach, few brown trout, sea trout, salmon, plentiful bream, few eels; all gamefish to be returned; contact David Deane, Crossmichael Marina, 4 Kirkland Terrace DG7 3AX (tel: 07810 693002); no ticket required for boat fishing; motor £65/day, rowing £30/day; bank fishing by permission of riparian owners. Accommodation plentiful.

New Galloway (Kirkcudbrightshire). Dee private. Forestry Commission Scotland controls fishing on eleven lochs, trout, coarse, or mixed, including Loch Dee, stocked brown trout; Lillies Loch, wild browns (ideal for beginners), and Stroan Loch, pike to 27lb and perch, and stretches of Rivers Palnure and Minnoch, with salmon and sea trout; day permits £6 to £35, with concessions; st coarse £50, no prawns, shrimp or live bait; st trout/coarse £75 (excludes lochs Dee and Braden); season salmon and trout 15 Mar to 30 Sept (season ends early to conserve spawning fish), from Forestry Commission Scotland, Galloway Forest District, Creebridge, Newton Stewart DG8 6AJ (tel: 01671 402420). New Galloway AA controls stretch of River Ken, occasional salmon, brown trout, rainbow trout, pike, roach, dace, perch; dt £5 from PO or Hopkins shop; stretch of Loch Ken, brown trout, pike, perch, bream and occasional salmon run through loch during season; Blackwater of Dee (N bank only), brown trout, occasional salmon, pike; Mossdale Loch, native brown trout and stocked rainbow trout, fly only; visitors permits, for all except Mossdale Loch, £15 per rod per day; Loch Ken, mainly pike and roach, dt £3 plus surcharge if permit bought from bailiffs; Mossdale Loch, dt £15 per boat (1 rod) (3 fish); permits from Mossdale PO; otherwise permits from Mr J R Hopkins, Grocer, High St, New Galloway, Castle Douglas DG7 3RN (tel: 01644 420229); New Galloway PO, High Str, New Galloway, Castle Douglas DG7 3RL (tel: 01644 420214). Barscobe Loch; brown trout, fly only; dt (incl boat and life jacket) £8 from Walter Stewart, Castle Cottage, Barscobe, Balmaclellan, Castle Douglas DG7 3QG (tel: 01644 420294).

Dalry (Ayrshire). Dalry AA has fishing on River Ken from Dalry; good stocks of brown trout; fly fishing only to 1 June, fly spinning or worm from 1 June, bank fishing only; Assn also has water on Carsfad Loch, brown and rainbow trout, bank fishing only; also Earlston Loch; visitors tickets sold from 15 Mar 30 Sept, dt £7, wt £35, conc for children: from N W Newton (Grocers), 17 Main St, Dalry, Castle Douglas DG7 3UP (tel: 01644 430225); Carsphairn PO (tel: 01644 460211).

DEVERON

Rises in Cabrach and flows some 45m into the Moray Firth at Banff. A salmon river, with brown trout fishing, some sea trout, June to September; finnock spring months.

Banff (Banffshire). Salmon, sea trout, brown trout. Banff Springs Hotel AB45 2JE (tel: 01261 812881) caters for anglers; best months: salmon, March to Oct; sea trout June to Aug; brown trout, April, May and Sept; salmon improving. Tackle shop: Turriff Tackle and Trophies, 6 Castle St AB53 7BJ (tel: 01888 562428). Hotels: Fife Lodge Hotel (tel: 01261 812436; see website for more info: www.fifelodgehotel.com); Station Hotel, Portsoy AB45 2QT tel: 01261 842327.

Turriff (Aberdeenshire). Turriff AA (tel: 01888 562428)has salmon, sea trout and brown trout fishing on Deveron; wt £150 Jun Oct; day tickets £30; 4 rods per day limit; permits from tackle shop; fly only when level falls below 6in on gauge; best months July, August and Sept; also a fishery on opposite bank, dt £10. Bognie, Mountblairy and Frendraught Group, has salmon, grilse, sea trout and brown trout fishing on Bognie Pool, Upper and Lower Mountblairy, 4m (part double bank), salmon, grilse, sea trout, brown trout; 11 Feb to 31 Oct; fishing is open to all, usually on a weekly basis along with holiday cottages; day permits only up until 31 July, from BMF Group, Estate Office, Frendraught House, Forgue, Huntly AB54 6EB (tel: 01464 871331). Tackle shop: Turriff Tackle and Trophies, 6 Castle St AB53 7BJ (tel: 01888 562428) (closed Wednesday). Hotels: Union; White Heather. B&B suitable for anglers, from Jenny Rae, Silverwells, St Mary's Well, Turriff AB53 8BS.

Huntly (Aberdeenshire). Salmon, sea trout, brown trout. Permits for Deveron, Bogie and Isla; st £150, mt £50, wt £40, dt £15 from J A Christie, Huntly Fishings Committee, 27 Duke Street, Huntly AB54 8DP (tel: 01466 792291); only 10 day tickets per day and none on Saturdays or Public Holidays. Castle Beat: $\frac{1}{2}$m double bank fishing for two rods 1 mile from Huntly; salmon, sea trout and brown trout, by arrangement either daily or weekly; wt £150 £220 per rod depending on season; contact tackle shop: Turriff Tackle and Trophies, 6 Castle St AB53 7BJ (tel: 01888 562428).

DIGHTY

Drains some small lochs and falls into the Firth of Tay not far from Dundee. Banks built up on lower reaches. Now considered a negligible fishery.

Dundee. Trout with occasional sea trout; free. 10m east, Monikie and Crombie Reservoirs leased to Monikie AC; access for disabled (Monikie only). Lintrathen Reservoir leased to Lintrathen AC; good brown and rainbow trout fishing up to 5lb; 20 boats for hire; catch limit 5 fish per rod (over 10in); club bookings from Jim Hardie, 41 Rowan Avenue, Northmuir, Kirriemuir DD8 4TB (tel: 01575 572412); during season, reservations from boathouse (tel: 01575 560327); access and boats for disabled. Tackle shop: Anglers Choice, Kingsway Circus, 259 Strathmartine Road, Dundee DD3 8QQ (tel: 01382 811211). Hotel: Station.

DON (Aberdeenshire)

Rises near Ben Avon and flows for nearly 80m to North Sea at Aberdeen. Long famed as a dry-fly trout water, the river is also important for its salmon, which run from April to October. Sea trout numbers are on the increase.

Kintore (Aberdeenshire). Salmon, browns and sea trout fishing on both banks of River Don; $2\frac{1}{2}$m on right bank and $3\frac{1}{2}$m on left bank. Permits from Sloans of Inverurie, 125 129 High St, Inverurie AB51 3QJ (tel: 01467 625181). No Sunday fishing.

Inverurie (Aberdeenshire). River Don, left bank ($2\frac{1}{2}$ miles) and River Urie, right bank, ($3\frac{1}{2}$ miles) salmon, brown trout and occasional sea trout; no Sunday fishing on Don. Salmon best March, April, May and Sept Oct. Permits from Sloans of Inverurie, 125 129 High St, Inverurie AB51 3QJ (tel: 01467 625181); who also issue tickets for the Manar beat on the Don.

Alford (Aberdeenshire). 25m from Aberdeen. Salmon, brown trout and some sea trout. Shire Council Buildings, Alford issues permits; wt £50 60 trout, £150 salmon; dt £10 £12 trout, £30 salmon; preference given to Alford Arms Hotel guests. Some good trout burns in vicinity. Sloans of Inverurie can supply permits for water at Alford; 2m fishing; tickets (see above).

Kildrummy (Aberdeenshire). Kildrummy Castle Hotel, AB33 8RA (tel: 019755 71288) has good stretch of salmon and brown trout fishing. Trout best early, salmon late.

Glenkindie (Aberdeenshire). Glenkindie Arms Hotel, Glenkindie, Alford AB33 8SX (tel: 019756 41288) issue permits for Don salmon and trout fishing; no Sunday fishing, guests only.

Strathdon (Aberdeenshire). Colquhonnie Hotel, AB36 8UN (tel: 01975 651210; see website for more: www.thecolquhonniehotel.co.uk) has 10m of salmon and trout fishing; day tickets from hotel; also for Tornasheen. For Tillypronnie: permits for salmon fishing from Kildrummy Castle Hotel, AB33 8RA (tel: 019755 71288).

DOON

Drains Loch Doon on the Firth of Clyde watershed and flows right through the old County of Ayr to the Firth of Clyde, near Ayr Town. Good salmon, sea trout and brown trout water.

Ayr (Ayrshire). On Rivers Doon and Ayr. Salmon and sea trout July onwards. Brig o' Doon House Hotel, Murdochs Loan, Alloway, Ayr KA7 4PQ (tel: 01292 442 466), has water on Doon. Salmon and sea trout fishing; 2½m double bank, 12 pools; permit by d or wk. Contact Mr Campbell Skeldon Estate, (1m from Dalrymple) Dalrymple, Ayr KA6 6AT (tel: 01292 560656; web: www.skeldonestate.com/fishing.htm) Ayr AC has stretch of Ayr from Craigie Gardens to Dalmilling Golf Course Burn; brown trout and salmon; club membership and permits for various club waters issued by GameSport of Ayr, 60 Sandgate, Ayr KA7 1BX (tel: 01292 263822; web: www.gamesportofayr.co.uk). Hotel: Parson's Lodge, 15 Main Str, Patna.

Dalmellington (Ayrshire). Good salmon and sea trout (July onwards). Loch Doon, 6m; plenty of small brown trout and occasional salmon and charr; fishing free. Craigengillan Estate KA6 7PZ (tel: 01292 551818; fax: 01292 551819) has 2½m both banks of River Doon from Loch Doon downstream, and coarse fishing at Bogton Loch (63 acres, brown trout and pike). Drumgrange & Keirs AC has 5m double bank fishing on river; dt available, apply Hon Sec; salmon, sea trout, browns to 5lb, pike.

EDEN (Fife)

Rises in Ochil Hills not far from Loch Leven and falls into North Sea in St Andrews Bay. Provides some very fair trout fishing. Slow flowing stream suitable for dry fly fishing. Some sea trout below Cupar.

St Andrews (Fife). Cameron Reservoir, brown and rainbow stocked by St Andrews AC (brown trout av 1¼lb, rainbow 1½ to 2lb); fly only; Sunday fishing; boat and bank fishing; boat hire (3 rods per boat max) £25 per person per session; bank permit £25 per session; juniors £15 per session; prices may vary from July; tickets for reservoir.

Cupar (Fife). For brown trout fishing on Clatto Reservoir; dt £12, evngs £12, dawn to dusk £18; boat hire: £5 morning, £5 evening, £10 all day; one boat available, no studded waders in boats; juniors half-price; apply J & T Rodgers (tel: 01334 653090). Eden AA has 15m fishing, including Balass, Crichtons, Kemback, Nydie through Cupar: salmon, sea trout, brown; st £50, dt £10 (Sept £15), conc; contact Hon Sec.

Ladybank (Fife). Fine dry fly fishing; trout. Some free, but mostly preserved. Golden Loch, nr Lindores Loch offers both bank and boat fishing; contact Clatterwallops House, Berryhill, Newburgh KY14 6HZ (tel: 01337 840355; web: www.goldenloch.co.uk); permits.

ESK (North)

Formed by junction of Lee and Mark, near Loch Lee, and flows for nearly 30m to North Sea near Montrose. Good river for salmon, sea trout and finnock.

Montrose (Angus). Salmon, sea trout, finnock (whitling) and occasional brown trout. Spring and Autumn best fishing; barbless hooks only 16 Feb to 1 June, no multi hooked lures (doubles or singles only). For Gallery fishing contact Matthew Ramage, Muir Cottage, Trinity, Brechin DD9 7PD (tel: 01356 625044); for information regarding Gannochy Lodge and Dalbog beats refer to Mr Ramage (above). For Mill of Criggie Trout Fishery, St Cyrus, nr Montrose DD10 0DR, rainbows and browns, open all year, contact Kevin and Helen Ramshore, custom rod builders and repairers (tel: 01674 850868); limited disabled access, tuition, tackle, snacks on site. Montrose & DAC fishes Craigo beat of North Esk and downstream from Bridge of Dun on South Esk; permits from £18 £25 on S Esk, £30 £55 on N Esk, if available; c&r until 1 May salmon, sea trout total c&r, from tackle shop: Montrose Guns & Tackle, 13 Murray Street, Montrose DD10 8AL (tel: 01674 660427). Hotels: Carlton, George, Hillside, Marykirk.

Edzell (Angus). Salmon and sea trout. Dalhousie Estate Office, Brechin DD9 6SG (tel: 01356 624566) has boats to hire for trout fishing on Loch Lee in Glen Esk; no bank fishing, and fly only; permits from Mrs Taylor, Kirkton of Invermark, Glenesk, by Brechin DD9 7YZ (tel: 01356 670208); also salmon beats to let by the week on North Esk at Edzell, dt when no weekly lets; details from Dalhousie Estates. Hotels: Panmure Arms Hotel, High St, Edzell, Brechin DD9 7TA (tel: 01356 648950) and Glenesk.

ESK (South)

Rises in Glen Clova and flows some 49m to North Sea near Montrose. Good salmon river with plentiful runs of sea trout. Best months for salmon are February, March and April. Good autumn river (mid September onwards), sea trout May July. Grilse run from July.

Brechin (Angus). Good centre for North and South Esk. Salmon and sea trout; fishing good, but mostly reserved. South Esk Estates Office, Brechin, let beats on 2½m, usually by the week or daily, but very limited; wt, dt from John R Gow (below), Kintrochat, Careston and Finavon Castle beats, who issue permits for Kirriemuir AC waters. Estate Management (Scotland) Ltd, Parklea, Park Rd, DD9 7AP (tel: 01356 625436; see website for more info: www.sporting-scotland.co.uk; email: info@sporting scotland.co.uk), offers 3 and 5 day fishing breaks in Grampian, Wester Ross, Lewis, Morayshire, Perthshire and Tayside, with accom, transport, ghillie, permits and equipment included in prices; issues wt and dt for most rivers and lochs. Brechin AC has fishing on Loch Saugh near Fettercairn, brown trout, fly only; dt £13.00 and River West Water, brown trout, salmon and sea trout; permits for L Saugh from Village Shop, Fettercairn; PO Edzell or Newsplus, Brechin (Saugh and West Water); dt from £10, other prices on application to Hon Sec. Hotels: Northern, Brechin; Glenesk; Panmure, both Edzell.

Kirriemuir (Angus). Kirriemuir AC has approx 7m on South Esk; salmon, sea trout, a few brown trout; permits from Hon Sec.; Day permits (£10) and weekly permits (£20) are now vailable from Thistle Newsagent, 48 High St, Kirriemuir, tel. 01575 572530; some fly only water, but much of it unrestricted; concessions to jun; no Sunday fishing and no permits on Saturdays. Strathmore AIA has rights on lower Isla and Dean, both near Blairgowrie; st £20 (trout), £10 (grayling), dt £5 (trout), conc (half), from tackle shops in Dundee (incl John R Gow (see above), Blairgowrie, Kerriemuir, Glamis, Meigle and Forfar.

EWE

This river has good runs of salmon (best May onwards) and sea trout (end June onwards) up to Loch Maree. Fishing is now restored to its pre-slump excellence. Owned by Inveran Estate, Poolewe.

Aultbea (Ross shire). Bank fishing for wild brown trout on Aultbea Hill Lochs. Permits from Laide Post Office, Laide, Achnasheen, IV22 2NB; tel 01445 731252). Hotels: Aultbea; Drumchork Lodge.

LOCH MAREE (Ross-shire). Spring salmon fishing from April until June. Sea trout from June until Oct. Also brown trout fishing.

Talladale (Ross shire). Salmon, sea trout, brown trout. Gairloch Angling Club has brown trout fishing in many hill lochs, including Bad na Scalaig, Tolliadh, Garbhaig; for permits contact Post Office, Anchorage, Pier Rd, Gairloch; pike in Lochs Bad an Scalaig, Dubh and Fuar, salmon fishing in IKerry, RiverR Kerry, (book chandlery in Pier Road); membership closed but for permits and information contact Cornerstone, Strath Square, Gairloch IV21 2BZ (tel: 01445 712400).

Kinlochewe (Ross shire). Brown trout, charr and sea trout fishing on Loch Bharranch; and brown trout, pike and perch fishing on Loch a'Chroisg.

Achnasheen (Ross shire). On A832, Loch a' Chroisg, brown trout, pike, perch; permits also for Loch Gowan) from Ledgowan Lodge Hotel, Achnasheen IV22 2EJ (tel: 01445 720252).

William B Currie searching for a springer on the Findhorn
Photo: Colin Bradshaw

FINDHORN

Rises in Monadhliath Mountains and flows over 60m to Moray Firth. Salmon, sea trout and brown trout. Good spate river with many rock pools, fishing begins mid to late April. Best months: May/June and August/Sept. Grilse from summer to end of season. Recent native hardwood regeneration schemes along substantial lengths of the river have enhanced the quality of the spawning beds; and helped to limit erosion previously caused by livestock.

Drynachan (Nairnshire). Cawdor Estate has fly only salmon fishing on Findhorn, 3 beats with 3 rods per beat; and trout fishing on Loch of Boath (brown); excellent accommodation is bookable on Estate at Drynachan Lodge (plus 5 cottages); contact the Lettings Manager, Cawdor Estate Office, Cawdor, Nairn IV12 5RE (tel: 01667 402402; fax: 01667 404787; web: www.cawdor.com). Good trout fishing on nearby lochs; Loch Lochindorb; bank fishing only; no charge. Tickets for 7m stretch of R Nairn with sea trout and salmon; fly fishing throughout, but spinning (high water) and worm allowed on the upper & lower stretches; middle section fly only; permits from tackle shop: Pat Fraser, 41 High St, Nairn IV12 4AG (tel: 01667 453038).

Forres (Morayshire). Forres AA water; 4m double bank, with salmon and sea trout; fly, spinning early season; dt £20 Feb May, £30 Jun Sept, wt £100, £150; permits from Fishing Tackle Shop, 97d High St, Forres IV36 1AA (tel: 01309 672936).

FLEET (Kirkcudbrightshire)

Formed by junction of Big and Little Water, empties into the Solway Firth at Gatehouse. Good sea trout and herling, and few grilse and salmon; best months July and August.

Gatehouse of Fleet
(Kirkcudbrightshire). Murray Arms Hotel, Gatehouse of Fleet DG7 2HY (tel: 01557 814207), issue permits for waters on River Fleet; sea trout and herling with some grilse and salmon; no sunday fishing. Gatehouse & Kirkcudbright AA has Loch Whinyeon, 160 acres, 3½m from town, brown trout, stocked, and wild; fly only; two boats; bank or boat fishing; assn also controls Loch Lochenbreck, 40 acres, 3m from Lauriston, rainbow and few brown trout; fly only; bank or boat fishing six boats; permits £18, boats plus £3, from Thomson Newsagent, St Cuthbert Street, Kirkcudbright DG6 (tel: 01557 330423) and Spar, Fleet Vale High Street DG7 2HP (Tel: 01557 815050); Hotel: Murray Arms Hotel, Gatehouse of Fleet, Castle Douglas, DG7 2HY (tel: 01557 814207).

FORTH (including Loch Leven and Water of Leith)

Formed from junction of Avendhu and Duchray not far from Aberfoyle, and thence flows about 80m to its firth at Alloa, opening into North Sea. Principal tributaries, Teith and Allan, flow above Stirling. A large salmon river, which at times, and especially on upper reaches, provides some good sport. Good run in lower reaches from August to October, as a rule. Trouting in upper reaches and tributaries, particularly in lochs, where salmon also taken.

Stirling (Stirlingshire). Forth, Allan and Teith may be fished from here. Herling/finnock in Forth in spring and autumn. Salmon fishing from Lands of Hood to mouth of Teith ($7\frac{1}{2}$m) including Cruive Dykes is controlled by Stirling Council: contact Countryside Manager, Room 124, Stirling Council, Viewforth, Stirling FK8 2ET (tel: 0845 277 7000; 01786 443322); st £248, 5dt £145, 3dt £100, dt £47, concessions available; good run in lower reaches, 1 Feb to 31 Oct. North Third Trout Fishery, Greathill House, Stirling, FK7 9QS (tel: 07767 831197): 140 acres, rainbow and brown trout (record rainbow, 19lb 13oz; brown, 9lb 14oz); fly only; 23 boats and bank fishing, tuition by appointment; open 15 Mar to 17 Oct; permits and season tickets from fishery.

Lake of Menteith, Scotland's premiere rainbow trout fishery, also has has brown trout and pike in the winter months. Largest brown trout 11lbs, rainbow 21lbs. 1,500 fish stocked weekly; fly only, boat and facilities for disabled; permits from Lake Menteith Fisheries Ltd, Port of Menteith, Stirling FK8 3RA (tel: 01877 385 664; web: www.menteith-fisheries.co.uk). Tackle shops: James Bayne Fishing Tackle, 76 Main St, Callander FK17 8BD (tel: 01877 330218); Angling Centre Stirling, Colquhoun Street, Stirling, FK7 7PX (tel: 01786 430400; see website for more info: www.anglingactive.co.uk).

Tributaries of Forth

LEVEN. Flows from Loch Leven to Firth of Forth at Leven, Fife. Fair sea trout runs and occasional salmon from Jul Oct; any legal method (on shrimp or prawn).

ALMOND. West of Edinburgh the river flows into the Firth of Forth at Cramond.

Cramond (West Lothian). Cramond AC has fishing leases on most of River Almond and tributaries. Salmon, sea trout and brown trout. Permits from Country Life, 229 Balgreen Rd, EH11 2RZ (tel: 0131 337 6230).

Livingston (West Lothian). River Cramond AC has $\frac{1}{2}$m of Almond with salmon and sea trout, and 2m with brown trout; permits from Country Life, 229 Balgreen Rd, EH11 2RZ (tel: 0131 337 6230) sell tickets for River Tyne, Water of Leith, and Upper River Tweed; also for Harperrig Reservoin (trout) and Edgelaw Reservoir (coarse); tickets should be bought beforehand. Morton Fisheries, brown and rainbow trout; fly only; bag limits apply; advanced bookings; permits from Morton Fisheries, Morton Reservoir, Mid Calder, Livingston EH53 0JT (tel: 01506 884500 or 07768 428647; web: www.mortonfishery.com).

NORTH ESK and **SOUTH ESK**. These two rivers are fed by Lothian regional reservoirs and join near Dalkeith to form the River Esk. The Esk flows a short way down to enter the Firth of Forth at Musselburgh.

Musselburgh (Midlothian). Musselburgh & Dist AA has salmon, sea trout and brown trout fishing on Esk, from estuary, 2m upstream of Musselburgh; permits from Mike's Tackle Shop, 46 Portobello High St, Edinburgh EH15 1DA (tel: 0131 657 3258); no Sunday fishing.

Glencorse and **Clubbidean** **Reservoirs**; brown, blue and rainbow trout; fly only; boat only; 52 acres, 13 acres; leased to Dooks Fisheries, 57 North Street, Ratho EH28 8RP (tel: 0131 3332693; mob 07817 221290); Clubbidean has disabled bank fishing. **Rosebery Reservoir**; 52 acres; brown and rainbow trout, pike, perch; dt £17, conc £11, contact Rosebery Fishery, Waterkeepers Cottage EH23 4SS (tel: 01875 830353). **Gladhouse Reservoirs** are managed by both Rosebery Estates (tel: 0131 331 1888) and Arniston Estates. Tackle shop: Fishers, 10 John Street EH26 8AD (tel: 01968 672877; see website for more info: www.fishersdirect.com).

West Linton (Peeblesshire). Brown trout fishing on West Water Reservoir; 93 acres; fly only; wild browns; fishing starts on 1 May; now let to West Linton Flyfishers; no dt.

DEVON: Fair brown trout stream; sea trout and salmon lower down; late season.

Alloa (Clackmannanshire). Devon AA has salmon, sea trout and brown trout fishing on beats of Devon, brown trout from Castlehill to Menstrie Tullabody bridge; salmon from Cauldron Linn to the Menstrie Tullabody bridge; assn also has brown trout fishing on **Glenquey Reservoir**, near Muckhart; fly only; bank fishing only; Sunday fishing permitted on reservoir, prohibited on river; season tickets for sea trout and salmon are only obtainable from Hon Sec (postal application only); permits for brown trout fishing from The Paper Shop, 50 Bridge St, Dollar FK14 7DG (tel: 01259 742825); and Marco Palmieri, The Inn, Crook of Devon KY13 7UR; Mona's of Muckhart tea shop; and Riverside Caravan Park, Dollarfield, Dollar FK14 7LX (tel: 01259 742896). 6m west of Kinross, Glensherrup Fisheries, Glendevon, Dollar FK14 7JY (tel: 01259 781631), has fly only, rainbow and brown trout, stocked regularly; boat and bank fishing; boat available; very varied permits. Gartmorn Dam Fishery, 167 acres, stocked rainbow, plentiful stocked browns also, fly and spinning, bait from the head wall, artificials only from bank; fly from boat and bank, 9 boats; permits from Gartmorn Dam Country Park, by Sauchie, Alloa FK10 3AZ (tel: 01259 214319). Fife Regional Council used to control reservoirs which were subsequently passed to East of Scotland Water (renamed Scottish Water); these are now largely and variously leased out (see later text): Lower Glendevon Reservoir; run by Frandy Fishery, Glendevon, Dollar FK14 7JZ (tel: 01259 781352; see website for more info: www.frandyfishery.com), part of Gleneagles Estate; rainbows, browns, blues; fly only; dt £18, conc on boat only, from lodge; Castlehill Reservoir; rainbow trout, some browns, perch and pike; fly and bait; contact David Duff (mob: 07748 011834); Cameron Reservoir leased to St Andrews AC; brown trout only; fly only; tickets from fishing hunt on site. Craigluscar Reservoirs to Dunfermline Artisan AC, rainbow trout dt from bailiff's hut (tel: Tel: 01383 732891); Glenquey Reservoir to Devon AA; Lochmill Reservoir to Newburgh AC; tickets from Betty Bryans, Albert Bar, High St, Newburgh (tel: 01337 842397). Upper Carriston Reservoir, run by Methilhaven and District Angling Club; brown trout only; 1 April 30 Sept; fly only, best times early month due to weed growth; tickets from The Village Store, Station Road, Windygates (tel: 01333 350319). Hotels: Castle Campbell, Dollar; Castle Craig, Tillicoultry; Tormaukin, Glendevon.

Gleneagles (Perthshire). The Gleneagles Hotel, Auchterarder PH3 1NF, has an attractive range of trout fishing on lochs available to residents and non-residents in hotel grounds; salmon, grilse and sea trout fishing on the River Tay can be arranged for residents. It has a membership package available to non-residents which will gain access to three lochs, and residents have exclusive access to five other lochs; lochs are either rainbow trout only or wild trout only; trout fishing lesson are also available on two lochs on the golf course; should venues be fully booked hotel will arrange alternative fishing; apply to The Shooting and Fishing School, Gleneagles Hotel, Perthshire PH3 1NF (tel: 01764 694344 or 01764 694351; fax: 01764 694429).

AVON: Flows 18m to estuary of Forth near Grangemouth. Lower estuary no longer polluted; sea trout and good brown trout elsewhere (av ½lb with few around 4lb). River fishes best in May, and then September.

Linlithgow (West Lothian). Linlithgow AC has 5m stretch of Avon north of Muiravonside Country Park, with brown trout; members only: st £25 + £15 joining, conc; contact Hon Sec or Lochside Tackle. Avon Bridge AA offer excellent value season tickets on a lengthy stretch in Avonbridge area; access to river regulated through R Avon Federation, which holds migratory fishing rights; membership is available to members of the local fishing clubs. For day permits contact Muiravonside Country Park, The Loan, near Whitecross, Linlithgow EH49 6LW (tel: 01506 845311): brown trout and coarse tickets, £7.40, concessions for juniors. Union Canal from Edinburgh to Falkirk: pike, perch, roach, carp, eel, bream, mirror and leather carp, and tench; no close season; st £15, dt £2 from Lochside Tackle & Sports, 254 High Street, Linlithgow EH49 7ES (tel: 01506 671477).

CARRON:

Larbert (Stirlingshire). Larbert & Stenhousemuir AC has fishing on Loch Coulter, near Carronbridge; brown and rainbow trout; fly only; no Sunday fishing; members only; club also fishes Carron; st £42, dt £7, conc, from: Rod & Creel, 50 North Main St, Carronshore, Falkirk. FK2 8HL (tel: 01324-570595).

Denny (Stirlingshire). Carron Valley Fishery controls Carron Valley Reservoir; bank fishing now permitted (4 miles), 20 boats, wild and stocked rainbow and brown trout fishing, fly only; dt £12, conc; booking (tel: 01324 823698; web: www.carronvalley.com). Drumbowie Reservoir, fly only; brown and rainbow trout; open all year; dt £10; 2 fish then c&r, visitors accompanied by member, st £70 + £10 joining fee: permits from Bonnybridge AC (tel: 01324 813136).

TEITH: Noted salmon and brown trout fishery, with good sea trout in summer.

Lanrick Castle (Perthshire). Strutt and Parker has fishing. Contact Mark Merison (tel: +44 (0)1635 576905; mark.merison@struttandparker.com) (see Agents). Total 3½m of water of which 2 are single bank; and 1½m double bank.

Callander (Perthshire). Stirling Council controls part of Teith in Callander, with excellent salmon, sea trout, and brown trout (average ¾lb); fishing open to visitors; contact Countryside Manager, Room 124, Stirling Council, Viewforth, Stirling FK8 2ET (tel: 0845 277 7000); visitor st £248, dt £47 (visitor juv £67), conc; no Sunday fishing; apply to James Bayne (below); 2m both banks (town water); salmon, sea trout; and also for brown trout fishing on L Voil (4m north of town) (dt £5.50). **Loch Venachar** controlled by L Ven Assn; mainly brown trout, but some sea trout and salmon; trout average 1lb; fishing from bank permitted on parts of loch; mapped details from Baynes, with prices (dt £6); boats for hire. Permits also for River Leny, 1m from town, trout only; dt £5; River Balvaig, 10m north, salmon and trout fishing; dt £6 lower stretch, £5 upper stretch; Loch Lubnaig, 2m north, trout, perch, charr, £6 (Forestry Comm side £5), £3 juv from James Bayne (below). Loch Drunkie (brown trout, dt £5); permits £3 £5 from Queen Elizabeth Forest Park Visitors' Centre, Aberfoyle, and James Bayne, Fishing Tackle, 76

Main St, Callendar FK17 8BD (tel: 01877 330218).

BALVAIG and **CALAIR** (Tributaries of Teith): salmon and brown trout.

Balquhidder (Perthshire). Salmon and brown trout fishing on R Balvaig, Loch Voil and Loch Doine; from Mrs Catriona Oldham, Muirlaggan, Balquhidder, Lochearnhead, FK19 8PB (tel: 01877 384219; web: www.lochsidecottages.co.uk) has

fishing dt £5, or st £15 on Loch Voil, salmon and brown trout, boats for hire; 2 self catering cottages on site with free fishing on L Voil. Tackle shop: James Bayne, Fishing Tackle, 76 Main St, Callandar FK17 8BD (tel: 01877 330218) for local permits.

Strathyre (Perthshire). Salmon, sea trout, brown trout, charr, eels on R Balvaig; R Leny; L Lubnaig, trout; James Bayne (tel: 01877 330218).

Loch Leven

Famous Kinross shire loch which produces quick growing trout. Loch is generally shallow so feed is good, and practically whole area is fishing water. Under efficient management, this has become one of the most notable trout fishing lochs of Scotland. For up-to-date fishing reports go to:
www.green-hotel.com/leisure-a-golf/fishing-report.html

Kinross (Kinross shire). Loch Leven, Scotland's premiere wild trout loch, is home to the famous Loch Leven trout; the trout average over 1lb with many specimen of 4-7lb being taken; fly fishing by boat only; boats are bookable by letter or phone; for full information on charges and booking conditions, apply (April to Sept) to The Pier, Kinross, Tayside KY13 8UF (tel: 01577 865386; email: fishing@green hotel.com). Kinross Trout Fishery, also known as Heatheryford Trout Fishery: a typical stocked water. Heatheryford, is a 10 acre spring fed water, with brown and rainbow trout; bank fishing only,

access for disabled; fly only; permits from office on site, Kinross KY13 0NQ (tel: 01577 864212).

Ballingry (Fife). Rainbow and brown trout fishing on Loch Ore; 260 acre loch, with bank and boat fishing, regularly stocked; access for disabled; wheely boat for wheelchair users; permits from Lochore Meadows Country Park, Crosshill, Lochgelly, Fife KY5 8BA (tel: 01592 583343).

Glenrothes (Fife). Permits may be had from Lomond Hills Fisheries (tel: 07949 256307) for reservoir trout fishing on Holl; dt on site; 42 acres; also for Harperleas; 39 acres; brown trout; fly only; c&r; dt available.

Water of Leith

Local people who know river well get fair numbers of trout.

Edinburgh (Midlothian). Water of Leith, running through the city, is stocked annually with brown trout; permits issued free of charge. Trout fishing at Gladhouse, Glencorse, Clubbiedean, Crosswood, and West Water Reservoirs; former Scottish Water fishings are now leased out (see above). Bank permits for Harperrig contact Colin Grieve (tel: 07904 085975). Rosebery Reservoir, brown

and rainbow trout, pike, perch; permits (dt £17, conc £11) from Mrs Grant, Keeper's Cottage EH23 4SS (tel: 01875 830353). Info on Whiteadder Reservoir from Scottish Borders Council (tel: 01835 825160); dt £8, £6 conc, or £4 bank dt; brown trout; boats available on Sundays if pre-booked. Coarse fishing on Duddingston Loch; carp and perch; Loch situated in a bird sanctuary, therefore a restricted area;

bank fishing by permit only, no charge; no lead weights; no close season; no dogs; permits from Historic Scotland Ranger Service, Holyrood Park Ranger Service, 1 Queens Drive, Holyrood Park, Edinburgh EH8 8HG (tel: 0131 652 8150). Union Canal from Edinburgh to Falkirk; pike, perch, roach, carp and tench; no close season; free. Tackle shops: Country Life, 229 Balgreen Rd, EH11 2RZ (tel: 0131 337 6230); Mike's Tackle Shop, 44 46 Portobello High St EH15 1DA (tel: 0131 657 3258); Gamefish Ltd, 6a Howe Street EH3 6TD (tel: 0131 220 6465).

Balerno (Midlothian). Trout fishing on Water of Leith; permits from Balerno PO, 36 Main Str, EH14 7EH (tel: 0131 4493077); and Colinton PO, 7 Bridge Rd, EH13 0LH. Brown trout fishing on Threipmuir and Harlaw Reservoirs, rainbow and blue trout; fly fishing only; bank fishing only; managed by Malleny AA; dt £15 from Balerno PO (above). Harperrig Reservoir, 237 acres; brown trout; fly only, bank fishing; permits from hut.

GIRVAN

Drains small loch called Girvan Eye and thence runs 25 miles to the Atlantic at Girvan. Good salmon and sea trout; fair brown trout. Salmon run March onwards; sea trout from June.

Girvan (Ayrshire). Salmon, rainbow, sea trout, brown trout. Penwhapple Reservoir, near Barr, stocked with brown trout; Penwhapple AC water; fly only; dt and boats available, Sundays members only; apply Mrs Hainey, Penkill Lodge Gatehouse, KA26 9TQ; tel: 01465 871226.

Straiton (Ayrshire). Salmon (late), sea trout, brown trout; Blairquhan Estate water on the R Girvan, fly only; permits from E Anderson, The Kennels, Blairquhan Estate, Straiton, Maybole KA19 7LY (tel: 01655 770239). Forestry Commission Scotland, Galloway Forest District, Creebridge, Newton Stewart DG8 6AJ (tel: 01671 402420), controls fishing in Galloway Forest Park, with brown trout fishing on Lochs Bradan, Loch Dee, Black Loch, and Loch of the Lowes; and Lilies Loch; pike and perch fishing, with other coarse on Linfern Loch, Spectacle, Garwachie, Eldrig, and Stroan.

HALLADALE

Rises on north slope of Helmsdale watershed and empties into sea at Melvich Bay. Early salmon March onwards, 10 16lbs. Grilse run from June, 5 7lbs. A small spate river which fishes well after rain.

Melvich (Caithness). 18m from Thurso. Apply for salmon permits on River Halladale from Strath Halladale Partnership, The Estate Office, The Kennels, Forsinard, Sutherland KW13 6YT (tel: 01641 571271); fly only.

Forsinard (Sutherland). Forsinard Hotel can arrange salmon fishing on River Halladale, fly only (usually heavily booked); hotel has trout lochs in 220,000 acres of Caithness, extending from Strathmore in the east to Strathy in the west. Excellent quality brown trout fishing in wilderness country. Apply to Forsinard Hotel, Forsinard KW13 6YT (tel: 01641 571221).

HELMSDALE RIVER

Formed by two headstreams near Kinbrace, this river flows 20m southeast through Strathullie to sea. The river is run by a conglomerate group of riparian owners and is divided into upper and lower river beats. Generally speaking, the lower beats are excellent spring salmon water, and the upper beats are very prolific and productive summer beats. Excellent salmon river, where there is now no netting. Water levels are controlled by releasing loch water into the river in periods of drought.

Helmsdale (Sutherland). Salmon and sea trout. Salmon beat lettings occasionally available from Roxton Bailey Robinson Worldwide Ltd, 25 High St, Hungerford, Berks RG17 0NF (tel: 01488 683222). Hotel: Belgrave Arms.

INVER (including Kirkaig and Loch Assynt)

Draining Loch Assynt, this river flows into a sea loch on the west coast of Sutherland known as Lochinver (village and loch having the same name), a little north of the old Ross shire border. Holds salmon and sea trout but fishing is hard to come by.

Lochinver (Sutherland). CKD Galbraith, Lynedoch House, Barossa Pl, Perth PH1 5EP (tel: 01738 451600; fax: 01738 451900; email: sporting@ckdgalbraith.co.uk)has salmon fishing on the River Inver. CKD Galbraith also has further River Kirkaig fishing, 3½m S of Lochinver; Inver Lodge Hotel has access to brown trout lochs in area including Loch Culag, LochAssynt, LochAwe, Loch Drumsuardalan; apply to Inver Lodge Hotel, Lochinver, Lairg, Sutherland IV27 4LU (tel: 01571 844496; fax: 01571 844395; see website for more info: www.inverlodgehotel.co.uk). The Assynt AA has 20 boats for hire and fishing on over 150 lochs in the locality of Assynt; six lochs, Culag, Awe, Shardalin, Lurgainn, Assynt and Ailsh hold migratory fish; there are 11 outlets for permits (see website or brochure); fly only, except Assynt where trolling is allowed; also restricted spinning; no bait fishing permitted; wt £25 (for one zone) £30 for all (south, east and west) zones, dt £5; the fishing is divided into three zones: south and west boats are controlled from the Cottage (see clubs list), the East boats from The Inchnadamph Hotel (see website). The Assynt Crofters (web: www.assyntcrofters.co.uk) own the North Assynt Estate; through the Trust, anglers may fish a large number of hill lochs, in a landscape of great natural beauty, including Loch Poll, the biggest, with boat obtainable from Old Drumbeg P O, Loch Drumbeg, Lochs Roe, Manse, Tuirk, which can produce excellent sea trout runs, and many others; 10 boats are for hire £10 per day, and st £45, wt £25, dt £5 permits may be bought at Mrs MacLeod, Old Post Office IV27 4NW (tel: 01571 833231), and Lochinver Tourist Office IV27 4LX (tel: 01571 844330). The Inchnadamph Hotel, Elphin, Lairg IV27 4HN (tel: 01571 822202) can arrange fishing on east end of Loch Assynt, and supplies permits for Assynt AA waters; permits free to guests; boats available for hire. Hotel: Kylesku, Lairg.

Ledmore (Sutherland). The Alt Motel, 20m N of Ullapool, has brown trout and first rate Arctic charr fishing on Loch Borralan; boat £20 and bank £5 per day; bed and breakfast, and self catering accommodation; further information from Bruce and Alba Ward, The Alt Motel, The Altnacealgach, nr Ledmore Junction,

By Lairg, Sutherland IV27 4HF (tel: 01854 666220). Mike Dwyer, The Altnacealgach Inn IV27 4HF

(tel: 01854 666260) supplies tickets, boats and engines for the east side of Assynt.

Loch Assynt

Inchnadamph (Sutherland). Salmon fishing from May on Loch Assynt. Inchnadamph Hotel, Elphin, Lairg IV27 4HN (tel: 01571 822202) has fishing on loch plus 10 other lochs, including the celebrated Gillaroo Loch and Loch Awe; £20 for boat (o/b £15) which includes 2 rods, 7 boats for hire; fishing free to residents; visitors require permits £5; season: salmon from 15 May until 15 Oct; trout, 15 Mar to 6 Oct.

IRVINE (including Annick).

Rises near Loudonhill and flows about 20m to Firth of Clyde at Irvine Town. Main tributaries are Cessnock Water, Kilmarnock Water and Annick. Fishing controlled largely by clubs. Salmon and sea trout July onwards; brown trout average ½lb; early season best.

Irvine (Ayrshire). Salmon, sea trout, trout; Irvine & Dist AA issues permits for 2m on Irvine and 3m Annick (no dt Saturdays) (see Torbets under Kilmarnock). Irvine Water runs from estuary to Red Bridge, Dreghorn, on north bank and to Bogie Bridge on south bank. Annick Water is from confluence with Irvine to Perleton Bridge, both banks.

Dreghorn (Ayrshire). Salmon, sea trout, trout; Dreghorn AC issues st, wt and dt for 12m water on both banks of Irvine and Annick; July to Sept best for salmon and sea trout; obtainable from Alyson's Flowers, 10 Bank Street, Irvine KA12 0AD (tel: 01294 276716). Brown trout average ½lb.

Kilmarnock (Ayrshire). Salmon, sea trout, trout. Permits for stretches on Irvine at Hurlford and Crookedholm from Torbets P & R, 15 Strand St, KA1 1HU (tel: 01563 541734); also for Kilmarnock AC water and Irvine AC.

GARNOCK: Trout, sea trout, salmon. Joins Irvine at harbour mouth. Its tributary is River Lugton.

Kilbirnie (Ayrshire). Kilbirnie AC has water on river Garnock and Kilbirnie Loch (brown and rainbow trout) and two reservoirs; yearly stocking of brown trout; Kilbirnie Loch best trout: brown 9lb 2oz; Kilbirnie Loch, any legal method; st £40; dt £8; club has excellent brown trout fishing on Camphill Reservoir; rainbow trout; fly and boat only; season holders £20 per boat per day and non holders £25 per boat per day; permits from R T Cycles, 73 Main Rd, Glengarnock, Beith KA14 3AA (tel: 01505 682191). Tackle from R T Cycles. For other trout fisheries in vicinity (see Greenock).

ANNICK: Brown trout; small runs of salmon and sea trout Sept Oct.

Irvine (Ayrshire). Dreghorn AC issues permits for 12m of water on Irvine and Annick; permits from Ticket Sec or Alyson's Flowers, 10 Bank Street, Irvine KA12 0AD (tel: 01294 276716).

Kilmaurs (Ayrshire). Kilmaurs AC has fishing on Annick and Glazert; sea trout and brown trout, with salmon in autumn; other fishing: North Craig Reservoir, Kilmaurs: Burnfoot Reservoir, Fenwick; Loch Gow, Eaglesham; st and membership from Hon Sec (see clubs list).

Stewarton (Ayrshire). Stewarton AC has water on Annick and tributaries, and White Loch; permits from Hon Sec, Alex Burt (tel: 01560 483870).

THE ISLANDS

The term 'The Islands' includes the Inner and Outer Hebrides, the Orkney and Shetland Islands and, for convenience, Kintyre. For detailed information, see Fish Hebrides website: www.fishhebrides.com.

ARRAN: In the rivers, brown trout are generally small, although fish up to 1lb have been recorded. In Aug, Sept and Oct there is often a good run of sea trout, especially in post spate conditions, along with good salmon catches, particularly in Sliddery, Kilmory, Sannox and Cloy. Benlister, Chalmadale and Monamore are also worth fishing under spate conditions. The Tourist Office at Brodick pier provides a free information sheet detailing all the main freshwater fishing opportunities on Arran, with charges; day permits from caravan site at Kildonan (£15) and Bay News shop at Whiting Bay (bag limit 2 fish) for various Arran AA waters; these include Kilmory, Cloy, Benlister, Monamore, Sannox, Ashdale, Sliddery Water and Loch Garbad (stocked with sizable brown trout and rainbows, fly only) (assn has own sea trout and salmon hatchery); there is no Sunday fishing on rivers.

Machrie. Machrie Fishings consistently record excellent sea trout and salmon returns. A fine spate river which has numerous named pools extending from the sea pool for approx 3 miles. Fly water, but worming area for 2 rods. Season, 14 Jun 30 Oct, 6 rods maximum (2 per beat); enquiries should be made to Mrs Margo Wilson, 10 Leysmill, by Arbroath, Angus DD11 4RR (tel/fax: 01307 466699: 9am 5pm), or to the Water Bailiff, Riverside Cottage, Machrie 840241; no Sunday fishing.

Dougarie. The Iorsa River has two beats, the upper beat includes Loch Iorsa (with boat). A spate sea trout river, with some salmon; the lower beat stretches from Gorge Pool to sea; catches (last 5 years) average 10 salmon, 45 sea trout; fishing is fly only and let by the week, from £145 (June) to £155 (July Aug), and £175 (Sept Oct); dt £35; enquiries should be directed to The Estate Office, Dougarie, Isle of Arran KA27 8EB (tel: 01770 840259).

Blackwaterfoot. Blackwater offers good sea trout catches and also salmon under suitable conditions; permits are obtainable from the Blackwaterfoot Post Office (tel: 01770 860220).

Brodick. The **Rosaburn** is now let to a local syndicate. Brodick Boat House, The Beach KA27 8AX (tel: 01770 302868): tackle and baits supplied, for fishing in Brodick Bay area; also permits from Tourist Information Centre, The Pier KA27 8AU (tel: 01770 303776) and other locations.

BENBECULA: Lies between N and S Uist. Numerous lochs, giving good sea and brown trout fishing.

Balivanich. South Uist AC has brown trout fishing on all lochs on Benbecula and many lochs in South Uist; Benbecula; bank fishing, wt £30, dt £6; boats on 14 lochs, £7/day: contact Hon Sec; PO; or contact D MacGillivray & Co HS7 5LA (tel: 01870 602525). Isle of Benbecula House Hotel, Creagorry HS7 5PG (tel: 01870 602024), has fishing for guests on seven lochs; waders useful; trout to 3lb; all within five miles of hotel; June Sept best for brown trout and August Sept for sea trout; sea trout up to 8lb in sea pools. Tackle: Macgillivray, HS7 5LA (tel: 01870 602525); tickets for South Uist AC.

BUTE: 5m from Ayrshire coast; 16m long and 3 5m wide. Trout and coarse fish.

Rothesay. Loch Ascog, 1½m pike, perch and roach. Loch Quien: 90 acres, wild and stocked browns, av 1lb, fly only; bank fishing and 4 boats; permits from Bute Angling & Outdoors, 9 Albert Place PA20 9AG (tel: 01700 503670); or Loch Fad office (tel: 01700 504871). Loch Fad, 175 acres, rainbow and brown trout fishing; boat and bank fishing; 30 boats; booking advisable; dt £18, OAP's £13, (juv £8); bag limits; permits from bailiff's hut at Loch (tel: 01700 504871); all information from Loch Fad Fisheries Ltd, Loch Fad, Isle of Bute PA20 9PA (tel: 01700 504871; web: www.lochfad.com; email: lochfad@btopenworld.com). Hotels: Palmyra, Ardbeg Lodge; B&B: Commodore. Sea fishing: from rocky shore popular and good.

Tighnabruaich is 25 miles from Dunoon. Kyles of Bute AC has fishing on Loch Asgog, brown and rainbow trout, fly only; on Upper and Lower Powder Dams, brown and rainbow trout, fly only; and on Tighnabruaich Reservoir, brown trout; tickets from Kames Post Office (tel: 01700 811877). Hotels: Kames, An Lochan, Kilfinan.

COLONSAY: Island of twenty eight square miles, reached by car ferry from Oban. Colonsay Fly Fishing Association was formed in 1989 with the aim of protecting the native Colonsay brown trout loch fishing, which includes Mid Fada, East Fada, na Sgoltaire; the season is from mid March to Sept 30, fishing is fly only, but children under 12 may spin; catch limit is 4 fish, sized 8" or more; permits cost £25 per week, boats £10 per day; contact Colonsay Estate, Argyll PA61 7YU (tel: 01951 200312) who also arrange boat hire. Isle of Colonsay Hotel, Argyll PA61

7YP (tel: 01951 200316) can arrange fishing for guests.

CUMBRAE: Small islands lying between Bute and Ayr coast. Largs is nearest mainland town, and there is a 10 minute ferry crossing from Calmac.

Millport. Cumbrae AC has fly only, brown and rainbow trout fishing on two reservoirs, Top Dam and Bottom Dam; juveniles must be accompanied by an adult and be over 12 years; permits, £15 dt and £40 wt from McFarlane's Newsagents, 2 Glasgow St; Ritz Cafe, 24 Stuart St, Millport KA28 0AJ (tel: 01475 530459). Sea fishing good from shore or boats. Tackle shops: Mapes, 4 Guildford St, Millport KA28 0AE (tel: 01475 530444); Hastie of Largs Ltd (Tackle Shop), 109 Main St, Largs KA30 8JJ (tel: 01475 673104) and hold permits for Largs & District AA. Hotel: Royal George.

HARRIS: Southern part of the island of Lewis and Harris, comprising the two distinct areas of North and South Harris. Accessible by car ferry from Ullapool, Uig in the Isle of Skye, and North Uist. Daily flights from Inverness, Aberdeen, Edinburgh and Glasgow to Stornoway. Most of the trout, brown trout, salmon and sea trout fishing in North Harris belongs to the Amhuinnsuidhe Castle Estate and is centred around Amhuinnsuidhe Castle, which is let along with the fishing on a weekly basis. There are nine river systems with lochs, which all contain salmon and sea trout. Ghillies are available and advisable. For dt available, incl boat, on Saturdays and unlet weeks, contact Castle Estate Office, Amhuinnsuidhe HS3 3AS (tel: 01859 560200).

South Harris, Good fishing for salmon and sea trout; brown trout lochs and lochans. Near Tarbert, brown trout fishing at Ceann an Ora Fishery, on Lochs Sgeiregan Mor, **A'Mhorghain** and **Na Ciste**; fly and bank fishing only; further information from The Anchorage, Ardhasaig, Isle of Harris HS3 3AJ (tel: 01859 502009); also salmon and sea trout fishing on Laxadale. Accommodation at Macleod Motel, HS3 3DG (tel: 01859 502364), with waterfront location. Borve Lodge, Borve, with fishing 7m west of Tarbert, has fishing on sea trout lochs; day tickets sometimes obtainable; enquire Gordon Cumming, Factor, Borve Lodge Estate Fisheries, Isle of Harris HS3 3HT (tel: 01859 550358). Finsbay Fishing, 4 Ardslave, HS3 3EY (tel: 01859 530318) (ghillie: A Mackinnon), has accommodation with over 100 lochs for salmon, land locked salmon, sea trout and brown trout fly fishing, including Lochs **Humavat** and **Holmasaig** ; also Finsbay, Flodabay, Manish, and Stockinish: interesting loch and stream fishing, bank and boat; for fishing contact Mrs Gale Tunnah (tel: 01859 530328). For salmon and sea trout fishing on the Obbe Fishings at Leverburgh, ferox trout, artic charr on Loch Langavat, and salmon and sea trout on Loch Steisabhat and Loch Moracha contact Tim Armstrong, Keeper, at Leverburgh (tel: 01859 520466).

ISLAY: Most southern island of Inner Hebrides. Lies on west side of Sound of Islay, in Argyllshire. Greatest length is 25m and greatest breadth 19m. Sport with salmon, sea trout and trout. Hotel: Harris.

Bridgend. Salmon and sea trout fishing on Rivers Laggan and Grey River; both within 2m of Bridgend; fly only; brown trout fishing on Lochs Gorm, Finlaggan, Skerrols and Ardnahoe, with boats; also trout fishing on numerous hill lochs without boats; permits and self catering accommodation from Islay Estate Office, Bridgend, Isle of Islay, Argyll PA44 7PB (tel: 01496 810221).

Port Askaig. For trout fishing in Lochs **Lossit, Ballygrant** and **Allan** and others apply for dt and boat from Dunlossit Estate Office, Knocklearach House, Ballygrant PA45 7QL (tel: 01496 840232); sport on other lochs by arrangement; salmon fishing in River Laggan; best months: July and Aug.

Port Ellen. Machrie Hotel can arrange any fishing on Islay for its guests; apply to Machrie Hotel, Port Ellen, Isle of Islay, Argyll PA42 7AN (tel: 01496 302310).

KINTYRE: This peninsula is part of Argyll and lies between Islay and Arran.

Campbeltown (Argyllshire). Kintyre AC has brown trout and stocked rainbow fishing on Loch Lussa; browns on Ruan, Aucha Lochy, Crosshill (including pike), and Southend River (small spate river, fishable Mar Oct (best Sept/Oct); wt and dt available, covering all lochs and river; Crosshill Loch dt), largely fly only, brown trout in all lochs, av $\frac{1}{2}$lb to $1\frac{1}{2}$lbs (rainbows to 5lb); permits from Brodie (below). Carradale AC has fishing on Tangy Loch, 60 acres, trout to 2lb; access road to waters edge; members only. Sea fishing in harbour and Firth of Clyde. Free fishing off pier. Tackle shop: Neil Brodie, Electrical Hardware, Long Row, Campbeltown. Hotel: White Hart; Argyll Arms, both Main St.

Carradale (Argyllshire). Salmon and sea trout fishing may be had on Carradale River, a small spate river. Carradale Estate lease the water to Carradale AC; bait and spinner under certain conditions, otherwise fly only; for permits apply to Mr William Shaw (River Keeper), 8 Toshs Park PA28 6QN (tel: 01583 431659).

Crinan (Argyllshire). Near west end of Crinan Canal, brown trout lochs controlled by Lochgilphead & DAC. Canal (trout). Permits: Fyne Tackle, 2 Colchester Square, Lochgiphead PA31 8LH (tel; 01546 606878); also for Loch Awe Improvement Assn.

Lochgilphead (Argyllshire). At east end of Crinan Canal, Forest Commission Scotland, White Gates, Lochgilphead PA31 8RS (tel: 01546 602518), has leased fishing on Loch Coille Bhar, Cam Loch, Loch An Add, Daill Loch, Seafield Loch, Lochs Glashan, Blackmill and Bealach Ghearran to Lochgilphead & DAC; brown trout, fly only; Lochgilphead & DAC lease a mile of the Add from Duntrune Castle mostly members only; salmon and sea trout; dt; apply Fyne Tackle (below). Duntrune Castle has 5m of River Add, both banks, from Kilmichael Bridge to the estuary; salmon and sea trout; 6 holiday cottages (fishing half price to residents); dt £15 and holiday bookings from Robin Malcolm, Duntrune Castle, Kilmartin, by Lochgilphead, Argyll PA31 8QQ (tel: 01546 510283). Permits: Fyne Tackle, 2 Colchester Square, Lochgiphead PA31 8LH (tel; 01546 606878) (they issue tickets for Loch Awe; ghillies; boat).

LEWIS: Some salmon and sea trout; almost unlimited amount of wild brown trout fishing on a large number of lochs and streams, most of which is free.

Stornoway. Permits available for salmon and sea trout fishing in River Creed and Lochs Clachan and An Ois, approx 5m from town, now controlled by Stornoway AA; tickets from Visit Scotland, Cromwell Street HS1 2DD (tel: 01851 703088) and Sportsworld (see below); Stornoway AA is local association, with boats on Lochs Breulagh and Achmore; they also fish the river Gress, sea trout and occasional salmon; tidal spate stream; good rough stream fishing; tickets from Back PO, 6m north of Stornaway. Tackle shop: Sportsworld, 1 3 Francis St HS1 2XD (tel: 01851 705464). Soval AA has brown trout fishing on several lochs within easy distance of Stornoway; wt £5 if staying in Soval area and £10 if not, dt £2, from Hon Treas: R Smith,

Treasurer, 55 Balallan, Lochs (tel: 01851 830351). Loch Keose, a beautiful 90 acre loch with plentiful wild brown trout; information & brochure from Murdo Morrison, Handa Guest House, 18 Keose Glebe, Lochs, Isle of Lewis HS2 9JX (tel: 01851 830334; see website for more: www.westernisleswelcome.com).
Hotels: Caberfeidh, Caledonian. Tackle and waterproof clothing from Lewis Crofters Ltd, Island Rd, HS1 2RD (tel: 01851 702350).

Garynahine. The Garynahine Estate control all the fishing on the River Blackwater and its freshwater lochs; salmon run from mid June to Mid October, sea trout from early April; accomm at Garynahine Lodge, Isle of Lewis HS2 9DS for parties of up to twelve; contact Garynahine (tel: 01851 621314). The Grimersta Estate Ltd owns fishing on Grimersta River and system of lochs. Grimersta Estate holds the UK record for the number of salmon caught on the same day. In 1888, Mr Naylor is recorded catching 54 salmon on the same day. The 'Grimersta System' is an integrated sytem of lochs and streams: fishing normally by the lodge week, but enquiries always welcome at estate office. The estate encourages access to the many trout lochs adjoining the main system, for which there is no charge; fly only, contact Simon Scott, Estate Office, Grimersta Lodge, Isle of Lewis HS2 9EJ (tel: 01851 621358; email: grimersta@lineone.net; web: www.grimersta.com).

Uig. Salmon, sea trout and brown trout fishing on Scaliscro Estate including Loch Langavat; bank and boat fishing; permits, boat and tackle hire, and ghillies; apply to Estate Office, Scaliscro Lodge, Uig, Isle of Lewis HS2 9EL (tel: 01851 672325; web: www.scaliscro.co.uk)). Uig and Hamanavay Estate, 10 Ardroil, Uig HS2 9EU (tel: 01851 672421) offers extensive fly only salmon and sea trout fishing, c&r, with self catering accom, on the Hamanavay, Red River; also Lochs na Craobhaig, and Fuaroil; Estate also has brown trout fishing on over 100 lochs; contact Simon Hunt, Estate Manager

Kintarvie. The Aline Estate, on the march of Lewis and North Harris, has four salmon fisheries, Loch Tiorsdam, two small rivers, Scaladale and Vigadale, plus 12 brown trout lochs and numerous lochans; boat and bank fishing for both salmon and trout on Loch Langavat and trout lochs; wild browns to 10lb have been caught in recent years, salmon are mostly grilse; Arctic charr taken every year in Loch Langavat; cottage and lodge to let; boat and ghillie; contact The Aline Estate, Lochs HS2 9JL (tel: 0207 808 8523). Further fishing contacts on Lewis are: Barvas Estate, Angus Macleod, Keeper, 01851 840267; Soval Estate, J Macleod, Keeper (tel: 01851 830223); Mike Reed, 23 Gravir, South Lochs, Lewis HS2 9QX (tel/fax: 01851 880233) who can arrange hill loch and salt water fly fishing.

MULL:

Tobermory. Salmon and sea trout fishing on Rivers Aros and Bellart. No Sunday fishing except for Loch Frisa. Salmon, sea trout and brown trout fishing on Loch Squabain; boat fishing only. Fishing on Torr Loch, sea trout, wild browns; no Sunday fishing; 1 boat; banks clear. Bank fishing on Loch Frisa (Sunday fishing allowed). Permits for all these, prices £5 £20 daily, £15 £45 weekly, depending on water and season, from Tackle & Books, 10 Main St PA75 6NU (tel: 01688 302336; fax: 01688 302140). Tobermory AA has fishing on Mishnish Lochs, well stocked, native brown trout only, 3 boats for hire on daily basis; and Aros Loch, open all year for rainbow; dt £12.50 and wt £35; boat hire: £7 for 4 hrs on Mishnish and £14 all day; permits from A Brown & Son, General Merchants, 21 Main Str, PA75 6NX

(tel: 01688 302020; web: www.browns tobermory.co.uk). Fishing on Loch Frisa, good brown trout, some salmon and sea trout; and River Lussa; permits from Tackle & Books (above). List of hotels from Tourist Office, The Pier PA75 6NU (tel: 01688 302182).

RAASAY:

The Isle of Raasay is near Skye. Free trout fishing in lochs and streams; waders should be taken.

RUM:

The fishing on the Isle of Rum is managed by the Isle of Rum Community Trust (tel: 01687 462404). Permits to fish are required, and Scottish Natural Heritage reserves the right to restrict fishing over certain areas in the interests of successful ornithological conservation, most particularly, red throated divers. But there are always fishing opportunities in various lochs on the island, along areas at the mouth of the Kinloch River, mainly browns and sea trout. Access by Calmac ferry from Mallaig PH41 4QD (tel: 01687 462403 ext 2).

NORTH UIST: Island in Outer Hebrides, 17m long and 3 13m broad. More water than land with over 400 named lochs and lochans, and many more unnamed, some probably un-fished. The machair lochs on the west side of the island provide challenging but excellent shallow water fishing for superb quality trout. The lochs on the east side are, perhaps, a less daunting challenge, with plenty of free-rising fish and the odd monster. Plenty of lochs by road side for elderly or infirm anglers.

Lochmaddy. Fishing on North Uist is controlled by the North Uist Estate, Lochmaddy HS6 5AA (tel: 01876 500329; fax: 01876 500428; email: george.macdonald@northuistestate.c o.uk); this covers all the salmon and sea trout systems on North Uist, and comprises brown trout lochs, sixteen of which are provided with a boat, and eleven salmon and sea trout lochs, six of which have a boat. Visitors' charges range between £40/day to £70/day for salmon and sea trout; and £6/day per rod, £30/week brown trout; brown trout boat £20/day. Salmon and sea trout fishing is available to guests staying at the Lochmaddy Hotel, Isle of North Uist HS6 5AA (tel: 01876 500331; fax: 01876 500210; see website for more info: www.lochmaddyhotel.co.uk; e-mail info@lochmaddyhotel.co.uk); residents have the first option; non residents day tickets cost from £40 to £70 per rod per day (salmon and sea trout), depending on season; residents conc £30 to £50; ghillies by arrangement; brown trout fishing costs visitors £30 weekly, or £6 daily, bank only, plus £20 per day boat hire; all permits obtainable from the Lochmaddy Hotel (brown trout fishing available at £4/day or £20/week to hotel guests). Langass Lodge Hotel, Locheport HS6 5HA (tel: 01876 580285) also has fishing. North Uist AC offers brown trout permits for the Newton Estate and Balranald Estate waters, comprising numerous lochs with boats on 5 of them; st £80, wt £30 and dt £6, from A & L Coleman, Clachan Stores,

Clachan, North Uist HS6 5HD (tel: 01876 580257). Other North Uist accommodation: Lochportain House, Lochmaddy HS6 5AS (tel: 0131 4479911), self catering; Sealladh Traigh, Claddach Kirkibost HS6 5EP (tel: 01876 580248).

SOUTH UIST: This island contains some of the finest wild trout fishing in the United Kingdom. It's machair lochs are world famous, providing a very fertile environment in which numerous trout grow large (specimen trout of over 4 lb are caught each season). There are also a number of sea trout and salmon systems which are capable of providing top-quality sport in from July – October. South Uist sea trout grow big and specimens into double figures are caught with surprising regularity.

Bornish. South Uist AC has trout fishing on many lochs in South Uist and all lochs on Benbecula. Bank fishing, wt £30, dt £6; up to 12 boats on various lochs, £8 p/day: contact Hamish Fraser, Hon Sec, South Uist Ac; tel: 01870 620394. Permits from Daliburgh PO. For South Uist Estates fishing, contact Lorna McLeod, Storas Uibhist (tel: 01878 700101); web: www.storasuibhist.com

ORKNEY

While sea fishing for skate, ling, halibut (British record), haddock, cod, etc, is general in waters about Orkney, good fun may be had in the evenings with saithe and pollack comparatively close to the shores.

Trout fishing is prolific, there are a multitude of lochs which hold excellent stocks of wild brown trout, and sea trout also are present in small numbers in specific lochs. Loch of Harray is the most famous and will produce fish from the first day of the season to the last, with May, June and July the best months. Bank fishing can be good but in the summer months it is best to go afloat. Catches can be phenomenal, equaling any comparable water in the UK. Midge and caenis hatches will bring vast numbers of trout 'on the feed'. Boardhouse Loch in Birsay is ideal for the visiting angler as there are no skerries and the fish average three quarters of a pound. Very surface active trout. Again, this is primarily a boat fishing venue with the best of the fishing being found in open water. The best months to fish at Boardhouse are May, June, and early July. Hundland is the neighbour of Boardhouse, and produces similar sport in the early months of the season, but can be troubled with weed growth in the later months. Loch of Swanney, again in Birsay, is another favourite with visiting local anglers, with the best months being May and June. This loch has a rather unique distinction in being locally considered an excellent dry-fly water. Swannay is capable of producing trophy wild trout, and fish over 2lb are relatively common. The Loch of Stenness is connected to the sea and is partly tidal. It is an exciting challenge for the fisherman and, with effort, the rewards are high. Native brown trout grow big and strong on the abundant marine life in this environment (a 29¼ lb fish was caught on a set-line in the early part of the last century). Sea trout from Scapa Flow also run through this loch. The Loch of Skaill and The Loch of Clumly in Sandwick should also be mentioned as they hold specimen trout, with fish in excess of two pounds. The lochs on the islands of Sanday, Westray and Stronsay also contain a number of very large trout.

The Orkney Trout Fishing Association is a non profit making voluntary body, dedicated to the preservation and enhancement of game fishing throughout the islands of Orkney. The Association constantly monitor the health and wellbeing of the trout habitat of the islands. Membership is open to visitors and non-residents. Membership entitles anglers to use Assn facilities, which include access to fishing on Loch of Skaill. Information at Visit Orkney, Kirkwall KW15 1NX (tel: 01856 872856); W S Sinclair, Tackle Shop, Stromness. Further information from OTFA Hon Sec, Stewart Topp, Choin, Marwick, Orkney KW17 2ND (tel: 01856 721488). A Trout Fishing Guide to Orkney by Stan Headley is on sale at most newsagents and booksellers in Orkney.

There is good quality accommodation throughout Orkney and there are taxi services to fishing waters. The Merkister Hotel, Loch Harray KW17 2LF (tel: 01856 771366; fax: 01856 771515; email: merkister hotel@ecosse.net) is close to Loch of Harray which offers excellent loch fishing: boats on Harray and other Mainland lochs, incl for disabled, outboards, ghillies. The Smithfield Hotel, Dounby KW17 2HT (tel: 01856 771 215) is convenient for the Lochs of Boardhouse, Harray, Hundland and Swanney.

SHETLAND

Shetland was formerly renowned for its sea trout fishing, but for a variety of reasons this fishing has now declined and anglers are recommended to concentrate on the excellent wild brown trout fishing in over three hundred lochs containing trout up to five pounds in weight.

Taking the Shetland Islands as a group, the majority of the fishing is controlled by the Shetland Anglers Association, who charge a fee of £25 per season for unlimited fishing, juniors free. Boats are bookable on five of the best lochs at an all in fee of £30. Details of all fishing and permits are obtainable from Rod and Line Tackle shop, Harbour Street, Lerwick, and also from the Association secretary, Alec Miller, 55 Burgh Rd, Lerwick, Shetland ZE1 0HJ (tel: 01595 696025; email: alec_miller@hotmail.com). There are now several hotels specialising in catering for anglers, and among the best is Herrislea Hotel, Tingwall; Baltasound Hotel, Baltasound, Unst. (tel: 01595 840208 fax: 01595 840630 email: hotel@herrisleahouse.co.uk)

SKYE

Trout and salmon fishing generally preserved. Sea trout historically good, but aquacultural practices in the area have added to a general decline. Excellent sea fishing.

Dunvegan. Numerous streams in area with some potential for sea trout in May and June. Hotels: Atholl House and others.

Sleat. Brown trout and Arctic charr fishing on a number of small rivers and lochs in the South of Skye; st £50, wt available £30; dt £7.50; ghillies £10/hour when available; £5 rod hire; boat on Loch Baravaig £10 per day: from estate office Mon to Fri: Fearann Eilean Iarmain, Eilean Iarmain, Sleat, Skye IV43 8QR (tel: 01471 833266).

Portree. The Storr Lochs called Fada and Leathan are 4m away, and have good brown trout (average 1lb, occasionally up to 5lb); good mayfly hatches; enquire Island Cycles, The Green IV51 9BT, tel: 01478 613121; bank fishing; 10 boats; mid May to mid June and early Sept best; permits for these and other hill lochs. The Portree AA controls all river fishing in the area, except south bank of R Lealt; Lealt is most productive of these; also Kilmuluag, Kilmartin, and Brogaig Rivers, small spate streams with the odd sea trout and salmon, suitable for fly, small spinner and worm; dt £15 for R Kilmaluig, Kilmartin, Brogaig; half dt R Lealt (north bank) £15; loch bank dt £10 from Island Cycles; bag limit 6/day; one Wheelyboat on Storr Lochs for disabled; enquiries to Hon Sec. Also sea fishing, for pollack and saithe in harbour. Tackle shop: Island Cycles, The Green, Portree, IV51

9BT, tel: 01478 613121. Hotel: Cuillin Hills.

Skeabost. riverlochy@btconnect.com). Skeabost Country House Hotel, Skeabost Bridge, Isle of Skye IV51 9NP (tel: 01470 532202) can arrange salmon and sea trout fishing (8m double bank) on River Snizort, reputed to be the best salmon river on Skye, and trout fishing; contact Derek Dowsit (tel: 01470 532297).

Sligachan. Sligachan Hotel IV47 8SW (tel: 01478 650204) currently issues permits at £20 for salmon and sea trout fishing in 2m Sligachan River, and brown trout fishing in Loch na Caiplaich, now heavily reeded; salmon few, sea trout quite plentiful; best months, mid July to end Sept; brown trout fishing by arrangement in Storr Lochs (15m) for hotel guests; boats for hire; season, May to end Sept. No permit is required for brown trout fishing in Loch Marsco.

Broadford. Sea trout and salmon in the Broadford River. 1½m south bank, fishing permits £10/day from Broadford Hotel IV49 9AB (tel: 01471 822204). Loch Sguabaidh and Lochan Stratha Mhor, brown trout, sea trout, occasional salmon, enquire locally.

LOCHY (including Nevis and Coe)

Drains Loch Lochy and, after joining the Spean at Mucomir, flows about 8m to salt water in Loch Linnhe close to Fort William. Very good salmon and sea trout river; river divided into 4 two mile beats fished in daily rotation; best months: July, August and Sept. Whole river is on weekly lets only: further information from River Lochy Association, (web: www.riverlochy.com; email: john.veitch@riverlochy.co.uk).

Tributaries of the Lochy

SPEAN: Fed mainly by River Roy and other minor streams. A rocky, spate river with good holding pools. Good fishing for salmon from May to October.

Spean Bridge (Inverness shire). No river fishing available; for Lochs Arkaig (browns) and Lochy; and a

further seven wild brown lochs, contact Fishing Scotland, tackle and permits PH31 4AG (tel: 01397 712812; see website for more info: www.fishingscotland.co.uk).

ROY (tributary of Spean): Salmon. A spate river; fishes best July onwards.

Roy Bridge (Inverness shire). Fishing Scotland Fishing School (fly fishing for experienced anglers; also tuition for beginners; all tackle &c included) have wild Atlantic salmon fishing, and wild brown trout fishing on 5 lochs; by pre reservation only; (tel: 01397 712812; see website for more info: www.fishingscotland.co.uk).

NEVIS: A short river flowing around south side of Ben Nevis and entering Loch Linnhe at Fort William, not far from mouth of Lochy. Very good salmon and sea trout fishing. Tackle shop: Rod & Gun Shop, 18 High St Fort William PH33 6AT (tel: 01397 702656) has tickets for river: dt £15; fly and worm only.

Fort William (Inverness shire). River Nevis; salmon, grilse, sea trout. Glen Nevis camp site has about 6m; wt £30, dt £10, conc; no spinning; best June onwards; c&r only; tickets from camp site or Rod & Gun shop (above). Good brown trout fishing on Loch Lundavra 6m from town; dt £17.50 boat; £5 bank; from Mrs A MacCallum, Lundavra Farm, Fort William PH33 6SZ (tel: 01397 702582). For Loch

Arkaig; permits from Achnacarry Estate, Bidwells, 33 High St (tel: 01397 702433)and Rod & Gun Shop, 18 High St PH33 6AT (tel: 01397 702656; www.fortwilliamfishing.com). Loch Lochy (free) rainbow trout and brown trout and pike Hotels: Imperial, Grand, Alexandra, West End, Milton.

COE. River flows through Glen Coe to enter Loch Leven and from there into Loch Linnhe. Salmon, sea trout and brown trout.

Glencoe (Argyllshire). The river fishing is for members of Glencoe AA; no tickets. Scorrybreac Guest House, Glencoe PH49 4HT (tel/fax: 01855 811354) supplies anglers, including disabled, with a gate key to enable vehicle access to Glencoe Lochan, nr Glencoe Village; rainbow trout, restocked monthly, April to mid Oct; Forestry Commission water. Tackle shop: The Arches, Loan Fern, Ballachulish PH49 4JB (tel: 01855 811111) (permits for Lochan).

LOSSIE

Drains Loch Trevie and flows about 25m to the Moray Firth at Lossiemouth. A good trout stream; salmon runs improving, July onwards. Provides good sport with sea trout from June onwards, especially near estuary.

Lossiemouth (Morayshire). Salmon, sea trout. Elgin & Dist AA has water; estuary and sea; salmon, sea trout and finnock. Permits and information on other fishings from the angling centre at Elgin.

Elgin (Morayshire). Elgin & Dist AA has water on Lossie at Elgin (salmon, sea trout and brown trout); about 17 miles in all mostly both banks, from mouth to about six miles south of of town; st, wt, dt available; no restrictions on membership; apply Angling Centre (below). Trout fishing can be had on the District Council's Millbuies Estate: Glenlatterach Reservoir, brown trout, boats on site; bank fishing dt £7; st £40, conc; boat:

dt £17 (single angler in boat), £24 for two, conc; Loch of Blairs, stocked rainbows, boat fishing only, and Millbuies Loch, mainly rainbow trout, also boat fishing only; boat: dt £17 (single angler in boat), £24 for two, conc; all lochs, 6 fish limit, 10in min; permits: for Millbuies and Glenlatterach from The Warden, Mr Jim Mitchell, Millbuies Lochs, Longmorn, Elgin IV30 8RJ (tel: 01343 860234); for Blairs: Fishing Tackle Shop, 97d High St, Forres IV36 0AA (tel: 01309 672936). Tackle shop: The Angling Centre, Moss Street, Elgin IV30 1LU (tel: 01343 547615); Info from Moray Council, Department of

Environmental Services, High Str, Elgin IV30 1BX (tel: 01343 543451).

Hotels: Mansefield House; Mansion House.

LUNAN

Rises near Forfar and flows about 13m to Lunan Bay in the North Sea between Arbroath and Montrose. Some good trout. Sea trout and finnock in July to October. Stocked with brown trout. A protection order now in force requiring all anglers to be in possession of proper permits, obtainable through Arbroath AC.

Arbroath (Angus). Lunan and the Vinney, about 8m of water, leased to Arbroath AC by riparian owners; restocked each year, holds good head of brown trout, also sea trout and occasional salmon; bag limit 4 fish; river mouth, sea trout and salmon; st £30, juv £15, OAP's £20; dt £6, £3: specify mouth or upstream; contact Angus Country Sport, 273 High street, Arbroath; tel: 01241 439988.

Forfar (Angus). Canmore AC (members of Strathmore Angling Improvement Association) have trout fishing on River Dean, fly only; Cruick; R Kerbet, fly only; Club also hold rights for Den of Ogil Reservoir, boat and bank fishing for brown trout; and Forfar Loch; all Canmore AC permits from W R Hardy Tackle Shop

(below) (also Strathmore AIA tickets for Isla and Dean). Rescobie Loch Development Assn runs Rescobie Loch, 200 acres, 3m E of Forfar; a Troutmaster loch with boat and bank fishing to rainbows and browns, fly only, c&r after bag limit; 12 inch size limit; st £195, OAP £150, juv £40, 4 fish limit (up to 8 fish per week); session ticket (9am to 5pm; or 5pm to dusk) £15, conc; boats all sessions 1 rod £5 (members only) (visitors £17), 2 rods £8 (visitors £34), 3 rods £9 (visitors £41); visitor bag limit 4 fish per rod; from Rescobie Boathouse, Clocksbriggs, Montrose Rd by Forfar (tel: 01307 830367). Tackle Shop: W R Hardy, 153 East High St DD8 2EQ (tel: 01307 466635).

NAIRN

Rises in Monadhliath Hills and flows about 36m to Moray Firth at Nairn. Salmon, sea trout, finnock and brown trout.

Nairn (Nairnshire). Tickets for the lower reaches (estuary to Cantray Bridge, approx 6½m) mostly both banks can be had for Nairn AA water; salmon and sea trout (st to be returned unharmed); best months: July to September for salmon; visitors permits £135 weekly, £35 day, conc for juv, from Pat Fraser, 41 High St, Nairn IV12 4AG (tel: 01667 453038). Clava Lodge Holiday Homes, Culloden Moor, by Inverness IV2 5EJ (tel: 01463 790228), also issues permits for 1¼m stretch on Nairn; dt £7 (free to residents). Lochs

Lochindorb (see Drynachan), Allan, and Loch an Tutach privately owned; brown trout; dt and boat. 2m east of Nairn on A96 road, Boath House, Auldearn, Nairn IV12 5TE; rainbow trout fishing on lake for residents (tel: 01667 454896). Newton Hotel, Inverness Rd, IV12 4RX (tel: 01667 453144) and Golf View Hotel, 63 Seabank Rd, IV12 4HD (tel: 01667 452301) both have river and loch fishing by arrangement. Tackle shop: J Graham & Co, 37 39 Castle St, Inverness IV2 3EA (tel: 01463 233178).

NAVER (including Borgie and Loch Hope)

Drains Loch Naver and flows about 24m to north coast at Naver Bay. The Borgie, which also debouches into Naver Bay, drains Loch Slaim and has course of about 7m. Both are good salmon and sea trout rivers; all preserved, but beats can be arranged, usually for weekly periods.

Altnaharra (Sutherland). Altnaharra Hotel, Lairg, Sutherland IV27 4UE (tel/fax: 01549 411222), which specializes in catering for fishermen, provides fishing in Loch Naver, Loch Hope and Loch Loyal; salmon, sea trout and brown trout; for details and tarrif on all lochs go to hotel website: www.altnaharra.com/home/fishing/; fishing in a number of lochs; all lochs have boats and are close to the road; some are open to non residents; no bank fishing; fly only; ghillies by arrangement; hotel also has fishing on River Mudale; Hotel supplies tackle and has drying room; and provides outboard motors, tuition and accommodation.

Tongue (Sutherland). Three limited day tickets (Mon to Fri: book personally 2 days beforehand) for quality salmon fishing on River Naver from The Store, Bettyhill, by Thurso, Caithness KW14 7SS (tel: 01641 521207; fax: 01641 521426); fly only, dt £20; 1 fish limit salmon or grilse (max 2 per week); sea trout fishing in the Naver Estuary, £5 d/t and £30 season ticket; no permits required for Loch Duinte; The Store also supplies permits for River Strathy; 3m salmon and sea trout; 8 rods per day, £20 per rod Mon to Sat; no Sunday fishing. Free fishing on the Bettyhill side of Lochs Meadie, More, Ghanu, Cool, all brown trout. Salmon and sea trout fishing on Loch Hope. Tongue & Dist AA (HQ at Ben Loyal Hotel see below) has brown trout fishing on several lochs; fly only; boats on Lochs Loyal, Craggie, Bealach na Sgeulachd, and Lochan Hakel, Bhuoaidh, Kyle of Tongue; ghillie by arrangement; st £30, wt £20, dt £6 from hotel: drying room and freezer space at hotel: Kyle of Tongue estuary also assn water; excellent sea trout when shoals are running; fly or spinner. Permits also from local hotels, post office and general store; Ben Loyal Hotel also has a rotating beat on s end of Loch Hope; dt £80 incl boat for 2 rods + ghillie. For R Borgie private beats, Mar Sept, fly only, contact Rebecca Stickland for information, Borgie Lodge Hotel (see below); brown trout boat dt £15 (free to residents); hotel has brown trout fishing on 20 lochs, with salmon in three, boats on five at £15 hire, spinning and worm permitted on some; hotel runs fishing packages with ghillie and all other facilities. Hotels: Borgie Lodge, Skerray by Tongue KW14 7TH (tel: 01641 521332); Ben Loyal, Tongue IV27 4XE (tel: 01847 611216).

NESS

Drains Loch Ness and flows to Moray Firth at Inverness. Notable salmon and sea trout river. Best July to October.

Inverness (Inverness shire). Salmon, sea trout, brown trout. Inverness AC has stretch from estuary upstream for about 3¾m, both banks; no Sunday fishing; permits £32 per day or £140 weekly, conc, from tackle shop, J Graham (below) (this tackle shop may from time to time have fishing on several private beats on several rivers; enquire at the time); Loch Ruthven, brown trout; fly only; boat only; permits from J Graham & Co, 37 39

Castle St, Inverness IV2 3EA (tel: 01463 233178); no Sunday fishing; £25 per boat per day; Loch Choire, brown trout; fly only; permits also from A Humfrey, Balvoulin, Aberarder IV2 6UA (tel: 01808 521283). Sea trout fishing on North Kessock sea shore; permits from North Kessock PO; and J Graham & Co (see above). Tourist Information Centre: Castle Wynd, IV2 3BJ (tel: 01463 234353; see website for more info: www.fishpal.com), for local fishing information. Hotels: Glen Mhor; Loch Ness House.

LOCH NESS: Sea trout at Dochfour and Aldourie; salmon, especially out from Fort Augustus and where Rivers Moriston and Foyers enter the loch. Brown trout all round the margins. Boats and boatmen from hotels at Fort Augustus, Drumnadrochit, Foyers, Lewiston and Whitbridge.

Drumnadrochit (Inverness-shire). Salmon and brown trout. Loch Meiklie, brown trout, fly only.

Foyers (Inverness shire).

Invermoriston (Inverness shire). River Moriston enters Loch Ness here. An early river, best February to June. Permits for river and trout fishing on hill lochs from Glenmoriston Lodge Estate Office, River Cottage, Invermoriston IV63 7YA (tel: 01320 351300); enquiries also for salmon fishing by boat on Loch Ness.

Fort Augustus (Inverness shire). Salmon and brown trout. Salmon season opens Jan 15. Trout season, March 15. Salmon fishing on River Oich (all south bank (4m); dt £25 plus ghillie fee, from J Graham & Co, 37 39 Castle St, Inverness IV2 3EA (tel: 01463 233178). Other hotels: Caledonian, Brae, Inchnacardoch.

Tributaries of Loch Ness

FOYERS. Free brown trout fishing.

Foyers (Inverness shire). Loch Mhor, 18m from Inverness, is 4m long by ½m broad, and contains trout averaging ½lb. Outlet from loch enters Loch Ness via River Foyers. Accommodation 2½m from loch at Whitebridge Hotel, Whitebridge, Inverness IV2 6UN (tel: 01456 486226), who have tackle for purchase or hire, and boats on Loch Knockie and Loch Bran (£25 per day); and information on fishing: Loch Ruthven (which can be fished), also River Fechlin.

Whitebridge (Inverness-shire). Whitebridge Hotel (see above) has boats for use of guests on Loch Knockie and Loch Bran; brown trout; fly only; arrangements also made for guests wishing to troll on Loch Ness.

MORISTON: Salmon, brown trout.

Glenmoriston (Inverness shire). Glenmoriston Lodge Estate Office, River Cottage, Invermoriston IV63

7YA (tel: 01320 351300; fax: 01320 351301) has fishing rights on Loch Ness, salmon and brown trout; R Moriston, salmon and brown trout; and Glenmoriston Hill Lochs, brown trout; (See Invermoriston) also Loch Cluanie, brown trout; no Sunday fishing.

OICH and **GARRY**: Garry rises in loch SW of Loch Quoich and runs into that loch at western end, thence to Lochs Poulary, Inchlaggan and Garry. Good salmon and trout river. Outlet to Loch Garry dammed by North of Scotland Hydro Electric Board. At Loch Poulary are fish traps; at Invergarry, a hatchery. River Oich good salmon fishing from opening day 15 January; brown trout from 15 March.

Invergarry (Inverness-shire): Upper Garry, Lochs Quoich, Poulary, Inchlaggan and Garry. Loch Quoich holds good brown trout and Loch Garry holds a few Arctic charr; both lochs hold charr; salmon only good Aug onwards, closing mid Oct; boats on all lochs and some of pools of Upper Garry from Tomdoun Hotel (see below). Excellent early spring fishing on both banks of R Garry (now syndicate water) and salmon fishing on Loch Oich; contact through Tomdoun Hotel. Tomdoun Hotel issues permits for Lochs Quoich, Poulary, Inchlaggan, Garry, and Upper River Garry (which is reserved for hotel guests only); trout, charr and pike; boat fishing only on Quoich; on the lochs, fly fishing and spinning for large brown trout; fly fishing only for wild brown trout on the river; bank fishing only on Loch Loyne; boats from hotel for all waters except Loyne; apply to Michael Pearson, Tomdoun Hotel, Invergarry, Inverness shire PH35 4HS (tel: 01809 511218; web: www.tomdoun.com/fishing).

NITH

Rises on south side of Ayr watershed and flows south and east to Solway, which it enters by an estuary with Dumfries at its head. Is the largest and best known river in the Dumfries and Galloway region and has established a reputation for the quality of its salmon and sea trout which continues to improve. Carries a good head of small trout.

New Abbey (Dumfriesshire). New Abbey AA has 2m on a small tributary of Nith; occasional salmon, good sea trout and herling, and stocked with brown trout and rainbow trout; dt £6, conc available from Criffel Inn, 2 The Square, DG2 8BX (tel: 01387 850305). Hotels: Criffel Inn (see above); Abbey Arms, 1 The Square DG2 8BX (tel: 01387 850489).

Dumfries (Dumfries & Galloway). Dumfries Common Good Fishing, 3m on Nith, 1½m on Cairn (tributary); salmon, sea trout, brown trout and grayling; best, March May and Sept Nov; visitors s/t £395, w/t £224, d/t £40 £50 depending on season;enquire about visitors concessions; reductions for residents, OAP, juveniles, from Dumfries & Galloway Council, 52 60 Queensberry Street, Dumfries DG1 1BF (tel: 01387 260739; fax 01387 260799), and d/t available from Tourist Board, 64 Whitesands, DG1 2RS (not open on a Saturday). Dumfries & Galloway AA has 3m on Nith and 16m on Cairn; salmon, sea trout and brown trout; fly fishing anytime; spinning and bait fishing also anytime; for reports contact Hon Sec (mob: 07595 922315); daily tickets; no daily tickets on Saturday; concessions for juniors; permits contact www.fishpal.co.uk (tel: 01573 470612). Glenkiln Reservoir (trout) Scottish Water reservoir, enquiries to Thomas Florey, Genkiln AC (tel: 01387 263066); dt £6 (bank), conc; boats on site. Tackle shops: D McMillan, 6 Friars Vennel DG1 2RN (tel: 01387 252075); Pattie's of Dumfries, 109 Queensberry St, Dumfries DG1 1BH (tel: 01387 252 891).

Jericho Loch, rainbow, brown and brook trout; fly only; bank fishing only; visitors should go directly to loch and pay on site or use honesty box. Tackle shops: D McMillan, 6 Friars Vennel, Dumfries DG1 2RN (tel: 01387 252075); Pattie's of Dumfries, 109 Queensberry St, Dumfries DG1 1BH (tel: 01387 252891).

Thornhill (Dumfriesshire). Mid Nithsdale AA has 3½m on Nith and tributary Scaur; salmon, sea trout and brown trout; tickets from Pets Larder, 101 2 Drumlanrig Street, Thornhill DG3 5LU (tel: 01848 330555) (closed pm Thurs and Sat). Buccleuch Estate has brown and rainbow trout fishing on Kettleton Loch 4m NE of Thornhill, 40 acres; Drumlanrig Castle Fishing on the Queensberry Estate offers salmon and sea trout fishing on River Nith, 7m, largely both banks, 4 beats; Lochs Morton Castle, Starburn, Slatehouse, and Coldstream, rainbow and brown trout: fly only on lochs, preferred on river; also Hillhead Loch, rainbow; Farthing Bank Loch, rainbow; Morton Pond and Dabton, coarse fish; st £275 (river, Nith Linns beat only), variety of weekly and 3 day tickets, dt £12.50 to £107 depending on season; also sea trout evng £29, otherwise prices as for river; loch fishing dt £26 (evng £18) for Kettleton, Morton Castle and Starburn; £21 (evng £16) for the remaining four; apply to Buccleuch Sportings, Drumlanrig Mains, Thornhill, Dumfriesshire DG3 4AG (tel: 01848 600415; fax: 01848 600244; web: www.buccleuch.com). Barjarg Estate has west bank stretch on Nith with named pools; salmon, grilse, sea trout, brown trout and grayling; daily or weekly permits until end August; normally weekly from Sept to end Nov; bag limit 3 sea trout and 2 salmon, then c&r; dt £15 £55 depending on season; apply to Dougie Smith, Brandyburn Farm, Auldgirth, Dumfriesshire DG2 0XG (mob: 07738 015793). Loch Ettrick Fishery, Blawbare, Loch Ettrick, Closeburn, Thornhill DG3 5HL (tel: 01848 330154); 20 acre loch, well stocked with rainbow and brown trout; boats available; tuition; suitable for disabled. Hotels: Buccleuch, George, Elmarglen.

Sanquhar (Dumfriesshire). Upper Nithsdale AC has approx 11m of Nith; and stretches on tributaries Kello, Crawick, Euchan and Mennock. Salmon, sea trout, brown trout and grayling; no Sunday fishing; reduced membership charge for resident juveniles; and Forsyth Shield presented each year in Jan to resident child for heaviest fish caught; permits from K McLean Esq, Solicitor, 61 High Street, Sanquhar DG4 6DT (tel: 01659 50241); also dt for grayling fishing, Jan and Feb. Hotels: Nithsdale; Glendyne; Blackaddie House.

New Cumnock (Ayrshire). New Cumnock AA has brown trout fishing on River Nith, Afton Water and Afton Reservoir; and on parts of Rivers Deuch and Ken, and Carsphairn Lane Burn; assn also has grayling fishing on River Nith and rainbow and brown trout fishing, also coarse, on Creoch Loch; Creoch Loch open all year; 2 boats; contact Hon Sec for tickets. Hotels: Lochside House, Cumnock KA18 4PN (tel: 01290 333000); Crown.

OYKEL (including Carron, Cassley, Shin and Loch Ailsh)

Rises at Benmore Assynt, flows through Loch Ailsh and thence 14m to enter the Kyle of Sutherland at Rosehall. Excellent salmon and sea trout fishing. The Lower Oykel has produced large average catch of salmon in recent years.

Oykel Bridge (Sutherland). Lower reaches fish very well for salmon early on and good grilse and sea trout run usually begins in the latter half of June. Loch Ailsh; good sea and brown trout fishing with occasional salmon. Best months Lower Oykel, March to September. Upper Oykel and Loch Ailsh, mid June to September; preference given to residents of lodge; for Beats 1 & 2 on upper River Oykel contact Mrs Betty Watt; Borralan, by Lairg IV27 4HF (tel: 01854 666368). Hotel: Inver Lodge Hotel, Iolaire Rd, Lochinver IV27 4LU (tel: 01571 844496).

CASSLEY: Some 10m long, river is divided at Rosehall into upper and lower Cassley by Achness Falls. Below falls fishing starts early. Upper Cassley fishes well from May to Sept.

Sea trout July and Aug. Now privately owned.

SHIN (Loch Shin and Kyle of Sutherland): Loch Shin is largest fresh water loch in Sutherland, 16m long. Brown trout in loch av ½lb, but very large fish taken early in season. Outlet from Loch Shin controlled by hydro electric works. River flows about 7m and empties into Kyle of Sutherland at Invershin. Salmon fishing privately let.

Lairg (Sutherland). Lairg AC has trout fishing in Loch Shin and hill lochs, including Loch Beannach (brown trout), 5m from Lairg, (½m walk); Loch Shin, brown trout including ferox up to 12lbs; competitions held on Loch Shin (18 club boats available) throughout the season (1 May to 30 Sept) details from club hut at loch side; st from Hon Sec; for bank wt for L Shin, and dt, juv conc, apply local tackle shop; club also holds 2 day fishing festival mid July; details from Hon Sec. Boats (only) for hire from Park House Sporting on hill lochs of Dola, Craggie and Tigh na Creig, wild browns; fly only; ghillies and electric outboards by arrangement: Park House Sporting, Lairg, Sutherland IV27 4AU (tel: 01549 402208; fax: 01549 402693; see website for more info: www.parkhousesporting.com); best start May to end of Sept; who also have fishing on Upper and Lower Shin, and Cassley, Brora and Carron (subject to availability). Overscaig House Hotel, on shore of Loch Shin, has boats there, and also on Lochs A' Ghriama and Merkland; many hill lochs within a short distance; hotel can arrange ghillies; advice and instruction; large brown trout caught on hotel waters in recent years; bank fishing free to residents; boats with o/b motors; for further information contact Overscaig House Hotel, Loch Shin, by Lairg IV27 4NY (tel: 01549 431203); there are usually facilities for sea trout and salmon fishing on Lochs **Stack** and **More**. Tackle shop: Sutherland Sporting Co, Main St IV27 4DB (tel: 01549 402229) (Lairg AC permits).

DORNOCH FIRTH: Dornoch (Sutherland). At entrance to Firth. Permits from Dornoch & DAA; Dornoch & District Angling Association. Brown Trout & Salmon fishing available on lochs within close proximity with Dornoch. Ticket sales from Dornoch Tourist Office 01862 810400;Contact Michael Banks; tel: 01862 810589; fax: 01862 811164. Brown trout, stocked with rainbows and blue on Lochs **Lannsaidh** Loch **Buidhe**, Loch **Laoigh**, Loch **Lagain**, Loch Laro, Loch **Ghuibhais** and Loch **Cracail Mor**; assn has also acquired salmon, sea trout and brown trout fishing on Loch Brora; boat only, £20 per day (£5/day/rod extra on Brora); fly only on lochs; Sunday fishing (except Brora); permits from Dornoch Pet & Country Store, 8 Castle street, Dornoch, IV25 3SN; tel: 01862 811812. Bank permits from Dornoch Outdoor Shop, Castle Street, Dornoch, Sutherland IV25 3SN; tel: 01862 811 111 for Buidhe and Laoigh. Royal Golf Hotel, The 1st Tee, IV25 3LG (tel: 01862 810283) has river and loch fishing by arrangement. Other hotels: Burghfield House, IV25 3HN; Dornoch Castle, IV25 3SD; Skibo Castle, Clashmore, IV25 3RQ.

KYLE OF DURNESS

Durness (Sutherland). Good salmon and sea trout fishing on Rivers Dionard Grudie and Dall, and the Kyle of Durness; big brown trout in famous limestone Lochs Calladale, Crosspool, Lanish, and Borralaidh well conditioned fish of 8lbs in weight have been taken; one of the finest wild trout fisheries in Scotland; for all information on fishing in the Durness area, see website for more info: www.durnesslimestonelochs.co.uk. Contact Martin Mackay; tel: 01971 511255; or contact via email: martin@durnesslimestonelochs.co.uk

SCOURIE (Lochs Stack and More)

Scourie (Sutherland). Excellent centre for sea trout, brown trout and salmon fishing. About 400 trout lochs. Scourie Hotel has extensive fishing rights on over 300; five with salmon and sea trout; 21 boats (only from hotel) on many; ghillies may also be hired; days on Loch Stack and Loch More open to guests May to Sept; salmon, sea trout (good), brown trout; for further information apply to Patrick and Judy Price, Scourie Hotel, Scourie, by Lairg IV27 4SX (tel: 01971 502396; web:scourie hotel.co.uk). Scourie & Dist AC has rights on 33+ lochs to N of village and 2 lochs S; wild brown trout $\frac{1}{2}$lb mark, but some larger fish; wt £20; dt £10 (for own loch) dt £5 (non beat); (boat £10 extra; buoyancy aids must be worn, hire £1) from Scourie filling station (tel: 01971 502422).

SHIEL (Argyll/Inverness shire) (including Moidart and Loch Shiel)

Short salmon river, only about 3m long, draining Loch Shiel. Moidart is a good spate river with excellent holding pools. Loch Shiel is fed by four major rivers, Slatach, Finnan, Callop and Alladale, which all tend to be spate rivers. Fishing in the loch has been poor of late, except for brown trout which have been returning in numbers in recent years.

Acharacle (Argyllshire). River preserved. The Ardnamurchan Peninsular has fly fishing in Lochs Mudle and Mhadaidh Riabhaich; wild brown trout, sea trout and the occasional salmon; permits obtainable from Estate Office, Mingary House, Kilchoan, Acharacle PH36 4LH (tel: 01972 510208), from local shop, T.I.C. (tel: 01972 510 222), and hotels and visitors centres; all other nineteen hill lochs and salmon and sea trout fishing on the Achateny water and Allt Choire Mhuilin reserved for estate guests; boat hire and self catering accommodation at Ardnamurchan Estate; Tickets and information from Kilchoan Community Centre, PH36 4LJ (tel: 01972 510711). Hotels: Sonachan; Kilchoan House.

Glenfinnan (Inverness shire). Loch Shiel: fishing now sub standard and not recommended, although it could produce good brown trout.

SPEY

One of the largest rivers in Scotland, from its source Loch Spey, it flows 97 miles to Moray Firth, emptying between Banff and Elgin. The total catchment area is 1,154 sq miles. The Spey is an alpine river, with melting snow supplementing flow well into spring. The waters are low in nutrients, and have remained fairly free from pollution. The main river is also relatively free from obstructions. Historically, one of the great salmon rivers, net fishing ceased at the end of the 1993 season, and there is now no commercial netting for salmon within the Spey district. The Spey is a Site of Special Scientific Interest (SSSI) and is a Special Area of Conservation (SAC).

Fochabers (Morayshire). The Gordon Castle sporting estate on the River Spey offers first class salmon fishing recognized to be amongst the very best in Britain; eight miles of river comprised of 8 double bank beats; 1 ghillie per beat, 3 - 6 rods per beat; fly only; salmon and sea trout; largely catch & release. Gordon Castle recently renovated and available for rent as are other smaller self catering properties on the estate; family groups welcomed. For all enquiries contact the Factor, Estate Office, Gordon Castle, Fochabers, IV32 7PQ; tel: 01343 820244 or 820078. Fochabers AA have four visitors day permits £20 £65 depending on season (subject to availability); these are booked from Hon Sec or President, Gordon Young (tel: 01343 821059). Hotels: Gordon Arms Hotel, 80 High St IV32 7DH (tel: 01343 820508/9); Mill House Hotel, Tynet, by Buckie, Banffshire AB56 5HJ (tel: 01542 850233) and The Garmouth Hotel, Garmouth IV32 7LU (tel: 01343 870226).

Craigellachie (Banffshire). Salmon, sea trout, trout. Craigellachie Hotel, Craigellachie, Aberlour, Banffshire AB38 9SR (tel: 01340 881204), arranges salmon fishing on Spey and brown trout fishing on local lochs for residents.

Aberlour (Banffshire). Salmon, sea trout. Aberlour Association water. Six tickets per day on first come first served basis; wt £150, dt £30; no day tickets issued on Saturdays; permits from J A J Munro, Fishing Tackle, 77 High St, Aberlour, Banffshire AB38 9QB (tel: 01340 871428); season 11 Feb 30 Sept; best season usually March till June but can be very good in July and August too; J A J Munro is a specialist supplier of hand tied salmon flies. Hotels: Dowans Hotel AB38 9LS (tel: 01340 871488); Aberlour Hotel, High Street AB38 9QB (tel: 01340 871287).

Grantown on Spey (Morayshire). Salmon and sea trout. Strathspey Angling Improvement Association (SAIA) has double bank fishing on 5m on Spey, and 12m on Dulnain; salmon, grilse and sea trout are the main quarry, but both rivers have brown trout. In recent years, salmon over 28lb, and sea trout over 13lb have been caught; av catch 275 salmon and grilse, 400 sea trout. Most of main stem of river is private and expensive. The Assn has a 13 pool beat of excellent fly water on the Reidhaven Estate, available only to st and wt holders. Daily permits are offered to temporary residents in Grantown, Cromdale, Duthill, Carrbridge, Dulnain Bridge and Nethy Bridge areas to fish AIA waters. Permits only available for Assn waters from Mortimers Fishing Tackle, (below). Strathspey Estate, Old Spey Bridge Rd, Grantown on Spey, PH26 3NQ (tel: 01479 872529), has four beats on Spey, incl three Castle Grant beats; contact Estate Office for further information. Trout fishing on Avielochan, bank fishing only; Abernethy AA water. Trout fishing is available on Loch Vaa; 2 rods per boat, no bank fishing; fly only. Permits from Boat of Garten Post Office (see below). Tackle shop: Mortimer's, 3 High St PH26 3HB (tel: 01479 872684). For other local fishing information apply to The Seafield Lodge Hotel, Woodside Ave, PH26 3JN (tel: 01479 872152; web: www.seafieldlodge.co.uk) who cater for anglers; fishing packages available.

Boat of Garten (Inverness shire). Salmon, sea trout, brown trout. Abernethy Angling Improvement Assn, incorporating Aviemore Angling Improvement Assn, issues tickets for Abernethy Waters, 6 mile stretch of Spey, both banks, 15 named pools; contact Boat of Garten Post Office (see below); certain stretches restricted to fly only when river below certain level, otherwise spinning and worming allowed; no prawn or shrimp allowed at any time; no Sunday fishing; all methods barbless hooks; brown trout fishing   fly only at all times; wt £150, dt £40; from Boat of Garten Post Office, Deshar Rd, Boat of Garten PH24 3BN (tel: 01479 831223).

Aviemore (Inverness shire). The principal Spey Valley tourist centre. Permits for Aviemore stretch from Aviemore Tourist Information Centre, Grampian Road, Aviemore, Highland, PH22 1PP; tel: 01479 810363.

Avielochan, 10 acre brown trout water; tel: 01479 831372. Trout and pike fishing on Rothiemurchus Estate, including rainbow (which are stocked) and brown trout lochs – Pityoulish (brown trout & pike), Lochan More (brown trout), Eilein (pike) - and beats on R Spey with salmon and sea trout; apply to Rothiemurchus Trout Fishery, Aviemore PH22 1QH (tel: 01479 810 703); ghillie service and instruction on site, disabled access on bank; tackle shop and boat. Trout fishing on

Loch Morlich at Glenmore; permits from Aviemore Tourist Information Centre (tel: 01479 810363) or Watersports Centre, Glenmore Forest Park by Aviemore, PH22 1QU (tel: 01479 861221; see website for more info: www.lochmorlich.com).

Kingussie (Inverness shire). Alvie Estate has fishing on Spey, salmon and trout; Loch Alvie, brown trout and pike; and Loch Insh, salmon, sea trout, brown trout, pike and Arctic charr; fly fishing or spinning; apply to Alvie Estate Office, Kincraig, by Kingussie PH21 1NE (tel: 01540 651255); or Dalraddy Caravan Park, Aviemore PH22 1QB (tel: 01479 810330). Loch Insh Watersports & Skiing Centre, Insh Hall, Kincraig PH21 1NU (tel: 01540 651272; fax: 01540 651208; or contact via email: office@lochinsh.com; see website for more info: www.lochinsh.com), also has 3 boats and bank fishing on Loch Insh, and stocked trout lochan; boats for hire, and tuition on site, facilities for disabled. Badenoch AA has fishing on River Spey from Spey Dam down to Kingussie, Loch Ericht at Dalwhinnie, and Loch Laggan on the Fort William Rd; all brown trout fishing, stocked monthly, very few salmon; Spey Dam has 2 boats, fly only, the other waters allow worm and spinning; fishing permits £12, conc, from Service Sports, 26 High St, Kingussie PH21 1HR (tel: 01540 661228); fishing permits and boat hire from Jock Dallas (tel: 01540 661207); and local hotels. Service Sports also supply fishing permits (and boat hire) for Loch Gynack, a private loch; £12 per rod and boats £6 per session.

Newtonmore (Inverness shire). Badenoch AA has trout fishing on Upper Spey, Loch Laggan, and Spey Dam and Loch Ericht; tickets, see Kingussie.

Tributaries of the Spey

AVON: Main tributary of Spey.

Ballindalloch (Inverness shire). (Banffshire). Ballindalloch Estate owns 5m stretch on Avon from junction with Spey; salmon, sea trout, brown trout; weekly and daily permits; permits from The Estate Office, Ballindalloch, Banffshire AB37 9AX (tel: 01807 500205; fax: 01807 500210; see website for more info: www.ballindallochcastle.co.uk, email enquiries@ballindallochcastle.co.uk).

Hotel: The Delnashaugh Hotel AB37 9AS (tel: 01807 500255).

Tomintoul (Inverness shire). (Banffshire). Sea trout, grilse and salmon. Permit holders can fish 7m of Avon and 1m of Livet; all hen fish to be returned; replace every second fish; upstream worming, spinning; fly only in Sept; Glenavon Hotel, The Square Tomintoul, Ballindalloch, AB37 9ET; tel: 01807 580218.

STINCHAR

One of west coast streams, rising on western slope of Doon watershed and flowing about 30m to Atlantic at Ballantrae. Has a late run of salmon, and fishes best from September till late October. Also good sea trout and brown trout from June onwards.

Colmonell (Ayrshire). River rises and falls rapidly after rain; salmon and sea trout. Boar's Head Hotel, 4 Main St, KA26 0RY (tel: 01465 881371) can assist with arranging fishings on river. For Knockdolian (best beat): Estate Office, Knockdolian, Colmonell, Girvan KA26 0LB (tel: 01465 881237; or contact via email: katrob1@btconnect.com); beats: for Badrochat/Almont and Dalreoch Estate: John Goodenough (tel: 07880 602922): these are the main beats on the river, of which majority are fly only; Hallow Chapel fishing: Tom Lothian, 'Craignelder', 1 Main St, Ballantrae KA26 0NA (tel: 01465 831277). Colmonell AC has water below bridge. Queen's Hotel, 21 Main St, KA26 0RY (tel: 01465 881213) can supply information to visiting anglers. Pinbraid Fishery (Bill Wood), Garnaburn, KA26 0RX (tel: 01465 891112); fly only; wild browns, rainbow; 7 days.

The glorious Helmsdale on opening day, January 11th!

TAY

A great salmon river. Tay proper runs out of Loch Tay, but its feeder, the Dochart, at head of loch, takes its head water from slopes of Ben Lui. After a course of some 119m it empties into North Sea at Dundee, by a long firth. River fished mainly from boats, but certain beats provide spinning and fly fishing from banks. Still notable for run of spring fish, but autumn fishing now produces better results. All netting has now been removed in the Tay estuary, and salmon and sea trout have run unhindered for several years. Owing to recent runs of salmon being lower than normal, for reasons beyond the control of the Tay District Salmon Fisheries Board (see Fishing in Scotland), the Board recommends strongly that all salmon caught in the River Tay and any of its tributaries should be released until 31 May. All female fish should be released thereafter, as well as all male salmon over 10lbs. Catch and release is now accepted by most anglers, and three-quarters of fish caught have in recent years been returned unharmed to the water. At least half a dozen of its tributaries are salmon rivers of slightly less repute than main stream. An excellent run of sea trout, big brown trout (less often fished for), grayling, and coarse fish (scarcely fished at all). Loch Tay itself has been improving over recent years as a salmon fishery, the largest taken being over 40lbs.

Perth (Perthshire). Scone Estate, Scone Palace, PH2 6BD (tel: 01738 552308; fax: 01738 552588; see website: www.scone-palace.co.uk; email: estate@scone-palace.co.uk) offers salmon fishing on two beats of Tay; daily lets in spring, and daily and weekly from July to October; for availability go to www.fishpal.com/Scotland/Tay.

Stormont AC has salmon fishing on Tay, 3 beats; and on R Almond, 2 beats; members only (c 550), apply Scone Estate (tel: 01738 552308); permits for 3 beats of brown trout and coarse fishing on Tay and Almond, from tackle shop (below). Perth & Dist AA has various leases for brown trout and salmon fishing on Tay; assn also has fishing on **Black Loch**, rainbow trout; Loch Horn, rainbow and brown trout; all game fishing members only. Brown trout on Tay permits from P D Malloch (below). Permits for Perth Town Water; salmon, trout, grilse and also coarse fish; from Perth and Kinross Council, Environment Services, Pullar House, 35 Kinnoull St PH1 5GD (tel: 01738 476476; fax: 01738 476410); and Visit Scotland Perth, Lower City Mills, West Mill St, Perth PH1 5QP (tel: 01738 450600) (Saturday only); dt £10 (Jan to June); £15 (July to Oct);

brown trout and coarse free; advisable to book in advance; only 20 permits per day. Tackle shop: P D Malloch, 259 Old High St PH1 5QN (tel: 01738 632316). Hotels: Royal George; Tayside, Stanley.

Stanley (Perthshire). Stanley & Dist AC has brown trout and grayling fishing at Luncarty, Upper Redgorton (dt for these 2 from Luncarty PO), Stanley Mill, Burnmouth, Taymount, and Meikleour; a limited number of permits are offered (Mon Sun) (dt £3) from Stanley PO (6am to 8pm), 2 Percy Str, PH1 4LU (tel: 01738 828206). Tayside Hotel, 51 Mill Str, PH1 4NL (tel: 01738 828249; fax: 01738 827216) issues trout permits for fishing on all beats: Linn Pool, Burnmouth, Catholes, Pitlochrie, Benchil, and Luncarty; special rates to residents; salmon fishing packages available; hotel has tackle for sale, and special anglers' facilities (drying room, freezers &c). Ballathie House Hotel, Kinclaven PH1 4QN (tel: 01250 883268; fax: 01250 883396; email@ballathiehousehotel.com; web: www.ballathiehousehotel.com) lets rods on the Ballathie beat and elsewhere, when available, to residents and non residents early in the season.

Dunkeld (Perthshire). Dunkeld & Birnam AA have trout fishing on Tay; permits are also issued for grayling, mostly in the trout close season. Permits from P D Malloch, 259 Old High St PH1 5QN (tel: 01738 632316) for Perth & Dist AA grayling tickets. **Loch Clunie**: no fishing now due to SSSI designation. Dunkeld & Birnam AA also has brown trout fishing on River Braan; permits from The Spar, 3 Murthly Terrace, Birnam, PH8 0BG (tel: 01350 727395). Amulree Hotel has fishing on Loch Freuchie; trout and pike, bank fishing only; and stretch of Braan (Dunkeld & Birnam AA water); dt £5 (browns) from Amulree Hotel, Amulree PH8 0EF (tel: 01350 725218). For Hilton Dunkeld House Hotel and Country Club, PH8 0HX (tel: 01350 728370) fishing, contact Simon Furniss (mob: 07736 379104), salmon and trout fishing on Tay; 2 miles double bank fishing; 14 named pools; fly and bait water; 2 boats with 2 rods; 6 bank rods; 3 experienced ghillies; no salmon fishing on Sundays. Butterstone Loch, (120 acres) rainbow, blue and brown trout;stocking up to upper teens pike in winter; fly only; 6 fish limit; 10 inch minimum; 24 boats on water plus wheelyboat; small shop; tackle; permits (day and evening) from The Cardney Sporting Estate, Butterstone Loch, Butterstone, by Dunkeld PH8 0HH (tel: 01350 724238; web: www.butterstonelochfishings.co.uk).

Dalguise (Perthshire). Perth & Dist AA (wt £10, dt £3) fishes Kinnaird and Dalguise beats: P D Malloch, 259 Old High St PH1 5QN (tel: 01738 632316). Permits, with boat and ghillie from CKD Galbraith, Lynedoch House, Barossa Pl, Perth PH1 5EP (tel: 01738 451600; fax: 01738 451900; or contact via email: sporting@ckdgalbraith.co.uk); salmon £65-£100 per rod per day, depending on season.

Grandtully (Perthshire). Salmon, brown trout and grayling; fly, bait or spinning; booking advisable for Aberfeldy AC water (not salmon) from Wade Newsagents (see Aberfeldy).

Aberfeldy (Perthshire). Salmon, brown trout and grayling on Tay. Trout and salmon fishing on River Tay from Bolfracts to south end of Aberfeldy is Aberfeldy AC water right bank only, trout and grayling; the club also fishes Grandtully Water, brown trout and grayling; dt £5; tickets for their Town Waters, grayling and brown trout also available; dt £5 for trout, grayling and coarse from Wade Newsagents, 31 Bank St, PH15 2BB (tel: 01887 820397); the club also has trout and grayling fishing on Bolfracts Estate, right bank only, dt £5 from Wade; for salmon permit (Aberfeldy water only), apply Hon Sec. Loch Tay permits from Kenmore PO, salmon and trout; and various hill lochs, including coarse fish and wild brown trout; fly fishing preferred; spinning and worming (sometimes) allowed; shrimps and prawns prohibited. Brown trout permit for left bank of Tay water from Roderick Kennedy, Borlick Farm, Killiechassie PH15 2JP (tel: 01887 820463). Ailean Craggan Hotel, Weem PH15 2LD (tel: 01887 820346) has fishing on the Upper Farleyer and Carse beats; salmon and trout; dt £25 55 (4 rods available). Trout and grayling fishing on the Lower Aberfeldy, contact Callum McDermott, Drumcroy Lodges, Aberfeldy PH15 2EA (tel: 01887 829899); self catering accommodation available.

Kenmore (Perthshire). Tay leaves Loch Tay at Kenmore. Salmon and trout fishing on river for guests at The Kenmore Hotel, Kenmore PH15 2NU (tel: 01887 830205); permits for non residents from hotel (salmon) or Post Office (trout).

Killin (Perthshire). Killin & Breadalbane AC has fishing on western end of Loch Tay, River Dochart, River Lochay, and Lochan an Laraig; salmon (members only), brown trout, rainbow trout, perch, pike and charr; stocking policy includes annual stocking with mature brown trout; salmon of up to 30lbs are caught; rainbows of 5 6lbs; an excellent venue for visiting anglers who are made very welcome; dt £6 and £3 (jun)trout and coarse only (salmon priced separately for members) for these waters apply News First, Newsagent & Tackle Shop, Main St FK21 8UJ (tel: 01567 820362). Tackle: James Bayne Fishing Tackle, 76 Main Street, Callander FK17 8BD (tel: 01877 330218).

Crianlarich (Perthshire). Trout fishing on Loch Dochart (good early in the season), Loch Luibhair and River Fillan, a tributary of Tay. In summer, salmon find their way into loch and up Fillan and tributaries; best months: May, June, July and Sept; dt £4; day tickets for River Fillan, 100 yards away, from Ben More Lodge Hotel, Crianlarich FK20 8QS (tel: 01838 300210; fax: 01838 300218; email: info@ben more.co.uk). Permits £7 for Lochs Dochart and Luibhair from Portnellan Highland Lodges FK20 8QS (tel: 01838 300284): boats and ghillies (weeks notice required) for hire.

Tributaries of the Tay

EARN: Salmon, sea trout, brown trout and excellent grayling. Loch Earn fishing closed in winter.

Auchterarder (Perthshire). Salmon, sea trout, brown trout and grayling. James Haggart, Haugh of Aberuthven, Auchterarder PH3 1HL (tel: 01738 730206) has fishing at Lower Aberuthven: salmon on application, grayling and trout ticket £5; all legal baits allowed. Dupplin Estate, Dupplin, Perth PH2 0PY (tel: 01738 622757); has fishing available for trout & grayling on the Foreteviot and Aberdalgie Beats; permits issued Mon Fri from Estate Office.

Crieff (Perthshire). Crieff AC has Drummond Castle, Braidhaugh and Upper Strowan beats, totalling 5½m, mostly double bank; brown, sea trout, salmon, grayling; dt £7 b trout, £15 £25 migratory fish, depending on month; season 1 Feb 15 Oct; no Saturdays in Oct; also Drummond Loch brown trout, dt £30 per boat for two (£20 single angler, or for 3 £40); electric outboards permitted; excellent access and parking. Laird Management Ltd; contact John Young (mob: 07970 274236) has Lochlane and Laggan fishings, with sea trout and salmon, dt £15 £70, 1 Feb 31 Oct. River permits for Crieff AC waters from A Boyd (below), or from Crieff Tourist Office, 33 High St PH7 3HU (tel: 01764 652578; fax: 655422) (Drummond Water, and Upper Strowan); loch tickets from E Boyd; Braidhaugh from holiday park; Crieff AC: membership £150 (2 year waiting list). At Comrie, Comrie AC has 6 miles right and left banks; dt from Thompsons, The Delicatessen, Drummond St (tel: 01764 670253); dt £10. For Laird Management waters tickets from Tourist Office, High Str, PH7 3HU (tel: 01764 652578). Crieff AC also has bown trout fishing on Loch Turret; fly only; bank only; no night fishing; permits (dt £6, conc £3) from A Boyd (below). Braincroft Loch: brown trout dt £10, at Comrie Croft, Braincroft Farm, by Crieff PH7 4JZ (tel: 01764 670140). Cowden Loch: brown and rainbow trout permit at Lochview Farm, Mill of Fortune, Comrie PH6 2JE (tel: 01764 670677). A £5 grayling permit is obtainable for

R Earn, from 15 Nov 15 Jan; also for brown trout (15 Mar to 6 Oct); and salmon (1 Feb to 15 Oct ecl Sat in Oct) £15 to 31 July, then £25: from tackle shop: A Boyd, Newsagents and Tackle, 39 King St, Crieff PH7 3AX (tel: 01764 653871) who also sell tickets for Loch Turret (wild browns dt £6), and boat fishing (only) on Drummond Loch (£30 2 anglers: see above).

St Fillans (Perthshire). Trout and charr fishing for visitors in Loch Earn. Drummond Castle (Alec Murray: 01567 830400) run loch; stocked with brown trout, between 12oz and 2E1/2lb.

Lochearnhead (Perthshire). Loch Earn, natural brown trout, stocked browns, occasional rainbows and charr. Lochearn Fishings water; day permits and boat hire available from Drummond Estate Boat Hire (tackle and bait available) Ardveich Bay, Lochearnhead FK19 8PZ (tel: 01567 830400); st only available from Loch Earn Fishings, Drummond Estate Office, Muthill, PH5 2AA (tel: 01764 681257). Permits also from Village Shop, Lochearnhead FK19 8PR (tel: 01567 830214); Post Office, Lochearnhead SPDO, FK19 8PR (tel: 01567 830201); and hotels. Nearest tackle shops A Boyd, Crieff; First News, Killin, Callander. The St Fillans & Loch Earn AA is only for those living within a 12 miles radius. Hotels: Drummond Hotel, St Fillans (tel: 01764 685212); Mansewood House; Lochearnhead; Clachan Cottage.

ISLA: Trout (av ¾lb and up to 3lb) and grayling. Pike also in lower reaches.

Dundee (Angus). Permits for brown trout and grayling fishing from Strathmore AIA, local tackle shops; assn also issues permits for Dean Water, tributary of Isla; brown trout. Cameron Loch, St Andrews, brown trout; Lintrathen Loch, Kirriemuir, brown trout; Mill of Criggie,

Montrose; Newton Farm, Newport on Tay; Rescobie Loch, Forfar; all brown and rainbow; details and permits from tackle shop: John R Gow Ltd, 12 Union St, Dundee DD1 4BH (tel: 01382 225427), who also arrange fishing on Tay (salmon) and North Esk (salmon and sea trout), and South Esk.

ALYTH (tributary of Isla):

Alyth (Perthshire). Several streams in neighbourhood. Isla contains trout and grayling in lower reaches. Above Reekie Linn trout very numerous but small. Alyth Hotel can supply information on salmon and trout fishing on River Tay and a number of its tributaries; also trout fishing on a selection of lochs; both day fishermen and coach parties are catered for; apply to The Alyth Hotel, Alyth, Perthshire PH11 8AF (tel: 01828 632447).

ERICHT (tributary of Isla):

Blairgowrie (Perthshire). Salmon and brown trout. Blairgowrie, Rattray & Dist AA has fishing on part of Ericht; st £200; dt £20, and £2 trout; from local tackle shops; salmon fishing for non club members on Mon to Fri; only from bridge to signpost down river (from bridge up, members only which is fly only, although dt may be had, subject to availability); no fishing at Cargill's Leap; about 2½m double bank in all. Advance booking only on 4m stretch: wt from £200, dt from £50; fly only; apply from Roger McCosh (tel: 01250 875518). Various fishings on tributaries R Ardle, R Blackwater, R Shee; permits from tackle shops. River Isla: Kate Fleming or James Crockart (below). For trout fishing on Isla and Dean, contact Strathmore AIA (tel: 01382 737938); or permits from local tackle shops. Bruce Reid, Coupar Grange, PH13 9HT (tel: 07850 236449) has 2m of double bank from confluence of Isla and Ericht d/s. Plentiful loch fishing in area, including Lochs Marlee, bank fishing only (coarse); Tullochcurran and

Shandra (wild browns); enquire at tackle shops. Loch Nan Ean and Loch Beinnie, brown trout, fly only, boat on Beinnie, permits from Invercauld Estate Office, Braemar AB35 5TW (tel: 013397 41224); and others. Tackle shops: Kate Fleming, Shooting and Fishing, 26 Allan St, Blairgowrie PH10 6AD (tel: 01250 873990), who also supply tickets for Blairgowrie, Rattray & Dist AA waters; also for 1½m of Ericht both banks, and 3m single bank of Isla above confluence of the rivers; James Crockart & Son, 28 Allan St, Blairgowrie PH10 6AD (tel: 01250 872056), who supply ghillie and instructor on R Isla; salmon dt £30 (Keithick Estate water); trout st £20, dt £5, conc; also Blairgowrie, Rattray & DAA tickets.

BRAAN: runs from Loch Freuchie.

Dunkeld (Perthshire). Forestry Commission Scotland, National Trust and riparian owners have leased water on R Braan to Dunkeld & Birnam AA; brown trout; permits for Hermitage beat and beats 1 and 2 from The Spar, 3 Murthly Terrace, Birnam, PH8 0BG (tel: 01350 727395); assn also has trout fishing on Murthly Estate and Glendelvin Estate; PO (Mace Store) Murthly or Spar Shop, Birnam; trout 15 Mar to 6 Oct; and grayling in winter (fly only during trout season). TUMMEL: Salmon, trout and grayling.

Pitlochry (Perthshire). Pitlochry AC has salmon fishing on R Tummel from marker post below Pitlochry Dam to bottom of Milton of Fonab Caravan Site; both banks; other beats sometimes available; for salmon: spinning, worm or fly; advance booking recommended, particularly for Apr Jun; recent average annual catch, 120 salmon and grilse; contact Club salmon secretary; dt £20 £35; 6 anglers per day; fly only for brown trout and grayling; browns: £10/day; club also has fishing for browns and grayling on Tummel (map on permit); and fishing on Lochs Bhac and Kinardochy, brown trout, (and rainbow, Bhac only); bank and boat fishing on Bhac; boat only on Kinardochy; fly only; permits from Pitlochry TI Centre (see clubs); or on line www.fishtay.co.uk (salmon); trout from various outlets incl TIC (sole outlet for Bhac and Kinardochy), Ballinluig Services, Quayles of Pitlochry. East Haugh House Hotel, Donavourd, Pitlochry PH16 5TE (tel: 01796 473121; web: www.easthaugh.co.uk) can arrange fishing on various salmon beats on R Tummel and R Tay, dt from £25 per rod. Permits for trout fishing on R Tummel, also Loch Tummel, from Tourist Information Centre, 22 Atholl Rd, PH16 5BX (tel: 01796 472215); Ballinluig PO, PH9 0LG (tel: 01796 482220); and Ballinluig Service Station. Loch Faskally; created in 1950s by damming of R Tummell. Salmon and sea trout ascent fish pass at dam, and may be caught from end of Mar Oct 15; brown trout, pike, perch; any legal lure; permits, boats and bait from C Dixon, Pitlochry Boating Station, Clunie Bridge Rd, Loch Faskally, Pitlochry PH16 5JX (tel: 01796 472919/470393). Tackle Shop: Quayles of Pitlochry, 23 Atholl Rd, PH16 5BX (tel: 01796 470222).

GARRY: Tributary of Tummel, good river for about 6m.

Killiecrankie (Perthshire). Pitlochry AC has salmon fishing on east bank, Ruan Ruarie (means Red Warrier from battle of Killiecrankie) beat; dt £20 per rod, 4 anglers; for advance booking and information contact Salmon Sec; also from TIC Pitlochrie (see clubs) or on line www.fishtay.co.uk.

Blair Atholl (Perthshire). Trout fly fishing on R Garry and Tilt (approx 4m) dt £6, wt £25, conc; rainbow trout on Blair Walker Pond, dt £2; permits from Blair Atholl PO, PH18 5SG (tel: 01796 481233). Atholl Estates office PH18 5TH (tel: 01796 481355) has salmon fishing on the River garry; wt £325 £645, dt £24 £45 May to 15 Oct.

Dalwhinnie (Inverness shire). Loch Ericht, 22 mile long brown trout loch, and rivers; weekly permit £30, day permit £10, conc; Badenoch AA has water: River Spey, Caldar, Tromie; Lochs Ericht, Laggan (pike ticket now available) and Truim; for dt contact Dalwhinnie Filling Station (opposite The Inn at Loch Ericht), PH19 1AF (tel: 01528 522311); open all year.

LOCH RANNOCH: Trout, some large but averaging 9ozs; best May to October, also ferox trout, charr, pike. Trout fishing in Upper River Tummel, below loch.

Kinloch Rannoch (Perthshire). Loch Rannoch Conservation Assn has fishing on Loch Rannoch; brown trout, ferox trout (up to 15lb), pike and charr; permits from Hon Sec, and local shops and hotels. **Dunalastair Loch** is a short distance east of Kinloch Rannoch, with brown trout and charr; boats, no bank fishing, fly only; permits available Loch Garry Cottage PH16 5PD (tel: 01882 632354); dt £20 per boat (2 rods). Rannoch & District AC has fishing on Loch Eigheach, 1m from Rannoch Station; brown trout and perch; fly fishing only; bank fishing only; June best month; wt £12, dt £3, from J Brown, The Square, Kinloch Rannoch PH16 5PN (tel: 01882 632268). Permits for Loch Rannoch, Loch Eigheach and R Tummel, dt £6, wt £20, st £35, conc, from Dunalastair Hotel PH16 5PW (tel: 01882 632323). Hotels: Loch Rannoch; Dunalastair.

LYON (near Loch Tay): Good salmon and trout river in the magnificently forested Glen Lyon, reputedly the longest glen in Scotland. River runs from two dammed lochs at glen head.

Glen Lyon (Perthshire). Brown trout and salmon permits from: David Pirie, Keeper's Cottage, Innerwick PH15 2PP (tel: 01887 866218); dt salmon £25, brown trout £5 (fly only). For North/South Chesthill beat, contact Hamish Rae, Keeper's Cottage, South Chesthill (tel: 01887 877233) for prices and availability. For brown trout only from Cashlie, contact Mr Sinclair, Keepers Cottage, Cashlie PH15 2PX (tel: 01887 866237); £3 £5 per day; fly only except in spate. Loch an Daimh: contact Steven Fraser, Croc na keys, Lochs PH15 2PU (tel: 01887 866224); dt £5; fly only from 1 May; bank fishing from dam to island. For Meggernie, contact Post Office, Bridge of Balgie (tel: 01887 866221); dt £7.50 (£1.50 refundable on submitting return). Further information from Aberfeldy Tourist Information Centre, 3 Bridgend PH15 2DD (tel: 01887 820276).

DOCHART (feeds Loch Tay):

Killin (Perthshire). At confluence of Dochart and Lochay, near head of Loch Tay. Salmon fishing best in July, Aug and Sept. Trout numerous and run to a fair size. Water is very deep and sluggish from Luib to Bovain, but above and as far as Loch Dochart there are some capital streams and pools. Auchlyne & Suie Estate Water; trout and salmon; permits issued by G D Coyne, Keeper's Cottage, Auchlyne House, Killin FK21 8RG (tel: 01567 820487), Luib Hotel (see below) and Sui Lodge Hotel (tel: 01567 820417). Luib Hotel, Glen Dochart, Crianlarich FK20 8QT (tel: 01567 820664); trout fishing best April May, good run of autumn salmon; Ardeonaig Hotel, South Lochtayside, Perthshire FK21 8SU (tel: 01567 820400) has own harbour with 7 boats on Loch Tay; salmon, trout and charr; salmon fishing and trout fishing; tickets and information only from www.fishtay.co.uk. Loch Tay Highland Lodges, by Killin FK21 8TY (tel: 01567 820323; fax: 01567 820581; see website for more info: http://www.lochtay-vacations.co.uk/marina/boats-for-hire.htm) have salmon and trout fishing on Loch Tay; 11 boats with outboard motors for hire, trolling is the usual method; this self catering complex is ideally placed for fishing middle and western beats of the loch. Tackle shops: James

Bayne Fishing Tackle, 76 Main St, Callander FK17 8BD (tel: 01877 330218) has tickets for Loch Tay (£6) and short stretch of River Dochart.

THURSO

A noted salmon river and one of the earliest in Scotland. The spring run has been improving recently, after a period of decline. In 2005 the estuary nets were removed and the salmon fishing has improved dramatically. Water level may be regulated by a weir at Loch More on the upper reaches. The river is entirely preserved.

Thurso (Caithness). Thurso AA has Beat 1 (from River Mouth up to the Geise Burn, including tidal water), which produces 10% of total river catch; members only, but possibility of permit if no members fishing; brown trout permit on Assn waters from The Bookshop, Princes Street; half day £25. Salmon fishing (fly only) on other beats can be arranged through Savills, 12 Clerk Street, Brechin DD9 6AE (tel: 01356 628600; see website for more: www.thursoriver.co.uk); bookings usually by week; weekly charges range from £450 to £550 + VAT, according to date; fishing improves progressively from opening on Jan 11 to close on Oct 5. First class loch, burn and river fishing for trout: brown trout loch fishing in vicinity: Loch Calder, Lochs Watten, St John's and Stemster; Loch Hielan; Broubster Lochs, Dunnet Head Lochs; permits for all these from tackle shop: Harper's Fly Fishing Services, 57

High St, KW14 8AZ (tel/fax: 01847 893179). Hotels: Park; Pentland; St Clair; Royal.

Halkirk (Caithness). The Ulbster Arms Hotel (tel: 01847 831641; email: info@ulbsterarmshotel.co.uk) can arrange fishing on many hill lochs; excellent accommodation (recently refurbished) and fishing, enquire at hotel. Salmon fishing on Thurso River; information from Eddie McCarthy, Superintendent's House, Braal Rd, Halkirk KW12 6XE (tel: 01847 831591 or Ulbster Arms Hotel, contact Keith (see above for contact details); www.thursoriver.co.uk); dt £70 £150 depending on season; now one of the most improved salmon rivers in the North of Scotland, demand for fishing is high.

Dunnet (Caithness). St John's Loch AA has fishing on St John's Loch; bank and boat fishing; permits from Northern Sands Hotel, Dunnet, Caithness KW14 8XD (tel: 01847 851270).

A fine 17lb salmon for Thurso ghillie Jimmy Sutherland. Beat 3

TWEED

Rises in corner formed by watersheds of Clyde and Annan, and flows over 100m to North Sea at Berwick upon Tweed, forming, for some of its course, the boundary between England and Scotland. The Tweed is probably the most popular of the large Scottish rivers, partly owing to its proximity to England. It contains over 300 named pools and its salmon harvest is considerable. It has the longest season (1st February to 30 November), but at its best in autumn, especially from mid to late October, when the run is noted for the size and number of salmon caught. There is a good spring run, and in summer even the most famous beats such as the Junction at Kelso are open for permit fishing, for around £45 per day. Summer fish may be difficult to catch at low water. Boatmen are employed by most beats. The Tweed produces a strain of sea trout, formerly called bull trout, which are remarkable both for size and distance they are known to travel in sea. The best sea trout fishing is on tributaries, the Till and Whiteadder, both of which fish well in summer. The season on the Tweed is the same as for salmon, and the permits are combined.

In the upper Tweed and Lyne research suggests that wild brown trout numbers are back to former levels. Stocking has therefore ceased. Furthermore significant numbers of grayling have reappeared. From 2008 catch & release was applicable. Enquiries for Peeblesshire fishing should be made to tel: 0870 1317128. There exists a code of conduct (The Tweed Angling Code) with regard mainly to fly fishing for salmon and sea trout, and the leaflet may be obtained from the River Tweed Commissioners or from most tackle shops and letting agents.

'Tweedline' is a service for fishermen provided by the Tweed Foundation, a charitable trust established by the River Tweed Commissioners to promote the development of fish stocks in the Tweed river system through scientific research and monitoring. Tweedline information is provided by other agencies for the Tweed Foundation, who benefit by receiving a share of the proceeds from each call. (Tweedline is a BT premium rate service.) Line available: Fishing reports and prospects (tel: 09060 400410); River levels (updated daily) (tel: 09060 400411); the last minute rod vacancies information is now on tel: 01573 470612 or web: www.fishpal.com. FishPal Ltd, Stichill House, Kelso, Roxburghshire TD5 7TB (tel: 01573 470280; fax: 01573 470259; web: www.fishpal.com/Scotland/Tweed/; email: info@fishpal.com) provide an information service. SEPA operate a local 24 hour pollution emergency response on 0800 807060. Anglers are requested to report incidents with urgency.

The Tweed Foundation may be contacted at Drygrange Steading, Melrose, Roxburghshire TD6 9DJ (tel: 01896 848271; fax: 01896 848277; email: info@tweedfoundation.org.uk).

Berwick-upon-Tweed
(Northumberland). Salmon, sea trout, trout, grayling, coarse fish. Tidal Tweed gives free fishing for roach and grayling. Salmon fishing on Tweed offered by FishPal Ltd, Stichill House, Kelso, Roxburghshire TD5 7TB (tel: 01573 470280; fax: 01573 470259; web: www.tweedsalmonfishing.co.uk and www.fishpal.com; email: info@fishpal.com); 14 beats between Horncliffe, near Berwick, and Peebles; early booking advisable. Berwick & Dist AA has brown trout fishing on 7m of River Whiteadder, including 2m of salmon fishing; river joins Tweed 1m from Berwick; brown trout st £50 (for locals), wt £30, dt £10, conc, from Game Fair (below). Till enters Tweed 2½m above Norham, 9m from Berwick. Coldingham Loch, 12m N: brown, rainbow and blue

trout; 10 boats, bank fishing for 12 rods; permits from Douglas and Kirsty Aitken, West Loch House, Coldingham, Berwickshire TD14 5QE (tel: 01890 771270), who have lodges and cottages to let; booking essential; Coldingham is noted for the quality and size of the trout caught there. Tackle shop: Game Fair Tackle, 12 Marygate, Berwick upon Tweed TD15 1BN (tel: 01289 305119)(tickets for Berwick & DAA water). Hotels: Castle; Kings Arms; Chirnside Hall, Chirnside; Hay Farm House, Cornhill on Tweed; Coach House, Crookham, Cornhill on Tweed.

Horncliffe (Northumberland). Tidal. Salmon, trout, grayling, roach, dace and eel. No permits required for trout and coarse fishing. Salmon fishing on 2½m single right bank Horncliffe beat, 6 rods, 1 ghillie, 2 huts; obtainable from FishPal Ltd, Stichill House, Kelso, Roxburghshire TD5 7TB (tel: 01573 470280; fax: 01573 470259; see website for more info: www.fishtweed.co.uk; or contact email: info@fishpal.com).

Norham (Northumberland). Salmon, trout. Salmon fishing on Ladykirk from FishPal Ltd, Stichill House, Kelso, Roxburghshire TD5 7TB. (Tel: 01573 470280, fax: 01573 470259, web: www.fishtweed.co.uk; e-mail info@ fishpal.com). Ladykirk, 3m single bank, 5 huts, boats and 1 5 ghillies, 6 rods; over 5 years average catch 520; also good sea trout water. For Pedwell, 1½m single bank for 2 rods with boat and ghillie; Mon, Tues, Fri, Sat only, contact Sale & Partners, 18 20 Glendale Rd, Wooler NE71 6DW (tel: 01668 280803); dt prices range from £36 to £175. Ladykirk & Norham AA has fishing from Norham boathouse to Horndean Burn, both banks, brown trout, grayling, eels; reputed to be one of the best waters along border; st £30, dt £5, wt £15; concessions OAP, junior free if accompanied; permits from Mace

Shop; Masons Arms Hotel TD15 2LB (tel: 01289 382326); and The Victoria Hotel, Castle Str, TD15 2LQ (tel: 01289 382437); see website for more info: www.fishtweed.co.uk.

Cornhill on Tweed (Northumberland). Strutt and Parker has fishing. Contact Mark Merison (tel: +44 (0)1635 576905; or contact via email: mark.merison@struttandparker.com). Tillmouth: 4m single bank from d/s of Coldstream Bridge; 22 named pools; up to 9 rods.

Coldstream (Berwickshire). Salmon, sea trout. Salmon fishing on West Learmouth obtainable from FishPal Ltd, Stichill House, Kelso, Roxburghshire TD5 7TB (tel: 01573 470280; fax: 01573 470 259; web: www.fishtweed.co.uk; email: info@fishpal.com): West Learmouth is a good spring and autumn beat for 2 rods opposite The Lees; ⅔m of single bank with boat and ghillie; prices vary considerably, from £55 to £750. Mrs Jane Douglas Home has rods to let at The Lees, TD12 4LF (tel/fax 01890 882706), from £55 per day; The Lees is a prime quality spring and autumn beat including the well known Temple Pool; 2m, 4 rods, 2 3 ghillies, 2 huts, 4 boats. Tillmouth Park Hotel, Cornhill on Tweed, TD12 4UU (tel: 01890 882255), has facilities for anglers, incl rod room, freezing and access to smoking facilities. Fishpal (www.fishpal.com) offer fishing by weekly or daily booking on beats 2 to 6 on Tillmouth Water, **Cornhill** on Tweed; prices on applicatiom from Fishpal (www.fishtweed.co.uk); all prices include boat, ghillie and use of fishing huts, Tweed levies and taxes. Dryburgh Estate Fishings, Melrose TD6 0RQ: dt £65 to £275 (plus VAT), depending on season; head ghillie: George Inglis (tel: 01835 822708); trout and grayling tickets from Borders Gun Room, Main St, St Bowells (tel: 01835 822844). Pedwell fishing, Norham (see Norham).

Hotels: Collingwood Arms; Tillmouth Park; Wheatsheaf, Swinton.

Lower Birgham (Berwickshire). Strutt and Parker has fishing. Contact Mark Merison (tel: +44 (0)1635 576905; mark.merison@struttandparker.com). ⅔m double bank; 3 rods; 2 ghillies in spring and autumn.

Sprouston (Roxburghshire). Strutt and Parker has fishing. Contact Mark Merison (tel: +44 (0)1635 576905; mark.merison@struttandparker.com). 2½m double bank, split into 2 beats for 2 rods only; 2 ghillies per beat.

Upper Hendersyde (Roxburghshire). Strutt and Parker has fishing. Contact Mark Merison (tel: +44 (0)1635 576905; or contact via email: mark.merison@struttandparker.com). 1m double bank for 3 rods.

Kelso (Roxburghshire). Salmon and sea trout preserved, trout and grayling. Strutt and Parker has fishing. Contact Mark Merison (tel: +44 (0)1635 576905; or contact via email: mark.merison@struttandparker.com); Junction extends to 1½m double ban; 6 rods; 3 ghillies. Salmon and sea trout fishing can be obtained daily during summer months on some of the best beats of the Tweed, including Lower Birgham with 2m of double bank, 3 rods, ghillie, hut, dt £55 £250; also Hendersyde beat, 4m left bank, 2 rods, 2 ghillies, 2 huts, dt £100 £850; for further information contact FishPal Ltd, Stichill House, Kelso, Roxburghshire TD5 7TB (tel: 01573 470280; fax: 01573 470259; web: www.fishpal.com; or contact via email: info@fishpal.com). Kelso AA has about 8m of Tweed and Teviot; brown trout and grayling; no Sunday fishing; size limit 10in; no spinning; trout season, April 1 to Sept 30; trout fishing good; st £25 (includes graying), wt £10, dt £5; concessions for OAPs and juniors; permits from local tackle shops. Tackle shops: Forrest of Kelso, 1 Bridge Street TD5 7HL (tel: 01573 224687); Tweedside

Tackle, 36/38 Bridge St TD5 7JD (tel: 01573 225306); Orvis, Bridge Street (tel: 01573 225810); Springwood Caravan Park (anglers can fish from the site) (tel: 01573 224596). Hotels: Cross Keys; Ednam House; Roxburgh.

St Boswells (Roxburghshire). St Boswells & Newtoun District AA rent miscellaneous stretches on River Tweed between Ravenswood and Rutherford; brown trout up to 7lb and grayling; rod limits on 4 stretches (6 fish); 28 anglers per day limit over the 7 miles; incl grayling (grayling only Dec, Jan). Tackle shop and permits: Borders Gunroom, Main Str, TD6 0AA (tel: 01835 822844) has tickets for all main waters.

Melrose (Roxburghshire). Salmon fishing on Bemersyde Beat, prime beat superbly set in beautiful wooded gorge; 1m with 4 6 rods, 1 2 ghillies, 4 boats; prices range between £40 and £300; Ravenswood beat: opposite Bemersyde, 1½m of right bank, 3 4 rods, 1 ghillie, 1 hut, £40 £280: apply to FishPal Ltd, Stichill House, Kelso, Roxburghshire TD5 7TB (tel: 01573 470280; fax: 01573 470259; web: www.fishpal.com; or contact via email: info@fishpal.com). Melrose & Dist AA has 2m of Tweed around Melrose open to visitors for wild trout and grayling fishing; no Sunday fishing; fly only; st £12, dt £4 from Hon Sec; season 1 Apr 6 Oct trout, 1 Dec 15 Mar grayling; barbless hooks and strict limit; 50% of permit sales donated to Tweed Foundation. Hotel: Burts.

Earlston (Berwickshire). A good centre for Leader and Tweed trout fishing. Earlston AA controls about 5m of Leader adjacent to Earlston, with the exception of two small private stretches; tickets from petrol station; no Sunday fishing and Saturday fishing for st holders only; 2 day permits on River Tweed at Gledswood estate for st holders; other portions of

Tweed are reserved. Hotels: Red Lion; Black Bull; White Swan.

Galashiels (Selkirkshire). Salmon fishing on Boleside beat, 1½m double bank, 5 6 rods, 1 ghillie, 2 boats, dt £40 £410; also Fairnilee Beat, good varied autumn beat in lovely scenery; 3m of single bank, 20 small pools; 9 rods; ghillie, 2 huts and full facilities;prices, from £45 to £175, depending on month; contact FishPal Ltd, Stichill House, Kelso, Roxburghshire TD5 7TB (tel: 01573 470280; fax: 01573 470259; web: www.fishpal.com; or contact via email: info@fishpal.com) for these and Peel, Nest, Ashiestiel, Holylee, Traquair and Glenormiston beats. Gala AA has trout fishing on 13m of Tweed, part Gala Water, and part River Ettrick, st £25, wt £17, dt £9, schoolchildren £2 (no Sunday tickets; no floats; no spinning; fly reels only); tickets from J & A Turnbull, Tackle Shop, 30 Bank St, Galashiels TD1 1EN (tel: 01896 753191); and hotels; April to Sept provides best daytime sport; Mid June to Aug best evenings. Sunderland Hall (tel: 01750 21298) has 2 rods let, dt £20 £130, up to 30 Nov. Hotels: Kings; Kingsknowes; Woodlands House; Philipburn House, Selkirk TD7 5LS (tel: 01750 20747) caters for the angler, and has freezer facilities; Windlestraw Lodge, Walkerburn EH43 6AA (tel: 01896 870636) overlooks Tweed and can arrange permits on river.

Selkirk (Selkirkshire). Salmon fishing preserved. Good centre for Tweed, Yarrow and Ettrick, covering 80m of trout fishing. Selkirk & Dist AA has water on Ettrick and Yarrow; c&r only; also Lindean Reservoir, rainbows, 2 boats at £18 per boat per session; limit 10 trout per boat; fly only; no bank fishing; av size 2lb: permits, conc, from Hon Sec; also (river only) from Honey Cottage Caravan Park, Hope House, Ettrick Valley TD7 5HU (tel: 01750 62246), who can also arrange fishing on

nearby St Mary's Loch (trout, pike); The Gordon Arms Hotel (Lorraine Martin), Yarrow Valley TD7 5LE (tel: 01750 82222); Bridge End PO; Rodgersons, 6 High St, Selkirk TD7 4DD (tel: 01750 20749); trout average 3 to the pound and go up to 3lb; c&r only; no spinning allowed; Rodgersons also have boat fishing permits at Lindean Reservoir, for rainbow trout; enquiries also to D Mitchell, 28 Scotts Place, Selkirk TD7 4DR (tel: 01750 20748). Tackle shop: J & A Turnbull, Tackle Shop, 30 Bank St, Galashiels TD1 1EN (tel: 01896 753191). Hotels: Glen; Heatherlie House; Woodburn; Philipburn House, Selkirk TD7 5LS (tel: 01750 20747) caters for the angler, and has freezer facilities.

Walkerburn (Peeblesshire). Salmon, trout. Windlestraw Lodge, Galashiels Rd, EH43 6AA (tel: 01896 870636; fax: 01896 870639), can arrange salmon fishing on request, including on Peeblesshire Trout FA water; open all season; hotel can also arrange fishing courses for adults; season: salmon, 1 Feb 30 Nov; trout, 1 Apr 30 Sep. George Hotel EH43 6AF (tel: 01896 870336) has permits from £50 £100 per day salmon (Oct, Nov); trout Apr to Sept £8 per day, £30 for season. For salmon, contact FishPal Ltd, Stichill House, Kelso, Roxburghshire TD5 7TB (tel: 01573 470280; fax: 01573 470259; web: www.fishpal.com; email: info@fishpal.com).

Innerleithen (Peeblesshire). Salmon, trout. Salmon fishing on Traquair Beat, good late autumn beat in grounds of Scotland's oldest inhabited historic house; 3m with easy casting and access for 9 rods; ghillie; contact FishPal Ltd, Stichill House, Kelso, Roxburghshire TD5 7TB (tel: 01573 470280; fax: 01573 470259; web: www.fishpal.com; email: info@fishpal.com). Peeblesshire Trout FA has trout and grayling fishing on Tweed; tickets sold by St

Ronans Hotel (tel: 01896 831487); The Village Store; Tweedside Caravan Park.

Peebles (Peeblesshire). Salmon fishing on approx 1½ miles of River Tweed; season Feb 21 to Nov 30; fly fishing only; tickets (limited in number) issued by Peeblesshire Salmon FA. Salmon fishing on Town Water (non-resident 3 day ticket £48 + £10 deposit; d/t £20 + 310 deposit) and Crown Water (non-resident w/t £130 + £10 deposit; d/t £35 + £10 deposit); permits from Borders Sport & Leisure Trust, Gytes Leisure Centre EH45 8GL (tel: 01721 723688). Peeblesshire Trout FA has approx 23m on Tweed and 5m on **Lyne**; trout and grayling; season April 1 to Sept 30 for trout, grayling 1 Jan to end Sept; no spinning or float fishing; fly only on all water; catch and release policy is described under main river heading; waders desirable; good trout April/May on wet fly then dry best; st £40, dt £10; permits from Peebles Hotel Hydro; and Rosetta Caravan Park, Rosetta Rd, EH45 8PG (tel: 01721 720770). Peebles Angling School, 10 Dean Park, EH45 8DD (tel: 01721 720331), offers instruction in salmon and trout fishing, and fishing parties on private water; salmon fishing available. Tackle shop: Cast Around Peebles, 20a Northgate EH45 8RS (tel: 01721 729229). **Kailzie Fishery**; 2 acres with rainbow trout up to 22lbs. Near Kailzie Gardens. (tel: 01721 729020; see website for more info: www.kailziefishery.co.uk)

Tweedsmuir (Lanarkshire). Apply Cast Around Peebles (see above) for permits for Peeblesshire Trout FA water on Tweed. **Talla Reservoir** (300 acres) and **Fruid Reservoir** (293 acres) are both privately leased from Scottish Water. Day tickets to fish both or either reservoir on the same day are available from Broughton Store, Broughton and Gamefish in Edinburgh. Season March 15 to October 7. Fly fishing only for wild brown trout. Day tickets £15 with 3 fish limit and unlimited catch & release. Some season-bank and season-boat permits available. Arctic char are also lurking in Talla.

Tributaries of the Tweed

WHITEADDER: Runs from junction with Tweed via Cantys Bridge and Allanton Bridge to source. The removal of the coastal and river nets has made the river one of the prime spring rivers for salmon and trout, with an ever increasing spring run. Upper waters, from Blanerne Bridge to source, including tributaries, are mainly controlled by Whiteadder AA (trout only).

Allanton (Berwickshire). Blackadder joins river here. Waters from ½m above Allanton Bridge (including lower Blackadder) down to tide are mainly controlled by Berwick & Dist AA; salmon and sea trout fishing tickets on five recognised beats brown trout st £50 (for locals), wt £30, dt £10, conc; R Welsh & Sons, 28 Castle St, Duns TD11 3DP (tel: 01361 883466); and Game Fair (see Berwick upon Tweed). Tickets for Tweeddale Fishery, Gifford (rainbow); Willowdean, Foulden (rainbow); and Whiteadder Reservoir (brown trout): at site. Allanton Inn has accommodation.

Chirnside (Berwickshire). Trout. Chirnside is good centre for Whiteadder. From here to source, except for stretches at Ninewells, Abbey St Bathans Estate, Chirnside Paper Mills and Cumledge Bridge, river is controlled by Whiteadder AA, including all tributaries entering above Chirnside, except Monynut above Bankend; Fasney above Fasney Bridge; and certain stretches of the Dye. Tickets from R Welsh & Son, 28

Castle St, Duns TD11 3DP (tel: 01361 883466) (tickets also for Berwick & DAA water and Blackadder); Nairns Newsagent, 26 Market Square, Duns TD11 3DP (tel: 01361 883233); J S Main, 87 High Street, Fishing Tackle Shop, Haddington EH41 3ET (tel: 01620 822148); Game Fair Tackle, 12 Marygate, Berwick upon Tweed TD15 1BN (tel: 01289 305119)(tickets also for Berwick & DAA water). River Eye, runs parallel to Whiteadder a few miles to N, entering sea at Eyemouth. Eye Water AC has water on River Eye at town, Ayton and East Reston, 3½m, and Ale Water; river stocked annually with brown trout; competitions held monthly, contact Hon Sec; st £15, conc £10, from Tourist Information Centre, The Auld Kirk, Eyemouth TD14 5HE (tel: 018907 50678). Hotels: Ship; Whale; Home Arms; Dolphin; The Churches.

Duns (Berwickshire). Trout. The following streams are within easy reach: **Blackadder**, **Whiteadder**, **Fasney**, **Bothwell**, Dye, Blacksmill, **Monynut** and **Watch**; these, except Blackadder, are, with main stream, largely controlled by Whiteadder AA; Berwick & DAA water below Chirnside. Tackle shop: R Welsh, 28 Castle Str, TD11 3DP (tel: 01361 883466) sells tickets for local associations. Hotels: White Swan, Barniken, Plough, Black Bull, Whip & Saddle.

Longformacus (Berwickshire). 7m from Duns. On Dye, Watch and Blacksmill burns. Permits from R Welsh, (see Duns). Trout fishing from boat and bank on **Watch Reservoir**; 119 acres, fly only, stocked with rainbows from 1¾lbs, also "blues" and browns; permits and refreshments;(tel: 01361 890331).

Cranshaws (Berwickshire). Whiteadder Reservoir; 193 acres, brown trout; fly only; permits available on site from ticket machines.

BLACKADDER (tributary of Whiteadder): Very good for brown trout early in season.

Greenlaw (Berwickshire). About 12m held by Greenlaw AC. Season from 1 April to 6 Oct, very good for brown trout, early in season, stocked every year; st, dt, conc for OAP and juniors from Butcher's Shop (tel: 01361 810291), Blackadder Mini Market, 20 West High St TD10 6XA (tel: 01361 810274); Village Store, 5 West High Street TD10 6XA (tel: 01361 810210). Hotel: Blackadder; Cross Keys.

TILL and **BREAMISH**: Trout, sea trout, salmon, good grayling, some pike and perch.

Milfield (Northumberland). Local beats on River Till all have good seasonal runs of salmon and sea trout with resident stocks of brown trout and grayling; no Sunday fishing; all fishing on Ford and Etal Estates is booked through Brian Thompson, Fishery Manager, Redscar Cottage, Milfield, Wooler NE71 6JQ (tel: 01668 216223); nearest towns: Redscar beat near Milfield, Wooler; Ford beat near Ford village, Wooler; Upper Tindal beat near Etal village, Berwick; Lower Tindal beat near Etal village, Berwick; tickets for Ford beat from Milfield or Ford PO's (st £120, wt £42, dt £12); Redscar, Upper and Lower Tindal beats from Ford and Etal Estates (above) (dt £20 to £25, wt £200). Hotel: Red Lion, Milfield NE71 6JD (tel: 01668 216224); Tankerville Arms, Wooler NE71 6AD (tel: 01668 281581).

Wooler (Northumberland). Upper Till private fishing, also **Glen**, now syndicate water. Some miles from Wooler, at Bewick Bridge, Breamish becomes Till. Wading in Till dangerous. **Bowmont**, also preserved. Kale Waters: Trout (small), grayling, with good sea trout in wet season. Tweed rules apply.

Chatton (Northumberland). Trout, grayling; and some fine roach: preserved by Chatton AA for 6½m; limited number of associated members' tickets, waiting list; st apply by 1 Jan to Hon Sec. Chatton Trout Fishery, Amerside Law Farm NE66 5RF (tel: 01668 215226; web: www.chattontroutfishery.com); open all year; 8.30am 7.30pm; 4 acre lake; trout; fly only; no rod licence required; disabled access; tackle shop; facilities. Hotel: The Old Manse, New Road NE66 5PU (tel: 01668 215343).

EDEN: Wild brown trout

Ednam (Roxburghshire). No salmon fishing; open to general public.

Gordon (Berwickshire). Permits for brown trout fishing from Gordon FC: contact Hon Sec; and from PO in village; £4 st, juvenile £1; no spinning; no Sunday fishing. Tackle shop: Tweedside Tackle, 36/38 Bridge St, Kelso TD5 7JD (tel: 01573 225306).

TEVIOT: First class for trout and grayling.

Roxburgh (Roxburghshire). Kelso AA controls some miles of brown trout fishing on Teviot and Tweed; visitors tickets, day £5, season £25, conc (under 13s free); from Kelso tackle shops (see Kelso).

Eckford (Roxburghshire). Morebattle & Dist AA has brown trout fishing on Kale Water, **Bowmont Water** and **Oxnam Water**; permits from Hon Sec; and Templehall Hotel, Kelso TD5 8QQ (tel: 01573 440249).

Hawick (Roxburghshire). Hawick AC has 10m both banks on River **Teviot** and tributaries **Slitrig, Borthwick** and **Ale**; salmon, sea trout, brown trout and grayling; club also has fishing on Lochs **Acremoor**, brown trout and perch; **Williestruther**, rainbow trout and brown trout; Acreknowe, rainbow trout and brown trout, fly only; Hellmoor Loch, brown trout, currently closed (wind farm development); st £50 (trout), dt £15; visitor salmon st

£140 from Hon Sec, dt £30 from Sandbed PO; Libbys' Pet Shop, High Street, Howick. Hotels: Mansfield House.

Jedburgh (Roxburghshire). Jedforest AA has 2 stretches on Teviot, salmon, sea trout, browns and grayling; Timpendean beat is 3m north on A68; 1½m south bank; Ormiston beat on A698 is 4m east of town; 600 metres south bank and 2m north bank; assn also has Upper and Lower Hass Loch, 8m south of town, 2 5 acre lochs (honesty box), brown and rainbow trout; brown trout st £40 (1 Apr (fly only until 30 Apr) to 30 Sept), dt £7, salmon wt £180 £60, dt £60 £30; conc for OAP & jun; visitors permits for salmon from Hon Sec (6 per day); grayling (Teviot only) st £40; dt £7; for Hass Loch dt £15, 3 fish then c&r; rainbows over 10lb and browns (browns c&r policy), no unattended juniors, from Swimming Pool, Jedburgh (tel: 01835 863430); otherwise tickets Taylor Newsagent, or fishpal.com. Jedforest Hotel, Jedburgh TD8 6PJ (tel: 01835 840222) has stretch of Jed Water, which runs by hotel (brown trout); residents only. Royal Hotel can arrange fishing in Jed Water and Teviot.

LEADER: Trout.

Lauder (Berwickshire). Lauderdale AA controls 6m of Leader and 20m of tributaries upwards from Whitslaid Bridge to Carfraemill with the exception of waters in Thirlestane Castle policies and Kelphope Burn above Carfraemill; st, dt, conc, from Hon Sec, shops, hotels and Post Office. Hotels: Carfrae Mill (4m from Lauder); Lauderdale; Black Bull.

Oxton (Berwickshire). Lauderdale AA has Leader Water from Carfraemill and tributaries.

GALA WATER: Popular trout water; fish average about 5 to lb.

Stow (Selkirkshire). Salmon and trout fishing on Gala Water. No permit required for local trout fishing.

ETTRICK and **YARROW**: Salmon.

Bowhill (Selkirkshire). Buccleuch Sportings has 12m double bank on Rivers Ettrick and Yarrow; salmon, sea trout; Tweed rules apply; dt £29.38 £92.83 depending on season, fishing best in autumn; Estate also has brown and rainbow trout fishing on Bowhill Lower Loch; fly only; dt £50 per boat (evng £40), 2 rods, 4 fish per rod limit, then c&r; permits for loch and salmon fishing from Estate Office, Bowhill, Selkirk TD7 5ES (tel: 01750 20753); all trout fishing in Ettrick and Yarrow by ticket. Permits from Buccleugh Estate (see above). The Gordon Arms Hotel, Yarrow Valley, Selkirk TD7 5LE (tel: 01750 82222); Rodgersons, 6 High St, Selkirk TD7 4DD (tel: 01750 20749).

St Mary's Loch (Selkirkshire). **Megget Reservoir**; 640 acres; stocked brown trout, also Arctic charr; fly only; 4 boats and bank fishing; permits £15 £30, conc, Megget Reservoir; tickets from Ben Miles, Cross Keys Inn, Ettrickbridge TD7 5JN (tel: 01750 52224; see website for more info: www.crosskeysettrickbridge.com). St Mary's AC has fishing on St Mary's Loch (500 acres) and **Loch o' the Lowes** (100 acres); brown trout, pike and perch; season 1 Apr 30 Sept, fly only until 1 May for trout, then to include spinning; pike and perch fishing all year round; boat and bank fishing; no private boats allowed; outboard motors must be supplied by the angler (max 4hp) as none are for hire; advance booking: permits £6 fly, £8 spinning or bait (no live bait), junior £2.50, boats £5 per boat extra from Loch Keeper (see clubs list).

TYNE (East Lothian)

Rises on north slopes of Lammermuir Hills and flows about 25m to North Sea a little south of Whitberry Ness, known best as brown and sea trout stream.

Haddington (East Lothian). East Lothian AA controls most of water in county. The Tyne and tributaries: most parts from Tyninghame Estate (south bank only) below East Linton, through Haddington, Samuelston and Pencaitland to Ormiston; brown trout, sea trout and a few salmon; several shops sell tickets, including J S Main & Sons, 87 High St (tel: 01620 822148); (others in East Linton, Dunbar, Tranent, North Berwick etc); st £30, dt £7, OAP/juv £15, under 12s £2; tickets also from East Linton Post Office, 39 High St; also river watchers; Sunday fishing allowed in most parts; no spinning. Tackle from Mike's Tackle Shop, 46 Portobello High St EH15 1DA (tel: 0131 657 3258); J S Main & Sons (above). Hotels: Maitlandfield.

East Linton. Markle Fisheries near Dunbar; 3 lochs total 10 acres, stocked with rainbow trout, also brown, blue, golden, tiger; fly only; one loch stocked with large carp, tench etc, also trout; open all year, partial access for disabled; permits from The Lodge, Markle Fisheries, East Linton, East Lothian EH40 3EB (tel: 01620 861213). North Berwick AC has no club water but organises 15 outings per year on various waters, for example, Loch Leven, Loch Fitty and North Third Fishery; sub £15, dt depends on water. Info on Tyne fishing, contact Ian Peacock, Post Office, High St (tel: 01620 860525). Tackle Shop: Mike's Tackle (above). Hotels: Bridgend. Tweedale Millenium Fishery, nr Gifford EH41 4PS (tel: 01620 810009), has 3 pools, 2 fly; 1 bait; it is regularly stocked with rainbows and browns, from 2lbs to more than 30lbs. Tackle from Mike's Tackle (see above). Hotels: Goblin Ha' Hotel, Gifford EH41 4QH (tel: 01620 810244); Tweedale Arms.

UGIE

A small river entering the sea at Peterhead. Salmon, good sea trout, some brown trout. Salmon and sea trout best from July to October; good run of finnock in February and March.

Peterhead (Aberdeenshire). Permits for approx 13m of fishing leased by Ugie AA; st £250, wt £80-£150, dt £30-£50, conc OAP & jun; permits available from Lunar Fishing's office, East Quay, The Harbour, Peterhead AB42 1JF (tel: 01779 473344) or Waterside Inn, North Rd (tel: 01779 471121). Braeside Fishery, Upper Stirling Brae,

Boddam AB42 3PB (tel: 01779 473903) has fly fishing for rainbow, brown and brook trout, on 2½ acre loch, stocked; £15 hours (2 fish), £25 (4 fish); c&r £10 5hrs, £14 day; open all year. Tackle shop: Dick's Sports, 54 Broad Street, Fraserburgh AB43 9AH (tel: 01346 514120). Hotels: Albert, Waterside Inn.

Tributaries of the Ugie

STRICHEN (or North Ugie):

Strichen (Aberdeenshire). Free trout fishing (subject to permission of riparian owners). Salmon fishing strictly preserved.

URR

Drains Loch Urr and flows to Solway. Late run of salmon; also sea trout, herling and brown trout.

Dalbeattie (Kirkcudbrightshire). Dalbeattie AA has Craignair beat, with salmon, sea trout, and brown trout, best Sept Nov; fly, worm, spinning; above Craignair beat assn has Firthead beat and East Logan bank, altogether 3½ miles; salmon open to end Nov; assn also has trout fishing on Buittle Reservoir; fly only; 2 boats (book through McCowans (below) only); stocked monthly with rainbows; various permits offered, incl dt for river £16 £35, wt £48 £105, both depending on season, reservoir £18 (3 fish), conc, evng £10 (1 fish)

from M McCowan & Son, 43 High Str, DG5 4AD (tel: 01556 610270) (branch also in Castle Douglas). Carp fishing on Barend Loch; permits from Barend Holiday Village, Sandyhills, by Dalbeattie, DG5 4NU (tel: 01387 780663); dt £10, 1/2 day £6; free to resident visitors. Near Kirkbean Village is Kirkhouse Trout Fishery (tel: 01387 880206), sporting ticket (c&r) £12, £17 for 2 fish. For coarse fishing on Cowans Loch, contact Cowans Farm, Kirkgunzeon, by Dumfries (tel: 01387 760284).

WEST COAST STREAMS AND LOCHS

Some complex fisheries and one or two smaller though not necessarily less sporting streams are grouped here for convenience. Other west coast waters will be found in the main alphabetical list.

AILORT

A short but good sea trout river which drains Loch Eilt and enters sea through saltwater Loch Ailort. One of the few rivers where run of genuine spring sea trout takes place.

Lochailort (Kirkcudbrightshire). Salmon and sea trout fishing on Loch Eilt and River Ailort; loch is renowned for some of largest sea trout caught in Britain; fly only; permit information from the ghillie: Euan Gillies (tel: 01687 470212). Hotel: Lochailort Inn, Lochailort PH38 4LZ (tel: 01687 470208). Loch Morar, a few miles north; good brown trout and occasional salmon and sea trout; fly, spinning and trolling allowed; permits and boats from Loch Morar Boat Hire (tel: 01687 462520); boats (incl fuel); permits from Morar Motors (tel: 01687 462118); Loch Superintendent (tel: 01687 462388; mob: 07733 356850).

LOCH BROOM
(including Rivers Broom, Dundonnell, Garvie, Oscaig, Polly and Ullapool)

Achiltibuie (Ross shire). Sea trout, brown trout and sea fishing. Summer Isles Hotel (see below) has much fishing for guests on rivers and lochs in the vicinity; sea trout and brown trout: Lochs Oscaig and Lurgain; boat on Oscaig £30; 1 boat on Lurgain; brown trout lochs, dt £6; enquire about boats for sea fishing; apply to Robert Mark Irvine, Summer Isles Hotel, Achiltibuie, by Ullapool, Ross shire IV26 2YG (tel: 01854 622282; web: www.summerisleshotel.co.uk). Inverpolly Estate, Ullapool IV26 2YB (tel/fax: 01854 622452; e-mail davies@inverpolly.freeserve.co.uk) has salmon, sea trout and brown trout fishing, with accommodation, on the following: River Garvie (very good little sea trout river which runs from Loch Osgaig to the sea); **River Osgaig** (running from Loch Badagyle to Loch Osgaig, fishes best in late season); **River Polly**, mainly below road bridge (numerous lies and pools), Polly Lochs, Loch Sionascaig and Loch Badagyle; Black Loch, Green Loch, Loch Lurgainn and others; mostly fly only, Sunday fishing allowed; loch permits with boat, £12 £15 (o/b £13); bank, £5; accommodation with fishing from £550 weekly.

Ullapool (Ross shire). Ullapool River, sea trout, brown trout and salmon; dt £10 (lower beat). Loch Achall, sea and brown trout; dt £8 (bank), £20 boat: inquire Loch Broom Hardware (below). Ullapool AC has brown trout fishing on Strathkanaird hill lochs: Lochs Dubh (brown trout), Beinn Dearg (brown and rainbow trout) and na Moille (brown trout and charr); membership for residents in area; no brown trout limit; all lochs fly only except Loch na Moille where under 15's may spin or bait fish; day tickets £5; permits from Loch Broom Hardware, Shore Street, IV26 2UJ (tel: 01854 612356). Tackle: North West Outdoors, West Argyle St IV26 2TY (tel: 01854 613383), who have large range of tackle. Hotel: Argyle; Arch Inn.

Inverlael (Ross shire). River Broom is a spate river sometimes suitable for fly spinning. Inverlael Estate has approx 1 ½m, single bank, including 10 pools; the bottom 2 pools are tidal; Inverlael Estate also has fishing on River Lael, its sea pool; fly only, except on sea pools; apply to Inverlael Estate office, Loch Broom, by Ullapool IV23 2RG (tel: 01854 655262).

Dundonnell (Ross shire). Dundonnell River; salmon and sea trout.

Loch DUICH (including Shiel and Croe)

Glenshiel, by Kyle of Lochalsh (Ross shire). Salmon and sea trout. Fishing on River Croe, a spate river with late runs. National Trust for Scotland, Morvich Farm House, Inverinate, by Kyle IV40 8HQ (tel: 01599 511231) has water; currently closed but under review. Sea fishing on Loch Duich. Hotels: Kintail Lodge, Loch Duich; Cluanie Inn, Loch Clunie.

EACHAIG (including Loch Eck)

Drains Loch Eck and flows about 5m into Atlantic by way of Holy Loch and Firth of Clyde. Salmon and sea trout.

Kilmun (Argyllshire). On Holy Loch and Firth of Clyde. Eachaig enters sea here. Salmon, sea trout and powan (protected) in Loch Eck (5m), where Whistlefield Inn, Loch Eck, Cairndow PA23 8SG (tel: 01369 860440) issues tickets: fly best at head of loch where River Cur enters. Other hotel: Coylet, Eachaie.

Dunoon (Argyllshire). Salmon and sea trout; limited weekly lets on River Eachaig from R C G Teasdale, Fishing Agent, Quarry Cottage, Rashfield, nr Dunoon, Argyll PA23 8QT (tel: 01369 840510). Loch Eck permits from Purdies. Forestry Commission Scotland has salmon, sea trout fishing on Lower Cur, dt £10, conc from David Marshall Lodge, Queen Elizabeth Forest Park, Aberfoyle FX8 3SX (tel: 01877 382258). Coylet Hotel, Loch Eck PA23 8SG (tel: 01369 840426) and Whistlefield Inn have salmon (mainly trolling), sea trout and brown trout fishing on Loch Eck for guests (preferential terms for residents); st £50, wt £25 and dt £5; boats for hire at Coylet Hotel. Loch Eck is about 7m long; no good for salmon until early June; best in August, Sept; apply to Whistlefield Inn, Loch Eck, by Dunoon PA23 8SG (tel: 01369 860440); no Sunday fishing. Dunoon & Dist AC has Rivers Cur, (wt £36, dt £12), Finnart (wt £24, dt £8) and Massan, salmon and sea trout, any legal lure (dt £12), and Ruel (dt £15); Lochs Tarsan (wt £40, dt £15) and Loskin, brown trout, fly only (dt £15) ; and Dunoon Reservoir, rainbow trout, fly only (dt £20); permits from Purdies of Argyll, 112 Argyll Str, PA23 7NE (tel: 01369 703232). Permits for River Finnart; sea trout, and occasional salmon, also mullet enter tidal parts and make very good fishing; any bait; £8, half day £4, conc, from S Share, River Warden, Keeper's Cottage, Ardentinny, Argyll PA23 8TS (tel: 01369 810228); and Purdies (see above). Good sea fishing in estuary for mullet, mackerel and flatfish, etc. Glendaruel Hotel at Clachan of Glendaruel, PA22 3AA (tel: 01369 820274) has salmon, sea trout and trout fishing on River Ruel (best Aug to Oct); permits available.

LOCH FYNE
(including Rivers Douglas, Fyne, Kinglas, Shira and Garron, and Dubh Loch)

Large sea loch on west coast of Argyll, which provides good sea fishing.

GAIRLOCH

A sea loch on the west coast of Ross.

Gairloch (Ross shire). Gairloch AC manages several trout lochs, including Lochs Bad na Scalaig, Tollaigh, Garbhaig; permits for these from Mr K Gunn, Strath; or Gairloch Chandlery, Pier Rd, IV21 2BQ (tel/fax: 01445 712458). Lochs Badacram, na Curra, and other fishing in remote mountain scenery; from Post Office, Pier Rd, Gairloch IV21 2BQ (tel: 01445 712175); fishing from mid June. Salmon and sea trout fishing in River Kerry, a spate river; easily accessible; season May Oct; best Aug Oct; information from Gairloch Highland Lodge, Gairloch IV21 2AH (tel: 01445 712068); tickets from the chandlery. Tackle and ghillie service from Gairloch Chandlery (see above).

GLENELG

Rises in Glen More and flows about 10m to the sea at Glenelg. Preserved by Scallasaig; no fishing at present, to allow stocks to replenish.

LOCH LONG (including Rivers Finnart and Goil)

A sea loch opening into the Firth of Clyde. Good sea trout, some salmon in streams. Finnart and Goil good in spates.

Ardentinny (Argyllshire). River Finnart enters Loch Long at Ardentinny. Dunoon & Dist AC lease both banks of River Finnart from Forestry Commission Scotland on condition that river is kept open to the public at a low cost. Grilse and sea trout, season July to end October; small brown trout in plenty; healthy wild stock; catch and return policy advised for late coloured spawning fish; spate and high rivers due to wet Argyll climate makes all parts of river fishable not many permits; fishing peaceful and enjoyable; permits for River Finnart and advice on local fishing from S Share, River Warden, Keeper's Cottage, Ardentinny, Argyll PA23 8TS (tel: 01369 810228), also Purdies of Argyll, 112 Argyll Street, Dunoon PA23 7NE (tel: 01369 703232).

Lochgoilhead (Argyllshire). River Goil AC has 15 years lease on River Goil salmon and sea trout fishings, and has bought the salmon netting stations on Loch Goil and has closed them for good; club also stocks the river; membership fee £100 pa; visitors ticket £40 Mon to Fri; dt £15 from Hon Sec or PO (tel: 01301 703201). Loch Goil (sea fishing) mackerel, dabs and cod.

FIRTH OF LORN (including Loch Nell)

Forming the strait between Mull and the mainland on the west coast. Lochs Linnhe and Etive open into it. Good sea trout and a few salmon.

Oban (Argyllshire). Oban & Lorn AC has trout fishing on twenty fly only lochs in the Lorn district; all brown trout, two with charr. Brown trout fishing include Lochs Nant and Avich, the largest of these waters; no bait fishing, and fishing with more than one rod is illegal; wt, dt from Anglers Corner (see below). Oude Reservoir, stocked rainbow and natural brown trout; boat located on this loch; bank fishing can be difficult because of fluctuating water level; also Ariogan Loch; rainbows; boat only; both dt water; apply Anglers Corner. Loch Nell, salmon, sea trout, brown trout and charr; salmon and charr preserved, best in summer; sea trout all through season; apply for dt to Anglers Corner. Permits from tackle shops in Oban. Tackle shops: Anglers Corner, 112 George St, Oban PA34 5NT (tel: 01631 566374); David Graham's, 11 15 Combie St, Oban PA34 4HN (tel: 01631 562069); Oban & Lorne tickets. Hotel: Ayres; Columba; Manor House; Cuilfail Hotel, Kilmelford, Argyll PA34 4XA (tel: 01852 200274).

Kilinver (Argyllshire). On **Euchar** estuary (10m south of Oban on A816). Tickets for 1m of good salmon, sea trout and brown trout fishing on Eucharr may be had from Mrs Hazel McCorkindale, Scammadale Farm, Kilninver, by Oban PA34 4UU (tel: 01852 316282); boat + 2 rods on Loch Scammadale £20 per day; bank and river fishing dt £5; as the Eucharr is a spate river.

Knipoch, by Oban (Argyll). Loch Seil, (sea trout and brown trout); bank fishing;under the control of Oban & Lorne AC; further information from Mrs J Mellor, Barrandromain Farm PA34 4QS (tel: 01852 316297).

LOCH MELFORT

A sea loch opening into the Firth of Lorn south of Oban. Sea trout, mackerel, etc.

Kilmelford (Argyllshire) 15m from Oban. Cuilfail Hotel, Kilmelford, Argyll PA34 4XA (tel: 01852 200274), can arrange fishing on Lochs nan Drimnean (10 min walk, trout; March May, Aug Sept best; fly only; 10in limit); a'Phearsain (15 min walk; trout, charr; fly only; April June, Aug Sept best); Avich (5m by road; trout; May Oct best); na Sreinge (8m by road and 35 min walk; trout; May Oct best), and Scammadale (8m by road; sea trout, salmon; end June Sept). Tickets from Kilmelford Stores. Glenmore and Glenbeg Estate hill lochs; 17 lochs; wild browns; some accessed after much walking; wt, 3 day and dt avilable from Anglers Corner, 112 George Street, Oban PA34 5NT (tel: 01631 566374).

MORVERN

Lochaline (Argyllshire). Salmon and sea trout fishing on both River Aline and Loch Arienas. Native brown trout in over 16 hill lochs. River fishing £25 per day for 2 rods; loch fishing dt £7.50; boats on site; contact Ardtornish Estate Co Ltd, Morven, by Oban, Argyll PA34 5UZ (tel: 01967 421288); very limited fishing tackle from Estate Information Centre and Shop; and self catering accommodation in estate cottages and flats.

LOCH TORRIDON

River Torridon, small salmon and sea trout river, flows into Upper Loch Torridon. Outer Loch Torridon offers excellent sea angling for a wide variety of species.

Torridon (Ross shire). Rivers Torridon, and Thrail, Lochs an Iascaigh and Damph, and hill lochs. Torridon Hotel, Torridon, by Achnasheen, Wester Ross, IV22 2EY (tel: 01445 791242), can advise on fishing on Loch Damph and Loch Clare, and may be able to arrange fishing on Loch Maree, subject to availability. Salmon and sea trout fishing on Loch Damph: Tigh an Eilean Hotel, Shieldaig IV54 8XN (tel: 01520 755251) can advise on local fishing including sea angling, and has good local contacts at the Shieldaig Angling Club, and Torridon House Estate. Fishing on River Balgy, which drains Loch Damph into southern shore of Upper Loch Torridon is now largely private.

WEST LOTHIAN, (lochs and reservoirs).

Allandale Tarn Fisheries, Gavieside, West Calder EH55 8PT (tel: 01506 873073; or contact through email: margo@thefishery.orangehome.co.u k); bank fishing only; brown, rainbow, blue; minimum 1½lbs to 16lbs plus; fly dt £24, conc; bait pool: dt £24 (five fish for both); any 4 hours (3 fish) £16.

Beecraigs Loch, Beecraigs Country Park, Linlithgow (tel: 01506 844516; web: www.beecraigs.com; email: mail@beecraigs.com); rainbow, brown trout, fly fishing, 8 boats on site; limit, 10 fish per boat (2 rods); no bank fishing, conservation area; all facilities, including tackle hire and visitors centre; advance booking essential; permits available. Tackle Shop: Lochside Tackle & Sports, 254 High St, Linlithgow, EH49 7ES (tel: 01506 671477).

Bowden Springs Trout Fishery, Carribber, Linlithgow EH49 6QE (tel: 01506 847269), 2 lochs: 5 and 2 acres, stocked daily with large rainbows; but including browns and blue trout; dt fly pond £27 (8 hours 5 fish) £23, 4 fish; bait pond £21, 6 fish; open 7 days a week.

Linlithgow Loch, Linlithgow; rainbow and occasional brown trout, Mar Oct, 20 boats incl one for disabled (Wheelyboat), and bank fishing; dt water; conc Mon to Thur; limit, 6 fish per rod; evng 6 fish limit; permits from Forth Federation of Anglers 12 Brodick Place, Falkirk, Central Region FK1 4SE, (tel: 07831 288921) or at lochside.

Morton Fisheries, Morton Reservoir, Mid Calder, Livingston EH53 0JT (tel: George - 07768 428647 or Paul - 07813 676159), fly only brown and rainbow trout, 12 boats on site, and bank fishing, limit 3 6 per rod, then c&r; all facilities, tickets from Fisheries.

Parkley Fishery, Parklay Place Farm, Linlithgow EH49 6QU (tel: 01506 671167), fly and bait fishing for rainbow trout; dt £20 8 hours (8 fish), £18 6 hours (6 fish), £15 4 hours (four fish) available.

WICK

Salmon, sea trout and brown trout fishing on Wick. Spate river with good holding pools. River controlled by Wick AA. Famous Loch Watten (trout) is 7m from Wick.

Wick (Caithness). Wick AA has fishing on River Wick; salmon, sea trout and brown trout; river well stocked from Assn's own hatchery; fly and worm fishing; apply Hugo Ross. Tackle specialist Hugo Ross, 56 High St, Wick KW1 4BP (tel: 01955 604200) has boat and bank fishing permits on Lochs Watten, St Johns, Toftingall, Calder, Stemster and Dunnett: wild brown trout; fly only on Watten and St Johns; all legal methods on Calder; bank fishing is open on most other Caithness lochs, including those on the Thrumster Estate.

YTHAN

Rises in "Wells of Ythan" and runs some 35m to North Sea at Newburgh. Late salmon river, noted for sea trout and finnock, which run up from June through to September, with some fish in October. Ythan has very large estuary for so small a river and is markedly tidal for the lower five miles or so of its course.

Newburgh (Aberdeenshire). Sea trout and finnock (no finnock may be kept) and salmon. Fishing on the large estuary controlled by Ythan Fisheries. Sea trout average 2 2½lb very occasionally run up to 12lb; finnock May onwards with large ones in September (c&r only); fly fishing and spinning only; spoons; Ythan Terrors, and devons fished on a 7 8ft spinning rod with 8 12lb line as most usual tackle; worm, maggot, bubble float and other bait not allowed; lead core lines, sinking lines not allowed; floating line with sinking tip allowed; fishing from bank; best months June to September; limited fishing open from 1 June to 30 Sept; prices on application to Mrs Audrey Clarke, Fishing Manager, Ythan Fishery, 3 Lea Cottages, 130 Main Street, Newburgh, Ellon, Aberdeenshire AB41 6BN (tel: 01358 789297).

Ellon (Aberdeenshire). Bruce & Partners, 21/23 Bridge St, AB41 9AA (tel: 01358 724442) issue permits for Ellon Water on River Ythan; st (waiting list), wt and dt available.

Methlick (Aberdeenshire). Some spring fish, but main run Sept to Oct. Good early run of finnock; a second, smaller run in the autumn. Sea trout; June Sept. Fishing on Haddo Estate water; now leased to Haddo House AA; dt £10 (Aug/Sept £20, Oct £25); permits from S French & Son, Main Rd, Methlick AB41 7DT (tel: 01651 806213). Hotel: Ythanview.

Fyvie (Aberdeenshire). Brown trout, sea trout and salmon. Sept and Oct best months for salmon. Fyvie AA has approx 3m on upper River Ythan, single bank; st £40, £25 conc, before 31 Aug only, and dt £10 Feb Aug, £20 Sept Oct; (£5 returned if return made); from Alldays Stores.

SEA FISHING LOCATIONS IN SCOTLAND

It is only in recent years that the full sea angling potential of the Scottish coast, indented by innumerable rocky bays and sea lochs, has come to be appreciated. Working in conjunction, tourist organisations and local sea angling clubs smooth the path for the visiting angler. He is well supplied in matters of boats and bait, natural stocks of the latter remaining relatively undepleted in many areas. The Scottish Federation of Sea Anglers can supply information about more than fifty annual sea fishing festivals, championships and competitions, at venues all around the Scottish mainland and islands. The local name for coalfish is 'saithe' and for pollack 'lythe'.

Kirkcudbright (Dumfriesshire). Centre for excellent shore fishing. Rocky points give good fishing for dogfish, with occasional conger, bull huss and thornback. Clear water gives pollack, garfish, mullet. The Dee estuary produces bags of plaice, dabs and flounders. Boats may be launched at harbour, Ross Bay and Brighouse. Baits: lug and ragworm may be dug locally, mackerel and herring are obtainable in town. Tourist Information, Harbour Square DG6 4HY (tel: 01557 330494; web: http://guide.visitscotland.com).

Stranraer (Wigtownshire). Loch Ryan, the W coast of Wigtownshire and Luce Bay offer first class sea fishing, boat and shore. Loch Ryan: codling, whiting, plaice, flounders, dabs, skate, conger, tope and dogfish. Other species found in Luce Bay and off Irish Sea coast include pollack, coalfish, bass, wrasse, mackerel, plaice, dabs, whiting, dogfish, conger. Tackle shop supply blast frozen ammo sea baits, and live baits. Local club: Lochryan Sea AA, David Goupillot, 50 St Ninians Ave DG9 7BE (tel: 01776 706915). Tackle shop: Sports Shop, 86 George St, Stranraer DG9 7JS (tel: 01776 702705; see web: www.fishingstranraer.com), which has information and tickets for Stranraer AA trout waters.

Girvan (Ayrshire). Pier fishing: mostly plaice, codling, flounder, pollack sea bass; from boat; pollock, codling, ling, wrasse, mackerel. Horse Rock, nr Stranraer Rd, is popular local fishing mark, approachable at half tide; lugworm and ragworm may be dug locally. Boat hire: Mark McCrindle, 7 Harbour St KA26 9AJ (tel: 01465 713219; see website for more info: www.ailsacraig.org.uk); Tony Wass, 33 Henrietta St KA26 9AL (tel: 01465 715934). Tickets for River Girvan from Wright's Hardware Store, 42 Dalrymple St KA26 9AB (tel: 01465 713213). Hotel: Mansefield.

Ayr (Ayrshire). On the estuaries of the Rivers Ayr and Doon. Beach fishing for flounders from Newton Shore, where baits may be dug; flounders and eels in harbour, mullet in tidal stretches of Ayr. Good mackerel and occasional herring fishing from May to October. Tackle shop: Gamesport of Ayr, 60 Sandgate, KA7 1BX (tel: 01292 263822; see website for more info: www.gamesportofayr.co.uk).

Saltcoats and **Ardrossan** (Ayrshire). Shore fishing in the South Bay, and around the harbours, for pollack, wrasse, dogfish, eels, cod, saithe, flat fish and herring. Ragworm and lugworm may be obtained locally, at Fairlie Pier and saltcoats Harbour. 3m north, Ardneil Bay, codling. Club: Ardrossan & Dist SAC.

Brodick and **Lamlash** (Isle of Arran). Mackerel fishing only. Lamlash is the main centre for sea fishing on Arran, with boats for hire for mackerel fishing at Lamlash Pier (tel: 01770 600998/349). Johnston's Marine

Store, Old Pier, Lamlash KA27 8JN (tel: 01770 600333) has tackle and comprehensive chandlery stock, with information on wrecks, etc.

Campbeltown (Argyllshire). Good sport with cod, haddock, flatfish, etc, in Kildalloig Bay and from The Winkie, causeway between Davaar Island and mainland. Plenty of loch and river trout fishing in vicinity. Details from the Tourist Information Office, Mackinnon House, Old Quay PA28 6EF (tel: 01586 552056). Tackle shop: Neil Brodie Hardware Shop, 15 Longrow, PA28 6ER; permits for Kintyre AC waters. Hotels: Argyll Arms; White Hart, both Main St.

Oban (Argyllshire). Best fishing off south and west sides of Kerrera Island. Best shore marks, Salmore Point, North Connel at road bridge. Good mackerel fishing in Oban Bay. Species found from shore and boat: tope, conger, whiting, codling, cod, pollack, coalfish, skate, thornback ray, spurdog, dogfish, mackerel, ling, wrasse and gurnard. Charter boat 'Gannet', licensed for ten, all tackle provided; contact Adrian A Lauder, 3 Kiel Croft, Benderloch, Oban PA37 1QS (tel: 01631 720262) (web: obanfishing.co.uk). Tackle shop: Anglers' Corner, 112 George Str, PA34 5NT (tel: 01631 566374) has information on all local fishing. Tourist Information, Argyll Square PA34 4AN (tel: 01631 563122).

Portree (Isle of Skye). Sheltered harbour, with fishing marks in and around it. Free anchorage. Cod, haddock, whiting, coalfish, pollack and mackerel. For bait, unlimited mussels and cockles in tidal areas. Camastianavaig is a sheltered bay 4m south east of Portree, where heavy bags of skate, cod, whiting, haddock, spurdog, gurnard, pollack may be caught with trace or paternoster. Tackle shop: Island Cycles, Rod & Reel, The Green IV51 9BT (tel: 01478 61 3121). For boat hire contact

Tourist Information, Bayfield House, Bayfield Rd IV51 9EL (tel: 008452 255121).

Kyle of Lochalsh (Ross shire). Pollack and mackerel frequent; occasional cod, ling, conger, skate. Wreck fishing around Isle of Skye waters. Mussels, clams and cockles are local baits. Tackle shop: Mr & Mrs Finlayson, Marine Stores, Station Rd IV40 8AE (tel: 01599 534208). For boats, enquire Tourist Information Centre, The Car Park, IV40 8AG (tel: 01599 534276).

Shieldaig (Ross shire). Skate, cod, conger, saithe, ling, huss, dabs, sole and mackerel. Fishing in sea lochs of Shieldaig, Torridon and Upper Torridon; sheltered water nearly always. Outside lochs conditions can be dangerous.

Gairloch (Ross shire). Cod, haddock, mackerel, whiting, pollack, saithe, ling, thornback and flatfish in Loch Gairloch. Disabled anglers have free access to Gairloch Pier. Charter boats from Kerry Sea Angling, Gairloch Chandlery, Pier Rd, IV21 2BQ (tel: 01445 712458; bookings tel: 0800 008 6833; see website for more info: www.sea-fishing-gairloch.com); also Gairloch AC tickets, and pike fishing; full and half day trips, tackle provided, common skate fishing and mixed. B&B and self catering accommodation Gairloch Tourist Information Centre, Auchtercairn, Gairloch IV21 2DN (tel: 01445 712071).

Ullapool and **Summer Isles** (Ross shire). Skate, also haddock, whiting, codling, pollack, coalfish, mackerel, gurnard, flatfish, thornback ray, conger, dogfish, turbot and wrasse. Inshore sport from dinghies and in charter boats around the Summer Isles. Good shore fishing at Morefield, Rhu and Achiltibuie. Tackle shop: Lochbroom Hardware, Shore Str, IV26 2UJ (tel: 01854 612356).

Lochinver (Sutherland). Cod, halibut, skate, tope, saithe, codling, lythe, mackerel. Fishing boats operate from harbour. Tackle from Lochinver Chandlery, Culag Square IV 27 4LG (tel: 01571 844398). Tourist Information, Main St IV27 4LX (tel: 01571 844373). Hotel: Inver Lodge.

Stornoway (Isle of Lewis). Cod, conger, pollack, ling, dabs, bluemouth, flounder, dogfish, wrasse, whiting, saithe, skate, etc. Fast growing centre with local club, Stornoway Sea AC, South Beach Quay, whose secretary will gladly help visiting anglers. Club organises Western Isles Sea Angling Championships in August. Accommodation and information from Stornoway Tourist Information Centre, 26 Cromwell St, Stornoway Isle of Lewis HS1 2DD.

Kirkwall (Orkney). Sheltered waters in Scapa Flow near Stromness hold variety of fish (record skate; halibut over 150lb, ling of 36lb). Also plaice, pollack, coalfish, haddock, mackerel, wrasse, from shore or boat. Orkney Tourist Information, The Travel Centre, West Castle St, Kirkwall KW15 1GU (tel: 01856 872 856). Tackle shop: W S Sinclair, 27 John St, Stromness KW16 3AD (tel: 01856 851523). Hotels: Stromness; Royal Hotel, Stromness.

Lerwick (Shetland). Excellent mixed fishing for ling, cod, tusk, skate, haddock, pollack, etc, and chance of halibut. Area has held British records for tusk, homelyn ray, grey gurnard and Norway haddock. Also Scottish hake record. Tackle shop: LHD Marine Supplies, Albert Building, Esplanade ZE1 0LL (tel: 01595 692379; see website for more info: www.lhdmarinesupplies.co.uk). Hotels: Lerwick, Shetland; and Busta House, Brae.

Thurso (Caithness). Conger from harbour walls, and rock fishing. Cod, ling, haddock, conger, pollack, coalfish, dogfish, spurdog, plaice, wrasse, mackerel, dabs, whiting, rays, halibut, porbeagle shark; turbot. Thurso Bay and Dunnet Bay are sheltered areas. Baits: mussel and lugworm at lower water. Most boats are based at Scrabster. Tackle shop: Harpers Fly Fishing Services, 57 High St. KW14 8AZ (tel: 01847 893179).

Wick (Caithness). Mainly rock fishing for conger, pollack, saithe, cod, haddock, mackerel and flatfish. Porbeagle shark off Caithness, and excellent halibut fishing. Good points are: Longberry, Broadhaven, Sandigoe and Helman Head. Excellent cod fishing off Noss Head. Best months: June to Sept. For further information contact Wick Tourist Information Centre: Whitechapel Rd KW1 4EA (tel: 01955 602596). Tackle: Bremner Fishing Co, Mara Vista, Whitehouse Park, KW1 4NX (tel: 01955 606408). Hotels: Nethercliffe; Mackay's; Norseman; Queen's.

Portmahomack (Ross shire). Good opportunities for cod, ling, pollack, mackerel, wrasse etc. The best of the season runs from April to October, probably peaking in August and September. Good reef and limited wreck fishing. Charter vessel for parties of up to 10; boats charged at £50 per hour or £250 per day including rods and lures. Accommodation can be arranged. Contact John R MacKenzie, Carn Bhren, Portmahomack, by Tain IV20 1YS (tel: 01862 871257; mob: 07970 220723). Tackle shop: R McLeod & Sons, 14 Lamington St, Tain IV19 1AH (tel: 01862 892171): wide and comprehensive stock including bait. Hotels: Caledonian; Castle: and Oystercatcher.

Lossiemouth (Morayshire). Notable centre for sea trout fishing off east and west beaches; spinning into breakers provides splendid sport. Also mackerel, saithe, flatfish from beach, pier and boats. Tackle shop: Angling

Centre, Moss St, Elgin IV30 1LU (tel: 01343 547615).

Aberdeen (Aberdeenshire). Excellent rock fishing for cod, ling, saithe, mackerel, whiting, haddock and flatfish. Few boats. Tackle shop: Somers Fishing Tackle, 13 15 Bon Accord Terrace AB11 2DP (tel: 01224 210008; see website for more info: www.grampianfishing.com). Hotels: Caledonian, Carmelite, Royal.

Stonehaven (Kincardineshire). Rock fishing for cod, coley, pollack, flounder and mackerel very good. Cod, haddock, ling, etc, from boats; available from I Watson (tel: 01569 765064) or Harbour Office, Old Pier AB39 2JU (tel: 01569 762741). Bait may be ordered from the above. Limited tackle from: Davids, Market Square. Tourist Information Centre, 66 Allardice St, AB39 2AA (tel: 01569 762806). Hotel: Arduthie House.

Nairn (Nairnshire). Sea angling on Moray Firth. Most fishing is done from two piers at the entrance to the harbour which is tidal, or on the beach at low water. Tackle shop: Pat Fraser, Radio, TV and Sports shop, 41 High St IV12 4AG (tel: 01667 453038); issues permits for 7m stretch of R Nairn, with sea trout and salmon. Tourist Information IV12 4DN (tel: 01667 452753). Hotels: Altonburn; and Greenlawns Guest House.

Dundee (Angus). Fishing from rock, beach and pier and boats at Tay Estuary, Easthaven and Carnoustie for mackerel, cod, saithe, lythe and flatfish. Tackle shop: Gow's of Dundee, 12 Union Str, DD1 4BH (tel: 01382 225427; see website for more info: www.gows-dundee.co.uk) who issue permits for Strathmore AA waters; tackle shop also has access to salmon and sea trout fishing on Tay, North Esk and South Esk; tuition; ghillies.

Dunbar (East Lothian). Excellent rock, pier and boat fishing. Saithe, cod (up to 10lb), codling, dabs, plaice, flounders, eels and, at times, small whiting, gurnard and mackerel can be caught. Tourist Information 143 High Str, EH42 1ES (tel: 01368 863353).

FISHING CLUBS & ASSOCIATIONS IN SCOTLAND

Included in the list of fishing clubs and associations in Scotland are those organisations which are in England, but which have water on the Tweed and its tributaries or on the Border Esk. Further information can usually be had from the Secretaries and a courtesy which is appreciated is the inclusion of a stamped addressed envelope with postal enquiries. Please advise the publishers (address at the front of the book) of any changed details for the next edition.

NATIONAL BODIES

Assn of Salmon Fishery Boards
Director: Andrew Wallace
CBC House
24 Canning Street
Edinburgh EH3 8EG
Tel: 0131 272 2797
Fax: 0131 272 2800
www.asfb.org.uk
andrew@asfb.org.uk

Federation of Border Angling Associations
Peter Reith, Secretary & Treasurer
St Fillens, Wellsbrae
Innerleithen
Peeblesshire EH44 6JE
Tel: 01896 830285
www.peeblesshiretroutfishing.co.uk
peter@reith.org.uk

Federation of Highland Angling Clubs
K Macdonald
30 Swanston Avenue
Scorguie
Inverness IV3 8QW
Tel: 01463 240095
(Over 30 clubs and associations registered)

Forestry Commission Scotland
231 Corstorphine Road
Edinburgh EH12 7AT
Tel: 0131 314 6508
Fax: 0131 314 6152
www.forestry.gov.uk/scotland
info@forestry.gov.uk

Greater Glasgow & Clyde Valley Tourist Board
(now incorporated into Visit Scotland)

Institute of Aquaculture
University of Stirling
Stirling FK9 4LA
Tel: 01786 467878
Fax: 01786 472133
www.aqua.stir.ac.uk

International Fly Fishing Assn
Ian Campbell, Secretary & Treasurer
Cruachan
16 Marindin Park
Glenfarg
Perth & Kinross PH2 9NQ
Tel: 01577 830582
www.iffa.net
iffa@glenfarg.com

Marine Scotland Science,
Freshwater Laboratory
Faskally
Pitlochry
Perthshire PH16 5LB
Tel: 01796 472060
www.scotland.gov.uk/marinescotland

Scottish Anglers' National Assn Ltd
The Pier
Loch Leven
Kinross
Perth & Kinross KY13 8UF
Tel: 01577 861116
Fax: 01577 864769
www.sana.org.uk
admin@sana.org.uk

The Scottish Country Sports Tourism Group
Ian Robertson
Croft Cottage
Trochry
by Dunkeld
Perthshire PH8 0DY
Tel: 01350 723226
Fax: 01350 723227
www.cstgscotland.com

Scottish Disability Sport
Angling co ordinator, John Hood
Caledonia House
South Gyle
Edinburgh EH12 9DQ
Tel: 0131 3171130
Fax: 0131 3171075
www.scottishdisabilitysport.com
admin@scottishdisabilitysport.com

Scottish Federation of Coarse Angling
www.sfca.co.uk
james.macdonald@btinternet.com

Scottish Federation of Sea Anglers
Sheila Muir
Unit 62, Evans Business Centre
Mitchelston Drive
Mitchelston Industrial Estate
Kirkcaldy
KY1 3NB
Tel: 01592 657520

Wheelyboat Trust
Director: Andy Beadsley
North Lodge, Burton Park
Petworth, West Sussex GU28 0JT
Tel/Fax: 01798 342222
www.wheelyboats.org

Scottish Government (The) Marine Directorate
Aquaculture, Freshwarer Fisheries & Licensing Policy Division
Pentland House
47 Robb's Loan
Edinburgh EH14 1TY
Tel: 0131 244 6231
Fax: 0131 244 6512
www.scotland.gov.uk

Marine Scotland Science
FRS Marine Laboratory
375 Victoria Road
Aberdeen AB11 9DB
Tel: 01224 876544
Fax: 01224 295511
www.frs-scotland.gov.uk

Scottish Record Fish Recorder
(Sea Fish)
Paul King
Harbour House
Hopeman
Moray IV30 5RU
Tel: 01343 830316
Aims as for British Record Fish Committee
pepekay@aol.com

Sportscotland
Templeton on the Green
62 Templeton Street
Glasgow G40 1DA
Tel: 0141 534 6500
Fax: 0141 534 6501
or
Caledonia House
South Gyle
Edinburgh EH12 9DQ
Tel: 0131 317 7200
Fax: 0131 317 7202
www.sportscotland.org.uk

Visit Scotland
(formerly Scottish Tourist Board)
Tel: 0845 2255 121
www.visitscotland.com/fish
(Gives information on fishing holidays in Scotland)

CLUBS

Aberdeen & District Angling Assn
Paul Toseland
27 Cove Circle
Aberdeen AB12 3DG
Tel: 01224 875452
adaal@tiscali.co.uk
www.adaa.org.uk

Aberfeldy Angling Club
Bob Stewart
P O Box 2000
Aberfeldy
Perthshire PH15 2BU
Tel: 01887 829512

Acconachie Angling Club
Okain MacLennan
Tel: 01381 620674

Achnasheen Angling Club
c/o Ledgowan Lodge Hotel
Achnasheen
Ross shire IV22 2EJ
Tel: 01445 720252
www.ledgowanlodge.co.uk

Airdrie & District Angling Club
Hugh Lucas
103 Park Road
Calderbank
Aidrie ML6 9TD
Tel: 01236 752336

Arbroath Angling Club
Tom Mill
39 Tarry Road, Arbroath
Angus DD11 4BB
Tel: 01241 879086

Arran Angling Association
Neil McLean
Hopefield
Bungalow Road
Lamlash
Isle of Arran KA27 8LD
Tel: 01770 600413

Assynt Angling Group
Peter Hendrich
The Cottage
Culag Square
Lochinver
by Lairg
Sutherland IV27 4LE
Tel: 01571 844076
www.assyntangling.co.uk

Avon Angling Club
www.theavonanglingclub.co.uk
webmaster@theavonanglingclub.co.uk

Ayr Angling Club
Andy Cannell
107 James Brown Avenue
Ayr KA8 9SF
Tel: 01292 268633
Mob: 07821 317810

Badenoch Angling Assn
Tommy Wade
Kingussie
Inverness shire PH21 1LB
Tel: 01540 661597
www.kingussie.co.uk

Ballater Angling Assn
Martin Holroyd
59 Golf Road
Ballater
Aberdeenshire AB3 5RU
Tel: 013397 55365

Beauly Angling Club
John Szarkiewicz
President
www.beauly-angling-club.co.uk

Berwick & District Angling Assn
David Cowan
129 Etal Road
Tweedmouth
Berwick TD15 2DU
Tel: 01289 306985
www.whiteadder.co.uk

Blairgowrie, Rattray & District Angling Assn
Peter Lock
White Loch Farmhouse
Carsie
Blairgowrie
Perthshire PH10 6HR
Tel: 01250 872149
www.brdaa.co.uk

Brechin Angling Club
Stuart Robertson
19 Dundas Park
Brechin, Angus
Tel: 01356 623713

Bridge of Weir River Angling Club
George Inglis
Hunthill
Bowfield Road
Howwood PA9 1BS
Tel: 01505 703809
www.bridgeofweirfishing.co.uk

Carradale Angling Club
David Shaw
17 Castlepark
Campbeltown, Argyll.
Tel: 01586 553469
Mobile: 0790 9991388

Castle Douglas & District Angling Assn
Stanley Kaye
2 Cairnsmore Road
Castle Douglas
Galloway DG7 1BN
Tel: 01556 502695

Chatton Angling Assn
Mrs Jane Douglas
10 Church Hill
Chatton, Alnwick
Northumberland NE66 5PY
Tel: 01668 215298

Coldstream & District Angling Assn
Paul Savage
Glen Priory
New Harper Ridge
Cornhill on Tweed TD12 4UP
Tel: 01890 883711

Colmonell Angling Club
Roger Pirie
Rose Cottage
Poundland
Pinwherry
KA26 0RU
Tel: 01465 841644

Crieff Angling Club
Patrick McEwan
11A Sauchie Road
Crieff
Perthshire PH7 4EN
Tel: 01764 655723
www.crieffanglingclub.org.uk

Cumbrae Angling Club
Maj Hugh Murphy, Ret'd
Bar End Street
Millport
Isle of Cumbrae KA28 0BL
Tel: 01475 531094

Dalbeattie Angling Assn
J Moran
12 Church Crescent
Dalbeattie
Kirkcudbrightshire DG5 4BA
Tel: 01556 610026

Dalry Angling Assn
Andrew Ruddock
Post Office
Dalry
Castle Douglas
Kirkcudbrightshire DG7 3UW
Tel: 01644 430201

Devon Angling Assn
David Mudie
19 Norwood Avenue
Alloa
Clackmannanshire FK10 2BY
Tel: 01259 213891
www.clacksnet.org.uk/hosted/daa

Dingwall & District Angling Club
Grant Mckenzie
Tel; 01349 830764

Dornoch & District Angling Assn
c/o Dornoch Pet & Country Shop
8 Castle Street
Dornoch
Sutherland IV25 3PE
Tel: 01862 811812

Dreghorn Angling Club
Wally Osborne: ticket secretary
18 Killoch Way
Girdle Toll
Irvine
Ayrshire KA11 1AY
Tel: 01294 214576

Drumgrange & Keirs Angling Club
Tom McClure
17 Riecawr Avenue
Dalmellington
Ayrshire KA6 7SR
Tel: 01292 551390

Dumfries & Galloway Angling Assn
Steve Ashworth
Raffles Burn
Ruthwell Station
Dumfriess DG1 4NY
Tel: 01387 870361
www.fishpal.com/scotland/nith

Dunfermline Artisan Angling Club
Jim Hay
6 Douglas Drive
Dunfermline
Fife KY12 9YG
Tel: 01383 724968

Dunkeld & Birnam Angling Assn
The Spar Shop
Murthly Terrace
Birnham
Perthshire PH8 0BG
Tel: 01350 727395
Or, Dunkeld Post Office
12 Bridge Street
Dunkeld
Perthshire PH8 0AH
Tel: 01350 727257
Or, Nisa Store,
Murthly
Perthshire PH1 4HG
Tel: 01738 710061

Dunoon & District Angling Club
Andrew Leech
Membership Secretary
Purdies of Argyll
112 Argyll Street
Dunoon PA23 7NE
Tel: 01369 703232
www.dunoonanddistrictanglingclub.co.uk

Earlston Angling Assn
John McLellan, 4 Arnot Place
Earlston
Tel: 01896 849162

East Lothian Angling Assn
Geoff Cusden
4 The Glebe
East Linton
East Lothian EH40 3EF
Tel: 01620 860045
www.elaa.co.uk

Eden Angling Assn
Ticket Secretary: R Young
33 Blalowan Gardens
Cupar
Fife KY15 5EL
Tel: 01334 654333
www.edenangling.co.uk

Elgin & District Angling Assn
Iain Mackay
42 Brucelands
Elgin IV30 1TS
Tel: 01343 541984

Esk & Liddle Fisheries Assn
Buccleuch Estates Ltd
Ewesbank
Langholm
Dumfriesshire DG13 0ND
Tel: 013873 80202

Evanton Angling Club
John McDonald
15 Camden Street
Evanton
Ross shire IV16 9XU
Tel: 01349 832966

Eye Water Angling Club
W Crombie
17 Gillsland, Eyemouth
Berwickshire TD14 5JF
Tel: 018907 50134

Fochabers Angling Club
Andy Milne
7 Institution Road
Fochabers IV32 7DZ
Tel: 01343 820259
www.speyfishingfochabers.com

Forres Angling Assn
The Forres Tackle Shop
97D High Street
Forres
Moray
IV36 1AA
Tel/Fax : 01309 672936
Mob 07880855543
www.faa.org.uk

Forth Federation of Anglers
12 Brodick Place
Falkirk
Central Region FK1 4SE
Tel: 07831 288921
www.fafa-linlithgowloch.org.uk

Fyvie Angling Assn
J D Pirie
Prenton
South Road
Oldmeldrum, Inverurie
Aberdeenshire AB51 0AB
Tel: 01651 872229

Gairloch Angling Club
Mrs L MacKenzie
4 Strath
Gairloch
Ross shire IV21 2BP
01445 712047

Galashiels Angling Assn
S Grzybowski
9 Annfield Gardens
Galashiels
Selkirkshire TD1 3DE
Tel: 01896 755712
gala.angling@btinternet.com

Gatehouse & Kirkcudbright Angling Assn
David Ferguson
Fergus Road
Kirkudbright DG6 4HN
Tel: 01557 331315

Goil Angling Club
(See River Goil AC)

Gordon Fishing Club
James H Fairgrieve
Burnbrae
Eden Road
Gordon
Berwickshire TD3 6JU
Tel: 01573 410357

Greenlaw Angling Assn
Mr T Waldie
26 East High Street
Greenlaw
Berwickshire TD10 6UF
Tel: 01361 810542

Haddo House Angling Assn
J French
Kirton Manse Road
Ellon
Aberdeenshire AB41 7DG
Tel: 01651 806205

Hawick Angling Club
Hon Sec: Bert Johnston
5 Sandbed
Hawick
Roxburghshire TD9 0HE
Tel: 01450 372266

Inverness Angling Club
Donnie MacKay
4 Maxwell Drive
Inverness IV3 5EX
Tel: 01463 239110
www.invernessanglingclub.co.uk

Jedforest Angling Assn
J M Oliver
67 Howden Crescent
Jedburgh
Roxburghshire TD8 6JY
Tel: 01835 863239
www.jedforest-angling.co.uk

Keithick Angling Club
Paul Chambers
Arnwood
Meigle Road
Alyth
Blairgowrie
Perthshire PH11 8EU
Tel: 01828 633115

Kelso Angling Assn
Len Bolton
www.fishpal.com

Killin & Breadalbane Angling Club
Gerry McCarron
Rowancroft
Main Street
Killin
Perthshire FK21 8SH
Tel: 01567 820833

Kilmaurs Angling Club
J Graham
99 East Park Drive
Kilmaurs KA3 2QP
Tel: 01563 538418

Kilsyth Fish Protection Assn
A McInnes
40 Arnbrae Rd
Kilsyth G65 9AS
Tel: 01236 821654

Kinlochewe Angling Assn
Kinlochewe Hotel
Kinlochewe
Achnasheen
Ross shire IV22 2PA
Tel: 01445 760253

Kintyre Angling Club
c/o Neil Brodie's Hardware Shop
15 Longrow
Campbeltown
Argyllshire PA28 6ER
Tel: 01586 552104

Kyles of Bute Angling Club
Tommy Simpson
Findhorn, Kames
Tighnabruaich
Argyll
Tel: 01700 811641

Ladykirk & Norham Angling Assn
J Cameron
53 Castle St
Norham
Berwick upon Tweed TD15 2LQ
tel: 01289 382481
jimalexandercameron@googlemail.com

Lairg Angling Club
Polson MacNeill
46 Ord Place
Lairg
Sutherland
Tel: 01549 402309

**Lamington & District Angling
Improvement Assn**
Secretary: Maggie Martin
Tel: 01555 750944.
www.lamingtonfishing.co.uk

Largs & District Angling Club
Maurice Dixon: Hon Sec
Tel: 01294 823314

Lauderdale Angling Assn
Graeme Sutherland
Kildonan
14 Brownsmuir Park
Lauder, Berwickshire TD2 6QD
Tel: 01578 722799

Linlithgow Angling Club
Lindsay McFadzean
56 Pilgrims Hill
Linlithgow EH49 7LW
Tel: 01506 844387
www.l-a-c.co.uk

Loch Awe Improvement Assn
Mrs J MacKay
Ardchonnel
by Dalmally
Argyll PA33 1BW
Tel: 01866 844226

Lochgilphead & District Angling Club
David Welch
Coig na Shee
1 Kilduskland Rd
Ardrishaig
Argyll PA30 8HE
Tel: 01546 603980

Loch Lomond Angling Improvement Assn
Michael Brady
379 Hamilton Road
Uddington
Glasgow G71 7SG
Tel: 0141 781 1545
www.lochlomondangling.com

Loch Rannoch Conservation Assn
Richard Legate
Perthshire Tel: 01882 632345

Loch Achonachie Angling Club
Okain McLennan
25 Station Crescent
Fortrose
Ross shire IV10 8SZ
Tel: 01381 620674
http://laac.cononfishing.com

Lochryan Sea Angling Assn
Mr McLean
86 George St
Stranraer DG9 7JS
Tel: 01776 702705

Malleny Angling Assn
A Howes
8 Addiston Crescent
Balerno
Edinburgh H14 7DB
Tel: 0131 4493041
www.mallenyangling.co.uk

Melrose & District Angling Assn
Tom McLeish
Fullarton, Abbotsford Road
Melrose
Roxburghshire TD6 9BB
mob: 0777 342 0191

Mid Nithsdale Angling Assn
Hon Sec: Brian Lord
6 New St
Thornhill
Dumfries DG3 5NH
Tel: 01848 330415

Monikie Angling Club
The Pier
Monikie Reservoir
Dundee
Angus DD5 3QN
Tel: 01382 370300
or
A Murray
26 Mill Hill, Montifieth
Dundee DD5 4PW
Tel: 01382 533467
www.monikie-angling-club.org.uk

Montrose & District Angling Club
John Sutcliffe
Leys of Dun Farm
Montrose
Angus DD10 9LW
Tel: 01674 810217

Morebattle & District Angling Club
D Y Gray
17 Mainsfield Avenue
Morebattle
Kelso
Roxburghshire TD5 8QW
Tel: 01573 440528

Muirkirk Angling Assn
Scott Hogg
30 Neanlour Drive
Muirkirk
Ayrshire KA18 3PX
Tel: 01290 661995

Musselburgh & District Angling Assn
George Brooks
19 Mayfield Crescent
Musselburgh
East Lothian EH21 6EY
Tel: 0131 665 4322

Nairn Angling Assn
Mrs Lorna Moffat
14 Manse Road
Nairn
Inverness IV12 4RW
Tel: 01667 459250

New Cumnock Angling Assn
Peter Bain
12 West Park Drive
New Cumnock
Ayrshire KA18 4LJ
Tel: 01290 338480

New Galloway Angling Assn
J Hopkins
Hopkins Shop, New Galloway
Castle Douglas DG7 3RN
Tel: 01644 420229

Newton Stewart & District Angling Assn
Billy McHarg
19 Maxwell Drive
Newton Stewart
Wigtownshire DG8 6EL
Tel: 01671 401127

North Berwick Angling Club
K Wood
3 Stevenson Way
Longniddry
East Lothian EH32 0PF
Tel: 01875 852712
Mob: 07980 599804

North Uist Angling Club
Philip Harding
Claddach Kyles
North Uist HS6 5EW
Tel: 01876 580341
www.nuac.co.uk

Oban & Lorne Angling Club
c/o Anglers Corner
112 George St, Oban
Argyll PA34 5NT
Tel: 01631 566374
www.anglerscorneroban.co.uk

Orkney Trout Fishing Assn
Malcolm Russell
Caolilla
Heddle Road
Finstown
Orkney Isles KW17 2EG
Tel: 01856 761586
www.orkneytroutfishing.co.uk

Peeblesshire Trout Fishing Assn
c/o Cast Around Peebles
16 Northgate, Peebles
Tel: 01721 729229
Or, Peter Reith
St Fillans
Wells Brae
Interleithen
Peeblesshire EH44 6JE
Tel: 01896 830285
www.peeblesshiretroutfishing.co.uk

Pitlochry Angling Club
Secretary: Ron Harriman
Sunnyknowe
7 Nursing Home Brae
Pitlochry
Pershire PH16 5HP
Tel: 01796 472484 (evngs)
or
Innes Smith (Club Salmon Secretary)
Tel: 01796 473651 (evngs)
or
c/o Pitlochry Tourist Information
Centre
22 Atholl Road
Pitlochry
Perthshire PH16 5BX
Tel: 01796 472215 (day)
www.pitlochryanglingclub.co.uk

Portree Angling Assn
Bernard Cooksoon
Tel: 01470 521819
www.portreeanglingassociation.co.uk

Prestwick Angling Club
David Allan
Pets Aquarium
124 Main St
Prestwick KA9 1PB
Tel: 01292 477863

Rannoch & District Angling Club
John Brown
The Square
Kinloch Rannoch
Perthshire PH16 5PN
Tel: 01882 632268

Rescobie Loch Development Assn
Rescobie Boathouse
Clock Briggs
Forfar
Angus DD8
Tel: 01307 830367

River Avon Federation
(controls migratory fishing on R Avon)
Lindsay McFadzean
56 Pilgrims Hill
Linlithgow EH49 7LW
Tel: 01506 844387

River Goil Angling Club
Ian K Given
"Bonnyrigg"
25 Churchill Drive
Bishopton
Renfrewshire PA7 5HB
c/o Tel: 01301 703201 (Post Office)

St Andrew's Angling Club
Clive Burhouse
6 Spinkie Crescent
St Andrews
Fife KY16 8SH
Tel: 01334 473304

St Boswells & Newtown Districts Angling Assn
W Rodger
Bruntyburn, Ancrum
Jedburgh TD8 6TZ
Tel: 01835 830714

St Fillans & Loch Earn Angling Assn
Donald Gow
6 Rintoul Avenue
Crieff
Perthshire PH7 3SJ
Tel: 01764 654439

St Mary's Angling Club
Peter Kokot, Loch Keeper
St Mary's Loch
Glengaber Cottage
Cappercleuch TD7 5LQ
Tel: 01750 423290
lochkeeper@progressiveorange.com

Selkirk & District Angling Assn
D Mitchell
28 Scotts Place
Selkirk TD7 4DR
Tel: 01750 20748

Shetland Anglers' Assn
Alec Miller
55 Burgh Road
Lerwick
Shetland Isles ZE1 0HJ
Tel: 01595 696025
www.shetlandtrout.co.uk

South Uist Angling Club
Hamish Fraser
191 Snishival
South Uist HS8 5SG
Tel: 01870 620394

Soval Angling Assn
Alastair McLeod
75 Leurbost
Stornoway
Isle of Lewis
HS2 9NU
Tel; 01851 860246

Stanley & District Angling Club
S Grant
7 Shielhill Park. Stanley
Perth PH1 4QT
Tel: 01738 828179

Stornoway Angling Assn
Ali Sugan
c/o 18 Keith Street
Stornoway
Isle of Lewis HS1 2QG
Tel: 01851 705453
alisugan@tiscali.co.uk
www.stornoway-angling-association.
com

Stornoway Sea Angling Club
South Beach Quay
Stornoway
Isle of Lewis HS1 2BT
Tel: 01851 702021
www.stornowaysac.co.uk

Stranraer & District Angling Assn
John Cathcart
21 Victoria Place
Stranraer DG9 7HE
Tel: 01776 700995
or
c/o The Sports Shop
86 George Street,
Stranraer DG9 7JS
Tel: 01776 702705

Strathgryfe Angling Assn
Kingsley Wood & Co, Solicitors
Burnside Chambers
The Cross, Kilmacolm
Renfrewshire PA13 4ET
Tel: 01505 874114

Strathmore Angling Improvement Assn
Hon Sec: G J McIntosh
4 Douglas Terrace
Broughty Ferry
Dundee DD5 1EA
Tel: 01382 737938

Strathspey Angling Improvement Assn (SAIA)
c/o 3 High Street
Grantown on Spey
Morayshire PH26 3HB
Tel: 01479 872684
Fax: 01479 872211
mortimers@spey.fsnet.co.uk
www.speyfishing-grantown.co.uk

Thurso Angling Assn
Stanley Ogrodnik
Millhouse
Millbank Road
Thurso
Caithness KW14 8PS
Tel: 01847 893355

Tobermory Angling Club
Mike Beckett
5 Erray Road
Tobermory
Isle of Mull PA75 6PS
Tel: 01688 302447

Tongue & District Angling Club
c/o Ben Loyal Hotel
Main Street
Tongue
Sutherland IV27 4XE
Tel: 01847 611216

Turriff Angling Assn
Frank Henderson
6 Castle Street
Turriff,
Aberdeenshire AB53 7BJ
Tel: 01888 562428

Ullapool Angling Club
Sandy Mackenkie
14 West Shore Street
Ullapool
Ross shire
IV26 2UR
Tel: 01854 612061
Mob: 07770 492719

United Clyde Angling Protective Assn Ltd
Joseph Quigley
39 Hillfoot Avenue
Wishaw
Lanarkshire ML2 8TR
Tel: 01698 382479
www.ucapaltd.co.uk

Upper Annandale Angling Assn
A Dickson
Braehead Woodfoot
Beattock
Dumfries shire DG10 9PL
Tel: 01683 300592
www.riverannan.co.uk/upper

Upper Nithsdale Angling Club
K McLean
61 High Street
Sanquhar
Dumfriess shire DG4 6DT
Tel: 01659 50241

Vale of Leven & District Angling Club
George McKenzie
Tel: 01389 756645

Whiteadder Angling Assn
Colin McLachlan, Chairman
39 Easter Street
Duns
Berwickshire TD11 3DW
Tel: 01361 882499
or
Sarah Watson
Tel: 01361 883500
www.whiteadderanglingassociation.viviti.com

Wick Angling Assn
c/o Hugo Ross
56 High Street
Wick
Caithness KW1 4BP
Tel: 01955 604200
www.hugoross.co.uk

Opening day celebrations on the Tay, Dalmarnock beat
Photo: Colin Bradshaw

FISHING IN NORTHERN IRELAND

Fishing Boards, Licences, Close Seasons, etc.

For game fishers and coarse fishers alike, Northern Ireland is still a largely un-discovered country. There is a wealth of lakes, large and small; miles of quiet, clean rivers, plentifully stocked with large and healthy fish. By the standards of most other parts of Britain, all of it is under-fished. In recent years, coarse fishers have begun to find out what Northern Ireland has to offer, and there is much on offer for the game fisher too.

The visitor as yet unfamiliar with the province is recommended to concentrate on the waters owned and managed by the **Department of Culture, Arts & Leisure (DCAL)**, possibly the largest single fishery proprietor in Northern Ireland. They include some of the very best. DCAL's Inland Fisheries Branch has overall responsibility for the supervision and protection of Salmon and Inland Fisheries, and for the establishment and development of Inland Fisheries, in Northern Ireland (except for the Foyle and Carlingford catchments which are the responsibility of the Loughs Agency).

DCAL Inland Waterways and Inland Fisheries, Inland Fisheries, Causeway Exchange, 1-7 Bedford Street, Belfast BT2 7EG. (Tel: 028 90515119: email: dcalangling@dcalni.gov.uk; web: www.dcal-fishingni.gov.uk). DCAL is the ultimate authority for fisheries in Northern Ireland and publishes Angling Guides to the waters under its control, available from Fisheries Division at the above address, and from many tackle shops.

The Loughs Agency (FCILC), 22 Victoria Road, Londonderry BT47 2AB (tel: 028 7134 2100; fax: 028 7134 2720; email: general@loughs-agency.org; web: www.loughs-agency.org) also acts as a conservator and issues rod licences in the Foyle area: i.e. the North-Western parts of the province drained by the Foyle/Mourne/Camowen river systems and the rivers Faughan and Roe. The Agency is also responsible for a number of river systems in Co Donegal, R.O.I., including the Finn, Culdaff and Deele; and in the east, the Carlingford catchment. The Loughs Agency is a cross-border body.

The Northern Ireland Tourist Board, St Anne's Court, 59 North Street, Belfast BT1 1NB (tel: 028 9023 1221; fax: 028 9024 0960; web: www.nitb.com; email: info@nitb.com) is also involved in angling, concerning itself with marketing and promotion, and produces literature on activities and accommodation; also visitor attractions.

Rod Licences & Permits

A whole range of licences and permits are available from both DCAL and FCILC with a price list too complex to list here. The reader is advised to visit the following websites or enquire at the local tackle shop or fishery. See the followig websites for pricing:

DCAL: www.dcal-fishingni.gov.uk/index/permits_licences/permit_prices.htm
FCILC: www.loughs-agency.org/angling/content.asp?catid=36

The following game fishing licences are currently available from DCAL and the Loughs Agency (FCILC): (Game fishing licences also cover coarse fishing).

- Season, 14 day or 3 day game fishing rod licence
- Juvenile licence
- Concessionary licence for disabled and persons aged 60 and over
- Endorsement to DCAL/FCILC season game fishing rod licence
- There are also joint 3-day and 14-day DCAL licence/permits available.

The following coarse licences are currently available:

- DCAL: Season, 14 day or 3 day coarse fishing rod licence
- DCAL: Concessionary licence for disabled and persons aged 60 and over
- DCAL & FCILC: Juvenile licence for season
- FCILC: Season coarse fishing rod licence

Note: Permits are also needed to fish the waters.

Permits and licences to fish the DCAL and Loughs Agency waters are available throughout Northern Ireland at authorised distributors including many tackle shops and fisheries. Licences and permits can also be bought online at (web: www.dcal-fishingni.gov.uk).

Regulations & Seasons

Fishing seasons vary for the species fished and on the location of the fishery. Generally there is no close season for pike, bream, roach, perch, tench, rudd, carp and rainbow trout fishing. The seasons for salmon and wild brown trout fishing vary mainly by river catchment. For example in the Foyle catchment the salmon fishing season operates from 1 April to 20 October, in the Carlingford catchment it is from 1 April to 31 October while in the Bann catchment and the Co Antrim rivers the season is from 1 March to 31 October (except the River Bush where the season ends on 21 October). The season on the Erne catchment is 1 March to 30 September except for Lough Melvin (1 February to 30 September).

The following limits apply to Loughs Agency fishings:

- No salmon, brown trout or sea trout of less than 25.4cm (10 inches) may be retained
- Anglers must gill tag all wild salmon and sea trout over 40cm that are caught and retained - immediately on landing the fish
- 1st March - 31st May inclusive: bag limit 1 salmon or sea trout over 40cm on any one day; maximum of 5 in this period.
- 1st June - 31st October: bag limit 2 salmon or sea trout over 40cm on any one day; maximum of 20 in this period.

Detailed regulations vary considerably within each area and local fishery rules may also apply. Please enquire at the time of licence/permit purchase.

FISHING LOCATIONS IN NORTHERN IRELAND

As in other sections, principal catchment areas are dealt with in alphabetical order, and details of close seasons, licences, etc, will be found on preceding page. Anglers wanting further details of accommodation, etc, should write to **The Northern Ireland Tourist Board**, St Anne's Court, 59 North Street, Belfast BT1 1NB, (tel: 028 9023 1221; fax: 028 9024 0960; web: www.discovernorthernireland.com; info@nitb.com). Additionally, there are extensive fishings controlled by the Department of Culture, Arts and Leisure.

BANN (Lower)

A mainly sluggish river running approx 30m from where it leaves Lough Neagh to where it enters the sea below Coleraine. River is canalised at upper end. Good coarse fish and salmonoid population; sea trout fishing in the tideway. Non canal stretches, both coarse and game, are controlled by Bann System Ltd (below), and permits are obtainable; 10 year average salmon catch, 1,300 on Carnroe Beat, which is catch and release only up to 1st June and from then to the end of the season there is a 2 fish daily bag limit for salmon.

Coleraine (Co Londonderry). River tidal below Cutts where there is excellent fishing for sea trout and mullet – permits available from Bann System Ltd. Good game and coarse fishing above tidal stretches. Bann System Ltd, The Cutts, 54 Castleroe Rd, Coleraine BT51 3RL (tel: 028 703 44796; see website for more info: www.fishpal.com/Ireland/Bann/), offers day tickets for all beats on the Lower Bann including Carnroe, Portna, Movanagher and Culliff Rock from www.fishpal.com/Ireland/Bann/ through www.fishpal.com. There are also a limited number of syndicate rods available (check availability through Bann System Ltd.). These are excellent game beats and are not normally available for day ticket use so check www.fishpal.com/Ireland/ for availability. For River **Bush**, contact Department of Culture, Arts & Leisure Northern Regional Office, River Bush Salmon Station, 21 Church Street, Bushmills BT57 8QJ (tel: 028 2073 1435). Coleraine AA allow dt fishing on R Ree, and Ballinrees Reservoir (fly only; bag limit 6 trout); no boats allowed; also on 8m of **Macosquin River**: mainly trout, a few late sea trout and salmon (season 1 March to 31 Oct; dt for the river from www.fishpal.com/Ireland/Bann/ and from The Great Outdoors and Smyths Country Sports (below); no boats allowed on Macosquin. Agivey AA has 12m stretch on R Agivey plus stretch on **Wee Agivey**, nr **Garvagh**; salmon and brown trout; permits (£20 Agivey; £10 Wee Agivey), (£5 March to end May)) from the website: www.fishpal.com/Ireland/Bann/ and Mrs J McCann, 162 Agivey Rd, Aghadowey BT51 4AB (tel: 028 7086 8686); or Albert Atkins (below) for visitors; fishing has access for disabled. **Ballyrashane** Trout Lake, Creamery Rd: fly only, stocked r trout, dt £15, 4 fish limit, season all year; contact Ballyrashane AC at Smyths Country Sports (below). Tackle shops: Albert Atkins, 71 Coleraine Rd, Garvagh, BT51 5HP (tel: 028 295 57691); The Great Outdoors, 58 Society St BT52 1LA (tel: 028 7032 0701); Smyths Country Sports, 1 Park Street BT52 1BD (Tel: 028 7034

3970). Hotels: Bushtown House Hotel; Portneal Lodge, Kilrea; Brown Trout, Aghadowey.

Kilrea (Co Derry). Bann System Ltd, The Cutts, 54 Castleroe Rd, Coleraine BT51 3RL (tel: 028 7034 4796), offers beats. Trout dt on Kilrea & Dist AC waters (season 1 Apr to 15 Oct) (evening fishing best); dry fly and nymph fishing; from Sean Donaghy, Donaghy Brothers, 34 Maghera St, Kilrea BT51 5QN (tel: 028 295 40429). Salmon and brown trout; permits for Lower Bann, excluding special game section, from Albert Atkins, 71 Coleraine Rd, Garvagh, BT51 5HP (tel: 028 295 57691). Pike, bream, rudd and perch in local canals and loughs. Hotel: Portneal Lodge.

Portglenone (Co Antrim). Clady River joins Bann below town. Bann System Ltd, The Cutts, 54 Castleroe Rd, Coleraine BT51 3RL (tel: 028 7034 4796), offers beats on this stretch; brown trout, late salmon and dollaghen; dt £5 (Mar Aug), £15 (Sept Oct), from Clady & Dist AC, who control whole river and tributaries;

obtainable from the website: www.fishpal.com/Ireland/Bann/ and M Cushanan, Maura's Shop, 60 Main St BT44 8HF (tel: 028 25 822197); bag limit 2 salmon per day after 1 June; before that, all fish to be returned.

Toomebridge (Co Antrim). Here, the Lower Bann leaves L Neagh. Dept of Culture, Arts & Leisure controls Lower Bann Navigational Canal at **Toome**, **Portna** and **Movanagher**; tickets from tackle shops. Lough **Neagh**, with an area of 153 sq miles, is the largest inland water in the British Isles. It supports an immense commercial eel fishery, but apart from that, its potential is as yet largely untapped. The bottom feeding habits of Lough Neagh trout and the exposed conditions on this enormous stretch of water have so far discouraged anglers from trying to exploit it. A principal problem is the absence of sheltered bays. Tom Woods; salmon; dollaghan; ferox trout; pollan; contact him on (mob: 07743 550804); boat fishing.

BANN (Upper)

Flows west and north from its source in the Mourne Mountains to enter Lough Neagh near the middle of its southern shore at a point north of Portadown.

Portadown (Co Armagh). Pike, perch, roach, bream and trout. Dept of Culture, Arts & Leisure has 10m stretch from Portadown to Lough Neagh; a designated coarse fishery; licences from Fisheries Conservancy Board (tel: 028 3833 4666). Tackle shop: McIlduff Fishing, 2b Gilpinstown Road, Lurgan, Craigavon BT66 8RL (tel: 028 383 49709); G I Stores, 5 Dobbin St, Armagh BT61 7QQ (tel: 028 375 22335). Hotels: Carngrove; Seagoe.

Banbridge (Co Down). Late salmon, brown trout and coarse fish. Water from Hilltown Bridge to **Katesbridge**, and at Drumlough, controlled by Rathfriland AC; membership £30 plus £30 joining;

contact Hon Sec; dt £15 (river), £15 (lough), conc, available from Graham's Confectionery, 11 Downpatrick St, Rathfriland BT34 5BG (tel: 028 4063 8179). Clonduff AC has upper stretches of this river; good salmon and trout later in season, which ends 31 Oct; dt from Downshire Arms, Main St, Hilltown BT34 5PS (tel: 028 4063 8899). Banbridge AC fishes from Katesbridge to **Lenaderg**; browns, dollaghen and late salmon, and has 76 acre **Corbet Lough**, brown and rainbow trout, 4m from town; dt £10 lake, 6 boats available + wheelyboat (prebook by phone: tel: 028 406 25039), £4 river, conc, from Coburn's Ltd (see below); Anglers Rest, 42

Aughnacloy Rd, Katesbridge. Lough **Brickland**, 62 acres, Dept of Culture, Arts and Leisure (tel: 028 2954 0533), fly only, b and r trout. Altnadue Lake, stocked with rainbows. Gilford AC fishes from Hazelbank Weir, Lenaderg to Dynes Bridge, Moyallen, plus **Kernan Lake**; dt £10 for Kernan Lake; 3 fish limit; fly and spinning for rainbows; and River Bann from Spar Shop, 40 Mill St, Gilford BT63 6HQ (tel: 028 38 831087); for Upper Bann, R Moffat, Newsagent, Mill St, Gilford BT63 6HQ (tel: 028 38 831501): dt £2.50, £1 conc. Coarse fishing: **Newry Canal** (roach, bream, rudd, perch, pike); Lough **Shark**; Lakes **Drummillar**, **Drumaran**, **Drumnavaddy**; **Skillycolban** (Mill Dam, perch, pike, eels); Lakes **Ballyroney**, **Hunshigo**, **Ballyward**, **Ballymagreehan**, pike, perch; FCB coarse licence required; information, tackle, licences and permits from Coburn's Ltd, 32 Scarva St, Banbridge BT32 3DD (tel: 028 4066 2207). Rathfriland tackle shop: Rodgers Fishing Tackle, 109 Castlewellan Rd BT34 5EP (tel: 028 406 30093); information and guiding on Upper Bann for trout and salmon. Hotels: Belmont; Banville; Downshire.

Hilltown (Co Down). Dept of Culture, Arts & Leisure, Northern Region (tel: 028 4377 8937), have four good trout lakes, totalling more than 350 acres in the area: **Spelga**, **Castlewellan**, **Hillsborough**, **Lough Brickland**. Clonduff AC have water; dt from Devonshire Arms (below) or Killens Service Station. Castlewellan & Annsborough AC fish **Ballylough**, **Annsborough**, a few miles north east; brown and rainbow trout, fly only; also **Writes Lough** (smaller); all legal methods; bag limit 4 fish; day tickets from King's Inn (Chestnut) (see below). Shimna AC has **Altnadue Lough**, stocked with rainbows; dt for lough; wt and dt also available for Shimna River; from The Four Seasons, 47 Main Str, Newcastle BT33 0AD (tel: 028 437 25078). For dt for Corbet Lough (brown and rainbow), fly fishing from 6 boats (electric engines) and shore; and Keirnon Lough (rainbow), also Lough Brickland, contact Coburn's Ltd. Tackle shops: Coburn's Ltd, 32 Scarva St, Banbridge BT32 3DD (tel: 028 4066 2207). Hotels: Downshire Arms; Belmont, Banbridge; King's Inn (Chestnut), Lower Square, Castlewellan BT31 9DW (tel: 028 4377 8247).

BLACKWATER

The largest of the rivers flowing into L Neagh, rising in South Tyrone to enter the lough at its SW corner. Coarse fish and trout.

Blackwatertown (Co Armagh). Dept of Culture, Arts & Leisure has 1½m, mainly coarse fishing but short stretch of good game fishing (salmon, brown trout and dollaghan in season); fly, worm and spinning; permits from K Cahoon. Ulster Coarse Fishing Federation has water from Bond's Bridge to end of Argory Estate, a mixed fishery with excellent match weights; individuals may fish free on FCB licence. Several trout lakes near **Dungannon**: **Park** Lake (4.85 hectares); rainbow; permits issued by fishery and cost depends on time and option chosen; excellent access for disabled fishers and Wheelyboat available (tel: 028 8772 8690). **Altmore Fisheries** (2.5 hectares); rainbow trout; permits issued by fishery and cost will vary according to permit chosen (tel: 028 8775 8977). **Ballysaggart Lough**: bream, eels, perch, pike, roach, rudd, tench; no permit needed. Other local fishings include **Lough More**, Clogher, wild

browns. **Annaginny Lake,** Newmills (2.5 hectares); rainbow trout; fly fishing, spinning and worm fishing from shore; permits issued by fishery; various tickets available and cost dependant on option chosen; bookings and further information contact Alan Abraham (tel: 028 8774 7808); also coarse lake; bream, roach; and a pike lake. **Carnteel Lough,** pike, perch and roach; **Carrick Lough,** bream, roach, perch, tench, pike &c and **Greeve** (18 hectares); bream, roach, perch, tench, pike (to 35lb) and eels; dt not required; disabled access available on both sides. **Brantry** (24.4 hectares); brown trout, fly fishing only; 4 fish per rod/day; min length 25.4cm; 1 Mar 31 Oct; boats only; permit required; information from Parks & Countryside Manager, Dungannon Park Pavilion, Moy Rd, Dungannon BT71 6DY (c/o tel: 028 8776 7259; fax: 028 8772 9169; email: dpreception@dungannon.gov.uk).
Tackle shops: K Cahoon, Cahoon Jewellers, 2/3 Irish St, Dungannon BT70 1DB (tel: 028 8772 2754) for licences; Lakeview Tackle, 106 Ballygawley Rd, Dungannon BT70 1 TA (tel: 028 8776 1133); G I Stores, 5 Dobbin St, Armagh BT61 7QQ (tel: 028 375 22335).

Moy (Co Tyrone). 250m upstream and 100m downstream of Moy town bridge; pike, bream, perch, rudd, roach; licence required for 12yrs and above; dt not required; no disabled access. Tackle shop: G I Stores, 5 Dobbin St, Armagh BT61 7QQ (tel: 028 375 22335). Hotels: Charlemont House; Tomney's Licensed Inn, 9 The Square, BT71 7SG (tel: 028 8778 4755) for Blackwater and Bann rivers, Brantry Lough and Lough Neagh.

Benburb (Co Tyrone). Trout for 2½m downstream. Armagh & Dist Game AC leases or owns stretch on river, and seven lakes; it also has its own hatchery, stocking brown trout from its own brood stock, and rainbows

reared from fingerlings; for day tickets contact tackleists; adult st £80, juv st £10, dt £15 from G I Stores (see Armagh). Dept of Culture, Arts & Leisure has **Brantry Lough** (brown trout), White Lough (rainbow); and Loughs **Creeve LoughEnagh** (5.3 hectares); bream, roach, perch, hybrids, tench, pike and eels; 22 disabled access points available (tel: 028 2954 0533). Tackle shop: Crawford Sports, 34 Main St, Maghera BT46 5AE (tel: 028 796 42672). Dept of Culture, Arts & Leisure (tel: 028 6634 3136) also has coarse fishing on **Clay Lake,** nr **Keady** (Co Armagh); 120 acres, pike rudd and perch, open all year.

Clogher, Augher and **Aughnacloy.** (Co Tyrone). Local stretch of river has undergone fishery rehabilitation following a major drainage scheme of the Blackwater River. Permits from Aughnacloy AC, and landowners. Dt from Farmers Maxol Garage, Augher/Clogher Rd; Gordon McLaren, Main St, Augher. Permission from landowners for tributaries: **Callan, Oona** and **Torrent.** For Coalisland & Dist AC water: brown trout, a few salmon and dollaghen later in season; free fishing; for membership contact Hon Sec. Dept of Culture, Arts & Leisure (tel: 028 9025 8870) has rainbow trout fishing on **White Lough** (9.3 hectares); rainbow trout; 4 fish per day, min. size 10in; fly only from boats, otherwise, spinning and worming permitted; permit required. **Carrick Lough** (4 hectares); bream, roach, perch, tench, pike and eels; licence required for 12yrs and above. Tackle shop: Glenkeen Trout Fishery, 194 Caledon Rd, Aughnacloy BT69 6JD.

Armagh (Co Armagh). Beside River **Callan,** centre for Blackwater and its tributaries, with many fishing lakes in district. Six of these are controlled by Armagh Fisheries Ltd, The Hatchery, 50 Ballinahonemore Rd, BT60 1HY (tel: 028 3751 1738) incorporating Armagh & Dist Game AC, who offer adult st £80, juv st £10, dt £15 from G I Stores (see below); fly only on **Shaw's Lake** (brown trout, rainbow & perch) and Segahan Reservoir (164 acres) (brown and rainbow); also **Tullynawood Reservoir** (148 acres) (mainly brown trout and rainbow, but also pike, perch, roach & rudd) and **Darkley Lake** (coarse fish) and **Lowrys Lake** (brown trout & rainbow); also for 9m of Callan and Blackwater; fly only on **Aughnagorgan Lake** (brown trout and rainbow); 6 fish bag limit on each lake; limited disabled access only on Lowrys Lake. Loughgall Country Park Coarse Fishery, 11/14 Main St, Loughgall BT61 8HZ (tel: 028 3889 2900; see website for more info: www.loughgallcountrypark.co.uk): coarse fishery: pike to 30lb, carp (up to 25lb), perch, bream, roach, rudd, eels, tench; stand for disabled; st and dt available, conc for juv; tickets on site £3.20, conc; disability facilities. Tackle shop: G I Stores, 5 Dobbin St, BT61 7QQ (tel: 028 375 22335; e-mail des@gistores.com). Hotels: Armagh City, 2 Friary Rd, BT60 4FR (tel: 028 3751 8888); Charlemont Arms, 63 65 Upper English St, BT61 7BH (tel: 028 3752 2028), both Armagh City.

SMALLER RIVERS EMPTYING INTO LOUGH NEAGH

MAINE (Co Antrim): Flows 25m from source in Glarryford Bogs to enter lough south of Randalstown, Co Antrim. With tributaries **Kellswater, Braid, Clough** and Glenwherry provides good fishing for salmon, trout and dollaghan. Braid AC waters: dt from McNeill's Hardware, 75 Main St, Broughshane BT42 4JP (tel: 028 2586 1629). Gracehill, Galgorm & DAC has 3m water at **Ballymena**, brown trout with salmon from July; 4 fish limit, no spinning until Aug 1, no maggot fishing; stretch for disabled; dt £5 Mar to Aug, £10 Sept to Oct, with conc, from Galgorm PO, 5 Fenaghy Rd; Clogh PO, 17 Main St; Mid Antrim Angling Centre, 14 William Street, Ballymena BT43 6AW (tel: 028 2564 8159). Randalstown AC controls Maine from **Randalstown** Road Bridge to Andraid Ford, Kellswater; trout, with salmon and dollaghan in season; dt £5 (per rod per day) Mar to Jun, £10 (per rod per day) rest of season, available from New Street Filling Station; no Sunday fishing permitted for dt; also from The Tackle Box, 6 New Street, Randalstown BT41 3AF (tel: 028 9447 9010). Demesne Anglers has water from Randalstown Bridge to Lough Neagh; wt, dt from The Estate Office, Shanes Castle, Antrim BT41 4NE (tel: 028 94 428216); advance booking recommended. Kells, Connor & Glenwherrey AC has dt £8 1 March to 31 June; Jul to Aug £12; Sept £15 to 16 Oct (no dt after that); bag limit 4 fish (incl 1 salmon per day); for fishing on Kells and Glenwherry; b trout, dollaghan and late salmon run; fly only 1 March to 31 July; shrimp and maggot not allowed; dt from Flack's Shop, Moorfields; and Kilgad Lake Trout Fishery, Kilgad, Kells BT42 3HY (tel: 028 2589 2806); also Mid Antrim Angling Centre (below). Dept of Culture, Arts & Leisure (tel: 028 2954 0533) has brown trout fishing on **Dungonnell** and **Killylane** Reservoirs, 70 and 50 acres; limit 4 fish. Maine AC issues dt £12 to £8 (depending on season) on 4 miles of river from above **Cullybackey** Weir to 1m above Dunminning Bridge; brown trout, dollaghen and salmon; dt from The Bridge Garage, Cullybackey, Ballymena BT42 1EB (tel: 028 258 80278). Tackle shops: The Great Outdoors, 20 Broughshane Street, Ballymena BT43 6EB (tel: 028 256 47187/53433), tickets for Department waters and Bann System; Mid Antrim

Angling Centre, 14 William Street, Ballymena BT43 6AW (tel: 028 2564 8159). Hotels: Adair Arms; Leighinmore House and Tullyglass House, Ballymena.

SIXMILEWATER: Flows 15m from Ballyclare to enter lough at Antrim, at its NE corner. A heavily fished but highly productive trout water, salmon and dollaghen Sept Oct; water has improved significantly over past few years, particularly in lower stretches for salmon, owing to restocking programme by both clubs. Antrim & Dist AC issues st £100, dt £5 (Mar July), £12 (Aug Oct), conc, for water between Doagh and Antrim; tickets from Country Sports (below); Twelfth Milestone, 954 Antrim Rd, Templepatrick, Ballyclare BT39 0AT (tel: 028 9443 2647); Antrim Town Tourist Office. Ballynure AC has water from Doagh to **Ballynure**; brown trout, salmon; dt from Doagh Service Station and Milestone Service Station at Ballyclare. Dunadry Hotel and Country Club, 2 Islandreagh Drive, Dunadry BT41 2HA (tel: 028 9443 4343), has fishing for guests on Sixmilewater, which passes through hotel grounds; salmon, browns, rainbow; also issues permits and licences for Straid, Ballyclare; Riverdale, Kells; Kildarg, Antrim; dt prices according to season. Ballynure AC issues dt £5 Mar Jul, £8 Aug Oct, for water between Doagh and **Ballynure**, from Ballyclare Milestone, 91 Templepatrick Rd, Ballyclare BT39 9RQ (tel: 028 9335 2063); Doagh Forecourt Centre, 10 Station Rd, Doagh BT39 0QT (tel: 028 9334 0215). **Potterswalls Reservoir**, off Steeple Rd, nr Antrim, has rainbow trout fishing (fly only) for members and visitors; dt £8 from Country Sports. Dept of Culture, Arts & Leisure (tel: 028 2954 0533) has trout fishing on **Woodburn Reservoirs** (six), nr **Carrickfergus**; Upper South (65 acres); Middle South (64 acres); Lower South (22 acres);

North (18 acres); Lough Mourne (127 acres); Copeland (Marshallstown) (24 acres); Upper and Lower South, fly only; the rest are fly, spinning, worm; North Woodburn, rainbow; others, rainbow and brown; bag limit 4 fish. Tackle shop: Vaughan Harkness, Country Sports & Tackle, 9 Rough Lane, off Steeple Rd, Antrim BT41 2QG (tel: 028 9446 7378). The Tourist Information, 11 Antrim St, Carrickfergus sells fishing permits for dams and reservoirs. Hotel: Dunadry Inn on banks of river. Ballyclare accommodation: Mr & Mrs Max McConnell, Five Corners Guest House, 249 Rashee Rd, BT39 9JN (fully licensed).

CRUMLIN and **GLENAVY** (Co Antrim): small rivers which flow west through these villages to enter lough. Trout fishing near their mouths. Crumlin & Dist AA water: dt from Glenview Service Station, 16 Mill Rd, Crumlin. Centre: Crumlin. Accommodation: Hillvale Farm, 11 Largy Rd.

BALLINDERRY: Flows east for approx 30m, through **Cookstown**, to enter lough about midway along west shore. Good fishing for brown trout, dollaghan, and occasional salmon for 20m up from the mouth. Kildress AC has fishing 3m from Cookstown, on A505 Omagh road, with trout, dollaghan and salmon, main species; members only, membership from Hon Sec: £15 per season; contact Hon Sec. Tickets from Hon Sec, David Hagan (028 867 37055) or Hon Treasurer for 2m of Unipork & Coagh AC water at Coagh, for dt contact Nearby, Main Street, Coagh. Ballinderry Bridge AC has 3m of water; membership £25; dt £5 from McCrystals Filling Station, Ballinderry Bridge Rd; P Devlin, Scotstown Rd (tel: 028 867 37420) and Ryans Shop, Ballyronan; access, facilities for disabled provided; for all other information contact Leo Cassidy MBE (see Clubs). Kingsbridge AC has 2m; water much improved by new water treatment works; 2 salmon per angler per day after 1 June (before, all fish to be returned); all legal methods, but no ground bait, maggots, prawn and shrimp; permit also covers stretches of Grange River: dt from Stanley Aspinall, 3 Rathbeg, Cookstown BT80 8HR (tel: 028 867 65905). 2m in the Ardtrea area and **Lough Fea** (also stocked with rainbows) is fished by the Mid Ulster AC; dt £10 from The Burnavon Arts Centre, Burn Rd; The Royal Hotel, Coagh St (tel: 028 867 62224); Millburn Filling Station, all Cookstown. Tackle shop: Crawford Sports, 34 Main St, Maghera BT46 5AE (tel: 028 796 42672). Hotels: Royal Hotel, Coagh St; Glenavon House, Drum Rd; Greenvale, Drum Rd, all Cookstown, Co Tyrone.

MOYOLA (Co Londonderry): Flows east and south from its source in S Derry to enter lough at NW corner. Brown trout in lower reaches and a run of salmon from July. Fishing rights held by Moyola AA, dt www.fishpal.com/Ireland/ and Huestons, 55 Main St, Castledawson, Magherafelt, BT45 8AA (tel: 028 794 68282); Crawford Sports, 34 Main St, Maghera BT46 5AE (tel: 028 796 42672). Accommodation: Laurel Villa Guest House, 60 Church St, Magherafelt, BT45 6AW (tel: 028 793 01459).

BUSH

The Bush flows 30m west and north through Bushmills, Co Antrim, to enter the sea near Portballintrae. The fishing rights of the entire catchment have been acquired by the Dept of Culture, Arts & Leisure primarily as an experimental river for studies into the biology and management of salmon. Within the terms of this programme, salmon angling is maintained at the highest possible level. Trout in the Bush and its tributaries are small but plentiful: there is a modest run of spring salmon and a grilse run for which the river is best known which begins in June or July, according to flow. It is important to report catches of fin clipped fish. Bush season has been extended from 1 Mar to 20 Oct. Full details from the booking office in the Salmon Station (tel: 028 2073 1435; web: www.dcal-fishingni.gov.uk).

For angling management, the river is divided into the following sections: the Dundarave Stretch; the New Stretch (500 yds); the Town Stretch about 200 yds downstream of the Project Centre at Bushmills; the Leap Stretch upstream (approx 600 yds of water); and the Unrestricted Stretch, the remaining 24m of fishing water. Special daily permits, which may be booked in advance, are required for the Dundarave, New, Town, and Leap stretches, as shown under 'Licences, permits and close seasons.' Weekend or Bank Holiday angling must be booked and paid for by 1300 hours on the preceding Friday or normal working day. Half day tickets are sold for the Dundarave, New, Town, and Leap stretches from 1 June to 20 Oct. Tributary: **Stracam River,** flowing through the village of that name, offers 2m of good trout fishing. (For details of permit charges see under Boards).

Bushmills (Co Antrim). Salmon, sea trout and brown trout. Dundarave Estates water now run by DCAL; excellent salmon fishing stretch from Bushmills to the sea; dt price depends on season; now run by Dept of Culture, Arts & Leisure which also has short stretches (Town, New, Dunderave and Leap) near Bushmills; stands for disabled on bank; dt from The Hatchery, and should be booked in advance; contact Northern Regional Office, 21 Church St, Bushmills BT57 8QJ (tel: 028 2073 1435). Tackle shop: Causeway Bait & Tackle, 106 Main St, Bushmills BT57 8QD (tel: 028 2073 0025). Hotels: Bushmills Inn; Antrim Arms, Ballycastle.

Ballymoney (Co Antrim). Bush River may be fished for salmon, brown trout, as can the Ballymoney Burn. Good coarse fishing on **Movanagher Canal** and R **Bann**, salmon, trout from 1 June. Brown and rainbow trout fishing on **Altnahinch Reservoir**, at head of R Bush; Dept of Culture, Arts & Leisure water, 44 acres, bag limit 4 fish, bank fishing only; fly, worm, spinning; permits from car wash, Rodeing Foot; E J Cassells & Son, 43/45 Main St, Ballymoney BT53 6AN (tel: 028 2766 3216).

LOUGH ERNE (Upper and Lower)

Upper and Lower Lough Erne, with the R Erne and tributaries feeding the loughs, comprise 15,300 hectares of mixed game and coarse fishing owned and annually restocked by the Dept of Culture, Arts & Leisure (tel: 028 6634 3166) and offering some of the best sport in Europe. The flow is in a NW direction, through the beautiful and largely unspoilt Fermanagh countryside, via Belleek, to where the R Erne reaches the sea at Ballyshannon. Infinitely varied fishing in the lakes, with innumerable secluded bays, inlets and small islands. Rich, unpolluted waters teeming with fish life, the Erne system is truly an angler's paradise. Centres: Belleek; Kesh; Enniskillen; Bellanaleck; Lisnaskea; Newtownbutler; Derrygonnelly (Tirnavar).

RIVER ERNE. River heavily populated with large bream and roach, pike of record breaking proportions. Good salmon runs in late summer and autumn. Belleek, Co Fermanagh, is a good centre for fishing river and Lower Lough; limit, 6 fish. Also brown and rainbow trout on Lough Keenaghan, 38 acres; fly only. Scolban Lough (171 acres) has pike to 20lb as main quarry, also perch, and is stocked with rainbow trout to 2lb by Dept of Culture, Arts & Leisure (tel: 028 6634 3136).

LOWER LOUGH ERNE. The trout fishing areas, in which the fish may run very large, are in the north and west of the lake. Recommended areas are from Roscor Bridge up to the Heron Island, and across to the Garvary River. South and east of a dividing line, the lake may be fished on coarse fishing licence and permit only.

TRIBUTARIES FEEDING LOWER LOUGH: Ballinamallard River flows south through the village of Ballinamallard, to enter the lake near St Angelo Airport. Dept of Culture, Arts & Leisure controls 1 mile nr Ballinamallard, brown trout; Ballinamallard & Dist AC controls the rest; brown trout; fishing by licence. **Colebrook** and **Tempo** enter lake from the east; Maguiresbridge & Dist AC has fishing here; dt from Hon Sec; also available is a small private rainbow trout lake, Colebrook lake; all fly only. 2 miles of Colebrook is Dept of Culture, Arts & Leisure Designated Coarse fishery, nr Lisnaskea: roach, bream, perch, rudd, eels, the occasional pike, trout and salmon. Ballinamallard and Colebrook rivers are currently being stocked with juvenile salmon as part of a cross border salmon enhancement initiative for the Erne system. Tackle shop: Home, Field & Stream, 18/20 Church Str, Enniskillen BT74 7EJ (tel: 028 663 22114).

UPPER LOUGH ERNE: Principally coarse fish: pike, eel, perch, rudd, bream, roach, occasional salmon and sea trout. Centres: **Lisnaskea**; **Newtown Butler**; **Enniskillen**. The National Trust at Crom Estate has fishing on Inisherk and Derryvore Islands, with excellent bream and roach; dt £5 in advance from Sharon Sey, Gate Lodge, Crom Estate, Newtownbutler, Fermanagh (tel: 028 6773 8825); stocked pike lake dt £10, very limited; boats for hire, contact Visitors Centre, Crom Estate BT92 8AP (tel: 028 6773 8118); also for accommodation at National Trust Holiday Cottages and Belle Isle (disabled facility). At Castle Coole, Lough **Coole**, National Trust water now private. Carrybridge Hotel & Marine Centre, 171 Inishmore Rd, Lisbellaw BT94 5NF (tel: 028 6638 7148), is situated on Upper Lough Erne, and has boats, engines, bait, tackle, storage on site. For Belle Isle Estate game and pike fishing including on **Colebrooke River**, contact agent, Lisbellaw, Enniskillen BT94 5HG (tel: 028 6638 7231; see website for more: www.belleisle-estate.com); William Ross Magee (tel: 028 6638 7077) supplies bait. **Mill Lough, Bellanaleck**: 100 acres Dept of Culture, Arts & Leisure r and b trout fishery 4 miles from Enniskillen, 4 fish limit. **Killyfole Lough**, 56 acres, nr Lisnaskea, has a variety of coarse fish, incl perch and pike; permits from Erne Tackle (below). Tackle shop: Erne Tackle, 121 Main Str, Lisnaskea BT92 0JD (tel: 028 677 21969). Hotels: Killyhevlin Hotel, Killyhevlin BT74 6RW (tel: 028 6632 3481): has chalets on banks of Erne, most with fishing stages; Manor House; Railway; both Enniskillen; and Donn Cara, Lisnaskea. Riverside Farm, Gortadrehid, Enniskillen BT92 2FN (tel: 028 6632 2725) has permits, accommodation with boats and bait supplied.

TRIBUTARIES FEEDING UPPER LOUGH ERNE: Swanlinbar River flows north from Co Cavan to enter the lough midway on the S side. Coarse fish in lower reaches, trout in upper. Permission from landowners. The **Sillees** River flows from above Derrygonelly to enter the lough between Enniskillen and Lisgoole Abbey. Excellent coarse fishing, some trout. **Arney** River flows from Lower Lough Macnean to Upper Lough Erne (large trout and exceptional pike fishing) to enter Upper L Erne near **Bellanaleck**. Good mixed fishing all the way to Lough **Macnean**. Upper and Lower L Macnean both have coarse fishing on them, notably pike. Permits from tackle shops in Bellanaleck and Enniskillen. Also four Dept trout lakes of various sizes in the area (5 acres to 100 acres), including the famous **Navar Forest Lakes**, and **Mill Lough** at Bellanaleck which holds trout to 5lb. Dept of Culture, Arts & Leisure permits for Mill Lough, Navar Forest Lakes, and Keenaghan Lough, from Belleek Angling Centre, Main St, Belleek, BT93 3FX (tel: 028 6865 8181), and tackle shops in Enniskillen, including Home, Field & Stream, 18 Church Str, Enniskillen, Co Fermanagh BT74 7EJ (tel: 028 663 22114).

FOYLE

The Foyle system is half in Northern Ireland, half in the Republic. It is formed by the **Derg** (draining Lough Derg) and the **Strule**, constituting the **Mourne**, which unites with the **Finn** at Strabane to become the Foyle proper, which enters the sea at Londonderry. That part of the system in Northern Ireland, including the **Faughan** and **Roe**, is the largest salmon and trout fishery in the country. It drains the north and west slopes of the Sperrin Mountains and most of Co Tyrone. Note there are new angling regulations on the rivers in the Foyle System most notable is that the River Foyle and River Finn are now catch and release only. Please check regulations on the Loughs Agency website.

Londonderry. River tidal here, with best fishing for salmon in tidal pools from July. Also a run of sea trout. Permits from Foyle Commission. Tackle shops: Rod and Line, 1 Clarendon St, BT48 7EP (tel: 028 7126 2877); Tom's Tackle Shop, The Gate Lodge, 31 Ardlough Rd, Waterside, Drumahoe BT47 5SP (tel: 028 7134 6265). Hotels: White Horse, 68 Clooney Rd, Campsie (tel:028 7186 0606); Everglades, Prehen Rd BT47 2NH (tel: 028 7132 1066); Broomhill, Limavady Rd, Londonderry BT47 1LT (tel: 028 7134 7995).

Strabane (Co Tyrone). Here **Mourne** and **Strule** unite to form Foyle.

Salmon and sea trout. No dt as such, but st £20 for **Finn** from Flushtown Bridge to Castlefinn Bridge; £20 for Foyle section; contact Martin McDaid, North West Country Sports, 19 Butchers Street, Strabane BT82 8BJ (tel: 028 7188 3021) who issues st and dt for rivers Foyle, Finn, Mourne, Derg, Dennett, Deel; he also can arrange accommodation and supplies ghillies; tickets also from Loughs Agency, 22 Victoria Rd, Londonderry BT47 2AB (tel: 028 7134 2100). Dept of Culture, Arts & Leisure has five lakes in the area (tel: 028 6634 3136). Fir Trees Hotel, Dublin Rd BT82 9EA (tel: 028 7138 2382), offers fishing breaks.

Tributaries of the Foyle

MOURNE: A big river which provides salmon, sea trout, brown trout; excellent fly fishing in the 10m between Strabane and Newtownstewart, but largely private; tickets obtainable from the website www.fishfoyle.com and from Abercorn Estates, Baronscourt Estate Office, Newtownstewart, BT78 4EZ (tel: 028 8166 1683; see website for more info: www.barons-court.com); bag limit salmon/grilse refer to Loughs Agency guidelines; ghillie essential; available to guests at apartments; prices on application.

Sion Mills (Co Tyrone). Excellent 4m stretch (both banks) from Strabane to Victoria Bridge managed by Sion Mills AC (membership closed, but dt available from www.fishpal.com only); salmon, sea, brown, white trout; bag limits 2 fish after end May (one before); season limit 25 fish; fly, spinning worm allowed; access for disabled; permits from Hon Sec. Tackle shop: N M Tackle, 131 Melmount Rd, Sion Mills, Strabane BT82 9PY (tel: 028 8165 9501); N M Tackle arranges fishing with day and week permits for various other waters including **Finn River**, **Derg River**

and **Ardstraw River**; advice and information on fishing, local clubs, and accommodation; also instruction. Hotel: Fir Trees, Dublin Rd, Strabane BT82 9EA.

Newtownstewart (Co Tyrone). The **Owenkillew** and **Glenelly** enter here, offering 30m of ideal game fishing waters noted for their sea trout, salmon and brown trout; bag limit 2/day (min 10"); Game licence £3.50/3 days, £8/14 days, £16.50 season; all waters Foyle System (available from Treanor's (below). Owenkillew is spate river, only worth fishing in Jun/Oct. For lower reaches (Glen Owen stretch) of Owenkillew at Newtownstewart contact David Campbell, 12 Killymore Rd, Newtownstewart, Omagh BT78 4DT (tel: 028 8166 1543); salmon, sea and brown trout; dt £20. For **Gortin** fishing on Owenkillew and Owenrea, contact Gabriel Treanor, Treanor's Butchers (below). Blakiston Houston Estate has fishing on 2m stretch of **Owenkillew**; salmon and sea trout; limited fly only dt £15, from Gabriel Treanor (Butcher's Shop), 56 Main St, Gortin, Omagh BT79 8NH (tel: 028 8164 8543). Omagh AA holds most of fishing rights on Mourne, Strule & Owenkillew around this area, (some 28 miles) and offers dt £20; also from C A Anderson. Also Gaff AC (membership £60) dt £20 on **Glenelly** River, and on Owenkillew from David Campbell, 12 Killymore Rd, Newtownstewart, Omagh BT78 4DT (tel: 028 8166 1543), who also offers B&B and self catering accommodation, also with private fishing on Rivers **Mourne**: salmon, brown trout, sea trout. Tackle shop: C A Anderson & Co, Guns & Tackle, 64 Market Str, Omagh BT78 1EN (tel: 028 8224 2311).

STRULE: Very good trout fishing from Omagh to Newtownstewart; salmon, sea trout and brown trout; bag limit 4/day (min 10"); Omagh AA; game licence: £20 dt, apply David Campbell (above).

Omagh (Co Tyrone). Dept of Culture, Arts & Leisure controls the coarse fishing on a stretch of R Strule by arrangement with Omagh AA; roach and eels; assn also controls stretches of Camowen, Owenkillew and Drumragh Rivers; salmon, sea & brown trout; bag limit 2/day (min 10"); game licence £5 /3days; rod £11 /14days; dt £20 (club permit). LoughMuck (35 acres), 3m south of Omagh; pike (up to 30lbs) and roach, perch and eels; privately owned; 12 pegs available and boats can be hired; dt £7 /rod (£1 for each extra rod) and boats £20 /day; contact Kenny Alcorn, Lakeview House, Loughmuck, Omagh BT78 1TG (tel: 028 8224 2618). More good fishing upstream of Omagh, to Camowen, but fish smaller; salmon in season. Owenragh, Quiggery/Fintona and Drumragh enter near **Omagh**. Dept stillwaters, Loughs Bradan and **Lough Lee**, 60 and 37 acres, 5 miles from Castlederg; brown trout fishing now private. Permits for Omagh AA water; new membership £45 +£45 joining, dt £20, conc, from

tackle shop, C A Anderson & Co, Guns & Tackle, 64 Market Street, Omagh BT78 1EN (tel: 028 8224 2311) or from David Campbell, 12 Killymore Rd, Newtownstewart, Omagh BT78 4DT (tel: 028 8166 1543). Hotels: Silverbirch, 5 Gortin Rd, Omagh BT79 7DH (tel: 028 8224 2520). Further information: Omagh TIC, 1 Market Str, Omagh BT78 1EE (tel: 028 8224 7831; fax: 028 8224 0774).

FAIRYWATER: Flows E from Drumquin (trout) to enter **Strule** below Omagh; remarkably good roach fishing in lower reaches; no permit required. **Burn Dennett River**, **Dunamanagh**: small brown trout, occasional salmon and sea trout in season; fly, spinning and worm; dt from Burn Dennet AA.

DERG: flows E from Donegal for 50m to enter **Mourne** N of **Newtownstewart**. Spate river. Good trout water for 15m to above Castlederg, Co Tyrone, with salmon (late June and July best), fine head of wild brown trout, and sea trout; Castlederg AC has 14m, both banks; d/s from the Border Bridge (near Lough Derg) to Spamount (except for short private stretch); dt £15, £40 weekly from H Irwin (see clubs); excellent fly water; spinning and worming permitted; wt £20; dt £15. Pettigo & Dist AA has much fishing on offer including 3m of R Derg and the Lough; dt £7; boat £10 for Lough; from Pettigo PO, Main St; Britton's Bar, Pettigo (tel: 00353 7198 61519) or contact Hon Sec (who does B&B and boat hire on Lough Erne). Tackle Shops: C A Anderson & Co, Guns & Tackle, 64 Market Str, Omagh BT78 1EN (tel: 028 82 8224 2311) or from David Campbell, 12 Killymore Rd, Newtownstewart, Omagh BT78 4DT (tel: 028 8166 1543/1167).

FAUGHAN and ROE

The Faughan flows N for 20m to enter the Foyle area E of Londonderry city; the Roe flows the same distance in the same general direction to enter the Foyle Estuary N of Limavady, Co Londonderry. Salmon, sea trout and brown trout in Faughan; principally sea trout in Roe, but also salmon from July.

FAUGHAN: River Faughan Anglers Ltd lease the fishing rights of tributaries and main river, a 30 mile stretch of water divided into two sections, approx 2m tidal and 28m freshwater, situated between Londonderry and Park; both sections are productive of sea trout and salmon; limited access for disabled anglers, left hand bank below Campsie Bridge and left bank at Claudy Bridge; waiting list for season permits; st £67, 2 week £120, 3 day £50, dt £20, conc 2 week £60; Foyle licences: season £21.50, 2 week £10.50, 3 day £5.00, all from www.fishpal.com and River Faughan Anglers Ltd (see clubs); or from Loughs Agency, 22 Victoria Rd, Londonderry BT47 2AB (tel: 028 7134 2100).

ROE:

Limavady (Co Londonderry). Good fishing for 15m from Limavady to Dungiven. Dept of Culture, Arts & Leisure has 1¼m at **O'Cahan's Rock**, S of Limavady, with salmon and sea trout. Roe AA offers 26 day tickets for most of a 34 mile stretch, both banks, from source to river mouth, from www.fishpal.com and Limavady tackle shops, £15; no dt during Oct; sea trout av 1lb, salmon 8lbs. Tackle shop: S J Mitchell & Co, Central Car Park, Limavady BT49 0ER (tel: 028 7772 2128) information on all local fishings, issues permits and is a reliable source of local information. Hotels: Alexander Arms; Raddisson, Roe Park; many guest houses.

GLENS OF ANTRIM RIVERS

CUSHENDALL: Enters sea at Cushendall. Good runs of sea trout Jul Oct. Occasional late salmon, small native brown trout. Fly, spinning, worm permitted, no bait digging allowed.

GLENARIFF: Small sea trout river which enters sea at Waterfoot. Good runs of sea trout Jul Oct, occasional late salmon, small native brown trout. Fly, spinning, worm permitted, but no bait digging allowed.

GLENDUN: Enters sea at **Cushendun**. Fair run of late salmon (c&r), primarily Sept Oct, and sea trout Jul Oct. Fly, spinning, no worm, no bait digging allowed. All three rivers controlled by Glens AC; dt £10 in Oct,

otherwise £5; available at O'Neills Country Sports, Unit 1, 25 Mill St, Cushendall, Co Antrim, BT44 0RR (tel: 028 217 72009). Many guest houses in locality.

MARGY/CAREY/
GLENSHESK/TOW: a system of small rivers entering the sea at **Ballycastle**. Sea trout, brown trout and salmon; Dept of Culture, Arts & Leisure waters; dt on bank; dt for non DCAL holders, from R Bell (below). Hotels: Antrim Arms, Ballycastle; Thornlea, Cushendun. Tackle shop: Moyle Outdoor Angling & Leisure, 23 Ann St BT54 6AA (tel: 028 2076 9521); R Bell, 40 Ann St, Ballycastle BT54 6AD (tel: 028 2076 2520).

LAGAN

A productive salmon and brown trout river which flows into the Belfast Lough. Trout fishing upstream from Magheralin, Co Down, for 12m.

Belfast (Co Antrim). Dept of Culture, Arts & Leisure has 2¼m of game and coarse coarse fishing on R Lagan; permits from: Tight Lines (below: not open Mon); J Braddell (below). Dundonald AC Ltd fishes **Lough Creevy**, Ballylone Rd, nr Saintfield: rainbow trout, pike; limited dt £15 from George Legge, 41 Geary Rd, Belfast BT5 7QS (tel: 028 9079 6061). Further information from TIC, 35 39 Donegall Place BT1 1NB (tel: 028 9024 6609). Holywood FFC fish lakes 4m from Dublin: Creitons Green, Upper Holywood; dt from Herrins Shop, Holywood; further information from Hon Sec. Tackle shop: Wolsey's Tackle Shop, 60 Upper Newtownards Rd BT4 3EN (tel: 028 9047 1131); Tight Lines, 198/200 Albertbridge Rd BT5 4GU (tel: 028 9045 7357); J Braddell & Son Ltd, 11 North St, BT1 1NA (tel: 028 9032 2657; fax 028 9032 0525).

Lisburn (Co Antrim). Iveagh AC has stretch of 7 miles from Thornyford Bridge, Dromore, to Spencer's Bridge, Flatfield; 10 free dt for holders of Dept of Culture, Arts & Leisure annual game season permit; dt £5 from: McIlduff Fishing, 2b Gilpinstown Road, Lurgan, Craigavon BT66 8RL (tel: 028 383 49709). Lisburn & Dist AC fish on 7 miles of **Lagan** between Lisburn and Moira, containing a fair head of b trout, roach, bream; also a stretch of a small tributary, the **Ravarnette**, with b trout to 3lb not uncommon, also roach and bream; this fishing is open to general public with no charge; club membership is £12 p/a. Dept of Culture, Arts & Leisure (tel: 028 9025 8870) has brown and/or rainbow trout lakes, totalling more than 700 acres, in the Lagan Valley area; near to Belfast, these waters are fished more heavily than most in N Ireland; they also include **Stoneyford Reservoir**, 160 acres, b and r trout, fly, spinning and worm, 4 fish limit, no boat angling; **Ballykeel Loughherne**, 53 acres, b and r trout, fly only. Abundant coarse fishing on canals and loughs Henney, **Begney**, **Aghery**, **Neagh**; all with pike, perch, etc. Tackle shop: Jack Smyth Angling & Outdoors, Unit 1F, Altona Business Park, Lisburn, Co Down, BT27 5QB (tel: 028 926 76600). Hotels: Beechlawn House, 4 Dunmurry Lane, Dunmurry, BT17 9RR (tel: 028 9060 2010).

Lurgan (Co Armagh). Dept of Culture, Arts & Leisure water: **Craigavon City Park Lakes**, 168 acres: South Lake, pike, perch, roach, bream hybrids, some r trout (season: all year): all lawful methods, 2 pike per day under 4kg fish limit; North Lake: r trout (season 1 Feb to 31 Dec); fly, spinning, worm; 4 fish per rod/day, minimum size 25.4cm. **Lurgan Park Lake**: coarse fishery (all year), pike, roach, perch, bream and carp (rod licence only needed); rod licences from: McIlduff Fishing, 2b Gilpinstown Road, Lurgan, Craigavon BT66 8RL (tel: 028 383 49709).

Dromore (Co Down). Dromore & DAC has 2 miles of river below, and 5 miles above Dromore: good trout water, for wet and dry fly; season starts 1 March; dt £4, juv £1, from Jackie McCracken's Confectionery, Gallow St, Dromore BT25 1BG (tel: 028 9269 3247). 5 miles away at **Hillsborough**, 40 acres r trout fishery, Dept of Culture, Arts & Leisure (tel: 028 4377 8937) water, season 1 Feb to 31 Dec; salmon, browns; fly, worm, spinning. Accommodation at Rhoda & Wilson Mark, B&B, 11 Bishops Well Rd, Dromore BT25 1ST (tel: 028 9269 3520).

LOUGH MELVIN

A 12,500 acre natural lake, approximately one fifth of which lies in Northern Ireland, (Co Fermanagh). A good spring run of salmon starts in February and a grilse run in June, but the lake is famous chiefly for the variety of its native brown trout. In addition to fish of orthodox appearance, there are dark 'sonaghan' caught over the deeper water and the yellow bellied 'gillaroo', found in the shallows near the shore. No coarse fishing. **Garrison**, Co Fermanagh is the centre for fishing the lough, **Lough Erne**, famous for its large browns and May/June hatches of mayfly, and Lough **Macnean**, Upper and Lower, also in the vicinity. (Pike, large trout, general coarse fishing.) Garrison & Lough Melvin AC has fishing here; dt from Sean Maguire, Melvin Tackle, Main Str, BT98 4ER (tel: 028 6865 8194/8975) who arrange boats and ghillies; and Melvin Bar (tel: 028 6865 8380); Riverside Bar, all Garrison. Small trout in L **Lattone** may be caught from the roadside between Belcoo and Garrison.

CLANRYE RIVER

A small system flowing into the head of **Carlingford Lough** at **Newry**, Co Down. 20m of fair salmon, sea and brown trout water above Carnbane Industrial Estate. Newry & DAC issues dt £15 for **Clanrye River**, (good run of large sea trout (to 10lbs) and occasional salmon), **McCourt's Lake**, **Poyntzpass**, occasional brown trout; fly only for rainbows; apply to Jack Smyth or Hon Sec. 3m from town, Cooper's Lake, fly fishing for brown trout; dt £10 from Jack Smyth (below). Dept of Culture, Arts & Leisure trout lake: Lough **Brickland**; tickets from Jack Smyth. Warrenpoint, Rostrevor & DAC has fishing at Mill Dam and also at Donaghaguy; dt £12, £10 conc, from Smyth or Bannatts Bar, Warrenpoint. Kilbroney AC has lower stretch of Kilbroney River at Rostrever; mostly sea trout, some brown; dt available. Tackle shops: Jack Smyth Angling & Outdoors, 5/9 Kildare Str, Newry BT34 1DQ (tel 028 302 52332); Fabb Tackle, Ballybot House, Cornmarket, Newry (tel: 028 302 65324); McA Boats, The Old Mill, Craigmore Rd, Newry BT35 6PL (tel: 028 302 62309); Bennett's Supermarket, Poyntzpass.

NEWRY SHIP CANAL

The first ship canal in British Isles, ceased operation in 1976. The fishable section which runs from Newry to sea locks on Omeath road, 3½m approx, has produced match weights of over 50lb. Summer algae improves roach and bream catches, while large pike are to be caught in winter. Most winter fishing is in Albert Basin.

QUOILE

Flows into **Strangford Lough** at **Downpatrick**, Co Down. Coarse fish and some trout in lower reaches; fair trout waters between Annacloy Bridge and Kilmore. Dept of Culture, Arts & Leisure (tel: 028 4377 8937) has fishing rights on **Quoile Basin** (100 acres) and 7m of Quoile River from Downpatrick to Kilmore; pike, perch, rudd, eels and brown trout; season all year; all legal methods; bag limit: 2 pike per day (pike of 4 kg and over to be returned); disabled car park at old flood gates; south bank fishing only; no fishing on nature reserve d/s of Steamboat Quay; no wading. Other Dept of Culture, Arts & Leisure fisheries, **Portavoe Reservoir**, nr Donaghadee and Bangor, 31 acres; rainbow trout, fly only, 20 rods per day, 4 fish limit; Lough **Money**, 53 acre, rainbow trout nr **Downpatrick** (tel: 028 2954 0533). Bridgewater Trout Fishery, I Logan, 93 Windmill Rd, Donaghadee (tel: 028 9188 3348): rainbow trout, B&B on site. Downpatrick & Dist AA hold fishing rights to **Loughinisland Lake** and

Magheraleggan Lake; guests only when accompanied by a member only on Loughinisland Lake; apply H W Kelly. Lough **Cowey**, 2 miles north of **Portaferry**, natural 70 acres lough with rainbow and brown trout mostly 2lbs plus, fly fishing; dt and boats on site, tickets from H W Kelly. Tackle shop: H W Kelly, Hardware, 54 Market Str, Downpatrick BT30 6LU (tel: 028 446 12193). Hotel: Portaferry; Denvers; The Mill; Cuan at Strangford.

SHIMNA

Small attractive river with deep rocky pools flowing from E slope of Mournes to enter sea at **Newcastle**, Co Down. Sea trout (holds Irish record 16½lb and salmon from July. Dept of Culture, Arts & Leisure fishery in forest areas now under the control of Shimna AC; no Sunday fishing; permits and local rules from Four Seasons (below); fishing is by all legal methods; no fly fishing in Tollymore Park; Dept stillwaters: **Spelga Reservoir**, 148 acres, b trout; **Castlewellan Lake**, 4 miles from Newcastle, regularly stocked, 103 acres, b and r trout, 4 fish limit per rod per day; fly (only from boat), spinning and worming; min length 25.4 cm; wheelchair access possible (tel: 028 4377 8664 first); (contact Peter Lynch, Senior Fisheries Officer, DCAL (tel: 028 4377 8937). Tackle shops: The Four Seasons, 47 Main Str, Newcastle (tel: 028 437 25078). Hotels: Slieve Donard, Downs Rd BT33 0AH (tel: 028 437 21066); Enniskeen,98 Bryansford Rd, BT33 0LF (tel: 028 437 22392).

WHITEWATER

Small attractive water flowing into sea west of **Kilkeel**, Co Down; 3m of fishing, mainly for sea trout, with some brown trout and a few salmon. Kilkeel AC offers six day tickets, £15 per rod day, for Kilkeel and Whitewater (except Mourne Park Estate water) rivers, from Sub Post Office, The Square, Kilkeel BT34 4AA (tel: 028 4176 2225), Rafferty's Garage, 42 Newry Road tel: 028 4176 3297)), or Kilmorey Arms (below). **Spelga Reservoir** is Dept of Culture, Arts & Leisure; wild brown trout fishery, bank only. Tackle shops: Graham Sports, 47 Greencastle St, BT34 4BH (tel: 028 4176 9267/2777). Hotel: Kilmorey Arms, 41 Greencastle St, Kilkeel BT34 4NR (tel: 028 4176 2220).

Details changed or missing? Please let us know, so we can update in the next reprint or edition; contact *Where to Fish* by email: editor@wheretofish.co.uk

A decent wave can help!
Photo: Mike Dobson

Fish Northern Ireland
www.dcal-fishingni.gov.uk

SEA FISHING IN NORTHERN IRELAND

The popularity of sea fishing in N Ireland has grown immensely in recent years, leading to the discovery of new and exciting possibilities. 300 miles of unpolluted coastline offers fishing for a variety of species from rock and beach alike. Sheltered inlets of which Strangford and Belfast Loughs are the largest and best known, offer protection to the boat angler when the open sea may be unfishable due to adverse weather. Twenty four species of sea fish are caught regularly, including blue shark, skate, tope, cod, bass and flatfish.

Magilligan (Co Antrim). From point, surf fishing for dogfish, flounder, occasional bass. From strand, where lug and ragworm can be dug, beach fishing for flounder. Other venues are: Benone Strand, Downhill Strand, Castlerock beach and breakwater, Barmouth pier (spinning for mackerel and sea trout) and beach; flatfish, coalfish, whiting, occasional mullet and bass. Tackle Shop: Bloomfield Guns & Tackle, 149 Bloomfield Avenue BT5 5AB (tel: 028 9020 9730).

Portrush (Co Antrim) and Portstewart (Co Derry). Near mouths of Lough Foyle and River Bann. Rock, pier and beach fishing for pollack, mackerel, wrasse, dogfish, coalfish, flounder, plaice, conger and bass. Conger fishing in Portrush harbour. Rock fishing from Ramore Head east and west, Blue Pool rocks, and Dunseverick. Skerries, 2m off Portrush produce good catches of turbot, plaice, dogfish, dab and big pollack. Causeway bank off Giants Causeway good rock fishing for wrasse, coalfish, pollack, plaice, turbot. Boats for hire: '*Causeway Lass*': contact Richard Connor (mob: 0771 2115751), rods supplied; '*The Brothers*' from the Stewart Bros (tel: 028 7082 3369); 'Boy Matthew': contact Peter Boston, 14 Movilla Rd, Portstewart BT55 7DW (tel: 028 7083 4734); 'Island Fisher': contact Robin Cardwell, 108 Coleraine Rd, Portrush BT56 8HN (tel: 028 7082 2359); Willie Verner, Portrush harbour (tel:

028 207 31343). Club: North Antrim Sea Anglers. Tackle shop: Flying Tackle, 74 Main Str, Portrush BT56 8BN (tel: 028 7082 2209)and also at 11 The Quays, Portrush Harbour (tel: 028 7082 2209). Hotels: The Ramada Hotel; Magherabuoy House; The Adelphi; all Portrush (and many more).

Ballycastle (Co Antrim). Rock fishing for wrasse, pollack, coalfish, mackerel from Ballintoy. At Ballycastle strand, little turbot, codling, plaice, small coalfish and whiting. Best in autumn, on high tides. Spinning or float fishing for cod and pollack. Night fishing at ferry pier is recommended, using float tackle with ragworm, obtainable in town. Rathlin Island, just off the coast opposite Ballycastle, has wreck fishing for conger in Church Bay; and cod, coalfish, dogfish, plaice, pollack, turbot, haddock, ling, herring, conger eel, spurdog off Bull Point; big skate (200lb+) in Ballycastle Bay. Conger fishing on Loughgarry off Rhu Point. Boats from C McCaughan (tel: 028 2076 2074; mob: 07751 345791), '*Lady Linda*': contact Sean McKay (tel: 028 20769665)and others. Tackle shop: R Bell, 40 Ann St BT54 6AD (tel: 028 2076 2520); Moyle Outdoor Angling & Leisure, 23 Ann St, Ballycastle BT54 6AA (tel: 028 20769521). Hotel: Antrim Arms, Marine Hotel.

Larne (Co Antrim). No fishing from harbour, but bottom fishing at nearby beach for coalfish, cod, dogfish, wrasse. Ragworm can be bought at Angling Supplies. Local venues are: Glenarm, popular night fishing mark for codling, flatfish; IMurlough BayMurlough Bay, spinning from rocks for coalfish, mackerel, pollack; Garron Point, codling, wrasse, pollack, coalfish, dogfish. Tackle shop: Angling Supplies, 131 Main St, BT40 1HJ (tel: 028 282 76634). Hotels which cater for anglers: Curran Court, Halfway House.

Whitehead and Carrickfergus (Co Antrim). Opposite Bangor at entrance to Belfast Lough (Belfast 16m). Pollack, mackerel, coalfish, cod, whiting, from rocks, beach and boats. Wrecks off Blackhead for cod, pollack, coalfish. Local venues are Whitehead Promenade, Carrickfergus Harbour and East pier, Ballycarry Causeway, nr **Islandmagee**. Below Blackhead lighthouse, conger, wrasse, cod, mackerel. No fishing boat trips, but enquire of Carrickfergus Marina, 3 Quayside BT38 8BJ (tel: 028 9336 6666) (website: www.carrickfergus.org). Clubs: Woodburn AC, Carrickfergus SAC and Greenisland AC. Hotels: Dobbins Inn Hotel, 6 High Str; Coast Rd, 28 Scotch Quarter, both Carrickfergus.

Bangor (Co Down). Bangor is on Belfast Lough, 12m from capital. Cod, plaice, turbot, whiting. Lugworm can be dug on beaches at Bangor, ragworm at Marino. Smelt Mill Bay and Orlock Point are good summer venues for wrasse, codling, coalfish, dogfish, mackerel. Bangor and Donaghadee piers for mackerel, coalfish. Boats from John Erskine (tel: 028 9146 9458; mob: 0780 157 1830). Tackle shop: Trap & Tackle, 6 Seacliff Rd BT20 5EY (tel: 028 914 58515).

Donaghadee (Co Down). Fishing from pier or rocks for pollack, codling and mackerel. Rigg sandbar (3m off Donaghadee) for cod, whiting, gurnard, coalfish, flatfish, mackerel, rays, dogfish, plaice, pollack. Back of Sandbar for big huss. Boats from Q Nelson, 146 Killaughey Rd BT21 0BQ (tel: 028 9188 3403) (web: www.nelsonboats.co.uk), specialising in wreck and reef drift fishing; twice daily June Sept, and weekends Jul Aug, around the Copeland Islands; all tackle provided for beginners on board.

Strangford Lough (Co Down). Good boat fishing in estuaries and inlets around the lough. Big skate (Aug Oct), spurdog, huss, thornback. Skate and tope are protected species in lough, and must be returned to the water alive. Codling, whiting, haddock, mackerel, spurdog and wrasse at deep water entrance to lough. Best fishing in slack water. Lugworm is plentiful at Island Hill nr Comber and shore at Kircubbin. Wreck fishing for big ling and conger outside lough. Boat in Portaferry: '*Cuan Shore*', D Rogers, 200A Shore Rd BT22 1LA (tel: 028 427 28297) (e mail: bernierogers@btinternet.com): £250 divided by no. of anglers, max 12; tackle on board extra. Hotels: The Narrows, 8 Shore Rd, Portaferry (tel: 028 427 28148); The Portaferry Hotel, 10 The Strand (tel: 028 427 28231).

Kilkeel (Co Down). Harbour fishing for coalfish and mackerel; West strand for flatfish, dogfish. Black Rock, Ballymartin, produces mackerel, dogfish, thornback and codling; Carlingford Lough, flatfish, dogfish, thornback, a few bass. Good points are Cranfield and Greencastle, mackerel, dogfish, bass, a few conger, and Bloody Bridge, 1½m outside Newcastle towards Kilkeel, rock cod, mackerel, pollack; Cranfield Point, 3m SW of Kilkeel, fishing for bass, sea trout, pollock and codling.

Lugworm can be dug in **Newcastle** harbour and **Greencastle**, rag and lug at Warrenpoint beach. Whitewater River has two piers for disabled. Boats for hire from O Finnegan, Carlingford Lough Sea Angling Centre, 25 Chestnut Grove, Newry BT34 1JT (tel: 028 3026 4906; see website: www.carlingfordlough.co.uk/fishing. htm), for wreck and deep sea fishing, species caught incl cod, pollack, tope, conger, ling. Tackle shop: J Graham & Sons, 47 Greencastle St, BT34 4BH (tel: 028 417 62777). Hotel: Kilmorey Arms, 41 Greencastle St BT34 4BH (tel: 028 4176 2220) is HQ of Kilkeel AC, who have trout and salmon fishing in Kilkeel and Whitewater Rivers.

Mark Patterson APGAI caught this blue shark off the Donegal coast

Photo: Mark Patterson.

NOBODY MOANED.
NOBODY COMPLAINED.
EVERYONE PRAISED IT.

BUT WE IMPROVED
IT ANYWAY.

How could we ever beat the legendary Greys GRX & GRXi rods? In short, with a totally new high-modulus blank, giving you more power in the butt section, faster recovery speed and – in the new 4-piece format – easier transportation. Then we added line-up marks and single-line ratings. Beat that.

See the full GRXi+ range at www.greysfishing.com

Available in 6ft #3 to 15ft #10 (double handed) from £89.99.
Reels available in #6/7, #8/9, #11/12 weight options, from £64.99.

GRXi+

GREYS
BORN TO FISH

FISHING CLUBS & ASSOCIATIONS IN NORTHERN IRELAND

The following is an alphabetical list of fishing clubs and associations who fish in Northern Ireland. Particulars of the waters held by many will be found by reference to the Index, in the section headed 'Fishing Locations in Northern Ireland', and information about the others, which may not have their own water, could be had from the Secretaries. A courtesy they appreciate is the inclusion of a stamped addressed envelope with postal inquiries. Please advise the publishers (address at the front of the book) of any changed details for the next edition.

NATIONAL BODIES

Department of Culture, Arts & Leisure
Inland Fisheries
Causeway Exchange
1-7 Bedford Street
Belfast BT2 7EG
Tel: 028 90515119
dcalangling@dcalni.gov.uk
www.dcal-fishingni.gov.uk

Fisheries & Aquatic Ecosystems Branch (AFBI)
Irish Specimen Fish Committee (marine)
Newforge Lane
Belfast
BT9 5PX
Tel: 028 90 255503
www.afbini.gov.uk
richard.briggs@afbini.gov.uk

Northern Ireland Tourist Board
St Anne's Court
59 North Street
Belfast BT1 1NB
Tel: 028 9023 1221
Fax: 028 9024 0960
www.discovernorthernireland.com
info@ nitb.com

The Loughs Agency (FCILC)
22 Victoria Road
Londonderry
BT47 2AB
Tel: 028 7134 2100
Fax: 028 7134 2720
www.loughs-agency.org

Ulster Coarse Fishing Federation
Chairman: Robert Buick
7 Knockvale Grove
Belfast BT5 6HL
Tel: 028 90 655373
or
Hon Sec: Victor Refausse
29 Georgian Villas
Omagh
Tyrone
Tel: 028 8225 5204

Waterways Ireland
2 Sligo Road
Enniskillen
Co Fermanagh
BT74 7JY
Tel: +44 (0)28 6632 3004
Fax: +44 (0)28 6634 6257
info@waterwaysireland.org
www.waterwaysireland.org

CLUBS

Agivey Anglers Assn
Kieran Tully
76A, Craigmore Road
Ringsend, Coleraine,
Co. Londonderry BT51 4HP
Tel: 02870868967
www.agiveyanglers.co.uk

Antrim & District Angling Assn
Alan Fleming
91 Hartswood
Cidercourt Road
Crumlin, Co Antrim BT29 4PY
Tel: 028 908 44636
www.sixmilewater.co.uk

**Armagh & District Game
Angling Club**
Trevor Dickson
93 Kilvergan Road
Portadown
Co Armagh
Tel: 028 3834 2364

Ballinderry Bridge Angling Club
Leo Cassidy, MBE
175 Spring Road
Coagh
Cookstown BT80 0BD
Tel: 028 7941 8642
or
c/o Hatchery
BFH Ltd
Cookstown BT80 9ND
Tel: 028 8676 1515

**Ballyrashane Fishing
& Conservation Club**
c/o Smyths Country Sports
1 Park Street
Coleraine
Co Londonderry BT52 1BD
Tel: 028 703 43970
www.smythscountrysports.net

Ballynure Angling Club
John Arneill
17 Collinview Drive
Ballyclare
Co Antrim BT39 9PQ
Tel: 028 933 24716 (after 6pm)

Banbridge Angling Club
J Curran
10 Old Manse Green
Banbridge
Co Down BT32 4KY
Tel: 028 406 29081 (home)

Belfast Anglers' Assn
Michael Crilly
20 Old Coach Road
Belfast BT9 5PR

Burn Dennett Angling Assn
W O'Neill
22 Carrickatane Road
Donemana
Co Tyrone BT82 0NG
Tel: 028 713 98512

Castlederg Anglers Club
R R Harron
Brookvale
Castlederg
Co Tyrone BT81 7AG
Tel: 028 816 12265 (9am to 6pm)
or
H Irwin
4 Eden Park
Castlederg
Co Tyrone BT81 7BD
Tel: 028 816 71494

**Castlewellan & Annsborough
Angling Club**
S P Harrison
Garden Cottage
Forest Park
Castlewellan BT31 9BU
Tel: 028 437 78240

Clady & District Angling Club
Margaret Dillon
33 Mayogall Rd
Magherafelt
Co Londonderry BT45 8PD
Tel: 028 796 43331

Coalisland & District Angling Club
Tony Kerr
9 Torrent Drive
Coalisland
Co Tyrone BT71 4SG
Tel: 028 877 48447

Coleraine Anglers Assn
Dr Mark Henderson
23 Ballyleague Rd
Limavady
Co Londonderry BT49 0NJ
Tel: 028 7776 6535

Dromore & District Angling Club
Michael Shanks
7 Drumiller Hill
Dromore
Co Down BT25 1EP
Tel: 028 9269 9688

Dundonald Angling Club Ltd
Peter Grahame
13 Cherryhill Drive
Dundonald
Belfast BT16 1JG
Tel: 028 904 82161

Dungiven Anglers Club
(Now amalgamated with Roe AA)

River Faughan Anglers Ltd
Pat McLaughlin
Office:
26A Carlisle Road
Londonderry, BT48 6JW
Tel: 028 712 67781
(10am to 1pm Tue or Thu)
www.nireland.com/faughan.anglers

Gaff Angling Club
David Campbell
12 Killymore Road
Newtownstewart
Co Tyrone BT78 4DT
Tel: 028 816 61543

Gilford Angling Club
Allen Tanner
Tel. 07939114061
alan.tanner7@btinternet.com

Glens Angling Club
Larry McCann
secretary@glensanglingclub.co.uk

Gracehill, Galgorm & District Angling Club
Stephen Gilmour
Riverside Cottage
Dromona Road
Cullybackey
Co Antrim BT42 1NT
Tel: 028 258 82274.
www.gracehillandgalgormac.homestead.com

Iveagh Angling Club
Gary Houston
43, The Grannery,
Waringstown
Lurgan
Co Armagh BT66 7TG
Mob: 078113 75420
www.iveaghac.com

Kells, Connor & Glenwherrey Angling Club
Michael Currie
19, Rockfield Heights
Connor, Kells,
Co Antrim BT42 3LH
Tel: 07725649678
info@kellsconnorglenwherryac.org

Kildress Angling Club
Robin Black
Lower Kildress Road
Cookstown
Co Tyrone BT80 9RN
Tel: 028 867 63809

Kilkeel Angling Club Ltd
Peter Rafferty
56 Burren Road
Warrenpoint
Co. Down BT34 3SA
Tel: 028 417 63297
info@kilkeelanglingclub.co.uk
or
c/o The Kilmorey Arms
41 Greencastle St
Kilkeel
Co Down BT34 4BH
Tel: 028 417 62220

Kilrea & District Angling Club
David Laughlin
Culmore House
Bann Road, Kilrea
Co Londonderry BT51 5RY
Tel: 028 295 40272

Kingsbridge Angling Club
Stanley Aspinall: Treasurer
3 Rathbegt
Cookstown
Co Tyrone BT80 8HR
Tel: 028 86 765905

Lisburn & District Angling Club
Hon Sec: Fred Lockhart
c/o Hammond Farm
Hammond Road
Ballinderry Upper
Lisburn
Co Antrim BT28 2RY

Maguiresbridge & District Angling Club
P Trotter
7 Tattinderry Heights
Maguiresbridge
Co Fermanagh BT94 4ST
Tel: 028 67 721877

Maine Angling Club
John Forsythe
Tel: 028 94469574

Mid Antrim Angling Assn
R Topping
24 Cameron Park
Ballymena
Co Antrim BT42 1QJ
Tel: 028 256 41642

Mid Ulster Angling Club
Tom Sterling
25, Killycolp Road
Cookstown
Co Tyrone BT80 8UL
Tel: 028 86 763926

Moyola Angling Assn
Edith Lees
12 Westland Drive
Magherafelt BT45 5BA
Tel: 028 796 32307
info@moyolaangling.com

Newry & District Angling Club
Ronald McCamley
28 High St
Newry
Co Down
BT34 1HB
Tel: 028 30 268768
www.newryanglers.com

Omagh Angling Assn

Terry Smithson
30 Sperrin View
Omagh
Co Tyrone
Tel: 028 822 49927
www.omaghanglers.org

Pettigo & District Angling Club

Davy Stinson
Drumgrenaghan
Kesh
Co Fermanagh BT93 8BD
Tel: 028 686 32391

Portstewart Sea Angling Club

A McCallion
23 Hillview Pk
Coleraine
County Londonderry
BT51 3EH
Tel: 028 703 21113

Randalstown Angling Club

John Ellis
92 Ahoghill Road
Randalstown
Co Antrim BT41 3DG
Tel: 028 944 79475
mob: 0780 3929102

Rathfriland Angling Club

Stephen Shimmons
44 Lisna Mulligan Road
Hilltown
Co Down BT34 5XA
Tel: 028 4063 8551

Riverview Angling Club

Billy Magee
21 University Park
Coleraine
Co Londonderry BT52 1JU
Tel: 028 7032 8121

Roe Angling Assn

Shane Lockhead
PO Box 30
Livamady
Co Londonderry BT49
roeanglingclub@hotmail.com

Shimna Angling Club

Ian Watts
7 Tullybrannigan Road
Newcastle
Co Down BT33 0DX
Tel: 028 437 22454

Sion Mills Angling Club

Angling Information Centre
151 Melmount Road
Sion Mills
Co Tyrone BT82 9PY
Tel: 028 816 58027
Fax: 028 816 59890
angling@sionmills.co.uk

South Armagh Angling Assn

J Cunningham
21 Forkhill Rd
Mullagh Bawn
Co Armagh BT35 9XJ
Tel: 028 30 889187

Warrenpoint, Rostrevor & District Angling Club

J.C.Smyth
7-9, Kildare Street
Newry
Co Down
Tel: 02830265303

MISCELLANEOUS

Ballinderry River Enhancement Association

Alan Keys
227 Orritor Road
Cookstown
Co Tyrone BT80 9ND
Tel: 028 867 61515
www.ballinderryhatchery.co.uk

Department of Culture, Arts & Leisure

South Eastern Regional Office
Fisheries Office
Castlewellan Forest Park
Castlewellan
Co Down
Tel: 028 4377 8937
www.dcal-fishingni.gov.uk

Department of Culture, Arts & Leisure

Western Regional Office
Riversdale
Ballinamallard
Enniskillen
Co Fermanagh BT94 2NA
Tel: 028 6638 8927
www.dcal-fishingni.gov.uk

Department of Culture, Arts & Leisure

Central Fisheries Office
Movanagher Fish Farm
152 Vow Road
Ballymoney
Co Antrim BT53 7NT
Tel: 028 2954 0533

River Bush Salmon Station

21 Church Street
Bushmills
Co Antrim, BT57 8QJ
Tel: 028 20731435
Fax: 028 20732130

Wheelyboat Trust (The)

Director: Andy Beadsley
North Lodge
Burton Park
Petworth
West Sussex GU28 0JT
Tel/Fax: 01798 342222
www.wheelyboats.org

FISHING IN IRELAND

The Irish Republic is world famous for the quality of its fisheries. Salmon, sea trout, brown trout, pike and other coarse fish, are to be found there at their best. The seas around Ireland contain very good quantities of many varieties of fish which provide excellent sport for visiting and local sea anglers. With a mild wet climate, an extensive coast line and a multitude of stillwaters, rivers and canals, fishing in Ireland can be enjoyed almost everywhere!

Fisheries are administered by a single national inland fisheries authority, **Inland Fisheries Ireland** and through its seven regional River Basin District boards.

Inland Fisheries Ireland (IFI) was formed on July 1, 2010 following the amalgamation of the Central Fisheries Board and the seven former Regional Fisheries Boards into a single agency. Inland Fisheries Ireland is responsible for the protection, management and conservation of the inland fisheries resource across the country. Ireland has over 70,000 kilometres of rivers and streams and 144,000 hectares of lakes all of which fall under the jurisdiction of IFI. The agency is also responsible for sea angling in Ireland.

Headquarters

Inland Fisheries Ireland, Swords Business Park, Swords, Co. Dublin
Tel: + 353 (0)1 8842 600
info@cfb.ie
www.fisheriesireland.ie (Corporate).
www.fishinginireland.info (Fishing Information).

Regional Offices:

The Eastern River Basin District Office

15a Main Street
Blackrock
Co. Dublin
Tel: +353 1 2787022
Fax: +353 1 2787025
Info@erfb.ie

The Southern Eastern River Basin District Office

Anglsea Street
Clonmel
Co. Tipperary
Ireland
Tel: +00 353 52 6180055
Fax: +00 353 52 6123971
enquiries@srfb.ie

The South Western River Basin District Office

1 Nevilles Terrace
Masseytown, Macroom
County Cork
Ireland.
Tel: +353 26 41221
Fax: +353 26 41223
swrfb@swrfb.ie

The Shannon River Basin District Office

Ashbourne Business Park
Dock Road
Limerick
Ireland
Tel: +353 61 300238
Fax: + 353 61 300308
info@shannon-fishery-board.ie

The Western River Basin District Office - Galway

The Weir Lodge
Earl's Island, Galway
Ireland
Tel: +353 91 563118
Fax: +353 91 566335
info@wrfb.ie

The Western River Basin District Office - Ballina

Abbey Street
Ballina, Co Mayo

Ireland.
Tel: +353 96 22788
Fax: +353 96 70543
info@nwrfb.com

The Northern Western River Basin District Office

Station Road
Ballyshannon
Co. Donegal
Ireland.
Email: info@nrfb.ie
Tel: +353 71 9851435
Fax: +353 71 9851816

Rod Licences

No licence is needed for trout, coarse and sea fishing in the Republic of Ireland, but **a licence is required for salmon and sea trout fishing**. This licence does not confer the right to fish for salmon or sea trout—you will still need to seek permission or permits from the fishery owner.

Salmon and sea trout licences may be obtained online at: www.salmonlicences.ie and from many tackle shops and some fisheries. There are very specific rules in force when salmon and sea trout fishing in Ireland. Three types of rivers have been defined, each with their own set of rules: **Open Rivers** (with bag limits), **Catch & Release Only Rivers** and **Closed Rivers**. The full details of these rivers and their regulations can be found here: www.fishinginireland.info/salmon/

Anglers in the Shannon Region must also have a Permit (ticket charge) to fish for trout, pike or coarse fish in the **Midland Fisheries Group** of controlled waters. This area comprises the following river catchments; River Suck, River Inny, River Brosna, Little Brosna River And Camlin River.

2010 Licence Prices (2011 prices not available when going to press)
- Salmon/Sea Trout - Season (All districts) 120 Euro
- Salmon/Sea Trout - Season (Single District Only) 58 Euro
- Salmon/Sea Trout - Juvenile (under 18) 18 Euro
- Salmon/Sea Trout - 21-Day 46 Euro
- Salmon/Sea Trout - 1 Day 32 Euro
- Area Extension 76 Euro

Fishing Seasons

The modified **close seasons** now in force for salmon, sea trout and brown trout differ not only between regions, but also within regions, in a formulation too complex for reproduction here in detail. The general pattern is that seasons for migratory fish tend to open early and close early, while that for brown trout opens early in many places (15 Feb) and does not close until a date in October. There are, however, important exceptions and anglers proposing to visit the Republic, especially early or late in the year, should make careful enquiries with the appropriate Regional Board before making firm plans, whether the intention be to fish for salmon, migratory or brown trout. Each fishery board has its own web site. There is no annual close season for angling for coarse fish or for sea fish, except bass locally.

Tagging: Ireland has introduced an important system of tagging and logging all retained salmon, and sea trout over 40 cms. Anglers should be careful to ensure that they comply with this system, and always have the tags, log book, as well as the licence, on them. Log books and tags are obtained from licence suppliers. Taggable fish must be tagged immediately they are caught. No rod-caught salmon or sea trout over 40cm may be sold.

Overall responsibility for the country's fisheries rests with the **Department of Communications, Marine & Natural Resources.** 29-31 Adelaide Road, Dublin 2, Ireland. (tel: +353 (0)1 678 2000; fax: +353 (0)1 678 2449; web: www.dcenr.gov.ie).

Enquiries about accommodation and general tourist angling information (e.g. leaflets, brochures about local angling resources and amenities throughout the country) should be addressed to **Failte Ireland,** Amiens Street, Dublin 1. Ireland. (If dialing from inside the Republic of Ireland; tel: 1890 525 525 or (01) 8847700; fax: (01) 855 6821; From outside the Republic of Ireland; tel: 00 353 1 8847700; email: info@failteireland.ie; web: www.failteireland.ie); **Tourism Ireland, Nations House,** 103 Wigmore Street, London W1U 1QS (tel: 020 7518 0800; fax 020 7493 9065; web: www.tourismireland.com; email: info.gb@tourismireland.com), which covers both Northern Ireland and Ireland.

Young Jamie Maher looking forward to a day's trouting with dad Philip
Photo: www.fishhunt.ie

Fish Ireland
www.fishinginireland.info

FISHING LOCATIONS IN IRELAND

Details of regional fishery boards, licences, etc, for Irish rivers and loughs listed alphabetically here will be found in the previous pages. Anglers wanting further details of accommodation should contact **Fáilte Ireland** (Irish Tourist Board), Amiens Street, Dublin 1 (tel: +353 (0) 1 8847700; info@failteireland.ie). Anglers in the **Western Fisheries Region** should note the fact that the killing of sea trout is now illegal. All sea trout must be returned alive to the water.

BALLYSODARE and LOUGH ARROW

River Ballysodare formed by junction of three rivers, **Unshin** or **Arrow**, **Owenmore** (not to be confused with Owenmore River, Co Mayo), and **Owenbeg**, near Collooney, flows into Ballysodare Bay. Near mouth of river, at Ballysodare Falls, is earliest salmon ladder erected in Ireland (1852). Salmon, trout, very few sea trout. R Arrow, which runs out of Lough Arrow, contains small stock of brown trout for which fishing is free. The Owenmore has good coarse fishing, especially bream, at Ballymote.

Lough Arrow (NWRFB) is a rich limestone water of 3,123 acres on the border of Sligo and Roscommon, situated 14 miles from Sligo town and 4 miles from Boyle. It is about 5m long and varies in width from ½m to 1½m. The lough is almost entirely spring-fed and has a place of honour among Ireland's best known mayfly lakes. The hatch of fly is rather less prolific than heretofore, but efforts were made to re-establish past hatches with significant success in the past two years. The brown trout rise to mayfly from late May to late-June and sport is varied at this time by dapping, wet-fly and dry-fly fishing with green drake and the spent gnat. This is followed soon after (mid-July to mid-Aug) by a late evening rise to big sedge called the Murrough and Green Peter which may give the lucky angler as much fun as mayfly. The lough is occasionally stocked with singerlings or fry; fishing free; boats and ghillies may be hired at all seasons and at many centres on lake shore.

Loughs Bo and **na Súil** are in close proximity, and ideal bank fishing for brown trout and rainbows, respectively; stocked annually by NWRFB; all legitimate methods; 1 Apr to 30 Sept; contact Ms.Mary McDonagh at the Public House immediately adjacent to the lake - (tel: +353 (0)71 9165126). Good coarse fishing may be found nearby at **Lough Haugh**. **Temple House Lake**, **Ballanascarrow (Ballymote)**, and the **Owenmore River**; contact Boyle & DAC. Trout fishing at **Cavetown Lake** (fly fishing for trout only); pike fishing (catch and take away to another lake only); stand for disabled; Cavetown & Clogher AC, Kit O'Beirne (tel: +353 (0)71 9668037); st Euro20. Salmon may be fished at Ballysadare (10 miles from Lough Arrow). Mary McDonagh, Heapstown, Castlebaldwin supplies permits for brown trout fishing in Lough Bo, and rainbow trout in Lough na Súil; boats and access for disabled in both Lough Bo and Louch na Súil; dt water; boats: F Dodd (*see Castlebaldwin*); Eileen Carty, Ballinafad (tel: +353 (0)71 9666001). For information about Lough Arrow, contact Lough Arrow Fish Preservation Society, F Dodd (tel: +353 (0)71 9165065); or John Hargadon, Annaghloy Boat Hire (tel: +353 (0)7196 66666). For Lough Arrow & Dist AC (tel: +353 (0)71 9165304); Murial Frazer. Tackle from

Brian Flaherty, Boyle; Barton Smith, Hyde Bridge, Sligo (tel: +353 (0)71 9146111); Louis Carty, Ballinafad (tel: +353 (0)71 9666001); also boat hire. Accommodation in Lough Arrow area includes: Cromleagh Lodge Country House Hotel, Castlebaldwin (tel: +353 (0)71 9165155); Tower Hill B&B, Castlebaldwin (tel: +353 (0)71 9666021).

Collooney (Co Sligo). Best season, May to July. Fishing dependent on sufficient rain. Permission to fish for sea and brown trout sometimes obtainable. Good dry fly. River contains sizeable pike. **Lough Bo** fished from here (*see above*). Tackle shop: Mac's Fishing Tackle, Main Street, Ballysodare (tel: +353 (0)71 9130512).

Castlebaldwin via **Boyle** (Co Sligo). Trout fishing on L Arrow, free. Season 1 Apr-30 Sept. Bank fishing not recommended. Boats can be hired on lake shore from Dodd Boats, Ballindoon, Riverstown (tel: +353 (0)71 9165065), and Annaghloy Boat Hire (tel: +353 (0)71 9666666). L Arrow FPS fishes in Loughs **Arrow** and **Augh** (brown trout in L Arrow). NWRFB permits required for L Bo and L na Leibe, Lough Nasool (rainbow trout), but not L Arrow;, conc, day tickets available and boat from Mary McDonagh, Heapstown, Castlebaldwin. **Lough Bo**, in hills, provides good shore fishing for brown trout; fly only; one boat for hire; season 1 Apr-30 Sept. **Lough na Leibe** has rainbow trout stocked occasionally by North Western Regional Fisheries Board; season 1 Apr to 30 Sept; fly only; contact Declan Feeney (mob: +353 (0) 87251 8215). Good stock of brown trout in **Lough Feenagh**; boats for hire. River fishing on **R Unshin** and **R Feorrish** (above Ballyfarnon); trout. Coarse fishing on **Templehouse Lake** and **Cloonacleigha Lake**; good pike and other coarse fishing; boats for hire.

Coarse and trout fishing on **Lough Key**, 3m east of Arrow; contact Boyle & DAC Hon Sec; trout 14" limit; 2 fish per day bag limit; pike strictly c&r; c&r encouraged by club. Contact Sec, or J Hargadon, Annaghloy Boat Hire (tel: +353 (0)71 9666666). For Lough Arrow & Dist AC (tel: +353 (0)71 9165304). Hotels: Cromleagh Lodge; Rock View.

Boyle (Co Roscommon). L Arrow, brown trout, free; contact Fishery Inspector (tel: +353 (0)7196 66033) for information. **River Boyle**, a tributary of R Shannon, connects **Loughs Gara** and **Key**, both with very large pike. Upstream of town are quality bream, rudd, perch, roach, eels, hybrid and brown trout. Boyle & DAC have fishing on **R Boyle**, **L Key** (c&r only), Oakport Lake and **Boyle Canal**; members only, information available from outlets (*see below*); the Club had some of its members (17) legally appointed as water keepers (Boyle, L Key and Canal) and operates under a strict catch and release policy; downstream, pike are to be found. **Lough Nasool**, 13m north, contains brown and rainbow trout, dt from Mary McDonagh (see above). **Cavetown Lake**, fly fishing only; wild browns and stocked fish; platform for disabled anglers; dt available and boats arranged locally at Post Office. **Ballysadare River** and **R Unshin**; salmon tickets from Mac's Fishing Tackle, Main Street, Ballysodare (tel: +353 (0)71 9130512). A short distance south-west at **Ballaghaderreen**, is the **Lung River** connected to **Breedoge Lough**, and several other waters, among them **Loughs Cloonagh, Urlaur**, and **Cloonholly**; this area holds some of the best coarse fishing in Ireland, with many species incl pike to 30lbs; contact Ballaghaderreen AC. Tackle shops: Abbey Marine & Field Sports, Carrick Rd (tel: +353 (0)71 9662959), provides ghillies; Boyle Tourist Office, King House, Boyle (tel: +353

(0)71 9662145); John Hunt, Castlerae (tel: +353 (0)9496 20111); Michael Rogers, Ballymote. Accommodation for anglers: Mrs Mitchell, Abbey House B&B (tel: +353 (0)71 9662385), situated beside R Boyle, with much fine game and coarse fishing within easy reach;

R and J Acheson, Andresna House, Lough Arrow, Boyle (tel: +353 (0)71 9666181), who also hire boats; Mrs Helen and Eileen Kelly, Forest Park House, Carrick Rd, Boyle (tel: +353 (0)71 9662227; see website for more: www.bed-and-breakfast-boyle.com).

BANDON

45 miles in length, rises in Shehy Mountains, West Cork and drains 235 square miles. Salmon fishing extends all the way from **Inishannon** u/s to **Togher Castle**, depending on conditions. An estimated 1,300 salmon are caught each season; about 300 of these are spring fish. Grilse (local name 'peal') run at end of June. Big run of sea trout (local name 'white trout') from early July to end of Aug (best caught after dark), and good stocks of browns, mostly small, but fish up to 2lbs taken. Fishing can be excellent on 4m stretch from Bandon to Innishannon, although permission from riperian owners may well be needed. Ghillies are for hire. Season 15 Feb to 30 Sept.

Bandon (Co Cork). About 7m double bank controlled by Bandon AA (web: www.bandonangling.com); dt water; bag limit 4 trout, 1 salmon (to 1 June) 2 thereafter, size limit 10in. Visitors welcome, tickets from Hon Sec. Visitors are not confined to fishing beats on the river, but may fish any part of the 7m Assn-owned waters. Tackle shop: Jeffersports, 7 Pearse Str, Bandon (tel: +353 (0)23 41133).

Ballineen (Co Cork). The 4m stretch of river to about 1m above Ballineen Bridge is controlled by Ballineen & Enniskeane AA; salmon and trout; st and dt from Tom Fehily, Bridge Str, Ballineen (tel: +353 (0)23 47173). **Kilcoleman Fishery**, Enniskeane (tel: +353 (0)23 47279; website info: www.flyfishing-ireland.com), offers self-catering accommodation and private fishing on Bandon with ten named salmon pools, and excellent stocks of wild brown trout; season 17 Mar-30 Sept, spate fishing, mainly fly only.

Dunmanway (Co Cork). Above Manch Bridge is Dunmanway Salmon & Trout AA water. Tickets from P MacCarthy, Yew Tree Bar,

Dunmanway (tel: +353 (0)23 55196). River fishable for about 8m. Many small trout loughs in region, incl **Cullenagh** (4½m west), **Coolkeelure** (2¼m north west), **Ballynacarriga**, **Atarriff**, **Chapel Lake**; free fishing, small browns; for **Curraghalickey Lake**, contact P MacCarthy, *(see above)*.

CAHA RIVER. Joins Bandon 3m north of Dunmanway. Holds good stock of trout to 14 oz, for 3m up from confluence. Free fishing, best in early season, because of weed. Free fishing on **Neaskin Lough,** 3¼m north of Dunmanway. Difficult access, but plenty of 6oz browns.

Clonakilty (Co Cork). **River Argideen**, rises n.w. of Clonakilty, flowing into Courtmacsherry Harbour, rated among best sea trout rivers in SW Ireland, occasional salmon. Lower fishery owned or managed by Argideen AA; maximum 6 rods per day, bag limit 10 trout, size limit 9in. Permits from Fishery Office, Inchy Bridge. Tackle shop: Jeffersports, 7 Pearse St, Bandon (tel: +353 (0)2341 133); Clontackle, 2 Pearse Street (tel: +353 (0)23 35580).

BARROW (including Suir and Nore)

(For close seasons, licences, etc, see The Southern Regional Fisheries Board)

A limestone river which has been underrated in its potential, and not heavily fished. The second longest in Ireland, it rises well in the centre of the country on the eastern slopes of the Shannon watershed (Slieve Blooms) and flows over 120m south to the sea at Waterford Harbour, entering by a long estuary. An excellent head of wild brown trout, salmon run from Apr, best angling during grilse run in June or July, then Sept. Bream, pike, rudd, roach, perch, dace and hybrids provide good coarse angling, and annual May run of twaite shad (protected under the EU Habitat Directive) (St Mullans, Co Carlow, best) is popular with visiting and local anglers near estuary. Suir and Nore currently operate on a catch and release basis.

Waterford (Co Waterford). Reservoirs managed by SRFB (tel: +353 (0)52 80055) **Knockaderry** (only fly fishing from the Board's boats permitted, which can be hired from the caretaker, but no fishing from dam wall and road) and **Ballyshunnock**: both 70 acres at normal level, with wild brown and rainbow,; apply to Centra Supermarket in Kilmeaden (tel: +353 (0) 51 384721); all legal methods on Ballyshunnock (where there is also coarse fishing), bank only, no maggots; dt from Centra. **Mahon River** (15m) holds sea trout and salmon, and mackerel, bass and pollack abound along the coast. Tackle shops: Army & Outdoor Stores, New Str (tel: +353 (0)51 857554; fax: +353 (0)51 38243); Angling & Outdoor Centre, Westgate Retail Park, Tramore Rd (tel/fax: +353 (0)51 844314); Shoot'n & Fish'n, 26a Ballybricken (tel: +353 (0)51 878007; and contact via email: shootandfish@eircom.net).

Graighuenamanagh (Co Carlow). Good coarse fishing, with pike and large bream. Local venues are Tinnehinch Lower Weir and Bahanna.

Carlow (Co Carlow). Bream, rudd, pike. Trout fishing on River **Barrow** at Milford and Maganey, 8m (best trout in fast waters below weir); **Lerr**, 4m, **Greese**, 3m approx, and **Burren**, 8m, controlled by Barrow AC and restocked yearly; mainly brown trout. Members only, membership from tackle shop, or Secretary. Other club:

Carlow & Graiguecullen Anglers. Free fishing from Milford Weir to canal mouth d/s of Milford Bridge. Tackle shop: Murph's Fishing, Lismard House, Tullow St, Carlow (tel: +353 (0)(0)59 9132839). Hotel: Dolmen, Kilkenny Rd.

Athy (Co Kildare). Trout, bream, rudd, pike. Several tributaries within easy reach. **R Greese**, from Dunlavin to Barbers Bridge, Kilkea, approx 8m, fishable on permit. Bream are regularly caught in Barrow, as well as pike above 22lbs, excellent perch, rudd and game fish. **Grand Canal** holds good head of tench, pike, perch, rudd and bream. There is some good free dry-fly water on left bank d/s of Athy, known as the Barrow Track. Enquire SRFB for fishing info (tel: +353 (0)52 80055) on 5m **Boherbaun River** from Milltown Bridge to Forth of Dunrally Bridge, Vicarstown, eastside, (natural browns, 1-4lb). **Stradbally River**, 6m away, with trout; permits from Griffin & Hawe *(see below)*; also a new put and take brown trout fishery has recently opened at Stradbally Village; community venture; contact Neil Harrison, The Square or Griffin & Hawe. Vicarstown & Dist AC club waters extend on west side of R Barrow from Laois/Kildare border northwards to the Glasha River. Athy & Dist AC fishes Barrow to Maganey Lock; in Sept 1992 club was releasing 20,000 brown trout into Barrow as part of a general improvement programme; there are no fishing rights on Barrow, but a club card allows access from landowners; membership 20 Euro, conc, and accom list from tackle shop: Griffin & Hawe Ltd, 22 Duke Str, Athy (tel: +353 (0)59 86 31221; web: www.griffinhawe.ie; e-mail: johnbutler@griffinhawe.ie). Self-catering accom: Mrs C Crean, Vicarstown Inn, Vicarstown, Co Laois (tel: +353 (0)5782 25189; web: www.vicarstowninn.ie).

Portarlington (Co Laois). River at town is easily accessible, and holds some salmon from March, if in flood, but usually Sept. Portarlington AC has approx 6 miles of good dry fly trout fishing on **Upper Barrow**. Best mid-May to mid-Sept. Mountmellick AC has 7m, good trout, a few salmon Sept (which are c&r); permits Victor Cox, The Square, Mountmellick (tel: +353 (0)57 8624107). Bracknagh AC has approx 5 miles of the **Figile River**, a tributary of the Barrow; mainly coarse, a few trout around Millgrove Bridge; st 20 Euro; conc; for all these waters are readily obtainable from (tel: +353 (0)872483261). Another tributary, the **Cushina River**, north of **Monasterevin** is fished by Cushina Trout AC. Tackle shop: M A Finlay, Rathangan Road, Monasterevin (tel: +353 (0)45 525331). Fishing Accommodation near aqueduct, where Grand Canal crosses R Barrow: Owen Cullen, Coole, Monasteravin.

GRAND CANAL (Co Kildare). Much free fishing. Canal runs through **Prosperous** and **Robertston** and **Sallins**, where there is first class fishing for bream, best early morning. Also rudd, tench, hybrids and some pike. Prosperous Coarse AC fishes on a length of some 20m from Naas to Thacknevin Lock. At **Edenderry**, Co Offaly, canal has large bream, tench, carp, rudd, roach, perch, eels; Edenderry Coarse AC controls 18m first class coarse angling, with bream, tench, roach, rudd, carp; all fishing is free; 3-day festival 5, 7, 9 June; contact Pauric Kelly, Edenderry Angling Supplies, 48 Fr. Murphy St, Edenderry (tel: +353 (0)4697 32071: home).

GRAND CANAL, BARROW BRANCH (Co Kildare and Co Laois). Fishing for bream, roach, tench, hybrids, rudd and pike, 5 minutes walk from **Rathangan**. At **Monasterevin** canal has pike, perch and bream. Contact M A Finlay, Tackle Shop *(see above)*. At **Vicarstown**, Co Laois, fishing for bream, tench, pike and rudd. Tackle shop: Countryman Angling, Leanne House, Pacelli Road, Naas (tel: +353 (0)45 879341; fax: +353 (0)45 875952; e-mail: countryman_angling@iolfree.ie). Bait stockists: Griffin & Hawe Ltd, 22 Duke Str, Athy (tel: +353 (0)59 8631221; web: www.griffinhawe.ie; e-mail: johnbutler@griffinhawe.ie).

SUIR

(For close seasons, licences, etc, see The Southern Regional Fisheries Board)

Considered to be one of Europe's finest dry fly trout rivers, with average trout size of ½lb, and fish up to 3lb often caught. Predominantly a trout river, it is fairly shallow with deep glides, and drains large areas of limestone. Runs into the same estuary as Nore and Barrow, reaching sea at Waterford. Fishes best from March to July. Daytime fishing is more productive in May, and evenings during the summer months. Record salmon for Ireland, 57lb, was caught in Suir, in 1874. Salmon fishing opens on 1 March, and in good years large springers up to 25lb are caught. Grilse run usually begins in late May and continues to end of Sept. Late Aug and Sept often bring bigger fish, over 10lb. There are large stocks of wild brown trout in river, but they not easily caught, and best fished in faster glides, from May to mid-June. Season 17 Mar-30 Sept. A wide network of tributaries, excellent fishing in their own right, includes the Rivers Nire, Tar, and Anner (*see below*).

Carrick-on-Suir (Co Tipperary). Start of tidal water. **Duffcastle** to Carrick-on-Suir is last freshwater section, well stocked with trout. Carrick-on-Suir AA has north bank from Miloko to Duffcastle, also **Coolnamuck Fisheries**, 3 miles south bank, fishing for salmon, trout, allis shad; tickets and ghillies through J O'Keeffe *(see below);* also dt fishing on tributary **Lingaun River**, which runs from north into tidal water east of Carrick-on-Suir. Up river there is good trout fishing and occasional sea trout for 400 metres on left bank d/s of **Kilsheelin**. About 4m to south mountain loughs, largest of which are **Coumshingaun** and **Crotty's**, provide very good fishing as also does **Clodiagh River**, which springs from loughs and is close to road for part of way. Good salmon and trout fishing from Carrick to Cashel. Most of river preserved for salmon, but some owners give permission to fish for trout. Tackle shop: O'Keeffe, OK Sports, New Str (tel: +353 (0)51 640626).

Clonmel (Co Tipperary). Moderate to good stocks of trout to 30cm. Free fishing between the bridges in town. Clonmel & Dist AC controls water from **Knocklofty Bridge** d/s one mile on south bank, also from Dudley's Mills (Clonmel) to **Anner River** (north bank) salmon and trout. Permits from Hon Treas *(see clubs list)*; dt 30 euro and wt 100 Euro (trout) available; conc. Private fishing u/s of Knocklofty Bridge reserved for residents of Knocklofty House Hotel, Knocklofty (tel: +353 (0)52 38222). Clonmel & Dist Salmon and Trout Anglers control fishing rights on both banks from Deerpark to Kilmanahan Castle. At **Kilsheenan** left bank d/s is free fishing for 400m; 2m salmon and trout fishing. Local tributaries of main river are **Nire** (mountain stream with

trout av ½lb, to 6lb), **Tar** (lowland stream with exceptional fly life, densely populated with trout av ½lb), **Duag**, **Anner** (fast moving stream with good stocks of trout av ¾lb, very good fishing in early season by u/s nymph method). Andrew and Eileen Ryan, Clonanav Angling Centre, Clonanav Farmhouse, Ballymacabry, Clonmel (tel: +353 (0)52 36141; web: www.flyfishingireland.com), offer accommodation and instruction, and arrange dry fly fishing on Nire, Tar, Duag, Anner, Suir, and Blackwater Rivers; Nire and Glenahiry Lakes; Knockaderry and Ballyshunnock Reservoirs; tickets sold for these waters, guide service and tackle shop; mountain loughs can also be reached from this centre. Tackle shop: Clonanav Angling Centre, Ballymacarbry *(see above)*; Baumann & Sons Ltd (Jewellers and Fishing Tackle), 6 St Mary St, Dungarvan (tel: +353 (0)58 41395). Hotels: Hearns, Parnell St; Hotel Minella, Spa Rd, both Clonmel.

Ardfinnan (Co Tipperary). Good numbers of trout to 30cm. Ardfinnan AC has much trout fishing in locality, d/s of Rochestown to Corabella. Permits from John Maher, Green View, Ardfinnan (see clubs list). Limited rods at Cloghardeen Fishery, Cloghardeen Farm.

Cahir (Co Tipperary). Cahir & Dist AA controls waters starting at Suirville, about 4m below Golden Village, d/s to Ballycarron Bridge; from Ballycarron down to Cahir; down both banks to Ballybrado; and down to Carrigatha; all fishing fly only, mostly brown trout, some salmon, depending on water levels; dt 20 Euro, wt 75 Euro for the full 13m of water, from The Heritage, Pat O'Donovan, 1 The Square, Cahir (tel: +353 (0)52 42730); association also has 4m of Aherlow River from Cappaghgates to confluence of Aherlow and Suir. Flies from Alice Conba, fly dresser (tel: +353 (0)62 52755). Hotels: Cahir House (tel: +353 (0)52 43000); Kilcoran Lodge (tel: +353 (0)52 41288); Theresa Russell, Bansha Castle, Bansha (tel: +353 (0)62 54187).

Cashel (Co Tipperary). Brown trout and salmon. Cashel, Tipperary and Golden AA issues visitors' permits for 8m both banks **Suir** from Camas Bridge south to **Ballycarron Bridge**, fly only, wild brown trout to 2lb, dt water, wt also from Hon Sec; Rahelly Sports Shop, Main Str, Tipperary; Bridge House, Golden. Best fishing from early spring to mid-summer. Tackle shop: Mr Tom Cahill, Casale 2000 Ltd, 4 Bank Place, Cashel (tel: +353 (0)62 63106); Rahallys Sports Shop, Main Str, Tipperary Town (tel: +353 (0)62 51252). Hotel: Ardmayle House; many excellent guest houses and B&Bs.

Thurles (Co Tipperary). Good centre for upper river trout fishing. Thurles Drish AA and Holycross & Ballycamas AA have water from **Holycross** to Kileen Flats both banks, fly only; dt/wt from Hayes Hotel, Liberty Sq (tel: +353 (0)504 22122); club also fishes **R Clodiagh** and **R Drish**; good stocks of trout to 40cms; u/s from Drish Bridge weeded in summer; d/s fishable throughout season, usually; Holycross tickets from village PO.

Templemore (Co Tipperary).
Templemore & Dist AA controls first 15m on R Suir (excellent for game fishing; wild brown trout at its best); coarse fishing on Templemore Town Lake, less than 5 min walk from town centre; tench, rudd, bream roach, pike and eel. Fishing available for visitors as well as club members; st (snr) 17 Euro, (juv: 16 or under on day of joining) 5 Euro, dt 7 Euro available from Hon Sec *(see clubs)* and Jim Hassey, Post Office, Main St, Templemore (tel: +353 (0)504 31098); no disabled angler boats, although the club has 3 special disabled anglers stands at Town Park Lake. Hotel: The Templemore Arms Hotel, Main St, Templemore (tel: +353 (0)504 31423; fax: +353 (0)504 31343).

BLACKWATER RIVER (Co Kilkenny). This tributary joins the Suir about 2 miles upstream of Waterford City. It is tidal as far as the weir below **Kilmacow**, and holds good stocks of small trout between Kimacow and **Mullinavat**. Some fishing with landowners consent. Enquire at local tackle shops. Hotel: The Templemore Arms Hotel, Main St, Templemore (tel: +353 (0)504 313423).

PORTLAW CLODIAGH (Co Waterford). Tributary, which joins **Suir** east of Portlaw. Moderate trout stocks. Fishing rights on entire river owned by the Marquis of Waterford, but fishing is open u/s of **Lowrys Bridge** and d/s of **Portlaw**.

ARA/AHERLOW (Co Tipperary). Tributary joins Suir north of Cahir, flowing from a westerly direction. Significant numbers of trout to 28 cm. Ara AC has trout fishing from **Tipperary Town** to **Kilmyler Bridge**, where R Ara meets R Aherlow; fly, spinning or worming, wt water.

NORE

(For close seasons, licences, etc, see The Southern Regional Fisheries Board)

River rises in Co Tipperary, flows east through Borris-in-Ossory and then south through Kilkenny to join River Barrow near New Ross, about 8 miles south of Inistioge. 87 miles long with a total catchment of 977 square miles, Nore is a limestone river with abundant fly life. Increased salmon run in recent years. Because the salmon fishing is good, the trout fishing is somewhat neglected, although trout are plentiful in the river. Mills and weirs are a feature of this river, and long deep stretches provide excellent dry fly fishing even in low water.

Thomastown (Co Kilkenny), Thomastown AA has excellent salmon and trout stretch of Nore and issues temporary cards to visitors. Trout fishing is fly or worm only. Inistioge AC controls 3 fields both banks at **Inistioge**, from Ballygalon weir to Red House Stream. Salmon, sea trout, brown trout and eels; visitors are welcome. Kilkenny AA has waters at **Brownsbarn**; both banks extend 1m above and below Brownsbarn Bridge; 1m left bank fishing at'Holdens' (2m above Brownsbarn Bridge) excellent salmon at both fisheries; apply Hon Sec. Tanguy de Toulgoet, Moyne Estate, West Hall Stables, Durrow, Co Laois (tel: +353 (0)57 8736578), organises dry fly fishing trips at Kilkenny, Durrow, Rathdowney, Kells and Callan, with instruction, and his own flies; he also has fishing on Castledurrow Hotel water, dt available; dry fly catch and release, permits through local clubs.

Kilkenny (Co Kilkenny). Kilkenny AA has some excellent salmon and trout fishing on **Nore**, left bank from **Dinin R** to Greenville weir, and from **Maddoxstown** to 1m u/s of **Bennetsbridge**; **Dinin R,** Dinin Bridge to Nore; also **Dunmore**. Assn issues permits and tickets to visitors from John McCormack (Assn Sec); also Leisure World (below). Durrow & Dist AC fishes from **Watercastle Bridge** to **Owveg** confluence, and **Erkina R** from **Durrow Castle** to R

Nore; all with 3m of Durrow; dt from Hon Sec; Durrow & DAC. Rathdowney AC fishes approx 4m of **Erkina R** from local meat factory to **Boston Bridge**, early season best for open fishing, May-Sept for fly; brown trout from 8oz to 2lb, dt from M White, Moorville, Rathdowney. **Kings River;** good brown trout. Club fishing at Ballinakill Lake: good tench, perch, rudd, pike; dt on bank. **Granstown Lake** nr Rathdowney, fishing is restricted to members of the Durrow and Ballinakill AC. Permits for Grantstown Lake can be arranged by contacting the Durrow and District Angling Club's officer Michael Walsh, 18 Erkindale Drive, Durrow on (057) 9736437 or Lawlors Gala Shop, The Square, Durrow on (057) 8736234.

Abbeyleix (Co Laois). Trout and salmon. Abbeyleix & Dist AC fishes from **Shanahoe Bridge** to **Waterloo Bridge**. **Mountrath** (Co Laois). Nore; brown trout, pike, perch, roach, eels. Mountrath & Dist AC stocks and fishes Nore main channel from Nore/**Delour** confluence to New Bridge at **Donore**, and **Whitehorse River**, which runs through town. Good salmon fishing for 2m between Mountrath and Castletown. Tourist membership from Hon Sec *(see clubs list)*. Tackle and salmon permits from Mrs Maura Kelly, The Tackle Shop, Main Str (tel: +353 (0)57 8732162).

KINGS RIVER (Co Kilkenny). Tributary which joins Nore above Thomastown.

BLACKWATER

(For close seasons, licences, etc, see The Southern Regional Fisheries Board)

Perhaps most famous salmon river in the Republic, and the most prolific for the late 1990s, with remarkable totals of over 8,000 fish caught in 1998, with over 5500 in 1999 and over 6000 in 2000, comparable in North Atlantic area only to Kola Peninsula, Russia. Rises west of Killarney Mountains and flows eastward about 70m until it reaches town of Cappoquin, where it becomes tidal and turns sharply south, entering sea by estuary 15m long at Youghal Bay. 20m tidal, from Lismore to Youghal. Salmon (best stretches mainly between Mallow and Cappoquin (dt from Cappoquin PO)), sea trout, brown trout, and abundance of roach and dace in some parts. Best fishing strictly preserved. Big runs of spring salmon from Feb to April; grilse June to Sept; and often good run of autumn salmon during Aug and Sept. Sea trout in Blackwater and Bride, June onwards.

Youghal (Co Cork). Youghal Sea AC has fishing on main river and tributaries. All arrangements through secretary. At **Castlemartyr** on Cork/Youghal road is **Lough Aderry**, rainbow trout fishery, fly, worm and spinning.

Cappoquin (Co Waterford). The freshwater here is backed up by the tide and fishing is best when the water is either rising or falling. Salmon and trout, good coarse fishing for roach and dace throughout year but best autumn and spring. Cappoquin Salmon & Trout AA have 4 miles of water on both sides of town. Salmon day tickets, wt on application, depending on season, from tackle shop; trout dt 6 Euro; wt 35 Euro; coarse dt 3 Euro, wt 15 Euro. Trout fishing on **Rivers Owenshed** and **Finisk** and on R Blackwater downstream of **Lismore Bridge**. Lismore Trout ACA fishes 1½m south bank from Lismore town d/s, and 1m north bank; also Abhan-na-Shad, Blackwater tributary, good in spate from July; fly only, browns and sea trout; dt water, Jack Maher, Main St (tel: +353 (0) 53 9377114). Tackle shop: Titelines Tackle Shop, Main St, Cappoquin (tel: +353 (0)58 54152). Hotels: Ballyrafter House, Lismore, (tel: +353 (0)58 54002). Anglers accommodation: Flynn's River View Guesthouse (tel: +353 (0)58 54073).

Upper Ballyduff (Co Waterford). Ballyduff Trout FAA has approx 3m E of bridge and 3m W, both banks; no dt. Blackwater Lodge and Salmon fishery, Upper Ballyduff (tel: +353 (0)58 60235; fax: +353 (0)58 60162; web: www.ireland-salmon-fishing.net) has 16 private and exclusive beats for salmon fishing between Lismore and Mallow; dt available for residents and non-residents alike; lodge provides guesthouse and self-catering accommodation, complete service for anglers incl tackle, smokery and ghillies, and website with up-to-date river report; recently voted best fishing guesthouse/ hotel by influential magazine.

Conna (Co Cork). 8 beats owned by Mr Justin Green, Ballyvolane House, Castlelyons (tel: +353 (0)25 36349). 2 beats: Mrs Esta McCarthy, Elgin Cottage, Ballyduff, Co Waterford (tel: +353 (0)58 60255).

Fermoy (Co Cork). Salmon, brown trout, dace, roach, perch, gudgeon and pike; free salmon, u/s of town, trout and coarse fishing for 1 mile single bank; salmon season: 1 Feb-30 Sept (trout from 15 Feb); any method on state permit water; dt for trout fishing on Fermoy & DTAA waters available from Bait All Tackle *(see below)*; Blackwater Lodge and Guesthouse (tel: +353 (0)58 60235); Ballyvolane House, Castlelyons (tel: +353 (0)25

36349); and (for Ballyduff salmon) Mocollop & Ballinaroone Fisheries (tel: +353 (0)58 60255). Coarse fishing available all year round. **Knockanannig Reservoir**: fishing clubs or assns for group bookings, contact Christy Roche (+353 (0)86 8564781) (2008 fishing free); beam, roach, tench, gudgeon. Fermoy Salmon AA controls water from approx ½m d/s of Fermoy on right bank for mostly about 3m to the weir at Careysville; also a large portion of fishing on opposite bank, but Assn confines dt water (coarse dt chargeable) to portions on right bank: 2 beats amounting to 1m of river, 1 beat being known as Hospital stretch and the other as Championship stretch; permits from Bait All Tackle *(see below)*. Salmon fishing on R Blackwater at **Careysville Fishery**, 1 ¾m stretch, both banks with well defined pools; grilse run in June; fishing peaks on the lower beats in June and on the rest of river in July; max 4 to 5 rods per day depending on month; ghillie price included in fishing charges; permits from Careysville House (tel: +353 (0)25 31712/31094, see website for more info: www.careysville.com). Salmon fishing arranged at Blackwater Fly Fishing, Doug Lock (a fly fishing instructor), Ghillie Cottage, Kilbarry Stud, Fermoy (tel: +353 (0)25 32720; web: www.speycast-ireland.com). Stretches near town which hold roach and dace; waters accessible and banks well kept; for information on coarse fishing contact Tommy Lawson (tel: +353 (0)25 33574) or Chris & Fionn O'Connell, Bait All Tackle, Fermoy (tel: +353 (0)25 33361; mob: +353 (0)8705 05643) (Fermoy & DAA tickets and also deep sea charters every month). U/s and d/s of Fermoy are eight private salmon beats controlled by Justin Green, Ballyvolane House, Castlelyons (tel: +353 (0)25 36349; fax: +353 (0)25 36781) at Ballyduff, Fermoy,

Killavullen and Ballyhooly; fishing Feb-Apr, May-Sept, spring run Apr/May; accommodation, tackle, and ghillies; chest waders essential; local facilities for smoking or freezing salmon. **Araglin** holds brown trout; dry fly. Hotel: Grand. B&B information from Slatterly Travel, 10 Pearse Square, Fermoy (tel: +353 (0)25 31811).

Mallow (Co Cork). Salmon fishing from 1 Feb to end of Sept; trout 15 Feb to end of Sept. Coarse fishing for dace, roach, pike. Mallow Trout Anglers have 4m both banks, salmon, trout, dace and roach. Dt for this and for other private beats (5 above and below Mallow) from tackle shop; coarse fishing free; various tickets (private, assn and club) available from tackle shop. Information from the Bridge House Bar. Nr Mallow is **Ballyhass Lakes**, Cecilstown (tel: +353 (0)22 27773; web: www.ballyhasslakes.ie); brown and rainbows by boat or from bank; main lake fly only, smaller lake fly, spinning and worm; dt, tackle, boats and equipment from pavilion on site. **BRIDE**. This tributary of the Blackwater holds salmon and sea trout as well as brown trout, also dace; fly only; season: 15 Feb to 30 Sept for trout; state salmon licence 21-day 50 euro, dt 28 Euro; during 2008, conservation initiatives on the River Bride only requires salmon fishing to be on a c&r basis only (barbless hooks); available from Bait All Tackle *(See Fermoy)*; and Bride View Bar. Private beats: Peter Collins (tel: +353 (0)22 25205) has tickets for fly-only Kildorrey Trout AC; as does Sean Dennehy (tel: +353 (0)22 25497) both Kildorrey.

FUNSHION. This limestone tributary of the Blackwater, flowing through three counties, rises in the Galtee Mountains; holds salmon and sea trout as well as brown trout; four clubs fish the water; limit 6 trout; thigh waders; contact Sean Dennehy (tel: +353 (0)22 25497) Kildorrey.

Tallow (Co Waterford). River is 500 yds from town. Tallow & Dist AC have 4½m fishing from Mogeely Bridge to Bride Valley Fruit Farm; brown trout, sea trout; salmon and peal from June onwards; fly only between Mogeely and Tallow Bridges, otherwise, worm, etc; there is also coarse fishing for big dace and roach; visiting anglers welcome; dt and wt from Hon Treasurer, Paul Hampton (tel: +353 (0)58 56358). Tackle shops: John Forde, Main Str (tel: +353 (0) 96 49037; Tite-lines, Main St, Cappoquin (tel: +353(0)58 54152. Hotels: Bride View Bar; (B&B) Kevin Ryan, The Grange, Curraglass, Mallow, Co Cork.

AWBEG. Tributary which runs into the Blackwater midway between Mallow and Fermoy. A very good trout stream, especially for dry fly.

BOYNE

(For close seasons, licences, etc, see The Eastern Regional Fisheries Board)

Rises near Edenderry and flows for about 70m, entering the sea near Drogheda north of Dublin. One of Ireland's premier game fisheries, in main channel and tributaries. Good salmon fishing between Navan and Drogheda. Currently all salmon and trout fishing is c&r only. Excellent run of sea trout as far up river as Lower Blackcastle. Superb stocks of brown trout in Boyne and tributaries. Virtually no free fishing, but permits are sold on many club waters. Fishable tributaries include **Rivers Trimblestown** (small browns), **Kells Blackwater** (trout, u/s of Headford Bridge; closed to angling for all salmon, and sea trout over 40 cm for 2008), **Borora** (7m good trout fishing from Corlat d/s to Carlanstown), **Martry** (small stream, trout to 1lb), **Stoneyford** (excellent trout water, Rathkenna Bridge to Shanco Bridge), **Deel** (trout), **Enfield Blackwater** (mainly browns, up to 3lb, excellent dry fly water), **Little Boyne** (spring trout fishery, club based at Edenderry), **Nanny** (sea trout up to Julianstown, browns to Balrath Bridge) (ERFB web: www.fishingireland.net.

Drogheda (Co Louth). Drogheda & District AC has prime salmon and sea trout fishing below Oldbridge and u/s at Donore, and **Nanny**; and also Reservoirs **Killineer** (fly only) and **Barnattin** which are stocked with brown and rainbow, and **Rosehall**, a mixed coarse fishery; dt from Drogheda Angling Centre *(see below)*. Lower parts of Boyne and Mattock largely preserved. Brown trout in two reservoirs; all tickets from Drogheda Angling Centre. Tackle shop: Drogheda Angling Centre, Fair Green (tel: +353 (0)41 9845442); The Cycle & Army Store, Balbriggan (tel: +353 (0)1 8413597). Hotels: Boyne Valley, Europa, Cooper Hill House (Julianstown).

Navan (Co Meath). Salmon and sea trout. Navan & Dist AA has approx 8½m of fishing on R Boyne and on R Blackwater; during 2008, conservation initiatives on both these rivers require salmon fishing to be on a c&r basis only (barbless hooks). Permits for these and various other angling waters in the eastern region available from ERFB (tel: +353 (0)1 2787 022). Tackle shops: Sportsden, Trimgate Str (tel: +353 (0)4690 21130); Anglers World Specialist Tackle, Balmoral Business Park (tel/fax: +353 (0)4690 71866; web: www.anglersworld.ie). Hotels: Newgrange; Ardboyne; both near river. Many B&B.

Slane (Co Meath). Rossin & Slane Anglers have salmon and sea trout fishing at Oldbridge, also excellent salmon and brown trout below Slane; dt from Hon Sec; Drogheda Angling Centre, Fair Green, Drogheda (tel: +353 (0)4198 45442). Hotel: Conyngham Arms; Glebe House.

Trim (Co Meath). Good trout in main river and tributaries. Trim, Athboy & Dist AA preserves and restocks Athboy River and some stretches on Boyne itself; dt water; concessions to jun and OAP, from sec. Deel & Boyne AA has trout and salmon water on tributary Deel. Longwood Anglers also have salmon and trout fishing on Boyne. Hotels: Wellington Court; Brogans Bar and Guesthouse.

Kells (Co Meath). Good trout fishing on River Blackwater, a tributary of R Boyne, dry fly. Mayfly fishing good. 15m preserved by Kells AA and two other clubs; these clubs have a reciprocal arrangement whereby anglers can fish rivers Blackwater (Navan (200 salmon a year) and Kilbride stretches) and Boyne; salmon is c&r only; permits from tackle shop below; trout up to 10lb may be had in the river, also large pike and salmon. Tackle shop: The Flying Sportsman, Carrick Str (tel: +353 (0)46 9241743); Clarks, Navan for Navan stretch. Hotel: Headford Arms.

Virginia (Co Cavan). On headwaters of R Blackwater. Lough Ramor gives good trout fishing and excellent fishing for bream, roach, perch and pike; boats for hire, two tributaries. Ten lakes and four rivers within 5m; trout and coarse fish. Virginia Coarse AC has fishing on Lough Ramor, with large bream, pike above 25lbs, 200lbs catches of coarse fish per day recorded. Lough also fished by Kingfisher Angling Club; contact Hon Sec (see clubs). Other fisheries: **Lisgrea Lake** (all species); and **Rampart River** (roach, perch and bream). **Mullagh Lake** is a popular pike fishery. To north east, **Bailieboro** is an ideal centre for good coarse fishing, with innumerable lakes within easy reach; all free, incl **Castle** (with disabled platform, wheelchair and car access); **Parker's**; **Town** (with wheelchair access); **Gallincurra**; **Drumkeery**; **Drummeague**; **Galboly**; **Skeagh**; **Rooskey**, **Gallin**, all containing perch, roach, bream, rudd, plentiful pike to 30lbs, and some tench; Club permit is required for **Grousehall Lake**. Tackle shops: Raymond Lloyd, Main St, Bailieborough (tel: +353 (0)42 9694449) (tickets for trout fishing on Grousehall Lake, 30 acres; dt 5 Euro); Joe Mulligan, Main St, Shercock (tel: +353 (0)42 9669184). Hotels: Bailie, Main St, Bailieborough. B&B: Mr & Mrs Peter Crosby, Hilltop Lodge, Curcish, Bailiebor, Co Cavan (tel: +353 (0)42 9666320); also provides tackle storage, bait fridge and drying room).

BUNDROWES RIVER AND LOUGH MELVIN

(For close seasons, licences, etc, see The Northern Regional Fisheries Board)

About 4m south of Erne , the Bundrowes River carries water of **Lough Melvin** to sea in Donegal Bay. The entire 6 mile river is open to anglers except for private stretch from Lareen Bay to the Four Masters Bridge. Kinlough & Dist AA have fishing on Lough Melvin. The lough is 8m by 2m, approx 5,000 acres; part of it is free and part under private ownership. It is renowned for its three different species of trout, these being sonnaghan, gilaroo and ferrox. Good run of big spring salmon in Feb and March; smaller fish arrive in Apr and May; grilse in late May and run right through to June. Best time for fly fishing for salmon late Apr to end June. Trolling baits, where permitted, takes place from early Feb. Disabled Anglers' International competitions has been held on the Lough on three occasions. For accommodation and information, contact Shane Gallagher, Lareen Angling Centre, Lareen Park, Kinlough (tel: +353 (0)71 9841055).

Bundoran (Co Donegal). Salmon, trout. Drowes R, 1½m, and west end L Melvin, 3m. Salmon season 1 Jan-30 Sept (Drowes); 1 Feb-30 Sept (Melvin). **Bunduff River,** 3½m from Bundoran, flows 8m to enter Donegal Bay near Castlegal; salmon, brown trout; best salmon, June to Aug; brown trout in upper reaches. Bunduff Angling Syndicate has water; dt from The Shop, Bunduff Bridge, Co Leitrim; Pat Barrett, Main St. Hotels: Allingham; Fox's Lair.

Kinlough (Co Leitrim). Salmon, grilse, trout. Season for spring salmon, Jan to Apr; grilse, occasional sea trout (few owing to lime in water), May to Sept. Boats, salmon licence and permits for **Bundrowes** fishing at Drowes and Lareen Fisheries from Shane Gallagher, Fishery Office, Lareen Park, Kinlough (tel: +353 (0)72 9841055); Thomas Kelly, Edenville, Kinlough (tel: +353 (0)72 9841497); boats: Brian Hallett (tel: +353 (0)71 9841451). Tackle shop: The Fishery Office, Lareen Park (above). Accommodation, information and ghillie service available (by arrangement) from T Kelly *(see above)* and J Gallagher (tel: +353 (0)71 9841736).

Rossinver (Co Leitrim). Salmon, grilse, sonaghan and gillaroo trout. Rossinver Bay strictly fly only, rule extended to Eden and Dooard, from 15 May. All legal methods elsewhere. Ghillies in vicinity. Boat and 2 rods 50 Euro, from Ruth Mettler, The Rossinver Fishery, Buckode, Kinlough (tel: +353 (0)71 9841451). Part of Lough Melvin is in Northern Ireland and is served by village of Garrison (Co Fermanagh). Tickets and boats for Garrison AC fishing from Sean Maguire, Tackle shop, Garrison.

CLARE

Flows into **Lough Corrib**, near Galway, web: www.sport.galway-ireland.ie/fishing and is one of best spawning rivers for salmon entering the Galway or Corrib River; best season: spring salmon, Apr and May; grilse, June and July; brown trout, Apr to Sept; holds large trout (av 2lb), similar to Corrib fish, and suitable for dry fly; fishing in main river and tributaries is controlled by riparian owners and angling clubs; fishing in Lough Corrib is free; WRFB Angling Officer (tel: +353 (0)91 563110), has detailed information.

Galway (Co Galway). For lower reaches. Sea and lake fishing. Several clubs have fishing rights, and issue permits; contact WRFB. At **Carraroe**, 26m west of Galway, Carraroe AC controls a number of brown and sea trout loughs, incl Lough Atoureen, Lough an Gleanna, Lough an Bric Mor, and Lough Cora Doite. Sea trout mainly from July onwards; boats on request; for local information, contact Failte Ireland West, Aras Failte, Forster Str (tel: +353 (0)91 537700). Tackle shop: Duffy's Fishing & Shooting, 5 Mainguard Str (tel: +353 (0)91 562367; Freeney's, 19 High Str (tel: +353 (0)91 568794).

Tuam (Co Galway). For upper waters. Tuam AA have a long association with the Central Fisheries Board and Western Regional Fisheries Board from whom they rent 2 fisheries: **Ballybanagher Fishery** (also known as **Turloughmartin Fishery**), ¾m stretch on the left bank on the River Clare (situated in Corofin, between Tuam and Galway City) and **Liskeavey Fishery** (situated between Tuam and Milltown) both have excellent trout, pike and salmon (Liskeavey has brown trout). Tuam AA are a community based club and membership is open to visitors as well as residents; st 40 Euro, dt 20 Euro and can be obtained; apply Ian Callander, (mob: +353 (0)86 0566 405).

Castlegrove Lake; pike, perch, bream, rudd. Tackle shops: Connaughton's Shop, Tuam (tel: +353 (0) 93 28915); Corrib Tackle, Liosban Ind Estate, Tuam Rd, Galway (tel: +353 (0)91 76 9974). Accommodation and supplier of fishing permits: Trevor Martin, Marberry House, Corofin, Co Galway (tel: +353 (0)93 41938; see website for more: www.marberryhouse.com).

Tributaries of the Clare.

ABBERT. Enters from east, 7m south of Tuam. Good trout fishing, with excellent fly hatches. Brown trout of 3lb regularly taken; salmon spawn there. The best angling is in the higher reaches.

GRANGE. Joins Clare from east, 4m south of Tuam. Brown trout and salmon in lower reaches; u/s of Castlemoyle for a distance of 3m is a very good area for large brown trout to dry fly; occasional salmon in high water.

SINKING. Enters from east, 8m north of Tuam. Salmon occasionally taken in lower reaches, following flood conditions anytime after the end of May, but primarily a brown trout fishery, the best areas being from Dunmore as far as Cloonmore; good fly hatches; river heavily weeded and difficult to fish from mid-summer onwards.

DALGAN. Runs into Sinking. Stocks of brown trout, occasional salmon may be caught from the end of May, depending on water conditions. Pollution now largely overcome.

Co. CLARE (streams and loughs)

A number of salmon and sea trout rivers and streams run from Co Clare to the Shannon estuary or to the west coast. Most of them offer free fishing, with landowners permission. Trout and coarse fishing lakes abound in the East Clare 'lakeland' and in the south west. The rivers are listed here in their geographical order, westwards from Limerick.

BUNRATTY. Enters Shannon at Bunratty Castle, and holds a small stock of ½lb brown trout; modest grilse and sea trout run, best in June/July, from tide to D'Esterres Bridge, 3m. Free fishing. At source, **Doon Lough** nr **Broadford**, is a fine coarse fishery with pike to 30lb, large bream, rudd tench roach and eels; boats on hire locally. Several other coarse fishing Loughs in region: **Rosroe** and **Fin**, nr Kilmurry: pike over 20lb, from boat; **Cullaun**, 400 acres, 2m from **Kilkishen**, specimen pike and large bream, best from boat; just south, **Stones Lough**: big tench. As well as these, there are other less accessible lakes for the angler to explore. Further north east is another notable group of coarse fishing loughs: **Kilgory**, nr **O'Callaghan's Mills**, with large bream; 4m West of Tulla are **Bridget Lough** and others, with pike, perch, rudd, bream, tench, roach, hybrids; by **Scarriff, O'Grady (Canny's Lough)**, shallow water, difficult access, but good bream fishing, with pike, tench and big rudd; and **Keel Lough,** inaccessible and unfished, with large tench, bream and rudd. On the **Scarriff River,** shoals of good bream and pike, easily accessible. On **R Graney** is **Lough Graney, Caher**, at 1,000 acres the biggest lake in the county with abundant perch, bream, pike, rudd and eel, boat essential, on hire at Caher and Flagmount. **Tulla** is central to much lake fishing: north are **Loughs Clondanagh** and **Clondoorney**, easily accessible with rudd, with pike and perch. At **Kilkishen** are **Loughs Cullaunyheeda, Avoher, Doon, Rathluby, Clonlea**, and others, with similar species. Accommodation at **Broadford**: Lake View House, Doon

Lake, Broadford, Co Clare (tel: +353 (0)61 473125); on shore of lake, anglers catered for, boats for hire, much excellent coarse fishing in easy reach.

RINE (QUIN RIVER). Runs from the lakes of East Clare to the estuary of the **Fergus**. Fishing similar to Bunratty; about 5m fishing from Latoon Bridge u/s to Quin. Permission to fish **Dromoland Castle** water from Rec. Manager. Castle also has 20 acre lough in grounds, stocked trout fishery. Rest of fishing free. A few miles SE of Rine are **Loughs Caherkine, Fin, Ballycar, Rosroe, Teereen, Castle** (at **Kilmurry**) and others, with pike, perch, bream and rudd.

FERGUS. This medium-sized, limestone river with several loughs along its course, rises in Burren region of North Clare and flows southward to join Shannon at Newmarket - on - Fergus. Holds good stocks of brown trout, av $\frac{3}{4}$lb, with fish to $3\frac{1}{2}$lb. Good dry fly water, both banks fish well for trout, best in Feb-May and Sept. Pike fishing also good, and other coarse. Approx 200 spring salmon and grilse each year, salmon Feb-March, grilse June-Sept, from Ennis u/s. Much free fishing in **Corofin** locality. **Loughs Dromore** and **Ballyline**. 6m east of Ballyline; limestone waters with trout to 5lb. Best March-May and Sept. Free fishing: contact M Cleary, Lakefield Lodge, Corofin (tel: +353 (0)65 6837675). Tackle shop: Riverbank Fishing Shop, Main Str, Sixmilebridge. **Ballyteige Lough:** 50 acre limestone fishery, trout to 7lb; best in March/Apr, at dusk in June/July. Boat necessary; contact M Cleary. **Inchiquin Lough,** 280 acres: excellent stock of wild browns, av $1\frac{1}{4}$lb; fishes well in early season, and Sept. **Lough Cullaun** (Monanagh Lake): limited stock of big trout; also a good pike fishery; trolling popular method. **Muckanagh Lough (Tullymacken Lough):** 60 acre

shallow lake with good trout and pike. Boat necessary. Boats through M Cleary for both these loughs. **Lough Atedaun**, 1m from Corofin, has excellent fishing for large pike, tench and rudd. Best fished from boat. **Lough Ballycullinan,** $1\frac{1}{2}$m from Corofin, has good stocks of large pike, perch, bream, tench and hybrids. Boat essential. Contact M Cleary *(see above)*. **Ballyeighter Lough**: a rich limestone water which holds pike, rudd and large tench. On this water in 1994, Mr Nick Parry of Tubber broke Irish record with 7lb 15$\frac{1}{4}$oz tench, then broke his own record with one 8lb 2oz (June 1995).

CLOON. This small river enters north east corner of Clonderalaw Bay. It gets a sea trout run in June/July, and is fishable for 2m d/s of new bridge on secondary road. Free fishing. Nearby trout loughs are **Knockerra**, 50 acres, **Gortglass**, 80 acres, and **Cloonsneaghta**, 30 acres. Boat hire on Gortglass, contact M Cleary (tel: +353 (0)65 6837675); free fishing on all.

DOONBEG. A better known salmon and sea trout river, rising in Lissycasy, flowing west to the sea at Doonbeg. Small spring salmon run, fair grilse and sea trout from June. Overgrown in places; best fishing on middle and upper reaches. Free with permission. For **Knockerra Lough** *(see Kilrush, under Shannon)*.

CREEGH. Small spate river, running to west coast north of the Doonbeg, on which 150 to 200 grilse are taken each season. Small brown trout, and sea trout under the right conditions. Free fishing. Near Kilmihil is **Knockalough**, with good stock of small browns. Boat is helpful; dapping with daddy-long-legs in Aug/Sept. Free fishing.

ANNAGEERAGH. Runs into **Lough Donnell**. Sea trout fishing at dusk for about 1m u/s of lough in June/July. Sea trout fishing and a few grilse in rest of river. **Doo Lough,** 220 acres, a little north west of Glenmore, holds good stock of small browns.

KILDEEMEA. A small spate river which enters sea 2m south west of **Miltown Malbay**. Excellent sea trout, to 3lb. Best June/July, fishable over ½m stretch on south bank from Ballaclugga Bridge u/s. Fly and spinner, fly best at night. Free fishing.

CULLENAGH (INAGH). This river is a good coarse fishery for 8m from Inagh towards sea. Open banks for pike and rudd fishing, easily accessible. Near village, **Inagh Loughs** contain good numbers of small brown trout. Free fishing. 2m west of Inagh, **Lough Caum**, 45 acres, pike fishery, boat fishing only.

DEALAGH. Joins sea from north east at Liscannor. Spate river with sea trout and grilse in June/July. Sea trout best at night, between first and fourth bridges u/s from tidal water. Free, with permission. **Lickeen Lough,** 200 acres, 2m south of **Kilfenora**, contains small wild brown trout with a large number of rudd. Now stocked by the Shannon Regional Fisheries Board with large brown trout from 2lb upwards, see website for more info: www.shannon-fishery-board.ie. Boats and fishing tackle for hire. Tackle shops: Joe O'Loughlins, Main Str. Lisdoonvarna (tel: +353 (0)65 7074038); Burkes, Corofin.

AILLE. Small spate river running from **Lisdoonvarna** to **Doolin**. Stock of 14" browns, moderate grilse and sea trout. Best between Roadford and Lisdoonvarna; access difficult, banks overgrown; free fishing. Tackle shop: Joe O'Loughlin *(see Dealagh)*.

CORK South West (rivers and loughs)

ARGIDEEN. Runs from west, above Clonakilty, and enters sea at **Timoleague**. A sea trout river, most of which is jointly managed by Argideen AA and SWRFB; best methods are single worm by day, or fly at night; tickets from Anthony Creswell, Flaxpond House, Inchybridge (tel: +353 (0)23 46026, or SWRFB (tel: +353 (0)26 41222). Fishing with accommodation is obtainable from Tim Severin, Argideen River Lodges, Inchybridge, Timoleague (tel: +353 (0)23 46127; fax: +353 (0)23 46233). To west of river, **Lough Atariff**, permission from P McCarthy, Dunmanway Salmon & Trout AC, Yew Tree Bar, Dunmanway; and **Curraghalicky Lake**, free fishing; both with good stock of small wild brown trout. At **Midleton**, 16m east of Cork City, **Lough Aderra**, a popular stocked trout fishery of 30 acres, fairly shallow water, with large stocks of rudd and eels; 6 boats on water, boats should be booked well in advance due to demand. fly, spinning and worm permitted; contact SWRFB (tel: +353 (0)26 41222), or The Two Mile Inn, Churchtown, North Midleton (tel: +353 (0)21 4613605) who also do boat hire.

ILEN. A medium sized spate river about 21 miles long, scenically pretty, rising on watershed of Bantry district and flowing into sea through long estuary, from Skibbereen. Spring salmon from late March. Main salmon runs in Apr-Jun. Average size 10lb. Good grilse run from mid-June. Sea trout begin in Feb; Aug is the most prolific month, fish run from ½lb to over 4lb. Fly, spinning and worming are practised. Prawn and shrimp not permitted.

Skibbereen (Co Cork). R Ilen AC has about 8m fishing on river, with salmon, grilse and sea trout; visitors welcome, access for disabled 1m from town; wt, dt available from Brendan Houlihan, Tig Na Gael, North Street (tel: +353 (0)28 21419 web: www.riverilen.com). 3m east, stocked rainbow and wild brown trout fishing on **Shepperton Lakes**; pike in winter (up to 27lb), 35 and 15 acres, with boats; Shepperton, Skibbereen (tel: +353 (0)28 33328). West nr Schull is **Schull Reservoir**, 5 acres, small native browns and stocked rainbows; both these are SWRFB fisheries. 2m north of **Leap**, **Ballin Lough**: wild stock supplemented with brown trout fingerlings and limited number of 2 year-olds, by Ballin Lough AC; contact Fallon's; boats and tickets at lough, season 1 Apr-30 Sept; information from HQ, Bee Hive Bar, Connonagh, Leap. 3m south west of Dunmanway is **Garranes Lake**, 25 acres, stocked rainbows and wild browns; jointly run by SWRFB and Dunmanway & Drinagh AA dt and boats from T & C Nyhan, Filling Station, Garranes, Drimoleague (tel: +353 (0)28 31843). 3m south of Leap, **Lough Cluhir**, free fishing on small lough for tench, pike and roach. Tackle shop: Fallon's Sports Shop, 20a North St, Skibbereen (tel: +353 (0)28 22264); Tig Na Gael, North Street. Full range of accommodation, from TI Office, North Str (tel: +353 (0)28 21766).

Bantry (Co Cork). Bantry Salmon & Trout Anglers fishes **Lough Bofinne**, 3m east of Bantry, 25 acres, first class rainbow and brown trout fishery, stocked weekly by Fisheries Board; tickets from McCarthy's Sports Shop; Quick Pick Shop. Tackle shops: Vickery's Store; McCarthy's Sports Shop, Main St, Bantry. Hotel: Bantry Bay Hotel, The Square (tel: +353 (0)27 50062).

MEALAGH. 1m north of Bantry, salmon and sea trout. Free except for bottom pool below falls.

OUVANE and **COOMHOLA**. Small spate rivers which run into north east Bantry Bay. Salmon and sea trout, the latter declined in Ouvane, better in Coomhola R. Ouvane has four good pools in first mile, and three more below Carriganass Falls. Coomhola has a good supply of brown trout.

Coomhola Anglers: contact Teddy O'Brien, Coomhola Bridge, Ballylickey, Bantry (tel: +353 (0)27 50563; mob: +353 (0)87 1241608) offer permits to fish some 20 pools.

GLENGARRIFF. This small river flows into Bantry Bay at north east end through one of Ireland's most beautiful national parks, and has good salmon fishing when in spate, sea trout and browns; rights are held by Glengarriff AA; st 20 Euro, conc for river or loughs (*see below*), from SWRFB (tel: +353 (0)26 41222; web: www.swrfb.com). Limited tackle from Shamrock Stores (tel: +353 (0)27 63347); McCarthy's Sports, Bantry (tel: +353 (0)27 51133); and Maureen's B&B, The Village, Glengarriff (tel: +353 (0)27 63201). Hotels incl Glengarriff Eccles; Casey's.

BEARA PENINSULA. (Co Cork). **Adrigole River** runs into Bantry Bay on north side: 6m long spate river with grilse and sea trout. Beara AA has tickets for local lough fishing. **Upper** and **Lower Loughs Avaul** contain wild brown trout, and are stocked with rainbows, fish to 17lb being caught; open Easter Friday to end Sept; st (11 stocked lakes) dt from Glengarriff AA; or Mrs Harrington, Maple Leaf Bar, Glengarriff (tel: +353 (0)27 63021). High in the Caha Mountains, SW of Glengarriff, fishing on **Loughs Eekenohoolikeaghaun** and **Derreenadovodia**, all club waters; apply J O'Hare (tackle) Kenmare *(see below)*. **Barley Lake**, 100 acres: small wild brown trout; from Glengarriff AA. Other small loughs in area with similar stock: **Glenkeel**, **Moredoolig**, **Begboolig**, **Shanoge** (larger fish, many over 1lb). Best in Apr/May and Sept. South of **Ardgroom** is **Glenbeg Lough,** leased by Berehaven AA; big stock of small browns; tickets from the Village Inn, Ardgroom, Béara: dt waters; apply to J O'Hare, 21 Main St, Kenmare (tel: +353 (0)64 41499). Hotel: Cametringane Hotel,

Castletownbere (tel: +353 (0)27 70379) has local fishing information. For further information: Béara

Tourism & Development Assn, The Square, Castletownbere Beara (tel: +353 (0)27 70054).

CORRIB SYSTEM

(For close seasons, licences, etc, see The Western Regional Fisheries Board)

River Corrib drains Lough Corrib and runs 5½m to Galway Bay passing virtually through the city of Galway. Salmon, trout. Salmon fishing very good. For particulars as to present conditions and rods apply Western Regional Fisheries Board, Nuns Island, Galway (tel: +353 (0)91 562388). Best fishing for springers early in season; grilse, May-June. Rods let by the day.

Galway (Co Galway). Salmon fishing at Galway Fishery, situated in City of Galway, less than ½m from sea; applications to The Manager, Galway Fishery, Nun's Island, Galway (tel: +353 (0)91 562388/ 61138; email: shartgalfish@eircom.net; web: www.wrfb.ie). The flow of the river is controlled by a regulating weir and the short stretch down stream of the weir is the salmon angling water. **Kilcolgan River** (10m E) part tidal, salmon and sea trout; WRFB controls 645 yards of north bank in town land of Stradbally East; dt from WRFB (tel: +353 (0)91 63118). Tackle shop: Corrib Tackle, 2 Kilkerin Park, Lioseaun Ind Est (tel: +353 (0)91 769974).

LOUGH CORRIB

This, the largest lough in the Republic is 65 square miles of water, and dotted with islands, around which are shallows that make for good fishing. Specially noted for large brown trout, each season a number of specimen fish are taken, and the record stands at 26lb. The lough is so immense that anglers unfamiliar with it will do best using the services of a local ghillie. Trout fishing opens on Feb 15, and commences with the duck and olive season, but lough best known for dapping with mayfly (beginning sometimes as early as first week in May), and daddy-long-legs (mid-July to end of season). Some dry-fly fishing on summer evenings. Salmon taken mainly by trolling, and in June on wet fly in many of the bays. Also big pike and other coarse fish in Corrib, so that angling of some kind is possible all year. Fishing free, but salmon licence required. Many hotels issue licences. Boats and boatmen at Portacarron, Oughterard, Baurisheen, Derrymoyle, Glan Shore, Cong, Greenfields, Doorus, Carrick, Salthouse, and Inishmacatreer; a detailed list and angling map of Lough Corrib may be purchased from WRFB, Weir Lodge, Earl's Island, Galway City.

Oughterard (Co Galway). Best fishing is from April to early June. **Owenriff River** flows through Oughterard; good in high water late summer. Local club is Oughterard Anglers & Boatmens Assn; actively involved in stream and river development, information from Tuck's Fishing Tackle Shop *(see below)*. There is additional good fishing for bream and roach on **Moycullen Lakes**, Moycullen, on Galway/Oughterard Rd. Currarevagh House, Oughterard, Connemara, Co Galway (tel: +353 (0)91 552312) provides boats, ghillies, outboard motors with fuel and tackle if necessary for residents only for a daily charge of approx 110 Euro (for ghillie and boat); they also fish top lake of **Screebe** sea trout fishery. Tackle shops: Tuck's Fishing Tackle Shop, Main Str (tel: +353

(0)91 552335); M Keogh. Galway tackle shop: Freeney's, 19 High Str (tel: +353 (0)91 562609). **Clonbur** (Co Galway). Good centre for **Loughs Corrib** and **Mask**. Clonbur AC fishes these waters, **Loughs Coolin, Nafooey** (pike over 36lb) and others, and is affiliated with Corrib Federation. Tackle shop: Anne Kyne's, Clonbur (tel: +353 (0)94 9546197); Fred O'Connor, Cong (tel: +353 (0)9495 46008). Accommodation plentiful.

Headford (Co Galway). Convenient for the east side of Lough Corrib. **Black River** (limestone stream) provides excellent if somewhat difficult dry fly water; affected by drainage work; best near village of **Shrule**; for info contact WRFB, Weir Lodge, Galway (tel: +353 (0)915 63118). Tackle shop: Kevin Duffy, Main Str (tel: +353 (0)93 35449; web: www.kduffy.com). Accommodation at Angler's Rest Hotel and guest houses.

Greenfields, nr **Headford** (Co Galway). Brown trout, salmon and coarse fish; fishing free. Situated on shore of **L Corrib**. Boatmen in vicinity.

Cong (Co Mayo). On shores of L Corrib, good centre for **Lough Mask** also; Cong Canal, coarse fishing; and R Mear, with salmon and trout, pike and perch. Boats and accommodation from Mike and Rose Holian, Bayview Angling Centre, Derry Quay, Cross P O, Cong (tel/fax: +353 (0)94 9546385; e-mail: bayviewac@eircom.net), open during winter for pike fishing; wet and dry flies available. Local club is Ballinrobe & District Anglers; fishing free, but visitors can subscribe to the club to stock lakes &c; very little bank fishing (all lake fishing) except for Cong Canal; gillies available; contact Billy Burke, Outdoor Pursuits, Glebe St, Ballinrobe (tel: +353 (0)9495 41262). Tackle shops: Fred O'Connor, Service Station, Cong (tel: +353 (0)9495 46008; fax: +353 (0)9495 46771).

Tributaries of Lough Corrib.

BLACK RIVER. Fifteen miles in length, it enters lough just north of Greenfields. Access is easy from Shrule, Co Mayo. A rich limestone river with a good stock of brown trout. Best in early season, before weed accumulates.

CREGG RIVER. Rises half mile upstream of old Cregg Millhouse, and flows four miles to Lower Lough Corrib. Upper stretch is nursery for stocking into Corrib, and fishing is not encouraged. Salmon and brown trout angling is permitted on lower stretches.

CLARE RIVER: for this river entering L Corrib at the easternmost end, and its own tributary system *(see Clare)*.

LOUGH MASK

Limestone lake of 22,000 acres connected by underground channel with Lough Corrib, holding large ferox trout, pike, eels, perch and a few char; angling is free; trout to 15lb are taken by trolling and on dap (5-6lb not uncommon); mayfly best in last 3 weeks of May; daddy-long legs and grasshopper, late June to Sept; wet fly, Mar-Apr and July-Sept. Dry fly fishing can be successful from May-Sept. **Ballinrobe, Cong, Clonbur** and **Tourmakeady** are good centres. At Cong is there is Cong Angling Centre: contact John Fahy, Lackafinna, Cong (tel: +353 (0)9495 46848); salmon licence required for L Corrib system; at Ballinrobe is Ballinrobe & Dist AA (st 60 Euro), open to visitor-membership. Tackle shops: Fred O'Connor, Cong (tel: +353 (0)94 9546008); Dermot O'Connor's, Main Str, Ballinrobe (tel: +353 (0)94 9541083); Billy Bourke's Outdoor Pursuits, Glebe Str, Ballinrobe (tel: +353 (0)94 9541262). Boats for hire at Cushlough Pier, Bay of Islands Park, Rosshill Park, Cahir-Tourmakeady Pier. Good anglers accommodation at Ard Aoibhinn Angling

Centre, Cappaduff, Tourmakeady (tel: +353 (0)94 9544009; email: info@loughmaskholidays.com; web: www.loughmaskholidays.com) (HQ of Tourmakeady AA), 4 holiday homes on lake shore, run by David and Helen Hall, Lakeshore Holiday Homes & Angling Centre, Cahir, Ballinrobe (tel: +353 (0)94 9541389; web: www.lakeshoreholidays.com; email: info@lakeshoreholidays.com); boatmen, boats, engines, ghillies provided; fly tying room on site; river fishing on **Finney** and canal joining Mask and Corrib; at Tourmakeady are some good spate rivers, and mountain lake fishing can be had in **Dirk Lakes**; brown trout.

LOUGH CARRA. Connected to **Lough Mask**, 4003 acres, limestone, relatively shallow with brown trout which are considered to be freer rising than those in Lough Mask, and average heavier. All are derived entirely from natural population of wild fish. Shore fishing, difficult, boat essential. Boats and anglers' accommodation from Roberts Angling Service & Guest House, Lough Bawn, Kilkeeran, Partry (tel: +353 (0)94 9543046); Joe and Lucy Flannery, Keel River Lodge, Keel Bridge, Partry (gillie service also available) (tel: +353 (0)94 9541706); Mr R O'Grady, Chapel St, Ballinrobe (tel: +353 (0)94 9541142); boats also from Tiernan Bros Angling Advice Centre, Upper Main St, Foxford, Co Mayo (tel: +353 (0)9492 56731; web: www.themoy.com). Local clubs: Ballinrobe & Dist Anglers, c/o Ballinrobe PO; Partry Anglers, c/o Post Office, Partry. East of L Carra, **Claremorris** and **Irishtown** are notable centres for little-known coarse lakes, containing large numbers of perch, pike, bream and roach; local fishery officer WRFB, Galway.

Lough Nafooey. Connected to Lough Mask, and contains trout, pike and perch.

Tributaries of Lough Mask.

ROBE RIVER, has brown trout fishing, free, best u/s of Robeen Bridge as far as Clooncormack, from Hollymount u/s to Hollybrook, and from Crossboyne through Castlemagarrett Estate as far as the Claremorris/Tuam road. Also d/s from Ballinrobe.

KEEL RIVER. Enters west of Ballinrobe, holds a fair stock of brown trout, and is an ideal dry fly water.

NORTH DONEGAL (streams)

(For close seasons, licences, etc, see The Northern Regional Fisheries Board)

Donegal is mostly salmon and sea trout country. Its waters are generally acid; rocky or stony streams and small lakes in which the brown trout run small - though there are one or two fisheries where they may be taken up to 5lb and more.

LENNON. Rises in Glendowan Mountains and flows through **Garton Lough** and **Lough Fern** before entering **Lough Swilly** at Ramelton. Historically is one of the best salmon rivers in Donegal (closed for salmon 2008). It is best known as a spring river and its most famous pool, The Ramelton Pool is privately owned. The rest of the river is a 'free fishery' and only a state licence is required. Season 1 Jan-30 Sept; June to Sept for grilse. Trout fishing equally good on upper and lower reaches; best Apr to July. Loughs Garton and Fern have stocks of small brown trout, and fishing is free.

Ramelton (Co Donegal). Salmon fishing on lower portion of river at Ramelton owned and fished privately by Ramelton Fishery Ltd. **Lough Fern** is best fished from a boat and produces mostly grilse and spring sal;mon. Other brown trout loughs in vicinity, Akibbon, Sessigagh, Glen and Keel.

SWILLY. Flows into Lough Swilly. Much free salmon and trout fishing of improving quality in region. Recently, the river has undergone major development with work being carried out by the Northern Regional Fisheries Board (NRFB) and the Letterkenny & Dist AA.

Letterkenny (Co Donegal). Letterkenny & DAA has salmon, sea trout and brown trout fishing on Rivers **Swilly**, **Lennon**, **Owencarrow**, and more than 25 lakes; trout av ½lb. Salmon run into Lakes **Glen**, **Gartan** and **Lough Fern**. Boats on Lough Keel. Hotel: Mount Errigal.

Churchill (Co Donegal). **Lough Beagh** situated in the heart of the **Glenveagh National Park**; 4m long by ½m wide; salmon, sea trout and brown trout. Best known for quality of sea trout fishing in Aug and Sept. Fly fishing from boats only (anglers supply own engine); 2 boats for hire. Anglers are requested to respect the bird life on this lake, as there are some rare and interesting species residing. Season mid-July-30 Sept. Info from Bernard Gallagher, Glenveagh National Park, Churchill, Letterkenny (tel: +353 (0)74 9137090/9137262).

CRANA. Enters **Lough Swilly** at Buncrana. Primarily a spate river which gets a good run of grilse and sea trout. Access to fishing is excellent.

Buncrana (Co Donegal). Salmon and sea trout. Buncrana AA issues permits; licences from Bertie O'Neill's Fishing Tackle Shop, Bridgend (tel: +353 (0)74 9368157).

Other waters: **Mill River;** brown trout to ½lb numerous; Letterkenny licence required; also **Inch Lake** (6m): good sea trout; also **Dunree River** (6m); brown trout, occasional salmon and sea trout; **Clonmany River** (5m); salmon, sea trout and brown trout fishing; fair sport in good water; best June onwards. Culdaff & Inishowen AA have water here; for wt and dt see clubs list; Inishowen Tourist Office, The Diamond, Carndonagh (tel: +353 (0) 74 9374933). Hotels: McGrory's of Culdaff, Inishowen (tel: +353 (0)7493 79104); Lake of Shadows.

CULDAFF. A small spate river on the Malin Peninsula, with brown trout, sea trout from mid-June onwards, and salmon in Aug and Sept. Nearest towns, Malin and Carndonagh. Season 1 Apr to 20 Oct. Fly spinning and worm, no float fishing. Culdaff & Inishowen AA have water; contact Hon Sec.

DEELE. East Donegal rather than North, a tributary of the Foyle which enters downstream of Strabane. Fished by Deele AC from 3m u/s of Convoy to 4m d/s, for brown trout, sea trout, and grilse from July on; season 1 Apr-20 Oct, fly, spinning; this is mainly a spate river with worm fishing on the day of the flood, and fly fishing and spinning in the next two days after the flood, or rise of water; tickets from Billy Vance, Milltown, Convoy, Co Donegal (tel: +353 (0)74 9147290); Mervyn McConnell, Milltown Road, Convoy (tel: +353 (0)74 9147702) Hotels: Friels, Raphoe; Central, Raphoe; Jacksons, Ballybofey; Kees Hotel, Stranorlar; B&B: Mrs Shirley Chambers, Strabane Rd, Raphoe (tel: +353 (0)74 9145410).

WEST and CENTRAL DONEGAL (streams)

(For close seasons, licences, etc, see The Northern Regional Fisheries Board)

EANY and **ESKE**. Eany fishery consists of Rivers Eany, Eany More, and Eany Beg, giving about ten miles of fishing. Eany itself is a spate river which flows for 10m SW from Blue Stack Mountains and enters sea in Inver Bay close to Inver village. Good run of salmon and sea trout and has resident population of small brown trout; the river produces around 600 salmon per season. **Eske River** drains **Lough Eske** (900 acres) then runs SW for about 5m to join sea at Donegal Bay. The system gets a good run of salmon and a fair run of sea trout; and has a resident stock of brown trout and char. Salmon 1 Mar-30 Sept (closed for salmon 2008). Trout 1 Mar-12 Oct. Most fishing is on the lake from boats and the river has a number of good pools. In recent years the system has been getting an increased run of salmon.

Donegal (Co Donegal). Donegal Town & Dist AC controls fishing on Eany. Eske Anglers with NRFB control fishing on Eske River and Lough Eske. Please phone Northern Regional Fisheries Board (NRFB), Station Rd, Ballyshannon (+353 (0)719 851435; web: www.nrfb.ie) for information. For permits and boat hire contact their Eske Angling Centre, Lough Eske, Demesne (tel: +353 (0)74 9740781); NRFB own both rivers; Eany contact their Eany Angling Centre, Gargrin, Frosses (tel: +353 (0)74 9736559) (open May 9am to 1pm; otherwise 7am to 1pm 7/7). Tackle shop: Charlie Doherty, Main Str (tel: +353 (0)74 9721119).

Frosses (Co Donegal). Fishing controlled by Northern Regional Fisheries Board (NRFB). Fishery has been upgraded with improved access; excellent run of salmon and sea trout, best fishing June to Sept. Day permits and licences from Eany Angling Centre, Gargrim, Frosses (tel: +353 (0)74 9736559);

GLEN RIVER. Flows S for 8m from Lough na Lughraman - headwater lake - to enter sea at Teelin Bay beside the town of Carrick. A spate river but has a number of good holding pools. Salmon, sea trout, brown trout. Fishes best in summer after a flood. The wild salmon and sea trout tagging regulations of 2003 apply. The Sliabh Liág Anglers Assn controls the **Glen**

River Fishery, which includes the following rivers: Glen, **Owenwee (Yellow) River**, Crow (Crove) and **Owenteskiny** and several loughs, **Agh, Auva, Unshagh, Unna, Divna, Lougherherk and Lough Nalughraman.** Meenacharvey River; dt 20 Euro for visitors; st 80 Euro; wt 50 Euro (anglers in local accomm applies); juv (to 18 yrs) 20 euro; contact Hon Sec; permits from Paddy Moloney, Aughra, Tellin, Carrick (tel: +353 (0)7497 39043). Tackle shops: Spar Shop McBriarty, Kilcar for licences (tel: +353 (0)7497 38492). Hotel: Bay View, Killybegs. Self catering and B&B available.

Carrick (Co Donegal). Salmon and trout. Private fishing, monitored by Sliabh Liág AA.

LACKARGH (Co Donegal). At Creeslough in extreme north of county, river system has spring salmon run mid-Mar to Mid-May. Creeslough & Dist Anglers, (see web: www.creeslough-anglers.com), permits available from PO, Creeslough, (tel: +353 (0)74 9138001); who also issues permits for Glen Lough; very good sea trout, and salmon; dt 15 Euro.

FINN. Governed by Foyle Fisheries Commission. Flows from Lough Finn nr **Fintown** in an easterly direction until it joins Mourne above **Strabane** and **Lifford**, to form River Foyle. Spring salmon best in Mar-May, between Lifford Bridge and Salmon Leap at Cloghan, depending on flow. Grilse, main run in May-July, best in middle section between **Liscooley** and **Letterbrick**, and at **Commeen** on **R Reelan**; sea trout, good runs in May-July, best in middle and upper sections. Brown trout and coarse, lower reaches. Foyle Fisheries Commission water, near **Clady**, is best for spring salmon. Finn AC and Glebe AC fish sections from Liscooley Bridge to near Edenmore. Ballybofey & Stranorlar AA fish water approx 4m above and below

Ballybofey and Stranorlar; limited rods; tickets from Ken Rule, Killygordon, and Ballybofey T I. Cloghan Lodge Fisheries, **Cloghan** (tel: +353 (0)74 9133003), has over 30m both banks of R Finn, from Dooish to Lough Finn, plus tributaries **Reelan, Cummirk, Elatagh**; excellent fly fishing, spinning and worm also permitted, with spring salmon and grilse, autumn salmon, average take per year increasing; good sea trout run in June-Aug; limited tickets, st & dt; ghillie service, B&B, by advance booking; some fishing is held jointly with Glenmore Estate; 20 loughs are also fishable, incl Finn, Nambraddan, Shivnagh, Muck. Dt and st available for **Glenmore Fishery**: Simeon Hay, Welchtown, **Ballybofey** (tel: +353 (0)86 813 3869) has good fly fishing; on 10m of Rivers **Reelan, Letterkillew** and **Finn**, and one bank of **Cummirk River**; spate system, with more than forty named pools; salmon with good grilse run, and sea trout. Tackle shops: Mr G's, Main St, Balleybofey (tel: +353 (0) 74 9132393). Hotels: Jacksons, Balleybofey; Kees, Stranorlar.

OWENEA AND OWENTOCKER.

Short rivers running into head of Loughrosmore Bay near Ardara. Owenea is primarily a spate river, taking 1 or 2 days to run after a good flood, with a run of spring fish, grilse, sea trout, and a resident stock of small brown trout. It has a nine beats on 8m of river, with good pools spread throughout river, much good fly water, and when in condition is one of the best in the country for salmon; producing around 700 salmon annually. Season 1 Mar-30 Sept.

Ardara and **Glenties** (Co Donegal). Fishing controlled by Northern Regional Fisheries Board (NRFB), Owenea Angling Centre, Glenties, Co Donegal (tel: +353 (0)74 9551141). Owenea Fishery has been upgraded and there are additional facilities for anglers, incl access for disabled along one section. Excellent run of salmon and sea trout from May to Sept (grilse from July); 8 beats of double bank over 9m of fishing; dt & wt available. Permits, licences and bookings from Owenea Angling Centre, Glenties. River Brackey closed for salmon; brown trout and sea trout fishing on River Brackey. Many mountain lakes free to fish. Hotels: Nesbitt Arms, Ardara; Highlands Hotel, Glenties.

GWEEBARRA. Drains **Lough Barra** and flows south-west about 7m to Doochary Bridge, where it becomes tidal and flows hence through long estuary between high hills a further 6m to the Atlantic.

Doochary (Co Donegal). Bridge here marks end of tidal water; several trout lakes in vicinity. Salmon, sea trout. Best season: Spring salmon, Feb-May; grilse and sea trout, end of June to Sept. Fishing is state-owned; inquire locally. Salmon and sea trout run into Lough Barra in large numbers and into tributaries.

THE ROSSES. Five salmon and sea trout rivers, including **River Dungloe**, and one hundred and thirty lakes, some of which contain salmon and sea trout, all of which contain brown trout.

Dungloe (Co Donegal). Salmon and sea trout. **Rosses Fishery** controlled by Rosses AA. **Loughs Meeala, Dungloe, Craghy** (Tulla), stocked with browns, sea trout and rainbows. Season: 1 Feb to 12 Oct (salmon). Fly only on all lakes; spinning for salmon. Prices are: assoc membership 35 Euro, dt 10 Euro (bank), boat 15 Euro; with ghillie 40 Euro, (juv free). River prices vary for season on **Crolly River** and **Clady River**; c&r only policy. Permits, tackle and boat hire from Charles Bonner & Sons, Bridge Str (tel: +353 (0)74 9521163), who also organise sea fishing trips (Charlie Bonner represented Ireland 3 times in World Trout Fly Fishing competition). Hotel: Ostan na Rosann. Many B&Bs.

EAST COASTAL STREAMS

(For close seasons, licences, etc, see The Eastern Regional Fisheries Board)

AUGHRIM RIVER. Approx 5m long, flows south-east to meet Avoca River at Woodenbridge; limestone catchment, good trout water. River and tributaries controlled by Aughrim & Dist Trout AC; permits from Woodenbridge Hotel & Lodge, Vale of Avoca, Arklow (tel: +353 (0)402 35146; see website for more info: www.woodenbridgehotel.com).

AVONMORE RIVER. Runs from **Loughs Tay** and **Dan**, approx 8m north; joins with the **Glenmacanass River** (from **Glendalough**) at Larach, on through Rathdrum, Co Wicklow; meets **River Avonbeg** at the famous region of the **Meetings of the Waters**, flows into the **Avoca** and reaches sea at Arklow. Big stocks of ½ brown trout, some larger and some smaller. Rathdrum Trout AC has 12m water from Clara-Lara Fun Park to Avoca; brown trout and some (very few) salmon and sea trout; permits from Tourist Office, Main St, Rathdrum (tel: +353 (0)404 46262); juv must be accompanied by an adult at all times, but permits not required; the club runs fly-fishing lessons in their club house and on the river. No hotels in Rathdrum but various B&B, incl Stirabout Lane Guest House, 36 Main Street, Rathdrum (Tel: +353 (0)404 43142) who caters for anglers with ghillie service, fly-tying room, etc. Further information from Wicklow Tourist Office, Rialto House, Fitzwilliam Square (tel: +353 (0)404 69117; fax: +353 (0) 404 69118; wicklowtouristoffice@eircom.net).

BROADMEADOW RIVER. Dublin District; trout. Drainage scheme has affected sport. Broadmeadow AC fishes river and **Tonelgee Reservoir**.

DARGLE RIVER. Short river which reaches sea at Bray. Principally sea trout, plenty of 2-4lb fish between May and Sept, salmon Apr-May, Aug-Sept, also occasional brown trout. Currently closed for salmon fishing and for sea trout which are over 40cm. Dargle AC has fishing rights on lower reaches; permits from Viking Tackle, The Anglers Shop, 79 Castle St, Bray (tel: +353 (0)1 286 9215). Tinnehinch Fishery: private water on Dargle, fly only; specialising in sea trout fly fishing at night; also Tinnehinch Lake, 4 acres spring-fed water in beautiful rural setting with 5 islands; rainbow trout; open all year; 40 Euro permits for visitors for both waters, from Hugh Duff, Tinnehinch House, Enniskerry (tel: +353 (0)1 2766089) who is also well known as a fishing guide and instructor.

RIVER DERRY. Rises near Knockanna, flows south through Tinahely, Shillelagh and Clonegal to meet R Slaney near Kildavin; occasional salmon, small brown trout. Fishing controlled by Derry & Dist AC.

DELVIN RIVER. In Drogheda District. Fair brown trout stream entering sea at Gormanstown; Holds few sea trout. Gormanstown & Dist AA has water; also Wavin Lake, stocked rainbows, all year round fishing; apply Hon Sec. River being stocked and developed with cooperation of landowners and members. Balbriggan is convenient centre. Hotel: Bracken Court.

DODDER. Dublin District; brown trout (av 9oz, but fish to 2lbs caught), with some sea trout fishing in tidal portion. Dodder AC controls all fishing; contact Rory's (below). Fishing on two Dublin City Council's waters: **Bohernabreena** (free for Dublin Trout AA and Dodder AC members); and **Roundwood Reservoirs** (10m from Dublin) (free for Wicklow AA members; others must buy dt); tickets from Dublin City Council, Block 1, Floor 3, Civic Offices, Fishamble St, Dublin 8; no boats, conc for OAP.

Tackle shop and permits, including for Dublin Salmon Anglers: Rory's Fishing Tackle, Temple Bar, Dublin 2 (tel: +353 (0) 677 2351).

GLENCREE RIVER. In Dublin District. Enniskerry is a centre; small brown trout. Mostly free.

NANNY RIVER. In Drogheda District. River enters sea at Laytown, Co Meath. Fair brown trout fishing; some sea trout in lower reaches. Drogheda & Dist AC has water and issues permits; club also fishes R Boyne, and three stillwaters. *(See Drogheda.)*

TOLKA RIVER. In Dublin District; a once excellent trout stream which has suffered from pollution. Best fishing is from Finglas Bridge to Abbotstown Bridge; 2008 closed for salmon and sea trout over 40cms; Eastern Regional Fisheries Board. For fishing information contact secretary, Tolka Trout AC; parmits from Rory's (see Dublin).

VARTRY. Small river which drains **Roundwood (Vartry) Reservoir** and flows into sea near Wicklow, with sea trout from late Aug, and small brown trout. Currently closed for salmon fishing and for sea trout which are over 40cm. Vartry AC controls lower reaches of river d/s of Newrath bridge; brown trout and salmon, also Ashtown Reservoir; brown trout and stocked rainbow trout fishery nr **Wicklow Town**. River by permission of landowners, no dt. Vartry Reservoir is fly only, brown trout water, run by Dublin City Council; permits st 12 Euro, 4 euro wt, 1.50 dt, conc, from Vartry Lodge near water, or D C C Vartry Waterworks (tel: +353 (0)1 281 8368). Tackle shops: Viking Tackle, The Anglers Shop, 79 Castle Street, Bray (tel: +353 (0)1 286 9215); Charles Camping, Blessington (tel: +353(0)45 865351; fax: +353 (0)45 891183). Hotels: Grand; Bridge Tavern (both Wicklow Town); Hunter's, Rathnew; Tinakilly House.

ERNE

(For close seasons, licences, etc, see The Northern Regional Fisheries Board)

A hydro-electric scheme has turned the River Erne into two large dams. Excellent sea trout fishing in estuary, for 2 miles from the Mall Quay in Ballyshannon to the Bar at the mouth, with easy access, especially on north shore, season 1 Mar-30 Sept (2008 closed for salmon). Coarse fishing excellent; bream, rudd and perch abundant and roach multiplying following their introduction in recent years, also large numbers of pike.

Ballyshannon (Co Donegal). Boats for sea trout fishing, on hire at Mall Quay. **Assaroe Lake** is a reservoir resulting from the Erne Hydro-Electric Generating Scheme, located above Cathleen's Falls Power Station where permits can be obtained. Fishing is available at four points on north side, controlled by ESB, and a permit to cover salmon, brown trout and coarse, may be purchased from ESB Fisheries Office, Ardnacrusha, nr Limerick; ESB Generating Station, Ballyshannon; boats available. Other ESB waters are Gweedore Fishery: Rivers **Clady** and **Crolly**; c&r only policy; tickets from ESB Office *(see above)*; for Assaroe Lake permits The Thatch Tackle Shop, Main Street, Belleek (tel: +353 (0)48 686 58181).

Belturbet (Co Cavan). Good centre for **Rivers Erne, Annalee,** and Shannon-Erne Waterway (formerly Woodford River), and some thirty seven lakes, with most coarse fish and some trout. **Putighan** and **Derryhoo Lakes** are popular venues, tench to 5lb in L Bunn, to 3lb in L Carn. New developments at Loughs Grilly, Killybandrick, Bunn, Drumlaney, Greenville, Round. Bait, boats and tackle from T McMahon, Bridge Str (tel: +353 (0)49 9522400). Anglers accommodation: Fortview House,

Drumbran, Cloverhill, Belturbet (tel: +353 (0)49 4338185), provides guide, bait, drying room, and all other facilities.

Cavan (Co Cavan). All lakes and rivers in the area hold coarse fish except **Annagh Lake** (100 acres) which holds brown and rainbow trout; fly only, no bank fishing, 6 fish limit. Trout season 1 Mar-30 Sept. **Lough Oughter**, a maze of lakes fed by **R Erne** and **R Annalee**, holds a wealth of coarse fish; bream, rudd, roach, pike, perch, trout, tench. Further details from Cavan Tourist Information, 1 Farnham Str (tel: +353 (0)49 4331942) (part of North West Tourism Authority, Temple St, Sligo (tel: +353 (0)71 9161201, fax: 9160360). Tackle shop: Sports World (prop: B R Webber), 11 Town Hall St, Cavan (tel: +353 (0)49 433 1812). Accommodation catering for anglers: Killykeen Forest Chalets, Killykeen Forest Park, Killykeen; (tel: +353 (0) 49 4332541; web: www.coillte.ie).

Lough Gowna (Co Cavan). Coarse fishing on Lough Gowna, the source of R Erne. Carrigallen is in a good position in the **Gowna**, **Arva**, **Carrigallen** area to explore the richest waters spread over three counties within 3m radius. Lakes include **Town**, **Gangin** (noted for the size of its bream), **Tully**, **Cullies**, **Beaghmore** and **Gulladoo** to name but a few. Tackle shops: Irish Bait & Tackle, Ballyconnell, Co Cavan (tel: +353 (0) 49 9526258; web: www.irishbaitandtackle.com.

Cootehill (Co Cavan). A notable fishing centre, with more than thirty coarse fishing lakes within fifteen mile radius, and **Rivers Dromore** and **Annalee**: trout, bream, rudd, tench, pike, hybrids, roach, perch. Fishing free in Dromore and Annalee, trout permit required for **Bunoe** and **Laragh Rivers**. **Moyduff Lake** is brown trout fishery, controlled by Northern Regional Fisheries Board (NRFB), contact NRFB Cavan office

(tel: +353 (0) 49433 7174); permit from Mulligan Supermarket, Shercock (tel: +353 (0) 42 96 69184); for info: Local clubs are Cootehill AC, Laragh AC, and Bunnoe AC: contact through Cootehill Tourist Development Assn, Riverside House, Cootehill (tel: +353 (0)49 555 2150). Boats, ghillies, available. Tackle shop: C J Bait and Tackle, Bridge Str; tel: +353 (0)49 55 52153). Anglers accommodation: Riverside Guest House (tel: +353 (0) 49 5552150); Cabragh Farmhouse (tel: +353 (0) 49 555 2153); Hillview House (tel: +353 (0) 49 5553039), Cootehill.

Clones (Co Monaghan). Coarse fishing. **River Finn**, a sluggish tributary of Upper Lough Erne, excellent bream fishing. There are sixty lakes within 5m of town: pike, perch, rudd, bream, roach, eel, salmon, trout and other species. A few miles north of **Monaghan** is **Emy Lake Fishery**, Emyvale, 136 acres trout fishing, fly only, 2 fish limit. 5m north-west of town is **Lough More** and **Ulster Blackwater** (which flows into Lough Neagh); also **Monaghan Blackwater**; its tributary; all trout fly-only; dt from Venture Sports. Also at Monaghan, **Peters Lake**, roach, rudd, tench, pike; overseen by Rossmore CAC. Tackle shops: Dick Kiernan, Venture Sports, 71 Glasslough St, (tel: +353 (0)47 81495; See website for more info: www.monaghan-outdoors.com) for tickets for above waters. Hotels: Creigh-ton, Lennard Arms.

SHANNON-ERNE WATERWAY (formerly **WOODFORD RIVER**). **Ballinamore** (Co Leitrim). Well developed centre for angling on the Shannon-Erne waterway; produces large catches of roach, specimen tench, bream av $2\frac{1}{2}$lb, also rudd, perch, pike and other coarse fish. Waterway runs into **L Garadice**, one of 25 fishing lakes in this area, good access, all free fishing; voluntary subscription appreciated. Riversdale

Farm Guesthouse (tel: +353 (0)71 9644122) beside Aghoo Lock and Weir caters for anglers (tackle shed, fridges, drying facilities); also McAllister's Hotel (tel: +353 (0) 78

44068); Glenview (tel: +353 (0)71 9644157). Tackle from G Owens, High Str (tel: +353 (0)71 964 4051) (agent for Irish Angling Services).

FANE

(For close seasons, licences, etc, see The Eastern Regional Fisheries Board)

Rises in **Lough Muckno** at Castleblaney and flows SE to enter sea at Blackrock, 4m S of Dundalk. Good supply of salmon in lower reaches, and well up river, depending on water levels; small run of grilse in June, autumn run of salmon. Upper reaches have wild brown trout, good fly fishing water, plenty of fish are caught as large as up to 3lbs.

Dundalk (Co Louth). Waters from Knockbridge to border (except 1m at Balintra), plus all **Castletown** and **Ballymascanlon** Rivers and tributaries controlled by Dundalk & Dist Trout AA; contact Hon Sec. Assn stocks each year with browns, and there is a good run of sea trout and salmon (Aug-Oct best). Membership and permits from tackle shops and tourist office. 7m both banks from Knockbridge to sea, Dundalk Salmon AA; catch returns approx 200+ salmon, 200+ sea trout; dt av 10 Euro, from Island Tackle. Tackle shops: Island Fishing Tackle & Firearms, 58 Park St, Dundalk (tel: +353 (0)42 9335698). Hotels: Ballymascanlon (3m north); Derryhale; Imperial.

Inniskeen (Co Monaghan). Waters in Inniskeen area controlled by Inniskeen AC; trout, fly only; salmon: fly, spinning, lure or shrimp; 2008 waters closed for re-development; membership from A Campbell, Monvallet, Louth, Co Louth; permits from Oliver Keenan, Drumass, Inniskeen (tel: +353 (0)42 937 8353).

Castleblayney (Co Monaghan). Good centre for Rivers Fane, **Clarebane**, **Frankfort** and **Mullaghduff**, brown trout. Several coarse fishing loughs in area; **Lough Muckno**, 325 hectares, with pike, perch, roach, bream, and other species; good free fishing from several islands in lough. **Lough Egish** (5m), pike, perch and eel. **Dick's Lake**, large roach; **Smith's Lake**,

good tench fishing, also bream, roach, perch; **Loughs Na Glack** and **Monalty**, big bream. Castleblayney Trout AA has trout fishing on **Milltown Lough** (3m); stocked annually with brown trout; dt from Hon Sec. Tackle shop: The Tackle Box, Main Street (tel: +353 (0)87 939 4990). Hotel: Glencarn.

Ballybay (Co Monaghan). Excellent coarse fishing centre for **Dromore River** and loughs, of which there are a large number; some, it is claimed, have never been fished. Boats and ghillies are to be found on the more important local fisheries, including **Bairds Shore, Corries, Convent, Derryvalley, Mullanary, Corkeeran and White Lakes**. There is much free coarse fishing for visiting anglers, and typical weights per day exceed 40lb, mainly bream and roach. Local pike fishing is also very good. Town holds annual coarse angling festival. Local Assn: Corkeeran & Dromore Trout & Coarse AA; dt water.

GLYDE: Rises near Kingscourt in Co Cavan and flows E for 35m to join River Dee before entering the sea at Annagassan. Flows through some prime coarse fisheries in upper reaches, notably **Rahans** and **Ballyhoe Lakes**. Small run of spring salmon and fair run of grilse in late summer depending on water levels. Good stock of brown trout. Excellent Mayfly hatch. Due to drainage works some years ago, there are some steep banks on which care should be taken. Currently closed for salmon fishing and for sea trout which are over 40cm. A good centre for anglers is **Carrickmacross**, with several fine coarse lakes near to hand with bream, roach, tench, rudd, hybrids, perch, pike, etc, incl **Lisaniske**, **Capragh** and **Monalty Lakes**, **Lough Na Glack**. **Castlebellingham** (Co Louth). Sea trout and brown trout; temporarily closed for salmon fishing; season 1 Feb-30 Sept. Dee & Glyde AC protect and fish river, contact Hon. Sec. Hotel: Bellingham Castle.

DEE: Rises above **Whitewood Lake**, near Kilmainham Wood. Flow E for 38m, joining **River Glyde** at **Annagassan**. Fair runs of spring salmon, some grilse and good runs of sea trout to 5lb (May). Lower reaches below **Ardee** and **Drumcar** yield most salmon and sea trout. Brown trout water above Ardee. Due to drainage works some years ago, many banks are steep and dangerous. Weeds can be a problem during dry summers, ruining fishing in many sections. Season 1 Feb-30 Sept. Currently closed for salmon fishing and for sea trout which are over 40cm.

Ardee (Co Louth). Dee & Glyde AC has water on Rivers Dee and Glyde. Tickets available from Hon. Sec (web: www.deeandglyde.com). Hotel: The Gables.

Drumconrath (Co Meath). There are several fisheries within a 5m radius; some are members only but tickets and permits are available for the rest; information and permits available from Drumconrath Coarse FC *(see Clubs)*; coarse fishing free, trout dt from and information also from Drumconrath PO (tel: +353 (0) 41 6854100). **Ballyhoe Lakes** (1 & 2), holds good stock of bream, roach, rudd, perch, pike, tench and eel; **Lagan River** which flows from Ballyhoe 2 also holds good stocks of coarse fish; coarse fishing in **Lough Mentrim**, (specimen bream and tench), **Lake Balrath**, **Corstown**. Fishing accommodation at Inis Fail (tel: +353 (0)41 685 4161).

Nobber (Co Meath). Nobber AC has stretch from **Whitewood Lake** to Yellow-Ford Bridge. Mainly brown trout, occasional salmon in late autumn, usually during flood water. Weeds can be a problem during low water.

MULLAGHDUFF: Tributary which enters Lough Muckno. A good trout stream, wet fly fishing best from April onwards, dry fly late in season.

FRANKFORT: Short river which connects Milltown Lough with Lough Muckno, stocked by local assoc. Trout to 3lb. Best in May-July.

FEALE

(For close seasons, licences, etc, see The Shannon Regional Fisheries Board)

Rises in North Cork on the southern slopes of Mullaghereirk Mountain, then flows west through Abbeyfeale, Listowel, and enters Shannon Estuary south of Ballybunion. Its total length is an estimated 46 miles, and there are eleven main tributaries: the **Gale**, Oolagh, **Allaghaun**, **Cahir**, **Brick**, **Smearlagh**, **Tullylease**, **Owveg**, **Glashacooncore**, **Clyddagh** and **Breanagh**. A spate river, with salmon, sea trout and brown trout. Season is from 1 Mar-30 Sept. Sometimes salmon run poor owing to low water. The Feale system is controlled almost entirely by five associations.

Abbeyfeale (Co Limerick). Best centre for Feale. Waders essential. Abbeyfeale AA has 5m of single and double bank d/s of town, with salmon and sea trout; membership, tickets and info Dennis Dennison (tel: +353 (0)68 31118). Mountcollins/Brosna AA has close to 8 miles of double bank fishing from a 1/4 of a mile below the confluence with the Owveg River, up past Mountcollins to within 1/2 mile of Ahane Bridge, contact Pat Danagher (tel: +353 (0)68 44281). Tackle shops: Ryan Brothers, New Str (tel: +353 (0)68 31411). Hotel: Leen's.

Listowel (Co Kerry). North Kerry AA has 7m single and double bank on R Feale and on River **Smearlagh**; salmon and sea trout, all legal methods allowed; wt and dt, from Hon Sec or tackle shops. Killocruin/Finuge Club controls 3m d/s of town, best stretch for spring salmon and grilse. Tralee AA has 5m u/s, both banks; dt issued; fly fishing for salmon quite good from mid-Aug. Salmon licences and permits for North Kerry AA from tackle shop: Jim Halpin Shooting & Fishing Supplies Ltd, 24 Church Str (tel: +353 (0)68 22392), who also advise on B&B, and arrange ghillie service. Hotels: Listowel Arms & many B&Bs.

GALWAY and MAYO (rivers and smaller loughs)

(For close seasons, licences, etc, see The Western Regional Fisheries Board)

BALLYNAHINCH

An extensive system of lakes, tributaries and connecting rivers draining into Bertaghboy Bay. One of the most important salmon and sea trout fisheries in the west of Ireland.

Recess. Salmon and sea trout. The famous Ballynahinch Castle Hotel Fishery consists of **Ballynahinch River** (2½m) and **Ballynahinch Lake**; situated at bottom of 25m long system of river and lakes. Salmon best June to Sept. Fly fishing dt water;; ghillies arranged. Permits for non-residents from Ballynahinch Castle Hotel (tel: +353 (0)95 31006; web: www.ballynahinch-castle.com); limited tackle. At Toombeola near **Roundstone**, **The Anglers Return Fishery** comprises several joined lakes draining into the Owenmore (Ballynahinch) River, as well as a chain of brown trout lakes; **Toombeola Lough**, south, has good browns, av 1lb; coarse and salmon fishing arranged by Lynn Hill, Anglers Return Hotel (18th century fishing lodge), Toombeola, Roundstone, Connemara (tel: +353 (0)95 31091); no charge for residents for trout fishing. Lough Inagh Lodge Hotel, Recess, is central to the **Lough Inagh Fishery**, seven beats including two outstanding loughs, **Inagh** and **Derryclare**, and associated rivers; situated at top of Ballynahinch system in heart of Connemara; dt, boats and Ghillies; permits from Maire O'Connor, Lough Inagh Lodge (tel: +353 (0)95 34706); tackle for sale or hire at fishery office. Tackle shops: Gerald Stanley & Son Ltd, Clifden, Connemara (tel: +353 (0)95 21039; fax: +353 (0)95 21721).

Maam Cross (Co Galway). Salmon and sea trout. Top Waters Ballynahinch Fishery comprises six lakes and part of **Owentooey** and **Recess** Rivers. Lough **Oorid**, at top of system, is 2m W of Maam Cross with Loughs **Shannakeela**, **Derryneen** and **Cappahoosh** forming a chain westward. Season mid-June to 30 Sept; wt (boat) and dt (boat) available; sea-lice have affected stocks in recent years; c&r in operation; permits from Mr L Lyons and Mrs Iris Lyons-Joyce, Tullaboy House (tel: +353 (0)91 552462).

CARROWNISKEY: rises in Sheefry Hills and flows 6m to sea beyond Louisburgh, and is owned and run by the WRFB local office, Ballyhip (tel: +353 (0)98 66404). Spate river, overgrown by trees in parts, making fishing difficult. Lower reaches characterised by long flat stretches. There are runs of salmon and sea trout from June onwards; some brown trout; **Roonagh Lough**, into which river runs, offers fishing for sea trout and browns, either by fly or dapping; fishing is by order of WRFB tickets (dt and licence), available at local office at Ballyhip (see above). Local club: Bunowen & Carrownisky Salmon & Sea Trout AC, contact John Staunton, Staunton's Pharmacy *(see Louisberg).*

Louisburgh (Co Mayo). Salmon and trout. Good shore fishing for bass, pollack, etc; boats by arrangement. Tackle shops: Hewetson's, Bridge St, Westport (tel: +353 (0)98 26018; fax: +353 (0)98 27075); John Stauntons Pharmacy (Gift shop/Fishing Tackle shop), The Square, Louisburgh (tel: +353 (0)98 66139; fax: +353 (0)98 66232.

BUNOWEN: spate river with some deep pools, providing excellent lies for salmon and sea trout. Currently operated on a catch and release basis. Sea trout and salmon, best from mid-June; season: 1 Apr to 30 Sept; it is run and is owned by the WRFB local office, Ballyhip (tel: +353 (0)98 66404); this includes **Lough Namucka**; tagged salmon were introduced into river in 1992, any tagged fish caught should be reported to an officer of WRFB; fishing is by order of WRFB tickets (dt and licence), available at local office at Ballyhip (see above). Local club: Bunowen & Carrownisky Salmon & Sea Trout AC, contact John Staunton, Staunton's Pharmacy *(see above).* **Moher Lough**, in vicinity of **Westport**; stocked annually by WRFB with 2,000 brown trout, ave 1lb; fly only, dt 30 Euro, 15 Euro evng (from 6pm), 4 fish limit; permits from Michael McDonnell, Curramore, Liscarney, Westport (tel: +353 (0)98 21638). Tackle shop: Hewetson's, Bridge St, Westport (tel: +353 (0)98 26018; fax: +353 (0)98 27075). Hotels: plenty of B&Bs. For sea fishing Bay View Hotel, Clare Island, recommended; boats for hire.

CASHLA: drains a complex system of lakes then flows into Cashla Bay at Costelloe. Good run of salmon up to 12lbs, but it is as a sea trout fishery that it really excels.

Costelloe (Co Galway). Sea trout, salmon. Costelloe and Fermoyle Fishery: Lower fishery includes R Cashla and **Lough Glenicmurrin**, and holds excellent sea trout and good salmon; Upper fishery Loughs **Fermoyle Clogher**, **Carrick** and **Rusheen** and **Shanawona**, and holds excellent sea trout and salmon; licences, permits, flies and tackle from Terry Gallagher, The Costello and Fermoyle Fisheries Co, Bridge Cottage, Costello (tel: +353 (0)91 572196; See website for more info: www.costelloandfermoylefisheries.com; or contact email: cosfer@iol.ie); accommodation may be booked through fishery. Tackle shops: Freeney's, 19-23 High Str (tel: +353 (0)91 568794); Duffy's Fishing & Shooting, 5 Mainguard Str (tel: +353 (0)91 562367; or contact e-mail: brianduffy@shoot.ie; see website for more info: www.fish.ie), all Galway.

DAWROS: drains Kylemore Lakes then flows 5m before entering Ballinakill Harbour. Run of spring salmon, grilse, sea trout. Best July to Sept (sea trout); May to Sept (salmon).

Kylemore (Co Galway). Salmon, grilse, sea trout. For river fishing, contact the Abbey (tel: +353 (0)95 41146); or Nigel (tel: +353 (0)95 41178). Mrs Nancy Naughton, Kylemore House Fishery (tel: +353 (0)95 41143; see web: www.kylemorehouse.net; email: kylemorehouse@eircom.net), issues permits. Tackle shops: Gerald Stanley & Son Ltd, Clifden, Connemara (tel: +353 (0)95 21039; fax: +353 (0)95 21721); Hamilton's, Leenane, Co Galway.

Owenglin River (Co Galway). Clifden. Spate salmon river, few sea trout; salmon best June to August; permits 25 euro/day, 80 euro/week. Clifden

AA has fishing on both Owenglin rivers as well as lakes in the Clifden area; lakes (trout) best April to July, Sept. Information: Western Regional Tourism Ireland, Town Hall, West Clifden (tel: +353 (0)9521163). All hotels and B&B cater for anglers.

DOOHULLA: drains a number of lakes, then flows into Ballyconneely Bay via The Pool at Callow Bridge; holds sea trout. Best sea trout July to Sept.

Ballyconneely (Co Galway). Between Roundstone and Ballyconneely lies the **Doohulla Fishery**, which has exclusive rights on a number of loughs including **Maumeen, Emlaghkeeragh, Barrowen, Barrcostello, Aturtaun** and **Carrick** and the rivers joining them, which enter the sea through The Pool at Callow Bridge. **ERRIFF AND BUNDORRAGHA**: good salmon and sea trout rivers lying short distance north of Ballynahinch country and flowing into Killary Harbour near Leenane.

Erriff Fishery, Aasleagh Lodge, **Leenane** (Co Galway) (tel: +353 (0)95 42252; web: www.wrfb.ie); WRFB fishery. At the east side of Killary Harbour, fishery consists of River Erriff (8m), **Tawnyard Lough & Derrintin Lough**; noted for salmon and some sea trout; fishery managed by Western Regional Fisheries Board since 2000; River season 1 Apr-30 Sept; contact WRFB for fishing and accommodation; accommodation at Aasleagh Lodge.

Delphi Fishery, Leenane (Co Galway). On the north side of Killary Harbour, fishery has the following waters: **Bundorragha River** (1m), 4 rods, salmon from 1 Feb-30 Sept, few sea trout from July onwards; **Finlough,** two boats, and **Doolough**, three boats, salmon from March onwards, few sea trout from July; **Glencullin** and **Cunnel Loughs**, few trout from July; fly only; see website for more info: www.delphi-salmon.com. **Knock** (Co

Mayo). Situated in east of county, a notable centre for coarse fishing. Local loughs include **Cloontariff,** pike and perch, **Carrownamallagh,** excellent pike, **Clooncurry**, pike and perch, **Curragh**, bream and pike, **Derrykin**, pike, **Lakehill Pond**, specimen tench, **Nanonagh**, mixed coarse. Boats are available on all lakes. Hotel and B&B accommodation is plentiful locally.

NEWPORT: drains Lough Beltra and runs into Clew Bay, at Newport. River over 7m long and usually fished from banks. Good for salmon and very good sea trout. There are about 20 pools, some for both day and night fishing. Fly only. River known for length of season, 20 Mar-30 Sept. Currently c&r only.

Newport (Co Mayo). Salmon and sea trout. Newport House Hotel has 8m fishing on **Newport River, Lough Beltra, West** (fine run of spring fish); **(River Skerdagh** (used for breeding) is a tributary used for redding); fly only, all sea trout to be returned alive; dt available; from The Fishery Manager, Newport House (tel: +353 (0)98 41222, see website for more info: www.newporthouse.ie). Hotel also issues tickets to non-members, when available. Newport AC, whose members are free to fish Newport River by concession of Newport House, issue permits for salmon and sea trout fishing (June to Sept) on **Owengarve**, a small spate river near **Mulrany**; fly only, all sea trout must be returned alive; dt available from Nevins Tiernaur, Newfield, Westport, beside Owengarve (tel: +353 (0)98 36959). Various small trout loughs around Newport. A few miles from Newport, boat fishing for salmon and sea trout at **Burrishoole Fishery** which consists of **Loughs Feeagh** (now open after 11 years) and **Furnace** with short tidal stretch of river (contact Pat Hughes, mob: +353 (0) 8723 77078); fishery owned and administered by the Marine Institute;

(tel: +353 (0)98 41107, web: www.marine.ie); fishing season effectively mid-June to end Sept; boats with or without boatmen, package holidays arranged by request incorporating local accommodation of varying grades. **Ballin Lough Fishery**, 54 acres, 3m north of Westport: stocked rainbow and brown trout, dt, fish limit; fly only; 1 May to 31 Oct; permits from Mrs Gill, Ballin Lough (tel: +353 (0)98 26128). **Clogher Lough** is 4m NE of Westport (also NWRFB); good stock of free rising browns; 1 Apr to 30 Sept; fly only; contact Mrs Gibbons (tel: +353 (0)98 25061). Tackle shop: Hewetson Bros, Bridge St, Westport, Co Mayo (tel: +353 (0)98 26018).

OWENDUFF: Good for salmon from end of Mar. Grilse and sea trout, mid-June to end of Sept. Provides excellent all-round fishing when water right.

Ballycroy (Co Mayo). Salmon, sea trout. Middle reaches owned by Craigie Bros, Owenduff, Celbridge, Co Kildare (tel: +353 (0)1 6272671); occasional weekly lettings with accommodation, for up to 16 guests and 8 rods; also lower middle stretch for 4 rods; no accommodation.

OWENGARVE: Spate river. Salmon, grilse and sea trout, early June to early Oct.

Mulrany (Co Mayo). Most of river controlled by Newport AC, which has mutual agreement with Dr J Healey, Rosturk Castle, Rosturk, Co Mayo, whereby whole river can be fished; daily, weekly and monthly rods from club Hon Sec or from Rosturk Castle; contact Eamon Kennedy, Kilbride.

ACHILL ISLAND: Off Mayo coast. Achill Sporting Club offers excellent brown, rainbow and sea trout fishing. There are three main trout lakes: **Loch Gall**, recently stocked with rainbows; **Loch na Breach**, with good stock of natural browns; **Keel Lake**, with a sea

outlet, and a good run of sea trout; controlled by club, permits from Hon Sec: dt 7 euro, fly only, no artificial baits; disabled access; contact Roger Gallagher, Valley House, Dugort (tel: +353 (0)98 47006). Tackle from Patrick Sweeney & Son Ltd, Achill Sound (tel: +353 (0)98 45211). Accommodation list from Achill Tourism, Achill Island (tel: +353 (0)98 47353).

OWENGOWLA and INVERMORE: two short rivers, each draining a complex of lakes. Owengowla flows into Bertraghboy Bay and Invermore flows into Kilkieran Bay. Both are sea trout fisheries.

Cashel (Co Galway). Sea trout. **Gowla Fishery** consists of **R Owengowla**, with holding pools, and about 14 loughs, permits from Fishery Office. Owing to paucity of sea trout, most waters unfished.

OWENMORE: 20m long and principally spate river from Bellacorick Bridge, rises near Ballycastle and flows into Blacksod Bay. Principal tributary is **Oweninny** (Crossmolina AA) (which flows down for 14m from Maumkeogh and joins the main river at Bellacorick). River divided among number of owners. Good for spring salmon from 1 Apr, given really high water; good grilse and sea trout from mid-June to end of Sept, if water is right. To the south of river are a number of small loughs with brown trout. Some of these have free fishing, including **Loughs Brack**, **Nambrock**, and **Nalagan**. They are remote, but worth exploring.

Bangor Erris (Co Mayo). Upper and middle reaches owned by syndicate, not for letting. Part of fishery let to Bangor Erris AC; permits from John Leneghan *(see clubs)*; enquiries respecting **Carrowmore Lough,** salmon, sea trout and brown trout, plus 4m of **Owenmore**, to John Leneghan *(see Clubs)*. Bellacorick Fisheries have salmon and trout fishing on **Srahnakilly** and **Oweninny** Rivers. For Oweninny fishing, contact landowners: John Gillespie, Shranakilla (tel: +353 (0)96 53053) who has 1m on west bank, ½m N of **Bellacorick**; John Ruddy, Shranakilla (tel: +353 (0)96 53144) who has 1m of west bank 1½m N of **Bellacorick**; Tony Cosgrove, Shranakilla (tel: +353 (0)96 53216) who has 2m, 3m N of **Bellacorick** (salmon and sea trout); wt and dt from each of the three.

SCREEBE: drains a group of lakes, including Lakes **Ardery, Shindilla, Loughanfree, Ahalia** and **Screebe**, then flows into Camus Bay at Screebe. Gets good run of grilse and some summer salmon.

Screebe (Co Galway). Salmon, brown trout and some sea trout. Screebe Fishery is professionally managed and includes Screebe River and numerous lakes; it also has its own hatchery; fly fishing only; permits from The Manager, Screebe House, Camus (tel: +353 (0)91 574110. Hotel: Currarevagh House Hotel, Oughterard, Connemara, Co Galway (tel: +353 (0)91 552312; web: www.currarevagh.com), situated beside L Corrib on NW shore, good centre for local fishing, caters for anglers. Tackle shops: Tuck's Fishing Tackle Shop (tel: +353 (0) 91 552335) (Oughterard AA).

MAYO North (streams)

Several small sea trout rivers run to the coast in north west of county. **Bunnahowen** is a short river near Belmullet, with free fishing for brown trout (to 1lb), and sea trout. **Glenamoy** (currently c&r only) and **Muingnabo** both empty into a sea lough at **Broad Haven Bay**, and have salmon and sea trout. Fishing on the Muingnabo R. is free. Near **Ballycastle** are **Glencullin** and **Ballinglen Rivers,** both with sea trout, late run on Glencullin, a few salmon in Ballinglen. Free fishing on both. The **Cloonaghmore River** runs into **Killala Bay**, west of the Moy. It has both salmon and sea trout. Free fishing with permission of local assn. **Leafony** is a small spate river which runs into east side of Killala bay, and has free fishing for salmon and sea trout (late run, Aug-Sept). **Easkey River** runs north from **L Easkey** (brown trout, free), and has salmon and sea trout. Some of this river is preserved, elsewhere free fishing. **Drumcliffe** and **Grange Rivers** run into sea loughs north of Sligo. Grange has brown trout, free fishing; Drumcliffe (connected to **Glencar Lough**) is Assn water, with salmon fishing; permits available from Barton Smith *(see below)*.

GARAVOGUE and LOUGH GILL

(For close seasons, licences, etc, see The North-Western Regional Fisheries Board)

Garavogue River connects Lough Gill with sea, which it enters in Sligo Bay to south of Donegal Bay and Erne. Salmon, trout, coarse fish. Lough Gill is a fine coarse fishery, with pike to 30lbs and excellent stock of bream at Hazelwood, Dooney, Aughamore and Annagh Bay.

Sligo (Co Sligo). Salmon, trout. **Lough Gill**, a large lake 5m long. Good run of spring salmon; best Feb to March. Northern and eastern shores controlled by Sligo AA; dt from Barton Smith *(see below)*; assn also fishes Glencar Lake; salmon and sea trout, and small browns; membership welcome; apply Hon Sec; also coarse fish. Fishing on the rest of the lake is free. **Drumcliffe River** and **Glencar Lake**, 6 to 9 miles north of Sligo, controlled by Sligo & Manorhamilton AC; salmon and white and brown trout; good spring salmon run from mid Feb; some very large sea trout caught; permits available from Barton Smith *(see below)*. On the **Ballisodare River**, 3m S of Sligo is **Ballisodare Salmon Fishery**; has two main areas - the falls at Ballisodare, and the river upstream of falls. The spring salmon run extends from start of May, when first run of grilse appears; the bulk of these grilse occur in Jun and Jul, with a small run of larger autumn fish in Aug and Sept; apart from State licence, a local permit is necessary: price varies according to time of year and area; booking essential; contact fishing club (tel: +353 (0)71 9130513); Ballisodare FC fishes these waters; dt (through village stretch), at falls (The Butts). **Lough Colga**, 4m; brown trout; free. Quotas apply on some waters. Tackle shops: Barton Smith, Hyde Bridge, Sligo (tel: +353 (0)71 9146111; fax: +353 (0)71 9144196) (Sligo AA tickets); Macs Tackle Shop, Ballisodare.

Dromahair (Co Leitrim). **River Bonet** feeds Lough Gill; salmon, trout. Best for salmon in summer. Dromahair AA fishes locally; permits from Spar Supermarket (tel: +353 (0)71 9164118). T McGowan, Stanford Village Inn (tel: +353 (0)71 9164140), has private fishing for guests, and patrons of bar and restaurant. **Glencar Lake**, contact NWRFB. Also abundance of coarse fishing in river and **Loughs Belhavel**, **Glenade** and **Corrigeencor**; all free, with pike and perch. 5m west of town (12m east of Sligo) is **Lough Doon**, an NWRFB fishery; fly only for wild browns up to 1½lb; 2 boats provided; 1 Apr to 30 Sept; for permits contact Mrs Martin (tel: +353 (0)71 9164989). Tackle from Spar, Main St.

Co. KERRY (rivers and loughs)

(For close seasons, licences, etc, see The South Western Regional Fisheries Board)

KENMARE BAY. Several small salmon rivers empty into this bay, which provides excellent sea fishing (large skate, tope, etc). Best season, May to Aug.

Kenmare (Co Kerry). Salmon, sea trout, small wild brown trout. Kenmare Salmon Angling Ltd owns 1¼m of **Roughty** at Ardtully Castle, 5 miles from Kenmare-Cork Road; spring salmon, Mar to June; good grilse runs, June to Aug; fly, spinning and worming permitted; spring salmon average 9lb, grilse 4lb; fishing hours 9am to 7pm; permits for visitors staying locally, from John O'Hare, 21 Main St, Kenmare (tel: +353 (0)64 41499); no Sunday fishing for visitors. **Sheen River** runs in on south shore and is preserved by owner (Sheen Falls Lodge (tel: +353 (0)64 41600); it produces approx 1,000 salmon and grilse every season; hotel guests only; contact the Leisure Centre, Sheen Falls Lodge (tel: +353 (0)64 40003). **Finnihy River** is currently closed. **Lough Barfinnihy** 35 acres, is 6½m from Kenmare, off Killarney Rd; good brown and stocked rainbows; **Lough Inchiquin**: char, sea trout, salmon, browns; one boat on site; permits for these and for **Uragh Lough** (shore only) from J O'Hare *(see above)*. **Cloonee Loughs,** on the south shore, have excellent game fishing; permits and boats (only) from May O'Shea, Lake House, Cloonee (tel: +353 (0)64 84205; or contact through email: mary@clooneelakehouse.com). For fishermen with taste for mountain climbing there are at least 40 lakes holding brown trout on plateau of **Caha Mountains**, all easily fished from Kenmare *(see also South West Cork)*. **Kerry Blackwater** 10m long, drains Lough Brin, spring salmon run, sea trout and browns. Fishing part over 4m long, with about thirty pools (Central Fisheries Board (CFB) water); permits from Blackwater Tavern (tel: +353 (0)64 82003). Good fly fishing up near Lough Brin itself; boat only; fly only; dt may be obtained from Fishery Manager, South West Regional Fisheries Board, Macroom, also from hut on river bank, from 15 Mar to 31 May 1 salmon per person per day; from 1 June 3 salmon; limit 20 salmon per season. **Lough Brin**, 65 acres, 10m northwest; trout to 1lb, and sea trout from Aug, dt water; boat only; fly only. **Sneem River**, further west, is controlled by Sneem River Assn; permits from Joli-Coeur Craft Centre/Tourist Office, South Sq, Sneem (tel: +353 (0)64 45270); 1 salmon per person per day; from 1 June 3 salmon; limit 20 salmon per season; fishing with accom at fishing lodge: Henry Cowper, The Huts, Sneem (tel: +353 (0)53 9236230). Run of grilse and sea trout July/Aug. For trout fishing on SWRFB **Lough Fadda**, contact Kenneth Mulcahy, Tahilla, Sneem (tel: +353 (0)64 45606); permits from Blackwater Tavern and Tourist Office. Hotels: Sheen Falls Lodge (reception: tel: +353 (0)64 41600) Park Hotel, Kenmare (tel: +353 (0)64 41200); Kenmare Bay (tel: +353 (0)64 41300). For state licence and tackle: Daybreak Supermarkets, North Square, Sneem (tel: +353 (0)64 89668); Sneem permits at Tourist Office, Kenmare (open June-Sept).

WATERVILLE RIVERS. Waterville River, or **Currane**, is the short gateway to the sea for all salmon and sea trout entering the Waterville system, and produces good catches throughout the season. It is state owned and requires a state licence to fish it. All other lakes and rivers in this area are private and require a private permit in addition to the state licence; available from Tadhg O'Sullivan *(see below)* For Waterville Fisheries Development Group see web: www.loughcurrane.com). **Butlers Pool** is a short fishery of only about 400 yds which drains Lough Currane and the entire Waterville system into Ballinskelligs Bay; tickets are available to fish this famous section from Waterville House (tel: +353 (0)66 947 4244). **Lough Currane** (locally known as Waterville Lake, 1100 hectares) is fished mostly by boat. Ghillie essential to those unfamiliar with the water. Famous for spring salmon, grilse from June, and good runs of large sea trout. The system as a whole produces the majority of all specimen sea trout (over 6lb) caught annually in Ireland. Prawn or shrimp fishing not allowed. Both bays at the inflowing rivers are strictly fly only; sea trout less than 30cm to be returned; 1 to 3 salmon per day limit, depending on season, a rule which also applies to sea trout over 40cms (limit st 4/day); the Waterville Fisheries Development Group (Manager: John Murphy) issue fishery reports and can assist with ghillies, accommodation and boat hire (tel: +353 (0)66 9475257; mob: +353 (0) 86 3991074; see website for more info: http://www.loughcurrane.com); Waterville Fisheries Development Group *(see above)* control **Upper Waterville Fishery** and has **Cloonaghlin** (122 hectares; salmon, large sea trout, and free taking browns); **Na Mona** (46 hectares); and **Derriana** (240 hectares; salmon, large browns); all fly only; licences, permits, ghillies and boat hire from Waterville Fisheries Development Group *(see above)*; Tadhg O'Sullivan, Fishing Tackle Shop, Main St, Waterville, Co Kerry (tel: +353 (0)66 9474433 (office) or +353 (0)66 9475384 (home)). Contact Joli-Coeur Craft Centre/Tourist Office, South Square, Sneem (tel: +353 (0)64 45270).

Cummeragh River, a spate river with five upper loughs, **Derriana**, **Niamona, Cloonaghlin, Na Huisce** and **Coppal**, feeding a catchment of 46 sq.miles (10 loughs in all) which flow into Lough Currane. All these loughs contain salmon, sea trout and browns, and producing occasional spring salmon, the river is better known for summer grilse fishing (to end of Sept) and excellent sea trout (July onwards). Tickets for all these may be obtained from Tadhg O'Sullivan, Fishing Tackle Shop, Main St, Waterville, Co Kerry (mob: +353 87 6705121; tel: +353 (0)66 9474433 (office) or +353 (0)66 9475384 (home)). Local hills contain numerous small loughs rarely fished.

Inny River, a fair sized spate river some 15m in length, with good run of salmon and sea trout from June onwards. Salmon fishing on these rivers is from 17 Jan-30 Sept; c&r only; single barbless hooks; no worming. Spring fish average 11lbs, fish over 15lbs caught, record 32lbs. An unusual feature is that fish may be caught by a small fly on a floating line from opening day, although many are taken on rapallas, toby spoons and other baits. The catchment is a long narrow mountain valley of some 47sq.m. Lough Currane is regarded mainly as a grilse fishery, although the system is noted for its large sea trout, with over 99% of Irish specimen (6lbs plus) fish taken. Season 17 Jan to 30 Sept. The bigger fish are caught in Lough Currane and Derriana. Tickets from from Tadhg O'Sullivan, Fishing Tackle Shop, Main St, Waterville, Co Kerry (tel: +353 (0)66 9474433 (office) or +353 (0)66 9475384 (home)). Waterville House (tel: +353 (0)66 947 4244) lets occasional rods, residents have priority; spinning allowed in spring, thereafter, fly only. Several other owners have or can arrange fishing on Inny, incl Butler Arms Hotel, Waterville (tel: +353 (0)66 947 4156) (no tickets); enquire tackle shop. Tackle shops: Tadhg O'Sullivan *(see above)*.

CARHAN and FERTA: small spate rivers which enter Valentia Harbour. Small run of grilse and sea trout.

Carhan is overgrown and worm is the best method. **Kells Lough** is between **Glenbeigh** and **Cahersiveen**. Plentiful stock of small browns.

CARAGH: river runs through **Caragh Lake** to sea at Dingle Bay. Salmon, sea trout, trout. Salmon best from May, sea trout late, good fishing at night. Bass and mullet in estuary. 7 beats on upper river from Fishery Manager, Glencar House Hotel at Upper Caragh Fishery (tel: +353 (0)66 9760199); dt and wt Mar 1-Oct 1; boat hire; access for disabled; tackle shop at fishery office (mob: +353 (0)87221 3835; web: www.glencarhouse.com; or email: info@glencarhouse.com). Immediately to the east of Caragh Lake is a large group of small loughs, incl **L Nakirka** (no longer fished).

Glenbeigh (Co Kerry). For **Laune** contact Upper Caragh Fishery (tel: +353 (0)66 9760199), **Feale**, **Flesk**, **Behy** and **Loughs Caragh** and **Currane**, and, to south west of Glenbeigh, a group of small trout loughs drained by **R Behy**, incl **Coomnacronia** and **Coomaglaslaw** (free fishing on all of them); information contact SWRFB, Sunnyside House, Macroome, Co Cork (tel: +353 (0)26 41222). Hotel: Towers Hotel (tel: +353 (0) 66 9768212).

Glencar (Co Kerry). Fishery Manager, Glencar House Hotel (tel: +353 (0)66 9760199); see website for more info: www.glencarhouse.com; e-mail: info@glencarhouse.com) has 7 beats, one rod per beat; salmon; best months, Feb to end of July; grilse mid-May to end July; sea trout; average salmon catch over 10 years, 310 per annum; for fishing contact their fishery operation (now separated from hotel itself) at Upper Caragh Fishery (mob: +353 (0)87221 3835); for **Loughs Cloon**, **Acoose** and **Reagh** contact Upper Caragh Fishery (see above). Many smaller rivers and lakes holding brown trout. Ghillies and boats in vicinity. Tackle and licences at Upper

Caragh Fishery. Seafin Fisheries has fishing on **Lower Caragh River** to the ocean, both banks.

MACGILLYCUDDY'S REEKS (Co Kerry). In the Gap of Dunloe, a line of three small lakes drain into **Laune** at Beaufort Bridge: **Black Lake**, **Cushvalley** and **Auger**. Free fishing for plentiful small brown trout that fight extremely well. Very small fly recommended. At head of Black Valley are **Cummeenduff Loughs** and **Lough Reagh**, which are approached via Gap of Dunloe. Free fishing with spring salmon and good grilse run.

DINGLE PENINSULA (Co Kerry). Several small rivers and loughs are fishable in this area; **Rivers Milltown**, free fishing with some sea trout; and **Owenascaul**, or **Annascaul** on south side, rights owned by Patricia Scully, Bunanear, Annascaul, permission required to fish; **Owencashla**, **Glennahoo**, **Scarid**, **Owenmore** on north side: some migratory fish in spate, worth fishing. Mostly free. Owencashla overgrown. Loughs incl **Annascaul**, with sea trout in Aug/Sept; **Gill**, west of **Castlegregory**: free, for small browns; **Adoon**, with sea trout from Aug, free; and many others worth exploring. **Lough Caum** at Castlegregory is SWRFB trout fishery with small native browns and stocked rainbows; boats for hire on water.

LAUNE and MAINE (including Killarney Lakes)

(For close seasons, licences, etc, see The South-Western Regional Fisheries Board)

LAUNE: Drains the lakes of Killarney and a chachment area of approx 320 sq.m. It flows 14m before entering the sea at Castlemain Harbour on Dingle Bay. Salmon, sea trout, brown trout. Late summer best time for trout. Laune Salmon & Trout AA has 16 fisheries on river and these waters are available to visitors; dt 25 to 35 Euro; fishing permits may be purchased at Dungeel Farm, Dungeel, Killorglin (tel: +353 (0)66 9761456); O'Sullivan's Foodstore, Beaufort Bridge (tel: +353 (0)64 44397). Daily permits to fish Beat 3 of the State Fishery, under the management of Laune Salmon & Trout AA, from O'Sullivan's Foodstore *(see above)*. Disabled facilites available on Killarney's Lower Lake, including wheelchair facilities and chair hoist; permits for Beats 1 and 2 of State Fishery from SWRFB. Tackle shops in Killorglin, Killarney and Tralee. **Beaufort** (Co Kerry). For upper reaches. Permits and limited light tackle from O'Sullivan's, Beaufort Bridge, Killarney (tel: +353 (0)64 44397). Self-catering house on banks. **MAINE**: Maine and tributaries **Little**

Maine and **Brown Flesk** hold salmon, sea trout and brown trout. Salmon fishing is at times very good. Brown Flesk has at least 35 holding pools; over 200 salmon per season, sea and brown trout fishing often good. River is late. Best at medium to low water; good grilse from end of June, sea trout in July. Little Maine has seven or eight salmon pools and good fishing for small browns. Sea trout best at night. Part of this system is free fishing: check with SWRFB.

KILLARNEY LAKES: Consist of three lakes: **Upper Lake, Muckross Lake, Lough Leane**, last being much the largest at 4,500 acres, connected with sea by **R Laune**. Good free trout fishing, excellent stocks of wild browns av 8ozs. Numerous boatmen for hire; boats for disabled. Boats from Harry Clifden, Ross Castle, Killarney Boats, (tel: +353 (0)64 32252). **R Flesk** feeds **Lough Leane**. Medium sized spate river, with good grilse run. Many small mountain lakes; free trout fishing. **Barfinnihy Lake**, 10m away on Sneem Road, is well stocked with rainbow trout, fishing by permit only, contact O'Neills or Buckleys (*see Killarney*).

Killarney (Co Kerry). Salmon fishing best in May/June. Sea trout fishing poor, brown trout excellent, best June, and Sept to mid-Oct. Fishing on R Flesk is open; wt 20 Euro from Lough Leane AA or tackle stores below.

Lough Leane (4,500 acres), largest of Killarney lakes; famous for beauty of scenery; estimated that local fishermen get hundreds of salmon and grilse by trolling baits every season. Free fishing; max rods 40-50. Boats with guide. Many hotels and guest houses in the area.

LEE

(For close seasons, licences, etc, see The South-Western Regional Fisheries Board)

Draining **Gougane Barra Lake** and flowing 53m in an easterly direction to Cork Harbour, Lee was formerly notable early salmon river, but fishing partly spoilt by hydro-electric schemes; salmon sport restricted to lower 9m, d/s of Inniscarra Dam. At least 300 salmon and 800 grilse are caught in a typical season. Trout are more plentiful below Inniscarra Dam. There is also good coarse fishing in system, for bream, tench, perch, eels. Salmon season, Feb-30 Sept. SWRFB Fisheries: **Inniscarra Lake**, River Lee: 530 ha, and over 25 miles of bank side, possibly Ireland's best bream fishing. Bags in excess of 100lb are common, also to be found are bream-rudd hybrids; permits from Kathleen Crowley, Kathleen's Shop, Coachford, Co Cork. There is ¾m double bank salmon fishing, below hydro-electric station; fishable from Mar, peaks in Apr to May, mid-June for grilse, brown trout 15 Feb to 12 Oct; state salmon permits required; additional payment for fishing to Amenity Officer, ESB Fisheries, Carrigadrohid, Co Cork; SWRFB, Sunnyside House, Macroom (tel: +353 (0)26 41222). Local club: South Munster Coarse AC; associate membership available; contact Hon Sec. Accommodation: Hogan's (The Village Inn).

Cork (Co Cork). Salmon fishing on lower R Lee at Inniscarra Dam and below Millbro; season begins 1 Feb-30 Sept: fishing is privately owned or leased and controlled mainly by Lee Salmon A and Cork Salmon A, tagging system in operation; salmon fishing licence is required, obtainable from tackle shops. Trout fishing on **R Shournagh**, **Martin**, **Bride**, **Sullane** and **Dripsey**; small streams with brown trout; fishing mostly free. Lough in Cork City, 10 acres, has large carp (Irish record 28lb) and eels, 2lb to 6lb. Tackle shops: T W Murray & Co, 87 Patrick Str (tel: +353 (0)21 4271089); Cork Angling Centre, Unit 14a, Kinsale Roundabout (tel: +353 (0)21 4321000); The Village Inn (John Hogan), Coachford (tel: +353 (0)21 7334430); coarse permits (st 25 Euro, wt 15 Euro and dt 8 Euro) from Kathleen Crowley, Kathleen's Shop, Coachford, Co Cork (tel: +353 (0)21 7334004); (coarse fishing on **Inniscarra Lake**); advance orders for bait: John Hogan (above), who also organises 2 festivals on lake.

Macroom (Co Cork). Stocked brown trout fishing on **Inniscarra Reservoir**; contact SW Fisheries Board, Macroom (tel: +353 (0)26 41222); tickets from Mary Anne's Bar (see below). **Carrigohid Reservoir** is good pike fishery, with perch shoals. Other venues for pike are lower **Sullane River**, **Middle Lee**, **Lough Allua**. Middle Lee, Rivers Sullane, Laney and Foherish, and **Gougane Barra** lake are good fisheries for small trout. Local club: Macroom Fly Anglers, c/o Mary Anne's Bar, Masseytown, Macroom (tel: +353 (0)26 41566); st & dt for River Sullane and tributaries (brown trout). Hotels: Castle, Victoria; Coolcower.

LIFFEY

(For close seasons, licences, etc, see The Eastern Regional Fisheries Board)

Winding river with two reservoirs along its course, rises some 13m SW of Dublin but flows over 80m before entering sea at Islandbridge, Dublin. Subject to hydro-electric floods, it has brown trout and some sea trout in lower reaches. Mayfly hatch end of May. Best trout fishing from Lucan upstream. Best salmon between Straffan and Islandbridge; closed to angling for all salmon and sea trout in 2010; (web: www.fishingireland.net).

Dublin (Co Dublin). Most water controlled by clubs. Dublin & Dist Salmon AA: Liffey at Islandbridge, Lucan, and below Leixlip Bridge; Dublin Trout AA: about 6m on Upper and Lower Liffey at Ballyward Bridge, Clane, Straffan/Celbridge, **Leixlip**, **Blessington** and **Upper** and **Lower Bohernabreena Reservoirs**; mainly trout fishing, some salmon in Liffey (salmon currently closed), and pike, also; dt 10 Euro average, depending on water. Clane Trout and Salmon AA: approx 4m of excellent brown trout water, best from early May; dt 15 euro from P.J. Wallace Cycle & Trophy Centre, Main Street, Clane (tel: 045)868936*)*; fly, bait fishing discouraged, no coarse. North Kildare Trout & Salmon AA: Kilcullen Bridge through Newbridge, Sallins to Millicent Bridge; brown trout, salmon and pike: tickets from Hon Sec; Rory's (below); Higgins, Arch Bar, Main St, Newbridge; Flemings, New Row, Naas; Moorefield, PO Moorefield, Newbridge and Rory's, Temple Bar, Dublin 2; new member st 30 Euro (juv 5 Euro), wt 10 Euro, dt 5 Euro; fishing classes 5 Euro. Kilcullen Trout & Salmon AA, Kilcullen u/s to Harristown; Ballymore Eustace Salmon & Trout AA, Ballymore Eustace to Harristown; Kilbride AC: Ballyfoyle to Ballysmutton; Lucan AC fishes Lucan stretch. Chapelizod AC has water from Old Mill Race River to Laurence Brook Weir, game and coarse fishing, no dt, membership available, conc. Broadmeadow AC fishes **Broadmeadow R** and **Tonelgee Reservoir**; tickets from tackle shops. Dt for Dublin Trout AA waters from Dan O'Brien, New Rd, Blackhall, Clane, Co Kildare. Dublin Corporation controls fishing on **Roundwood Reservoir** (20m) and on **Bohernabreena Reservoir** (8m); fly only; bank fishing; st, wt & dt available. **Grand Canal**, which runs alongside Liffey for some distance, holds few brown trout, bream, rudd, perch and pike. Coarse fishing also in **Royal Canal**, similar species; fishing free. Tackle shops in Dublin area: ABC Fishing Tackle Specialists, 15 Mary's Abbey, Dublin 7 (tel: +353 (0)1 873 1525); Patrick Cleere & Son Ltd, Unit 16B, Kilcock Rd, Clane, Co Kildare (tel: +353 (0)45 893551); Henry's Tackle Shop, 19 Ballybough Road, Dublin 3 (+353 (0)1 8555216); Southside Angling, Cork St, Dublin 8 (tel: +353 (0)453 0266); Angling & Shooting Centre, Ballydowd, Lucan (tel: +353 (0)1 628 1112); Boland's Hardware, 349 Ballyfermot Rd, Ballyfermot, Dublin 10 (tel: +353 (0)1 626 4777; fax: +353 (0)1 623 1911); Tallaght Rod & Gun Shop, Unit 2 Castletymon SC, Tallaght, Dublin 24 (tel: +353 (0)1 452 6522); Rory's Fishing Tackle, 17a Temple Bar, Dublin 2 (tel: +353 (0)1 677 2351; web: www.rorys.ie), who sells permits for Dublin Salmon A, Dodder A, North Kildare A, Tolka A, and Blessington A. Accommodation: Dublin Tourism, Suffolk Street, Dublin 2 (tel: +353 (0)1605 7700; www.visitdublin/accommodation).

Naas (Co Kildare). Ballymore Eustace Trout & Salmon AA has fishing on

Liffey from **Ballymore Eustace** to **Harristown**; brown trout, pike; and also **Golden Falls Lake**; dt enquiries to Publican, The Square, Ballymore Eustace; or Hon Sec. Kilcullen & Dist Trout & Salmon AA fishes Liffey at Kilcullen, u/s to Harristown. Prosperous Coarse AC fishes 20m of **Grand Canal** *(see Grand Canal);*

North Kildare Trout & Salmon AA fish 18m from Kilcullen Bridge to Millescent Bridge; tickets for Blessington Lake from Charles Camping, Blessington (tel: +353(0)45 865351). Hotels: Ardenode, Ballymore Eustace; Town House Hotel, Naas. Several guest houses.

Luke and Fionn caught this beautiful brown trout on the River Nire

Photo: www.fishhunt.ie

MOY

(For close seasons, licences, etc, see The North Western Regional Fisheries Board)

Flowing 63m from its source in the Ox Mountains to enter Killala Bay at Ballina, its tributaries drain an area of some 800 square miles. One of Ireland's premier salmon rivers, particularly famous for its grilse and summer salmon, the average rod and line catch in the last 5 years being 7660 salmon. Stretches to suit all forms of angling from fly fishing to spinning to worm fishing. Spring run starts in early Feb; main grilse run starts in May and peaks in June/July. Estuary contains good stocks of sea trout, boats obtainable. Detailed information on all fisheries from North Western Regional Fisheries Board, Ardnaree House, Abbey St, Ballina (tel: +353 (0)96 22788; fax: +353 (0)96 70543; e-mail: info@nwrfb.com).

Ballina (Co Mayo). Famous salmon water, with catches of over 5,000 in a season. Fishing on seven beats (Ridge Pool, Cathedral Beat, Polnamonagh, Spring Wells, Ash Tree Pool, Freshwater Beat (disabled anglers access) and The Point) owned by **Moy Fishery**; State Salmon Rod Licence required; dt available, various fees apply (non-refundable and non-transferable); all must be booked in advance with exception of The Point. Apply to Moy Fishery Office (NWRFB), Ardnaree House, Abbey St, Ballina (tel: +353 (0)96 21332; fax: +353 (0)96 78850; e-mail: info@moyfishery.com); permits and licences also available from local tackle shops. NWRFB can also arrange boats and engines for **Lough Conn** fishing (wild brown trout and salmon). Ballina Salmon AA has a 3m stretch of double bank fishing from weir in Ballina to confluence of Corroy river, with estimated 1,000-3,000 salmon per season; Ballina SAA issue permits for their waters, limited st (apply for vacancy, waiting list), wt (seven days), dt; apply to local tackle shops; also provide access for disabled anglers as they have installed two wheelchair-friendly access points. 4m south of Ballina, Mount Falcon Fishery has 2m double bank fishing upstream from Corroy river, split into 2 beats, lower beat spin & bait, upper beat fly, incl fly fishing on one bank of famous Wall Pool; also contains other pools such as Connor's

Gap; ghillie service and casting instructors provided; limited to residents only; apply to Fishery Manager, Mount Falcon Castle (tel: +353 (0)96 74472). Knockmore AC (in assn with Mount Falcon) has lease on two stretches on left bank between Wall Pool and Coolcronan Fishery; dt available. Scott-Knox-Gore & Mount Falcon Fishery own 3m double bank fishing opposite Mount Falcon Castle; the Attymass Fishery (Attymass AA waters) has 3 separate beats of 1½m, bait and spinning water (but bubble and fly can be effective); permits from Padraig Garret (tel: + 353 (0)94 58151); Pat Gaughan (tel: +353 (0)94 58147) and Padraig Hughes (tel: +353 (0)94 58146); for Coolcronan Fishery, contact Mary Carlisle (tel: + 353 (0)94 57055, web: www.salmonrod.com). There is a short stretch comprising ¾m on left bank opposite junction of Yellow River which is Byrne's Fishery; permits from Jim Byrne, contact (tel: + +353 (0)96 36733). Armstrong Fishery has adjoining single left bank stretch of about 1½m; permits and information fr George Armstrong or Mrs Bridie Armstrong at fishery (tel: + 353 (0)94 56580). Hotels: Ridge Pool, Bridge Str; Bartra House, Pearse Str; Downhill Hotel, Sligo Road; Belleek Castle.

Foxford (Co Mayo). Foxford Fishery, double bank, from 400 metres north of Foxford Bridge, double bank for 1 1/2m; limited rods, book in advance; contact Granville Nesbitt (tel: +353

(0)86 8032350). Baker's New Fishery, about 400m d/s from the old Eel Weir, Foxford; 2 good salmon pools (Eddie Moloney, Maloneys Lodge, The Green (tel: +353 (0)94 9256475)); Foxford Salmon Anglers (known as Baker's Water), 1m double bank from Foxford Bridge upstream and joins Cloongee Fishery ½m north of Cross River; this fishery is now combined with Scotts Fishery at Rinaney; wt, dt, conc; permits from Tiernan Bros *(see below)*. Cloongee Fishery, a prolific salmon and grilse fishery comprising 2m of right bank and 1m of left bank, incl stretch of Cross River; famous Joinings Pool is located here, considered one of of the most productive salmon pools on the Moy; dt available without reservation; few multiple-day permits; two beats; contact John Ruane, Cloongee (tel: +353 (0)87 2796243); Tiernan Bros for permits (see below). East Mayo AA, 8m both banks above Foxford, fly, spinning and worm only (apart from 3m stretch where fly only), ghillie service; baliff on bank dt: contact Bolands Lounge, Swinford (tel: +353 (0)94 9251149). Permits for most of these fisheries from Tiernan Bros *(see below)*. Free fishing on **Loughs Conn** and **Cullin**; wild brown trout and salmon, 2m from town, and on a short stretch of R Moy up and downstream of Foxford Bridge (locals only). Healys Restaurant and Country House, **Pontoon**, Foxford (tel: +353 (0)94 9256443; see website for more: www.healyspontoon.com), has boats at southern end of Lough Conn and at **Lough Cullin. Lough** Muck is a

NWRFB fishery, 1½m north; large stock of wild browns; all legitimate methods; 15 Feb to 30 Sept; fishing free, not suitable for bank fishing. The Board also controls Callow Loughs, 2 loughs of 100 acres each, joined by a narrow channel, which is navigable by boat; 15 Feb to 30 Sept; Tackle shop: Tiernan Bros Angling Advice Centre, Upper Main St, Foxford (tel: +353 (0)94 9256731).

Crossmolina (Co Mayo), a small town north of **Lough Conn**. Salmon, grilse, trout. Free fishing on Lough Conn. Boats and ghillies from J Murphy, Mossbrook, Boseenaun (tel: +353 (0)96 51079/51294); Padraic Kelly, Kelly's Angling Service, Cloghans, Ballina (tel/fax: +353 (0)96 22250); provides a complete angling service covering brown trout fishing on Lough Conn, and salmon fishing on Loughs **Carrowmore**, **Furnace** and **Feeagh**; accom arranged. Local club is the Crossmolina Angling Club. Accommodation: Kilmurray House, Castlehill (tel: +353 (0)96 31227); can also be arranged by Kelly's Angling Service *(see above)*.

Swinford (Co Mayo). Spring salmon best from mid-Mar, grilse June onwards. East Mayo AA controls the largest stretch of water on the River Moy (6m fishing on both banks); wt 190 Euro, dt 35 Euro available from East Mayo AA office (tel: +353 (0)94 9253955, see website for more info:: www.eastmayoanglers.com). **Lough Talt** is good brown trout lake (200 acres); free. For disabled facilities, contact East Mayo AA office.

Tributaries of the Moy

BUNREE. Joins just below Ballina. End of season salmon fishing, sea trout, brown trout. Free fishing.

GWEESTION. Glore River and **Trimoge River** join to become **Gweestion**, flowing from south easterly direction. Both have a large

stock of small brown trout, with free fishing.

MULLAGHANOE and OWEN -GARVE These two rivers flow from the **Charlestown** area westwards. They contain a good stock of browns to 1½lb. Fishing free, excellent on Owengarve d/s of Curry Village.

EINAGH. Joins main river from **Lough Talt** near **Aclare**. Brown trout to 1½lb, but average at 10oz. Sea trout run; free fishing in river and lough (browns, av ½lb).

LOUGH CONN SYSTEM. Lough Conn, 12,000 acres, together with **L Cullin**, main run from end of Mar through Apr, grilse run from May through July. Salmon adhere to known localities, and are taken by trolling spoon or Devon minnow, a few on wet fly. Trout fishing starts around 17 March. The vast majority of trout caught on Lough Conn are taken on any flies during seasonal hatches. L Conn has one of the longest mayfly hatches in the country, from about 20 May until almost the end of Sept. Trout fishing slows in July, but improves in Aug. Specimen fish are sometimes taken. Several rivers run into **Loughs Conn** and **Cullin**. From north west, **Deel River**: salmon in spring and summer, brown trout u/s of Deel Bridge. From the south, **Clydagh River** (spate river) and **Manulla River** (limestone based), and the outflow from **Castlebar Lakes** all join a few miles above lough. On Clydagh free salmon fishing; on Manulla Roundtower AC water between **Moyhenna** and **Ballyvary** bridges. Stocked browns on location (tickets on bank) in **Islandeady Bilberry Lough**. There is a wide range of accommodation approximate to the Lough Conn fisheries. Contact NWRFB, Ardnaree House, Abbey St, Ballina, Co Mayo (tel: +353 (0)96 22788; fax: +353 (0)96 70543; e-mail: info@nwrfb.com; see website for more: www.northwestfisheries.ie), for further information on L Conn fishing. Tackle shops: Field & Stream, Main St, Castlebar (tel: +353 (0)94 9021030).

Two happy Swedes with a salmon of about 10lb, caught on the Castle Stream Kilsheelan beat, river Suir. *Photo: www.fishhunt.ie*

SHANNON

(For close seasons, licences, etc, see The Shannon Regional Fisheries Board)

Largest river in these islands, 160m long with catchment area covering greater part of central Ireland. Enters Atlantic on west coast through long estuary. A typical limestone river, rich in weed and fish food, of slow current for most part, and though some its sources rise in peat, acidity counteracted by limestone reaches. Many of the adverse effects of hydro-electric scheme now overcome by re-stocking and other forms of fishery management. With exception of the famous Castleconnell stretch, Shannon mostly sluggish. Salmon run from Mar to May, grilse from end of May to Sept. Primary sea trout waters are **Rivers Feale** and **Doonbeg**. Permits from local tackle shops. Trout fishing is a feature of Shannon and tributaries, **Mulcair**, **Newport**, **Nenagh**, **Brosna**, **Little Brosna**, **Fergus**, and **Maigue**. There is a mayfly rise, when excellent sport can be enjoyed, free of charge, in **Loughs Derg** and **Ree** at Athlone. Trolling is the usual method, otherwise; trout grow large. Salmon fishing rights on Shannon and tributaries are reserved by the ESB, and a permit is required, which is sold as st, wt, or dt, from ESB Fisheries Office, Ardnacrusha (tel: +353 (0)61 345589). Currently the only rivers open for salmon fishing are the Feale, Mulcair and a section of the lower Shannon (from O'Briensbridge to Thomond Bridge); local restrictions are also in place: check with Shannon Regional Fisheries Board. Brown trout fishing is in part free, and in part leased to the Central Fisheries Board or fishing clubs. River has well-deserved reputation for its coarse fishing. Excellent fisheries for rudd, perch, shoals of bream and roach, at Plassey, O'Briensbridge, u/s of Portumna, Banagher, Shannonbridge. The three main pike fisheries of the system are R Shannon itself, Lough Derg, and R Fergus. There is a limit on the killing of pike: one per angler per day, max size 50cms. Coarse fishing may also be had in Derg and Ree; max 4 coarse fish retained per day; not larger than 25cm. **Lough Allen**, northernmost lake of Shannon, specially good for pike. Eel fishing is growing more popular in Shannon region, which has sluggish stretches ideal for the species, large catches coming from Shannon, **R Fergus, L Derg** and **East Clare Lakes**; Mouth of Suck at Shannonbridge and mouth of Brosna are good spots to try. A share certificate is required to fish for brown trout and coarse fish on Shannon upstream of Banagher Bridge, and a licence is required to fish for sea trout and salmon in whole of region, where applicable. For angling guide and detailed pamphlets on angling in Shannon region contact Shannon Development, Shannon Town Centre, Co Clare (tel: +353 (0)61 361555; fax: +353 (0)61 363180; e-mail: meehanc@shannondev.ie); or Shannon Regional Fisheries Board, Ashbourne Business Park, Dock Rd, Limerick (tel: +353 (0)61 300238; fax: +353 (0)61 300308; e-mail: info@shannon-fishery-board.ie); also Brian McManus of Shannon Regional Fisheries Board (Angling Section (tel: +353 (0)5791 21777). For more angling information, see www.shannonregiontourism.ie and/or www.shrfb.ie. *Wheelchair anglers:* Much of the accommodation featured have special access facilities for wheelchair users. Likewise, many of the rivers and lakes in the region are equipped to make fishing accessible to persons with physical disabilities. Car parking is available close to the water's edge, and purpose-built fishing stands enable access by wheelchairs at the following better-known angling venues: the Shannon at O'Briensbridge (Rowing Club stretch) 6 pegs; Annacotty stretch 10 pegs (there are problems accessing Pumphouse stretch); Lough Bridget in East Clare 20 pegs; Lough Derg shores at Rossmore Quay 6 pegs; from the pier at Scariff Harbour there is limited access at Twomilegate near Killaloe, and at Dromineer Bay. Check accommodation facilities first, though, and for up to date information visit www.shrfb.ie. A *Three Counties Angling Guide* is also available, covering fishing in upper Shannon catchment, from Mr Michael Flaherty, Lack, Whitehall, Co Longford (tel: +353 (0)43 26439).

Kilrush (Co Clare). West Clare AA has fishing in this corner of Co Clare, on Lakes **Knockerra** (50 acres), **Knockalough, Doo Lough, Kilkee Reservoir**, all fly and worm only; plenty of trout; trout fishing free, however membership of West Clare AA would be appreciated; permits from Kilkee Tourist Office. National, regional, district and local permits as well as tackle, information and advice from Michael O'Sullivan & Son, 49/50 Moore St, (tel/fax: +353 (0)65 9051071). Accommodation: several hotels in Kilkee, including Strand; various B&B available, including Kilrush Creek Lodge, Kiely's Grove House and several in Kilrush. Salmon in spate, brown and sea trout fishing locally on **Cree**, **Annageeragh** and **Doonbeg Rivers**.

Limerick (Co Limerick). On tidal Shannon. Clancy's Strand is the lowest bottom fishery on Shannon, mainly trout fishing, which can be very good, on fly, worm, dead minnow or spinner. ESB permit required. On outskirts of city is the Long Shore Fishery: wide, deep tidal water with spring salmon run; it can be fished from both banks. Good spring salmon fishing at **Plassey** (2m); 500 yds salmon fishing which peaks in May, and trout. ESB permits required; licences and permits available from The Fishing, Shooting Archery Store *(see below)*. Limerick tackle shops: Bonds Tackle, 40 Wickham Str (tel: +353 (0)61 316809; fax: +353 (0)61 473017); The Fishing Shooting Archery Store, The Milk Market, Ellen Str (tel: +353 (0)61 413484; websites with more: www.flyfish.ie and www.whattododirectory.com); e-mail: info@stevenormoyle.com), who also offer a comprehensive range of services such as guided boat trips for pike and trout; tuition in fly fishing and spinning/trolling &c.

Castleconnell (Co Limerick). Principal centre for salmon angling on Shannon and within 3m of **Mulcair River**. Traditional big fish water; catches improved recently. Good run of spring salmon, grilse from May, and Sept fishing is usually good. Fishing on six Castleconnell beats controlled by Regional Manager, ESB Fisheries, Ardnacrusha (tel: +353 (0)61 344511/3), who will book beats and provide information; also Kingfisher AC *(see below)*. Permits and licence from Kingfisher Angling Centre *(see below)*. Advance booking advisable from ESB (tel: +353 (0)61 345589). Best beats can be the lower beats. Best months for spring salmon, Apr to mid-May, grilse mid-May to end June. Fly and spinning. The best coarse fishing in Limerick area is located just below Castleconnell Salmon Fishery; annual rod catch is 800 salmon in the season; this is free fishing, but has eight private positions, available as dt and should be reserved in advance; landowner consent is required on some parts. About 10 mins drive from Castleconnell Fishery, one of Ireland's famous fishing houses, Millbank House, Murroe, is located; contact Richard & Eleanor Keays (tel: +353 (0)61 386115); Millbank has a well stocked tackle shop and all facilities required for the experienced fisherman; the Mulcair River flows by the property; famous for its salmon and trout. Also, contact Nancy or Niall O'Donnell, Lake View House, Doon Lake, Broadford, Co Clare (tel: +353 (0)61 473125); b&b on shore of lake, anglers catered for, boats for hire, much excellent coarse fishing in easy reach. Tackle shops: Kingfisher Angling Centre, Castleconnell (tel: +353 (0)61 377407), supplies boats, ghillies (book well in advance), hires tackle, supplies permits and licences, and runs Kingfisher AC (also agent for stocked fishery, with trout

2lbs-12lbs); Moloneys; T J's Angling Centre, Ballina, Killaloe (tel: +353 (0)61 376009); see website for more information: www.tjsangling.com). Accommodation: Edelweiss, Stradbally (tel: +353 (0)61 377397).

Killaloe (Co Clare). At outlet from Lough Derg, good centre for trout and coarse fishing on lake. Trout angling can be very good in May and autumn; fish average 3-4lb. Boats for hire. **Doon Lough**, 8m west, is a fine coarse fishery, with a good stock of bream to 3lb, also boat fishing for large pike. Boats for hire. Good bream fishing at caravan park on west shore. Tackle shop: T J's Fishing Tackle & Angling Centre (tel: +353 (0) 61 376009), Ballina. Hotel: Lakeside.

Scariff Bay (Co Clare). From Aughinish Point into bay there is good fishing for specimen pike, also stocks of bream, tench, perch and rudd. Boat essential. Further west shore centres for coarse fishing are **Mountshannon/Whitegate**: Church Bay contains large tench, pike, bream and rudd; **Williamstown Harbour**: big tench from boat, quay fishing for pike, perch and bream; **Rossmore** pier: good place for same species, and a nice spot for camping. Boats and ghillies are for hire.

Dromineer (Co Tipperary). Best centre for middle sections of **Lough Derg**. Large trout taken spinning or trolling; also good centre for dry fly and dapping; trout up to 10lb caught. Mayfly starts about first week in May. Coarse fishing very good at **Youghal Bay**, Dromineer, **Kilgarvan** and **Terryglass** from quays, harbour walls and shore; Carrigahorig Bay has shoals of big bream and large pike: boat essential. Lough fishing free, although there is a voluntary share membership of Lower Shannon Trout & Coarse Fisheries Development Society; eight fishing clubs on lake are represented by Lough Derg AA. **River Nenagh** flows into R Shannon at Dromineer; a major trout fishery

with small number of salmon; in wider stretches trout can reach 2lb, about ½lb in narrows. No coarse fish except between Ballyartella Weir and mouth of river (1m); 22m of fishable water. Fly fishing best Mar-May, wet and dry fly. Minimum size removable, 10". Nenagh and tributary **Ollatrim** (trout fishery only, no maggot fishing) are controlled by Ormond AA; membership, season and day tickets from tackle shop: Open Season, 45 Pearse Street, Nenagh (tel: +353 (0)67 31774). Hotels: Abbey Court; Hibernian Inn. 3km from **Nenagh** town, Ashley Park House, Ardcroney (tel: +353 (0)67 38223), has Lough Ourna, private lake in grounds of Ashley Park, stocked with brown trout; fish may be taken under prior agreement.

Lough Rea (Co Galway). 19m NW of Portumna; fairly large limestone lake with trout, pike and perch; fishing on lough and river open to members of Loughrea AA, which has improved and restocked water; trout average 2lb, pike run to over 30lb; for dt and boats contact Hon Sec. Loughrea tackle shop: Beatty's, Main Street (tel: +353 (0)91 841403). Hotel: O'Deas, Bride St; Meadowcourt.

Banagher (Co Offaly). Brown trout, coarse fishing good: bream, rudd, hybrids, pike, perch, eels. River is wide at **Meelick**, with islands, pools and weirs. There is some east bank fishing for salmon, mainly from boat. Access to west bank is from **Kilnaborris**: bank fishing possible, in fast water. Occasional spring salmon, mainly grilse. **Brosna** and **Little Brosna River** and small tributary **Camcor River**, nr **Birr**, controlled by Shannon Regional Fisheries Board; brown trout; a permit to fish required. Coarse fishing on **Grand Canal**. **Ferbane** is a good centre, with bream, rudd, pike. Shannon Regional Fisheries Board stock **Pallas Lake** (18m E) with rainbow and brown trout; season 1 May-12 Oct; bank fishing; fly only; 4 fish limit; bank only; pike fishing subject to local regulations; permits from Jim Griffin, The Tackle Shop, Rahan, Co Offaly tel: +353 (0)57 9355979); other tackle shops: The Old Forge, West End, Shannonbridge (tel: +353 (0)57 9151504); Kellehers Angling Services, Taylors Cross, Banagher (tel: +353 (0)57 9151273). Hotels: Brosna Lodge; Shannon.

Shannonbridge (Co Offaly). Junction of Shannon and **Suck** is a fine centre for coarse fishing; long stretches of bank ideal for bream, hybrids, tench and rudd; specimen pike regularly 20lb plus, occasionally 30lb plus. Hot water from the Power Station attracts tench. Eel and roach fishing also is good here. Five bog lakes, Boora Park Lands, have been opened 10-14m distance, stocked individually with few trout, tench, small carp, roach. Assn: Shannonbridge AA. Tackle shops: Dermot Killeen, Killeen's Village Tavern, Main Str (tel: +353 (0)90 967 4112; web: www.shannonbridge.net). For further information contact Information Centre, Shannonbridge (tel: +353 (0)90 967 4344).

Athlone (Co Westmeath). Athlone AA has water within 20m radius; stocked with pike and trout. Some salmon. Shannon and Lough Ree abound with trout (good rise to mayfly, late May to late June), pike, roach and bream; bank or boat. Tench plentiful on **Lough Ree** Inner Lakes, particularly on Coosan Lough; also large rudd. At Barrymore Point, Lough Ree, is good fishing for rudd and bream; generally Zebra mussel has allowed for extreme water clarity for summer fishing; best late evening or overnight. Boats: Lough Ree House, Glasson (tel: +353 (0)1 4923 150), who provide accommodation and angling facilities. Tackle shops: Scully Guns & Tackle, 3 Pearse Court, Pearse Str, Athlone (tel: +353 (0)90 6492486); Strand Fishing Tackle, Strand (tel: +353

(0)90 6479277; mob: +353 (0)86 825 4141). Anglers accommodation: Mrs Duggan, Villa St John, Roscommon Rd (tel: +353 (0)90 6492490); Mark & Linda Egan, Shannonside House, West Lodge Road (tel: +353 (0)90 6494773).

Lanesborough (Co Longford). Bream, rudd, rudd-bream hybrids, perch, pike, eels. Coarse fishing on **R Shannon, Suck, Lough Ree** and **Feorish River**. Good stock of big fish early in season on hot water stretch of Shannon below Power Station, from July these move out into lake. Baits from M Healey, Lakeside Stores. Tackle shop: Lakeside Stores Fishing Tackle, Main Str (tel: +353 (0)43 21491); Edward Denniston & Co, Centenary Square, Longford (tel: +353 (0)43 46345). Hotel: Abbey Hotel Conference & Leisure, Galway Rd, Roscommon (tel: +353 (0)90 66 26240/26250; fax: +353 (0)90 66 26021; web: www.abbeyhotel.ie).

Strokestown (Co Roscommon). Free fishing in locality, some on dt. Convenient centre for Shannon and **Lough Lea**; a chain of 65 lakes within 7m radius of the town; rudd, perch, bream, pike and tench. **Cloonfree Lake**, one mile from town, is another good coarse fishery, especially for rudd. **Kilglass Lake**, a five-mile long chain, is 4 miles out on Dumsa Rd: plentiful bream and rudd. **Annamore Lake**, record rudd caught in 1995. **Lough na Blaithi** has new fishing development with 60 fishing stands erected; rudd, bream, tench, roach. **Finlough** contains quality rudd and specimen tench (difficult to locate and catch). **Grange Lake** (known locally as Trout Lake) produces trout to 12½lb, specimen rudd, pike and tench. Boats can be hired locally; advance booking advised. Local club, Strokestown AC. Hotel: Abbey Hotel Conference & Leisure, Galway Rd, Roscommon (tel: +353 (0)90 66 26240/26250; fax: +353 (0)90 66 26021; web: abbeyhotel.ie); Mrs H

Cox, Church View House, Strokestown (tel: +353 (0)71 96 33047), central for much local free fishing.

Rooskey (Co Leitrim). Centre for coarse fishing on Rivers Shannon, **Rinn** or **Rynn**, and many small lakes in the area. Bream, tench, rudd, perch, pike, roach. Some brown trout in Shannon. Good catches in **Drumbad Lake** near **Mohill**. Mohill is also a good centre for **Loughs MacHugh, Erril, Lakes Cloonboniagh** and **Creenagh**: fine waters for tench and bream, with pike. Tackle shops: Roosky Quay Enterprises, The Creel, Main St. Accommodation catering for anglers: Mrs Davis, Avondale (tel: +353 (0)71 963 8095).

Carrick-on-Shannon (Co Leitrim). Centre for **Shannon, Boyle, Loughs Key, Allen, Corry, Drumharlow, Scur, Keshcarrigan, Oakport** and many others, including **Hillstreet Lakes**. Trout and coarse fish. Boyle carries heavy head of roach. Good venues are: **Hartley Bridge, Drumsna, Carrick, Albert Lock**. Normal coarse fishing, pike good, roach (April-May). Local club: Upper Shannon AC (tel: +353 (0)71 966 3184). Tackle shops: Tooman Angling & Leisure, Bridge Str (tel: +353 (0)71 962 1872). Many guest houses and hotels offer special anglers accommodation, including Mayfly Lodge, Dromad (self-catering apartments with private jetties) (tel: +353 (0) 71 9165065) with 200m Shannon and 41 lakes within 6 miles;

also Shannon Guest House (tel: +353 (0)71 964 1438); boats for hire. **LoughBran**, roach, bream and hybrids. Hotel: Aisleigh House.

Drumshanbo (Co Leitrim). R Shannon rises in Cuilcagh Mountains a short distance N of here. Free coarse fishing on R Shannon, **Lough Allen** and twelve small lakes, incl.**Acres, Derrynahoo, Carrickport** and **Scur**; roach, bream, perch, pike. Trout fishing on Shannon, esp. below **Bellantra Bridge**, in fast water. Lough Allen Conservation Assn has stocked L Allen with over 100,000 trout in past ten years. Lough also has a good stock of coarse fish, including specimen pike over 30lb and some big trout. However, as lough acts as a reservoir for the power station near Limerick and has sluice gates at lower end, the waters fluctuate considerably and at low water there are many hazardous rocks; and also there can be sudden strong winds. Local club is Lough Allen CA, visitors welcome, membership fee (voluntary). Two trout streams run into L Allen, on which fishing is regarded as free. The **Yellow River** enters from east, a spate river, with brown trout in lower reaches. The **Owennayle** is a mountain stream entering from north. Trout average ½lb. Anglers accommodation: Paddy Mac's, High Str (tel: +353 (0)71 964 1128); Woodside Guesthouse (tel: +353 (0)71 964 1106); Mrs Costello, McGuires Rent-a-Cottage (tel: +353 (0)71 964 1033).

Principal Tributaries of the Shannon

DEEL. Enters estuary near Askeaton some miles below Limerick. Fishing stations; **Rathkeale** (Limerick), and **Askeaton** (Limerick), (best Feb-May), white trout (on summer floods), a few salmon and good brown trout (best mid-Mar to Sept). Parts of river private. Tackle and services: Celtic Angling, nr Adare (tel: +353

(0)69 68202). Hotels at Rathkeale; Central. Deel AA issues low-price st for 15m at Rathkeale. Nearest tackle shop at Limerick.

MAIGUE. Enters estuary between mouth of Deel and Limerick. Brown trout and occasional salmon.

Adare (Co Limerick). Adare Manor Hotel & Golf Resort (tel: (freephone)

0800 904 7523; +353 (0)61 396566; www.adare manor.com) has 2m stretch for guests; two lakes on site fully stocked with brown trout; also ghillie; fishing: strictly members and guests. Dunraven Arms Hotel (tel: +353 (0)61 396633; fax: +353 (0)61 396541; see website for more info: www.dunravenhotel.com) can arrange fishing through ghillie. For Rathkeale, 7m, trout, with ghillies and boats, enquiries at hotels. Some free tidal water below town. Tackle shop: The County Dresser, Station Rd (tel: +353 (0)61 396915).

Croom (Co Limerick). Shannon Regional Fisheries Board has brown trout fishing. Season 1 Mar-30 Sept; fly only; bag limit applies; trout ¾lb-3lb; contact Shannon Regional Fisheries Board. Preserved water below town, free above to Bruree and beyond. Tributaries Camogue, Loobagh and Morningstar mostly free and very good for trout.

Kilmallock (Co Limerick). Kilmallock & Dist AC has brown trout fishing near town on **R Loobagh**, from Riversfield Bridge to Garrouse Bridge, fly only. River is recovering from drainage scheme, and fish average small. Tickets from club members.

MULCAIR. Enters Shannon 4 miles east of Limerick, and is joined by **Slievenohera River**, which is a confluence of the Newport and Annagh Rivers. Mulcair River is spate system, mainly grilse, salmon from March, small brown trout d/s of Annacotty Bridge. The Slievenohera system gets spate runs of grilse from late June; st, wt and dt from Regional Manager, Hydro Generation Region (belongs to ESB), Ardnacrusha, nr Limerick.

KILMASTULLA. Enters Shannon above O'Briens Bridge from east, near Montpelier. River holds some good trout at Shalee, and a moderate stock to 1lb immediately upstream of Kilmastulla Bridge. ESB permit reqd.

FERGUS. Limestone stream with gin-clear water, trout fishing good; few salmon in spring. Fishing free (except salmon). *(See also Co Clare Streams and Loughs).*

Ennis (Co Clare). Good centre for fishing principal waters of Co Clare, including several coarse fish lakes and rivers (tench, pike, perch, rudd). Good brown trout fishing in Fergus and lakes it drains. **Knockerra Lake** has rainbow trout to 8lb. Tackle shop in Ennis: Noel Tierney, Fishing & Cycle Centre, 17 Abbey Str (tel: +353 (0)65 682 9433; see website for more info: www.shannon-fishery-board.ie). Accommodation: Auburn Lodge Hotel, Galway Road (tel: +353 (0)65 682 1247); Old Ground; Queen's; West County Inn.

Corofin (Co Clare). Numerous lakes very good for trout, others for perch, rudd and tench, and all for pike. Accommodation at number of family guest houses. Lakes Inchiquin, Atedaun and Ballycullinan and R Fergus close by; boats.

Tulla (Co Clare). Area is noted for its excellent bream fishing; also roach, tench and pike; fishing free in about 20 lakes within 10m radius (Ennis 10m).

BROSNA. Enters Shannon from the north east, at junction with Grand Canal, north of Banagher. A brown trout fishery, controlled by Inland Fisheries Trust, Dublin 9.

SUCK. Flows through 30 mile valley (5 mile wide) linking West Roscommon and East Galway, joins Shannon at Shannonbridge, between Banagheer and Athlone. Wild brown trout and excellent coarse fishing for tench, pike, bream and rudd. Tench to 6lb at Shannonbridge Power Station, where "hot water stretch" attracts fish. Specimen rudd in L Ree. Good fishing in Coreen Ford area, nr Ballinasloe.

Ballinasloe (Co Galway). River Suck deep and slow, providing excellent coarse fishing with large shoals of bream to 8lbs, bags of 100lbs common, also rudd to 2lbs. Other local waters include **Lough O'Flyn**, **Ballinlough**, 600 acres trout fishery, controlled by Shannon RFB. **Bunowen** and **Shiven** hold good stock of trout, especially good early in season. **Lough Acalla**, nr Kilconnell; browns, rainbow trout, season 1 May to end Oct, st and dt purchased locally; 4 fish limit; artificial fly only; bank only; Shannon Regional Fisheries Board permits from Salmon's Department Store, Ballinasloe (tel: +353 (0) 90 9642120). Hayden's Hotel, Ballinasloe (tel: +353 (0)90 964 2347), offers anglers accommodation with salmon and coarse fishing in Rivers Shannon and Suck.

Ballygar (Co Galway). For middle R Suck and also tributaries, **Rivers Bunowen** and **Shiven**; excellent coarse fishing; tickets from Castlecoote Stores, Castlecoote Village (tel: +353 (0)90 6663394); permits, tackle, bait.

Roscommon (Co Roscommon). One of Ireland's renowned pike fishing areas is on the main **R Suck** and **Hollygrove** and **Blacks Lakes**; in recent years, the R Suck around Athleague and Hollygrove Lakes has produced many fine double figure pike to 20lb plus. River is good for trout in mayfly season. There are several coarse angling centres located in what is known as the River Suck Valley, about 10-15 kms from Roscommon. **Lough Ree** is controlled by ESB, with open fishery angling rights; is a mixed fishery; wild brown trout av 1½lb - 3lb (larger specimens possible; daily bag limit 4 trout) and pike/coarse fishing. The once Irish record rudd (3lb 1oz) caught in nearby **Kilglass Lake**. Shannon Regional Fisheries Board have upgraded facilities at a number of lakes, which includes those for

disabled anglers. Local contacts: Athleague Fuerty AC; Boyle & DAC, John Gallagher (tel: +353 (0)86 387 1616); Cavetown AC; Ballaghderreen & Dist AC (tel: +0353 (0)9498 60077); Tulsk AC (Tel: +353 (0)71 9639038). Accommodation: Abbey Hotel Conference & Leisure, Galway Rd, Roscommon (tel: +353 (0)90 66 26240; fax: +353 (0)90 66 26021; web: www.abbeyhotel.ie). For further information, contact: Angling/Visitor Centre, Athleague, Co Roscommon (tel: +353 (0)90 6663602; fax: +353 (0)903 63014; see website for more info: www.suckvalley.com); Ireland West Tourism, Aras Failte, Forster St, Galway (tel: +353 (0)91 537700). Tackle shop (also supplies permits for R Suck): Oscar Neilan, Castlecoote Stores, Castlecoote (tel: +353 (0)9066 63394). Hotels: Grelly's, Royal, O'Gara's.

Castlerea (Co Roscommon). For upper R Suck reaches which hold trout in some areas. **Lough O'Flynn** now has excellent trout fishing, thanks to CFB improvement work; Shannon Regional Fisheries Board permit required *(see Mount Nugent)*; permits and boats from Padraig Campbell, O'Flynn Bar, Ballinlaugh. Trout and coarse fish in **Lough Glinn** and **Errit Lakes**. Hotels: Don Arms, Tully's.

INNY. A slow-flowing river densely populated with roach, pike, and large bream. Trout between Abbeyshrule and Shrule Bridge where water runs faster. Inny AA have much fishing; Shannon Regional Fisheries Board waters.

Mullingar (Co Westmeath). Many coarse loughs in area, including **Kinale** (roach, pike), **Slevins**, bream, tench, pike, perch (with new platform for disabled), **Patrick** (tench), **Sheever**, (bream, tench, pike, perch), **Ballinafid** (specimen bream, carp), **Doolin** (tench, bream), **Derravaragh** (renowned pike to specimen size, roach, hybrids and trout); trout loughs are **Lene**, north of Collinstown, fly and trolling, good fly hatches on water; boats: Derravaragh Boat Hire (tel: +353 (0)86 823 0363); **Bane**, northeast of Mullingar, access through ghillies only, very large brown trout; **Glore**, 4km from Castlepollard, excellent stocks of wild browns, average over 2lbs, good fly hatches; famous limestone loughs, **Sheelin** (4,654 acres) (*see below*), **Ennell** (3,200 acres) and **Owel** (2,500 acres); and also **Mount Dalton Lake**, a small fishery stocked with brown trout by Shannon Regional Fisheries Board; season 1 Mar-12 Oct Ennell and Owel; on Ennell, wet fly fishing productive in March, fly hatches from May; on Owel, large hatches of fly from Mid Apr, and sedges from end of Jul to mid-Aug; on both lakes, dapping grasshopper and daddy longlegs in Aug; Mt Dalton season 1 May-12 Oct; size limit 30cm; bag limit 4 fish; fly only on Mt Dalton Lake; boat only; st, 21-day tkt and dt available, conc, from Shannon Regional Fisheries Board, Tudenham, Mullingar (tel: +353 (0)44 9348769; mob: +353 (087259 5286). **Royal Canal** nr Mullingar contains tench, roach, rudd, pike, perch. West of Mullingar to Ballinea Bridge is one of Ireland's prime tench fisheries. Local assns: L Owel Trout PA, membership 30 Euro pa; Mullingar Coarse AC. Boats on L Ennell from Peter Gandley, Lilliput Boat Hire (also permit supplier) (tel: +353 (0) 44 9226329; see website for more info: www.lilliputboathire.com) or Jim Roache (tel: +353 (0)44 9340314); L Owel: John Doolan Boat Hire, Levington, Mullingar (tel: +353 (0)44 9342085), boats 25 Euro per day; Mount Dalton: Mrs C Gibson-Brabazon, Mt Dalton, Rathconrath, Mullingar (tel: +353 (0)44 9355102); L Sheelin: Stephen Reilly, Finea (tel: +353 (0)43 81124). Tackle shops: David O'Malley, 33 Dominick Str, Mullingar (tel: +353 (0)44 9348300). Hotels: Bloomfield House, Greville Arms. Lakeside accommodation: Mrs A Ginnell, Lough Owel Lodge (tel: +353 (0)44 9348714).

Castlepollard (Co Westmeath). Trout and coarse fish. **Lough Derravaragh** (2,700 acres), a limestone lake once famous for trout but in recent years trout stocks have decreased to be replaced by coarse fish, roach bream hybrids to specimen size and large pike. **Lough Glore** (86 acres) holds excellent stock of wild brown trout; boat fishing only. **White Lake** (80 acres) (Eastern Regional Fisheries Board) is stocked annually with rainbow trout and some brown trout; **Lough Glore** controlled by Shannon Regional Fisheries Board; season 1 Mar-12 Oct (Derravaragh and Glore); bag limit 3 fish; st 39 Euro, dt 12 Euro, (www.shannon-fishery-board.ie), for **Lough Lene** (900 acres); stocked rainbows and browns, both to 7lb; good hatch of duck fly in April, July/Aug Green Peter; daddy-longlegs and grasshopper Aug/Sept; dt (tel: +353 (0)4496 61359).

Mount Nugent (Co Cavan). Brown trout fishing on **Lough Sheelin** (4,654 acres); rich limestone lough which produces and maintains a large stock of big brown trout, av 2-3lb and up to 10lb; size limit 14"; fishing controlled by Shannon Regional Fisheries Board; method subject bye-law; season: 1 Mar to 12 Oct; mayfly from about mid-May to early June; hatches from Derry Point to Curry Rocks, Merry Point, Sandbar, Plunkett's Point to Crane Island; bag limit 4 fish; no live bait fishing; suitable flies and dt from Kilnahard Pier, Mountnugent, L Sheelin; dt also direct from Shannon Regional Fisheries Board, Angling Section (tel: +353 (0)509 21777; web: www.shannon-fishery-board.ie; www.shannon-fishery-board.ie/shopping/licences-online.htm (for permits). Local assn: Lough Sheelin Trout PA; membership available; st; 21-day and dt available from Flying Sportsman; tackle, in-depth fishing information and licences from The Flying Sportsman, Carrick St, Kells, Co Meath (tel: +353 (0)46 924 1743); Geraldine Clarke, Finae (tel: +353 (0)43 81158), all Loch Sheelin. Hotels: Crover House (tel: +353 (0)49 854 0206), Mountnugent for boats. B&B accom: Mabel Chambers, Boat & Engine hire, also supplies maps of the lake. **Two tributaries of the Inny** are fishable, on a fisheries board permit: the **Tang River** joins Inny downstream of Ballymahon, and the **Rath River**, upstream; both have a stock of small brown trout, and are best fished early in the season, before they run low; information from tackle shop: David O'Malley, 33 Dominick Str, Mullingar (tel: +353 (0)44 9348300). Hotels: Crover House Hotel; Percy French Hotel, Ballyjamesduff, Co Cavan.

SLANEY

(For close seasons, licences, etc, see The Eastern Regional Fisheries Board)

Rises in corner between Barrow and Liffey watersheds and flows south 73m to Wexford Harbour. During most of course has rocky beds, rapids alternating with deep pools. Good spring salmon river, especially in Tullow-Bunclody reaches (Mar, Apr, May best; no autumn run) but of little account for brown trout save in upper reaches and in some tributaries. Good sea trout lower down and in tributaries Urrin and Boro. Best sea trout fishing in lower reaches, late June to Aug. Most salmon fishing private, but certain parts let from season to season and no permission needed to fish for salmon or sea trout from Enniscorthy Bridge to Ferrycarrig (10 March to 15 Sept); fly fishing rules (check bye-laws) (web: www.fishingireland.net); salmon, trout and sea trout fishing is currently c&r only.

Wexford (Co Wexford). Garman AC has made efforts to restock. **Owenduff**; good white trout fishing in June, July and Aug. **Sow River** near Castlebridge good for brown trout and sea trout; permits from angling club. Fishing for brown trout on **Wexford Reservoir**. Sea fishing (incl. sea trout, bass and mullet) in estuary. Hotels: Talbot, White's.

Enniscorthy (Co Wexford). Sea trout good; brown trout poor; free fishing downstream of bridge. Hotel: Portsmouth Arms.

Bunclody (Co Wexford). Salmon and sea trout, browns and rainbows, coarse fishing for eels. Much fishing in area on Slaney, Clody and Derry, either free or for nominal fee. Bunclody Trout AC has fishing for visitors. Licences: Jack Maher, Main St (tel: +353 (0) 53 9377114). Accommodation: Phyl Kinsella, Meadowside, Ryland St (tel: +353 (0)53 9377459/76226).

Tullow (Co Carlow). Tullow Trout & Salmon AA have water on Slaney; permits from Hon Sec for salmon; in 2008 fishing only open for brown trout. Trout and salmon fishing is free on Slaney from Rathvilly to Baltinglass, and also on **River Derreen** with permission from landowners. Hotel: Bridge House.

SEA FISHING LOCATIONS IN IRELAND

As elsewhere, the sea fishing in the Irish Republic has been growing in popularity. The inshore potential of these waters is now widely appreciated. Bass are much sought after along the south and west coasts, and pollack are abundant off the rocks. Deep-sea boats land specimen skate, conger, halibut, turbot and so on. Fishing facilities are improving all the time. Space will not permit more than a few centres to be listed, but club secretaries and local tackle shops will be pleased to give further information and to help visitors.

Dundalk (Co Louth). Bay is shallow for the most part, but contains spurdog, ray and flatfish for boat anglers off north shore. Tope Irish record holder. Quay fishing from **Gyles Quay** at high water for flatfish and dogfish; the quay on **Castletown River** south bank, mullet in summer. 8m south at **Glyde** and **Dee** junction, spinning from southern breakwater for bass, mackerel, occasional sea trout. Good fishing rocks north of **Drogheda** at **Clogher Head**: pollack, coalfish, codling, mullet and mackerel. Greenore Point provides good mackerel, cod, pollack and rock salmon, sea trout and bass; deep water, strong current; best from low to high water: not ebb tide. Club is North Louth Sea Angling Club (www.louthanglers.8k.com). Tackle shops: Island Fishing Tackle, Park St (www.islandfishingandshooting.com) (permits and licences). Boats operate from **Carlingford**; (but north of the border): contact Oliver Finnegan, Newry. (boat: Sharon Michèlé), (tel: 028 30264906; mob: 07703 606498; web: www.carlingfordlough.co.uk). Hotels: Ballmascanlon, McKevitts, Beaufort House and others.

Dublin and **Dun Laoghaire** (Co Dublin). To north, **Howth Harbour** is popular venue: from piers, whiting, pollack, coalfish and codling; from rocks, mackerel, flatfish and others. Good boat fishing for large spurdog. Howth club holds annual festival. Estuary at **Sutton** is a good place to dig lugworm and clam. Ragworm can also be found. In Dublin Bay good points are: **Dollymount Strand**, (some large bass, flounder, eels, codling, good in autumn at evening); sea wall running south, (pollack, codling, whiting, bass and flounder); Liffey between Ringstead Basin and Pidgeon House Power Station (mullet and bass in large numbers); spinning below Poolbeg Lighthouse (bass, mackerel); Sandymount Strand, a large beach with gullies and pools, with bass, mullet, big flounder. This beach can be dangerous at flood tide.

Ferryport at **Dun Laoghaire** provides pier fishing from head of West Pier, and bandstand at East Pier: dabs and conger in summer, whiting, codling, pouting, coalfish in autumn/winter. Sandymouth Strand, north towards Dublin, produces flatfish and bass. There is no fishing off both Marina breakwaters or Traders Wharf. South, from Bullock Harbour to Greystones Harbour there are seven popular fishing venues, with pollack, coalfish, codling, whiting, flatfish, conger, and mackerel. Dublin has over thirty sea angling clubs affiliated to the Leinster Council of the IFSA; information from Inland Fisheries Ireland (tel: +353 (0)1 884 2600). Dublin Tackle shops: Rory's, 17a Temple Bar, Dublin 2 (tel: +353 (0)1 677 2351; web: www.rorys.ie); Henry's Tackle Shop, 19 Ballybough Road, Dublin 3 (web: www.henrystackleshop.com) and several more.

Arklow (Co Wicklow). Local boats offer deep sea angling over inshore banks for dogfish, ray, codling, whiting, bull huss, plaice, flounder, and tope. Codling and dabs may be fished for from Roadstone Pier. Beach fishing on Clones Strand: codling, bass, flounder. There are more than two dozen good shore venues between Arklow and **Wexford**. (popular sea fishing venue for Dublin anglers and from the UK with Smooth Hounds). Tackle: Power Sound, Main Street, Arklow. Hotel: Arklow Bay.

Rosslare (Co Wexford). Good pier fishing for conger, occasional bass and flatfish. Access is difficult because of shipping and permission is needed from Harbour Master. Fishing from shore at St Helens for bass, flatfish, mackerel and other species. Rock and surf fishing for bass and tope between Rosslare and **Kilmore Bay. Ballyteigue Lough** is a fine venue for flounders, and beach fishing is very good at **Cullenstown**, for bass and flounders. Ballytrent beach is good for flatfish by night. Boats can reach Splaugh Rock, a massive reef, and Tuskar Rock: mainly cod fishing. Charter boat from Kilmore Quay, 14m from Wexford Town. Tackle shop: Murphy's Fishing Tackle Shop, 92 North Main Str, Wexford Town (tel: +353 (0)53 9124717).

Kilmore Quay (Co Wexford). Record Irish Pouting taken in 1983, and large coalfish taken recently. Fishing at high tide from pier produces flounder and occasional bass. Mullet may sometimes be taken by ground baiting. **St Patrick's Bridge**, reef of rocks to east of harbour, is boat mark for good bass fishing. Excellent pollack, bass and tope around **Saltee Islands**. Surf fishing for bass and tope at **Ballyteigne Bay**. Mullet and flatfish abound. Lugworm from harbour. **Burrow** shore is popular beach for competitions, best at night. Charter boat: Autumn Dream, Eamonn Hayes

(Mob: +353 (0)87 2135308, web: www.kilmoreangling.com) Club: Kilmore Quay SAC. Tackle shops in Rosslare, Wexford and Kilmore Quay.

Fethard Bay (Co Wexford). Bottom fishing for flounder, bass, plaice, best at night. Hook Head has spinning at high tide for pollack, coalfish, mackerel, bottom fishing for conger and other species. Along shore at Cummins Quay, **Ballyhack**, conger fishing.

Dunmore (Co Waterford). Shore fishing in estuary: bass, dogfish, coalfish, codling, pollock, wrasse, flounder, ray, plaice, conger, river eel, dab, shark. Reef, wreck and shark fishing; base for charter boats. Contact J A O'Connor, Dunmore East Angling Charters, Fairybush House, Dunmore East (tel: +353 (0)51 383397; mob: +353 (0)87 2682794); daily charters available up to 12 persons. Clubs: Dunmore East SAC; Waterford Crystal SAC; Rinnashark SAC. Tackle shops: Shootin' & Fishin', 26a Ballybricken, Waterford (tel: +353 (0)51 878007); Angling & Outdoor Centre, Westgate Retail Park, Tramore Rd, Waterford (tel/fax: +353 (0)51 844314; email: bait@eircom.net); Army & Outdoor Stores, New St, Waterford (tel: +353 (0)51 857554; see website for more: www.gooutdoorireland.com; email: info@gooutdoorireland.com).

Dungarvan Bay (Co Waterford). From **Ballinacourty** pier, bass, flatfish and dogfish, half flood to early ebb. Abbeyside and Barnawee; spinning for bass, bottom fishing for flounder. Fishing at Dungarvan for bass and flatfish. A number of large bass, 6lb to 9½lb are caught; mackerel recently abundant, and cod; blue shark plentiful at times. Pier at **Helvick** provides good sport with congers; distance casting catches ray. Flounder taken in Helvick Harbour. Fewer blue shark than there were. Conger, mackerel, pollack, dogfish, wrasse, bream, ray and bass off Helvick Head. Crab and lugworm on foreshore. Boats for hire. Tackle shop: Baumann & Sons Ltd (Jewellers and Fishing Tackle), 6 Mary St, Dungarvan (tel: +353 (0)58 41395). Hotels: Dun Ard, Clonea, Gold Coast.

Ardmore and **Youghal** (Co Cork). Several venues around Ardmore and Ram Head, incl surf fishing from Ballyquin Strand for bass and flatfish (flounder to 3½lb), Ardmore beach and pier, bass, flatfish; Goat Island and Whiting Bay, similar species. Fishing from Mangans Cove through Youghal, to Knockadoon Head and pier offers more than a dozen venues. Species caught include flounder, plaice (to 5lb), codling, ray, turbot, bass, dogfish, conger (to 41lb), ling (to 38lb), cod (to 28lb 12oz), pollack, coalfish, gurnard, whiting, wrasse, blue shark (135lb) and most deep sea species. Clubs: Ardmore Sea Anglers has freshwater fishing on Blackwater and tributaries Information: Youghal Heritage and Tourist Centre, Market House, Market Square, Youghal (tel: +353 (0)24 20170). Hotels: Devonshire Arms, Youghal, and Green Lawn Guest House.

Ballycotton (Co Cork). One of the best-known of Irish sea fishing centres for both deep sea and shore fishing; large catches of prime fish and excellent facilities. Many specimen caught, including blue shark, conger, ling, pollack, cod, mackerel, coalfish, bass, hake, spur and spotted dog. Big cod in winter months. Fishing from pier at Ballycotton and **Knockadoon**, rocks from Knockadoon Head, Ballinwilling Reef and other marks, or boat; surf fishing at **Ballymona**; bass, flounder and codling. Good mullet in harbour. Lugworm may be dug at Ballycrennan and Ardnahinch. Boat hire: The Sarah Marie, Ballycotton Angling. (see website for more info: www.ballycottonangling.com; tel: +353 (0)214646002); (380 Euro per boat, 50 Euro per hour; Groups of 9;

9.30 to 17.00hrs); The Cleona, Peter Manning, (tel: +353 21 4646773). Monthly competitions May to Oct. Local clubs: Ballycotton Deep SAC; Ballycotton SAC; Aghada SAC; Guileen SAC; Cloyne SAC. Tackle shops: T H Sports, Main St, Midleton (tel: +353 (0)21 4631800). Hotels: Bayview (tel: +353 (0)21 464 6746); Garryvoe (tel: +353 (0)21 464 6718; see web: www.garryvoehotel.com); Inn-by-the-Harbour (B&B and pub: tel: (0)21 464 6768), Sunville House, Sunville. Many hotels around Midleton.

Cobh (Co Cork). Good area for fishing Cork harbour; conger, ling, dogfish, cod, pollack, rays, also base for shark fishing. Cobh Sea AC, runs an international sea angling festival each year in first week of September (catch and release). Species caught include skate, bass, pollack, coalfish, cod, whiting. Conger 44lb 12oz has been weighed in. For deep sea fishing there are charter boats from Geary Angling Services, Sycamore House, Ballynoe, Cobh (tel: +353 (0)21 481 2167). Tackle shop: Cobh Fishing Tackle, Sycamore House, Ballynoe, Cobh (tel: +353 (0)21 481 2167; see website: www.sea-fishing-ireland.com); (email: seaangling@esatclear.ie). Hotels: Commodore, WatersEdge Hotel, Delmar B&B.

Cork (Co Cork). Fishing both inside and outside Harbour offers the following species: dogfish, codling, conger, pollack, turbot, plaice, ray, wrasse, blue shark and angler fish. Various charter boats operate from Cork Harbour and **Crosshaven**, for shark, wreck and bottom fishing; apply T W Murray, Tackle shop: T W Murray & Co. Ltd, 87 Patrick Str (tel: +353 (0)21 4271089). Club: Cork Sea Anglers.

Kinsale (Co Cork). Fine natural harbour. Best-known centre on the south coast for deep-sea fishing, especially for shark, ling, conger, dogfish, ray, pollack, coalfish, red bream and wrasse. Well-equipped boats and experienced skippers; all operators offer rod and tackle hire. Bishopstown Kinsale Sea AC run many competitions during season. For boat hire: *The Harpy*, Carroll O'Donoghue, Crohane, Old Head, Kinsale, Co. Cork. (tel: +353 (0) 21 4774946; see website for more info: www.kinsaleangling.com); *The Sundance Kid*, Butch Roberts (tel: +353 (0) 86 1036 905; web: www.anglingkinsale.com), licensed for 12; tea & coffee supplied. Tackle shop: Cork Angling and Outdoor Centre, Kinsale Rd Business Park, Kinsale Rd Roundabout (tel: +353 (0) 21 432 1000; see website for more info: www.fishingandhunting.ie). Hotels: Blue Haven Hotel, White House, Carlton Kinsdale Hotel, Desmond House B&B.

Rosscarbery (Co Cork). Noted for surf fishing for flatfish, mackerel, occasional bass; three fine beaches. Bass and mullet also taken in small harbour, and from mouth of estuary. Mackerel spinning from pier. Lugworm and ragworm in estuary, sand eel from beach. Club: Rosscarbery SAC.

Baltimore (Co Cork). Excellent boat fishing for shark (mid-June to Oct), common skate, conger, ling, pollack, coalfish, cod, etc. Wreck fishing for conger, ling, pollack, coalfish, cod. Shore fishing for mackerel, pollack, wrasse, bull huss, conger, mullet, etc. Deep sea boat charter: *Rooster*, Nick Dent, Fastnet Charters (tel: +353 (0)86 824 0642; see website for more info: www.wreckfish.com); *Algerine,* Pat Fehily, The Haven (tel: +353 (0)28 20549). Self-drive: Atlantic Boating Services (tel: +353 (0)28 22145). Nearest tackle shop: Baltimore Diving Centre and Tackle Shop (tel: +353 28 20300; web: www.baltimorediving.com). Hotel: Fastnet House, Casey's B&B.

Sea Fishing in Ireland
Photo: Mike Dobson

Mizen Peninsula (Co Cork). Fishing in harbours, rocks, coves, for pollack, mackerel, coalfish, flatfish, bass, etc. Schull Pier offers bottom fishing for flounder, float fishing for mullet. Barley Cove at point of Peninsula is recommended. Wreck fishing within easy reach. Boat operator: Nick Dent, *Rooster* (see Baltimore); in Schull, Iain O'Driscoll, *Blue Thunder* (tel: +353 (0)8638 62876); good shark fishing and large skate; reef and drift fishing for large pollack, ling, coalfish, a few spurdog, bull huss. Several B&Bs.

Bantry (Co Cork). Town is convenient centre for Bantry Bay deep sea fishing. Large conger are caught, rays, ling, whiting, bull huss, l/s dogfish, pollack. Shore fishing best on south side of bay. Club: Bantry Sea AC. Hotels: The Maritime Hotel (tel: +353 (0) 27 54700; see website for more info: www.themaritime.ie), West Lodge (tel: +353 (0) 27 50360); Bantry House B&B (see website for more: www.bantryhouse.com), Dromcloc House B&B (see website for more info: www.dromclochouse.com).

Castletownbere (Co Cork). Fine harbour for sheltered fishing in Berehaven and offshore at marks in Bantry Bay. Shark, pollack, ling, conger, tope, ray, skate, pouting, bass, bream, wrasse, spurdog, gurnard, flounder, plaice, grey mullet, whiting and mackerel. Boats are available: *Tigger*, John Angles, (tel: +353 (0)27 74494; see website for more info: www.irelandseaangling.com). Shore fishing at harbour pier, Muccaragh, Seal Harbour and Zetland Pier. **Kenmare**: charter boats operated: *The Sturdy*, Sean McCarthy (tel: +353 (0)87 2592209; see website: www.kenmareanglingandsightseeing.com), Seafari, 3 The Pier (tel: +353 (0)64 83171; see website for more info: www.seafariireland.com); boat licensed for 12. **Sneem**: Two deep sea boats operate from here, for cod, ling, skate, blue shark, etc. See John

O'Shea boats entry in Waterville (below). Hotel: Island View House (tel: +353 (0) 27 70415; web: www.islandviewhouse.com). Sea Breeze B&B (tel: +353 (0) 27 70508; www.seabreez.com). For further information: Béara Tourism & Development Assn, The Square, Castletownbere Béara (tel: +353 (0) 27 70054; see website for more info: www.bearatourism.com).

Waterville (Co Kerry). Centre for Ballinskelligs Bay, which has various points for rock and surf fishing. Bass readily taken. Angling club: Waterville Fisheries Development Group. Boats may be chartered for shark and other species: John O'Shea, Bealtra Boats, Bunavalla Pier, Caherdaniel (tel: +353 (0)66 947 5129; mob: +353 (0) 87 6898431; www.sneem.com/seanoshea.html). Hotels: The Old Cable Historic House (tel: +353 (0)66 9474233; see website for more: www.oldcablehouse.com), Brookhaven House (tel: +353 (0)66 9474431; see website for more info: www.brookhavenhouse.com), Clifford's B & B (tel: +353 (0)66 9374283; www.cliffordbandb.com).

Cahersiveen (Co Kerry) and Valentia Island. Rock fishing for mackerel, pollack, wrasse, dogfish, pouting, conger, and others, over twenty species. Deep sea angling for ling, cod, conger, pollack, skate, blue shark, bull huss, and other species. Charter boats operate. Catches include conger (up to 50lb), ling (to 35lb), cod (to 30lb), pollack (to 15lb); also cuckoo wrasse, gurnard, haddock, and others, record fish caught here, in various species. Club: Cahersiveen SAC. At Valentia, Brendan Casey operates charter boats (tel: +353 (0)66 947 2437; web: www.skelligislands.com), shark and bottom fishing. Boats from Hugh Maguire, Anchorage, Rocky Rd, Cahersiveen; Anchor Bar, Main St (tel: +353 (0)66 9472049; web: http://www.anchorsiveenfishing.com) Also: *The Mary Francis*, Nealie Lyne,

Valentia Island, (tel: +353 66 (0)9476300; see website for more: www.valentiaislandseaangling.com).

Dingle Peninsula (Co Kerry). Rock fishing for pollack, wrasse, conger. Inshore fishing for ray; offshore for pollack, coalfish, bream, conger, ling, tope, cod, whiting, huss, spurdog, gurnard, pouting and shark. Club: Dingle SAC. Charter boats operate from Dingle: *The Emma Delia*, Tommy Russell, (tel: +353 (0) 66 9151344; see website for more info: www.dinglebaycharters.com). *The Molly'O*, Rory O'Connor, (tel: +353 (0)87 2213 900; see website for more info: www.deepseadingle.com). Of interest is also the Gallarus Oratory and Visitor Centre, Ballydavid (tel: +353 (0) 66 915 5333). Hotels: Castlewood House Hotel (tel: +353 (0) 66 9152788; see website for more info: www.castlewooddingle.com). Brownes B&B (tel: +353 (0) 66 9151259; see website for more info: www.brownesdingle.com)

Shannon Estuary. Locations for shore fishing on the south side are: **Beal Point** and **Littor Strand**, bottom fishing for dogfish, flatfish, and bull huss; several marks around **Carrig Island** and **Saleen Quay**, where good bottom fishing is to be had from rocks and quay: ballan wrasse, dogfish, bull huss, some tope. **Tarbert** and **Glin** piers are best at high tide for flatfish, conger at night; **Foynes** piers produce conger, thornback ray, codling, whiting and flounder. Best baits, crab, lugworm, mackerel. North side of estuary has pier fishing available at **Kildysart** (flounder, crab bait essential), and **Innishmurray** (bull huss, thornback, conger, freshwater eels), Kilrush, *(see below),* and **Carrigaholt** (bottom fishing for dab and flounder, spinning for pollack and wrasse). Beach fishing at **Shanahea** and **Killimer** for bass, flounder, flatfish, Spanish Point for bass, and rock fishing at **Aylvaroo Point** for similar species, plus codling and

whiting in winter. Plenty of opportunities for bait digging. Charter boats for estuary from Kilbaha, Kilrush. Car ferry runs from Killimer to Tarbert hourly, summer: 7am to 9.30pm, (Sundays: 9am to 9pm), winter: 7am to 7.30pm (Sundays: 9am to 7.30pm). Limerick SAC fish all along the estuary and in the open sea.

Kilrush (Co Clare). Important sea fishing centre. Pier fishing from Cappagh pier, bass, conger, whiting, flounder, dogfish on flood tide, large catches of mackerel in warm weather. Beach fishing at White Strand and Doughmore, Sandhills and Seafield Beaches. Mackerel and pollack fishing from Dunlickey cliffs and Bridges of Ross. Species commonly caught in Lower Shannon include large tope, pollack, conger, thornback ray, bull huss, dogfish, bass. Several towns on the coast of Co Clare have charter boats available for shark, wreck and bottom fishing, 35 ft average, tackle for hire. Boats: The Seka, Gerry Norton, Kilbaha, (tel: +353 (0)87 2502546; see website: www.loopheadangling.com). The Deva, Michael Fennell, Kilbaha (tel: +353 (0)65 9058174; see website: www.gofishing.ie). Kilrush Creek Marina (tel: +353 (0)65 905 2072) (www.kilrushcreekmarina.ie), has every facility for hiring and mooring boats, incl hoist and repair services. Accom, shops, bars, restaurants are a 3 mins walk. Tackle, information and advice from Michael O'Sullivan & Son, 49/50 Moore St (tel/fax: +353 (0)65 905 1071) can also assist in arranging deep sea angling boats &c.; B&B: Hillcrest View, Doonbeg Road, Kilrush. The Central (tel: +353 (0)65 905 1332).

Kilkee (Co Clare). Short distance from Kilrush, on north of peninsula. Fishing for mackerel, eel, pollack, ray, and cod. Rocks near golfcourse are good mark, also Pollack Holes, at low tide. Bourkes Fishing Tackle Shop and Charters, Kilkee. (tel: +353

(0)65 9056363; see website for more info: www.fishing.westclare.net).

Liscannor (Co Clare). Boats: contact Willie O'Callaghan, Angling Charters, Roslevan, Tulla Rd, Ennis (tel: +353 (0)65 682 1374; email: mocallaghan.ennis@eircom.net; web: www.ocallaghanangling.com); day fishing/cruise trips around the three Aran Islands. Tackle shop: Patrick Cleary, Westcliffe Lodge, Spanish Point (tel: +353 (0)65 708 4037) closed Sept-May.

Galway Bay (Co Galway). **R Spiddal** enters on north side, with skate, tope, ray, huss, dogfish, monkfish, cod, ling, conger, flatfish. Boats from Galway Bay Sea Safaris, Kevin MacGabhann, Spiddal (mob: +353 (0) 86 854 7890) (see website for more info: www.galwaybayfishing.com), larger boat licensed for 12; Also *The Leaca Rua*, Max Couque, Galway Bay Fishing, Spiddal, (tel: +353 91 595 352; see website for more info: www.galwayfishing.ie).

Clifden (Co Galway). First-class boat and shore angling in sheltered conditions. Blue shark, coalfish, pollack, skate, ray, ling, cod and plaice. Good marks include: Slyne Head; Barrister wreck off **Inishark**; Inishbofin; Inishturk and Fosteries Shoals. Other good bays are Mannin, Killary, Roundstone, Cleggan and Bunowen. Deep sea charter boats from Clifden: John Brittain with *Blue Water*, Sharamore House, Streamstown Bay; (tel: +353 (0)95 21073; www.seafishingireland.net); charter boats from **Cleggan**: *Western Kingfisher*, Johnny King (tel: +353 (0)95 44649; see website for more info: www.clegganseaangling.com), transport and B&B and self-catering accommodation available by arrangement. Charter boats from **Letterfrack**: John Mongan (tel: +353 (0)95 43473), 31 ft, licensed for 12 persons, all tackle and bait included, evening trips (6-8 pm), morning trips by arrangement. Club: Clifden Sea AC. Tackle shops: Stanley's, Market St, Clifden (tel: +353 (0)95 21039); Hotels: Clifden Station House (tel: +353(0)95 21699; see website: www.clifdenstationhouse.com), Ardagh Hotel, Dolphin Beach House B&B, Ardmore House B&B.

Louisburgh (Co Mayo). Sea fishing in this area is excellent, including various locations such as the foreshore at Carrowniskey (flounder, dogfish, turbot and bass); Emlagh Strand (stand and rock casting); Roonagh Quay (mackerel, pollack & wrasse), Carramore Strand (flounder, dabs, sea trout & bass, and more); Old Head (mackerel, coalfish & wrasse &c.) and Old Head Pier and Killsallagh Rocks. Fish include mackerel, coalfish, flounder, dabs, gurnads and the occasional tope.

Westport (Co Mayo). Good boat and shore fishing in shallow water. Local clubs run sea angling competitions in the area each year. Fish caught include: the record monkfish (69lb), skate (up to 167½lb), tope and conger (to 40lb and more), cod, codling, pollack, flounders, plaice, gurnard, coalfish, bass, wrasse, turbot, dogfish, white skate (146lb), blue shark, and porbeagle shark, buss huss. Good marks include Tower in Inner Bay, off Lighthouse, Pigeon Point, Cloghormack Buoy. Sheltered sport in **Clew Bay**. Charter boats available from The Helm *(see below)*; R Roynon (tel: +353 (0)98 26514; mob: +353 (0) 87 7647789); boat licensed for 10. Clubs: Westport Sea AC, Secretary (tel: +353 (0)98 27297); runs 3 day annual boat festival and 1 day shore event in last weekend in June (web: www.westportseaanglingfestival.eu); Tackle shop: Hewetson's, Bridge St, Westport (tel: +353 (0)98 26018; fax: +353 (0)98 27075); Westport Marine Supplies Ltd, Shop St (tel: +353 (0)98 28800). Hotels: **The Helm**, Westport Quay (tel: +353 (0)98 26398; fax: +353 (0)98 26194); West Port Plaza Hotel (tel: +353 (0)98 51166; web:

www.westportplazahotel.ie), Augusta Lodge B&B (tel: +353 098 28900; see also website: www.augustalodge.ie), Brooklodge B & B, Woodside Lodge.

Achill Island (Co Mayo). Excellent boat fishing; up to 40 species, incl pollack, conger, ling, ray, cod, etc; fish run large. Noted area for blue shark and porbeagle. Holds records for heaviest fish caught in Irish waters for both men and women: 365lb (man), 362lb (woman), plus blue shark record, 206lb. Pollack and wrasse fishing off rock produces specimens in 15lb class. Good marks are Carrick Mor, Gubalennaun, Alennaun Beag, Dooega and Dugort. Flatfish from **Tullaghan Bay** on north side of island. Good shore fishing at Keel Strand and Keem Bay; Mackerel and pollack fishing from **Cloughmore Pier**. Sea trout late June to early Aug (plentiful and good size); mackerel; plaice etc. Charter boats from **Purteen Harbour**: Tony Burke (tel: +353 (0)98 47257), daily charter available (Apr-Oct). Hotels: Bervie Guest House, Keel (tel: +353 (0)98 43114; see website for more info: www.bervie-guesthouse-achill.com), Atlantic Breeze B&B, Pollagh, Keel, Achill Island, (tel: +353 (0)98 43189).

Newport (Co Mayo). Central for Clew Bay, which has more than twenty popular shore fishing venues. Flounder fishing at outskirts of estuary. Good shore fishing at Mallaranny and Corraun. At Newport Quay, bottom fishing for flounder; Rossmoney, casting over mud for dogfish, bull huss and conger; Rossanrubble, bottom fishing for ray, dogfish and bull huss; also Ross and Rossnakilly, dogfish, bull huss, small pollack, flounder. Other species found in Clew Bay include mackerel, gurnard, whiting, common skate. Bait may be dug at Carrowmore Strand and Mallaranny (sand eel), Murrick, Rossbeg, Rossturk, Rossmurrevagh, Corraun (lugworm). Charter boat for shark and bottom fishing from Mary

Gavin Hughes, Clynish View, Derradda, Newport (tel: +353 (0)98 41562; mob: +353 (0)86 806 2282; see web: www.clewbayangling.com), Europe's only lady charter skipper; disabled with assistance provided for; reef and general fishing, common skate a speciality. Tackle from Hewetson's, Bridge St, Westport (tel: +353 (0)98 26018; fax: +353 (0)98 27075). Hotels: Newport House (tel: +353 (0)98 41222; see website for more: www.newporthouse.ie), Bridge Inn (tel: +353 (0)98 41524).

Belmullet (Co Mayo). Rapidly rising in popularity as sea-fishing centre. Sheltered water. 39 species and many specimens caught to date, incl present Irish record red gurnard and halibut; turbot, bream, coalfish and pollack especially good. Belmullet Sea AC has been active in improving sea fishing in the area, and holds competitions in June, July, Aug. Local venues include Annagh Head: spinning for pollack, coalfish and mackerel from rocky outcrops, float fishing for wrasse, bottom fishing for dogfish and occasional conger; Cross: beach fishing for flounder, dogfish and small turbot. Lugworm may be dug at various nearby localities, including the shore lying west of town. Deep-sea charter boats for shark, reef and bottom fishing from Blacksod Bay: Mattie Geraghty, Geraghty Charters, *Brú Chlann Lir,* Tirrane, Clogher (tel: +353 (0)97 85741); 2 boats licensed for 12; *The Doloree*, Sean Lavelle (tel: +353 (0)86 8365983; see website for more: www.fishwestireland.com). Tackle shop: Erris Autoparts & Accessories, American St, Belmullet (tel: +353 (0)97 82093). Hotel: Broadhaven Bay Hotel Belmullet (tel: + 353 (0)97 20600; www.broadhavenbay.com), Western Strands, Main St (tel/fax: +353 (0)97 81096); Leim Siar B&B, Blacksod (+353 (0)97 85004; see website: www.leimsiar.com).

Ballina (Co Mayo). Estuary of R Moy opens into Killala Bay. Lugworm may be found in sandy patches, sand eel, crab and clam are alternative baits. From Kilcummin Head at the west, to Lenadoon Point at the east, there are eight recognised shore fishing areas. These include Palmerstown Channel (Cloonoghmore Estuary), spinning for sea trout and bottom fishing for flounder; Ross Beacon, the same, Innishcrone Strand (beach fishing for flounder, dab, dogfish) and Pier (conger, dogfish, occasional ray, wrasse.

Donegal Bay (Co Donegal). There are more than twenty good shore fishing points in and around bay, which include **Darbys Hole** in south (spinning for pollack; floatfish for wrasse); **Erne Estuary** (spinning for seatrout and bottom fishing for flounder, 2 hrs either side of low water) (NWRF licence required), **Donegal Quays** (float fishing for mullet; ground baiting essential); **St John's Point** (spinning for pollack, mackerel and coalfish; bottom fishing for wrasse, ray, dogfish and occasional conger (specimen wrasse recorded here); **Killybegs Harbour** (freelining and floatfishing for mackerel, coalfish, pollack and mullet from East Pier; bottom fishing for conger at West Pier); **Muckross Pier** and **Head** (spinning for mackerel and pollack; floatfishing for wrasse); **Teelin Pier** (spinning for mackerel and coalfish; botton fishing for conger, dab, flounder and dogfish; high water best). Various other areas include **Silver Strand**, **Shalway Pier**, **Fintragh**, **Nun's Cove**, **Polladoirt**, **Drumanoo Head**, **Gunwell**, **Sandloop**, **Heelin Port**, **Rossnowlagh**, **Mermaids Cove**, **Mullaghmore** and **Milk Haven**; rock and shore fishing, with more than 20 species to be caught, incl red & grey gurnard, whiting, conger, mackerel, haddock, cod, ling, pollock, ballam & cuckoo wrasse, plaice, dory, dab, megrim, pouting, rockling; and

White Strand, flatfish from beach plus mackerel. Any further information required may be obtained from Mary Rouiller, Killybegs SAC. Shark fishing for blue shark Jul-Sept through charter boats. Deep sea charter boats operating from **Mullaghmore**: *Ellen Louise*, Gerry Sheerin, Cloystarra, Grange (tel: +353 (0)86 8282782), licensed for 12, incl bait; **Killybegs**: *Huntress Blue*, Micheal McGettigan (tel: +353 (0)74 9731401; mob: +353 (0) 87 2871423), evening trips also available; 33 ft charter boat for shark or bottom fishing, 6 rods shark, 12 rods bottom; Brian McGilloway (tel: +353 (0) 74 97 31181; mob: +353 (0)87 2200982; see website for more info: www.killybegsangling.com), 40 ft *The Meridian,* 12 persons. Local clubs are Donegal Bay SAC; Killybegs SAC contact Sec; club holds various fishing events - all participants must be a member of club affiliated to IFSA. Hotels: Bay View Hotel & Leisure Centre, Main St (tel: +353 (0)74 9731950; fax: +353 (0) 74 9731856; web: www.bayviewhotel. ie); Drumbeagh House B&B, Drumbeagh, Killybegs.

Kilcar (Co Donegal). Boat and shore angling, from rocks, reefs, estuary and sandy beaches, for pollack, coalfish, cod, ling, conger, bull huss, spurdog, whiting, tope, shark, skate, flatfish, etc. Charter boats operate. **Teelin**, 36 ft charter boat *Nuala Star* from Paddy Byrne (tel: +353 (0)74 9739365); (mob: +353 (0)8762 84688); web: www.nualastarteelin.com); licensed for 12.

Burtonport (Co Donegal). By Aran Island, and the Rosses, famous trout fishery. Good base for shark and bottom fishing, with up to 30 species caught. Boats and tackle for hire, licensed for 12; *Loinnir* 43ft, contact Neil Gallagher, Annagry East (tel: +353 (0)74 9548403; see website for more: www.donegalseaangling.com); *Surose* 31ft, Liam Miller (+353 (0)74

955 1533; mob: +353 (0)87 9253534; web: www.inish.ie), licensed for 10.

Downings (Co Donegal). On Rosguill Peninsula, in Sheep Haven Bay; site of Home International Competition in 1999, and selected by Shark Club of Ireland for first shark competition; has hosted the FIPS-M World Boat Angling championships. Beach, rock, estuary fishing for sea trout and other species; charter boats operate; information on sea angling and boats, contact Marion Buchanan, Hon Sec, Downings SAC (Tel: +353 (0) 74 9155386). Boats: *Summer Rose* 36 ft, licensed for 12, contact Sammie Scott (tel: +353 (0) 74 9155386, web: www.fishingdonegal.com); *Bonito* 33ft, Trevor Ryder (tel: +353 (0) 74 9155261; web: www.bonitocharters. com). Tackle shop: Top Tackle, 55 Port Rd, Letterkenny (tel: +353 (0)74 9167545). Hotels: Rospenna, Downings (tel: +353 (0)74 91 55301 web: www.rosapenna.ie); Beach Hotel (tel: +353 (0)74 9155303; web: www.beachhotel.ie).

Lough Swilly (Co Donegal). Sea trout in estuaries, good sea fishing to be had, with rays, flatfish, tope, May-July; mainly cod, haddock, pollack, coalfish, gurnards, tope, ling, conger, wrasse on offshore wrecks; blue shark and porbeagle shark in Aug/Sept. Lough Swilly SAA is local assn, at Rathmullen, runs a major annual tope angling festival, first week in June. Easy access via floating pontoons available for disabled anglers. At Rathmullan pier, *Enterprise I*, 38ft and *Swilly Explorer*, 42ft, for 12 persons (reduction for Lough Swilly SAA); tackle on board, disabled access, rod and reel hire; Rathmullen Charters: Angela Crerand (tel: +353 (0) 872480132) or Niall Doherty, Skipper, (mob: +353 (0) 870507464); rathmullencharters@eircom.net; web: www.rathmullancharters.com). Hotels: Watersedge Inn (+353 (0)74 9158182; see website for more info: www.watersedgedonegal.com); Rathmullen House (see website for more: www.rathmullanhouse.com); also B&B accommodation available.

Malin (Co Donegal). Charter boats operate from Bunagee and Culduff, specialising in wreck fishing; species caught are whiting, haddock, cod, conger, ling, gurnard, pollock, tope, turbot, plaice. Boats: *Gemini 2*, Derek Harley, Inishowen Boating, Bunagee, Culdaff, County Donegal. (tel: +353 (0)74 9370605. More on website: www.irishanglingcharters.ie) 087 2480132/087 0507464. Hotels: Malin Hotel (Tel: +353 (0) 74 93 70606; web: www.malinhotel.ie); Radharc Dun Cinn, Drumcarbitt, Malin. liamandsusan@mydonegalhome.com ; web: www.mydonegalhome.com.

Moville (Donegal). Estuary of River Foyle; pollack, cod, tope, whiting, red gurnard, wrasse, flatfish and dogfish. Boats (20ft-30ft) and bait. Hotels: Carlton Redcastle Hotel; Corner Bar, Admiralty House B&B.

FISHING CLUBS & ASSOCIATIONS IN IRELAND

The following is an alphabetical list of angling clubs and associations in the Ireland. Particulars of the waters held by many will be found, by reference to the Index, in the section headed 'Fishing Locations in Ireland', and the information about the others, which may not have their own water, could be had from the Secretaries, whose addresses are given. An addressed envelope should be enclosed with inquiries. Please advise the publishers (address at the front of the book) of any changed details for the next edition.

NATIONAL BODIES

Inland Fisheries Ireland,
Head Quarters
Swords Business Park
Swords
Co. Dublin
Tel: + 353 (0)1 8842 600
info@cfb.ie
www.fisheriesireland.ie   (Corporate).
www.fishinginireland.info (Fishing).

Department of Communications,
Energy & Natural Resources
Head office:
29 - 31 Adelaide Road
Dublin 2
Tel: +353 (0)1 678 2000
www.dcenr.gov.ie
email: press.office@dcenr.gov.ie

Fáilte Ireland (National Tourism
Development Authority)
Baggot Street Bridge
Dublin 2
Tel: +353 (0)1 602 4000
Fax: +353 (0)1 602 4100
www.failteireland.ie

Federation of Irish Salmon &
Sea-Trout Anglers (FISSTA)
Noel Carr
Teelin Road
Carrick
Co Donegal
Tel: +353 (0) 74 9730300
dgl1@indigo.ie
www.fissta.com

Irish Disabled Fly Fishing
Association
Miss E J Black
6 Old Park Drive
Ballymena BT42 1BG
Tel: 028 2564 2539
www.idffa.org.uk

The Irish Federation of Pike Angling
Clubs
Terry Sheridan
Hon Treasurer
Cloncovid
Kilcogy P.O.
Co. Cavan via Co.
Longford
www.angling-in-ireland.com

Irish Federation of Sea Anglers
Hon Sec: H O'Rourke
Sports Headquarters
13 Joyce Way
Park West Business Park
Dublin 12
Tel: +353 (0)1 280 6873/6901
email: ccifsa@yahoo.ie
www.ifsa.ie

Irish Specimen Fish Committee
Swords Business Campus
Balheary Road, Swords
Co Dublin
Tel: +353 (0)1 884 2600
www.irish-trophy-fish.com

National Anglers Representative Association (NARA)
Eamonn Ross
Ardlougher
Ballyconnell
Co Cavan
Tel: +353 (0)87 943 6655
email: nara@iol.ie
www.nara.ie

Wheelyboat Trust (The)
Director: Andy Beadsley
North Lodge
Burton Park
Petworth
West Sussex GU28 0JT
Tel/Fax: 01798 342222
www.wheelyboats.org

The Loughs Agency (FCILC)
22 Victoria Road
Londonderry
BT47 2AB
Tel: 028 7134 2100
Fax: 028 7134 2720
www.loughs-agency.org

National Coarse Fishing Federation of Ireland
Hon Sec: Mr T. Lawton
NCFFI Treasurer
Rath-Healy
Fermoy
Co. Cork
secretary@ncffi.ie
www.ncffi.ie

IRISH FISHING CLUBS

Anglesea Sea Angling Club Cork
Pete Davis
Tel: +353 (0)862 370162
anglesea.sac@gmail.com
www.anglesea-sac-cork.webs.com

Ballaghderreen & Dist Angling Club
Jimmy Coogan
Tel: +353 (0)9498 60077
or
Joe Madden
New Street
Ballaghderreen
Co Roscommon
Tel: +353 (0)94 9860186

Ballina Salmon Anglers' Club
Mrs. Josephine Egan
3 Barrett Street
Ballina

Ballisodare Fishing Club Ltd
Dermot Glannon
Ballisodare Fishery
The Falls
Ballisodare
Sligo
Tel/Fax: +353 (0)71 91 30513
ballisodarefc@eircom.net

Ballymore Eustace Trout and Salmon Anglers
Thomas Deegan
Broadleas
Ballymore Eustace
Co Kildare
Tel: +353 (0)4586 4477
www.kildare.ie/ballymoreanglers/

Bandon Angling Association
Fergal O'Regan
Oliver Plunkett St
Bandon
Co Cork
Tel: +353 (0)23 41674
bandonangling@eircom.net
www.bandonangling.com

Bangor Erris Angling Club
Seamus Henry
The West end bar
Nagor Erris
Co Mayo
Tel: +353 (0) 97 83487
www.bangorerrisangling.com

Belturbet Trout Angling Club
Irwin Morrow
Milltown House
Belturbet
Co Cavan
Tel: +353 (0)49 9522186

Boyle & District Angling Club
Jane Suffin
Tel: +353 (0) 86 8301261
www.boyleanglers.blogspot.com

Cahirciveen Sea Angling Club
Johnny Griffin
griffin.johnny2@gmail.com
www.cahersiveenseaanglingclub.com

Cahir & District Anglers' Association
Kevin Rowe
Reiska Rd
Cahir
Co Tipperary
Tel: +353 (0)52 42729
Mob: +353 87 6409271
www.visitcahir.ie/ThingsToDo/Thing
sToDoFishing.html

Cappoquin Salmon & Trout AA
Jeremy Nicholson
Littlebridge Inches
Cappoquin
Co Waterford
Tel: +353 (0)58 52302
www.cappoquinsalmonandtroutangle
rs.com

Cavan Anglers Club
Secretary:
Francie McNally
secretary@cavananglersclub.com
www.cavananglersclub.com

Cavan Coarse Anglers Club
Mr. Mark Handsley
60 Pearse Park, Dundalk,
Co Louth
Tel: +353 (0)87 7505630
www.cavanfishingcac.com

Clane Trout & Salmon Anglers
Denis Madden
5 Balreask Manor
Trim Road
Navan
Co Meath
Mob: +353 (0)86600 4940
www.ctsaa.ie

Clifden AA
Mr. John Stanley
c/o The Pharmacy
Clifden
Connemara
Co Galway
Tel: +353 (0)95 21039

Clodiagh AA
Timmy Delaney
Rathmoy
Borrisoleigh
Co Tipperary
Tel: +353 (0)504 51346

Daingean & District Match Anglers
Jim Delaney
Chairman
Tel: +353 (0) 879034945
jimdelaney1957@eircom.net
www.freewebs.com/dainglers/

Dargle Anglers Club
Peter Carton
Treasurer
53, James Everett Park
Bray
Co.Wicklow
Tel: +353 (0) 860745033
www.dargleanglers.com

Dee & Glyde Fishing Club
Co Louth
www.deeandglyde.com

Deel & Boyne Angling Association
Patrick Connaughton
Joristown
Raharney
Mullingar, Co Westmeath
Tel: +353 (0)44 9374595

Deele Angling Club
Billy Vance
Milltown
Convoy, Lifford
Co Donegal
Tel: +353 (0)74 9147290
www.deeleangling.com

Drogheda & District Anglers' Club
c/o John Murphy
39 Anneville Crescent
Drogheda
Co Louth
Tel: +353 (0)41 9834078

Dublin Telesport Sea Angling Club
Frank McNamee
Secretary
Tel: +353 (0)87-9610659
dtsacs@eircom.net
www.dublintelesport.com

Dublin Trout AA
Ronnie Miley
4 Dodder Park Road
Dublin 14
Tel: +353 (0)1490 2163

Dunfanaghy Angling Association
Jim Curran
Hon Secretary
Faugher
Port-na-Blagh
Co. Donegal
Tel: 074 9136232
jemcurran@eircom.net
www.dunfanaghyangling.com

East Mayo Anglers' Assn
Secretary
Market St
Swinford
Co Mayo
Tel/fax: +353 (0)94 9253955
eastmayoanglers@eircom.net
www.eastmayoanglers.com

Edenderry Coarse Angling Club
Pauric Kelly
Tel: +353 (0) 86-3503117
http://edenderrycoarseanglingclub.w
ebs.com

Fermoy Coarse Angling Club
Tommy Lawson
Rath-Healy
Fermoy, Co.Cork
Tel: +353 (0)25 33574
Mob: +353 86104 3040

**Glengormley & District Sport
Angling Club**
greggj92@talktalk.net
Tel: +353 (0) 2894 460395
www.gadsac.freeuk.com

Gormanstown & District Anglers
The Secretary
Gormanston & District Anglers
14 Knightswood Park
Balrothery
North County Dublin
Tel: +353 (0) 87-6825619
gormanston@gmail.com
www.gormanstonanglers.com

Howth Sea Angling Club
Peter Gaffey, Hon. Secretary
15a West Pier
Howth
Co Dublin
info@howthsac.ie
www.howthsac.com

Inagh Angling Club
Michael Dillon
Tel: +353 (0)8767 42779
inagh.fishing@gmail.com
www.inaghanglingclub.com

Kells Angling Association
Ciarn O'Kelly
County Meath
Mob: +353 (0)86 375 2050
www.kells-anglers.com

Kenmare Salmon Anglers
John O'Hare
21 Main Street
Kenmare
Co Kerry
Tel: +353 (0)64 41499

Kilkee Boat And Fishing Club
Tony Stapleton
Chairman KBFC
The Boathouse
East End, Kilkee
Co Clare.
www.fishkilkee.ie

Killybegs Sea Angling Club
Kellys Quay
Killibegs
Co Donegal
+353 (0)74 973 1137
See also: www.killybegsangling.com

Kilmore Sea Angling Club
Chris Busher
9 Columba Villas
Wexford
Co Wexford
Tel: +353 (0)53 914 5227
kilmoresac@hotmail.com
http://homepage.eircom.net/~beach/ki
lmore/kilmore.htm

**Laune Salmon & Trout Anglers'
Association**
Sec: Billy Downes
10 Pairc Na Dun
Mounthawk
Tralee
Tel: +353 (0)66 712 3950
billydownes@hotmail.com
www.launesalmonanglers.com

**Leixlip & District Angling
Association**
http://leixlip.blogspot.com

Letterkenny & District Anglers' Assn
Derek McHugh
Tel: +353 (0)8793 73332
email: derek.mchugh@ldaa.ie
www.ldaa.ie

**Lough Allen Conservation
Association**
www.allen.ie/conservation/home.htm

Lough Derg Anglers
Kevin Grimes
Canal Bank
Killaloe
Co Clare
Mob: +353 (0)87 678 4539
www.loughderganglers.com

Lough Glore Anglers Club
Fred Murray
Secretary
gloreanglers@gmail.com
www.gloreanglers.com

Lough Lene AA
Mr D. Mockler
Club Secretary
Lough Lene Angling Association
No 3 Greenville
Kildalkey
Navan
Co. Meath.
info@loughleneanglingassociation.com
www.loughleneanglingassociation.com

Lough Sheelin Trout Protection Assn
Eamonn Ross
Hon Secretary
www.loughsheelinanglers.ie
eamonnoruis@eircom.net

Monaghan AA
Dick Kiernan
Venture Sports
71 Glasslough St
Monaghan
Tel: +353 (0)47 81495
venturesports@monaghan-outdoors.com
www.monaghan-outdoors.com

Mountmellick Anglers
Brian A Lynch
Mob: +353 (0)87 981 8197
info@mountmellickangling.com
www.mountmellickangling.com

Mullingar Coarse Angling Club
Ned O'Reilly
Mullingar Coarse Angling Club
Riverstown
Killucan
Co Westmeath
mullingaranglingclub@eircom.net
www.mullingaranglingclub.com

Navan & District Angling Association
Diarmuid Maguire
Hon Secretary
navananglers@gmail.com
www.navananglers.com

Newbridge And District Pike Anglers
Tommy Winders
Club Secretary
www.newbridgepikeanglers.com

Newport Sea Anglers
Mary Gavin Hughes
Clynish View
Derradda
Newport, Co Mayo
Tel: +353 (0)98 41562
Mob: +353 (0)86 8062282
www.clewbayangling.com

North Kerry Anglers' Association
Convent Street
6 The Square, Listowel
Co Kerry
Tel: +353 (0)68 22537
info@northkerryanglers.com
www.northkerryanglers.com

North Kildare Trout & Salmon Anglers' Association
Michael Deeley
32 Langton Park
Newbridge
Co Kildare
Tel: +353 (0)45 435024
n.k.t.s.a.a@gmail.com

North Louth Sea Anglers
Gerry Casey
Pursang House
carrickedmond
Kilcurry
Dundalk
Tel: +353 (0)876 645938
www.louthanglers.8k.com

Portobello Angling Club
Colm O'Gaora
Secretary
Tel: +353 (0)87 220 1578
www.portobelloangling.com

Rinnashark Sea Angling Club
Declan Flanagan
3 Aldergrove
Mount Pleasant
Grantown
Waterford
Mob: +353 (0)87 610 3031
www.rinnasharksac.net

River Ilen Anglers' Club
Bob Cooke
Hon. Secretary
Ballincolla House
Union Hall
Co Cork
Tel. +353 (0) 28 33635
www.riverilen.com

Rosses Anglers' Association
June McKenna
Secretary
Pole Rd
Dungloe
ds67@eircom.net
www.rossesanglers.com

Rossmore Coarse Angling Club
Secretary
Rossmore Coarse Angling Club
Killygola
Castleblayney
Co. Monaghan
secretary@
rossmorecoarseanglingclub.com
www.rossmorecoarseanglingclub.com

Sliabh Liág Anglering Association
Paddy Maloney
Secretary
Carrick
Co. Donegal
Tel: 073 39231
Fax 073 30300
dgl1@indigo.ie
www.fissta.com/glen

Tralee Bay Sea Angling Club
Tralee Bay Sea Angling Club
Fenit Harbour, Fenit
Tralee, County
Kerry
Ireland
www.traleebaysac.org

Trim, Athboy & District AA
Pat O'Toole
Club Secretary
Mob: +353 (0)86 8777039
trimathboyanglers@gmail.com
www.trimathboyanglers.net

Tulla & District Angling Club
Club Secretary
Seamus Ó Cualáin
Tel: +353 (0)86 6014837
www.fishingintulla.com
fishingintulla@yahoo.ie

Waterford & District Angling Club
Pat Dalton
2 The Terrace, Cannon Street
Waterford, Co Waterford
Tel: +353 (0)51 354619
mail@waterfordangling.com
www.waterfordangling.com

Other Clubs

Abbeyfeale Anglers' Assn
Abbeyleix & District AC
Achill Island Sea AC
Achill Sea Anglers'
Achill Sporting Club
Aghada Sea AC
Ardfinnan Anglers
Ardmore Sea Anglers
Arklow Fly Fishers
Athleague AC
Ballinakill AC
Ballineen & Enniskeane AA
Ballinrobe & District Ang.
Ballybofey & Stranorlar AA
Ballycotton Deep Sea AC
Ballyduff Trout Fly AA
Banteer Salmon Anglers
Bantry Salmon & Trout Ang
Barrow Anglers
Belmullet Sea AC
Borora AC
Broadbridge AC
Broadmeadow AC
Bundrowes Estuary Fishing
Bunowen&Carrowniskey
S&ST
Carraroe AC
Carrick-on-Suir AC
Carrigallen AC
Cashel, Tipperary & Golden

Castle AC
Cavetown & Clogher AC
Chapelizod Anglers Club
Clonbur AC
Clonmel Salmon & Trout A
Clonmel & District AC
Cloyne Sea AC
Cobh Sea AC
Cork Salmon AA
Cork Sea Anglers
Cork Trout AA
Corofin Fishing Club
Culdaff & Inishowen AA
Derravaragh AA
Downings Sea AC
Drumconrath Coarse FC
Dundalk & District TAA
Dundalk & District SAA
Durrow & District AC
Edenderry & Castlejordan
AA
Erriff & District S&T A
Fermoy & District Trout AA
Fermoy Salmon AA
Foxford Salmon AA
Glengarriff AA
Guileen Sea AC
Inistioge AC
Kilbride AC
Kilkenny AA

Killaloe, Ballina & D Ang.
Killashandra Trout AC
Kilsheelin Anglers
Kingfisher AC
Kinlough & District AA
Knockmore AC
Laragh AC
Lee Salmon Anglers
Lisdoonvarna Fanore SA
Lismore Salmon Anglers
Lismore Trout Anglers &
Conservation Association
Lough Arrow & District AC
Lough Arrow Fish
Preservation
Lough Bane AA
Lough Ennel Trout
Preservation
Lough Gill Anglers
Lough More & Blackwater
AA
Lough Owel Trout
Preservation
Lough Swilly Sea AA
Macroom Fly Anglers
Mallow Coarse AC
Mallow Trout Anglers' Club
Mountrath & District AC
Mourne AC
Ormond AA

Oughterard AA
Portarlington AC
Prosperous Course AC
Rathangan & District
Anglers
Rathdowney AA
Rathdrum Trout AC
Rossin & Slane Anglers
St Colman's AC
Schull Sea AC
Shannonbridge AA
Sligo AA
South Munster Coarse AC
Tallow & District AC
Templemore & District AA
Thurles/Hollycross/Ballyca
mas
Tramore/Waterford Sea AC
Tuam AA
Tullow T&S Anglers
Tulsk AC & Services
Upper Shannon AC
Vartry AC
Vicarstown & District AC
Virginia Coarse AC
Waterford Crystal Sea AC
Waterville/Caherdaniel SAC
Waterville Fisheries
Development
West Clare AC

farlows

9 PALL MALL LONDON

By Appointment to
H.R.H The Prince of Wales
Suppliers of Fishing Tackle
and Waterproof Clothing
Farlows Group Ltd, London

All the best brands
with a personal service…

Pure essence
of fishing…

We have had the pleasure of providing our customers
with the finest in fishing tackle, shooting equipment
and country clothing since the early nineteenth
century. Our west-end store is a London landmark
bringing the best of the country to town; Farlows
are the only supplier of fishing equipment to
hold a prestigious Royal Warrant.

If you need the best tackle and advice for
fishing travel anywhere in the world we
are here to help – our stock reflects our
customer's wanderlust.
Farlows staff have centuries of
experience of every kind of fishing,
there is a good chance we have
fished your chosen destination
and will know exactly what
gear you should take.

ensure you get the very best
fishing experience, worldwide.

How to find us…

We are short walk away from Piccadilly
Circus tube station with meter parking
close at hand.

Our address
9 Pall Mall, London SW1Y 5NP

Opening times
Monday - Friday 9-6pm, Thursday 9-7pm
Saturday 10-6pm

Contact us on: fishing@farlows.co.uk
Tel: 020 7484 1000 **Fax:** 020 7839 8959

Shop online: **www.farlows.co.uk**

FISHING ABROAD

The primary purpose of this section is to give the angler contemplating visiting, or even, in the case of Commonwealth countries, emigrating to, one of the countries listed a brief description of the fishing to be had. It is neither necessary nor practicable to enter into such detail as in the British sections, but the addresses of various authorities from whom further information can be obtained are given, together with that of the appropriate London tourist or Government information office, at the end of each description. Web addresses are also given.

CENTRAL AFRICA

ZAMBIA. Most rivers and lakes carry good stocks of fish, giving very reasonable sport. But the angler must be prepared to travel long distances over rough roads, carrying his own camp equipment and finally making his camp beside the river he intends to fish. There are very few hotels off the main roads, and fewer still in fishing areas, though the Tourist Board is conducting a successful drive for more hotels and rest houses, particularly the lodges in the national wildlife parks, where good fishing is to be had on the rivers. For parties who appreciate camping holidays in the bush, some delightful trips can be planned, particularly in August and September, when there is little fear of rain and the nights are warm enough to make camping pleasant. Most of the rivers are either heavily wooded right down to the water or are swamp-edged, so the addition of a boat and outboard motor to the camp equipment is a sound policy. On the other hand, canoes and paddlers can be hired, and the latter are usually good guides to the best fishing grounds. Youths are also very helpful as camp attendants, and little trouble is normally experienced in hiring one or two to take care of the heavy work of the camp. The visiting fisherman must remember that the hippopotamus and crocodile are found in nearly all Zambian waters. Wading in rivers can be a dangerous pastime, and hippos, especially with calves, should be given a wide berth. An insecticide spray against tsetse fly and a malarial prophylactic are recommended.

Indigenous species. These include tiger-fish, which probably provide the best sport, and goliath tiger fish, a separate species running up to 80lbs or more (found only in part of the river systems that run into the Congo River basin); fish of the Nile perch variety and their close relatives, giant perch (top weight around 200 lbs); giant vundu (sampa); large- mouthed, small-mouthed and humped bream; catfish; barbel; local pike; lake salmon; labeo; and nkupi. There are two species of fish which are referred to as nkupi, one is found in Lake Tanganika and is a cichlid, it is also called a giant yellow belly; and the other is a

citharinid found in the middle Zambezi including Lake Kariba.

The great **Zambezi** and its large tributary, the **Kafuwe**, are outstanding among the rivers. A good centre for the Zambezi is **Livingstone**, with record breaking tiger and bream. There are a number of excellent lodges along the Upper Zambezi River, and various companies that offer half and full day fishing to guests not staying at a lodge (or hotel) that specialises in fishing. Another town which has become a tourist centre is Siavonga on Lake Kariba. There is an all weather road from Lusaka (capital of Zambia) to Siavonga, which can be reached within a two-hour drive. The centre has several modern lodges, some of which are air-conditioned. Sport fishing including angling and spearing are very important here. Good fishing centres on the Karfue are at Itezhi-tezhi, Lochinvar and the Lower Kafuwe, near Chirundu. At Itezhi-tezhi, the angler will come across the famous small yellow belly and the Kafuwe pike. At Lochinvar, bream are important sport fish and at Lower Kafuwe, vundu. All three centres are served by good lodges: Musungwa (at Itezhi-tezhi), Lochinvar (at Lochinvar near Monze), and Gwabi (at Lower Kafuwe near Chirundu).

The Lower Zambezi, the stretch from Lake Kariba to Mozambique, offers excellent tiger fishing as well as bream and a variety of other species, including very large vundu (catfish). There is an excellent choice of lodges and camps along the Zambian banks of the lower Zambezi that cater for the fisherman. Tiger is being caught on fly and has been referred to by a well-known fisherman and author as 'the fiercest fresh water fishing in the world'.

Lake Tanganyika is another anglers' mecca and a good centre is Kasaba Bay, where there are three small lodges. The lake holds giant perch, tiger-fish, yellow belly and vundu among a wide variety of sporting fish.

Apart from Nile perch and sampa, which call for heavy tackle, most of the fish mentioned can be landed with a spinning rod. Steel traces are necessary for tiger-fish, nkupi and pike. A light bait-casting rod will usually cover other species. Fishing is free as a rule and can take place all the year round, but most rivers are in spate during the rainy season from December to April.

Zambia is unlikely to prove to be a land in which trout will thrive, owing both to the high temperature range and the lack of suitable highlands, but an exception may be provided by the picturesque **Nyika Plateau**, north of **Chipata** on the Malawi border, where an experimental stocking with rainbow trout in the headwaters of the **Shire River** is being carried out.

Anglers are required to purchase an angling permit, obtainable from the offices of the Department of Fisheries in Chilanga. The department also has offices in all the major fishery areas, and permits may be bought from them.

Useful addresses are: **Department of Fisheries, Ministry of Agriculture, Food & Fisheries, Headquarters, Kafuwe Road, PO Box 350100, Chilanga** (tel: +260 211 278418; email: piscator@zamnet.zm)**; Zambian National Tourist Board, 2 Palace Gate, Kensington, London W8 5NG** (tel: 020 7589 6655; fax: 020 7581 1353; web: www.zambiatourism.com).

ZIMBABWE

Zimbabwe offers some of the best fishing to be found in Central Africa. The angler has scope to pit his skills against a diversity of species, ranging from the fighting tiger-fish of the **Zambezi** and **Save** river systems, to introduced species like the rainbow and brown trout in the mountain streams and dams of the Eastern Highlands.

Much of centre of the country acts as a watershed, with the streams forming rivers which flow north to the Zambezi river system, on which lies the huge expanse of Lake Kariba; south to the **Limpopo**; southeast to the Save and Runde; and east into the **Pungwe** system of Mozambique. Many dams exist on all of the rivers feeding the various systems. Not all of the 117 species of fish found here are of interest to the angler, but he will certainly find more than enough to suit his tastes. There is an excellent road, rail and air network ensuring that chosen fishing locations are readily accessible.

The main area of interest to fishermen is the Zambezi River, with **Lake Kariba** (250km in length with a surface area of some 5,250 square kilometres) and the **Victoria Falls** forming the chief focal points. Tourist facilities in both these locations are excellent, the visitor being able to choose from a varied list of accommodation ranging from basic camping and National Parks sites to luxury houseboats, lodges and hotels.

Tigerfish are most commonly taken using trolling or spinning methods, but they may sometimes be tempted with a fly. They are lightening-fast, fighting fiercely after the first vigorous take. The average size is between 2-6lbs, but double figure fish are common, especially in the legendary stretch above Victoria Falls. The current Zimbabwean and world record for this species stands at 34¼lbs.

Another freshwater fish which is proving popular with British anglers is the mighty vundu. The vundu is a giant catfish, in Africa, second only in size to the Nile perch. This species, although not often fished for by local anglers, is a formidable opponent, growing to well over 100lbs and is found only below the Victotora Falls. Prospective fishermen would do best to try Lake Kariba first, using a sturdy boat rod and multiplier type outfit (capable of withstanding powerful runs often exceeding 100yds) plus the services of a guide.

The other most commonly sought after species are members of the *tilapia* and *serranchromis* families, known to local fishermen as bream. Besides being a popular table fish, the various species give an excellent account of themselves on light tackle and may be caught using a variety of methods ranging from conventional coarse fishing techniques to the use of spinners and flies.

Other indigenous species include the Cornish Jack, bottlenose, chessa, nkupe, hunyani salmon, purple labeo and the sharptooth catfish. Introduced species include the largemouth bass, a fine fighting fish introduced from USA several years ago and now widespread in Zimbabwean waters; rainbow, brown and brook trout, well stocked in the rivers and lakes of the **Nyanga** and **Chimaniamni** mountain ranges (a picturesque region often likened to Scotland); and carp, which are stocked in selected waters such as the **Mazowe Dam** near Harare and fish in excess of 50lbs have been caught.

The fishing season is any month with an 'R' in it and so ideally suits European anglers, who will, moreover, find that the high cost of the international airfare is pleasantly offset by the excellent value for money once there.

For more information, contact **Zimbabwe Tourist Office, 429 Strand, London WC2R 0JR**. (tel: 020 7836 7755) (web: www.zimbabwetourism.co.zw); **Department**

of National Parks & Wildlife Management, PO Box CY 140, Harare (tel: +263 4 792783/9; fax: +263 4 726089; email: natparks@africaonline.co.zw).

MALAWI

Excellent sport with rainbow trout may be enjoyed in the bracing climate of the **Zomba, Mulanje** and **Nyika Plateaux** as a result of consistent restocking of rivers and streams by the Government. **Lake Malawi** holds over 400 species; including varieties of catfish, perch and carp; also yellow fish, lake salmon and lake tiger. Most of these are found in the **Shire River** above **Livingstone Falls**, but below the falls the main species are related to those found in the **Zambezi** (which include the famous tiger-fish). Further information may be obtained from the **Malawi Tourist Office, c/o High Commission of Malawi, 70 Winnington Road, London N2 OTX** (tel: 020 8455 5624; fax: 020 32351066; web: www.visitmalawi.mw; email: malawitourism@aol.com); **Malawi Department of Tourism**, P O Box 402, Blantyre, 265, Malawi (web: www.visitmalawi.mw) and **Ministry of Information & Tourism**, P/bag 326, Lilongwe 3, Malawi (tel: +265 (0)1755 (0)702/499; fax: +265 (0)1770 650) (email: psinfo@sdnp.org.mw and **Fisheries Department**, P O Box 593, Lilongwe, Malawi (tel: +265 (0)788 511/788 716; fax: +265 (0) 788 543; web: www.malawi.gov.mw).

EAST AFRICA

KENYA

Kenya is well-developed for the sporting tourist and offers a variety of fishing off the coast, in its rivers and in the lakes or the **Great Rift Valley**. Licence fees: are modest; accommodation of some variety is established at or near virtually all main centres.

The coast. Black, blue and striped marlin, broadbill swordfish, sailfish, yellow fin tuna, wahoo, barracuda, cobia, dorado, mako shark. Centres at **Mombasa**, **Shimoni**, for fishing in the famous **Pemba Channel**, a natural corridor between the mainland and Pemba Island, **Kilifi**, **Watamu**, **Lamu** and **Malindi**, the latter the largest. Accommodation at club premises or hotels. Charter boats operate, with good fishing almost all the year round, peaking Oct-April: at its least attractive May-June.

The mountain rivers. Stocked early in the century with brown trout, later with rainbows. Camps with rondavel accommodation at **Thiba**, **Thego**, **Kimakia**, **Koiwa**. Rest house at **Kaibabich**; lodges at **Ngobit** and **Kiandorogo**. A dozen or more specially recommended hotels and clubs. Camp accommodation may be primitive; nothing should be taken for granted. There are limits on size, method and bags, but wholesale poaching is an ever-present problem despite determined governmental efforts to curb it.

The lakes. **Naivasha** is famous for black bass, but the angler in pursuit of them should forget any preconceptions he might have. Smallish coppery-tinted bar-spoons are the most successful lure and the bigger fish are found not so much in the shallows as in pockets of deeper water inshore, where they shelter in the papyrus. In **Lake Turkana** (formerly Rudof) the principal quarry are Nile perch and tiger-fish, the former growing to more than 250lbs. Also in Turkana, the rare and beautiful golden perch, which may weigh 150lbs. **Lake Baringo**, well off the beaten track, is noted for its tilapia fishing; also for its wildlife watching potential, but that is a bonus attaching to much of the Kenya fishing. Sport-fishing is now developing in **Lake Victoria** and the **Sasamua Dam**. Accommodation at all centres, but the extreme variety of types calls for detailed investigation in advance. The **Pemba Channel Fishing Club** address is **PO Box**

84851, Mombasa (tel: +254 (0)722 205020/1; fax: +254 (0)41 49 1265; web: www.pembachannel.com; email: info@pembachannel.com). The **Kenya National Tourist Board** is at Colechurch House, 1 London Bridge Walk, London SE1 2SX (tel: 020 7367 0900/27; web: www.magicalkenya.com; email: info@kenyatourism.org).

TANZANIA

Tanzania can provide some of the finest big-game fishing in the world.

Big-game fishing: From October to March there is first-class sport with sailfish, shark, tunny, marlin, wahoo, horse mackerel and dolphin, particularly off **Dar es Salaam**, around **Bagamoyo, Latham Island** and **Mafia Island**, and also in the **Pemba Channel** off **Tanga**. Mafia has now been declared Tanzania's first Marine Park. Mafia offers some of the finest sport in the world in quantity, variety and excitement, and here particularly, and in addition to those already mentioned, can be found king fish, barracuda, red snapper and rock cod. There are two lodges on Mafia Island. Boats and equipment can be hired from the Seafaris Company. Flights to Mafia Island from the mainland (about 40 minutes run) are operated daily in each direction by air charter services from Dar es Salaam.

Lake fishing: the great **Lakes Victoria**, **Nyasa** and **Tanganyika** provide the best sport fishing where, from **Kigoma, Mwanza, Bukoba** and **Itungi**, it is possible to catch Nile perch, tiger fish and tilapia, which provide excellent sport. The **Great Ruaha River** and the **Rufiji River Basin** are further inland fishing grounds.

Trout fishing: At the moment, less organised than other branches of the sport, but can be arranged on request.

For visa enquiries &c, contact **Tanzania High Commission, 3 Stratford Place, London W1C 1AS** (tel: 020 7569 1470; web: www.tanzania-online.gov.uk). Further information (licences etc) may be obtained from the **Tanzania Tourist Office/Trade Centre, 3 Stratford Place, London WC1 1AF** (tel: 020 7569 1470; fax: 020 7495 8817; email: tanzarep@tanzarep.demon.co.uk; web: www.tanzaniatouristboard.com); **Tanzania Tourist Board, PO Box 2485, IPS Building, Dar es Salaam** (tel: +255 22 2111244; fax: +255 22 2116420; email: safari@ud.co.tz).

MOZAMBIQUE

The New Mozambique can provide excellent fishing and has something to offer everyone, both the amateur and experienced (keen) fisherman, with a wealth of fishing venues to choose from.

A former Portuguese colony that gained independence in 1975, Mozambique has approximately 2500 kilometres of pristine coastline. The warm waters of the Indian Ocean create lagoons, coral reefs and island, all of which offer superb fishing.

There is a variety of game fishing, which is excellent: Marlin: The **Bazaruto Archipelago** (a National Marine Park off the coast of Vilanculos, consisting of 4 main islands – **Bazaruto, Benguerra, Magaruque** and **Santa Carolina**, and a number of smaller islands) is ranked the best marlin angling destination in the Indian Ocean (av. 350 kg with a record 590 kg landed in 1998), and best months are Oct - March. Sailfish: Av weight 32 kg, while the record is nearly 60 kg; best months May - Sept. Other species include several tuna species, wahoo, prodigal son, yellow fin, skipjack, dorado, giant kingfish, barracuda and king and queen mackerel;

Angling for Kingfish is excellent throughout the year, though the Giant Kingfish is more likely to be seen during September to April. The King and Queen mackerel appear in the cooler months from March to August. Kawakawa fishing picks up in late spring into summer, which is November through to June. The elusive Bone fish, which to date has only been hooked in deeper water, are more likely to be caught during April to July, whilst the "almost un-catchable" milk fish are more prevalent during the same months. Springer are present all year round.

Catch and release of all species is encouraged.

The **Bazaruto Archipelago** is becoming exceedingly popular with fly-fishermen. When trying for the giant trevally and sailfish on fly, a 12 weight outfit, competent reel with good drag and plenty of backing (300 m) is necessary. Favoured fly patterns include Clouser Minnows and Lefty's Deceivers, especially in chartreuse.

A few years ago a world record Kingfish was caught at **Guinjata Bay**, south of **Inhambane** which is approximately 530 kms north of **Maputo**. In the same area is the **Barra Peninsula**, another excellent fishing area.

Inhaca Island, 40 kms off the mainland close to Maputo, is another natural reserve that is popular with fishermen. Top catches of blue and black marlin are recorded regularly. To the south of Mozambique is Ponta Malongane and **Ponta do Ouro**, both known for their excellent fishing opportunities. Just south of Maputo this area is easily accessible by vehicle from South Africa. All the fishing areas along the Mozambique coast offer a range of accommodation from the budget to the expensive exclusive lodges. The infrastructure in Mozambique has improved immeasurably over the last few years, and even the more remote areas are now accessible, albeit some only by 4 x 4 vehicles.

Although the coastal waters are the most popular, inland the **Cahorra Bassa Dam** (located in **Tete Province**, in the north of Mozambique) is the second of the Zambezi's great man-made lakes. For the past 25 years it has been largely unfished, but it has been growing in popularity; angling is good throughout the year, with excellent tiger fish up to 14kg caught in the dam, with av wt of 4-8kgs. There are also more than 40 species of angling fish in the dam, of which bream, chessa, nkupe, Cornish jack and vundu are among the most popular; best results obtained from boats. Accommodation is available at Ugezi Tiger Lodge, situated near the town of **Songo**, at the dam wall; it is recommended anglers provide their own tackle; tackle for spinning and trawling (not fly) can be hired from the lodge. The best angling is done from boats.

For further information contact **Mozambique Tourism, EuroCenter - First Floor, 363 Rivonia Boulevard (P O Box 2042), Rivonia, Sandton 2128, Gauteng, South Africa** (tel: +27 11 803 9296 or +27 11 803 9296; fax: +27 11 803 9299; web: www.mozambiquetourism.co.za; email: travel@mozambiquetourism.co.za).

SOUTH AFRICA

EASTERN and WESTERN CAPE

Since the establishment of large-mouthed and small-mouthed black bass, the inland fisheries of the Cape area have been greatly extended; but this development has not been at the expense of the rainbow trout fisheries, which are as flourishing as ever. A few rivers hold brown trout, and brown trout were also introduced to upland waters some time ago. All the inland waters fall under the laws of the Cape Provincial Administration. In proclaimed trout rivers no fishing may be done at all except with the artificial fly and during the open season for trout, which extends from the beginning of September to the end of May. Trout licences are required but the charges are extremely moderate. In addition, however, the permission of riparian owners will be needed and sometimes a fee is payable.

Most of the rivers in the Western Cape are within a day's motoring of Cape Town on tarred roads, and some of the best waters are on State Forest Reserves, to which anglers have access on permit. This area has a winter rainfall and the best months are September, October and November, late April and early May. Steenbras Reservoir holds a rare hybrid known as 'tiger trout' which is a cross between brown trout and the American eastern brook trout.

The Olifants River in the **Citrusdal** and **Clanwilliam** districts provide excellent fishing for small-mouthed bass and the indigenous yellowfish, *Barbus capensis*. The latter takes artificial lures, is very game and runs as large as 20lbs. Further afield, the mountainous area of **East Griqualand** has rivers which provide boundless opportunities for the trout fisherman.

Sea fishing along the coastline is very good indeed, with hundreds of species to be caught. Cape Town has emerged as the world's leading Broadbill Swordfish fishing venue. The big-game potential is only beginning to be realised, and remarkable catches of yellowfin and longfin tuna have been taken. Tuna catches predominate throughout spring, summer and autumn; snoek in the winter months. Skiboat fishing is an interesting and highly successful technique for taking many varieties of off-shore fish. Every type of tackle is obtainable and accommodation is plentiful and comfortable.

KWAZULU-NATAL

The streams originating in the **KwaZulu-Natal Drakensberg** mountains, which rise to 11,000 ft, form several river systems before emptying into the Indian Ocean. Although the sources are in general too steeply graded to support fish life in any quantity, below the torrent source each river enters a series of pools and rapids suitable for trout and other fish. Moreover, the construction of numerous dams in the KwaZulu-Natal Midlands has been the means of providing many extra fishable waters.

Only waters at an altitude of about 4,000 ft and more have, in general, been stocked with trout. Below this level most rivers are too warm and silt-laden for the species to thrive. Black bass and carp have been established in a number of these midland dams with tilapia species inhabiting the warmer areas. However, other species to be caught are the indigenous 'scaly' (yellowfish), catfish, and eels. The State dams administered by the KwaZulu-Natal Parks, Game and Fish Preservation Board (**Albert Falls, Midmar, Wagendrift, Spioenkop, Chelmsford, Hazelmere** and **Craigie Burn**) not only provide abundant angling for many types of fish, including those mentioned above, but also provide a wide range of other recreational facilities and comfortable accommodation.

Rainbow and brown trout are the most important sporting fish of the **Drakensberg** area (midlands) and warm-water angling (carp, black bass, catfish, scaly, eels and tilapia) of the lower inland areas. The open season for trout streams is from September 1 to June 1, but dams are open throughout the year. The best fishing is usually obtained at the beginning and end of the season. From November to February the heavy summer rains and thunderstorms are apt to discolour the lower waters and render fly fishing difficult. It is almost always feasible, however, to obtain fishing on the headwaters or on artificial lakes and dams. The average size trout runs from about $\frac{1}{2}$lb to 2lbs, but on the larger waters, especially dams, much heavier fish can be expected and each season a few trout of more than 5lbs are taken. The province's record for a rainbow trout is 5.54kg (12¾lbs) caught in the Swartberg district in May 1958.

Public waters and the Provincial nature reserves (where accommodation may be found close to fishing areas) were controlled by the KwaZulu-Natal Parks, Game and Fish Preservation Board. They have now changed their name to **Ezemvelo KZN Wildlife**; all queries regarding licences, accommodation etc should be directed to **Ezemvelo KZN Wildlife, P O Box 130** (tel: +27 (0) 33 845 1000; fax: +27 (0) 845 1001; email: webmail@kznwildlife.com; web: www.kznwildlife.com) who will supply full information to visitors and handle reservations. Parks Board rangers are stationed at the more important public fishing areas to assist visitors and enforce regulations for the protection of trout, black bass, carp and indigenous fish.

Sea fishing. The majority of salt water anglers fish in the surf, casting their baits and lures from sandy beaches or from rocky promontories. Estuaries offer sport, while the open sea attracts those who have access to suitable craft. A wide variety of fish may be caught in the surf, ranging from sharks to small members of the bream family. Tackle varies accordingly, but a light fibre-glass rod of about 10-13ft together with a fixed-spool or multiplying reel gives a chance of catching many of the inshore species. Visitors should acquaint themselves with size restrictions and open seasons which apply to certain species of fish.

In June and July the annual migration of 'sardines' may attract game fish such as king mackerel into the surf and sport is likely to be fast and furious. The best estuarine fishing is **Lake St Lucia**, a nature reserve-controlled by the Ezemvelo KZN Wildlife; large numbers of grunter and kob enter the estuary leading to the main lake in spring and autumn. Deep sea angling takes place from ski-boats (small, speedy, flat-bottomed craft) as well as from the larger types of vessel. Advice on the organisation of deep sea trips will be provided by the Ezemvelo KZN Wildlife. Tackle for every branch of angling is obtainable. Innumerable hotels, holiday cottages, holiday flats and rest camps provide accommodation for visitors to the coastal resorts (with marlin, sailfish and tiger fishing).

NORTHERN PROVINCE and MPUMALANGA

Rainbow trout can be caught in a number of fine mountain streams at altitudes varying from 4,000 to 6,000ft in this north-eastern region of that was previously called the **Transvaal**. **Magoebaskloof, Sabie, Pilgrim's Rest, Lydenburg, Machadodorp, Belfast, Dullstroom** and **Waterval Boven** are the principal trout fishing centres. Some waters contain only fish over 3lbs in weight. There is no closed season for trout fishing although fishing conditions are at their best in October and April. The rule is fly only, with dry and wet flies being used. Most waters are privately owned and, except where angling clubs have fishing rights, the permission of the riparian owner must be obtained. Good bass fishing is to be found in a large number of public, club and private waters. Large-mouth bass are widely distributed but some of the best waters are in the **White River** area of **Mpumalanga**: dams in that region, such as **Longmere, Klipkoppies, Witklip, Stanford** and **Dagama** have produced excellent fishing in recent times. Tiger-fish may be caught in the **Komati River** at **Komatipoort** and in the **Limpopo**. Minimum takeable size, 12in, daily bag limit, 6. Tiger-fish are best caught in September and October.

Yellowfish abound in the waters of the northern provinces There are four species, all belonging to the genus *Barbus*. In the **Vaal River** they grow to 30lbs in weight and can be caught on mealiemeal dough, earthworms, grasshoppers or crabs. The two species of the east-flowing rivers grow to 15lbs and take crab, earthworms, mealiemeal dough and spinners.

Tilapia, commonly known as 'kurper', is a very popular fish. There are two species, both being restricted to warmer waters. They can be caught on earthworms, mealiemeal dough (a paste bait) and spinners, with a light trout rod. They average about 1¼lbs, but specimens of 4½lbs are commonly caught. The best waters for this species are the **Hartebeestpoort, Rust der Winter, Roodeplaat, Loskop** and **Njelele dams**, also those in the White River area - although they may be caught in almost any lowveld water. Not just the north, but the whole of the Republic of South Africa is a carp angler's paradise, with the fish attaining exceptional weights in very short periods, due to the nature of South Africa's waters. The record caught on rod and line is 48lbs 10oz, although much larger specimens have been caught but not recorded, and the heaviest known fish was a monster of 83¼lbs which was trapped in an irrigation furrow near **Bon Accord Dam** north of **Pretoria**. Carp are found throughout South Africa in many public and private dams. No bag or size limits apply to these fish.

It is also possible to stay in and fish within some of South Africa's game reserves, including Loskop and Willem Pretorius.

General Information: Licences relative to the particular province can be obtained from Receivers of Revenue, magistrates' offices and reputable tackle stores throughout the Republic.

For further information contact the **South African Tourism Board & Tourist Office, 5/6 Alt Grove, Wimbledon, London SW19 4DZ** (tel: 0870 1550044; fax: 020 8944 6705). **South African Tourism** head office is located in **Bojanala House, 90 Protea Road, Chislehurston, Johannesburg 2196, Gauteng, SA**; postal address: **P/Bag X10012, Sandton 2146, Gauteng, SA** (tel: +27 11 895 3000; fax: +27 11 895 3001; web: www.southafrica.net; email: info@southafrica.net).

FISHING IN AUSTRALASIA; INDIA; SRI LANKA AND MALAYSIA

AUSTRALIA

As a result of acclimatization and planned research in Australia, many of the lakes and rivers in the State of Tasmania, New South Wales, Western Australia and Victoria are well stocked with trout, which sometimes reach a large size. The island State of **Tasmania** is world-famous as a trout fishing centre, and continues to attract anglers from all parts of the Commonwealth each year.

Many rivers are still subject to flooding despite hydro schemes and this imposes a standstill on angling, so that the tendency is to reduce close seasons. The angler is strongly advised to check on river levels before going to fish. Before water temperatures have warmed up will be found to be the best times - midsummer is generally worst for trout fishing.

Freshwater Murray cod, perch and blackfish are found in good number in Australia. The **Murray River**, which forms the boundary of the eastern States of **Victoria** and

New South Wales, and its many tributaries provide good sport for thousands of anglers, including trout in the upper reaches, Murray cod may weigh up to 150lbs; another Murray River fish, the callop or golden perch, grows to over 50lbs. Macquairie perch (to 11lbs) and silver perch or grunter (to 6lbs) are also taken. Another perch, or Australian bass, is taken in coastal streams and estuaries.

Australia was said by the late Zane Grey, noted big game authority, to possess the finest big game fishing grounds in the world. Centre of interest for sportsmen is **Montague Island**, off the coast of New South Wales, where there are marlin, tuna, shark and other big fish. The island is 14m from **Bermagui**, a safe harbour that can be used in all weathers. The tropical waters of the **Great Barrier Reef**, which extends for about a thousand miles along the east coast of Queensland, form Australia's most fascinating grounds; there are many unusual varieties of fish. There is good beach and rock fishing almost everywhere.

The Tourism Australia, Australia Centre, Australia House, 6th floor, Melbourne Place, The Strand, London WC2B 4LG (tel: 020 7438 4601; web: www.tourism.australia.com). For information on Australian holidays contact **The Aussie Helpline**: web: www.australia.com. There is also an excellent website, www.recfish.com.au, which is the national body dealing with recreational fishing, and which can be accessed state by state.

NEW SOUTH WALES

The streams near **Sydney** are mostly too small to support a large trout population, but good sport may be had in parts of the Blue Mountains area. Easily best from the fishing point of view, however, is the **Snowy Mountains** area. Very large reservoirs constructed as part of the hydro-electric scheme in the Southern Alps are now ranked equal to any in the world for brown and rainbow trout. The scenic beauty of the streams and these lakes is outstanding. **Lake Eucumbene** is the largest of the dams and in recent years has become the mecca of Australian trout anglers, Lake **Jindabyne** is the other principal fishery, but the total number of man-made lakes is 16. Brown trout average 1 to 2kg, rainbows from 1 to 3kg. Lakes Jindabyne and **Burrinjuck** have stocked Atlantic salmon. There is also good river trout fishing in the region, including **Maclaughlin River**, **Bobundara Creek**, **Bombala River**, and others, and little explored creeks and streams. Good accommodation and camping sites are to be found and many fine fishing waters are reached easily over good roads. Another good area for trout fishing is the **New England Tableland**, north of Sydney. Centred on the University Town of **Armidale**, the area's many streams and high altitude provide excellent fishing.

Apart from these new waters, one of the most renowned centres is **Cooma**, which has produced many of the heavier fish caught in the state. The **Murrumbidgee** and its tributaries near **Kiandra** are well worth fishing at the right time.

With the exception of a number of small spawning creeks, which have extended close seasons, and the larger impoundments, which are open all the year round, the trout streams are open to fishing from early-October to mid-June. Other inland waters are open the whole year. The most popular times for trout fishing are in the cooler months of the open season; that is October, November, March, April and May.

There are many attractive native species inhabiting the freshwater streams. Murray cod being perhaps the most popular, and the taking of fish up to 50lbs is not uncommon; these fish do, in fact, run much larger. There are size and bag limits for trout and native fish and there is a closed season for Murray cod during September, October and

November. Trout cod, Macquarie perch, eastern cod and Australian grayling are protected. Silver perch may be taken from stocked impoundments only.

There is now a **NSW recreational fishing fee** (required by law) for fishing in BSW waters both freshwater and saltwater, applicable to all except Commonwealth pensioner concession card holders, under 18's and charter-boat fishers with registered guide. Fees range from: Aus$6 for 3 days; Aus$12 per month; Aus$30 for one year, and Aus$75 for a 3 year licence. All revenues go into the Recreational Fishing Trusts to be spent on improving recreational fishing in NWW. Further information may be had by writing to **NSW Department of Primary Industries, PO Box 21, Cronulla 2230, Australia** (tel: +61 2 9527 8411; web: www.fisheries.nsw.gov.au; email: information-adv isory@dpi.nsw.gov.au).

The State is noted for its attractive coastal lagoons and estuary fisheries. At many excellent resorts bream, flathead, whiting, black fish, etc, give good sport, while big game fish like tuna, marlin and shark abound in waters off the coast. For rock fishing, there are hundreds of locations on the Central Coast, some little known, where big yellowtail kingfish, tuna, mulloway, drummer, marlin, snapper and shark may be caught. Recommended among these are the Haven and Skillion at **Terrigal**, and **Avoca**.

Tourist information can obtained from **The Sydney Visitors Centre, Level 6, 66 Harrington Street, The Rocks, Sydney 2000** (tel: +61 9240 8500; email: visitorinformation@shfa.nsw.gov.au; web: www.therocks.com).

NORTHERN TERRITORY

The **Northern Territory** has some of the most prolific fishing in Australia. With vast, unique wetlands, with their numerous freshwater rivers and billabongs (waterholes resulting from seasonal rivers drying up), it is the perfect environment for barramundi, and is commonly known as the centre for barramundi in Australia.

The top end of the Northern Territory has two distinct seasons: the Wet and the Dry. On average 92% of the top end's rainfall occurs during the tropical summer season, between November and April, and flooding can affect access to many inland areas by road. The Dry finds many rivers and creeks dried up, leaving isolated billabongs and lakes in difficult-to-access areas.

Fishing in the Territory is a year-round pursuit, and the different seasons offer different fishing opportunities, with the main attraction, barramundi, available all through the year. Known for its aggressive nature and fighting characteristics, the barramundi is found in both fresh and saltwater. It is the favourite quarry of the Australian angler, fish 10 to 15 kilos being not uncommon, and running sometimes to 20 kilos. For fly fishermen, the saratoga offers good sport, and fights hard (average 1-2kg).

The Northern Territory is also famous for its saltwater and estuary fishing in its many mangrove-lined creeks, tidal rivers, bays, offshore islands and reefs. Some of Australia's best light and medium tackle game fishing is found in the coastal waters of the Northern Territory, in **Arnhem Land,** which is territory set aside for Aborigines. Varieties include mangrove jack, queenfish, tuna, threadfin salmon, blue salmon, trevally, Spanish mackerel; even sailfish and marlin.

Reef fishing provides excellent sport for golden snapper, saddletail snapper, red-finned emperor, red emperor, estuary rock-cod, coral trout, moonfish, mangrove jack, bream, black jewfish, tuna, and Spanish mackerel. The best times for barramundi are March to May, and September to December.

Other recommended locations are the **Mary River**, east of **Darwin**, the **Daly River**, south of Darwin, **Bathurst** and **Melville Islands** to the north of Darwin, and the estuaries, and many rivers and billabongs in **Kakadu National Park**. These are all popular fisheries. Anglers are advised, a hat, sunglasses, 20+ factor sunscreen, long-sleeved cotton shirt, long cotton trousers in this tropical environment are a must.

Weather and tides play an important role in fishing productivity. The Northern Territory has large tidal changes and low tide can leave boats stranded for long periods with large tides often creating strong currents in the river systems. Obtaining tidal information before departing on fishing expeditions is a necessity. Such information can be obtained from local newspapers as well as from news and weather reports on radio and television. Regulations for recreational fishing deal mainly with bag limits and minimum size regulations. Details can be obtained from the **Fisheries Division Group, Department of Primary Industry, Fisheries, Mines & Energy, PO Box 3000, Darwin, NT 0801** (tel: +61 8 89992144, fax: +61 8 89992065; email: fisheries@nt.gov.au; web: www.nt.gov.au). The Department can also supply names and addresses of fishing tour operators.

QUEENSLAND

There are no trout fishing centres, no licence fees and no close season except for barramundi angling (Nov 1 to Feb 1). Among other species, golden perch (or yellowbelly) are found in the **Darling River**, **Lake Eyre** and **Bullo** drainages, and also in the **Dawson-Fitzroy** system; a freshwater table fish which gives a determined fight; Murray cod are found in the **Murray-Darling** system, and Mary River cod are indigenous to **Mary River**; this is an endangered species, and must be returned to water alive; and freshwater perch and grunters (several species) are found in most inland streams. Barramundi are taken from all inland rivers of eastern Queensland from around Mary River to Gulf of **Carpentaria**. Saratoga are excellent sportfish, and are found in **Fitzroy** system, growing to maximum length of 3ft.

Off the coast are the **Greater Barrier** coral reefs (1,230 miles long), which abound in fish life. Big game fish are plentiful along the whole coastline, and the following species are commonly caught: Marlin, spearfish, tuna, Atlantic bonito, Spanish mackerel, sharks (white pointer, mako, tiger, whalers, etc), amberjacks, emperor, trevally, etc.

Cairns and Tropical North Queensland are known world wide as a big game area for the big black marlin in the last quarter of the year. Also mackerel, tuna, big trevally, queenfish, and outside the reef, wahoo, dolphin fish, as well as marlin.

The area off **Brisbane** and **Moreton Bay** produces whiting, flathead, trevally, larger mackerel species in summer, and in winter whiting, bream, tailor, jew, perch, school mackerel, tarwhine, blackfish; all year round cod, snapper, sweetlip, drummer. Deep sea charters produce snapper, parrot, pearl, perch, sweetlip, cod, and big game such as tuna, sea-pike, black king, dolphin, small marlin, and larger mackerel species.

The mainland coast provides excellent estuary beach and rock fishing for bream, whiting, flathead, tailor, trevally, giant perch, grunter, jew fish, and so on.

Information on regulations can be had from **Director, Fisheries Branch, Dept of Primary Industries and Fisheries, GPO Box 46, Brisbane, Qld 4001** (tel: +61 7 3404 6999; email: callweb@dpi.qld.gov.au; web: www.dpi.qld.gov.au); and on tourism from the **Tourism Australia (attn: Tourism Queensland), Australia**

Centre, Australia House, 6th floor, Melbourne Place, Strand, London WC2B 4LG (tel: 020 7438 4601; fax: 020 7240 6690; web: www.tourism.australia.com).

SOUTH AUSTRALIA

South Australia has very few freshwater streams if the **River Murray** is excluded. Relatively little trout fishing is to be found except in some streams near capital city of Adelaide and in farm dams. There is no closed season on trout fishing but there is a legal minimum length of 28cm.

The River Murray, which flows through the State to the sea, supports a recreational fishery for native freshwater species, callop, silver perch and catfish and yabbies. Introduced species, including European carp and redfin may be caught, but must not be returned to the water alive. Fishing for Murray cod is now permitted between 1 August to 31 December (c&r is encouraged); Murray crayfish, silver perch and catfish are now fully protected in South Australia.

Very enjoyable and profitable sea fishing can be had along most of the coast of South Australia with rod and line or hand line. Amateur anglers do not require licences.

South Australia's premier saltwater table fish is the King George whiting and these are accessible to boat anglers in most waters of the State, including waters adjacent to Adelaide. Snapper up to 30lbs or more and sweet tasting garfish are also taken by boat anglers in the relatively sheltered waters of **Gulf St Vincent** and **Spencer Gulf**. A large number of piers along the South Australian coast allow good fishing for a variety of species. Excellent sport fishing for Australian salmon (*Arripis trutta esper*, a sea perch, and not related to the family *Salmonidae*), sharks and large mulloway may be had by shore anglers along the surf beaches of the more exposed parts of the coast.

The coastal waters of the **Innes National Park** are home to a wide variety of fish life, and there are at least seven excellent beach and rock fishing locations where good catches of garfish, Tommy ruff, King George and yellowfin whiting, squid, bream, mullet, flathead, and leather jacket may be had. Fishing boats take anglers on sea fishing trips from **Port Lincoln**, and commonly taken are snapper, various species of shark and tuna, and whiting.

Kangaroo Island, 4,500 square km, lying off the coast south-west of Adelaide, is an important national centre for wildlife and has a great potential for fishing. At **Kingscote**, **Penneshaw** and **American River** wharves garfish, tommy ruffs and snook may be caught on fast running tides; jetties at Emu Bay and Vivonne Bay produce good fishing at times; surf fishing at **Emu Bay**, **Stokes Bay**, **D'Estrees Bay**, **Vivonne Bay** and Middle River, where, where salmon, mullet, and large flathead may be caught; swallowtail are caught by rock fishing, and inland the Middle, **Sou'West**, **Chapman** and **Cygnet** Rivers, and the **Western River** mouth all provide excellent bream fishing; at the mouth of the **Cygnet River**, salmon, mullet and tommy ruffs are to be found. Charter boats operate on the island, found through information centres at **Penneshaw** and **Kingscote**, and snapper are caught along the north coast in large numbers, whiting to 1.5kg, and snook are also taken. Fishing in National Parks rivers or creeks is prohibited. Tourism is well organised on the island, and there is a wide range of good accommodation.

Anglers do not require a licence to fish with a rod or hand line, but must observe legal minimum lengths of fish, bag limits, boat limits, and closed areas, and must not take protected species. Fishing is not permitted in most Aquatic Reserves.

Tourist information can be had from the **South Australian Tourism Commission, Travel Centre, 18 King William Street, Adelaide**, (tel: +61 (0)88 4634547; email: informationAndBookings@SouthAustralia.com; web: www.southaustralia.com); and further information on fishery matters from the **Primary Industries and Resources, SA Fisheries, PO Box 282, Adelaide, SA 5015;** (web: www.pir.sa.gov.au/fisheries) and the **Honourary Secretary, South Australian Fly Fishers Association Inc, PO Box 489, North Adelaide, SA 5006;** (web: www.saflyfishers.asn.au). For houseboat hire in a wide range of river locations, often with fishing opportunity, contact **Houseboat Hirers Association, Marine House, 300 Morphett St, Adelaide SA 5001** (tel: +61 (0) 8823 18466; fax: +61 8 8231 7821; web: www.hha.asn.au).

TASMANIA

Tasmania, not without justification, describes itself as Australia's fly fishing capital. More than 3,000 lakes and rivers contain self-supporting populations of brown, rainbow and brook trout, species which have achieved growth-rates on the island second to none. The size-bracket in which the angler expects his captures to fall spans 1-5 kg, with even larger trout an ever-present possibility. Most of the waters are within motoring distance of Hobart and Launceston. Mobile campers are widely employed. Guides operate in vicinity, and can arrange, where necessary, flies, lures, boats and accommodation.

Popular waters include **Great Lake**, 158 square km (situated in the central plateau of the island at an altitude of 1,000m, 83 miles from Hobart, the capital, and about the same distance from Launceston, second largest city in the island, situated in the north), **Lake King William, Lake St Clair, Lake Echo, Little Pine Lagoon**, (perhaps Tasmania's best known fly fishing water,) **Brady's Lake, Dee Lagoon, Arthurs Lake** (64.4 square km), **Lake Rowallan** and **Lake Pedder** (which reached a legendary peak in the late 1970s, with trout over 10kg. Now, trout average a more modest 1$\frac{1}{2}$ to 2kg). Other popular fishing waters are **Lake Leake** and **Tooms Lake** on the east coast, and **Lake Sorell** in the central midlands, 43 square km, at 823 m above sea level, with fine hatches of mayfly and caddis. Browns to 3kg are caught. Another popular group is the Bronte system, between Bronte Park and Tarraleah, as are the many small lakes in the Nineteen Lagoons district centred around **Lakes Ada** and **Augusta**. The **Western Lakes** are a scattering of countless lakes, lagoons and tarns across the Western Central Plateau (1,150 to 1,200m above sea level), between the **Great Lake** and the **Cradle Mountain Lake, St Clair National Park**. They are also know as the **Wilderness Lakes**. The more accessible amongst them include **Howes Bay Lagoon, Carter Lakes, Lake Botsford, Lake Ada** and **Lake Kay**. Mainly brown trout are to be found in the area. Other famous Tasmanian fisheries are **Brumbys Creek**, near Cressy and Longford, and the **Macquarie River**, flowing northwards through the midlands, with 'red spinner' mayfly hatches: stream fishing for small brown trout. **London Lakes** is a private trout fishery of 5,000 acres in the Central Highlands, with abundant stocks of wild browns, generally in the 1-1$\frac{1}{2}$ kg size range. Contact **London Lakes Lodge, P.O. Bronte Park, Tasmania 7140** (tel: +61 (0)3 628 91294; fax: +61 (0)3 6289 1122; web: www.londonlakes.com.au; email: greg.beecroft@ozemail.com.au).

The northern part of the island is more richly endowed with trout streams than the south, having the **South Esk, North Esk, Macquarie** and **Brumby**. The north-west has the **Mersey, Forth, Leven, Blyth, Duck** and **Inglis**. In the south are the **Derwent**, and **Huon**.

Sea fishing abounds in Tasmania, mainly in the east, but in the north Port Sorell and the **Tamar River** (65km, with jetty and estuary fishing) are popular venues, and in the west, Macquarie Harbour. The **Derwent River** at Hobart also provides many spots for jetty and estuary fishing, with catches of mackerel, flathead, cod, squid, barracouta, perch, bream and australian salmon. There are also many excellent beaches, particularly in the north from Cape Portland to Stanley, where flathead, Australian salmon, flounder and whiting are taken. Most of the rivers on the east coast from **St Helens** to **Bruny Island** hold large populations of bream, best fishing in Nov. Bruny island also has excellent beach fishing. Bait is sold in many spots on the coast, and accommodation is first class.

Species caught either from shore or from boat are southern rock cod, leather jacket, blue eye, school whiting, barracouta, yellow-eyed mullet, black bream, flathead, warehou, leatherjacket, wrasse, mullet, silver trevally, southern garfish, greenback flounder, school, "gummy", shark, marlin, various species of tuna, blue pointer, and bronze whaler sharks, elephant fish, Australian salmon, trumpeter, silver trevally, snapper, tailor, garfish and yellowtail kingfish. Boats may be chartered. There are various laws and restrictions practised, including bag limits; details should be obtained from **Dept. of Primary Industries, Water & Environment, GPO 44, Hobart, Tasmania 7001** (tel: +61 (0)3 6233 8011; web: www. dpiwe.tas.gov.au). The Department does not manage freshwater fishing in Tasmania; for inland fisheries information see below (web: www.ifs.tas.gov.au; email: infish@ifs.tas.gov.au). It also has an excellent section of related sites for quick access to various other websites relevant to fishing throughout Australia.

Angling licences are required. For inland waters these are: full season Au$65.00; 28 days $51.50; 7 days $33.00, with concessions for pensioners and juveniles and are sold at most sports stores, police stations and Tasmanian travel centres or the Inland Fisheries Service. The *Tasmanian Angling Code*, which is free with each licence should be consulted for details on fishing restrictions. The main season runs from the Saturday nearest 1 Aug to Sunday nearest 30 Apr. There are some exceptions. Specific reglations have been introduced for six waters in the Western Lakes area. For professional trout guides and/or lodges (web: www.troutguidestasmania.com.au).

Further information can be obtained from **Tourism Tasmania, Level 2, 22 Elizabeth Street, Hobart TAS 7000** (tel: +61 3 6230 8235; fax: +61 3 6230 8353; email: reception@tourismtasmania.com.au; web: www.tourismtasmania.com.au); **The Inland Fisheries Service** (web: www.ifs.tas.gov.au; email: infish@ifs.tas.gov.au) and **Trout Guides and Lodges Tasmania** (web: www.troutguidestasmania.com.au).

VICTORIA

The smallest in area of the Australian mainland States, Victoria offers a considerable diversity of opportunities for freshwater river and lake, estuary, bay and inlet, beach and sea fishing. Many fishing locations are among or near National, State and other Parks that provide an attractive scenic environment and comprehensive touring/holiday experience. Anglers are able to use natural baits, artificial lures and flies in Victoria's public waters.

Freshwater Fishing. Victoria may be known for the **Yarra River** that passes through Melbourne, the capital of Victoria, but the State has many excellent opportunities for freshwater fishing. The Yarra R. has edible fish throughout its accessible length which is confined to bank fishing (headwaters are closed water catchment) with trout, blackfish, roach, redfin, carp, Macquarie perch, some Murray cod in the urban area and within 1 hour's drive from the city centre. The estuarine section from the city to Port Phillip Bay contains a wide variety of species fishable from the bank, including bream, mullet, luderick, some mulloway and tailor. Other major streams entering Port Phillip Bay are the **Maribyrnong** and **Werribee Rivers**, which have trout in the headwaters, coarse fish in the middle sections and estuary fish in the lower sections. Except in the far north-west of the State where it is very dry, there are numerous streams, lakes and reservoirs fishable from bank, shoreline or boat, throughout Victoria. Many waters have self-supporting fish populations, but Fisheries Victoria have active stocking programs of the native golden perch, Murray cod and Macquarie perch and the introduced brown trout, rainbow trout and chinook salmon into selected, suitable waters. Trout fishing is providing in hundreds of waters but is most popular in the north east (**Ovens River**, **Kiewa River** system, **Lake Dartmouth**), Wimmera region (**Fyans Lake**, **Wartook Lake**), the south west (**Purrumbete Lake**, **Lake Bullen Merri** , **Merri River**) and central (**Goulburn River**, **Lake Eildon**). Native fish angling can be had throughout much of Victoria, although the waters in the northern half of the State provide the best Murray cod and golden perch fishing in the streams and lake systems draining into the Murray River - which forms the boundary between Victoria and New South Wales. Coarse fishing is practised State-wide with good populations of redfin, roach, and tench. Carp are abundant throughout the State, however, they are listed as noxious, and must not be returned to the water alive.

Saltwater Fishing. Melbourne and its suburbs are situated around **Port Phillip Bay**, which together with **Western Port Bay** about 1 hours drive to the south east, dominate Victoria's saltwater fishing scene, providing boat and shore anglers with a variety of fish including snapper to 11 kg (mainly October to March), salmon, elephant fish, flathead, whiting, mullet, garfish, trevally and gummy shark. Victoria's coastline has many estuaries, inlets, lakes, surf beaches and rocky shorelines that provide ample opportunities for shore, jetty, rock, beach and boat fishing. The most popular eastern area is the major **Gippsland Lakes** system where a series of large lakes provide excellent year-round fishing. Many of Victoria's coastal fishing areas are popular and well-serviced holiday locations complete with accommodation, facilities and boat hire. The **Glenelg River** in the west provides a 70 km estuary which is very popular for mulloway fishing. The commonly caught saltwater fish are bream, flathead, mullet, luderick, estuary perch, sharks, tailor, Australian salmon, sweep, leatherjackets and garfish.

There are too many angling locations around Victoria to mention individually. Tackle stores and newsagents provide numerous publications and video tapes about where and how to catch fish in the State. A useful publication is *Fishing Guide to Victoria's Salt Water* - Wilson and Classon, (RRP $A29.95), which is designed to help the angler find and fish hundreds of locations along the coast.

Anglers fishing in either saltwater or freshwater or both, require an Recreational Fishing Licence to fish, unless they are under 18, or over 70 years of age, or in receipt of certain pensions. Annual licences cost A$24.50; 28 day A$12; 48 hour A$6. Information on licensing and fishing regulations, including bag limits, size limits and closed seasons are provided in the *Victoria Recreational Fishing Regulations Guide* which is issued free from over 700 fishing tackle and sporting goods stores in Victoria, or from the **Department of Primary Industries** offices, and are issued when buying a licence. Detailed information on recreational fishing in Victoria is available (website: www.dpi.vic.gov.au). A very popular website with Victorian anglers is www.fishnet.com.au. It contains up to date reports on hundreds of fishing locations, as well as chat boards and links with other popular fishing websites. The Department of Primary Industries also maintains an on-line Guide to Inland Angling Waters of Victoria that identifies more than 600 streams and freshwater lakes, the fish present and advice about fish sizes and abundance.

Public enquiries about fishing locations and types of fish should be directed to Dept's **Customer Services Centre** (tel: +61 (0)3 5332 5000; web: www.dpi.vic.gov.au; email: customer.service@dpi.vic.gov.au). Information of fishing regulations should be directed to **Fisheries Victoria, Department of Primary Industries** (web: www.dpi.vic.gov.au/fishing/). Tourist information is issued by **Tourism Victoria, Level 32, 121 Exhibition st, Melbourne, 3000 Victoria, Australia** (Tel: +61 (0)3 9653 9871; fax: +61 (0)3 9653 9777; fax: +61 (0) 3 9653 9722); web: tourism.vic.gov.au). Further information from **Tourism Australia (attn: Tourism Victoria), Australia Centre, Australia House, 6th floor, Melbourne Place, Strand, London WC2B 4LG** (tel: 020 7438 4601; fax: 020 7240 6690; web: www.tourismaustralia.com).

WESTERN AUSTRALIA

Stretching from the tropical north to the cool southern oceans, the vast coastal waters of Western Australia provide superb ocean sports fishing, and some of the best angling in the world can be found on the doorstep of Western Australia's major cities.

Around 300,000 West Australians go fishing at least once a year, and the State attracts many visiting anglers. Boat ownership is the highest in Australia.

Principal centres for ocean fishing are: Kununurra, **Broome, Port Hedland, Dampier, Exmouth, Carnarvon, Shark Bay, Kalbarri, Geraldton, Fremantle, Lancelin, Perth, Rottnest Island, Mandurah, Bunbury, Busselton, Augusta, Albany** and **Esperance**. Fishable rivers include **Margaret River, Kalbarri, Murray**. Species to be caught include: herring, silver bream, garfish, mulloway, whiting, tailor, tuna, Australian salmon, pink snapper, dhufish, barramundi, sailfish, flathead, whiting, black bream, and Spanish mackerel. Annual gamefishing classics are held in the tropical waters of **Exmouth** and **Broome** where marlin and other gamefish are target species. In the **Swan River**, on Perth's doorstep, locals hand-trawl for prawns and black bream. Flounder and flathead are also prolific. World famous western rock lobsters can be taken from the reefs around many mid-west coastal centres. Fishing boats operate from all principal centres.

A Recreational Fishing Licence must be held for the taking of lobster, marron, freshwater fishing, abalone or to use a gill net, and is sold by Fisheries Department offices. Bag limits apply to all species of fish.

The **Fisheries Department** is located at **168/170 St George's Terrace, Perth WA 6000** (tel: +61 8 9482 7333; web: www.fish.wa.gov.au) and the address of the **Western Australian Government, European Office** in London is: **5th Floor, Australia Centre, Corner of Strand and Melbourne Place, London WC2B 4LG** (tel: 020 7240 2881; fax: 020 7240 6637; email: agent_general@wago.co.uk).

NEW ZEALAND

Fishing in New Zealand divides into three parts - Trout, Salmon and Big Game angling.

Trout, both brown and rainbow, were introduced about 100 years ago and have long been fully distributed on both islands. Rainbow predominate in the North Island, and browns in the South, but many waters have a mixture of the two in varying proportions.

The main areas in the North are centred on **Lake Taupo** and the **Rotorua** district with its group of important lakes. The rivers flowing into and out of these lakes are also noted fisheries, particularly late in the season when the main runs commence. The **Tongariro**, **Waitahanui**, **Tauranga-Taupo** and others flow into Lake Taupo, while in the Rotorua area there are the **Kaituna**, **Ohau Channel**, **Ngongotaha**, and the **Motu**, which is the best dry fly river in New Zealand. The summer trout fishing season runs from Oct to Apr in most districts. Winter trout fishing is found in the Taupo/Rotorua regions, with Apr/May. Sept/Oct the best months. May to Oct is the best time for the Tongariro. The top dry fly fishing in the more remote areas of the North Island is best Nov/Apr inclusive.

The South Island has thousands of miles of rivers and streams, and numerous lakes of all sizes. It was once calculated, at the turn of the century, that there are 17,000 miles of river fishing in New Zealand, and of course it is all open to the public, subject only to right of access and to reasonable accessibility. The best time for trout fishing in South Island is from Oct to May.

Good trout fishing is widely spread, and large trout can still be caught within an hour's drive of the main cities, but obviously many of the best waters are more remote and some are seldom fished, although helicopter or floatplane services operate out of the towns of **Queenstown**, **Wanaka** and **Te Anau** to reach places like **Lakes Alabaster** and **McKerrow**, or the **Pyke** and **Hollyford** rivers for example.

The main, and also the lesser, rivers of **Southland** and **Otago** provinces offer excellent dry fly and nymph fishing for brown trout, and fish of from 12-15lbs are caught each season, but a good average would be from 3-4lbs. Guide services are again easily found, although obviously concentrated somewhat in the more popular areas. An Angling Guides Association was formed some time ago, all professional guides are licensed, and are fully supported with 4-wheel drive vehicles and boats as necessary for their local areas.

In general, the open season is from Oct 1 until the end of April (North Island - 1 Oct to end of June) but some waters open early to take advantage of the runs of whitebait which provide feed for sea-run trout, while others, principally in the Taupo and Rotorua areas, stay open all the year, particularly the lower reaches of the larger streams feeding Lake Taupo, Rotorua and Wakatiou themselves. Regulations vary throughout the twenty-six fishing districts, but fishing usually starts at 5 a.m. and finishes at midnight on any day. Generally fly only on all rivers and streams flowing into lakes (no spin rod, and fly and bubble). Fly only includes the area within 300m radius from the point where a stream joins a lake. Streams flowing from lakes or mountains to the sea are generally open to all methods. With the exception of Lake Taupo, which requires a local licence, licences apply in any area of New Zealand, and are obtainable from guides, shops, petrol stations, visitor centres &c. The cost ranges from about NZ$21 per day to season, NZ$105. A few rivers also require a special back-country on controlled fishing licence.

Salmon, the Pacific Quinnat or King Salmon, introduced to the main **Canterbury** rivers, are fished for in about eight of them, the main ones being the **Waimakariri**,

Rakaia, **Ashburton**, **Rangitata** and **Waitaki**. Best between mid December and late April, the fishing is mainly heavy spinning, with spoons most favoured as lures, in the lower rivers, estuaries and even in the surf at the mouths. A certain amount of fly fishing, using very large lures or flies, is done upriver, notably in the **Rakaia Gorge** area. In all the salmon rivers the fish are mostly in the 10-20lb class, but are sometimes caught as large as 40lbs. The rivers are often unfishable for many days at a time due to cloudy glacial melt water, and trips undertaken with salmon exclusively in mind are not to be recommended. Season: 1st October to 30th April. Licence costs as for trout.

Coarse fishing: there is very good coarse fishing to be had in the areas of Greater Auckland and Waikato (around Hamilton), and the Greater Wellington and Christchurch areas. Large rudd, perch, tench, are caught regularly. Other species include eels, goldfish, and koi carp. There is no close season for this, and no charge, just the permission of the owner required, and a licence fee of $21. All coarse tackle has to be bought from overseas, however.

Big Game Fishing: the main bases for this are **Russell, Paihia** and **Whangerei** in the **Bay of Islands**, and also out from **Bay of Plenty**, and from **Tauranga** to the **Mayor Island** area. There are ample charter boats, with professional skippers and hands, based in these places, catering for parties of up to four anglers. The tackle and bait are provided in the charter. Main species caught are striped, Pacific blue, and black marlin, broadbill, mako, thresher and hammerhead shark, yellowfin tuna, yellowtail, and are taken with natural bait or lure. The southern part of the West Coast of the South Island, known as 'Fiordland', is now assuming increased importance for big game fishing. Boats are now based there, at Milford Sound and elsewhere.

Big Game angling is mainly from January to the end of April, with the period from mid-February on offering fine sport.

Licences are needed for trout and salmon fishing. There is a special Tourist Licence which covers the whole country and is only sold at the Tourism Rotorua Information Office in Rotorua. Alternatively licences may be purchased from other districts which allow the visitor to fish in any district with the exception of Rotorua and Taupo, separate licences being needed for these two districts. Rods may be brought freely into the country, although airport agriculture officials may want to fumigate flies made with real feathers.

For further information and advice on angling in New Zealand, contact **New Zealand Professional Fishing Guides Association Inc, PO Box 213, 295 Gladstone Rd, Gisborne** (tel: +64 6 877874, fax: +64 6 867 1563, email: secretary@fishingguides.co.nz; web: www.fishingguides.co.nz) or **New Zealand Tourism Board, New Zealand House, The Haymarket, London SW1Y 4TQ** (tel: 020 7939 1662; fax: 020 7839 8929; web: www.newzealand.com). Useful web sites: **The New Zealand Fish & Game Council** (web: www.fishnhunt.co.nz); **Fish & Game New Zealand** (web: www.fishandgame.org.nz); **Ministry of Agriculture & Forestry (MAF)** for quarantine requirements regarding your equipment (web: www.maf.govt.nz).

INDIA

One of the big attractions for the fisherman in India - in more senses than one - is the mighty mahseer. Mahseer country stretches between the Hindu Kush-Kabul-Kohistan watershed in the west all the way to the eastern tributaries of the **Brahmapurta**. It is found in some rivers in the Deccan plateau region and the River Kaveri in the south central plain region of **Karnataka**. Mahseer is essentially a migratory fish, running up and into side streams for spawning, at heights of up to 2000 metres during the monsoon. The fish avoids very cold water and therefore frequents the lower portion of the Himalayan streams during winter. Fish breeds three times a year, Jan-Feb, May-June, July-Sept, the peak season. The big ones are generally landed when returning from the breeding grounds when they chase shoals of minnows.

The mahseer can be taken on a spoon, but strong tackle is essential. It not only runs large - the biggest caught on rod and line weighed 119lbs (Cauvery River, South India, 1919) - but is a splendid fighter. The sport has, in fact, been compared most favourably with salmon fishing.

Mahseer are generally found in the rivers of the Terai regions of the Himalayas, the Shivalik Hills in the north, and the river **Kaveri** in the south. The following river stretches have been specifically cited as mahseer fishing areas, and are accessible for accommodation or camping: **River Jhelum** (J & K), below the Wular lake on the Sopore-Rampur stretch 80 kms from Srinagar. (Permits from J&K Fisheries Dept. in Srinagar). **River Beas** (Himachal Pradesh and Punjab), from Dehra Gopipur up to the Pong Dam reservoir; Below Pong Dam at Talwara (Punjab); Harike barrage on the Ferozpur Road. (Permits from Fisheries Officer at Dehra, or Director Fisheries, Palampur). Best seasons Feb-May, Sept-Nov. **River Ganga**, stretch above Tehri (10 km); Beashgat, and Gangalehri. (Permits from UP Fisheries Dept., Dehra Dun). **River Bhoroli** (Arunachal), 60 km from Tezpur, the river is fished between Tipee and Bhalukpong, as it flows through the Balipara reserved forest. Inflatable raft recommended. (Permits from Fisheries Officer, Tezpur). **River Manas** (Assam), Located in the famous Manas wildlife sanctuary. (Permits from Fisheries Officer, Gauhati - foreign nationals require restricted area permits from the Ministry of Home Affairs to visit this area). **River Kaveri** (Karnataka), $2\frac{1}{2}$ hours by road from Bangalore. Mahseer of 43 kgs landed here on 20 Jan, 1985. (Permits from Karnataka Fisheries Dept, Bangalore).

Kashmir is renowned for sport with brown and rainbow trout, which have thrived since they were introduced at the turn of the century. The snow trout is found in high altitude waters. The many streams in the area are regularly stocked from two large hatcheries and are divided into 'beats' of about two miles. Each beat has a local *shikari* or guide, and a watcher from the Fisheries Dept supervises a few beats. (Permits from Director, Game & Fisheries at Srinagar). Great variety is to be found, the rivers ranging from foaming torrents, when spinning is permitted, to gentle streams suitable for dry fly. There are 'fly only' beats. The most suitable flies are those usually included in every angler's selection, but in Kashmir they are usually dressed on hook sizes between No. 9 and No. 5 (old sizes). The season lasts from May to September. The major trout waters in Kashmir are as follows: **River Sindh**, flows along main Srinagar highway. Wide and shallow in places, upper beats are deep and narrow. Fishing early or late in the day is recommended; **River Lidder**, originates north of Pahalgam, and has two major tributaries, the **Aru** and the **Sheshnag**. excellent trout fishing, also for 'chush', a local species of bartel (inedible). Pahalgam is a convenient base for the system; **River Bringhi**, runs along the Anatnag-Dakshum road, beyond Acchabal. Narrow and boulder strewn, it has always been a great favourite with anglers. Three tributaries are the Dyus, Naubaug, and the Alhan. **Kokernag** and **Verinag** streams, springfed waters in the Kashmir valley, have easily accessible bank fishing, with good sized brown trout. There are a number of high altitude lakes in the north of the valley, well stocked with large brown trout. The average size of these waters is around 3000 sq meters, and they are only approachable by three-day treks, with camping necessary. Amongst these are lakes **Tarsar, Marsar**, approached from Pahalgam; **Kishensar, Vishensar, Gadsar** and **Gangabal**, approachable from Sonmarg, Gund or Nichnai.

India's rivers contain numerous other species. The **Jamuna** at **Okhla**, in **Delhi**, for instance, holds no fewer than eight species, including heavy catfish, the silund - a predator running up to 50lbs, which can be taken on a spinner - and a humpbacked fish called the cheetul or moh, which will be seen constantly rising to the surface and turning over broadside. There is also plenty of huge carp in the slow-flowing rivers and the lakes and tanks. The sea fishing can be excellent, too, but is dependent upon seasonal migrations and the weather. A considerable body of angling literature has now been published by the **Bombay Natural History Society** (web: www.bnhs.org; email: bnhs@bom4.vsni.net.in).

While the tourist-angler should not expect to find luxurious cabins on his expeditions, numerous camping-sites and comfortable rest-houses have been provided, often in the most beautiful surroundings and at **Corbett**, the call of the tiger and the trumpeting of wild elephants may sometimes be heard.

So far as tackle is concerned, the trout or mahseer fisherman will be specially well catered for at **Srinagar**, capital of Kashmir, where he may obtain first-class gear, but rates are rising due to restricted imports, and it is preferable to take one's own equipment.

Further information from the **Government of India Tourist Office, 7 Cork Street, London W1S 3LH** (tel: 020 7437 3677).

SRI LANKA

Nuwara Eliya is the best centre for trout fishing. As it is above the 6,000ft level, the climate is temperate. There is good hotel accommodation. The fishing is, with few exceptions, restricted to fly only and most common patterns of wet fly are successful. Dry fly is rarely used, there being little natural fly. There is no statutory close season, though the club imposes one in parts following restocking. Size limits vary from 8in to 15in.

The main waters are: **Nuwara Eliya** stream (flows through the golf course and park); **Ambawela** stream (8m from Nuwara Eliya; jungle and grassland); **Bulu Ella** stream (2 ½m jungle); **Portswood Dam** (4m; tea estate); **Agra Oya** and **Gorge Valley** rivers (10-15m; tea estates), and the magnificently spectacular **Horton Plains** stream (30m; jungle and grassland, Nature reserve). Motor transport can be hired. On any of these waters it is possible to maintain an average of 1lb and several fish over 3lbs are caught.

Trout fishing is now controlled by the Nuwara Eliya District Fishing Club. Stocking has so far been carried out in Portswood Dam, the Horton Plains, Agra Oya and Gorge Valley. For licences application should be made to the **Honorary Secretary, Nuwara Eliya District Fishing Club, Court Lodge Estate, Kandapola**. Visitors are advised to bring their tackle as fly tackle is scarce in Sri Lanka.

The two main species of indigenous sporting fish in Sri Lanka are the mahseer and the walaya (freshwater shark), found in the jungle rivers of the Low Country, particularly the **Mahawehi**, the upper reaches of the **Kelani** and the **Amban Ganga**. Ceylon mahseer, though small compared with those in some Indian rivers, provide good sport, but fishing for them can be somewhat difficult. Fishing for indigenous sporting fish in Sri Lanka is free. With a shoreline of 1,140 miles and a continental shelf of 10,000 square miles, the seas around Sri Lanka have an unlimited fishing potential hardly exploited.

The outfalls of 103 major river basins and hundreds of other estuaries, lagoons and coastal lakes all round the island are the most popular spots frequented by local surf casters as well as bait fishermen. Many varieties of game fish of the Carangid family, locally called paraw and know elsewhere as trevally, horse mackerel, etc, are taken. These swift and powerful carnivorous fish attain a length of 5ft and a weight of 150lbs. The schooling habits of the caranx, their keen eyesight and some built-in sensory mechanism make them congregate in estuaries immediately after monsoons and rains.

Next in popularity among surf-casters come the barracuda and Spanish mackerel. Both these species of voracious predatory fish attain lengths of 6ft as do other species known locally as 'giant perch', 'threadfins' and 'tassel fish' which frequent the estuaries.

Trolling over the continental shelf yields catches of tuna ranging from the 2-3ft skipjack to the 6ft yellowfin and bluefin, the acrobatic dolphin, swordfish and marlin which attain a size to provide a challenge to the best big game fishermen of any country. The broadbill swordfish found in deeper waters reach a length of 15ft and a weight of well over 1,000lbs. Though reaching only 10ft and 250lbs, the sailfish compensate for their smaller size by their remarkable agility.

The monsoons regulate the fishing in Sri Lanka Seas. The western and southern coasts are favoured during the North-East monsoon (from October to April) and the east coast during the South-West monsoon (from May to September).

Further information can be obtained from **London Director, Sri Lanka Tourist Board, 52 High Holborn, London WC1V 6RI'** (tel: 0845 880 6333 Ext 201; fax: 0845 880 6444; web: www.srilanka.travel; email: sanjika@srilanka.travel).

MALAYSIA

There is good sport in the jungle-covered highlands where fast-flowing, clean streams will delight the eye. These are well stocked with cyprinids or members of the carp family, which include the well-known mahseer of India, known locally as kelah. This group of which the most common species are kelah (up to 20lbs), sebarau (up to 12lbs), and kejor or tengas (up to 8lbs), are sporting fish which fight well when hooked. Kelah and tengas are good to eat. They are best when curried and provide a good change or diet in the jungle when living on operational 24-hour pack rations.

All these fish will take an artificial bait; the most popular being a 1in or 1½in silver or silver/copper spoon. A normal salmon spinning outfit is ideal. For those who prefer it, a fixed-spool reel can be used provided it will hold sufficient line. Owing to the crushing power of the jaws of the kelah, extra strong treble or large single hooks should be used and some people recommend the use of a 2ft wire trace.

Taman Negara, on the borders of **Kelantan**, **Trengganu** and **Pahang**, provides the best fishing, and a visit to the HQ at **Kuala Tahan** is well worth the journey. It may be reached by rail to **Kuala Tembeling** and thence by water, in long, narrow, locally-built boats fitted with 40hp outboard motors which can do the journey up the **Sungaï**

Tembeling in three to four hours depending on the condition of the river. At Kuala Tahan there are bungalows and chalets providing full board. A number of visitors' lodges and halting bungalows have been built throughout the park so the fishermen can stay near the river they are fishing.

From Kuala Tahan all onward movement is by smaller boats with lower-powered engines to negotiate the shallower rivers, such as the Tahan itself. There are many large pools well stocked with fish in the lower reaches, and above the **Lata Berkoh** barrier many pools and rapids, all excellent fishing water. Malay and Aborigine boatmen are happy to act as guides and are delightful companions.

It is easier and pleasanter to cast from the bank, but this will necessitate some wading where the bank is steep and overhung by the jungle. The water is pleasantly warm and waders would be far too hot to wear. Those with a good sense of balance can try fishing from a slowly paddled perahu, but as this is only a shell at the most 2ft wide, it is liable to be something of a circus act.

Most reliable times to fish are the months February/March and July/August, because in other months fishing will be spasmodic owing to the heavy rainfall. Spates and floodwater so colour the rivers that fishing is a waste of time.

In **Terengganu State** is the massive **Kenyir Lake,** a well known attraction to visiting anglers, where baung, toman, sebarau, kelah, kelisa (arowana) can be caught, and houseboat holidays are organised: for information contact **Kenyir Lake Resort & Spa, PO Box 32, 21700 Kuala Berang, Terengganu Darul Imam** (tel: +609 666 888; fax +609 666 8343; email: resort@lakekenyir.com; see website for more info: www.lakekenyir.com), for **Kenyir Dam** area.

Apart from the fishing there is always the chance of seeing the wild animals of Malaysia at the many salt licks. There are usually monkeys, monitor lizard, snakes and flying foxes to be seen, as well as many varieties of birds such as hornbill eagle and kingfishers.

The Kelah Fish Sanctuary is situated at the **Tahan River**, in the heart of Taman Negara which offers a guided fishing experience in one of the world's oldest tropical rainforests.

Intending visitors should write well before the date of their visit, giving as much information as possible on their special interests to the **Director-General, Dept of Wildlife and National Parks, KM10, Jalan Cheras, 56100 Kuala Lumpur, Malaysia** (tel: +3 9086 6800; fax: +3 907 52873; web: www.wildlife.gov.my) so as to enable the Dept of Wildlife & National Parks to plan their itineraries or contact **Malaysia Tourism Promotion Board, 57 Trafalgar Square, London WC2N 5DU** (tel: 020 7930 7932; email: info@tourism-malasia.co.uk; web: www.tourismmalaysia.gov.my).

FISHING IN NORTH AMERICA

CANADA

On the Atlantic side of Canada there are plenty of salmon rivers in **Québec** and **New Brunswick**, and a good deal of fishing is open to the non-resident who takes out the appropriate provincial licence. There is a great deal of splendid trout fishing in many of the inland lakes and rivers, while in the **Great Lakes** region there are big muskellunge, and fine black bass fishing in various waters. The land-locked salmon is found in Québec, both in the tributaries and discharge of **Lac St John**, and in some lakes in **Nova Scotia**, such as **Grand Lake** and **Beaver Bank Lake**. The 'trout' of this side of Canada are charr *(Salvelinus fontinalis),* while some of them are migratory and become 'sea trout'. In the lakes are 'grey trout', some of which reach a great size. There are also charr *(Salvelinus namaycush)* in the Arctic.

On the other side of Canada, British Columbia offers splendid opportunities of sport with Pacific salmon, steelhead and rainbow trout. Fishing for Pacific salmon has until recently been considered of necessity a matter for tidal waters. The **Campbell River**, **Vancouver Island**, has been the most favoured, and there quinnat (now known locally as tyee) up to 70lbs have been caught on the troll. At **Prince Rupert** a 93lbs quinnat was caught on a spoon in 1929 by Mr O P Smith, a professional fisherman. An 82lbs tyee was caught in August, 1951, at **Rivers Inlet**. The coho has been caught on fly, also in tidal waters. Of late years it has become clear that quinnat will take in fresh water in certain conditions. To the far north there are evident possibilities of sport in **Yukon** and NW Territories.

So far as tackle is concerned, the trend is towards lighter outfits. Brook trout, for instance, are almost universally taken on a nine-foot, five-ounce fly rod, and many anglers use the same rod for steelhead or Kamloops trout, although this is probably foolhardy. Tackle should always be carefully geared to the area and quarry, and on-the-spot advice is desirable.

Much work is done by the Federal and Provincial hatcheries, and waters in various parts of Canada are supplied with fry of species suitable to their needs, chiefly salmonidae, but also bass and other kinds of the best big game fishing so far discovered anywhere.

Throughout Canada there are many regulations controlling all aspects of freshwater fishing, which vary from one province to another. Information on these laws is readily obtainable from a large number of public outlets.

Note: The Canadian Tourist Office has provincial brochures and general information relevant to fishing in the country. For further information please contact **Visit Canada, P O Box 170, Ashford, Kent TN24 0ZX** (tel: 0870 (0906 871 5000 960p/min); web: www.travelcanada.ca; email: visitcanada@dial.pipex.com).

ALBERTA

Alberta is fortunate in having more than 4,000 miles of good fishing streams and more than 1,000 lakes found in the mountains, foothills and prairies, and in the boreal forests of the northern region of the province.

There are 18 species of sportfish in Alberta of which there are 9 cold water and 9 warm water sportfish. The cold water sportfish include brook, brown, cutthroat, golden, rainbow, and lake trout, bull trout, Arctic grayling and mountain whitefish. These fish are generally found in the lakes and streams in the foothills and mountain areas in the west of the province.

The warm water sportfish include lake whitefish, walleye, perch, pike, goldeye, and lake sturgeon. These fish are generally found in rivers and lakes throughout the south east and northern areas of the province.

Since the 1960s, the numbers of anglers fishing in Alberta has increased dramatically from 150,000 to peak nearly 350,000 in 1986. Subsequently, the numbers of anglers has declined and stabilised at between 225-250,000. Perch, pike, walleye, trout, and lake whitefish are the most widely taken fish, accounting to 95% of total harvest but pike fishing is predominant. Fewer than half Alberta's lakes can produce game fish, owing to a short summer season when warm water temperatures produce sufficient aquatic insects, plants, and other food, and the supply of fish is supplemented by stocking. Hatchery production of 3.5 million trout are stocked annually throughout the province into lakes that do not contain native fish and which are readily accessible to the public.

As throughout Canada, there are many fishing regulations, which the angler must know before setting out. Licences are obligatory, and obtainable in most retail sports outfitters. Prices are as follows: Youths (under 16), none required. Non residents annual, C$40; limited (3 day), C$30;(1 day); youths under 16 years: no permit required.

Further information may be obtained by writing to **Alberta Sustainable Resource Development, Fisheries & Wildlife Division, 2nd Floor, Great West Life Building, 9920-108 Street, Edmonton, AB T5K 2M4** (tel: +1 780 944 0313; web: www.srd.alberta.ca; email: srd infocent@gov.ab.ca).

BRITISH COLUMBIA

The province has a coastline (including islands) of 27,000 km and is drained by innumerable rivers and freshwater lakes. The game fish of British Columbia comprise five species of salmon: sockeye, chum, chinook or spring (large specimens often referred to as 'Tyee'), pink (tidal waters only), and coho, which may be taken with the fly, but are more easily caught by trolling; all varieties of Pacific Coast trout, particularly steelhead, rainbow, and cut-throat; Arctic grayling; two species of char, of which the more common is Dolly Varden; and Eastern brook trout which has been introduced.

Some of the most important freshwater fishing areas are **Kootenay District, Okanagan District** (including **Beaver, Bear, Dee, Ideal, Mabel, Sugar, South** and **Woods Lakes), Kamloops District** (including **Adams, East Barriere, Murtle, Shuswap** and **Nicola Lakes), Cariboo District** (including **Quesnel, Horsefly** and **Canim Lakes,** and **Fraser** and **Thompson Rivers**), and **Merrit District**, which abounds with small productive, accessible lakes, such as **Chataway, Dot, Gypsum, Antler, Corbett, Peter Hope** and **Roche Lakes**. Most of the southern lakes and rivers are easily accessible, especially by car, and yield excellent fishing. Flying in to the less accessible waters is now a common practice. Lodges, cabins and boats are abundant.

The **Skeena Region** of northwest **British Columbia** has a wide variety of attractive fisheries. The **Burns Lake** area boasts a number of great trout fishing lakes, and **Terrace** is the centre of exceptional sport fishing for steelhead trout and chinook and coho salmon. Some restrictions apply on certain steelhead waters as conservation is a priority. Information may be obtained from the Victoria address below.

Vancouver Island offers excellent cut-throat trout and steelhead fishing. The important waters are **Cowichan, Cameron** and **Sproat Lakes, Alberni** and **Qualicum Districts** and the **Campbell River** area. Steelhead trout are in **Sproat, Somass, Ash** and **Stamp Rivers,** to name but a few. Chinook (or spring) salmon and coho are found in good quantities in many of the main rivers and streams draining into the Pacific Ocean. On Vancouver Island there is splendid salmon fishing in tidal water to be had near the following cities: **Campbell River, Comox, Nanaimo, Gold River, Port Alberni, Tofino, Ucluelet** and **Victoria.** On the mainland excellent fishing for salmon is to be found within 20 minutes drive from downtown Vancouver. Other famous salmon fishing locations include: **Pender Harbour, Powell River, Hakai Pass, Rivers Kitimat, Prince Rupert** and the **Queen Charlotte Islands,** including Langara Island. For the sea angler, charter boats operate from Prince Rupert Island, and halibut are plentifully found, among other species.

Salmon conservation: a salmon conservation stamp must be purchased ($6.30) before fishing to keep a salmon of any legal size or species (except) kokanee) from non-tidal waters (this does not apply to c&r); catches of adult chinook salmon must be recorded on the back of the basic angling licence. Due to conditions which are subject to change at short notice, it is no longer possible to publish daily limits or size limits for any of the five species of salmon. Before fishing contact nearest DFO office.

Licences are obligatory, and obtainable in most retail sports outfitters. For freshwater licence fees and supporting information, visit the **British Columbian Government's website: www.fishing.gov.bc.ca**. For saltwater fishing, contact: Department of Fisheries and Oceans Canada, web: www.pac.dfo-mpo.gc.ca. For travel information, contact **British Columbia Tourism, British Colombia House, 3 Regent St, 3rd Floor, London SW1Y 4NS** (tel: 020 7930 6857 Ext 203; web: www.hellobc.co.uk.

MANITOBA

Manitoba is at the centre of a country more than 4,500 miles wide, from **St John's, Newfoundland** on the east to **Victoria, British Columbia** on the west.

The province is enormous by British standards, covering 250,000 square miles and measuring 735 air miles from north to south. Lake Winnipeg, 40 miles north of the capital city of **Winnipeg**, is the seventh largest inland body of freshwater in North America. The northern three-fifths of the province is laced with innumerable streams and rivers, and someone claims to have counted more than 100,000 lakes, although many are too small to even appear on a map.

The species most commonly fished are walleye, pike, channel catfish, lake trout, rainbow trout, brook (speckled) trout, arctic grayling, whitefish, smallmouth bass, lake sturgeon, goldeye (superior to eat, smoked), and carp. Trout fishing is some of the finest in North America, in particular, the **Knife** and **Gods Rivers** in north-eastern Manitoba are famous for trophy-sized brook and lake trout, northern pike and walleye. Lake trout *(Cristivomer namaycush)* are widely distributed from the south-eastern area of the province through to the northern boundaries in the deep, cold-water lakes of the Pre-Cambrian shield. Specimens over 35lbs are taken each year.

The Arctic grayling *(Thymallus arcticus)* is common along the north-western coast of Hudson Bay and its tributary streams, which include the **North Knife, Seal, Little Seal** and **Wolverine Rivers**. With its spectacular beauty, it is the delight of those fly-fishermen who are able to travel to the Churchill area or the fly-in areas of **Big Sand, Knee, Nueltin** or **Nejanilini Lakes** in the far North.

Other fish. In the smaller lakes and streams in the southern part of the province, walleye, northern pike and yellow perch are plentiful. In **Lake Winnipeg** and the tributary **Red River**, carp and channel catfish to 30lbs are taken in large numbers at certain seasons. **Winnipeg River** is the locale for large walleye, and great northern pike, together with an abundance of smallmouth bass, which provide excellent sport.

Large numbers of lakes throughout the province are stocked for trout fishing. As elsewhere in Canada, ice fishing is a popular winter sport, often with shelters. Holiday sport is well organised, with many fishing lodges offering packages with accommodation and other facilities.

Licences are required, and obtainable in most retail sports outfitters. There are two types of licence (a) conservation licence for anglers who keep reduced limits of fish (b) regular licence. Fees include the &% GST.

regular licence $57.12; conservation $32.59; youths under 16 years do not require a licence. There are many fishing regulations in Manitoba, including a complete ban on barbed hooks, prohibition of open fires from 1 Apr to 15 Nov, and bait restrictions, including the number of live baits permissable. Anglers should know all details before starting out. Fishing in the province is governed by **The Manitoba Government Water Stewardship, Head Office, 333 #450 Broadway, Winnipeg, Manitoba, R3C 0V8** (tel: +1 204 945 3730; web: www.gov.mb.ca/waterstewardship/fisheries), and their 6 other offices.

Further information (including details of licence charges and open seasons) can be had from www.manitobafisheries.com.

NEW BRUNSWICK

Atlantic salmon in the **Restigouche, Nepisiquit, Tabusintac, North-West Miramichi, South-West Miramichi, Little South-West Miramichi, Sevogle, Renous, Dungarvon, Cains** rivers. Salmon run large, particularly in the Restigouche, where fish from 30-40lbs are taken each year, and occasionally larger. Other rivers include **Rocky Brook, Clearwater Brook, St John River, Nashwaak** and **Tobique** rivers. New Brunswick rivers usually yield over 30,000 fish each season. Conservation methods such as hook and release are used, to ensure future stocks, and fishing is fly only. Non-residents are required to employ a guide while fishing for Atlantic salmon or any other species on Atlantic salmon waters. Only grilse, fish less than 63cm in fork length, are allowed to be retained. The season varies from river to river, but generally runs from 16 May to 15 Oct. Licences are required, and obtainable from most outfitters. Seasonal prices range from C$149.50 per season to C$40.25 for 3 days, covering all species. Non-residents licences for all species except Atlantic salmon range cost C$57.50 per season to C$23.00 for 3 consecutive days. (Updated information on angling regulations and licence information can be viewed on the website below.)

In addition to salmon fishing, there is fishing for small-mouth bass in the south-west of the province. Several waters yield good-sized fish, and these are considered to be some of the best bass resources in North America. Other popular angling pursuits include spring Atlantic salmon, brook trout and land locked salmon. On the seashore, jigging for cod, casting for mackerel, and deepsea fishing are possible at some locations along the coast. Angling for striped bass occurs in the St John River and Bathhurst Harbour.

Non-resident licences must be obtained from a DNR or Service New Brunswick office in the province. These must be carried by the holder at all times, but do not convey right of fishing on Crown Reserve Waters or any private fishery without the consent of the lessee or owner. Further information, including details of licences and open seasons, can be had from the **Department of Natural Resources, Fish & Wildlife Branch, PO Box 6000, Fredericton NB E3B 5H1** (tel: +1 506 453 2440; web: www.gnb.ca/0254/Index-e.asp. Outfitters may be contacted via **Business New Brunswick, 5th Floor, 670 King Street, Fredericton NB, E3B 1G1** (tel: +1 506 453 3707; web: www.gnb.ca/0398/index-e.asp).

NEWFOUNDLAND and LABRADOR

Newfoundland and Labrador, Canada, has probably some of the best game-fishing in North America. Almost a quarter of the province's area is water, and its many fine wild Atlantic salmon rivers flow through unspoiled forest and hill country. Fishable waterways vary from wide and roaring rivers to intimate brooks tumbling down from highland plateaus; the **Sandhill River**, the famous **Eagle River**, the **Flowers River**, **Gander River**, the **Exploits River** and the **Humber River** to name but a few. Newfoundland and Labrador is home to nearly two-thirds of North America's Atlantic salmon rivers - more than two hundred rivers, some with annual runs in excess of 20,000 wild fish. Anglers can fish everything from Trophy Brook trout and land-locked salmon (Ouananiche) to wilder cousins such as lake trout, northern pike and arctic char. Eastern brook trout can run in excess of 9 lbs. and Arctic charr approaching 20lbs have been caught. Sea-run brown trout streams in the province are mainly concentrated along a 100-kilometre coastal area immediately south of St. John's, the capital city; where fish over 20lbs have been taken. Scheduled (licensed) rainbow trout waters comprise a small group of steams and ponds immediately north of St. John's; rainbows are also frequently caught in unscheduled water throughout the province. All the trout except the brown trout are as plentiful (and on average significantly larger) in Labrador where most angling waters are much more remote than that on the Island portion of the province.

The salmon season varies among groups of rivers and from year to year, ranging from early June to mid-September, with most rivers open from mid-June to the first week in September, fishing is restricted to fly only. Scheduled rainbow trout waters are open from late May-early June to mid-September. The province has scheduled salmon rivers on the Island of Newfoundland and in Labrador, and scheduled rainbow trout streams.

Fishing in all inland waters in the province is restricted to rod, hook, and line, with a variety of baits and lures permissable in most unscheduled waters; angling in scheduled salmon rivers is further restricted to fly fishing only. The province has scheduled salmon rivers on the Island of Newfoundland and in Labrador, and scheduled rainbow trout streams. Fishing in all inland waters in the province is restricted to rod, hook, and line, with a variety of baits and lures permissible on most unscheduled waters. Angling on scheduled salmon rivers is restricted to fly fishing only, using only barbless hooks. There are bag limits in force which vary, depending on a river's classification; on Class 1 rivers, 4 salmon may be retained; on Class 2 rivers, which are the large majority, 2 fish; on Class 3 rivers, 2 fish; on Class 4 rivers, catch and release only. Current regulations require that a non-resident must either be accompanied by a resident relative, a licensed guide or in parts of Labrador, engage the services of an outfitter.

Annual licence fees for non-residents are as follows. Salmon: $C53, $53 family; Trout $C8 $C8 family. Special licences are required to fish inland waters within the boundaries of National Parks and anglers should consult with park officials regarding their fishing regulations. Salmon and trout angling licences are obtainable at most sporting goods shops, outfitters, tackle and hardware shops and some department stores. Further information on non-resident angling is available from **Department of Tourism, Culture and Recreation, Tourism Division, P.O. Box 8700, St. John's, Newfoundland, Canada A1B 4J6** (tel: +1 709 729 0862); fax: +1 709 729 0870; email: tcrinfo@gov.nl.ca; web: www.newfoundlandlabrador.com). For a listing of fishing outfitters, go to the Newfoundland and Labrador Outfitters Association website at www.nloa.ca

NOVA SCOTIA (including Cape Breton Island)

Atlantic salmon in some rivers continue to have good runs of salmon but stock status, water levels and conditions are a major factor in the annual take. There are 16 rivers scheduled and posted for fly fishing only, but it should be noted Atlantic salmon may only be taken by fly; brook trout are common in streams and lakes, many of which are accessible from woods roads known as roads to resources; sea trout (brook and brown) in most tidal streams in the Northern and Eastern part of the province.

For the saltwater angler the province has 4,625 miles of shore, and over one hundred harbours and marinas dotted around the coast, mainly in areas of Victoria, Cape Breton, Richmond, Halifax, Lunenbourg, Yarmouth, Pictou, Antigonish, and Inverness. There is currently no saltwater/tidal water licensing for recreational fishing purposes. Species taken are cod, pollack, haddock, striped bass, flatfish, and from boats, bluefish, blue shark, tuna, dogfish, etc. Charter boats are hired for ground fishing in all areas except the upper reaches of the **Bay of Fundy**. Tuna charter boats operate in the **St George's Bay** and Halifax areas. Licence fees for non-residents are as follows: salmon: C$142.96 seasonal; C$57.48 7 day; trout C$57/84 seasonal; C$31.63 7 day. **Nova Scotia Fisheries and Aquaculture**'s website www.gov.ns.ca/fish/sportfishing/angling contains the latest Nova Scotia Anglers' Handbook which you can either view on line or download.

For further information on travelling to and around Nova Scotia, please contact **Nova Scotia Tourism & Culture, PO Box 456, Halifax, NS, B3J 2R5** (tel: +1 902 425 5781; fax: +1 902 424 2668; web: www.explore.gov.ns.ca; email: explore@gov.ns.ca); **Nova Scotia Salmon Association, P O Box 396, Chester NS BOJ 1JO** (web: www.novascotiasalmon.ns.ca; email: nssalmon@yahoo.ca.

ONTARIO

With over 250,000 inland lakes, thousands of streams and rivers, and shorelines on four of the five Great Lakes, Ontario offers a wide diversity of angling opportunities. Although probably best known for its trophy muskellunge waters and highly sought walleye (pickerel) fisheries, Ontario is home to an astounding 158 of Canada's 228 species of freshwater fish.

Brook Trout: Ontario boasts more than 2,100 inland lakes and at least 1,700 streams and rivers which support brook trout. Some of the more popular areas for brook trout anglers include the **Lake Nipigon** watershed, the Algoma area of northeastern Ontario, and the southcentral Ontario highlands including **Algonquin Park** and the **Muskoka lakes** area. In addition to these native populations, Ontario has an active brook trout stocking program comprised of approximately 1.3-1.4 million fish being released annually. The world record brook trout (14.5lbs, 6.6kg) was caught in the **Nipigon River** . A colour variant of the brook trout, known as the Aurora trout, is found in several northeastern Ontario lakes which are open to provide limited angling opportunities. Included among the many other waters are the **Haliburton** and **Hastings** highlands and the **Magnetawan** area; farther south and west, some streams tributary to

Lakes Huron, Erie, Ontario and **Georgian Bay**. Lying between the eastern and western areas of northern Ontario there are numerous brook trout waters, among which are the **Sudbury, Manitoulin, Sault, Michipicoten, Mississauga, Gogama, Chapleau, Missinabi-White River-Franz, Elsas, Oba, Hornepayne, Hearst, Kapuskasing, Nakina** and **Albany** River areas.

Bass: largemouth and smallmouth bass are among the most popular sport fish species in Ontario with largemouth bass primarily in the southern portion of the province (south of the French River); smallmouth bass are more broadly distributed across the province. The Ontario record largemouth bass was a fish weighing 10.4lbs (4.7 kg) while the current record for smallmouth bass is 9.8lbs (4.5kg). Most bass angled from Ontario waters would average between 1-3lbs (0.5-1.4kg) however. Some popular bass areas include **Long Point Bay (Lake Erie), Rideau lakes** in southeastern Ontario, the **Trent-Severn** waterway and **Kawartha lakes** of southcentral Ontario, and **Lake of the Woods** in northwestern Ontario. Other areas include **Haliburton Lake District, Muskoka lakes, Lake Nipissing,** the **French** and **Pickerel rivers,** and the Georgian Bay District areas. In the north-west section of Ontario bass are found in **Quetico Provincial Park**.

Muskellunge and Northern Pike : two closely related species, are common in Ontario waters. Northern pike are distributed across the province while muskellunge are concentrated in the northwestern and southcentral portions of Ontario. There are waters which are managed to provide trophy fisheries for each species and there are many other waters where opportunities exist to catch numerous, but smaller, fish. Some of the world class muskellunge waters include **Georgian Bay**, the mouth of the **Moon River,** the **Lake of the Woods, Lac Seul, Ottawa** and **St. Lawrence Rivers,** and **Eagle Lake**. The Ontario record muskellunge was a 65lb (29.5kg) fish angled from Georgian Bay. The **Kawartha lakes,** and many smaller lakes in northwestern Ontario, provide popular muskellunge fisheries. Trophy northern pike are found in many remote northern Ontario lakes while many other waters across the province provide good angling for pike.

Carp: rapidly becoming more popular in Ontario, particularly among non-resident anglers from Europe, they achieve weights of up to 35-50lbs (15.8-22.7kg) but are more commonly in the 10-20lbs (4.5-9.0 kg) range. There is a year-round season for carp in Ontario, and some of the more popular waters for carp angling include Lake Erie, the **Bay of Quinte,** the **Trent-Severn** and **Rideau** canal systems, and the **Long Sault Parkway** portion of the St. Lawrence River.

Rainbow Trout and Brown Trout: while neither rainbow trout nor brown trout are native to Ontario, both have been introduced and have successfully established self-sustaining populations throughout the Great Lakes and their tributary streams. Rainbow trout fishing is booming in southern Georgian Bay especially in the **Owen Sound-Collingwood** area and is popular in many tributaries along the north shore of Lake Ontario in the **Port Hope** area. Rainbow trout fishing is best either in the spring or fall; brown trout are found in nearshore areas of the Great Lakes and can easily be caught fishing from shore. Once again, Lake Ontario and Lake Huron provide the best fishing locations. The province of Ontario stocks approximately 7-800,000 brown trout annually. There are designated areas (river mouths) which have extended angling seasons for these two species. Many south-western Ontario streams also provide excellent fly fishing opportunities for stream-resident brown trout.

Pacific Salmon: three species of Pacific salmon (coho, chinook and pink) have been successfully introduced into the Great Lakes. Open water angling for chinook salmon is best in mid-late summer; chinook salmon have reached sizes up to 45lbs (20.4kg) but are more commonly in the 10-20lbs (4.5-9.0kg) range. **Lakes Ontario** *(Port Credit-Niagara area)* and **Huron** provide the best chinook salmon fisheries in Ontario. Coho salmon are stocked in Lake Ontario and provide some good fall angling opportunities in several tributary streams. Pink salmon are most common in Lake Superior and the North Channel of Lake Huron and are most readily fished in the fall.

Splake: a cross between lake trout and brook trout (speckled trout), approximately 800,000 splake are stocked annually into inland lakes across the province to provide recreational angling opportunities. They are relatively easy to catch and are delicious to eat. There is good splake fishing at **Owen Sound, Parry Sound** and at **Providence Bay** on **Manitoulin Island**.

Walleye: without doubt, the most highly sought fish in Ontario. There are well over 4,000 lakes and hundreds of rivers which contain walleye. Some of the more popular angling locations for walleye include the **Bay Quinte** (Lake Ontario), **Kesagami Lake, Lake Nipissing, Lac des Milles Lakes,** Lake Erie, and Lake of the Woods. There are many remote (fly-in) angling opportunities particularly in northwestern Ontario. Walleye are angled during the open water season and also during the winter (ice) fishery, and are highly prized as a food fish. The Ontario record walleye was a fish weighing 22.3lbs (10.1 kg) but most angled walleye are in the 1-2 pound (0.5-1.0 kg) range. A close relative of the walleye - sauger - is known to occur in over 200 Ontario waters and are most common in northwestern Ontario.

Lake Trout: are found in more than 2,300 Ontario lakes and is highly prized by anglers and esteemed as a food fish. Lake trout live in deep cold lakes scattered across the **Precambrian Shield** and may be caught in nearshore waters in the spring, in deep waters during the summer, and through the ice in the winter. Some popular lake trout fisheries include **Lake Nipigon, Lake Superior, Lake Simcoe, Lake Ontario,** and **Lake Temagami**. Ontario stocks almost 5 million lake trout on an annual basis into various inland lakes as well as the Great Lakes.

Other Species: There are many other popular sport fish species in Ontario, which include lake whitefish, channel catfish, black crappies, bluegill and pumpkinseed (panfish), and bullheads. Information on angling locations for these species can be obtained by contacting the Ontario Ministry of Natural Resources.

There are more than 500 fish and game associations in the province, many of which are affiliated with the **Ontario Federation of Anglers and Hunters, P O Box 2800, Peterborough, Ontario K9J 8L5** (tel: +1 705 748 6324; fax: +1 705 748 9577; email: ofah@ofah.org; web: www.ofah.org). Other notable organizations include **Trout Unlimited, Muskies Canada Inc.**, and the **Ontario Federation of Fly Fishers**. For angling information, enquiries about non-resident fishing regulations, or to obtain a copy of the annual summary of fishing regulations, write to the **Ontario Ministry of Natural Resources Information Center, Whitney Block, #6630, 99 Wellesley Street West (6th floor), Toronto Ontario, Canada M7A 1W3** (tel: +1 416 314 2000; web: www.mnr.gov.on.ca.

PRINCE EDWARD ISLAND

This island, which lies in the Gulf of St Lawrence off the north coast of **Nova Scotia**, has an enviable reputation for its speckled trout fishing. The streams and rivers are spring fed, and the whole province may be considered a natural hatchery for trout and salmon. The salmon fishing, however, is not first class, and the best runs, with the exception of early runs on the **Morell** and **Trout Rivers**, do not begin until towards the end of the season. Both non-migratory and migratory trout are to be caught. Fishing for rainbow trout can be had in **Glenfinnan**, and **O'Keefe's Lakes**. Noted trout streams are the **West**, **Morell**, **Trout** and **Dunk** rivers, and large freshwater dams also afford good sport. Many estuaries contain white perch, and a few are home of the striped bass. During late summer and autumn, mackerel and smelt fishing is popular. There are bag limits of 10 trout per day, not more than 5 being rainbow, and one grilse per day, 7 per season. Salmon greater than 63 cm or less than 30 cm must be returned alive and unharmed. Trout season is from 15 April to 15 Sept. Salmon season on the Morell River begins 1 June and runs to 31 Oct. Salmon season is also extended to Oct 31 on certain stretches of Rivers Midgell, Naufrage, Valleyfield, West, Dunk, Mill. Rainbow trout season on Glenfinnan and O'Keefe's lakes, April 15 to November 15. Non-residents trout day licences cost $10 + GST, Atlantic salmon licence $10 + GST, a Wildlife Conservation Fund License. These are obtainable from sports outfitters or from **Department of Environment, Energy and Forestry**, Jones Building, 4th and 5th Floors, 11 Kent St, Charlottetown (tel: +902 368 5000; web: www.gov.pe.ca/enveng/ff aw-info).

Further information may be obtained from the **Tourism PEI** (website: www.peiplay.com) and **Department of Fisheries, Aquaculture & Environment, Fish & Wildlife Division, PO Box 2500, Charlottetown, PEI, C1A 7N8.**

QUÉBEC

Stretching over a vast expanse of territory, Québec boasts more than one million rivers and lakes. These waters teeming with fish offer the possibility of catching various species, including Northern pike, walleye, brook trout, Arctic char, landlocked salmon, lake trout, Atlantic salmon and bass. However, to fish in parks, wildlife reserves and ZECs (controlled zones), certain specific conditions apply over and above the general rules. In most parks and wildlife reserves, a reservation is required, and, just as for the ZECs, a right of access is emitted. Private firms offer outfitting services in Québec, including accommodation. Some hold exclusive fishing rights in specific areas. In Northern Québec, a right of access must be obtained from the Native authorities in question (Cree, Inuit, Naskapi) in order to fish in certain waters. On land under Inuit jurisdiction, fishermen must be accompanied by an Inuit guide. Any non-residents wishing to fish north of the 52nd parallel must use the services of an outfitter. Licence fees vary tremendously, depending on where and what is being fished for.

The **Société de la Faune et des Parcs du Québec (FAPAQ)** 880 Chemin Sainte-Foy, RC 120-C, Québec G1S 4X4; email: services.clientele@mrnf.gouv.ca; web: www.mrnf.gouv.qc.ca), determines the rules governing recreational fishing.

SASKATCHEWAN

Pike, perch and walleye are found throughout the province and represent the largest portion of the sport catch. Lake trout and arctic grayling are plentiful in the northern areas. Rainbow, brook, brown and lake trout are stocked in streams and lakes throughout the province. Current licence fee for those over 16 is $78.51 annual; $39.25 for 3-day.

For further information (including details of limits, accommodation, outfitters and guides) contact **Tourism Saskatchewan, 1922 Park Street, Regina, Saskatchewan S4N 7M4** (tel: +1 306 787 9600; web: www.sasktourism.com; tollfree: +1 877 237 2273) who also issue a guide free of charge. Tourism Saskatchewan has just launched a new fishing website (web: www.sasktourism.com/things-to-do/saskatchewan-fishing).

THE UNITED STATES OF AMERICA

The United States of America covers an enormous area of land and water space, offering everything between the near-Arctic conditions met in winter near the 49th parallel and the semi-tropical climate of Florida, Louisiana and Arizona, providing almost every conceivable environmental opportunity for freshwater or saltwater fish-species to exploit to their full advantage. This creates a great swathe of corresponding angling opportunities on such a scale that holidays spent fishing and camping in the backwoods have long been a commonplace of the American way of life as holidays on the coast - and, more recently, on the shores of the Mediterranean - have been of the British.

Such a demand compels a supply: and there is nowhere in the world where so sophisticated a blend of modern comfort and primitive atmosphere can be found at the waterside, made, as it were, to measure. And signs reading 'Keep out: fishing private' are not readily to be found in America. Apart from small lakes on private land immediately adjacent to private homes, the water and its inhabitants are the property of the community, managed expertly for the good of all by the community's public agencies. Fishing may not literally be 'free', but it is open to all with a few dollars to invest in recreation. The US population is four times Britain's; but the space open for it is ten times greater.

Because of the way in which, traditionally, exchange-rates and living costs have related, the USA has never in the past figured as a place where the adventurous British angler was likely to take a fishing holiday. All that though has now changed and it makes just as much sense, financially and otherwise, for an Englishman to holiday in **Tennessee**, fishing for large-mouth bass, or in **Minnesota** in search of *Esox masquinongy,* as for a Texan to come to Scotland to catch a Spey salmon. Going out from the **Florida Keys** in pursuit of marlin, sailfish or tarpon has for many years been a branch of the sport attracting a trickle of wealthy Britishers, but fishing American fresh waters has been a practice confined to angling writers and such, out to broaden their professional education.

Since it is the state geographically nearest to Britain, let us begin our review of the northern tier of states and their fishing with **Maine**, whose beaches offer the classical opportunity to contact the greatest of all saltwater sporting fish to be angled feasibly from the shore anywhere, the striped bass. Though scarcer now than in years gone by, unfortunately, there are still fine specimens to be taken by the persistent specialist surf-caster. Offshore, there are cod and pollack, the bluefin tuna, some of these registering on the beam-scale weights of more than 500lbs.

Inland, there is a multitude of wilderness lakes and streams offering sport with smallmouth bass, brown and rainbow trout and the unique native of Eastern North America, the brook trout, actually a fine handsome member of the charr family. Atlantic salmon which ran Maine's rivers by the ten thousand a hundred years ago suffered near-extermination, but are now being nursed back by conservation technology.

Moving west to the **Great Lakes,** thoughts turn back to another char, the 'lake trout', a fish which grows to great size in deep and cold water throughout this latitude and in Canada. One fishes for them in hopes of a 40-pounder. An attempt to pass over without comment the damage done to some waters, the Great Lakes included, by the consequences of unthinking industrialisation would be dishonest, but remedy is now the order of the day. None has been more spectacular in its success than the stocking of **Lake Michigan** with coho salmon from the Pacific shore. Here, a new and tremendously exciting sport-fishery has been created, as it were, out of nothing, based on a food-supply left uncropped by lake trout no longer present in sufficient numbers to preserve a natural balance. Most see that as a net gain. The coho gives better sport than the 'Mackinaw', as it is sometimes named farther north.

On to a state where water-area challenges land-space: **Minnesota**, as the North American Indian dialect-name implies, and the cream of the fishing for great northern pike (our pike), walleyes (resembling our zander) and the greatest lantern-jaw of them all, *Esox masquinongy,* the muskellunge or 'muskie'. While these predators are distributed throughout the region, Minnesota is the heartland. Muskies there may grow to 80lbs weight and leap like trout when hooked.

Passing through a varied landscape, some of it watered by trout streams, we arrive eventually among the foothills of the **Rockies**, where the brilliantly-coloured dolly varden and cut-throat trout (the former another char, to be pedantic) and representatives of the five sub-species of the so-called 'golden' trout join the ranks awaiting the angler's thinning, not to mention the sea-going rainbow trout, the steelhead. It was in the Rocky Mountain watershed that the rainbow, sedentary and sea-going, was first encountered and employed to provide the bloodstock for the eventual artificial populating of the entire temperate world with this enormously successful species.

Over the mountains: the ocean: and the feeding grounds of the Pacific salmon, five species, of which two, the king or 'Tyee' and the coho, are of sporting significance.

Going back East and starting again farther south, we traverse a band of warmer states, less favourable to the cold-water salmonids, but affording an ideal environment for pickerel (another pike-species) and for the small-mouth and large-mouth bass, the fish on which the romance of North American angling is largely founded. These big athletic cousins of the European perch (called there, incidentally, the 'yellow perch') hit surface flies and lures with astonishing ferocity, fight like tigers when hooked and lie habitually in the shade and cover of the water-plant zone where only the most expert of tackle-handlers can present the offering and cope with the ensuing seizure without disaster. As the cooler uplands are again reached, the typical population of the upland waters is met again, and the pattern replicates.

Repeat the journey starting in **Georgia**, and one covers territory with a yet warmer climate, swamplands, and then an area of low rainfall. Traditionally, what fishing there was did not enjoy sporting prestige. The image was one of a poor coloured man employing crude tackle to harvest cheap protein; a typical quarry, the Mississippi catfish. One is south of that section of the lowland region where water temperature falls low enough to permit salmonids to spawn successfully in natural waters.

But the water-demand for growing population growing also in affluence has necessitated the construction of chains of dams in the drier states; vast new sheets of deep water offering environments novel in their setting, with a variety of temperature regimes encouraging the successful introduction of some of the great sporting species found naturally to the north and west. Even **Arizona** - the 'dry county' itself - now provides fine fishing for sport, and offers it in hot sunshine, a combination of pleasures not frequently encountered by the proverbially frozen-fingered angler acquiring lumbago from his water-logged nether end.

It would not do to dismiss the terrific sport potential to be enjoyed generally in the U.S.A. without some mention of the fantastic angling offered in its largest state,

Alaska. Known by Alaskans as the last frontier, it is comparatively untamed, but if you seek the five species of Pacific salmon, wild rainbow trout and Arctic grayling, it offers sport beyond your wildest dreams.

Alaskan Department of Fish and Game is the Licence and Permits website (web: www.admin.adfg.state.ak.us). Most visiting anglers settle for residence in one of the many lodges which cater for those who do not wish to suffer any hardships when divorced from civilisation. Most of the best and more productive lodges are in the **Bristol Bay** area. This is easily accessible by hour-long scheduled flights from **Anchorage** to the little town of **King Salmon**. There you are within short flying times by bush or floatplane to many of the best lodges.

Some lodges offer daily fly-outs to choice fishing venues, but this adds considerably to the expense and there are many advantages in seeking a lodge which offers fishing on the river at which it is sited, and where jet boats take you to good fishing within a matter of a half-hour boat ride. One lodge popular with British visitors (they even fly the Union Jack) is **Katmai Lodge** on Levelock Native land on the **Alagnak** river. This is but a mere 80 minute flight by twin-engined turbo-prop aircraft from Anchorage direct to the lodge's own airstrip. Early July offers prime time for the king (chinook), sockeye and chum salmon. The pink salmon or "humpie" runs in late July (and only every other year), while the coho or silver salmon run in early August.

King salmon are not always easy to get on fly tackle, but those caught on baits may run to 60lbs and more. Sockeye salmon may be taken on a single-handed fly rod but require a different technique to that used for Atlantic salmon here in Britain. The chum and coho have similar taking habits to Atlantic salmon, but it always pays to take great heed of your guide before assuming that you know it all.

Several sporting agencies in Britain have Alaskan fishing on offer. For saltwater king salmon and halibut fishing on the Kenai Peninsula, and freshwater king salmon and silver on Kenai River, and other locations, with accommodation, contact **Alaskan Adventure Charters, P.O. Box 4273, Soldotna, AK 99669** (tel: +1 907 262 7773; fax: +1 907 262 7765 (season); +1 360 371 8973 (winter); web: www.alaskancharters.com; email: rufishn@alaska.net).

We have discussed none but the prime sporting species. They, however, are not the last word. US waters are inhabited also by others; carp, blue-gill sunfish, crappies and what-have-you, fish present in higher population densities and easier to catch, fish whose presence has traditionally ensured that the less expert members of the specialist angler's family on holiday may take their share of the pleasures and the triumphs. The travel business had now started international operations in this field and British anglers can expect a rapid growth in attractive opportunities.

MEXICO

Freshwater fishing: river trout fishing has been spoilt by local netting, but during the past few years black-bass fishing has become popular in Mexico, with exaggerated claims of 100 to 200 bass per day. **Vicente Guerrero Dam**, near **Ciudad Victoria**, (fishing licence 25.80 dollars per week). For **Diaz Ordaz Dam**, contact Santa Anita Hotel, Los Mochis, Sinaloa. 8lb bass are common here, and at the **San Lorenzo Dam**, near **Xicotencatl**. Sea fishing: there are over 850 species to be caught, and in the Los Cabos region alone over 40,000 marlin and sailfish are hooked each year. Popular centres are **Acapulco, Puerto Vallarta, Manzanillo, Mazatlán, Guaymas, Loreto, La Paz, Cancun, Cozumel, Tampico, Veracruz, Cabo San Lucas** and **San Jose del Cabo**, with good facilities. Good charter boats are on hire, with expert crews. Amongst coastal species are pargo, yellowtail, rock bass, grouper, barracuda, totoava, snook, giant sea bass. Pelagic species include blue and striped marlin, yellowfin tuna, black marlin, Atlantic bonito, sailfish, swordfish and mackerel. These are usually found a good distance from the shore. Bonefishing is a sport practised by anglers from all over the world at Boca Paila, near Cancun, **Quintana Roo**. Contact **Frontiers International, The Dovecot Workshops, Barnsley Park, Barnsley, Cirencester, Glos GL7 5EG** (tel: 01285 741340; email: info@frontierstrvl.co.uk; web: www.frontierstrvl.co.uk) for further information.

The **Mexican Tourism Board** has an office at **Wakefield House, 41 Trinity Square, London EC3N 4DJ** (tel: 020 7488 9392; fax: 020 7265 0704; web: www.visitmexico.com; email: uk@visitmexico.com) from which more detailed information can be obtained.

Pesca Maya Fishing Lodge, Ascension Bay, Mexico
Photo: Paul Sharman

THE CARIBBEAN

Forty years ago, so little was the Caribbean exploited by the indigenous peoples dwelling on its islands and about its shores that the United Nations Food & Agriculture Organisation gave a priority to the encouragement of commercial fishing there. What little fish was eaten in Central America had come traditionally in the form of salted fillets imported from countries - Norway and North America particularly - which had well-established cold water fisheries for cod in the prolific waters of the North Atlantic and the Arctic.

Various geophysical features were thought at that time to inhibit the Caribbean from ever becoming a region rich in exploitable fish populations. That, in one sense, may have been correct, but there are more ways than one of exploiting a resource, a fact already known by that time to charter-boat proprietors operating out of Florida resorts to crop the wonderful harvest of American anglers in search of sport more dramatic than the salmon or the muskellunge could offer in freshwater.

Thus the possibilities of the **Gulf of Mexico** and the seas around the **Bahamas** became known - marlin, swordfish, sawfish, sailfish, barracuda, tarpon and tuna the quarry, individual fish which took angling statistics from measurement by the pound to measurement by the hundredweight. The same geophysical conditions which had led to doubts as to the possibility of upgrading national catches of readily marketable fish for human consumption in the region had concentrated the big predators at water-depths where they could be found and profitably angled for.

During these forty years, facilities for Big Game fishing as it soon became known, spread progressively throughout the area and one may now fish for these splendid creatures from bases in **Mexico, Honduras, Nicaragua, Costa Rica, Panama, Colombia, Venezuela** (which was the first country in the region seriously to exploit its fish stocks in the traditional fashion) and the oceanic islands all the way south to **Trinidad.**

Originally, the big fish were angled for with a trolled dead bait and tackle powerful enough to master a bolting horse. Nowadays they are sought for with the fly rod, too, reflecting the fact that official records are maintained not only for maximum species weights, globally speaking, but for tackle categories, too, expressed in terms of line-strength - i.e. IGFA rules.

Astonishingly, billfish - to use the up-to-date term for swordfish and sailfish species grouped together - five feet in length have been brought to the glove in ten minutes from hooking with a conventional fly rod and single-action fly reel.

Tourist offices in London maintained by Mexico and Islands in the West Indies give details on hotels, facilities for boat charter, (with professional help integral to the hire-package) and of what restrictions apply to limits, seasons, and species of fish and other marine quarry which are excluded locally from the angler's activities. These restrictions are not onerous.

ANTIGUA and BARBUDA

Antigua and **Barbuda** have developed their big game fishing. Blue marlin, sailfish, tuna, wahoo, snapper, grouper, angel, trigger, margate, amber jack, black jack, and barracuda are all present around the islands, according to the conformation of the sea-bed. There are many reefs and coral formations. Lobster fishing is particularly good around the wrecks off Barbuda, which number more than 50. Anglers should note that use of dynamite is strictly forbidden. Many species of fish are reserved for commercial fishermen. Contact Phil's Eco Fishing who specialise in snook, tarpon, tuna & bone fishing; fly fishing and light tackle spinning, (tel: +1 268 560-4882; mob: +1 268 786-4347; email: fish@eco-fish.com; web: www.philsecofishing.com). All persons wishing to fish are required to hold a licence, obtainable locally. Charter boats operate from a variety of locations. Deep sea fishing aboard 'Overdraft' and "H2O", further information and reservations (tel: +1 268 720-4954/463-3112 or +1 463-3112; fax: +1 268 462-3119; email: nunesb@candw.ag; web: www.antiguafishing.com) or your tour representative.

For further information contact the **Antigua and Barbuda Tourist Office, 2nd Floor, 45 Crawford Place, London W1H 4LP** (tel: 020 7258 0070; fax: 0207 258 7486; email: tourisminfo@antigua-barbuda.com; web: www.antigua-barbuda.com).

THE BAHAMAS

The Bahamas comprise twelve major groups of islands, numbering over 700 in total, spaced over 1,000 square miles or more of ocean. **Bimini** is probably the best known of the fishing centres and it was here that the largest Bahamian marlin recorded by an angler - a fish weighing more than 1,000lbs - was brought into harbour.

Other notable islands are **San Salvador**, marlin, yellowfin, fine reef and flats fishing; **Exuma**, good bonefishing, reef fishing, and light tackle opportunities; **Long Island**, deep sea, bonefishing and reef fishing; **Cat Island**, for marlin and tuna; **Andros**, world class bonefishing, trophy sized bottom species, marlin and tuna; **Nassau**, bluewater fishing, for marlin and tuna, wahoo, kingfish, sailfish; **The Abacos**, deep and shallow water fishing, with a good variety, main attractions being yellowfin tuna, marlin, good flats and reef fishing; **Grand Bahama**, also good flats and reef fishing; **Chub Cay,** white marlin, dolphin and other species; and **Eleuthera**, with blackfin tuna, blue marlin, good bonefish flats and reef fishing, as well as big game. Seasons for best fishing:, bonefish Mar-Apr; snapper, spring summer, barracuda, Jun-Aug; blue marlin, May-Jun; white marlin, Mar-Jun; sailfish, Apr; broadbill and swordfish, Jun peak time; Allison tuna, Mar-May, blackfin, Jun; bluefin, May. Tournaments are held frequently throughout the islands, hotels catering specially for anglers abound, and there are many fishing lodges. Charter rates vary with duration of fishing trips and species sought.

Contact **The Bahamas Tourist Office, 10 Chesterfield St, London W1J 5JL** (tel: 020 7355 0800; web: www.bahamas.co.uk; email: info@bahamas.co.uk; web: www.bahamas.co.uk), for more information.

CUBA

Fishing in Key Largo Cuba. *Photo: John Wolstenholme*

Cuba is a saltwater fisher's dream being awash with flats and blue water. Take your pick: Barracuda, Bonefish, Cubera Snapper, Jack Crevalle, Permit or Tarpon. Best areas: Cayo Largo, Casa Batida Santa Maria, Cayo Romano, Isle of Youth, and Jardines de la Reina.

Specialist fishing agents operate hosted trips from the UK: **Avalon Cuban Fishing Centers** (web: www.cubanfishingcenters.com).; Aardvark McLeod; (web: www.aardvarkmcleod.com); Farlows (www.farlows.co.uk); WhereWiseMenFish (web: www.wherewisemenfish.com); See also the **Fly Fisher Group**, (web: www.flyfisher-travel.com). For more, see earlier chapter: "FISHERY AGENTS".

BERMUDA

Licences are not required: charter boats in deep water produce catches of wahoo, greater amberjack, almaco jack, dolphin fish, grey and yellowtail snapper, great barracuda, rainbow runner, Atlantic Blue marlin, Great Blue marlin, white marlin, little tunny, blackfin, Wahoo and Yellowfin and skipjack tuna. Also all species of shark, the prize being the blue marlin with 9 fish over 1,000lbs. recently caught. Reefs produce greater amberjack, almaco jack, great barracuda, little tunny, Bermuda chub, grey and yellowtail snapper, and assorted bottom fish. Shore fishing from beaches, docks piers is free, and may produce bonefish, palometa, grey snapper, great barracuda. Charter boats operate the year round, from the BSFA and St George's GFCA (below), the majority independently, supply and demand peaking from May to November. There are quite a few charter boats operating in Bermuda, almost all are independently owned and operated, which include Capt Allen DeSilva, "De Mako", Fishbermuda Ltd, 11 Abri Lane, Spanish Point, Pembroke HM02 (tel: +1 441 295 0835; fax: +1 441 295 3620; mob: +1 441 234 8626; web: www.fishbermuda.com; email: mako@logic.bm); "MV Messaround" Charters, St. George's Game Fishing and Cruising Association, PO Box GE 107, St. George's GE BX (tel: +1 441 297 8093; fax: +1 441 297 1455; mob: +1 441 334 8953; web: www.fishandfun.bm; email: joekelly@northrock.bm); further information from the **Bermuda Tourism, 26 York Street, London W1U 6PZ** (tel: 0800 883 0857; web: www.bermuda tourism.com)and **Bermuda Sport Fishing Association, Creek View House, 8 Tulo Lane, Pembroke HM O2** (tel/fax: +1 441 295 2370). Hotel facilities are excellent.

LESSER ANTILLES

South of Puerto Rico is the chain of small islands known as the **Lesser Antilles** - the **Leeward** and **Windward** groups.

TRINIDAD AND TOBAGO

Finally, **Trinidad & Tobago**, the large islands which lie just off the coast of Venezuela and terminate the chain. Their waters, too, are abundantly supplied with billfish species, tuna, tarpon, barracuda and many other species of interest to the angler, if offering rather less dramatic sport than the 'stars' on the angler's stage. For further information, contact **Trinidad & Tobago Tourism Office, 111 Hare Lane, Claygate, Surrey KT10 0QY** (tel: 0137 246 9818, or freephone: 0800 804 8787; web: www.visittnt.com; email: trinbago@ihml.com) or **Tourism & Industrial Development Co (Trinidad & Tobago) Ltd, P O Box 222, Maritime Centre, 29 Tenth Ave, Barataria, Trinidad WI** (tel: (868) 675 7034/5/6; fax: (868) 675 638 7962; web: www.tdc.co.tt). Names and addresses of charter-boat operators in both islands are available on various websites.

SOUTH AMERICA

BRAZIL

This is a vast country in the same league as China, Canada, Australia and the United States of America. Brazil boasts not only the Amazon basin (the largest hydrographic basin in the world) but also the Prata basin (the second largest in Latin America) as well as the Araguaia-Tocantins, the Sao Francisco and Atlântico Sul Basins. With the world's biggest river draining it, it lacks neither water nor fish. Brazil has five main regions, each one has its own fishing areas and fish variety (too many to be fully detailed in this section). The regions are listed, along with a few varieties in each area:

Northern: (**Amapa, Amazonas, Para, Rondônia, Roraima** and **Tocatins**): fish variety: *rivers*: peacock bass, surubim, aracu, tambaqui, red-tail catfish, dorada, cachorra, apapa, great barracuda, tarpon, grey snapper; *coastal regions*: dolphin, piramutaba, club shark.

North East (Alagoas, Bahia, Ceará, Maranhao, Piaui, Paraiba, Pernambucco, Rio Grande do Norte, Sergipe); fish variety: rivers & dams: peacock bass, dorado, surubim, freshwater croaker, curimatas; *coastal regions*: snook, tarpon, crevalle jack, catfish, grey & Southern red snapper, king mackerel and pompano; *coastal rivers*: snook, hake and tarpon.

Central West: (**Goias, Mato Grosso, Mato Grosso do Sul**); fish variety: *rivers & dams:* peacock bass, apapa, surubim, chachorra, great barracuda, pirahna (red & black), catfish (varieties), pacu.

SouthEast: (**Espirito Santo; Minas Gerais, Rio de Janiero, Sao Paulo**); fish variety: *rivers & dams*: catfish (var); peacock bass, catfish, tilápias, black-bass, croaker; (trout is found on **Aiurioca River**); *coastal regions*: Bluefish, snook, grouper, pampo, snook, blue runner, blue marlin, white marlin, Greater Amberjack, Yellowtail (Lesser Amberjack).

Southern: (**Paraná, Rio Grande do Sul, Santa Catarina**); fish variety: *rivers & dams:* tilápia, carpa, jundiá, mandi, corvina, pacu, corimba, catfish (varieties), peacock bass, cascudo, surubim, pacu, pintado, blackbass (trout is found on **River Silverira and Pelotas River**); *coastal regions*: snook, croaker, Greater Amberjack.

Anglers from the USA have already explored its possibilities with excellent results. Brazil as an exciting new destination for fishing holidays is now being widely developed and available through numerous travel web-sites.

For further information, contact the **Brazilian Tourist Office, 32 Green Street, London W1K 7AT** (tel: 020 7399 9221; fax: 020 7399 9102; web: www.brazil.org.uk/tourism; email: tourism@brazil.org.uk).

ARGENTINA

Here, although the South Atlantic is probably now the world's most productive fishing zone, the emphasis in terms of sport shifts back to freshwater fishing. Salmonids were introduced from the northern hemisphere many years ago - land-locked salmon *(Salmo salar sebago)* the brown trout (in both its sedentary and migratory forms) and the brook trout *(Salvelinus fortinalis)*. The home of these species is in the Andean lake district. Specimen brook trout up to 10lbs, have been caught; in the case of the other species named, specimens topping 30lbs.

In the river-catchments of the lower-lying regions of the country, especially those of the **Parana** and **Plata,** there are two fine native species of fish, the dorado *(Salminus maxillosus)* and the perch *(Percicathys trucha)* which are rated as highly or higher than salmonids. The perch grows to weights approaching 20lbs, while the dorado reaches a weight of 50lbs.

In the same habitats are found other species which grow to be enormous - the mangururu (200lbs), the surubi (120lbs) and others which do not reach such spectacular weights but still offer splendid sport.

Spinning from a boat piloted by a guide is the usual method of fishing for dorado, but they will also take a fly (not exactly a blue winged olive!) and in an Argentinean torrent quite a challenge to the fly rod, also the fish it naturally feeds on, offered as either a live or a dead bait. This splendid sporting fish is found throughout the catchments of the rivers Plata and Parana. Centres specially recommended for the quality of the fishing guides, boats and accommodation are **Paso de la Patria** (Corrientes), **Isla del Carrito** (Chaco) and **Posadas** (Misiones).

The best fishing is in the summer - August to March. Annual competitions are held early in the season. Five vast National Parks offer the best of the fishing for salmonids, all of them on the west side of the country, in the uplands bordering Chile.

In **Patagonia,** the lakes and rivers in the mountainous region of **Cholila** contain abundant stocks of trout, usually fished with wet and dry fly, or Devon minnow. Average sizes are large: brook trout to 10lbs, rainbow from 3-6lbs with specimen fish running to 20lbs, brown trout 3-8lbs, with record from this area, 32lbs. Other fishable species are landlocked salmon, perca, and Patagonian pejerrey. The principal lakes are: **Lago Cholila**, the biggest in Cholila (15 km long), with beautiful surroundings; the water is very cold due to glacier melt; access via Estancia Lago Cholila; **Lago Lezama**, the highest and warmest in the area, deep, with permanent undercurrents of warm streams; **Lago Mosquito**, the smallest (8 km long, close to village, with small hostel alongside the lake. Largest rivers are **Rio Carrelefu, Rio Tigre, Rio Pedregoso,** and **Rio Blanco**. All these waters are excellent for fishing, and only a handful of anglers can be found in any one season for the place is virtually unknown internationally.

From **Punta Piedras** in the north to **Tierra del Fuego** in the extreme south, Argentina has more than 2,200 miles of Atlantic coastline. The water so far south is too cold for tuna, billfish and tarpon, but their place is taken for the big game angler by all the Atlantic species of shark.

For the Argentineans themselves, though, the peak of the sea angling year is when the warm current from Brazil brings down the black corvina, whose shoals provide many specimens of 40lbs, and better. **San Clemente de Tuyu** is the most famous centre for fishing the corvina, where the fish arrive in December. They then work their way down the coast, arriving in **Bahia Blanca** in February. There is plenty of shore fishing, but boats are to be had, though not on quite the sophisticated scale to be met with in the Gulf of Mexico and the Caribbean.

Tourist information may had from the **Consulado General de la República Argentina, 27 Three Kings Yard, Mayfair, London W1K 4DF** (tel: 020 7318 1340; fax: 020 7318 1349: web: www.argentine-embassy-uk.org). **Secretaría de Turismo de la Nación, Centro de Informes, Av. Santa Fe 883 P.B - Buenos Aires** (tel: 004 11 312 2232; web: www.turismo.gov.ar; email: info@turismo.gov.ar). The secretariat can supply telephone numbers with information on the Litoral network, on mountains and forests, on hills and streams, on Patagonia fishing stations, on sea fishing, on tides, including in the river Plate and the river Plate basin rivers, and on meteorology.

Anglers who have fished in areas infected with whirling disease must wash their waders, because Argentina is free of it.

CHILE

Chile's coastline matches that of the neighbouring Argentine, but the fishing promoted is largely for introduced salmonids, especially in Chilean Patagonia. The trout run extremely large; the country in that region is thinly populated and attractively wild, the climate mild. Mid-Nov to Apr is the trout season in Chile. In November trout begin to feed actively. January and February are height of summer, with plentiful insect life, and fish feed heavily in March. In April the weather cools, but the largest fish tend to be hooked then, up to 12 or 14lbs. Fishing lodges are run in several locations, including on the **Nireguao** and **Futaleufu** Rivers, with good accommodation. Other first rate fisheries in the Chilian Patagonia are the **Baker** and **Cochrane** Rivers, and **Frio** and **Pollux** lakes, with spectacular fly fishing for large brown and rainbow trout, regularly in the 4-7lbs range. The cities recommended as start-points for the angler are **Temuco, Puerto Montt** and **Coihaque**. Temuco is accessible by rail from **Santiago** daily, Puerto Montt, depending on season. Coihaque is accessible by air only, either from Santiago or Puerto Montt. Fishing licences can be obtained from the offices of the Regional Municipalities. Further information from **Sernatur, Av Providencia 1550, Santiago**; (tel: 00 562 731 8300/8336; fax: 00562 251 8469; email: info@sernatur.cl; web: www.sernatur.cl); **National Tourist Board of Chile, Regional Headquarters of Aisen, Bulnes No 35, Coyhaique, Chile** (tel/fax: (67) 231752/233949; email: sernatur coyhai@entelchile.net) or **Chilean Consulate, 12 Devonshire St, London W1N 7DS** (tel: 020 7580 6392; fax: 020 7436 5204; see website for more info: www.chile.embassyhomepage.com; email: embachile@embachile.co.uk).

THE FALKLAND ISLANDS

One of the growing, but still largely undiscovered attractions in the South Atlantic, this group of islands is the best researched and most promising for the angler. How else? Natural and spacious, enjoying clean air and majestic scenery, the Islands are a dynamic Overseas territory of the United Kingdom, with over 94% of the 2,379 strong population of British descent. After the events of 1982, these shores remain protected by the British forces. From nowhere else south of the equator has *Where to Fish* received such comprehensive information. The whole development of sea trout fishing in the Falklands has taken place in less than a lifetime. Nature left the Islands with only the Falkland trout - *(aplochiton zebra)* which is not a trout or even a char, and a few minor species in its rivers. The first real trout *(Salmo trutta)* were introduced less than forty years ago, but a fast growing migratory strain quickly became established and spread around the islands, giving us today some of the finest sea trout fishing in the world.

Sea trout 2-5lbs are common, and many fish in excess of 10lbs are taken every season. The best recorded sea trout taken on a fly to date was 22¾lbs, caught on the **San Carlos River** by Alison Faulkner.

The main sea trout rivers - the **Warrah** and **Chartres** on West Falkland and the **San Carlos** on East Falkland - are ideal for fly fishing, with treeless banks being free of casting obstructions. However a strong wind often blows, so this is no place for a poor caster with mediocre tackle.

Most rivers have fair numbers of resident brown trout, but most are small, dark fish, typical of acid rivers.

Major sea trout rivers with visitor accommodation and guides.

West Falkland

Warrah River: Can be fished from **Port Howard Settlement**, where there is accommodation. The Warrah River is about 12 miles from the settlement, and the Chartres River about an hour's drive. The main tributary, the **Green Hills Stream**, which is crossed on the way to the Warrah, is well worth fishing.

East Falkland

San Carlos River: Controlled by local farmers, the river is accessed from the Stanley Port - San Carlos track. Blue Beach Lodge offers comfortable accommodation.

Mullet fishing: as a bonus, you will probably come into contact with the Falkland mullet *(Eleginus falklandicus)* if fishing in tidal water. Like the British mullet, the Falkland species follows the tide right into shallow water, where it can be seen swimming just below the surface with a very obvious wake, but there the similarity ends. It is not even related to our mullet and is much larger, with fish recorded up to 20lbs and mullet of 8lbs are quite common. The dorsal fin runs virtually from head to tail along a tapering body, and the pectoral fins are huge in relation to the size of the fish.

The Falkland mullet is a powerful fish which makes long runs and would be much valued as a game fish if it existed in Britain. It often takes the sea-trout angler's fly or spinner, but the local method normally used is to suspend a piece of mutton (fresh sheep meat) on a size 4 or 2 hook a couple of feet below a small pike bung. This tackle is cast out wherever there are signs of mullet activity, and the response is rarely long delayed.

Small to medium mullet can be caught virtually on your doorstep at places like **Port Howard**. The really large fish are often found in specific locations, at some distance from the settlements. It is worth considering setting aside a little time for a trip specifically for big mullet.

The commercial route flies via South America, where Lan Chile operates a weekly Saturday service linking Santiago and Punta Arenas in Chile with Mount Pleasant, Falkland Islands. Alternatively, a limited number of seats are available on the RAF Tristar service, which flies direct from the UK via Ascension Island. This service departs six times a month.

There is accommodation for fishermen at Stanley, Port San Carlos, Darwin and Port Howard. There are also lodges in wildlife centres (fishermen may like to take some time off to see the large colonies of penguins, seals and other wildlife).

The **Falkland Islands Tourist Board** office is at **Falkland House, 14 Broadway, Westminster, London, SW1H 0BH**. (tel: 020 7222 2542; see website for more info: www.falklands.gov.fk). A useful website is www.visitorfalklands.com.

FISHING IN EUROPE

AUSTRIA

Austria is understandably popular with anglers from all over the world, with its abundance of streams and lakes, providing first-class sport with brown and rainbow trout, grayling, char, and coarse fish such as pike and pike-perch, huck, sheat-fish and carp. Some of the main centres tend to be overfished, so a car is valuable; many beautiful mountain streams are easily reached by road. Much of the sport is on the lower reaches of these mountain rivers, but the more venturesome can often find better fishing on the high alpine streams and lakes. Grayling are highly regarded, often more so than trout, the **Drau**, **Salzach** and **Traun** being three of the best grayling rivers in Europe. The River **Mur**, **Ybbs** and **Steyr** are other recommended rivers. 'Fishing in Austria' *(see below)* is a co-operative of 35 areas and hotels specialising in angling; and issues temporary permits for several trout preserves, as well as dt. Temporary permission and information can be obtained from the Association's office. The same applies to the VÖAFV and 'Fishing in Austria.'

To keep the sport at a high level, the authorities maintain strict conservation measures and a specially close watch is kept on pollution and abstraction. Generally speaking the rule is fly only for trout, grayling and char. Spinning is usually only permitted for larger fish such as lake trout, pike, huck, pike-perch (depending on the local authority) and so on, and natural bait and sheatfish only for coarse fisheries. Many waters are controlled by the two principal fishing associations, the Austrian Fishing Association (ÖFG) and the Association of Austrian Workers' Fishing Clubs (VÖAFV).

In some parts of Austria, the visitor usually needs two permits, a general licence issued by the State, costing according to the province - and a private permit from the local owner.

Accommodation is no problem, as many fine hotels offer anglers first class facilities on the more important lakes and rivers. More information can be obtained from the **Austrian National Tourist Office, P O Box 83, A-1041, Vienna** (tel: 08451 011818; fax 08451 011819; web: www.austria.info; e-mail holiday@austria.info). Addresses of the main angling associations are **Österreichische Fischereigesellschaft, 1010 Wien 1, Elisabethstrasse 22** (tel: +43 1 586 52 48; fax: +43 1 587 59 42; web: www.oefg1880.at; email: office@oefg 1880.at). **Verband der Österreichischen Arbeiter-Fischerei-Vereine, A-1080 Wien, Lenaugasse 14** (tel: +43 1 403 21 76; fax: +43 1 403 21 76 20; web: www.fischerei.or.at; email: verband@fischerei.or.at).

BELGIUM

Although Belgium has never made a name for itself as a visiting fisherman's country, it has, in fact, in its many canals and rivers, most of the fish which British fishermen know, with sea fishing along its 40 miles of coast.

In general terms the freshwater fishing water can be divided thus: The **Scheldt** basin, with the rivers **Scheldt, Lys, Rupel, Dyle, Demer, Dendre** and **Nèthe** holding bream, roach, perch, pike, burbot, smelt, shad and eels; the **Meuse** basin, with the rivers **Meuse, Semois, Lesse, Sambre, Ourthe, Amblève, Warche** and **Vesdre** holding trout, grayling, chub, barbel, perch, roach, bream, pike, pike-perch, carp, tench and eels; and the streams between the Sambre and the Meuse, holding trout, grayling, chub, perch, pike, roach, bream, carp, tench and eels. Many waters of the lowlands and near industrial centres have suffered from pollution and overfishing, but the situation is improving.

All Belgian waters fall into one of three categories; closed water, not subject to fishing laws; public, or navigable water, belonging to the Walloon, Flemish or Brussels regions; preserved, or non-navigable water belonging to the landowners. Waters in the last two groups are subject to the fishing laws, and anyone fishing in them must possess a current licence. There are three different licences in Belgium: 1) sold by the Flemish authority, for fishing in the northern part of the country; 2) sold by the Brussels region, for Brussels; 3) sold by the Walloon region for fishing in Wallonia. The cost varies according to the type of fishing. Licences may be obtained only at post offices of the region concerned. The **close seasons** are: Pike, perch, grayling or pike-perch: January 1 to first Saturday in June; trout, October 1 to third Saturday of March. Fly fishing falls off sharply on the Ardennes streams after June.

For visiting trout fishers the greatest attraction probably lies in the streams of the **Ardennes**, where there is a good deal of association water. These are mostly mixed fisheries on the lines of the Hampshire Avon in England, with trout and grayling predominating in the upper reaches and being increasingly joined by coarse fish on moving downstream. The best fishing will usually be found in the least accessible places. Standard British fly patterns will take fish on the Ardennes streams but the local flies should be tried where possible.

Sea fishing along the sandy, shelving coast is largely for dabs and plaice (Oct-June), flounders (all year) and sole (May-Oct), with piers and breakwaters providing sport with conger (all year), cod (Sept-Mar), and whiting (Oct-Jan). Turbot are occasionally taken (May-Sept) and rays, shad and garfish are also caught (Sept-Oct), **Zeebrugge, Ostend, Nieuwpoort, Blankenbergh**, and **Knokke-Heist** are good centres.

Just after the last edition was printed, the-then Belgian Tourist Office was divided into two sections *(see below)*. Belgian fishing legislation is extremely complex and anglers are strongly advised to consult the local tourist centres. For example, **Namur** province publishes a special angling brochure in French. Further detailed information (in English) from (i) **Belgian Tourist Office - Brussels & Walloonia, 217 Marsh Wall, London E14 9FJ** (tel: 020 7537 1132; fax: 020 753' 0393); free brochure line: 0800 9545 245; see website for more info: www.belgiumtheplacetobe.com; email: info@belgiumtheplaceto.be) and (ii) **Tourism Flanders-Brussels, 1a Cavendish Square, London W1G 0LD** (tel: 020 7307 7738; free brochure line: 0800 9545 245; web: www.visitflanders.co.uk; email: info@visitflanders.co.uk); finally, in Belgium itself, from the secretary of the **Fédération Sportive des Pêcheurs Francophones de Belgique, Rue Grandgagnage 25, 5000 Namur** (tel: +32 (0)81 41 34 91; fax: +32 (0)81 42 10 43; web: www.pecheurbelge.be; email: info@fspfb.be); and from the secretary of the **Vlaamse Vereniging Voor Hengelsport Verbonden, Astridlaan 30, 8370 Blankenberge** (tel: +50 41 40 77; web: www.vvhv.be). Information on the specifics of fishing legislation can be obtained from the **Service de la Pêche, du Ministère de la Région Wallonne (Ministry of the Wallonian Region)** (tel: +32 (0)81 32 74 88; web: www.wallonie.be).

DENMARK

Fishing in Denmark is plentiful, varied and easy to come by. A few of the rivers hold salmon, and many of them sea trout, brown trout and grayling, as well as coarse fish, which are found also in many lakes.

In many places visitors can fish by purchasing tickets from the local fishing association. The association tickets are invariably cheap and sold at local tourist offices, post offices and large tackle shops.

The principal rivers are all in **Jutland**. They are **Skjern Aa, Store Aa, Varde Aa, Ribe Aa** and **Karup Aa**. All are game-fish waters, but of them the best salmon fishing is probably to be had on the Skjern and the best sea trout fishing on the Karup. The water is generally good for fly fishing, and the flies used are much the same as those used in this country. Spinning is much practised. Added variety is given by the sea trout fishing which can be had from the rocks and from boats off both the mainland and the various Baltic islands.

For the coarse fisherman, the **River Guden** holds prolific stocks of bream and roach, and hundreds of lakes contain large bream, tench and other species, and are hardly ever fished. The lakeland area of East Jutland, for instance, produces very heavy net weights. Notable centres are Viborg, Silkeborg, Ry, Århus, Skanderborg (beside **Lake Skanderborg**, teeming with fish), and Horsens. Please note, there are restrictions on use of groundbait, and in some areas it is prohibited. In **Zealand**, the lake fishing is more predominant.

The **Funen Islands** between Jutland and Zealand have been in recent years systematically developed into an important centre for breeding and increasing sea trout, as a response to dwindling native populations. More than 400,000 smolts have been introduced each year since 1999; more than 100 barriers in the Funen river system have been removed by establishing fish passages and runs, and now, there exist one hundred different fishing locations on the coast round about these islands. Fishing is permitted all the year round, best times are Jan-May, and Aug-mid Nov. Normal methods are fly, and spinning with spoon or lure. A brochure may be obtained from **Visit Fyn, Sivmosevaenget 4, DK-5260 Odense 5** (web: www.seatrout.dk; email: info@fyntour.dk) and also information on their guide service and casting trips.

There similar opportunities for sea trout fishing from the coast of Eastern Jutland, **Sjaelland**, and the island of **Bornholm**, in the Baltic. Excellent trolling for salmon is also to be had off Bornholm, salmon weighing over 42lbs are caught every year.

Denmark has a coastline of 7,500 kilometres, much of it unfished but nearly all stretches are accessible, with good possibilities for cod, coalfish, flatfish, tope, mackerel, garfish, whiting, ling and pollack, and for turbot, brill, plaice, sole, dab and flounder. One should not fish within 50 metres of a private dwelling place without the owners permission. Anglers are warned about the danger of breakwater fishing from **Jutland** west coast in rough weather, and on North Sea coast, jetty fishing is prohibited in several places for security reasons. Fishing boats will take anglers out to sea for a reasonable charge, and may also be chartered at **Copenhagen, Elsinore, Korsør** and **Frederikshavn**.

Salmon and sea trout fishing in fresh water is best from Apr/May to July, and September (salmon), June to Sept, and Oct/Nov, smaller rivers (sea trout).

A fishing licence is obligatory, and costs DKK 100. It is obtainable from post offices or tourist offices. A tourist licence may be obtained for one day, cost DKK 30, or one week, DKK 90. Those under 18 or over 67 are exempt. Fishing rights in natural lakes and streams are nearly always private, but often let to local angling societies, who issue day or week cards. These are priced between DKK 40-150 per day, DKK 100-350 per week and may be bought at tourist offices. There are close seasons and size limits on game fish and large variety of other freshwater and sea fish.

Further information about both fishing and accommodation can be had from the **Visit Danish, 55 Sloane Street, London, SW1X 9SY** (tel: 020 7259 5958; fax: 020 7259 5955; email: London@visitdenmark.com; web: www.visitdenmark.com); **Danish Directorate of Fisheries** (web: www.fisketegn.dk).

FINLAND

Finland can offer the angler no fewer than 187,888 lakes and rivers, and some 3,000 miles of sea-shore and archipelago. In the north and centre of the country the angler can catch very big fish on very big, remote waters; conditions which, in Europe at any rate, are becoming increasingly harder to find. The long days of midsummer give plenty of fishing time - the best sport in fact is often enjoyed in the brief twilight which elsewhere is called 'night'. In the South and in the archipelago area the best fishing periods are spring and autumn. Ice fishing for perch is popular in the winter months, and spear fishing with a lamp is practised during autumn, in dark, calm, or cloudy weather.

Salmon, sea trout, brown trout and brook trout all run well above the European average, and the size of grayling, too, is often remarkable; four-pounders are not rare. There are also arctic charr *(Salvelinus alpinus)* which in the right conditions will take a fly. The most notable salmon-fishing rivers in Finland are **Tenojoki** in Lapland, **Tornionjoki** and **Simojoki** in Northern Finland, and **Kymijoki**, which empties into the Gulf of Finland in Kotka. Other popular salmon-fishing sites are the delta areas of **Kemijoki, Oulujoki** and **Aurajoki** rivers.

Excellent trout rivers and rapids are to be found in **Central Finland, Karelia, Kuusamo, Northern Finland** and **Lapland**, while the best waters for catching grayling are in the north. Worthy of particular mention are the seaspawning grayling of the western **Oura** archipelago, and the **Lake Saimaa** grayling.

The cream of the sport is to be found in **Lapland**, though there are individual waters further south which can match them in quality. Some of the best game fishing in Europe is to be found in the region north of **Lake Inari**, and especially the rivers emptying into the lake. A very good possibility is the lake itself, holding taimen, very big grayling and brown trout to 20lbs and more. Best fished for during their migratory runs up the tributaries in late summer.

Although hydro-electric schemes have impaired the salmon runs in many famous waterways, rivers are recovering and several of them can be offered for salmon and sea trout fishing - the **Kiiminki**; the **Simo**; the **Lesti**; the **Tornio**, which Finland shares with Sweden yielded in 1996 an estimated 20,000 kilos, the quieter stretches of Lappea producing more than 600 salmon, and the **Kymi River** produced 3,000 kilos, with salmon fishing well organised all the year round. The **Kuusinkijoki** at Kuusamo has been the venue of the world fly fishing championships.

The many guides will help you avoid problems. Many rivers are so wide, deep and fast flowing that comfortable fishing from the bank may be out of the question; it may often be impossible to reach the salmon and sea trout lies. Hence on great rivers like the **Teno** (claimed to be the best river in the world for Atlantic salmon), and **Näätämö** which flow along the frontier with Norway, the fishing is mainly from a boat with an outboard motor from which large flies are cast by short but stout rods over enormous pools and streams - a technique known as 'harling'. Reels carrying 250 yards of line of up to 1mm thick and over 40lb breaking strain are employed.

One problem which may be encountered is transport - many of the best waters are 'off the beaten track' and although there are excellent air services between the main centres, after that the angler is on his own and may have to be prepared for a good deal of foot-slogging and camping. A car, with a fibreglass boat strapped to the roof, is a valid alternative where the roads are not too bad. Nearly half of the farm holiday sites in Finland offer fishing; information may be had from local Tourist Information Centres.

One important accessory for the angler is some form of repellant to ward off mosquito attacks, which can often be unbearable - some Finnish fishermen wear head-nets. There are many fishing holiday resorts in Finland, and many organised package fishing holidays.

The Finnish coast with its large archipelago, not to mention the 6,500 **Åland Islands**, offers very good prospects for trout, salmon and perch fishers, and the pike fishing is outstandingly good. Even the immediate surroundings of big cities should not be ignored. As to the catch - the sea area is best.

The coarse fisherman will find first-class pike fishing in high summer, trolling a popular method on Finnish lakes, and large perch, which are very edible, may be caught during this season by worming. Some very good coarse fishing is to be found in the south, notably for pike and perch and pike-perch - not, as many believe, a hybrid, but a separate species. Opportunities for the fly fisherman in the south have been extended in recent years by the stocking of ponds with rainbow, brown and brook trout.

The National Board of Forestry administers 85 fisheries, which it manages mainly by restocking. Most of these are in eastern and northern Finland.

Fishing permits: Fishing regulations are strict and strictly enforced - there are game wardens even in remote districts. Two documents are required when fishing by means other than hook and line (ice fishing is free of charge). The first is a receipt for payment of the fishing management fee, the second the actual fishing permit. The fishing management fee is 20 Euro per calendar year or 6 Euro per week (seven days). Those under 18 or over 65 need not pay this fee, nor do those who merely assist in the fishing and do not handle the fishing equipment during the actual fishing. The fishing management fee is paid by bank giro to the state giro account: Nordea 166030-101496.

The second required document is a receipt of payment of a fishing permit. This may be obtained in two ways. Special fishing sites require permission from the owner of the water area. Such permits also include specific information concerning the fishing methods allowed, fishing times and other pertinent rules and regulations. Provincial lure fishing permits allow fishing with one rod, at sea and on lakes, at the cost of 29 Euro per year or 7 Euro per week.

Certain limitations apply to provincial lure fishing permits. Lure fishing fees may be paid into the following giro accounts, according to province:
- Province of Southern Finland: Nordea 166030-106594
- Province of Western Finland: Nordea 166030-106602
- Province of Eastern Finland: Nordea 166030-106610
- Province of Oulu: Nordea 166030-106628
- Province of Lapland: Nordea 166030-106636.

Separate regulations apply in the Åland Islands and the aforementioned licence system is not in force there. For additional information on fishing licences and fishing in Finland, visit the **Federation of Finnish Fisheries Associations, Malmin kauppatie 26, 00700 Helsinki:** (tel: +358 (0) 9 6844 590; email: kalastus@ahven.net; web: www.ahven.net/english; **Ålands Tourist Information** (web: www.turist.aland.fi).

Close seasons *(with minimum measurements)*: salmon *(60cm)*, land-locked salmon *(40*cm), sea and brown trout *(50cm)* and brook trout *(no min)* in rivers, brooks and rapids and in tide rips: Sept 1-Nov 30; with rod and lure: Sept 11-Nov 15; grayling *(30cm)*: 1 April-31 May; Arctic charr *(40cm)* in the Vukosi water: Sept 11-Nov 15; crayfish: Nov 1-July 21 (noon); lamprey: Apr 1-Aug15. (In the Åland Islands shore fishing is banned between 15 Apr and 15 June, in order to protect nesting sea birds.)

Further information can be obtained from the **Finnish Tourist Board, P O Box 33213, London W6 8JX** (tel: +44(0)20 7365 2512; fax: +44(0)20 8600 5681; web: www.visitfinland.com/uk; email: finlandinfo.lon@mek.fi).

FRANCE

Excellent sport with trout and some salmon fishing is open at reasonable cost in this country. French waterways are divided into the navigable public rivers, where fishing rights are owned by the State, and private rivers, where they belong to the riparian owner, fishing association or local authority. Even on the public rivers, however, anglers must belong to an angling and fish-breeding association and pay a tax based on the method of fishing adopted. Most rivers of this type provide coarse fishing only.

Trout and salmon rights will nearly always be privately held, but the visitor should have little difficulty in obtaining a permit. Information should be sought from the local club or tackle dealer.

To fish in first and second category waters you normally require a **licence**, and a day (or sometimes) weekly card. The annual licence varies in price according to the Department. There is now a 'holiday pass' (carte vacances) for over 16 year-olds. To fish public stretches of rivers you only need the licence; juveniles can buy La Carte Jeune for the year.

Close seasons vary a great deal according to the locality, especially for salmon, and it is best to make local enquiries. A rough guide, however, would be, first category waters: salmon and trout, mid-Sept. to mid-March. Second category waters, fishing permitted all year round, although there are restrictions for various types of fish, such as pike. Fishing is allowed 30 mins. before and 30 mins. after sunset.

Information from local clubs, tackle dealers and **Ministère de l'Agriculture et de la Pêche, 78 Rue Varenne, 75349 Paris** (tel: +33 1 49 55 57 46).

Perhaps the best salmon fishing in France is to be found on a small number of fast flowing streams in the **Western Pyrenees**. The noted **Gave d'Oloron** is in this area. **Oloron, Sauveterre** and **Navarrenx** are good centres for this river. The **Gave d'Aspe**, which joins it at Oloron, and its tributary, the **Lourdios**, have provided good sport in recent years. They may be fished from **Lurbe**. At **Peyrehorade** the Gave d'Oloron is joined by the **Gave de Pau,** on which sport has also been improving, and Pau itself makes a fine place to stay. Salmon also run up the **Gaves d'Ossau** and **de Nive**. Because of melting snow, the season begins later here than elsewhere in France, but it extends later, too. For the Oloron area the best months are from June to the end of August.

Brittany, too, provides some opportunities for the salmon fisherman, with 12,400 miles of water courses, though the fish are on the small side, especially on the **River Aulne**, which flows into the sea near **Brest**. Generally, March, April, then June to end of season is the best time for salmon. Try the **Châteaulinn** area until April and **Chateauneuf-du-Faou** later on. Châteaulinn is also a good centre for the **Ell'le** and from **Landerneau** and **Landivisiau** the **Ellorn** may be fished. This salmon and trout river has been improved, pruned, and made accessible by the local angling society. Other productive streams are the **Blavet**, which passes through many locks, and is a first-rate coarse fishing stream, **Laita** and **Odet**, which flow into the Atlantic; the **Trieux** and its tributary the **Leff**, with **Guingamp** a suitable venue. In Cotes d'Armor region, the **Guer** and **Guic** are excellent and easily accessible trout streams, also the **Jaundy**, and tributary the **Théoulas**, brown trout and occasional salmon.

Flowing northwards through picturesque countryside to feed the **Loire**, the **Allier** offers the best opportunities for salmon fishermen in **Auvergne**. This is a region comparatively unknown to British anglers. The place to make for is **Brioude**, on the upper reaches of the river. The **Bajace dam**, where salmon congregate before taking the leap, is half a mile away. **Vichy, Pont-du-Château, Veyre** and **Issoire** are other centres. The upper reaches of the Loire itself can provide good sport. **Cantal** in the heart of the Auvergne, has 2,500 miles of rivers and mountain streams, with abundant brown trout. Best time, March to June. **Roanne** is a suitable place to stay. In the **Languedoc-Roussillon** region of southern France, there are almost 1,800 miles of game fishing stretches, mostly on the three major river basins, the **Garonne**, the **Loire** and the **Rhône**, and a multitude of lakes, some 50 up in the mountains. 15 May to 15 June is the best time for fly fishing, April to Oct for coarse, and June, July, Sept for mountain lake fishing.

Some of the **Normandy** rivers have good runs of fish, but the best of the fishing is hard to come by, being largely in the hands of syndicates. The visitor may find opportunities, however, on the **Orne** and **Vire**, the **Sée**, the **Sienne** and the **Sélune; Pontfarcy, Quetteville, Avranches** and **Ducey** are suggested centres.

France is a splendid country for the trout fisherman, with an abundance of well-stocked streams flowing through glorious scenery. He may find solitude and beauty not very far from Paris - in fact, on the upper reaches of the **Seine** and its tributary, the **Ource**. A little farther south lies **Avallon**, from which the **Cure** and its tributaries may be fished.

But the visitor will find the **Pyrenees** very hard to beat for trout. The **Gave d'Ossau** is one of the best of the many first-class streams in this area, offering particularly fine sport at the **Fabrège dam**. From **Lurbe** the **Gave d'Aspe** and its tributary, the

Lourdios, may be fished, and excellent sport may be had on the **Gave d'Oloron** above **Pont-de-Dognen**, the **Nive** above **Itxassou**, and the **Gave de Pau** upstream of **Pont-de-Lescar**. The best trout fishing is from the end of May, once the snow has melted, and from June for salmon; April/Nov for coarse fish.

In eastern France, the **Franche-Comté** region offers a wealth of fishing for trout and grayling in such fine rivers as the **Loue**, **Doubs**, **Ain**, the **Dessoubre**, **Bienne**, **Usancin**, **Breuchin** and **Saône**, as well as the **Saint-Point** and **Remoray** lakes, and the huge **Vouglans** reservoir. March is the best month for trout fishing with worm, dead minnow, and spinning, and very large fish are caught then. In May/July, dry fly and nymph. There is good coarse fishing to be found in the region, too, in June/July, and Sept/Oct

In the fascinating and comparatively unexplored regions of **Creuse**, **Haute-Vienne**, **Corrèze** and **Lot**, are innumerable streams with torrential upper reaches holding fine trout. Downstream they become less tumultuous and wider until, in the **Dordogne**, they harbour a variety of coarse fish. Figeac is a good centre for the trout. Farther east lies the wild, mountainous region of **Lozère**, where grand and beautiful rivers like the **Lot** and its tributary, the **Colagne**, may be fished. The **Bès** and **Truyère** should also be tried.

Wherever one turns in France, it seems, there are trout to be caught. In the **Savoy Alps** are innumerable streams of quality, like the **Isère** and **Doron**, near **Albertville**, and the **Sierroz**, **Tillet** and **Chéron** near **Chatelard-en-Bauges**, the **Arvan** and **Arc**, near **Saint-Jean-de-Maurienne**. Auvergne and the **Dauphiny Alps** are ideal for the explorer with a fly rod. **Grenoble** commands a number of valleys through which flow some noted trout streams.

Normandy has some trout fisheries of high repute, like Risle, Eure, Charenton and Andelles, but they are strictly preserved for the most part. Fishing on the streams of Brittany is more easily obtainable. **Quimper** is an excellent centre for the large fish of the **Odet** and its tributaries. Trout abound throughout **Finistère**, notably in the **Aulne** tributaries.

The lake fisherman is also well catered for in France, with some splendid opportunities in the Pyrenees, especially near **Luz-Saint-Sauveur**, and in the Alps. **Lakes Leman**, **Annecy** and, farther south, **Lauvitel** and **Beason** are good for trout.

One cautionary note for the fly fisherman - many French rivers are so torrential and boulder-strewn that they cannot be fished with fly. It is as well to check with a club or tackle dealer in the area to avoid disappointment. Best months of the fly are generally May, June and Sept in the north and before April and in Sept in the south. British patterns do well in the north, but are not so good in the south.

Further details from the **French Tourist Office, 178 Piccadilly, London W1J 9AL** (premium rate tel: 09068 244123; email: info.uk@franceguide.com; web: www.uk.franceguide.com) who will supply literature. (Useful website: Union Nationale pour la Pêche en France - www.unpf.fr).

GERMANY

The **Black Forest** and **Bavaria** offer the best prospects for the trout fisherman. Although pollution and over-fishing are producing a decline in sport, Bavarian waters like the **Wiesent** (with fishing stations Gössweinstein, Streitberg and Ebermannstadt), **Pegnitz**, **Loisach**, **Isar**, **Ammer**, **Saalach** and **Salzach**, to name only a few, still offer fishing of high quality amid beautiful surroundings. Brown and rainbow trout, as well as grayling, are widely distributed. For anglers who like to fly-fish for trout and charr from a boat, the **Hintersee** at **Berchtesgaden** is highly recommended - the charr in particular are good, reaching weights of 6lbs and more.

In the Black Forest, some of the best rivers are **Kinzig**, **Murg**, although there are many others such as the **Obere Wolf**, **Grosse Enz**, **Nagold**, **Jagst**, **Kocher**, **Bernbach**, and many more that provide good sport with trout and grayling. The best waters are usually fly-only. Trout, tench, barbel, eel, bream, pike and some carp are found in rivers and lakes in various other regions.

The **Harz** mountain area, south-east of **Hanover**, is also well worth exploring - the **Radau**, fished from **Bad Harzburg**, is good. Trout are found, too, in some of the streams and lakes of the **Rhineland-Palatinate**, especially in the Eifel district, and in some parts of **North Rhine-Westphalia** and **Lower Saxony**.

Elsewhere there is good coarse fishing. In **Baden-Wuerttemberg** (apart from the Black Forest) carp, bream, tench, whitebait, roach, barbel, pike, eels and trout can be had in the **Neckar Valley**, the Hohenloe district, the **Swabian Forest** area and elsewhere, including trout, pike and barbel fishing in the **Danube**. Other coarse-fishing areas are the Rhineland Palatinate (Moselle, Ahr, Lahn), and most of Lower Saxony.

The angler will need an Angling Permit (Angelschein) obtainable from the Landratsamt or Ordnungsamt (rural district council) or from the local police and also a local Angling Permit which is issued by the owners or lessees of the fishing grounds. It should be noted that some Federal States may require a UK fishing licence in order to obtain a permit in Germany. Many Hotels and clubs also have fishing rights. The principal seasons are as follows: red river trout, Mar 2-Oct 9; sea trout, March 2-Oct 9; lake trout, Jan 1-Sept 30; river char, Jan 11-Oct 9; lake char, Jan 1-Oct 31; pike, May 1-Dec 31; pike-perch, July 1-Mar 31; huck, May 1 to last day of Feb. (The seasons vary slightly in the different Federal states).

General tourist information can be had from the **German National Tourist Office, PO Box 2695, London W1A 3TN** (tel: 020 7317 0908; fax: 020 7317 0917; web: www.germany-tourism.co.uk; email: gntolon@d-z-t.com) who advise.

HOLLAND

Fishing has become one of the most popular of outdoor sports in Holland. There are about 150,000 acres of fishing waters which hold eel, carp, pike, perch, pike-perch *(Stizostedion lucioperca)*, roach, bream. For fishing in public waterways, anyone over the age of 15 must have a sportvisakte or national fishing document, which is inexpensive and can be obtained from any Dutch post office, angling club or tackle shop. It is valid for a year, from 1st January to 31st December. For most of the rivers, canals and lakes both a licence and fishing permit is required. A permit can be bought at any post office. One also needs the right licence, and this is usually obtainable by joining one of the fishing clubs affiliated to the national angling organisation NVVS *(see below)*. It is also possible to obtain a "Grote Vergunning", an extensive licence by becoming a member of the NVVS. This document consists of an identity form and booklet which gives information about 1000 places to fish in Holland.

For general tourist information and details on accommodation, contact the **Netherlands Board of Tourism, PO Box 30783, London WC2B 6DH** (tel: 020 7539 7950); fax: 020 7539 7953; web: www.holland.com/uk; email: info-UK@holland.com).

ICELAND

There are five species of fish found naturally in fresh water in Iceland — salmon, trout, charr, common eel and stickleback. Iceland has close on 100 self-sustaining salmon rivers, and at least 20 of these are regarded internationally as first class. Icelandic salmon usually weigh between 4 and 12 lbs and are mostly 55–85 cm in length. Each year, however, several fish of over 20 lbs are caught. Sea trout are normally between 1 and 4 lbs in weight but occasionally can reach as much as 20 lbs. Charr normally range between 1 and 2 lbs, although some as heavy as 12 lbs are caught.

The salmon fishing season is short, from early June into late September. July and the first days of August are usually considered the time best for fishing but this fluctuates every year. Almost all the first class rivers insist on fly-fishing only throughout this prime period and some rivers are fly-only all season. Catch and release is becoming the norm. The best months for sea trout are September into October with the south of Iceland the best region. Most of the best charr fishing waters are located in the north and east, and prime time is normally late July and August.

Detailed information on all fresh water fishing is to be found on the website of FIRO (the Federation of Icelandic River Owners; web: www.angling.is) The most notable salmon rivers on the west coast are the Thverá-Kjarrá, Nordurá, Langá, Haffjardará, Grimsá, Laxá í Dölum, Laxá í Kjós, Haukadalsá and Laxá í Leirársveit. In NW Iceland the most popular rivers are Midfjardará, Blanda, Vídidalsá, Vatnsdalsá, Laxá á Ásum and Hrútafjardará. In NE Iceland the most famous river is the Laxá í Adaldal (Big Laxá). Further east are Selá, Hofsá, Hafralónsá, Sandá, Svalbarðsá and Vesturdalsá.

Iceland's famous Laxá í Adaldal (Big Laxá) where it meets the sea
Photo: Colin Bradshaw

The most noteworthy rivers on the south coast are the Rangá rivers. They are too cold for self-sustaining salmon stocks, but the release of hatchery-reared smolts in great numbers every year has turned them into excellent salmon waters. Of self-sustaining salmon rivers in that area one might mention the River Sog, the Stóra-Laxá and Vatnsá. The east coast only has one noteworthy salmon river, the Breiddalsá. It has a moderate natural salmon stock, but smolt releases have turned it into a prolific salmon fishery.

Good sea trout rivers in southern Iceland would include the Grenlaekur, Vatnamót, Tungulaekur, Hörgá, Geirlandsá, Eldvatn and Tungufljót. For brown trout rivers we recommend the outstanding Laxá í Adaldal (upper and lower sections) and Litlaá in Kelduhverfi in the north and the Minnivallalaekur ("Minni") in the south. Good fishing for sea-run arctic charr can be had in the Hördudalsá, Midá and Hvolsá and Stadarhólsá in the west and the Fljótaá, Vídidalsá and Vatnsdalsá, Eyjafjardará, Hörgá and Fnjóská in the north. There are many small remote rivers with arctic char, particularly in the Western Fjords and on the east coast.

There are also numerous lakes in Iceland, offering good catches of resident brown trout and arctic char. The demand is not very high so fishing licences can be obtained at short notice and often at low cost. One might mention the Thingvallavatn, Veidivötn á Landmannaafrétti and many lakes on the Arnarvatnsheidi. Details on all those fishing waters can be found on the above-mentioned web-site. FIRO will also do its best to assist interested anglers.

Iceland is still free of all the most virulent fresh-water diseases and maintains a strict disinfection regime. Visiting anglers must have their tackle and other equipment disinfected. Sterilisation can easily be carried out at Keflavik Airport at customs, but a certificate of disinfection issued by your local veterinary office will be accepted at the airport when you enter Iceland. Arrangements can also be made by the Icelandic Angling Club at Akureyri and Egilsstadir airports. The certificate should be clearly worded on officially headed paper with the appropriate stamp of approval.

Guidelines for disinfection are as follows: The equipment should be immersed in the disinfection solution and then dried with a soft cloth. Examples of approved disinfectants are as follows. 1. Virkon (1% solution) 2. Caustic soda (0,2% solution) 3. Crystalline soda (5% solution) 4. Setex (0,3% solution) 5. Korsolin (3% solution) 6. Formalin (2% formaldehyde soltuion) 7. Phenol solution (2-5% solution)

The Federation of Icelandic River Owners publishes information about national fishing: Baendahollinni, 107 Reykjavík (tel: +354 (0)553 1510; fax: +354 (0)568 4363; email: angling@angling.is or info@angling.is web: www.angling.is) with weekly update on salmon catches during the season.

There are several well known angling operators in Iceland: Icelandic Angling Club (Big Laxá and Fljótaá) fljotaa@icy.is and Strengur Syndicate, Skipholt 35, 105 Reykjavík for Selá and Hofsá; orri@sela.is, www.sela.is.

Angling Service Strengir for Breiðdalsá, Hrútafjarðará, Minnivallalaekur, Jokla and Tungulaekur; Tel: +354 567 5204, ellidason@strengir.is, www.strengir.is

Angling Club Lax-a ehf, Akurhvarf 16, 203 Kópavogur, Iceland (tel: +354 (0)557 6100; fax: +352 (0)557 6108; web: www.lax-a.is; email: lax-a@lax-a.is. It has venues on 30 salmon and trout rivers, with salmon, trout and salmon and sea trout fishing and also arranges tackle hire and accommodation.

Iceland is easily accessible by air from a good number of cities in Europe and North America, from which Icelandair maintains frequent flights. Icelandair, Adam House, 2nd floor, 1 Fitzroy Square, London W1T 5HE (tel: 0844 811 1190; fax: 0207 874 1001; web: www.icelandair.co.uk; email: uk@icelandair.is).

The Iceland Tourist Board (www.iceland.com) no longer has an office in the UK but the Embassy of Iceland, 2A Hans St, London SW1X OJE can deal with all enquiries (tel: 020 7259 5959, brochure request line: 020 7636 9660; web: www.iceland.org/uk).

Orri Vigfússon, chairman of the North Atlantic Salmon Fund and winner of the Goldman Environmental Prize for his conservation work, returning a fine Icelandic salmon to the River Sela. (www.nasfworldwide.com). *Photo: Colin Bradshaw*

ITALY

In Italian rivers, mountain torrents and lakes above the 1,800 ft contour, trout, char, grayling may be fished for. The trout fishing close season is Oct 15 to Jan 15. Lowland waters contain mainly bleak, chub, carp, tench, pike, perch, roach, etc.

Sea fishing is unlicensed and first class. Deep-sea sport with tuna, albacore and swordfish has become increasingly popular, and so has underwater fishing. Underwater fishing with aqualung is prohibited in all Italian waters. Only those over sixteen are allowed to use underwater guns and such equipment. Use of an underwater gun for recreational fishing is prohibited. When submerged, an underwater fisherman is required to indicate the fact with a float bearing a red flag with a yellow diagonal stripe, and must operate with a radius of 50m of the support barge or the float bearing the flag. Fishing is prohibited: at under 500m from a beach used by bathers; 50m from fishing installations and ships at anchor. Sea sport fishing may be practised both from the shore and from a boat.

The most suitable coasts for underwater fishing are those of Sardinia, **Sicily**, **Aeolian Islands**, **Pontine Islands**, **Tremiti** Islands and the rocky shores of **Liguria**, **Tuscany**, **Latium**, **Campania**, **Calabria**, **Basilicata** and **Apulia**.

For fishing in rivers, streams, lakes and in all inland public and free freshwaters, a "Libretto di Pesca" and a "Licenza per la Pesca" issued by the Provincial Administration are required, and for foreigners cost about £20 in total. These amounts are paid to local post offices. The Local Tourist Board will advise about further details for obtaining these. With exception of 10%, all waters liable to exclusive rights are managed by the Italian Angling Federation. Fishing in private waters requires the owners permission, while fishing in all other waters requires a provincial licence, easily obtained, and it is valid all around Italy for three months and costs Euro 8.52; the Federation licence, which may be obtained from Federazione address below, at cost of Euro 21. The list of places where you need licences is on www.pescambiente.it.

Further information is available from the **Italian State Tourist Board** in London, **1 Princes Street, London W1R 2AY** (tel: 020 7408 1254; fax: 020 7399 3567; web: www.italiantouristboard.co.uk), from the **Federazione Italiana Pesca Sportiva e Attivita' Subaquee, Head Office, Viale Tiziano, 70-00196-Roma,**(web: www.fipsas.it) or from the provincial tourist boards (their addresses may be obtained from the Tourist Board in London).

LUXEMBOURG

Most of the rivers of Luxembourg are mixed fisheries holding trout, grayling and coarse fish, including pike, barbel, chub, roach, carp, eels, pike-perch and tench. There is a fine reservoir at the head of the **Sûre**, heavily stocked with lake trout, charr and roach, and carrying a good head of pike, some of them very large. In inland waters, fishing is only allowed in public waters, that is, at present, the Mid-Sûre sector between the mouth of the **Alzette** at Ettelbruck, and the mouth of the **Our** at Wallendorf. Fishing is not allowed in the fish reserve between the Moestroff weir and the bridge at Reisdorf. In the ponds at Boulaide, Clemency, Clervaux-Reuler, Erpeldange/Ettelbruck, Fischbach/Mersch, Grevenmacher, Kockelscheuer, Lamadelaine, Olingen, Pétange, Pratz, Redange/Attert, Remerschen, and the lakes of Echternach and Weiswampach, fishing is allowed with a national licence. For angling on the Vianden lake (from 1 June to 30 Sep) an annual permit is available from the Tourist Office, Maison Victor Hugo in Vianden. A useful website for regulations when fishing in Luxembourg's border waters is www.luxembourg.co.uk.

A licence is required in order to fish in the Grand Duchy, border fishing 15 Euro per year, 10 Euro per month 5 Euro per week; inland fishing 12 euro per year, 2 euro per month. The legislation regulating the practice of fishing is rather complex so check with the local tourist information office about the local regulations and licensing before going fishing. The fishing is regulated by the **Services de la Gestion de l'Eau**, 51-53 rue de Merl, L-2146 Luxembourg (tel: +352 26 02 86-1; fax: +352 26 02 86-63; email: peche@eau.etat.lu). Visitors are advised to contact the **Administration des Eaux et Forêts, 16 rue Eugene Ruppert, L-2453 Luxembourg** (tel: (00352) 402201-1; fax: (00352) 402201-250); or **Fédération Luxembourgeoise des Pêcheurs Sportifs, 47, rue de la Libération, l-5969 Itzig** (tel: +352 36 6555; fax: +352 36 9005; email: flps1@pt.lu; web: www.flps.lu) for up-to-date information.

Further information, including details of hotels with fishing, from the **Luxembourg Tourist Office,** Sicilian House, Sicilian Avenue, London WC1A 2QR (tel: 020 7434 2800; fax: 020 7434 2800; fax: 020 7430 1773 web: www.luxembourg.co.uk.

NORWAY

Norway has acquired a world-wide reputation for its BIG salmon, which can be fished for in superb surroundings of mountains and fjords, spectacular waterfalls and peaceful valleys. Beats on such renowned rivers as the Gaula, Lakselv, Namsen, Orkla and Stjørdal, fetch high prices and some are in the hands of specialized agencies as well as direct booking via the internet. Excellent sport at more modest charges may be had from farms, fishing camps and guest houses at rivers like the Beiar, Mandal, Maalselv, Numedal, Otra, Rana, Saltdal and Verdal. The salmon season is normally from 1 June to 31 August (best in June and July). Combining salmon fishing on some rivers with sea-trout would have to take place at the end of July and August, although on some rivers, the season extends into September.

Axel Wimmer happy to return a 44lb River Gaula salmon to the swim again.
Norway is justly famous for its huge salmon.

Less well known, and much less expensive, is fishing for brown trout and charr, which can be very good indeed. Countless streams and lakes, well stocked with trout, lie within easy reach of Oslo, while anglers prepared to travel further afield will be amply rewarded. Trout of 25lbs and over have been caught in the Lake Steinsfjorden, near Vikersund, and the Randselven, near Kistefoss, and Lake Mjösa, near Gjövik. Several fish of around this weight have fallen to fly.

Arctic charr are mostly found in the deep and cold mountain lakes, where they can provide thrilling sport, though this is a difficult art. There are taxi flights to the lakes from the big towns. The brown trout season varies with altitude, the extremes being late May until mid-Sept. As several rivers have rather swift currents, strong tackle is recommended. Most fishing rights are owned privately, but there are vast areas of Crown land where good fishing may be enjoyed at no great cost. Any fisherman in Norway, in addition to the application fee, is required to take out a licence sold at post offices. It covers the entire country for a year, and prices vary. Many hotels in the country have their own rivers and lakes for brown trout fishing, making no charge to guests.

Dry-fly fishing is very popular, especially in smaller lakes and tarns or slow rivers. Most suitable gear is a fly-rod of 9ft to 10ft, with a No.7 line, which may be used anywhere at any time. Best flies are those in dull colours, such as March brown and Greenwell's Glory etc. For red charr fishing, use stronger colours such as Red Cardinal, Butcher or Coachman, etc. The best all-round spinning lures are those with slow movements and in golden or red colours. For hooking, use Devon or Phantom lures, or artificial minnows.

Anyone, fishing for salmon, sea trout or sea going charr in Norway, must hold a mandatory Government licence, sold at post offices or arranged online at www.inatur.no. It covers the entire country for a year and costs around NOK 220.

Fishing in the sea or fjords is free; likewise is freshwater fishing for trout, grayling, pike and charr. A local fishing permit (day, week, season) must then be purchased in addition. The cost of this varies from place to place. These are sold at sports suppliers, kiosks, tourist offices, hotels, and campsites etc. A permit (ticket) generally covers the waters in a certain area, whilst some are valid for one lake or part of one only. A permit can be purchased for a day, a week, a month, or a whole season. Restrictions are normally stated on the permit.

Offshore sea fishing in Norway for members of the cod family and other sea fish can be spectacular and many overseas visitors travel to Norway for the thrill. In places off the north east coast 30lb cod are commonplace and 50lb fish are not just a dream. The spectacular Lofoten archipelago is the most famous location, and a magnet for cod fishers from far and wide.

Live bait is banned in Norway. Also, to protect trout, charr and salmon stocks, fish must not be transferred from one water body to another. Restrictions have been introduced to protect stocks of anadromous salmonid fish. For further information on fishing opportunities, visit www.fishnorway.co and www.salmonatlas.com or contact FishNorway, Scanholt, Croasdale Drive, Parbold, Lancs. WN8 7HR (tel: 01257 46 4805; mobile: 07801 46 5072; see website for more info: www.fishnorway.co; email: harald.oyen@fishnorway.co. See also www.visitnorway.com the official Norwegian Tourist website run by Innovation Norway.

PORTUGAL

Salmon and trout are found mostly in the **River Minho** and its tributaries in the far north, but the lack of controls has diminished sport. Very good sea trout fishing may be enjoyed in the Minho estuary near **Moledo** and on the **Lima** near **Viana do Castelo**. The fish are usually taken on bait or spinner, but fly fishing should prove productive. The coarse fisherman, too, can find sport. All Portuguese rivers hold barbel, while those in the centre and south of the country hold good carp and black bass.

The open season for salmon and trout fishing is from 1 March - 31 July, sea trout Feb - Oct; open seasons for other species vary, but most coarse fish either from 16 May - 31 Dec, or 1 Jan - 14 March. Licences for visitors are not as a rule required.

The sea fishing is excellent, partly owing to the structure of the continental shelf, and the narrow strip of 50 to 100 miles shallower water. More than 200 different species are taken. Among these are many of the fish known to British fishermen in home waters, but in the south it includes game species such as swordfish, blue and white marlin, tunny, bonito and amberjack, as well as blue porbeagle, and blue shark. School tunny and meagre (the so-called salmon-bass) are also taken.

Many of the fish known to British fishermen reach heavier weights in Portuguese waters. Bass of around 20lbs are reported to be taken inshore from boats, for instance, and smaller fish of 10-14lbs from the shore. Large shoals of mackerel up to 61b were found by a British team fishing off Peniche in 1956. Good shore fishing for bass can be had more or less everywhere. Other fish regularly caught include: red mullet (to 5lbs), conger and dogfish, various types of bream, some running up to 25lbs; pollack, cod, turbot, rock gurnard, wrasse, John Dory, tope, dorado to 10lbs, grouper to 10lbs, peacock fish, croaker. rays, and garfish. Meagre attain weights up to 90lbs, amberjack to 18lbs, and school tunny to 80lbs. The comparatively recent discovery of this vast potential has led to a rapid development of a number of small fishing ports. Boats and boatmen operate at most of them, and hotel accommodation is reported to be good. Most important of the new-found fishing centres is perhaps **Sesimbra**, south of **Lisbon**. Others are **Praia da Rocha** (near **Portimao**) and **Faro** in the south, **Cascais** (near **Estoril**), **Nazaré**, and **Ericeira** (all to the north-west of Lisbon) and **Sines** (south of Sesimbra). Apart from the fishing, most of these places have good beach and rock casting, and are good holiday and tourist centres. Boats are for hire at many places, including **Albufeira**, **Lagos** and **Monte Gordo**.

In the **Algarve**, several hotels provide or can arrange sea fishing parties. They include the Hotels Praia, Algarve and Baleeira. The best centres in this region are in the **Sagres** and **Carvoeiro** areas where large mackerel are frequently taken. More information can be had from the **ICEP Portugal - Portuguese Trade and Tourism Office, 11 Belgrave Square, London SW1X 8PP** (tel: 020 7201 6666; fax: 020 7201 6633; brochure line tel: 0845 355 12112); web: www.visitportugal.com; email: icep.london@icep.pt).

RUSSIA

The Kola Peninsula. Over the last few years the Kola Peninsula has built up a reputation for some of the most prolific Atlantic salmon and sea trout fishing to be found anywhere in the world. Situated in north-western Russia, jutting into the White Sea from its border with north-eastern Norway, the peninsula is approximately the same size as Scotland, with as many rivers supporting salmon and sea trout runs.

With few roads, a very small population, and lying mainly above the Arctic Circle, the peninsula is a truly remote wilderness, and it has taken some years to overcome the geographical problems this incurs. Although in recent times western fishermen have only fished the Kola since 1989, its rivers were a topic of great interest in the *Fishing Gazette* as long ago as 1925, a few Englishmen having fished there shortly after the turn of the century.

Hard work by a few western specialist organisations over the last few years has now made it possible to fish the Kola relatively easily. They have all combined their experience with Russian local knowledge, to build camps on the most productive and consistent rivers. The remoteness means that it is still not possible to fish there except through these organisations. To get to the rivers one must fly via Moscow, St Petersburg or Helsinki to the peninsula and then onward to the rivers by helicopter.

The season runs from the beginning of June, the winter snows having melted in May, until late September, when the onset of the severe Arctic winter prohibits access. The rivers may be grouped into those which flow north into the Barents Sea, and those which flow east and south into the White Sea.

The southern rivers were the first upon which fishing was organised. There, the main salmon run is in June and July, and a smaller run in September. Sea trout run throughout the season, not starting until July on some rivers. Large catches may be expected, with salmon of between 5-20lbs being normal. The main salmon run in the northern rivers, which have only been fished seriously since 1991, is from mid-June to mid-July, although it does extend into August. To date, fish from these rivers have averaged 15-20lbs, with many in the 30-40lb range. The 1993 season saw a fish caught exceeding 60lbs.

The majority of fishing is on floating, intermediate or sink tip lines using traditional salmon flies. A sink line may be necessary on the northern rivers. A surprisingly large number of fish are taken on dry fly. The majority of the rivers require chest waders and wading staffs.

The rivers vary greatly in character. The **Panoi**, flowing east into the White Sea, is large, with prolific runs of salmon. Running South is the **Varzuga** system, including the **Pana** and **Kitsa**, which has, perhaps, the largest salmon runs in the world, and in parts is comparable with the Aberdeenshire Dee. The **Polanga**, **Babia**, **Likhodyevka** and **Pyalitsa**, fished together, are probably the prettiest rivers on the peninsula, requiring little wading and are similar to the Scottish Carron, Oykel and Cassley; their salmon run is not quite as prolific, but is boosted by large runs of sea trout. The **Kharlovka**, **Eastern Litsa**, **Varzina** and **Yokanga** in the north, all have runs of large salmon, but in places are very rocky and steep, with fast water and difficult wading.

Fishing is mostly fly only, and all rivers operate a policy of catch and release for salmon, allowing each rod no more than one or two fish a week for the table.

For further information, contact **Russian Travel Centre, 9 Mandeville Place, London, W1U 3AT** (tel: 020 7224 4678)

SPAIN

Spain is a well-endowed country, offering the most southerly fishing for Atlantic salmon in Europe; brown and rainbow trout, coarse fish including large carp and barbel, tench, pike-perch, black bass, chub, pike, and Boga or *Chondrostoma polylepis*; and shore fishing for sea bass, mackerel, mullet, conger and other species. Black bass, pike and Danube salmon are among comparatively recent introductions.

Twenty-six rivers draining the Cantabrian range and the Galician Coast are entered by salmon. The **Deva-Cares**, **Navia**, **Sella**, **Narcea**, and **Asón** provide the best sport. Arrangements for licences and permits for visitors are not uniform and the British angler contemplating salmon fishing in Spain is advised to contact the **Spanish National Tourist Office, PO Box 4009, London W1A 6NB** (fax: 020 7486 8034; web: www.spain.info). 24-hr automated brochure line: 0845 9400 1800. Much the same is to be said of the trout fishing, applying equally to seasons and permitted methods. In some areas, trout grow impressively large. Spain has not yet become as notable for high-grade coarse fishing as it may at some future date, but few who have connected with large carp or barbel in a deep, fast-flowing Spanish river fail to cherish ambitions to renew the experience.

SWEDEN

Sweden presents an inviting prospect for game and coarse angler alike, and with 9,000 km of coastline, a large variety of locations and species for sea fishing. Salmon fishing has a long tradition in the country, and western Sweden was explored for this purpose during the 19th century by British anglers. Several of these centrally located waters, the **Ätran, Säveån, Göta** and **Klarälven Rivers** still provide good sport, but there is more salmon fishing to be found than on the west coast alone. The whole coastline is dotted with attractive salmon rivers, and every year the most famous, **Mörrumsån, Emån** and **Dalälven** attract many anglers. Along the northern coastline there are a rich variety of rivers ideal for both spinning and fly-fishing. In recent years these have improved and produced more and larger salmon, weighing between 20 and 30 kg. During the 1990s a good quantity of very large salmon have come from the **Hanöbukten** (Baltic Sea) area of southern Sweden. In addition, Sweden figures highly in the world's ratings for landlocked salmon. In summer, spinning and fly fishing are the most popular methods in the rivers, while trolling is favoured in the Baltic. Trolling is also popular in the two largest lakes **Vänern** and **Vättern**, where salmon of more than 17 kg have been caught.

For the game and coarse fisherman Sweden abounds in lakes. Amongst these, various in the **Hökensas** area near Lake Vättern have stocked rainbow and brown trout, and rainbow trout may be caught in the **Ångebytyärnet Lake** from jetty or shore. The **Svågadalen** wilderness has hundreds of lakes, tarns, rivers and brooks, and the main species are trout, charr and grayling. The forest **River Svågan** runs through this area, with many exciting fishing spots. The brook trout, lake trout and sea trout run large in Sweden, lake trout to 17 kg, and may be caught in cold, fast-flowing water, on fly, spinner, jigger, or by trolling, depending on season and conditions. Pike fishing is wide spread in the country, and some lakes can produce pike around 20 kg, as well as large shoals of big perch. In the mountainous region of **Hemavan** are lakes with first rate trout and charr fishing.

Coastal fishing for sea trout may begin in January, and is popular on the coast of **Blekinge County**, where good spots include Björkenabben at Listerlandet, Lörby Skog in Pukaviksbukten, Sternö Island, and the coast east of Torhmans udde near Karlskrona. Bleckinge also has good pike fishing in its lakes, streams, and in the Baltic.

Lapland fishing for trout and grayling is well organised for small groups of anglers, and an informative website is www.laplandfinland.com.

For salmon and trout fishing, licence charges vary considerably; charges for trout fishing in stocked lakes and ponds are somewhat higher than for natural waters. No charge is made for rod and line sea fishing.

Some of Sweden's foremost fisheries have entered into a partnership, with the purpose of encouraging angling in their respective areas. These include mountain, forest, rivers, lakes, and coastal fishing, for pike, rainbow trout, perch, carp, salmon, sea trout, brown trout, char, grayling and sea fish. The fishing is of a high quality, also the reception, accommodation and service, in the form of information, transport and guiding. Contact **Visit Sweden** (web: www.visitsweden.com).

Close seasons vary widely. For salmon and sea trout it usually runs from Sept 1 to Jan 1, though fishing is prohibited in some waters after Aug 15.

Further and more detailed general information can be had from the year book published by **Sportfiskarna** (The Swedish Anglers Assn), **Svartviksslingan 28, S-16739 Bromma, Sweden** (tel: +46 (0)8 704 4480; fax +46 (0)8 795 9673) which lists about 1,800 fishing waters. The assn cannot, however, answer detailed enquiries from abroad. These should be directed to **Swedish Travel & Tourism Council, 5 Upper Montagu St, London W1H 2AG** (tel: 00800 3080 3080 (freephone); fax: 020 7724 5872; web: www.visit-sweden.com; email: info@swetourism.org.uk); or to **Swedish Board of Fisheries, Box 423, S-401 26 Göteborg, Sweden** (tel: +46 (0)31 743 03 00; fax: +46 (0)31 743 04 44; web: www.fiskeriverket.se). For a wide range of fishing holidays in Sweden, contact **Cinclus C Sport Fishing Guide** (All you want to know about fishing in Sweden), **Cinclus C, Lägervägen 31B, 25456 Helsingborg, Sweden** (tel: +46 (0)42 155 755; web: www.cinclusc.com *(where there is an English version)*; email: cinclusc@cinclusc.com).

SWITZERLAND

There is no shortage of water in Switzerland - 20,000 miles of rivers and streams, and 520 square miles of lakes within a small area - and as most of these waters hold trout, the country is a fly-fisherman's dream.

Unfortunately, the dream is often of brief duration, as the streams at appreciable altitudes are in snow spate often until July. But in the lower valleys there is sport to be had from May to the end of the summer. Lake fishing consists mainly in trolling at great depth. Swiss waters may be classed as follows:

The **Lakes**. Most of the lakes contain trout and char, pike, perch and other coarse fish. The trout and charr (Ombre chevalier) run to a great size, but they lie at such depths that fly fishing or trolling with a rod is practically useless. Best results are obtained by spinning with light tackle.

The **Great Rivers**. Both the **Rhine** and **Rhône** hold very big trout. Spinning with a 2 ¼in silver Devon is the best method, though a small silver-bodied salmon fly will sometimes give good results. The Rhône, above the lake of **Geneva**, is fishable only till the middle of April. In summer months it is thick with snow water. Many Swiss rivers contain good stocks of coarse fish, including barbel, carp and pike.

Plain and Lower Valley Streams. Trout in these streams run from ¼-2½lbs or more. There is always a good hatch of fly, and the Mayfly is up on most of them from May to July. Wading is not as a rule necessary. Fine tackle is essential. Carry a couple of small silver Devons for thick water.

The **Hill Torrents**. Trout run four or five to the pound in the best of the hill torrents, rather smaller in the others. As the hatch of fly is usually poor, the upstream worm pays best. The coch-y-bondhu is sometimes useful, while in July and Aug the 'daddy-long-legs' is deadly. Wading is usually an advantage. Watch for the spate that often occurs towards midday owing to melting snow. Of the mountain rivers, the **Kirel**, **Fildrich** and **Simme** of the Bernese Oberland are recommended, holding wild brown trout, rainbow and brook trout. Fishing there begins in early April and ends 30 Sept, best time, mid-May to mid-Sept.

It should be said that Switzerland, in common with most European countries, is experiencing a growth of angling pressures, but the authorities, concerned to ensure that sport remains at a high level, release at least 100 million fish, mostly trout, from hatcheries every year.

The close season for trout runs most commonly from 1 Oct to 15 Mar, and for grayling from 1 Mar to 30 April.

Fishing regulations vary. Generally speaking the angler will require a canton licence and may also need a permit for private waters. Further information is obtainable from the local Tourist Offices in the area to be visited or from a very useful website: www.switzerland.angloinfo.com/countries/switzerland/fishing.asp General tourist information can be had from **Switzerland Travel Centre Ltd, 30 Bedford Street, London WC2E 9ED** (tel: Freephone: 00800 100 200 30; Freefax: 00800 100 200 30; or tel: 020 7420 4902; web: www.stc.co.uk).

For the latest fishing opportunities please visit:

www.wheretofish.co.uk
www.salmonatlas.com
www.troutatlas.com
www.carpatlas.com
www.fishnorway.co
www.watercams.co.uk

For news, features, reviews and fishing chat visit:
www.flyforums.co.uk
www.flyforums.com
www.fishingmagic.com
www.speycast.co.uk

About the Publisher:
www.fishandfly.com

Shimano Felindre Trout Fishery, South Wales.
www.shimanofelindre.co.uk

INDEX

Also in the *Where to Fish* Series:

The ***Where to Fish Map*** of the Fishing Rivers, Lakes and Reservoirs of England, Scotland, Wales and Ireland. Only £6 + 60p p&p

The ***Where to Fish Map*** of the Fishing Rivers, Lakes and Reservoirs of Scotland. Only £7 + 60p p&p

In handy pocket size
(no charge for p&p if more than one copy is ordered)

FROM: Thomas Harmsworth Publishing Company
Old Rectory Offices,
Stoke Abbott, Beaminster
Dorset DT8 3JT.

thomasharmsworth@btconnect.com

www.fishandfly.com